Principles of
ANIMAL ECOLOGY

By

W. C. ALLEE
Professor of Zoology, The University of Chicago

ORLANDO PARK
Professor of Zoology, Northwestern University

ALFRED E. EMERSON
Professor of Zoology, The University of Chicago

THOMAS PARK
Professor of Zoology, The University of Chicago

KARL P. SCHMIDT
Chief Curator of Zoology, Chicago Natural History Museum

W. B. SAUNDERS COMPANY
PHILADELPHIA AND LONDON

Reprinted January, 1951 and, August, 1955

☆

COPYRIGHT, 1949, BY W. B. SAUNDERS COMPANY

☆

COPYRIGHT UNDER THE INTERNATIONAL COPYRIGHT UNION

☆

20195

"As concerns 'Relations Physiology', i.e., the study of the relations of the animal organism to the external world, this in turn falls into two segments, ecology and chorology. By ecology we mean the body of knowledge concerning the economy of nature—the investigation of the total relations of the animal both to its inorganic and to its organic environment; including, above all, its friendly and inimical relations with those animals and plants with which it comes directly or indirectly into contact—in a word, ecology is the study of all those complex interrelations referred to by Darwin as the conditions of the struggle for existence. This science of ecology, often inaccurately referred to as 'biology' in a narrow sense, has thus far formed the principal component of what is commonly referred to as 'Natural History'. As is well shown by the numerous popular natural histories of both early and modern times, this subject has developed in the most close relations with systematic zoology. The ecology of animals has been dealt with quite uncritically in natural history; but natural history has in any case had the merit of keeping alive a widespread interest in zoology."

ERNST HAECKEL, 1870

PREFACE

In writing this book we hope we have a start at supplying the orientation of which ecology, a subscience of biology, is in need. The time seemed ripe for a group of ecologists, approaching the science from various points of view and with various techniques, to attempt to gather together fundamental concepts, supported in so far as possible by well-verified evidence. Others have accumulated many facts that we have drawn upon freely, from both published compilations and original research reports, but our effort has been directed primarily towards the presentation and documentation of general ecological principles. We have not been wholly successful. Many concepts and principles of a future science of ecology are only beginning to be recognized, and many important ideas that will be taught to future classes in biology have not yet been conceived by the present generation of ecologists.

We hope that, as a result of our efforts, the general biologist may more easily grasp the scope and implications of ecology and that profitable lines of investigation will be more readily apparent to interested students. We are encouraged by remembering the stimulus gained some years ago from Elton's small books, in which he emphasized ecological principles.

From our point of view there is an urgent demand for three different types of books about ecology. On the one hand we could well use an encyclopedic treatise of present-day knowledge of the subject. In distinct contrast, a brief statement of the underlying principles would also be useful. We felt that there was also a need for a study of the underlying principles together with a sampling of the evidence on which they are based. This is the task we have undertaken. So far as possible, no fact is admitted to these pages for its own sake, and although no general concept is stated without the presentation of evidence supporting it, an attempt has been made to give no more than the necessary minimum of factual support.

At one point we are immediately on the defensive. In limiting our discussion, at least in certain chapters of the book, primarily to the principles of *animal* ecology, we appear to be recognizing a logical dichotomy between ecological relations of plants and of animals where none exists. The decision not to extend our work to include the whole scope of ecology, the so-called bio-ecology of some writers, was based primarily on convenience and workability. Yet, although this book stresses animal ecology, we have felt free, in fact we have been compelled, to draw on ideas from plant ecology and to make continued use of the concepts in which plants and animals are necessarily considered together. The distinction between our "animal ecology" and ecology in the most comprehensive sense lies in our emphasis on the animal factors.

We stress ecological generalizations from two vantage points. First, there are those principles concerned with the functions or physiology of contemporary individuals and ecological assemblages of whatever rank. Second, there are those ecological principles concerned with organic evolution. We are not interested in helping to continue the separation between these two aspects of ecology. Rather, our aim is to point out their essential interrelation, and we hope we may have depicted ecology in better perspective in this connection.

In addition to attempting the correlation of the shorter-term contemporary phenomena with a longer-term evolutionary perspective, we have also been impressed by the need for an historical approach to many aspects of the subject. Besides the fairly full section on ecological history, the historical approach is frequently made elsewhere in the book. This emphasis has not necessarily affected the selection of supporting examples, since neither the older, more widely known illustrations nor the most recently discovered ones have been regularly used.

We discuss ecological principles dealing with the nonliving physical environment more or less as a unit, whether they are concerned primarily with the individual (autecology) or with the population or the community (synecology). The consideration of the biotic environment of the individual organism is less unified and perhaps less comprehensive. It is hard to avoid some duplication in dealing with the environmental relations of these different biological units, and the inherent difficulties have not been resolved formally and logically. In discussing principles dealing with the organism in its nonliving physical environment, we have anticipated many somewhat similar interrelations with the higher ecological categories. In contrast, much of the discussion of the biotic environment is given in direct connection with populations, communities, and evolution, rather than in a single part of the book.

In our treatment of the ecological principles that emerge with the population as the unit of study, our attention centers first on the population in both laboratory and field and, later, on aggregations and on certain aspects of societies. The analysis of functional contemporary principles leads naturally to the examination of interspecies groups. Here our primary concern is with the underlying structure, organization, successional development, and distribution of the ecological community. In this section our emphasis is on terminology only in those instances in which the term itself is a well-authenticated index of the principle. The multiplication of terms represents a juvenile stage of the science as a whole, and it is hoped that a critical definition and sifting of the concepts that support the terminology may lead to a reduction of their complexity and to an advance toward maturity.

Finally, in examining the problems of evolution we attempt to bring out those ecological aspects that are particularly significant, such as isolation, selection, adaptation, distribution, regressive evolution, and others, insofar as they contribute to ecological principles or as the ecological approach aids in their solution.

The book was planned jointly. Each author undertook primary responsibility for preparing the first draft of sections or chapters for the handling of which he showed particular competence so far as our group membership was concerned. Early working outlines and successive copies of each chapter or section were distributed to the other authors and received criticism concerning both manner and matter, particularly with regard to possible omissions. Eventually all parts of the manuscript were read aloud to the other authors, and there was much discussion of questioned points. We feel that in the main we have reached a truly remarkable degree of agreement both on the major and minor principles of ecology, though some generalizations, emphases, and conclusions are not shared with equal enthusiasm by every author. Fortunately, these are usually matters of relatively minor significance.

Many parts of the manuscript were read critically by persons outside our circle, and the revised version was again distributed to the other authors. Finally there was a period of collation between pairs of authors. Near the end of the writing each author was instructed to use his own judgment in the final polishing of the chapters for which he prepared the first draft.* Chapters from various sections were also read to the

* We had originally hoped that many traces of personal origin of chapters would disappear during this extended and detailed critical treatment and that final responsibility would rest entirely with the group. This hope has been realized in large part, but, as was to be expected, each author feels decidedly more responsibility for the selection, organization, presentation and interpretation of the material he has himself written than he does for other chapters, or even for the book as a whole. Particular responsibility for the different chapters was distributed as follows:

Preface and Introduction (Chapter 1): K.P.S. (based on drafts by W.C.A. and T.P.).

Chapters 2, 4 to 16, inclusive, and 23: W.C.A.

Chapters 3 and 18 to 22, inclusive: T.P.

Chapter 17: W.C.A. and K.P.S.

Chapters 24 and 31 to 35, inclusive: A.E.E.

Chapters 25 to 29, inclusive: O.P.

Chapter 30: K.P.S. and O.P.

General editing of the manuscript: K.P.S.

The four junior authors here acknowledge the leadership of Dr. Warder Clyde Allee and their indebtedness to him throughout the preparation of the present work.

Chicago Ecology Club, and the resulting discussions were stimulating and profitable.

We take this opportunity to thank many people for their help in this enterprise. Of course, final responsibility for all remaining errors rests with the authors.

Dr. Theodor Just (Chicago Natural History Museum) and the late Dr. Chancey Juday (University of Wisconsin) read all of Section I, and the latter also criticized the material on limnology in Section IV. The late Dr. F. R. Lillie, Dr. Elizabeth A. Beeman (University of Chicago), and Dr. Ruth M. Merwin (National Cancer Institute, Bethesda, Maryland) read Chapter 2, and the last mentioned checked its bibliography. Dr. Garrett J. Hardin (Santa Barbara College) criticized Chapters 4 to 18, inclusive. Mr. Peter W. Frank and Mr. Gerson Rosenthal (University of Chicago) each read certain of those chapters. Among others from the same University, Dr. T. F. W. Barth (Geology) checked over the paragraphs on earthquakes, Dr. Ralph W. Gerard (Physiology) and Dr. Clay G Huff (Parasitology) gave similar advice and aid concerning other matters in Section II, and Dr. Charles E. Olmsted (Botany) gave helpful botanical aid. Dr. Fritz Haas (Chicago Natural History Museum) was helpful on various sections.

Dr. L. C. Birch (University of Sidney) read Chapters 3 and 18 to 22, inclusive. Of the staff of Northwestern University, Dr.

William Powers aided with Chapter 28, Dr. Orrie J. Eigsti read the material on bacteria, Dr. L. H. Tiffany was consulted with respect to photosynthesis, and Dr. Albert Wolfson was helpful on the subject of bird migration (Section IV).

The following men, all from the University of Chicago, helped in the section on Evolution. Dr. Sewall Wright read the whole section. Dr. Herluf H. Strandskov read parts, especially the matters dealing with population genetics. Dr. Clay G Huff and Dr. W. H. Taliaferro criticized and made suggestions concerning parasitism. Dr. O. H. Robertson helped similarly with the treatment of *Pneumococcus,* as did Dr. E. J. Kraus with the portion on rusts and with plant ecology, and Dr. John M. Beal with botanical names, evolution of chromosomes, rusts, and at various other places. Dr. Ernst Mayr (American Museum of Natural History) read Chapter 32. Mr. Robert F. Inger was extremely helpful in checking bibliographic references, and our few references to the Russian literature were put in correct form by Mr. D. Dwight Davis (Chicago Natural History Museum).

The authors are indebted to the Ridgeway Memorial Fund of the University of Chicago for the support that made possible the illustration of the book and to Winifred Emerson for a critical polishing of the illustrations. We have freely selected, modified, and redrawn figures from varied sources.

THE AUTHORS

CONTENTS

CONTENTS

SECTION V. ECOLOGY AND EVOLUTION

INDICES

1. INTRODUCTION

Ecology may be defined broadly as the science of the interrelation between living organisms and their environment, including both the physical and the biotic environments, and emphasizing interspecies as well as intraspecies relations. The *living organism* may be defined, though somewhat incompletely, as a physicochemical mechanism that is self-regulating and self-perpetuating, and is in process of equilibration with its environment. The *environment* of any organism consists, in final analysis, of everything in the universe external to that particular organism. Those parts of the total environment that are evidently of direct importance to the organism are regarded as constituting the *effective environment*. The relations of any organism or community of organisms with the environment are, in the language of Raymond Pearl (p. 266), (1) particular: specific for every organism; (2) continuous: the organism living in its environment for its total life; (3) reciprocal: the environment affecting the organism, and *vice versa;* and (4) indissoluble: dissociation of an organism from its environment being impossible. The organism and groups of organisms are the essential biological units in ecology, and we exclude the intraorganismal or cellular environment except as special cases demand its examination.

The reciprocal relations require especial attention. The interaction of the environment and the organism is obvious in almost every field of biology. Physiological processes are correlated primarily or secondarily with environmental fluctuations: energy for life is derived from the environment; growth and development show relationship to environmental factors; environmental forces and substances impinge upon the sense organs of animals and the reactive systems of plants; behavior patterns in large part are responses to environmental patterns; distribution of plants and animals is determined by variations in the environmental complex; isolation through environmental factors has profoundly influenced genetic systems of organisms, and the environment has acted as a selective agent in determining the survival of organisms and populations, thus leading to the evolutionary development of living systems.

In its more scientific aspects, ecology is intrinsically a difficult subject. In its relations it depends on many other phases of biology, and it is built directly, as well as indirectly, on the physical sciences. The subsciences of biology and the physical sciences are in turn dependent upon and affected by ecology. Yet in its close relationship to natural history, ecology is near the stolon from which all biology has developed. As such it sometimes seems deceptively simple, and under many conditions ecology may really be simple. Almost any good, precise observation within its extended borders makes a useful contribution to the mass of needed ecological information. Its wide range of subject matter, open to exploration by diverse techniques, is a major reason for the lack of ready integration of the field of ecology as a whole. It is at any rate obvious that the development of generalizations and principles in ecology and the orientation of its subject matter with respect to such principles, have been slow.

Workers in ecology, like those in any other broad field, face reproach from more narrow specialists. Physiologists, for example, are hard pressed to meet the rigorous standards of biophysics or biochemistry, to say nothing of those of physics or chemistry proper. In part this particular difficulty is not directly related to subject matter, as evidenced by the relative precision gained by specialists as contrasted with generalizers in any field. In part the diffi-

1

culty in biology is associated with the intrinsic complexity of the materials to be analyzed or synthesized.

Biologists working with the social life of insects, or of other animals, are frequently tempted to regard their own work as more precise than that done by equally competent students of human sociology; and those dealing with human material often feel compelled to explore subjective psychological aspects of sociology that are almost or completely closed to the student of social insects.

Much of human sociology is an integral part of ecology. There are reciprocal influences between these two sciences, influences that are especially apparent in such practical matters as the development of the Canal Zone in Panama, with the details and outreach of the Tennessee Valley Authority, with stream pollution, and with the whole set of problems centering about the potential or actual dust bowls of semiarid regions of the world. Much that is now being done in such projects is recognized as ecology.

A major difference between human relationships and those of other animals is the role played by the symbolic language of man, and by ideas, as contrasted with the restricted use of both among nonhuman populations. The extent to which animals other than primates communicate with each other, and the means employed, are still matters for investigation. We know much about the importance of odors as signals, particularly among such animals as dogs, ants, and moths. We also know about various cries, songs, and visual displays that reveal sexual receptivity, or nonreceptivity, that facilitate aggregation or warn of danger. We have evidence that the complex activities within the ant colony are integrated primarily by touch and odor; to regard such manifestations as language emphasizes the distinctiveness of human speech. The demonstration of ideas—particularly of abstract ideas—among the mental processes of nonhuman animals is still more difficult.

We have purposely avoided emphasis on human sociology, but we hope that in time a maturing ecology will be properly fused with that field.

The line between ecology and physiology is equally difficult and perhaps equally impossible to draw with exactness. One of the most helpful distinctions concerns the working units in the respective subject matter. The physiologist seldom gets beyond considering an individual as his upper limit; often he is content with some organ or even with an individual nerve fiber; his research may focus finally at the molecular level. In contrast, the ecologist usually regards an individual organism as his smallest unit, except as he needs information about the functioning of the liver, pancreas, muscles, or other organs in order to understand the general environmental relations of the whole organism, or of the community. The kidneys give a remarkably good illustration of the close correlation that may exist between an inner organ of the body and the general environment. For ecology, the supra-individualistic units are real entities. Aggregations, populations, societies, and various units at or near the community level present problems rarely recognized by physiologists working as physiologists. Yet the problems of this level are real and lie so near the center of ecology that Shelford (1929, p. 2) makes the statement that ecology is the science of animal communities.

A single *Asellus* moving upstream in a small brook has an ecology of its own, even though it is not at the moment in direct association with any organisms other than the bacteria and other nannoplankton of the water or those minute forms residing on its own surface or acting as its parasites. We have no reason to believe that this particular isopod remembers or anticipates contacts with another living creature. It is essentially alone, a creature of the moment, responding to an innate urge to move upstream against the current of water. The positive reaction is not free from environmental influences; it is dependent on such external relations as the amount of oxygen and of carbon dioxide present, and on the ionic content of the surrounding water. The isopod is also, without knowing it, a member of the community of the brook and so is related to the ground water that feeds the stream and, to some extent, to the body of water into which the brook flows. At a different level, the single, isolated isopod may well have been and may soon become again a member of an isopod aggregation with which other animals are also associated.

The physical environment impinges directly on the individual as it does on populations or on a whole community, and it initiates and directs the course of action of innumerable small-scale events. Phenomena on the largest scale may likewise depend directly on the physical environment, as exemplified by isostasy, the condition of equilibrium in which the heavier portions of the earth's crust sink to form the ocean basins, while the lighter parts are pushed up as the continental platforms.

The definition of ecology as the science of communities may be valid in its total implications. The isopod illustration presents a phase of a much larger problem. In another example, is the cell, the tissue, or the organism as a whole the unit? The cell may itself be broken into parts, and in genetics we hear much about chromosomes, chromomeres, and genes. So in ecology there may be ecological relations of parts of organisms—the nephridial system, for example—of the whole animal, of populations, whether aggregated or dispersed, of associations and communities, and of biomes. At whatever level one begins, and whatever the point of view, one must study all possible unitary levels before coming to a full understanding of the ecology of either an isolated isopod moving slowly upstream in a small brook, or of the vast biome in which the brook itself is a minor and almost negligible incident.

Close interaction exists between genes and the general environment, both in development and in evolution. A gene may be helpfully regarded as a reagent in the process of development; the environment also enters intimately into the developmental processes. Aside from supplying continuity under suitable conditions, much that is produced by the gene system can be duplicated by appropriate surroundings, either as a result of shock furnished by an environmental insult or from the more steady pressure of a steadily continuing physical or biotic induction. Such subjects are treated in some detail in any modern work on physiological genetics (Goldschmidt, 1938), in more specialized books such as Hogben (1933) or Newman, Freeman and Holzinger (1937), and even in more popular accounts, as in the small book by Dunn and Dobzhansky (1946).

Animals do not develop without an environment; contrariwise, even given optimum environment, organisms do not start to grow without the presence of a spore or zygote or of a group of cells from a preceding organism. Both a bearer of heredity and a suitable environment are necessary for development. After much discussion, lasting from the time of Darwin, Galton, and Weismann, we can now ask fairly exact questions in this field and expect to find fairly exact answers. Some pertinent data are available at various evolutionary levels such as those of the micro-organisms, the insects, and man. The relation between heredity and environment is frequently called the problem of nature versus nurture. In its present dress the discussion does not center about environment versus heredity in general, but rather concerns the functions of these two necessary components with regard to some particular characteristic, such as the color of the shanks in hens, the width of the bar in bar-eyed *Drosophila*, coat color in certain mammals, or intelligence or stature in man.

Concrete examples may clarify what is meant by the ecological relations of such characters. Yellow fat in rabbits or yellow shanks in hens require a source of yellow coloring matter, such as is furnished by yellow corn or by the xanthophyll from green foliage or other similar foodstuffs; but, for yellow to be developed, the enzyme that breaks down xanthophyll must be absent, and this lack in the hen or rabbit is associated with gene action. Absence of xanthophyll from the food yields equally white fat or white shanks, and one cannot know whether the absence of yellow is primarily environmental or genetic, or both, without more direct knowledge of both the heredity and the feeding routine. The effect of temperature on the width of the bar in bar-eyed *Drosophila*, of heat on the production of feathers in young frizzle fowl, or of the absence of iodine in water containing frog tadpoles fed on an iodine free diet, all demonstrate significant effects of the environment on the development of characters that are also definitely related to the gene complex (Hogben, 1933).

In man, the best assay of nature in association with or in contrast to nurture has come from studies of identical twins reared apart compared with those of others reared together, and further compared with similar qualities in fraternal twins. Identical twins have an identical gene pattern, fraternal twins do not. A good study of this kind is that of Newman, Freeman, and Holzinger

(1937), which shows that "physical characters are least affected by the environment, that intelligence is affected more; educational achievement still more; and personality or temperament, if our tests are to be relied upon, the most."

Reasons for the slow development of ecology can be found in the general state of nonecological science, in the relative inability of ecologists to work with intellectual and physical tools of precision, and especially in the scope and innate complexity of the subject.

There are few good reasons other than the convenience of authors and readers for not treating ecology as a whole. Plant ecologists can make a strong case for focussing on plant relations and largely neglecting animal life, since the plants are primary producers and play a highly important role in providing shelter for many types of animals. Even so, the neglect of animal activities omits or minimizes such phenomena as grazing and browsing, working of the soil, seed scattering, and the pollination of many important flowering plants. Students of animal ecology must give due attention to plants if for no other reason than that animals live in an environment largely conditioned and controlled by the plant matrix. Acknowledging the failure of the present work to develop a unified ecology, we fully recognize the need for a future work on the Principles of Ecology which will make the logical synthesis of the two fields.

Plant ecology presents two aspects, vegetational and floristic. Animal ecology largely lacks the vegetational phase so far as land animals are concerned. It is true that forest animals differ in general appearance from those of grasslands, but the differences in body proportions by no means approach the contrast in growth forms between grasses and trees. The general aspect of aquatic animals stands in marked contrast with that of land forms, and various convergences exist among both series that approach what we understand when a vegetational type is mentioned. Thus the fishlike form of whales, seals, walruses, fossil sea reptiles, tadpoles, certain larvae of lower chordates, and of the whole galaxy of fishes stands in distinct contrast with typical terrestrial structures. The sessile animals of coral reefs and oyster banks approach the terrestrial vegetational concept even more closely.

Contrary to first impression, the fact that animal ecology is based primarily on faunistic considerations tends to simplify its study, since the student of animal relations is not so much tempted to pursue the superficial types of inspection that make the carwindow approach one of the charms and also one of the pitfalls of plant ecology.

The application of even a well-formulated generalization to a given situation may require further research. Thus in the control of mosquito-borne diseases of man, the mosquitoes that transmit epidemic yellow fever behave according to rule. A trained executive can sit at his desk in New York, after he has fully learned the principles involved, and give directions which, if faithfully carried out, will lead to the control of the disease. It is not so with the anopheline mosquitoes that carry malarial parasites. Each type of malarial vector is a special case, and, without further knowledge, the general principles may seem inapplicable to the given situation. In the southeastern United States, malaria is transmitted by a marsh-dwelling mosquito characteristic of sluggish water; in Italy, by a form that lives in the cold running water of the uplands; in Puerto Rico, by a brackish-water mosquito. Under such varied conditions the needed local detail is of equal value with knowledge of the underlying general principles.

An example of the benefits to be derived from an approach to ecology through general principles is given in the summarizing paragraph of ocean currents by Sverdrup, Johnson, and Fleming (1942, p. 399), who conclude:

"From this brief summary it is evident that it is virtually impossible to obtain knowledge of the ocean currents on an entirely empirical basis. If this were to be accomplished, it would be necessary to conduct measurements from anchored vessels at numerous localities for long periods and at many depths."

A word is in order about "principles." We do not wish, nor are we competent, to enter into a philosophical evaluation and definition of "laws," "concepts," and "principles." Ecology proceeds, as does any empirical science, (1) by the collection of relevant facts; (2) by the arrangement of these facts into ordered series according to their relations and patterns; and (3) by the development of higher-category knowledge or principles that synthesize and correlate the material at hand. Thus the "principles" we shall attempt to formulate and interrelate are simply those generalizations inductively derived from the data of ecology. We regard the so-called "laws of nature" as empirical, derived from the facts, and not the facts from the laws. In this view, a principle is a means of description of nature in succinct and compressed form. This is true in the relatively well-organized physical sciences, in which the principles frequently can be reduced by mathematical statement to the extreme of simplification. In the vastly more complex biological sciences, mathematical formulation of generalizations is more difficult, and possible only in limited segments of the complex. The process of inductive generalization is useful at every stage. The principles derived from the compression of a mass of data into a science form the main basis for deductive thinking and for hypotheses which ask new questions and make possible new advances, on the one hand by opening up new fields of inquiry and on the other hand by progressive correction of the older generalizations in the light of additional data.

We subscribe to the general principle of scientific parsimony ("William of Occam's razor"), which may be stated as follows: "Neither more, nor more onerous, causes are to be assumed than are necessary to account for the phenomena" (Pearson, 1937, p. 340). For ecology in particular, the number of entities should not be unnecessarily increased. Furthermore, Morgan's canon (1894) concerning animal behavior is essentially a quantitative development of "Occam's razor" and an application of the law of parsimony: "In no case may we interpret an action as the outcome of the exercise of a higher psychical faculty, if it can be interpreted as the outcome of one which stands lower in the psychological scale."

There is an understandable tendency in any synthesizing discussion to review chiefly the progress made in recent years or decades. This is sound practice in many ways, but one result is that work, often excellent work, of previous decades or even centuries may be neglected. A false idea of rapidity of progress is thereby encouraged, and the concept of the relatively complete modernity of subject matter tends to be built up in the thinking of younger readers, although the minds of authors and editors may have been entirely free from such a misconception. We have accordingly made a serious effort throughout this book to supply historical perspective and regard the history of ecology and of its antecedent sciences as an integral and significant part of our treatment.

Ecological history, like that of zoology in general, can be summed up briefly as follows: In the Greek period—either because such was the case, or because Aristotle did not cite sources—it was the apparent rule to study nature directly and to think over the implications of observations made at first hand. During the long scholastic period in the Middle Ages, the influence of which unhappily lingers on here and there, the fashion changed to a study of books, or at least a part of those available. The spirit of the scientific awakening was at length summarized by the dictum of Louis Agassiz: "Study nature, not books."* Too often this became perverted, by practice rather than by precept, to the study of preserved specimens, and some books. A gradual change occurred until in the early decades of the present century the tacit advice became: Study living and preserved organisms in the laboratory together with the pertinent books.

One constant effort of the modern ecological movement has been to take the study of nature again out under the sky. This could not entirely succeed, in part because of the difficulties in doing accurate analytical work in the field. A partial compromise is attained by our turning to the greenhouse and breeding cage, where experimentally-minded ecologists have been met by workers moving out of orthodox laboratories into these substitutes for field conditions. Some ecologists have remained stubbornly in the field, where they are being joined by a trickle of the more orthodox indoor students. Laboratory and field ecology are interdependent, and both are essential. At the same time, the check of knowledge gained directly against printed accounts, both as to empirical content and

* An amusing and even paradoxical commentary on this famous aphorism may be derived from the fact that Agassiz prepared the first comprehensive bibliography of zoology—the four volume *Bibliographia Zoologiae*, published by the Ray Society (1848–1854).

philosophical implications, is being given more balanced consideration.

The reality and usefulness of the population as an ecological unit were apparent to us when we outlined the present book, and our subsequent work has reinforced our conviction of the importance of the principles that center on the population. We view the population system, whether intraspecies or interspecies, as a biological entity of fundamental importance. This entity can be studied with some measure of precision, and the emergent principles are significant throughout the field of ecology. The population is forged by strong bonds with autecology through the physiology and behavior of individuals; communities are composed of recognizable population elements; and evolutionary ecology depends directly upon population systems, since selection acts upon populations that evolve and become adapted to their environments, to a more important degree than upon individuals. The study of populations as such, as operational systems, yields principles that clarify the nature of group interactions, interactions that do not exist at the level of the single organism, and that are too complex at the community level to be analyzed in a quantitative way.

The major relations of animals center around nourishment, reproduction and protection. The reaction to these needs may be summarized by the concept of a "drive" towards favorable ecological position. This usually implies a drive for security of one kind or another, or of all kinds. The partially mystical idea of a "drive" hides the nonmystical one of the survival values furnished by the attainment of nourishment, protection and sufficient reproduction, or even by the attempt to secure them.

The situation can be clarified somewhat by attending to only one of the three fundamental needs—protection, for example. The given animal, or population, may orient and move actively toward protected places as a generalized reaction that may become much more marked in times of particular stress. Or the individual or population may wander about, apparently at random, and come to rest under favorable conditions. Animals may invade a more stable physical environment such as that furnished by a pond or a forest, or in winter there may be a movement down to the forest floor or an active invasion of its superficial carpet of leaves and of the soil beneath them. Security may be gained by attaining control of a portion of the environment through the slow processes of ecological succession leading toward the establishment of an ecological climax or through the more active animals moving into natural safe niches or building their own shelters. A third mode of progress toward ecological security, or more assured ecological position, is found in societal evolution. These are all aspects of the tendency toward ecological homeostasis, and this sort of homeostasy is one of the major inclusive principles of ecology and, with a different emphasis, of physiology as well.

The tendency towards homeostasy extends through the diverse phases of ecology, whether the subdivisions are based on habitat differences such as those characteristic of oceanography, of limnology, or of the land, or of the living habitats of parasites. Such tendencies are found under primarily physical relations with nonliving environments and also when all the relations are primarily biotic.

The physical universe is indifferent to life in general and resistant to the influence of living organisms even in slow-working long-time trends. For that matter, organisms are largely indifferent to each other. Dramatic incidents occur, and there is a strong tendency to record and to overemphasize these. Animals, under many conditions, and plants as well, may merely persist; it is then needful to search out the undramatic relations that allow them to continue to live when little or nothing beyond mere existence is involved. Often only a saving few individuals survive in a given habitat, and these may spend much of their time apparently doing nothing at all except remaining alive. Hibernation, aestivation, "resting" cysts, and resistant or so-called winter eggs represent periods of marked quiescence. The quiet retirement of animals capable of extreme activity is often a fundamental part of living. Hens fight and actively establish social orders based on dominance and subordinance, yet they spend much more time in which no activity is evident. Chimpanzees exhibit a strong drive for status in a social group, and yet they too pass only a small percentage of their time in active social tension. Outdoor nature is a place where there is much inactivity. Even in the teeming tropics an observer frequently has nothing to do except wait and watch. In fact, patience is one of the prime prerequisites for naturalistic study of undisturbed wild life, even when attention is limited to selected birds or mammals. The essential impatience of observers is one of the dominant reasons for the growth of experimentation in ecology; but great patience is required for any adequate long-term program of experimentation, the ramifications of which may seem endless.

Such considerations lead naturally to thinking about the interrelations between ecology and animal behavior, since the active behavior of animals both in field and laboratory may be striking, and behavior studies can yield important indications of current environmental effects. This does not imply that all studies of animal behavior as developed at present are directly or even indirectly ecological (except in a quite remote sense). Students of behavior are much concerned with psychological problems, which in turn may lead into physiology and into philosophy rather than into ecology proper.

Many of the ecological phases of animal behavior cluster about the central problems of distribution, being concerned with the closely related matter of so-called habitat selection or, objectively expressed, of modality. Gradients of important environmental factors exist in nature both on small and on large or even gigantic scales. Gradients of concentration of oxygen, carbon dioxide, and other chemicals, including food, heat, moisture, light and pressure, to mention no more, give stimuli to which animals react. The responses may be fairly direct and oriented, amounting at times to forced movements, or there may be random reactions of the trial-and-error variety. The results may either be apparent immediately or they may be deferred for days, weeks, seasons, years, centuries or millenia; or finally they may be discoverable only in the vast perspective of geological time. Migrations such as those of birds and butterflies are frequently large-scale spectacles; in contrast, important emigrations may be inconspicuous events, the effects of which have not become fully apparent during recorded history.

Emigrations may have evolutionary as well as contemporaneous importance. These time scales sometimes blend, as they do in illustrations of what is known as the host selection principle (p. 615). In theory, it is only a short step from the host selection shown by wood-boring beetle larvae that tend to live in and feed upon a particular species of tree, to the more crystallized behavior shown by solitary wasps that catch, sting, and oviposit on a particular kind of caterpillar, grasshopper or spider. (The implied evolution can be explained by modern assumptions centering about natural selection.) This brings up also the problem of search for the right animal to be captured, stung and parasitized, in which the innate behavior patterns, commonly and somewhat roughly called instincts, have real and far-reaching ecological implications. (The interested reader is referred to Tinbergen, 1942, for a behavioristic approach to the subject.)

Some behavior patterns of higher vertebrates appear to resemble innate, instinctive behavior, and yet have been demonstrated for certain birds to result from a specialized type of early learning, called "imprinting" by Lorenz (1935). Imprinting results when a young animal at an impressionistic age, when the learning threshold is low, is exposed to a meaningful stimulus or to some suitable substitute. Normally at such times the stimulus that becomes imprinted, so to speak, initiates persisting behavior that may dominate the animal's activities for the rest of its life. A common example concerns the following of an adult of the species, often the female parent. This behavior results from a few contacts, or even from a single contact at the proper age. In the absence of the parent, the tendency to follow a given individual may be imprinted by exposure to some other animal at the crucial time, with amusing and incongruous results. The tendency is important in the normal building of family or flock integration; the interesting psychological mechanisms and implications lead beyond our scope.

Other types of integrations with the biological or physical environment are also apparent, as are many fundamental questions. How does an animal find and settle in a given habitat? How much so-called search is involved? Is there an element of active preferential choice, or, more simply, is there a reaction to the relative absence of disturbing stimuli? To what extent is the behavior innate, and how much is reestablished each generation? This leads to curiosity concerning the possible presence of tradition among nonhuman animals. How much learning, if any, is involved? To what extent, if at all, are animals conscious of their actions or surroundings?

These are troublesome questions concerning which it is difficult to collect exact and pertinent information, whether from existing literature, directly from outdoor nature, or by means of planned experiments. Elton (1933) recognized the existence of such problems and suggested some conclusions that depart from current trends of thought in scientific circles. Apparently speaking primarily of birds and mammals, he says (p. 46):

"Changes in habitat are frequent, and we do not yet know precisely what relative importance to attach to psychological factors (new ideas, or broken traditions or accumulative fatigue with old habits) and how much to organic changes in the form of mutations affecting behaviour. Finally it is of great interest to inquire whether animals are actually conscious of their actions, and whether in this consciousness there is any element which is at variance with the usual concepts of animal behaviour current among physiologists and also many ecologists. There is definite evidence that animals often migrate in response to stimuli which cannot be called danger signals but which appear to be unpleasant to them (Elton, 1930). Whether in this behaviour we can discern feelings akin to aesthetic feelings or whether they are to be looked upon as mechanical aspects of mental balance, cannot be decided. The whole question of animal behaviour in relation to the choice of habitats and habits in general is of profound importance both in theoretical science and in practical economic biology."

These are matters that we cannot yet solve, but it is important that we should not continue to ignore their existence. A major difficulty lies in the absence of an objective terminology. The use of vaguely defined terms is associated with the uncritical humanizing tendencies of many naturalists, who in turn give strong avoiding reactions to the carefully objective and perhaps overcorrected point of view of critical modern students.

Recognition of community of interests between the general and comparative phases of psychology and of ecology calls for commendation of the modern tendency toward objective terminology in both subjects, as well as in general biology and other phases of science. General anthropomorphic con-

cepts and language are to be avoided, admitting that other considerations such as clarity and brevity or entrenched usage may sometimes require exception. It is unfortunate to have to use a Greek or Latin root meaning "loving," for example, to denote an ecological relation, when the English form would be objectionable or ridiculous. This is a language ideal that is frequently difficult to apply even with conscious and conscientious effort. There is a severe strain when one is convinced (a) that the Cartesian doctrine is essentially unsound, (b) that scientific writing should be simple, clear, and direct, and (c) that even the words used should not carry partially hidden suggestions unsupported by direct evidence.

A binding principle in ecology, as in many other phases of biology, deals with the integration of individual units into larger wholes. Cells of more complex animals combine into tissues, organs, and systems, and yet all this complexity develops from a single cell. Even at the cell level, certain cells living in close association with each other—as in lichens, for example—may not be germinally related. All ecological communities lack the germinal continuity characteristic of populations of single species and particularly characteristic of colonial animals like sponges or many hydroids, or the typical societal colonies of social bees, wasps, or ants. Interspecific populations also obviously lack germinal continuity. Their evolution is traced to a combination of ecology and genetics that will be outlined in the section on Evolution.

The relationships between these ecological categories may be traced either by the type method or by the principles treatment attempted in the present book. Neither approach is automatically preferable. The cataloguing of one category after another gives a readily indexed treatment that orders the details in a workable manner, but may conceal the underlying principles. The approach through principles may confuse the issue so far as facts are concerned and may be unsatisfactory for those interested primarily in a catalog of existing data.

The type treatment deals directly with the ecology of the oceans, one after another, of bays and gulfs, of the fresh water, and of the land. The principles treatment draws evidence now from one and now from another type of habitat, and then passes on to repeat the process with another principle. The two approaches continually tend to become mixed when the documentation of principles is given in any detail. Recognition of the existence of a physical environment as contrasted with a biotic environment illustrates the principles approach; even when the physical environment is broken down into component parts, the treatment continues to present principles, when, within the subdivisions such as temperature, light, and moisture, the discussion centers about principles such as the temperature "laws," Bergmann's rule, and Corioli's force.

A fresh definition of the community concept is offered in the present work: In large, the major community may be defined as a natural assemblage of organisms which, together with its habitat, has reached a survival level such that it is relatively independent of adjacent assemblages of equal rank; to this extent, given radiant energy, it is self-sustaining.

This definition places special restrictions on a term that has often been a useful catch-all, correctly applicable to any ecological assemblage ranging from the inhabitants of a small clod of earth to the animals and plants living in the northern evergreen forests of the world. Under the older usage, "community" might refer to a simple ecological unit illustrated by a thin mat of floating algae as well as to the complicated, multistoried tropical rain-forest (J. R. Carpenter, 1938). A practical solution seems to be to recognize the usage of the term "community" both in the restricted sense indicated by our definition, and in the extended loose sense. It will occasionally be necessary, under the conditions, to add or to imply "s.s." or "s.lat.," "in a strict sense" or "in a broad sense." We have wished to avoid further implementation of the facetious definition of ecology as being that phase of biology primarily abandoned to terminology.

There are two fundamental approaches to ecological communities that are best presented by considering the two extremes. As biocoenoses, they may be organized primarily by the interrelations of the plants and animals as associates; in contrast, the basic organization may rest on the common habitat in which the constituent organisms serve primarily as indicators and secondarily as associated individuals. Both types of communities exist in fairly pure form, and there are closely graded interconnections. The biota of the desert presents many aspects of a community controlled by its physical habitat, and the oyster bed is a classical example of a biotically controlled biocoenosis. Both types present many different orders of complexity and size; one of the larger of these, the biome, requires further mention.

The biome, represented by the northern coniferous forest in North America, includes three major plant associations: viz., the spruce-pine forest of Alaska and northwestern Canada; the spruce-balsam fir forest of northern Canada from the Mackenzie River through Labrador and southward; and the pine-hemlock forest of southeastern Canada, the region around Lake Superior, and northern Michigan. The climax dominants of the last two associations are radically different, but they resemble each other closely in having a large number of identical animal constituents that characteristically range through both.

Shelford and Olsen (1935, p. 395) list the common animals of the coniferous forest biome, pointing out that they range through the three major plant associations without conspicuous change. Their analysis shows the importance of the animals in defining biotic units and the weaknesses inherent in biome concepts based solely on data concerning plants. The vegetation is not the sole key to the biome. Furthermore, the pine-hemlock community has a clear unity with the transcontinental spruce-balsam fir forest and even with the Alaskan spruce-pine association. This unity is based on subclimax stages and on animal constituents some of which may be relatively unimportant ecologically.

The universality of the biome concept meets a severe test in the geographic fragmentation of the major biotic formations. New Guinea and northern Australia, for example, tend to be separated by plant geographers into two areas (Scrivenor et al., 1943). Contrariwise, most students of animal distribution unite the two into a common major zoogeographic region. The concept of the biome, like many other ecological generalizations, must be accepted with proper reservations and adjusted to the historical problems involved.

Ecological formations are not static. Given time, the advance and retreat of glaciers affects the location of the tundra. Grasslands expand and contract on a vast geographic scale; deserts wax and wane. Bodies of water, including whole oceans, overflow their basins; in another geological age, the land masses stand high out of water. These changes follow certain more or less irregular periodicities that have a geological time scale. Shorter temporal progressions also occur. Given sufficient freedom from man's interference, striking vegetational changes may occur within the life of a single human generation. Burnt-over areas "heal," and, given longer time, seral successions advance from pioneer through intermediate stages to the climax characteristic for the given climate. A community in this temporal series undergoes development and maturation before the succeeding one replaces it. The processes of biotic *development* in combination with those of physiographic *succession* are referred to as "Community Ontogeny." "Community Phylogeny" involves the whole range of continuing adaptational change of the components of the community. Community evolution, in a broad sense, has been made to include several meanings:

1. The development of the climax through successive biotic changes and stages—a process comparable to the development of the individual.

2. The organic development of the climax when there is a series of underlying and correlated physiographic changes, succession in the strict sense.

3. The convergence of community life-forms, which is implied, so far as plants are concerned, by speaking of the evolution of vegetation as contrasted with the evolution of the species composition of the community flora. The animal constituents show the same kind of interrelations in structures and in physiological adjustments, and the whole biota can be similarly considered.

4. The community evolves also as a result of converging immigration. Thus in the Chicago area we have elements that have come from both southeastern and southwestern centers of dispersal, immigrants from the more northern grasslands and from the northern forests, relicts from the glacial age, and regional endemics. The combination of this third sort of community evolution with the convergencies allows us to think of the evolution of the bio-sociological climax community as a whole without giving particular consideration to the evolution of the constituent species. From this point of view the evolution of forest or grassland, or other communities, focusses on their evolution as biotic complexes. Mesozoic and modern forests, for example, have biotic equivalence, regardless of the great differences in the species and higher groups of both plants and animals.

5. Such considerations lead to another aspect of community evolution, namely, "The phylogeny of the definitive grouping of species within the community." The subject is too complex for thorough treatment, and of necessity we have been essentially limited to tracing the evolution of pairs of ecologically related species, or at most to small groups of species that have apparently evolved under close mutual relationships. This has the advantage of forcing us to test fundamental interrelations that stand near the simplest level of community organization, and it emphasizes our lack of knowledge of more complicated ecological phylogenies.

Reconstruction of the cause of evolution of the biosociological whole requires consideration and integration of all these aspects. We recognize and can outline the problem without being able to advance far toward its solution.

In community relations it is important to consider the fundamental relations of protocooperation, disoperation, and, as a somewhat different category, competition. These are matters difficult to discuss with clarity. In part the difficulty lies in the need to consider both short-run operational aspects and long-run evolutionary phases. Aside from such complications, and from the innate complexities, there is the lack of sufficient exact and carefully documented information with which one may test and modify, and reject or strengthen, tentative conclusions.

The competition among plants for space and light and for nutrients is obvious under many conditions. Such competition is one of the important relationships that find expression in the evolution of life forms with resultant layering. There is also competition for pollination when, or if, potential pollinators are scarce, and for effective mutualism, if one of the mutualistic pair lacks local abundance. Competition is avoided, at least in part, by the evolution of space and of time separations, or by some combination of these. Important as competition may be, it can readily be overstressed; Clements and Shelford (1939, p. 166) help to correct this tendency when they state that "It is desirable to stress again the fact that competition comprises a relatively small number of the countless coactions among animals." So far as predation is concerned, this conclusion is supported down to the species level—or to different races within the species—by the generalization of Volterra (1931), elaborated by Gause (1935) and illustrated by Lack (1946), showing that competition is lessened until it may become relatively unimportant as a result of differences in habitats and habits of predators even when they otherwise show much similarity. Such a qualification does not affect conclusions concerning competition between individuals of the same subspecies unless these, too, come to develop some slight dissimilarity in individual habits.

With all these reservations, competition is a potent factor in animal life, and its results are not always disoperative. In fact, there is evidence for what may be called the biological necessity of predacious types that eliminate surplus populations by killing off weaker animals, especially when these occupy marginal habitats filled beyond their year-round carrying capacity.

The basic cooperative relations, particularly the more obscure protocooperations, or biological facilitations, often are difficult to demonstrate conclusively under laboratory conditions even when using selected situations and favorable organisms. They become still more elusive in the field, especially at the community level, and particularly for students well grounded in skepticism. Some of the more apparent protocooperations under these conditions include:

1. The role of bacteria in the formation of soil and in its yearly renewal of fertility.
2. The similar role of bacteria in the mineral nutrient cycles of the sea and of fresh-water communities.
3. The full range of subtle interactions between soil organisms and the soil.
4. The mass effects of organisms on the toxicity of media.
5. The "rain" of dead organisms from the surface of the ocean that permits the development of life in the great lightless depths of the sea.
6. The protocooperations inherent in the definition of a dominant organism in the community as one that receives the full impact of environment and so modifies it that associated species can live in areas they could not otherwise invade.

The effects produced by plants and animals on their physical, chemical, and biotic environment that prepare the way for continuing the community development show both disoperative and protocooperative aspects. The disoperation concerns those present occupants of the habitat whose activities are making their own continuance impossible in that particular place. The protocooperations come in the preparation of conditions that will permit the whole series to move on towards the climax.

In the community, as well as in its component biocoenoses or smaller fragments, the forces making for ecological facilitation are, in the long run, generally somewhat stronger and more widespread than those tending towards disoperation.

In our ambitious attempt to set forth ecological principles, it is fitting to emphasize the unknown elements remaining in the field. The very existence of some of these is just beginning to gain recognition. Others, at the present time, can be outlined in qualitative terms only; still others, doubtless, are as yet wholly unknown. Some few relations can be given fairly exact mathematical treatment. There is much room for pure humility among ecologists who are trying to cope with these loosely formulated relationships, most of which cannot be expressed in exact quantitative formulations.

The relations of individuals to temperature, light, and gravity, and to other environmental factors, can often be stated with approximate precision. Population ecology is quantitative with respect to description, at least under certain controlled laboratory conditions, but even students of this phase of the subject edge away from prediction except on the basis of statistical probability based on accumulated data. For some students this situation produces an avoiding reaction; for many it constitutes a challenge; for others of us, less well-equipped for quantitative studies, it has a strong primary attraction. We enjoy working under the necessity of making needed reservations and keeping in mind the many and varied qualifications that should prevent us from making dogmatic generalizations.

The inadequacy of the framework of ecological principles presented in the following chapters is evident; supplementation and correction are urgent needs for the advancement of ecology. But it is also important to point out that it is often impossible to find exact and well-chosen data concerning a given point. The minimum temperature at which death occurs immediately for any population of a species of animals is a good illustration. For that matter, the limits of toleration for all elements in the physical environment except in general terms are unknown for any one species of animal, even for man. With all our emphasis on the need of ecological principles, it must be emphasized again that in the formulation of principles, as in testing and extending them, evidence is basic.

SECTION I. THE HISTORY OF ECOLOGY

2. ECOLOGICAL BACKGROUND AND GROWTH BEFORE 1900

Carnap (1938) recognized "physics" as a common name for the nonbiological field of science and stated that "the whole of the rest of science may be called biology (in the large sense)." He immediately saw the necessity of dividing this wider biology into two fields, the first of which contains "most of what is usually called biology, namely, general biology, botany, and the greater part of zoology." The second part "deals with the behavior of individual organisms and groups of organisms within the environment; with the dispositions to such behavior, with such features of processes in organisms as are relevant to the behavior, and with certain features of the environment which are characteristic of and relevant to the behavior, e.g., objects observed and work done by organisms."

Carnap proceeds to discuss the distinctions between the two phases of biology primarily from the point of view of human relations and suggests, among other things, that the second phase might be made up by "selecting the processes in an organism from the point of view of their relevance to achievements in the environment . . . ." He continues by saying that "there is no name in common use for this second field. . . . The term 'behavioristics' has been proposed. If it is used, it must be made clear that the word 'behavior' has here a greater extension than it had with the earlier behaviorists. Here it is intended to designate not only the overt behavior which can be assayed from outside but also internal behavior (i.e., processes within the organism); further, dispositions to behavior which may not be manifested in a special case; and finally, certain effects upon the environment."

Carnap distinguishes between such relations of individual organisms and groups of organisms and adds that "it seems doubt-ful whether any sharp line can be drawn between these two parts." He also states that such considerations extend to non-human animals as well as to men.

Thus, late in the 1930's, a philosopher of high attainments compounded logical necessity with ignorance of the history and present development of biological ideas, and announced as new the discovery of the field of "bionomics," "ethology," "ecology," or "relations physiology." This happened at the University of Chicago, where research and teaching concerning the relations between organisms and their environments had been an active feature of the biological program since the late 1890's. The long, respectable history of this phase of biology forms the subject matter of the present section. Carnap's statement is a valuable introduction to this history, since it demonstrates anew that ecology fills a natural niche in biological science. It also gives warning of the lack of general knowledge among scholars as to the mass of information in this field.

Near the turn of the present century, W. K. Brooks, founder of the great Johns Hopkins tradition in biology, expressed much the same need for an understanding of the environmental relations of organisms as that given by Carnap. He stated: "To study life we must consider three things: *first,* the orderly sequence of external nature; *second,* the living organism and the changes which take place in it; and *third,* that continuous adjustment between the two sets of phenomena which constitutes life. The physical sciences deal with the external world, and in the laboratory we study the structure and activities of organisms by very similar methods; but if we stop there, neglecting the relation of the living being to its environment, our study is not biology or the

13

science of life." The idea was already old when Brooks expressed it.

Now, having placed two shots on this side of our target, we may try a much longer range and come up on the historical development of the basic ideas of ecology in conventional fashion. The first half of this historical section will deal with the beginnings of ecology up to about 1900 and will be followed by a survey of the rapid growth of the subject during the present century.

While the word "ecology" was put together from Greek roots and is based on *oikos,* which means home, the Greeks did not have a word for it, and it is problematical to what extent they appreciated the basic ideas and relationships that the word now summarizes. In this respect, ecology does not differ essentially from many other phases of modern biology. The Greeks did observe the home life of animals after the relatively unorganized methods of what is still called natural history, and they were aware of the necessity for interrelations between living things and their environment.

Empedocles, about the middle of the fifth century B.C., said that plants procure nourishment through pores in stem and leaves; he obviously realized that plants have relations with their environment.

Pre-Aristotelian Greeks had developed a considerable stock of information about some of the environmental influences in relation to human health. Hippocrates, so-called father of medicine, emphasized such matters. Among the extant writings that Adams (1849) considers genuine works of Hippocrates, that "On Airs, Waters and Places" is strongly environmental in its medical emphasis. There is a recognition of the influence of location, exposure, and season upon health, but Hippocrates also knew that in order to estimate the effect of a given season, the nature of the preceding seasons must also be considered. The first paragraph of this essay gives his approach to medicine:

"Whoever wishes to investigate medicine properly, should proceed thus: in the first place to consider the seasons of the year, and what effects each of them produces (for they are not at all alike, but differ much from themselves in regard to their changes). Then the winds, the hot and the cold, especially such as are common to all countries, and then such

as are peculiar to each locality. We must also consider the qualities of the waters, for as they differ from one another in taste and weight, so also do they differ much in their qualities. In the same manner, when one comes into a city to which he is a stranger, he ought to consider its situation, how it lies as to the winds and the rising of the sun; for its influence is not the same whether it lies to the north or the south, to the rising or to the setting sun. These things one ought to consider most attentively, and concerning the waters which the inhabitants use, whether they be marshy and soft, or hard, and running from elevated and rocky situations, and then if saltish and unfit for cooking; and the ground, whether it be naked and deficient in water, or wooded and well watered, and whether it lies in a hollow, confined situation, or is elevated and cold; and the mode in which the inhabitants live, and what are their pursuits, whether they are fond of drinking and eating to excess, and given to indolence, or are fond of exercise and labour, and not given to excess in eating and drinking."

The applications that follow are not usually impressive in the light of present day knowledge, but the point of view is modern. These early teachings are important in the history of ecology since they give some inkling of the state of Greek thought before Aristotle's activities began.

Aristotle (384–322 B.C.) is usually regarded as the founder of biological science. Ramaley (1940) suggested that Aristotle "hardly takes a place in ecology, although he did study the habits of animals to some extent." This calls for a look at Aristotle's writings.[*] The material given in Section 1 of Book 1 may be outlined in part as follows:

Animals differ in modes of subsistence, Aristotle says, in actions, in habits, and in their parts. They include:

I. Water animals
   1. Entirely aquatic
   2. Animals that live and feed in water, but breathe air and bring forth their young on land.
   3. Sea dwellers
   4. River dwellers
   5. Lake dwellers
   6. Marsh dwellers

Elsewhere Aristotle definitely recognized amphibious animals.

[*] D'Arcy Thompson's 1910 translation of *Historia Animalium.*

II. Land animals, which may, however, invade water

Water-"inhaling" animals do not derive subsistence from the land. Some of them live in water and then change shape and live on land. Stationary animals live only in water, where they may be (*a*) attached or sessile; (*b*) unattached but motionless.

Means of locomotion of animals: swimming, walking, flying, wriggling, creeping.

No creature is able to move solely by flying as fish move by swimming.

Flocks of birds differ in power.

Some birds are present at all times; others are seasonal.

Some are gregarious; others are solitary.

Some gregarious animals are social.

Some birds are gregarious, but none with crooked talons have that habit.

Many fish are gregarious.

Social animals have a common object in view.

Some social animals have a ruler; some do not.

Animals may have a fixed home or be nomadic.

Diets differ: they may be (*a*) carnivorous, (*b*) graminivorous, (*c*) omnivorous, or (*d*) special, e.g., honey.

Some animals have dwellings; some do not.

Some are nocturnal, others diurnal.

Some are tame, some wild; some wild animals are easily tamed, e.g., the elephant.

Domesticated animals all have wild relatives.

Some emit sounds; others are mute.

All animals without exception exercise their power of singing or chattering chiefly in connection with intercourse of the sexes.

Some live in fields; others on mountains; some frequent abodes of men.

Some are salacious, e.g., the cock; others are inclined to chastity.

Some marine animals live in open sea, some near shore, some on rocks.

Animals differ in character:
(*a*) Good-natured, sluggish
(*b*) Quick-tempered, ferocious
(*c*) Intelligent, timid
(*d*) Mean, treacherous
(*o*) Noble, courageous
(*f*) Thoroughbred, wild, treacherous
(*g*) Crafty, mischievous
(*h*) Spirited, affectionate, fawning
(*i*) Easy-tempered
(*j*) Jealous, self-conceited
Many animals have memory.

Aristotle's observations on the breeding behavior of animals are scattered through his writings on zoology, which, in general, are not so well organized as might appear from the foregoing outline. They are not yet ecology. They do constitute good natural history, for the first major attempt, and they represent a part of the stuff from which ecology has developed. It may be remembered that natural history contains elements of other phases of biology, of anatomy and taxonomy, for example, as well as much of ecological importance.

Ramaley (1940) regards Theophrastus as the first ecologist in history. Theophrastus was a student and friend of Aristotle's and succeeded him as leader of the Athenian Lyceum. Ramaley says that Theophrastus wrote sensibly of the communities in which plants are associated, of the relations of plants to each other and to their nonliving environment. According to Greene (1909, p. 125), Theophrastus definitely forecast the natural associations of plants in particular places. He distinguished (1) marine aquatics, (2) marine littoral plants, (3) plants of deep fresh water, (4) those of shallow lake shores, (5) plants of wet banks of streams, and (6) of marshes. He wrote of trees that grow on exposed, sunny mountain slopes, of those that flourish only on northern exposures, and also of those limited to the more frigid summits.

As has been shown, Aristotle gave a somewhat similar classification of animals in relation to their habitats. In fact, Zeller (1931, p. 202) states that the extant writings of Theophrastus on plants follow Aristotle in their leading ideas. Theophrastus did found plant systematics, wrote on plant geography, and developed a sort of plant physiology. He also knew enough about color changes in animals to show that he had some grasp of the color adaptation of animals to their environment.

Even the best of the Greeks did not have all their facts straight and showed tendencies toward accepting travelers' tales uncritically, which some moderns have at last outgrown. They used anthropomorphisms with plants and animals alike about on a level with those found in "nature study" today. Aristotle, great as he was, apparently was no greater genius than are our best modern thinkers, and perhaps not less great, either. It may be added that Aristotle was probably no stronger in sheer mental ability than the best of the ancients who lived 2500 years before him, though there were more facts accumulated by his time with which he could deal. We judge a man or a group of men historically by the end product they leave behind, and a good lasting end product, even in affairs of the intellect, does not necessarily trace back to the work of one brilliant man.

Certain rule-of-thumb ecological knowledge was evidently widespread among the Hebrews of 2000 years ago, though they were not notably a scientific people. The "parable of the sower," for example, shows that the relation between habitat and yield was well understood, though not in these words.

The Romans used widely distributed folk knowledge in creating the science of agriculture. In their hands, this grew primarily from hunting and fishing, enriched by early experience with plant and animal husbandry. Roman agriculture was fertilized by the writings of the Greeks and put into practice with their own common sense. It was based on empirical ecological observations and was frankly economic in outlook.

Pliny the Elder (A.D. 23–79), one of the best of the Roman writers of the period, owes his reputation to his *Natural History,* which was the starting point of modern faunal study. Pliny's account tends to be a confused jumble of compiled notes without logical organization. Nordenskiold (p. 53) defends Pliny against overharsh critics who accuse him of being a soulless compiler, because, "more honest than Aristotle, he quotes his sources." Like Aristotle, Pliny used an ecological system of classification. Among his categories we find the recognition of terrestrial, aquatic, and flying animals.

Ramaley (1940) also recognizes the good in Pliny's work. He quotes with approval the following: "A soil that is adorned by tall and graceful trees is not always a favorable one except of course for those trees. What tree is taller than the fir? Yet what other plant could exist in the same spot? Nor are verdant pastures so many proofs of richness of soil. What is there that enjoys greater renown than the pastures of Germany? But they are a mere thin layer of earth with sand underneath." Here we have a suggestion, not only of plant indicators, but also of some of the pitfalls in their use.

After the Roman spark of interest there were few signs of activity in what we now call ecology. The foundation sciences of geography and climatology were undeveloped. Even chemistry and physics could not yet lay the groundwork for physiology, so that ecology had to wait. For a thousand years there was stagnation. When Greek writings again became popular, they were all too slavishly accepted as ultimate authority.

The Greek spirit of inquiry was rediscovered in the Renaissance. Albertus Magnus (1193±–1280) wrote, like Theophrastus, of plants of streamsides and marshes and of the relation between the habitat of a tree and the quality of its wood. While there were some signs of scholarly growth from within Europe, yet the development of ecology, as of other phases of biology, stood still or even regressed until the geographic experiences of Marco Polo and of the Portuguese and the catalyzing discovery of America forced biologists to turn from authority to the study of the thing itself. The interest in new animals and plants, their habits, and their possible usefulness, thus helped to bring on the reawakening of science, especially as regards the forerunners of ecology.

The writings of Gesner (1516–1565) and Aldrovandi (1522–1605) mark the beginning of this movement, which was forced by the accumulation of greater knowledge of local and exotic animals. Greene (1909) writes with high appreciation of the German herbalist, Cordus, who lived briefly about this time (1515–1544). Concerning the bearing of his work on ecology, Greene says (p. 310): "We have already been learning that even from most primitive times every botanist was an ecologist; at least to the extent of observing and recording the special environment which every kind of wild plant affects, and sometimes to the mentioning of some of its associate species. Valerius Cordus, being well-skilled in both chemistry and mineralogy, goes beyond all his predecessors in that he names the petrography of a plant's habitat or otherwise indicates the constituency of the soil in which it is to be looked for."

Robert Boyle (1627–1691) is sometimes referred to as the first of the modern chemists. His biological observations were incidental. In 1670 he published the earliest experiments upon the effect of low atmospheric pressures on animals. The forms tested comprised mice and young kittens, various birds, including a duck and a duckling, snakes, frogs, and different invertebrates, among them several kinds of insects. The point of view from which he made his experiments is shown in the following passage (p. 2012):

"We put a full-grown *Duck* (being not then able to procure a fitter) into a Receiver, whereof she fill'd, by our guess, a third part or somewhat more but was not able to stand in any easy posture in it; then pumping out the Air, though she seemed at first (which yet I am not too confident of upon a single tryal,) to have continued somewhat longer than a Hen in her condition would have done; yet within the short space of one minute she appeared much discomposed and between that and the second minute, her struggling and convulsive motions increased so much that, her head also hanging carelessly down, she seemed to be just at the point of death; from which we presently rescued her by letting the Air in upon her: So that, this Duck being reduced in our Receiver to a gasping condition within less than two minutes it did not appear that, notwithstanding the peculiar contrivance of nature to enable these water-Birds to continue without respiration for some time under water, this Duck was able to hold out considerably longer than a Hen, or other Bird not-Aquatick might have done."

Boyle was impressed by the resistance of cold-blooded animals in his vacua. He experimented with recently born kittens: "Being desirous to try, whether Animals, that had lately been accustomed to live without *any*, or without a *full* Respiration, would not be more difficultly or slowly killed by the want of Air . . . and found that: These tryals may deserve to be prosecuted with further ones, to be made not only with such Kittens, but with other very young Animals of different kinds; for by what has been related it appears, that those Animals continued three times longer in the Exhausted Receiver, than other Animals of that bigness would probably have done."

These quotations show that the approach to Boyle's experimentation was distinctly ecological in the present usage of a word unknown to him and that his experiments were well conducted and not overinterpreted. His main technical weakness lay in failure to record for many of his experiments any indication of the degree of reduction of air pressure in his self-styled "Vacuo Boyliano."

Réaumur (1683–1757) has a place near the beginning of the great modern tradition of natural history. His most notable work, "Mémoires pour servir à l'histoire des insectes," filled six large volumes. He was concerned with the conditions of life of insects, as well as with their structure, and he experimented with their habits of life, including leaf-mining, gall formation, and, more especially, the community life of social insects. He studied parasitism among the Hymenoptera. He made observations on shell formation in mollusks, movement of primitive animals, and the digestion of food. Réaumur was a man of much influence in his own day, and his work is still held in high esteem, as witness the appearance in 1926 of one of his hitherto unpublished manuscripts, translated and annotated by William M. Wheeler.

The modern aspect of ecology did not begin to take form until early in the eighteenth century. Linnaeus (1707–1778) and Buffon (1707–1788), each in his characteristic style, made notable contributions. Nordenskiold (p. 215), with some truth and pardonable patriotism, proclaims that in addition to founding modern systematics, Linnaeus originated all that is now called "phenological, ecological, and geographic zoology and botany" by his descriptions of the influence of external conditions.

Of Buffon, Lankester (1889) said that he "alone among the greater writers of the three past centuries emphasized that view of living things which we call 'bionomics.' Buffon deliberately opposed himself to the mere exposition of the structural resemblances and differences of animals, and, disregarding classification, devoted his treatise on natural history to a consideration of the habits of animals and their adaptations to their surroundings. . . . Buffon is the only writer who can be accorded historic rank in this study." Buffon's great principle of environmental induction is still an important rallying point in dynamic biology. This should not be confused, as apparently it is at times, with Lamarck's principle of the inheritance of effects of use and disuse.

ENVIRONMENTAL PHYSIOLOGY: RANGE AND ADJUSTMENT

We now know that there are two types of environmental effects that may be distinguished conveniently as examples of (*a*) developmental, maintenance and/or toleration physiology, and (*b*) response physiology. The line between them is not necessarily sharp, nor are they mutually exclusive.

In addition to his work on the natural

history of insects, Réaumur was a pioneer in developmental physiology. Interestingly enough, he laid the foundation for the mass of modern work on the summation of temperature when (1735) he found that the sum of the mean daily temperatures of air in the shade made a constant for any given phenological period. Abbe in a book compiled in 1891 and finally published in 1905 quotes a translation from Réaumur as follows: "It would be interesting to continue such comparisons between temperature and the epoch of ripening and to push the study even further, comparing the sum of the degrees of heat for one year with the similar sums of temperature for many other years; it would be interesting to make comparisons of the sums that are effective during any given year in warm countries with the effective sums in cold and temperate climates, or to compare among themselves the sums for the same months in different countries."

Réaumur expanded this statement elsewhere into the suggestion that, since the same grain is harvested in different climates, a comparison should be made of the same temperatures for the months during which the cereals accomplish the greater part of their growth and maturity in warm countries like Spain and Africa, in temperate countries like France, and in cold countries like those of the extreme north. Here we have the background for the geographic application of temperature summation that underlies, in theory at least, certain modern work such as the life zone concept of Merriam and the "bioclimatic law" of Hopkins.

Gasparin in 1844, in commenting on Réaumur's ideas on this subject, recognized in them the germ of all work on the quantity of heat necessary to mature different kinds of plants. According to Abbe, Adanson, soon after Réaumur, disregarded subfreezing temperatures and took only the sums of those above freezing. More than three-quarters of a century later Boussingault in 1837 in his *Rural Economy* computed the total heat required to ripen grain essentially according to Adanson's suggestion. His data indicate that the required number of day degrees increases as the latitude decreases.

Quetelet (1846) added the idea of a threshold of awakening from winter dormancy; even so, in his summary (cf. Abbe,

1905, p. 188) Quetelet used the sum of temperatures, or the sum of the squares of temperatures above freezing for his basic data. Alphonse de Candolle, by 1865, knew that if the time in days required for seed germination is multiplied by the accumulated degrees centigrade, the results are more consistent if the minimum germinating temperature for the species, rather than freezing of water, is taken as the base.

It remained to work out the physiological zero for different plants. Gasparin (1844) adopted 5° C. as the beginning of "effective temperature." By 1852 (*fide* Abbe) he had recognized that these early preoccupations with temperature were faulty in that the effect of other meteorological conditions was also important in phenological affairs. He suggested that rainfall, sunshine, and related meteorological data should also be considered in such analyses.

Candolle (1865) found that, contrary to the opinion of certain workers, some seeds will germinate at 0° C. and possibly at even lower temperature if the water can be kept liquid. He knew about minimum, maximum, and optimum germinating temperatures and emphasized the difference between effective and ineffective temperatures.

Abbe summarizes these and many other records of the measurement of environmental factors and their effects on plants. Among other matters, he reviews the modification of Boussingault's day degrees by Tisserand (1875), who used hours of light between sunrise and sunset multiplied by the mean temperature to give "sunshine-hour degrees." The data indicate that, for the maturation of spring wheat and barley, this mixed summation appears to decrease as the latitude increases.

Abbe also traces the development of information concerning the effect of light on germination and growth of plants from that of Edwards and Colin in 1834 through the cautious conclusion of Pauchon (1880) that light favors germination when the seeds are below their optimum germinating temperature. Abbe discusses the invention by Arago before 1850 of thermometer couples composed of black-bulb and colorless-bulb pairs to measure total insolation, which Marie-Davy improved. By 1867, Roscoe knew from measurements in Europe and Brazil that, unlike heat, the chemical action of light reaches its maximum effect at noon

The measurement of the evaporating power of the air with a Piche evaporimeter had been recorded in the *Montsouris Annuaire* for 1888. Knowledge of other effects of wind is much older. The relation of wind to the dispersion of spores had attracted attention, and certain of the relations to vegetation were also known. For example, Wollny (1891, vol. 14, p. 176) records that the catch of living spores on suitable glass plates in forests is about one-third of that found in the open country.

Interrelations between living organisms were also being studied. Cordus, the German herbalist, in his *Historia Plantarum,* published posthumously in 1561, had described the tubercles on lupine roots. It is a far cry from this initial description to the experiments on nitrogen fixation that flourished in the 1880's. By the end of that decade, much of the basis for present day knowledge of the symbiotic functioning of root tubercles had been experimentally outlined (see Abbe, 1905, p. 136 ff).

It is perhaps pardonable to pause in the midst of this historical survey to point out a fact that is steadily becoming more and more evident. When Brooks was writing the passage referred to earlier in this chapter, or when, to anticipate, Warming was studying the vegetation of the Danish dunes in the early 1890's, there already existed a rich literature concerning the relations of organisms to their environment. Having made this point, it is unnecessary to trace out each detailed advance. We do need to turn to the zoological developments of the nineteenth century to find how far general knowledge about the environmental relations of animals had progressed by the end of that period.

The work of tracing the history of ecology is made easier by the books of Davenport and Semper. Davenport brought together much ecological information in his *Experimental Morphology* (1897–1899, 2 vols., 508 pp.) and documented his writing in modern style. The excellent review by Semper (1879 to 1881), called *Animal Life,* covers a part of the same literature. Both these men had a hand in the rise of self-conscious ecology, a topic that will be considered in due time.

The advances in animal ecology during this period can be more soundly evaluated if the history of plant physiology is also considered. This is summarized by Sachs (1882) and Pfeffer (1900–1906). The more distinctly ecological discussion by Klebs (1896) of the conditions of existence as they affect the reproduction of algae and fungi is also significant.

It had been suggested before the 1890's that respiration of anaerobic bacteria and of other parasitic organisms resulted from the breaking down of oxygen-containing compounds present in the nutritive medium (cf. Loew, 1891, p. 760). Much earlier, Kühne (1864) had shown experimentally that protoplasmic movement in the ameba is slowed down in the absence of oxygen, while subsequently it was found that the presence of increased amounts of carbon dioxide immobilizes quickly, but kills slowly (Demoor, 1894).

The preliminary information concerning acclimatization to poisons had been worked out both with man (Binz and Schulz, 1879) and other animals (Ehrlich, 1891). Observations on many organisms had yielded the generalization that an organism which produces an albuminoid poison is resistant to that poison. Thus Fayrer (1872) reported that snakes were not killed by injections of their own poison; modern studies show that such immunity is only relative (Keegan and Andrews, 1942).

Determinations by Bezold as early as 1857 showed that the amount of water ordinarily present in body tissues varies with different species. By 1896 it was known that seeds do not germinate if they contain only 10 to 15 per cent of water and that certain animals can revive after being desiccated. Leeuwenhoek mentioned in a letter written in 1702 that when dry stuff from a gutter was put in water, organisms appeared, and Hall (1922) states that Baker in 1764 had revived nematodes after they had been in a dried state for twenty-seven years. Spallanzani, in the late eighteenth century, similarly revived dried rotifers. Preyer (1891) coined the modern term "anabiosis" to apply to apparent death, and Davenport believed (1897), but admittedly could not prove, that anabiosis could result from acclimatization rather than selection. Semper (1881, p. 174) doubted whether, after the protoplasm was actually and truly desiccated, revival could take place, though he knew that eggs of the phyllopod crustacean *Apus* could be kept in mud for years and still hatch out if properly moistened. Other cases of recovery after extended drying were known. For example, Cooke (1895) summarized instances that show the tenacity of life of desert snails. One of the most spectacular concerns two specimens of *Helix desertorum* that were glued to appropriate supports and exhibited in the British Museum from March 26, 1846, to about March 15, 1850, when one revived and fed after being placed in water.

Bachmetjew (1907) cites a fairly rich literature which grew during the latter half of the nineteenth century dealing with the effect of humidity upon the development of insects and insect populations and upon such other matters as body form and color.

By 1890 many of the essential relations of osmosis had been worked out for plant cells by Pfeffer (1877) and De Vries (1884). It had been known for an even longer time that the ameba shrinks in a weak saline solution and swells on return to fresh water (Kühne, 1864). In the late 1870's Schmankewitsch reported that if the fresh-water flagellate *Anisonema acinus* is cultivated for many generations in water to which sea salt is added gradually, its structure is modified, and Grüber (1889) changed the marine form of the heliozoan *Actinophrys sol* to the more vacuolated fresh-water form, and *vice versa*.

Davenport (1897) could make the generalization that the capacity for resistance to stronger salt solutions seems to be closely correlated with the conditions of the medium in which the organism has been reared; he cited a series of observations dating back to those of Beudant (1816) and showing that mollusks living in the diluted sea water of littoral regions, such as *Ostrea* or *Mytilus*, could resist the ill effects of exposure to fresh water better than mollusks from the open sea. Beudant also showed experimentally that fresh-water and marine organisms could go far towards becoming accustomed gradually to the opposite type of medium, or, in more general language, that by varying the density of the culture medium slowly, we may, with time, vary the resistance of individuals. Such experiments were much extended during the nineteenth century as, for example, by Plateau (1871) on the fresh-water isopod *Asellus* and by others on representatives of almost all the principal animal groups. Schmankewitsch's oft-quoted experiments (1875) in which he transformed the brine

shrimp *Artemia salina* to the so-called *A. milhauseni* and back by rearing it in different concentrations of salt water are probably the most dramatic of these otherwise half-forgotten experiments. A consideration of the relation of mineral nutrients, especially those of the soil, to the growth of plants led to the strong emphasis that Liebig (1840) placed on what is now known as Liebig's "law of the minimum" (see p. 198).

Experimental analysis of the effect of light extended throughout this period. Edwards (1824) stated that tadpoles would not develop well in the dark. Others in the fifties and sixties found no effect of light or darkness on the rate of growth, while Yung (1878) claimed that tadpoles grew more rapidly in length in the light. Wood (1867) reported a positive influence of reflected light on the color of butterfly chrysalids.

Modern work on the effect of wavelength of light on animal development apparently began with that of Béclard (1858), and the foundation for present knowledge concerning the relation between wavelength and photosynthesis was laid by Draper (1844), Sachs (1864), and Pfeffer (1871). For plants that contain chlorophyll, it became known that, within limits, the rate of assimilation decreases as light intensity decreases (Reinke, 1883, 1884). For plants and other organisms, the most diverse upper limits of intensity were known by 1896. Experimentation on the lethal effect of light on bacteria dates back to Montegazza, according to Nickles (1865), and was first studied with thoroughness by Downes and Blunt (1877, 1878), who found that the blue end of the spectrum was actively bactericidal, but that red was not similarly effective.

Organisms are normally subjected to a diurnal period of darkness and of light. Smith (1933) says that the first mention in literature of the influence of the length of day on plants is found in the writings of Linnaeus, in 1739. Linnaeus thought, however, that the rapid growth and speedy maturity of arctic plants result from heat rather than from the light supplied by the lengthened days. Davenport (1897, p. 421) records that Trew in 1727 had studied the effect of alternation of light and darkness on the rate of growth in plants. Once opened, the subject attracted attention, but it was not until the work of Sachs (1872) that a continuous curve of plant growth was obtained, demonstrating clearly that growth increases during the night, has a maximum about daybreak, and then falls to a minimum about sunset. Garner (1936) traced the development of photoperiodicity. Moleschott (1855) reported that the frog, *Rana esculenta*, produces carbon dioxide more rapidly in light than in darkness; and Bidder and Schmidt (1852) had found that starving cats show a diurnal rhythmicity in loss of weight, with least rapid loss during the night. It would be interesting to know if temperature changes were properly controlled.

Schäfer (1907) was the first person in the present century to present evidence that length of day is a factor in bird migration. He traces the idea back to a Swedish poet, Runeberg, who was reported in 1874 to have thought that "it is the longing after light, and that alone, that draws the birds southward" in the autumn, and that they return to the long days of the Scandinavian summer for the same reason. The views of Runeberg did not pass unchallenged, for Newton (1874) objected that since both autumn and spring migrations are initiated before the respective equinoxes, the birds in both instances are journeying toward increasingly shortened days.

Apparently without knowing about Runeberg's ideas, Seebohm (1888) wrote concerning the autumnal migration: "The ancestors of the Charadriidae were probably not in search of *warmth* for the climate of the Polar Basin was in those remote ages mild enough: nor in search of *food*, which was probably abundant all the year round; but in search of *light* during the two or three months when the sun never rose above the horizon." Schäfer comments on the fact that Seebohm apparently did not realize that birds might return to the arctic region on account of the lengthened days to be found there.

The custom of providing domestic fowls with added light in order to increase egg production is said to be traceable to Spain in 1802. The practice was introduced into North America in 1895. The effects of the increased length of the light period on the egg production of hens becomes evident in ten to twelve days' exposure. The same practice is now applied in the raising of fowls for food.

Many observers, from Spallanzani (1787) and Saussure (1796) down to Brues (1939), have been interested in collecting data on animals and plants of thermal waters.

Dutrochet (1837), for plants, and Kühne (1859), for animals, head a long line of distinguished workers who agree that, within limits, an increase of heat accelerates protoplasmic movement. Semper (1881, p. 129) could cite sound data to show that an increase in temperature strikingly increases the rate of development of many animals and concluded, accurately enough: "Many other examples might be added . . . all providing the same effect of a rising temperature; but, unfortunately, so far as I know, none give an exactly determined thermal curve for particular species . . ." The first such curve to be published appears to have been that by Lillie and Knowlton (1897).

Modern interest in the degree of heat required to produce death dates to Spallanzani (1787). Edwards (1824), Dutrochet (1837), and Bert (1876) are among those who investigated it. Unfortunately, experimental conditions were not carefully controlled and standardized. Even so, the work of this period fairly well fixed the ideas that prevail today and supplies much of our present information on this subject. In general, this early work showed that while certain flagellates were not killed, under the conditions used, until about 50° C., and while for many groups 45° C., or thereabouts, represents a common death point, the majority of the metazoa are killed below 40° C. or even below 35° C.

Temporary cold rigor and death point as a result of low temperature similarly attracted attention, particularly from 1860 to 1890. The information was sufficient to allow Davenport (1897) to make the sound generalization that there is no fatal minimal temperature for desiccated protoplasm. At the other extreme, according to Doyère (1842, p. 29), rotifers and tardigrades, which in water are killed before the temperature reaches 50° C., after drying may be heated to 120° C. and still survive. This supplies further evidence of the increased resistance of dried protoplasm. Semper (1881, p. 111) cited as a recent discovery that hibernating mammals have a considerably lowered temperature, which Horvath had found to reach 2° C. in the ground squirrel, *Citellus citellus*.

Experiments on acclimatization to high temperatures were also carried on in the later decades of the nineteenth century.

Those of Dallinger (1887), still cited extensively, covered several years, during which time he slowly acclimated a population of flagellates to heat. At the beginning they started to die if raised to 23° C.; finally they were living at 70° C. At this point the experiment was terminated by an accident; neither the nature of this event nor Dallinger's emotions at the time are revealed in the original reports.

Davenport's conclusions, based on knowledge available in 1896, have a distinctly modern sound. In general terms, not in exact quotation, he says (1897, p. 277) that when dynamic conditions vary quantitatively, a quantitative variation in metabolism will follow such that metabolism begins to slow down as limiting conditions are approached. And finally: "A vital phenomenon occurring in a given protoplasmic mass can be reproduced only when the dynamical conditions are reproduced, and the structural limiting conditions are in no wise closely approached."

Semper's earlier *Animal Life* (1881) is less fully documented and hence is somewhat less helpful in strict chronology. His book has the distinct advantage of being written from much more nearly the modern ecological point of view than was Davenport's. A brief review of some of his points will increase our knowledge of, and respect for, the ecological information available at the close of the 1870's.

Semper knew of monophagy in the strict modern sense among both carnivores and herbivores. He also knew that monophagy is often closely connected with the occurrence of special organs or structural relations, or with special adjustments in the life history. He clearly foreshadowed the modern conception of "key-industry" animals, and he worked out in principle what has come to be called the "pyramid of numbers" (p. 52).

Protective color changes in animals have long been a matter of interest. Semper (p. 91) reports that Stark in 1830 recorded observations on color changes in several different kinds of fishes; Shaw in 1838 was perhaps the first to conclude that fishes that can change color are apparently protected thereby from predators. Lister (1858) found by experimentation that a connection exists between eyes and chromatophores in frogs, a relationship later independently confirmed by Pouchet (1876),

who experimentally demonstrated that the connection existed through the sympathetic nervous system. Except in the growth of detailed knowledge and the formulation of the ratio hypothesis to explain background matching (Keeble and Gamble, 1904), the next important advance in the matter of knowledge about chromatophore activity came with the relatively recent insight into the role of hormones and of neural humors in the ecological relations of animals capable of color change to fit their environment.

Semper strongly doubted the significance of the classification of animals according to the temperature zones in which they live in "fortuitous community." He thought that the well-being of animals that live in association depends far more essentially on the variations and extremes of temperature than on the absolute degree of heat to which they may be simultaneously exposed at any given time. Hence he found the distinction that Möbius had made between stenothermal and eurythermal to be as important as we now hold it to be.

In a much more specialized field, Semper anticipated the modern human preoccupation with "Lebensraum" and extended the earlier experiments of Hogg (1854) to show that the fresh-water isopod *Asellus* and the pond snail *Lymnaea* would be stunted if grown in too small a volume of water. He failed to find an adequate explanation experimentally and invented the hypothesis of the presence of an unknown, but necessary, substance, which was present in the water, probably in a minute quantity. Since a certain quantity would be needed, it follows that below a minimum volume, growth would be retarded. While we know much more now than when Semper was experimenting, this problem is still essentially unsolved; the present knowledge about the importance of vitamins and other trace substances lends significance to Semper's guess.

Semper was a morphologist, uninterested in ecological relations before he went to the Philippines on his great expedition. Close contact with coral reefs in particular, and with the wealth of life in general, appears to have changed his approach to biology. This is a dramatic, though not an isolated, example. The effect of similar personal experience with varied and, to them, exotic aspects of nature, during their voyages on the "Beagle" and the "Rattlesnake," respectively, exerted strong formative influences upon Charles Darwin and T. H. Huxley. Many others have had and continue to have their biological thinking channelized and intensified by direct observations on the unaccustomed richness of the ecological relationships of plant and animal life of the tropics.

Milne-Edwards (1857) published a basic contribution on the processes and organs of respiration in animals. In the next two decades, knowledge of the respiration of aquatic animals was advanced decidedly. In this connection, the work of Bert (1870) and Fritz Müller was available to Semper.

Bert (1878) emphasized the interrelations between barometric pressure and oxygen tension. He knew that the effect of lowered or increased atmospheric pressures can be obviated by adjusting the final partial pressure of oxygen to that to which the animals are acclimated. Fairly large changes from this pressure are normally harmful. Animals with closed, or nearly closed, internal reservoirs of air show mechanical effects from variations such as might be expected from a general knowledge of the physical principles involved. Bert also knew about the internal release of nitrogen in decompression. It is an item of more than passing interest that a translation of this thousand-page monograph was published in 1943.

The importance of the evaporating power of the air on animal distribution was well recognized by 1880. There was also a considerable body of knowledge concerning mechanisms that allow gill-breathing animals such as crabs, and fishes such as *Periophthalmus*, to invade the land, sometimes for extended periods of time. Forel's observations on the reinvasion of deep water by the air-breathing Lymnaeidae were also on record.

The ecologically-minded zoologist of the 1870's was also interested in the influence of water in motion upon such matters as the clinging power of mollusks, erosion of shells, form of coral reefs and the relation of currents of water (or air) to the distribution of species. The importance of the substrate was recognized, and many natural history aspects of reciprocal reactions of living organisms upon each other were given much attention, especially the relations of sexes and various sorts of symbi-

osis, including commensalism, mutualism, and parasitism. Semper was also quite aware of the relationship between his data and the Darwinian theory of evolution. In this he seems to have been in advance of some of the more self-conscious ecologists who followed him.

RESPONSE PHYSIOLOGY[*]

Ecological aspects of response physiology are mainly concerned with phases of behavior. The attention centers on the behavior of animals, since their reactions are much more marked than are those of plants. The responses of organisms are important in ecology because they are frequently initiated primarily by the environment and in turn react upon it. Since vocalization, which may be easily and sometimes precisely interpretable in communication from man to man, is not equally revealing among other animals, the most sensitive clue to the effect being produced by an environment is frequently gained from the response physiology of the reacting animals.

The history of this aspect of ecology also traces back to Aristotle, who recorded a somewhat systematic account of the behavior of many sorts of organisms. His observations, despite their defects, exerted an influence in this phase of developing ecological knowledge which, with the possible exception of that of Réaumur (1683–1757), was hardly equalled before the time of Charles Darwin.

Wallace in Malaya and South America, Hudson in the Argentine, Bates on the Amazon, Belt in Nicaragua, and many others made sturdy contributions to our knowledge of the behavior of little-known animals, which they observed on expeditions or in out-of-the-way places. Espinas' consideration of social animals (1877) was based on records or observations concerning native as well as exotic forms. Brehm's *Tierleben* in its successive editions was the outstanding natural history of the period as Buffon's *Histoire Naturelle* had been a century earlier. Romanes made good observations, not only on the behavior of *Cebus* monkeys, but also on jellyfishes, starfishes and sea urchins. Preyer experimented on

[*] The interested student is referred to Holmes (1916) and Warden, Jenkins, and Warner (1935) for the history of the study of animal behavior.

the behavior of starfish. Darwin contributed his classic and essentially ecological study on the earthworm; although, as usual, his observations were exact, his long-range conclusions on earthworms appear to have been erroneous (cf. Keith, 1942). Fabre, Lubbock, the Peckhams, and many others reported penetrating field observations of insect behavior.

In animal behavior, as in self-conscious ecology and other phases of biology, the decade and a half centering about 1900 showed a remarkable outburst of important biological work which, while firmly grounded historically, was still unusually original. A mature contribution came from Whitman (1898) in his Woods Hole lecture on "Animal Behavior" in which he demonstrated a naturalist's sensitivity regarding the necessity for full acquaintance with the normal behavior of animals before experimenting on them. He insisted, on the basis of pertinent original observations on the behavior of a leech, of *Necturus*, and of pigeons, that often the origin and significance of a given behavior pattern antedate individual acquisitions and are a part of the problem of the origin and history of organization itself, as well as reveal adjustment between the animal and its normal environment. Whitman's work on animal behavior, though many of his results were too long left unpublished (cf. Whitman, 1919), still influences current programs for the analysis of ecological and other aspects of behavior.*

The late 1890's and the early years of the present century were enlivened by the controversy that developed between the forced movement, nonadaptive explanations of animal behavior of Loeb and his school and the adherents of the more complicated "trial and error" adaptational system of Jennings. Happily we can now see that the views are largely complementary, and they have already been knit, notably by Kühn, along with other elements, into a comprehensive system of orientational behavior (cf. Fraenkel and Gunn, 1940).

By 1897, Davenport, in his *Experimental*

* Whitman was himself an able naturalist. He brought C. B. Davenport to the recently founded University of Chicago, in part to foster field studies, and he had much to do with the early development of C. C. Adams and V. E. Shelford.

Morphology, which reviewed a much wider field, was able to summarize a literature in response physiology almost as extensive as in developmental and toleration physiology. The topics he treated historically include chemotaxis, hydrotaxis, tonotaxis, thigmotaxis (stereotaxis), rheotaxis, geotaxis, electrotaxis, phototaxis, photopathy, and thermotaxis. Much of the literature cited is from the decades immediately preceding publication, but Davenport calls attention to early work, such as that of Trembley (1744, p. 66) that *Hydra viridis* moved toward the light even when the lighted slit is turned toward cooler air.

Some of the ecological queries that such studies helped to answer are:

1. Do animals have definite reactions that enable them to find the habitat suitable to their ecological tolerances?

2. Are animal reactions adaptive?

3. Is a given behavior pattern innate or conditioned (learned)?

4. Do any animals other than man seem to be conscious of their behavior? if so, to what extent? Is there a choice of habitats? Do animals show preferences?

RELATION OF POPULATIONS TO ENVIRONMENT

General biologists, and even ecologists, who have read thus far, may ask: Is this the history of ecology? Without referring to the discussion of the rise of self-conscious ecology, which will be considered when the background is adequately prepared, an answer may be quoted from an early ecological summary. Adams (1913) said:

"There are also so many degrees and kinds of work that go by the name ecological, which may or may not be, and so many also which are truly ecological but which do not pass under that name, that it is necessary that the student shall be able to see through its diverse guises and recognize its essential character. Whenever the question arises as to the ecological character of a fact, inference, or conclusion, its ecological validity may be tested in the following way: Do the facts, inferences, or conclusions show a *response* to the inorganic or organic environment:

"1. As an individual of a species or kind of animal?

"2. As a group of taxonomically related animals?

"3. As an association of interacting animals?"

According to Adams, any of these responses might properly be considered ecological.

The treatment of developmental, toleration, and response physiology may be tested by the first of these queries. The present section is written about the second; the third point will be considered later. At the turn of the century, the present discussion would have centered about the history of the ecology of species as distinct from that of individuals. Now, in the 1940's, it is concerned with populations. The difference is not great, since current definitions of a species are in terms of natural populations or groups of populations.

The study of populations is not so far removed from developmental, toleration, and response physiology as at first appears. Even the mathematical theory of populations is built around a framework of facts or assumptions concerning animal behavior (cf. Thompson, 1939). The primary biological functions of a population include the birth, nutrition, growth, reproduction, and death of its members. As organisms or populations grow, they draw their food from outside themselves and may effectively diminish the surrounding food supply.

Malthus (1798), an early student of populations, calculated that while numbers of organisms may increase in geometrical progression, their food supply may never increase faster than shown by an arithmetical progression; a resulting discrepancy frequently develops between the population to be fed and the available food. Malthus identified the drive for coitus with that for reproduction, and at first thought both were inexorable in man, as in other organisms. As a result, there arises, he said, a violent competition, which leads to a struggle for existence (his phrase) until population increase is finally controlled by catastrophe or, in man (1803 edition), by purposive restraint from procreation.

As ecologists, we may happily avoid the bitter controversy that sprang up almost immediately about the matter of human birth control and focus our attention on the more general implications of the *Essay on Population.* The ideas were not entirely new, and much of the earlier history can be found in the discussion of pre-Malthusian doctrines of population by Stangeland (1904). Machiavelli, 275 years before Malthus, had realized the danger that human populations may increase beyond the means of subsistence in limited areas and that such an increase would then be checked by want and disease. Botero presented a similar thesis in 1590. Hale (1677), Buffon (1751), Franklin (1751), Wallace (1761), and Brückner (1767), among others, anticipated Malthus. In fact, Hale stated that the increase in human population tends to occur in geometrical ratio, which is one of the important propositions of Malthus. Yet it was Malthus who focussed attention on the problem and so set the stage for all demographic studies in sociology and for the controversy about the "struggle for existence" in biology.

Darwin (1859) found one of the bases for his theory of natural selection in the reasoning of Malthus, and A. R. Wallace was also influenced by it when independently arriving at nearly the same evolutionary ideas (Darwin and Wallace, 1858). Twenty-four years before the publication of the *Origin of Species,* Quetelet, the Belgian statistician, assumed (1835) that resistance to the growth of a population increases in proportion to the square of the rate of population growth, much as the resistance to a projectile increases with the square of its speed. Quetelet speaks of a population as though it were an entity.

Verhulst, a student and a colleague of Quetelet's, in 1838 published a short essay entitled "Notice sur la loi que la population suit dans son accroissement," in which he cited the ideas of "le célèbre Malthus" and those of Quetelet and proceeded to develop briefly an equation describing the course of population increases in proportion to population density. His equation plotted into the now well-known S-shaped population curve with upper and lower asymptotes, which he called the logistic curve. In his original paper, Verhulst gave certain tests of goodness of fit of this curve against data for a few human populations of western Europe. Verhulst died in 1849 at the age of forty-five. His work on populations attracted little attention. Miner (1933) found only one reference to it in "modern times" before the rediscovery of the logistic curve by Pearl and Reed in 1920; thus population studies were long dominated by the cruder and partially erroneous ideas of Malthus.

There seems to have been a general interest in human populations in the early decades of the nineteenth century. Doubleday (1841), stimulated by his skepticism concerning the validity of the population theory of Malthus, brought forth his "true law of population." He said in part (p. 6):

"The great general law then, which, as it seems, really regulates the increase or decrease both of vegetable and of animal life, is this, that whenever a species or genus is endangered, a corresponding effort is invariably made by nature for its preservation and continuance, by an increase of fecundity or fertility; and that this takes place whenever such danger arises from a diminution of nourishment or food, so that consequently the state of depletion . . . is favorable to fertility; and that, on the other hand, . . . the state of repletion, is unfavorable to fertility, in the ratio of intensity of each state, and this [holds] probably throughout nature universally, in the vegetable as well as in the animal world . . . ."

Doubleday was mainly concerned with human phenomena. He accurately detected the fact that the well-to-do and rich reproduce less rapidly than the poor, and inaccurately thought that this human situation and similar phenomena in plants and animals were wholly explicable in terms of the effects of overrich mineral nutrients on plants and overfeeding with domestic animals, including man.

The next contribution, that of William Farr, did not grow out of the same set of considerations that had intrigued Malthus, Quetelet, Verhulst, and Doubleday. Farr was especially concerned with mortality. In 1843 he discovered that, within limits in England, there was a relation between the density of the human population and the death rate such that mortality increased as the sixth root of density. Farr returned to the problem in 1875 and tested his earlier discovery against population and mortality data from all districts of England and Wales for the years 1861 to 1870, finding that when the districts were listed in the order of their mortality, the latter always increases with the density, but less rapidly. In general terms, Farr's rule states that if the death rate is represented by R and the density of the population per unit area by D, then $R = {}_cD^m$, where c and m are constants.

Brownlee (1915) rehabilitated this rule by showing that the statistics used by Farr, which came from the decade 1861 to 1870, compared favorably with those from the decade 1891 to 1900. The only correction needed arose from the improvement of sanitation in the intervening years.

It is easy to jump ahead of our chronological story. In 1852 Herbert Spencer published an outline of "A Theory of Population, Deduced from the General Law of Animal Fertility," which he later incorporated in his *Principles of Biology* (1867) and expanded to make a whole section of that work. The essence of his later statement is:

"Individuation and Genesis are necessarily antagonistic. Grouping under the word Individuation all processes by which individual life is completed and maintained, and enlarging the meaning of the word Genesis so as to include all processes aiding the formation and perfecting of new individuals; we see the two are fundamentally opposed. Assuming other things to remain the same—assuming that environing conditions as to climate, food, enemies, etc., continue constant; then, inevitably, every higher degree of individual evolution is followed by a lower degree of race multiplication, and *vice versa*. Progress in bulk, complexity, or activity involves retrogress in fertility; and progress in fertility involves retrogress in bulk, complexity, or activity."

We sympathize with Doubleday, who complained (1853, p. xxix) about an earlier version of this idea: "The author will now venture a few brief remarks on positions of a very erudite review of the 'True Law of Population' . . . published . . . under the name of 'Herbert Spencer.' It is not easy to evolve the exact doctrine of the reviewer from the load of learned diction . . . "

Stated simply, Spencer's ideas were that when the amount of energy is limited, the greater the proportion used in the growth of nutritive aspects of the individual, the less there is left for reproduction. Doubleday found this suggestion entirely unacceptable.

Darwin took over without criticism the whole of the Malthusian doctrine as regards the geometric ratio of population growth and the resulting struggle for existence. He documented these ideas extensively with data from nonhuman as well as from human populations. The use he made of them is well and generally known. In the *Origin of Species* he also clearly recognized that populations exist as units. Thus the evolution of instincts of neuter insects can be explained on the ground that the colonies (populations) are selected as units. As with many other phases of biology, Darwin's work gave direction to population studies without containing much that was strictly concerned with this particular field.

Farr, as we have seen, returned in 1875 to his discussion of problems related to the human population of England as revealed by the accumulated vital statistics. He saw clearly that a decrease in death rates and a resulting increase in longevity do not necessarily lead to an increase in population, since, as he cogently remarks, the associated birth rate may fall to an equivalent extent. He knew that in man, as in other organisms, the possibility of population increase in geometrical ratio exists; but (and here Malthus had erred) so also may the means of man's subsistence. Not only had the population of the United States of America doubled itself every twenty-five years for a century and a half, but the means of human subsistence had also increased in geometric ratio and at an even greater rate. This must frequently hold true, since the plants or animals on which man feeds can increase (or decrease) even more rapidly than longer-lived, slow-breeding man. Restated in terms of the pyramid of numbers, which Farr did not do, this can be turned into another general principle.

A close consideration of the ideas of Malthus concerning population growth and control, and of Darwin concerning evolution, would seem to require oscillations in the populations of what would now be called key-industry animals and in those of the carnivores that feed upon them. Spencer (1863) wrote about this "rhythm in number of each tribe of animals and plants" in approximately modern terms. We have recently been reminded by Elton (1942) that knowledge of mouse plagues, which represent an outstanding oscillation in nature, dates back to early Hebrew history and that such plagues were well known to Aristotle, Theophrastus, Pliny, and others of the classical period. They were observed somewhat critically during the last decades of the nineteenth century, the formative years for much of modern ecology.

Knowledge concerning populations had another line of ancestry in the biometricians, Galton, Weldon, and Karl Pearson. Aside from Weldon's work (1898) on the relation of the survival of crabs in Plymouth Harbour (England) to the width of the carapace, and a few similar papers, these men contributed disappointingly little directly to the knowledge or theory of populations. It remained for an American disciple, Raymond Pearl, to make the transition from biometry to population studies that somewhat approximates the ecological approach to the subject. Like his rediscovery (with Reed, 1920) of Verhulst's logistic curve and his effective use of that curve as a quantitative expression of potential rate of increase and of environmental resistance, these developments by Pearl came too late to affect the early rise of ecology. Their modern aspects and their relations to other phases of present day ecology will be treated later (p. 46).

ECONOMIC BIOLOGY

Many population studies have a strong economic trend, and the pressure of economic problems not only accelerated the development of an adequate basis for modern ecology, but continues to stimulate ecological development today. Three broad economic interests of man—fisheries, agriculture, and certain aspects of medicine—are closely related to ecology. The need for more precise information concerning food fishes and the conditions of their existence has been one of the potent drives in the study of the ecology of aquatic habitats. The relation between ecology and agriculture is even more obvious; many of the environmental relations of plants were studied in the eighteenth and nineteenth centuries, as well as in earlier and more recent times, because of their direct bearing on agricultural problems. The data reviewed by Abbe (1905) were discovered primarily because of their immediate economic application, and Abbe's comprehensive review was itself similarly motivated.

On the animal side, an important element in the background of ecology came from work with insects in relation to man-grown crops and to the control of diseases of domestic animals and of man. Precise summaries of the history of these developments will be found in books devoted to economic and to medical entomology, especially those on the history of entomology, notably Howard (1930) and Essig (1931). The treatment here will be suggestive rather than comprehensive.

The regulation of population size of

noxious insects is a primary problem which has long been attacked. One ecological method uses the natural controls of trouble-making insects. Fungus diseases attracted attention at an early date; Forbes, (1895) traced the history of knowledge of such diseases of insects in Europe and America and described in detail additional experiments designed to stop the inroads made by the chinch bug, *Blissus leucopterus,* upon farm crops in Illinois. As early as 1880 Thomas had observed a relation between temperature and rainfall and the development of excessive populations of chinch bugs.

Another phase of insect control, distinctly ecological in approach and in general implications, comes from the use of predatory species and insect parasites to attack destructive species. Sweetman (1936) has summarized the history of such efforts. It appears that Forskål (1775) gave the first written account of this usage when he described the introduction of colonies of predatory ants from the nearby mountains into Arabian palm orchards to attack other ants that were feeding on the date palms.

Sweetman (1936) notes that Erasmus Darwin wrote about the possibilities of biological control in 1800. In 1840 in France large numbers of native carabid beetles were placed on poplar trees to destroy caterpillars of the gipsy moth. The interna-

tional transfer of parasites to prey on introduced insect pests was suggested by Fitch in 1854 and was put into effect by Planchon and Riley in 1873. Other early experiments of this nature in the 1870's and 1880's were almost forgotten in the success achieved, largely as a result of the work of C. V. Riley, by the importation of a coccinellid beetle from Australia into California in 1889 to control the cottony-cushion scale.

Oscillations between insect pests and their parasites were demonstrated independently by Howard (1897) and Marchal (1897) for different species. Two other workers, (Bellevoye and Laurent, 1897) provided the outline of a mathematical theory of the biological control of population size. They set up a fairly simple equation to show how such a state, now called a steady state, would be maintained.

Growth of knowledge about the interrelations of organisms with respect to mammalian disease also proceeded at a rapid pace in the closing decades of the last century. Herms (1939) records that Josiah Nott of New Orleans published an essay on the origin of yellow fever in 1848 in which he expressed the belief "that mosquitoes give rise to both malaria and yellow fever." This was a fortunate guess. Carlos Finlay of Cuba set forth a similar theory for yellow fever about 1880 and conducted

Table 1. Important Diseases Known before 1900 to Be Insect-Borne (Data Extracted Chiefly from Herms, 1939)

Disease	Causative Organism	Principle Vector	Discoverer* of Vector (or Name Closely Associated)
Filariasis.........	*Wuchereria bancrofti* (Filaria)	*Culex fatigans* (Mosquito)	Patrick Manson, 1878
Texas cattle fever..	*Babesia bigemina* (Protozoan)	*Boöphilus annulatus* (Tick)	Theobald Smith, F. L. Kilbourne, 1893
Nagana...........	*Trypanosoma brucei* (Protozoan)	*Glossina morsitans* (Tsetse fly)	David Bruce, 1895
Malaria..........	*Plasmodium* (Protozoan)	Anopheline mosquitoes	Ronald Ross, 1897
Bubonic plague....	*Bacillus (Pasteurella) pestus*	*Xenopsylla* (Rat flea)	P. S. Simond, 1898
Yellow fever.......	A filterable virus	*Aëdes aegypti* (Mosquito)	Walter Reed, 1900

* Names of other men closely connected with these discoveries, or some of them, can be found in Herms' text and are not repeated here, even though their omission may do an injustice to worthy workers.

experiments on the subject. King (1883) gave nineteen reasons why mosquitoes should be considered as possible vectors of malaria. King knew about Finlay's work, but he deserves credit for extending it to malaria at a time when even certain entomologists well acquainted with mosquitoes rejected the idea.

The relations that had been established by 1900 are summarized in Table 1. We have taken the liberty of bringing information concerning the causative organisms and insect vectors up to date rather than give here the more imperfect statements of 1900.

Medical entomology was in a state of rapid growth at the end of the period covered by the present chapter, and scholarly consolidation of the field had already begun; this was shown by the appearance of the first comprehensive, critical and historical study of the known disease-carrying activities of arthropods, that by Nuttall (1899). The medical masterpiece by Smith and Kilbourne (1893) deserves independent mention, not only because of its medical significance, but also because of its careful and critical use of the techniques of field experimentation.

Forbes, an alert student of the literature of the subjects with which he dealt as well as with natural phenomena themselves, may well have had many of these developments in applied entomology in mind when he wrote the following orienting paragraph (1895) as an introduction to his discussion of the diseases of the chinch bug:

" . . . Another division of biological science, little known to the general public by its name as yet, and but lately distinguished as a separate subject, . . . is now commonly called *oecology*. It is the science of the relations of living animals and plants to each other as living things and to their surroundings generally. It deals with the ways in which heat and light, moisture and drouth, soil and climate, and food and competitors and parasites and predacious enemies, and a long list of agencies additional, act upon living things, and the ways in which these living things react in turn; it includes, in short, the whole system of life as exhibited in the interactions between the plant or animal and the environment, living and without life. It is a very comprehensive, complicated, and important subject; how comprehensive and important we see at once when we learn that the whole Darwinian doctrine belongs to it on the one hand, and that all agriculture depends upon it on the other. It

covers, indeed, the whole field of active life and all forms of matter and energy as affecting living things in any way."

EVOLUTION:
STRUGGLE AND COOPERATION

The history of the growth of knowledge of organic evolution has been told frequently and well. We need only call attention to the twin facts (*a*) that the history of the rise of evolution in its modern biological connotation repeats much of the history of ecology in that many of the same men were involved, and (*b*) that the subject matter of each of these two aspects of biology strongly overlaps.

The nearer we approach modern times and modern preoccupations, the greater is the divergence in men as well as in matter. Although shadowy ideas of evolution, and even forerunners of the theory of natural selection, are much older (cf. Zirkle, 1941), for the purposes of this sketch we may well begin with Buffon, the great theoretical biologist of the eighteenth century. We get a glimpse of the essence of his evolutionary ideas from the following quotation from his *Histoire Naturelle* (Paris, 1749 ff.: translation quoted from Dendy, 1914):

"If we again consider each species in different climates we shall find obvious varieties both as regards size and form; all are influenced more or less strongly by the climate. These changes only take place slowly and imperceptibly; the great workman of Nature is Time: he walks always with even strides, uniform and regular, he does nothing by leaps; but by degrees, by gradations, by succession, he does everything; and these changes, at first imperceptible, little by little become evident, and express themselves at length in results about which we cannot be mistaken."

Buffon's main contribution to evolutionary biology was the idea that the environment can permanently affect the life of organisms by the process now called environmental induction. Buffon influenced Erasmus Darwin's ideas, and also those of Lamarck. Although he anticipated Malthus in understanding the implications of population pressure, and while he had a clear appreciation of the struggle for existence, Buffon was not a consistent thinker, and he may be as truly classified with Cuvier as a catastrophist as with Lamarck and Erasmus Darwin as a forerunner of modern evolutionary views.

Lamarck's contributions are more widely known as a result of the publicity, mainly adverse, given to his now generally abandoned theory of evolution through the inheritance of characters acquired by use and disuse or by a more direct effect of the environment. Lamarck summed up his conclusions in the *Histoire Naturelle des Animaux sans Vertèbres* (Paris, 1815; cf. Dendy, 1914, p. 382). Lamarck's *Philosophie Zoologique* (1809) is better known. He placed the effects of needs and of resulting habits of animals, together with their manner of life and the conditions under which their ancestors have lived, in the forefront of his explanation of the bodily form and general qualities of a given animal.

Darwin's (and Wallace's) theory of evolution is based on principles equally ecological though radically different. Among the important ones we may recognize Malthusian overpopulation and the resulting struggle for existence with ensuing natural selection. Except for the fundamental part, which is concerned with the nonenvironmental origin of many, probably of the majority, of heritable variations, the remainder of the factors involved in Darwin's theory are now recognized as being clearly ecological in nature. The exception just noted is even more important than Darwin thought, since he was not altogether free from Lamarckian environmentalism. The ecological substratum of Darwin's and of Wallace's thinking is brought into clearer light when we recall the extent to which each was influenced by zoogeographic considerations.

The supporting theory of geographic isolation (Wagner, 1868; Gulick, 1888, 1905) also grew out of zoogeographic studies and has even more of an ecological bent than does general Darwinian theory.

It would be interesting, and perhaps not without value, to consider briefly the reasons for the failure of some early ecologists to recognize and insist upon the close connection between their newly vivified subject and the important generalizations of evolutionary theory. Perhaps, however, such a discussion can be dismissed with the suggestion that a part of the psychology involved is not wholly unlike that of a vigorous adolescent in establishing his independence from actively possessive parents.

From a certain viewpoint, there are two main approaches to the phenomena of ecology and of biology in general, and each yields its element of truth. The more usual approach has been by way of the individualistic, egocentric position of the neo-Darwinians that Darwin himself emphasized. This approach is usually developed about some phase of person-to-person competition, and hence the word "competition" has wrongly come to be wholly associated with the harmful interactions of organisms that yield results which are the opposite of cooperations, and may be called disoperations. The history of the use of this approach is almost identical with much of that of evolutionary theory since Darwin's time. Opposed to the individualistic emphasis, there is the concern with group-centered, more or less altruistic tendencies, such as have frequently been considered under the heading of cooperation, which careful students nowadays consider as entirely nonconscious proto-cooperation in all lower forms. The word itself in this connection should imply merely that the interactions under consideration are more beneficial than harmful for individuals or group units.

The germ of the idea of natural cooperation, along with that of natural selection, can be traced to the biologically absurd poetry of Empedocles (p. 14). Thereafter the idea was kept somewhat alive, often in barely recognizable form, by the succession of thinkers from Aristotle to Herbert Spencer and others who saw human society as a natural outgrowth from the life of other animals. They were opposed by an equally impressive succession of men who thought of society as an artifact. A fairly exhaustive history of this phase of the subject is given by Espinas (1877).

More positive philosophical emphasis on the nonegocentric interpretation of nature began with Anthony Cooper, third earl of Shaftesbury, who about 1700 recognized that racial drives exist that can be explained only by their advantage to the group. Adam Smith emphasized the same qualities in his *Theory of Moral Sentiments* (1759) under the heading of "sympathy" or "fellow feeling"; his more famous *Inquiry into the Wealth of Nations*" (1776) is completely based on the opposed force of self-interest, and he did not publicly reconcile the two Later, Feuerbach (1846–1890) emphasized the same idea under the heading of "love,"

ency is by no means new, but stems rather from the long line of excellent naturalists, whether travelers or stay at-homes, who contributed much to the background of the subject. This is not the place to set forth the needed history of natural history; combined with what has already been said on the subject, the barest outline must suffice. Basic as is their service to ecology, we must pass over the host of taxonomists of the latter half of the nineteenth century, except as they contributed directly to ecological observation.

The contributions of the Greek, Roman, and earlier naturalists of northern Europe have already been mentioned. The writings of many others have been or will be discussed in other connections. We want to call attention to such observations as those furnished by Martin (1698), who gave an early description of the breeding and something of the populations of the sea birds of St. Kilda in the Outer Hebrides, and to those of White (1789), who described the natural history of his native village of Selborne.

The varied contributions of explorers and collectors like Bates, Belt, and Humboldt, and of observers like Fabre, Forel, and the Peckhams, to name no more, are not limited merely to the background of modern ecology; their observations often emerge into the foreground.

Wallace's *Island Life* and *Malay Archipelago,* Bates' *Naturalist on the Amazons,* Belt's *Naturalist in Nicaragua,* Fabre's fascinating accounts of the habits of insects of the countryside in France, Audubon's recently reprinted *Birds of North America* and Brehm's *From North Pole to Equator,* with his greatly expanded *Tierleben*—again to name no more—are still desirable reading for any alert animal ecologist.

Louis Agassiz, the many-sided naturalist, played an important role in laying the foundation on which ecology was later built. In 1846, when he was almost forty years old, Agassiz came to America from his native Switzerland with an established reputation based on teaching and on much scholarly work with fossil and living fishes and on his study of glaciers. His later scientific work was also of high quality. In America, Agassiz had an extraordinary career as a naturalist both at home and on expeditions. His influence as a lecturer and above all as a teacher revivified the study of

nature in this country and made naturalists more respected members of many communities. He taught the men who in turn trained the pioneer American ecologists. His final success was with a summer seaside laboratory on Penikese Island off Woods Hole, Massachusetts, established in 1873, the year after Anton Dohrn completed the first building of the zoological station at Naples. Agassiz at the Penikese laboratory exerted an influence on American biology out of all proportion to the length of the short summer session in this, the last year of his life.[*]

The naturalists of the later decades of the nineteenth century rounded out certain phases of ecology or of allied subjects in approximately their present form. Thus the zoogeographical regions of the world, outlined on the basis of the taxonomic relationships of animals, and the smaller faunal areas of North America and Europe remain on the maps much as the nineteenth century naturalists left them. Though often used, especially by nonecologists, the limits of Merriam's life zones have undergone only slight change since early in the present century, and, moisture considerations aside (see p. 114), they appear in modern works much as Merriam outlined them in the 1890's. The whole vast field of the reciprocal relations between flowers and pollination by insects was largely established in its present form by the eighteenth and nineteenth century naturalists (cf. Müller, 1883; Knuth, 1898–1905).

Fortunately for ecology, robust work in natural history still continues in the twentieth century and will be discussed in the next chapter.

[*] Many marine biological laboratories have arisen as a direct or indirect result of the lasting success of Dohrn's "Stazione Zoologica" at Naples and of the influence of Agassiz's meteoric venture at Penikese. The Marine Biological Laboratory at Woods Hole is the direct descendant of the latter. We wish to record our judgment that many of these laboratories, despite their favorable locations, have not as yet had an important direct influence on the development of ecological science. The more recently established "Oceanographic Institution," also at Woods Hole, is becoming an exception in its relation to the marine ecology of the future. The much more humble laboratories scattered about the fresh waters of Europe and the United States have been more consistently important in ecological research.

THE COMMUNITY CONCEPT

Recognition of the existence of communities of living organisms in nature is not new. As shown earlier in this chapter, the idea dates back to the classical Greeks. In the modern period, according to Braun-Blanquet (1932), Heer (1835), Lecoq (1854), Sendtner (1854), and Kerner (1863), all sought to understand the basic causes of the interrelations of certain plants, and Kerner "brought even to the laymen an understanding of the principal plant communities of Austria-Hungary to the environment."

Clements (1905) traced recognition of the plant formation to Grisebach (1838), who recognized it as the fundamental feature of vegetation. Earlier writers, Clements continues, "notably Linné (1737, 1751), Biberg (1749), and Hedenberg (1754), had perceived this relation more or less clearly, but failed to reduce it to a definite guiding principle." Clements adds that the acceptance of the "formation" as a unit of vegetation took place slowly, but this point of view came to be more and more prevalent as a result of the work of Kerner (1863), and a half-dozen others, including Warming (1889).* Clements and Shelford (1939) state that "the idea of the plant community in general extends backward for nearly two centuries," and, as regards the biotic community, "Post (1868) recognized that the organic world should be dealt with in its entirety, but seems to have had no definite idea of the community as a unit."

Darwin's recognition of the web of life concept has already been mentioned. His famous illustration of the relationship between the number of cats and the amount of clover seed in an English community illustrates his understanding of possible intracommunity relationships. Saint-Hilaire (1859) foreshadowed the concept, and Haeckel (1869), in his classical definition of "Oecology," also vaguely recognized the existence of communities.

Edward Forbes (1843–1844), in studying the animal distribution in British waters and the Aegean Sea, discovered "provinces of Depth" which "are distinguished

* Warming's bibliography in the 1909 edition of his *Oecology of Plants* does not list a title for 1889 among his thirteen publications between 1869 and 1894, inclusive.

from each other by the associations of the species they severally include. Certain species in each are found in no other; several are found in one region which do not range into the next above, whilst they extend to that below, or *vice versa*. Certain species have their maximum of development in each zone, being most prolific in individuals in that zone in which is their maximum, and of which they may be regarded as especially characteristic. Mingled with the true natives of every zone are stragglers, owing their presence to the secondary influences which modify distribution."

Forbes clearly recognized the dynamic aspect of the interrelations between organisms and their environment. He stated his conclusions as follows (1843, p. 173):

"The eight regions in depth are the scene of incessant change. The death of the individuals of the several species inhabiting them, the continual accession, deposition and sometimes washing away of sediment and coarser deposits, the action of the secondary influences and the changes of elevation which appear to be periodically taking place in the eastern Mediterranean, are ever modifying their character. As each region shallows or deepens, its animal inhabitants must vary in specific associations, for the depression which may cause one species to dwindle and die will cause another to multiply. The animals themselves, too, by their over-multiplication, appear to be the cause of their own specific destruction. As the influence of the nature of the sea-bottom determines in a great measure the species present on that bottom, the multiplication of individuals dependent on the rapid reproduction of successive generations of Mollusca, etc., will of itself change the ground and render it unfit for the continuation of life in that locality until a new layer of sedimentary matter, uncharged with living organic contents, deposited on the bed formed by the exuviae of the exhausted species, forms a fresh soil for similar or other animals to thrive, attain their maximum, and from the same cause die off."

This is an early, perhaps the first, statement of ecological dynamics, a subject much emphasized in recent decades (see p. 563). Elsewhere, Forbes (1844) regarded self-produced, local destruction of a species as a kind of "rotation of crops" and shows clearly that he was more concerned with the alternation of fossiliferous and nonfossiliferous geological strata than with the processes that we now know are connected with the biotic control of some important phases of ecological succession.

The subdivision of the littoral region of the ocean into faunal provinces, as Dana (1852, 1853), Packard (1863), and Verrill (1866) have done for Atlantic coastal waters, is based primarily on the observed distribution of species and groups of species and secondarily on physical factors such as temperature and geographic features such as capes. From the most southern Floridian, through the Carolinian, Virginian, and Acadian, to the most northern Syrtensian province, the geographic faunas of these naturalists suggest the biomes (biotic formations) of more recent workers (cf. Shelford et al., 1935). If proposed today, they might be designated by biological terms to suggest their taxonomic composition, rather than by geographic names that suggest their distribution.

We now know that this is the historical background against which to view the remarkable work of Verrill and Smith (1874) which, despite the praise given by Adams (1913), did not receive the recognition or have the influence among ecologists that it merited. They found "three quite distinct assemblages of animal life, which are dependent upon and limited by definite physical conditions of the waters which they inhabit." These three primary groupings were: (1) the animals of the bays and sounds; (2) those of the estuaries and other brackish waters; and (3) those of the cold waters of the ocean shores and outer channels.

In each of these assemblages, Verrill and Smith recognized that certain kinds of animals are restricted to particular localities because of their relation to the character of the bottom or of the shore. "Thus," they say, "there will be species, or even large groups of species, which inhabit only rocky shores; . . . others that prefer the clean gravelly bottoms where the water is several fathoms deep." These may be still further divided. The mud, for example, has different characteristics in different places, and "the different kinds are often inhabited by different groups of animals." In describing the animals that live in these habitats, they report: "It has not been found desirable to mention, in this part of the report [the general discussion], all the species found in each, but only those that appear to be most abundant and important." They also knew

that the population during the day differed from that found at night in the same spot and that there were seasonal changes as well.

This somewhat extended report of Verrill and Smith's work indicates correctly that they were impressed with the organization of communities upon the basis of their relation with their physical habitat rather than as a result of interrelations between constituent organisms. The latter were not unknown to them, for, among other instances, they state that "Shells of oysters provide suitable attachment for various shells, bryozoans, ascidians, hydroids, sponges, etc., which could not otherwise maintain their existence on muddy bottoms, while other kinds of animals such as crabs, annelids, etc., find shelter between the shells or in their interstices." Thus Verrill and Smith saw certain of the interrelationships that exist on an oyster bank.

A few years later Möbius (1877) wrote of these in greater detail; his much-quoted passage will be repeated here (from the 1883 translation) both because of its historical significance and because of its distinctly modern tone.

"Every oyster-bed is thus, to a certain degree, a community of living beings, a collection of species and a massing of individuals, which find here everything necessary for their growth and continuance, such as suitable soil, sufficient food, the requisite percentage of salt, and a temperature favorable to their development. Each species which lives here is represented by the greatest number of individuals which can grow to maturity subject to the conditions which surround them, for among all species the number of individuals which arrive at maturity at each breeding period is much smaller than the number of germs produced at that time. The total number of individuals of all the species living together in any region is the sum of the survivors of all the germs which have been produced at all past breeding or brood periods; and this sum of matured germs represents a certain quantum of life which enters into a certain number of individuals, and which, as does all life, gains permanence by means of transmission. Science possesses, as yet, no word by which such a community of living beings may be designated; no word for a community where the sum of species and individuals, beings mutually limited and selected under the average external conditions of life, have, by means of transmission continued in possession of a certain definite territory. I propose the word *Biocoenosis* for such a com-

munity. Any change in any of the relative factors of a biocönose produces changes in other
factors of the same. If, at any time, one of the
external conditions of life should deviate for a
long time from the ordinary mean, the entire
biocönose, or community, would be transformed. It would also be transformed, if the
number of individuals of a particular species
increased or diminished through the instru-
mentality of man, or if one species entirely
disappeared from, or a new species entered
into, the community."

S. A. Forbes (1887) apparently took over
and expanded the ideas of Möbius. The
quotation already given (p. 32) shows that
Forbes recognized a "*close community of
interest*" even between predators and prey
in a community. Warming (1895) saw the
unity of plant communities as a result of
his study of the vegetation of Danish dunes.
Braun-Blanquet, disregarding the zoological
studies we have just reviewed, ranks Warming's work as the most important landmark
in the development of community ecology
since that of Heer. In one important respect, this estimate is just: modern community studies have mainly been stimulated
by Warming's findings rather than by those
of his zoological predecessors, Edward
Forbes, Verrill, Möbius, and S. A. Forbes.

Communities may be integrated by the
requirements imposed by a uniform, circumscribed habitat as well as by the mutual
interactions between organisms such as
those that characterize a biocoenosis. The
two kinds of integration do not necessarily
yield similar results. Caves furnish one of
the striking examples of a unity imposed by
the habitat. Interest in cave life was strong
in the Darwinian period of the last century.
Attention was focussed particularly on the
origin and evolution of cave faunas. This
involved a consideration of adaptations,
especially those of sense organs, the migration of preadapted animals into caves, the
degeneration of eyes and other features, and
the conditions of existence to be met there.
Food habits of cave animals, including what
we now call food chains, and ultimate
sources of food were also studied. Absolon
in Europe, and Packard and Eigenmann in
America, engaged in such investigations.
The summaries of progress to date and
bibliographies by Packard (1888, 1894)
indicate that a fair knowledge of the general relations of cave animals had been
attained by the closing years of the nineteenth century. Active work along the

same lines continued into the new century
(see p. 48) and will be critically discussed in the section on Evolution.

Quantitative studies of the plants and
animals of a given community appear to
date from the work Hensen began in 1882,
the results of which were published in the
latter part of 1887. Hensen was primarily
interested in two questions: (1) What
quantities of living plankton organisms does
the sea contain in a given area at a certain
time? And (2) how does the quantity of
plankton vary from place to place and
from time to time? He attempted to find
answers to these questions by collecting
plankton quantitatively by means of small-
meshed nets drawn through a known volume of water.

A large and critical literature soon developed, much too voluminous and complicated for us to review thoroughly. An early
summary is given by Johnstone (1908),
and some of the more important papers
are listed by Adams (1913) in his excellent annotated bibliographies.

Hensen's work at once stirred up controversy. Haeckel (1890) doubted the
validity of Hensen's conclusions in a mem-
oir done in his usual attractive style, to
which Hensen (1891) replied effectively.
Kofoid (1897), though also engaging in
quantitative studies, dissented from Hensen's conclusions, and Lohmann (1901)
undertook to show that Kofoid had not
understood the nature of the method he
criticized. Kofoid (1903) gave an excellent
and detailed report on a quantitative study
of the plankton of the Illinois River. In
fact, quantitative as well as qualitative
plankton studies flourished to such an extent that Shelford used to warn his classes
in the early years of the present century
that ecology was not a synonym for plankton study.

Quantitative methods were soon applied
to the investigation of communities of the
inshore bottom of the ocean by Petersen
(1893 and later) and to those of the land
by Pound and Clements (1898), Dahl
(1898), and others.

HYDROBIOLOGY

Discussion of the rise of self-conscious
ecology will be delayed only for a brief
further consideration of the development
of hydrobiology or, more exactly, of its

components, oceanography and limnology. These subjects are concerned with all matters that apply closely to oceans, bays, gulfs, and seas on the one hand, and to inland waters, especially lakes, ponds, and streams of fresh water on the other. Forel (1892) called oceanography and limnology sister subjects, and such they remain, with a close family resemblance, but without having fused into a unified science.

In so far as oceanography and limnology deal with organisms in relation to their aquatic environment, or with bodies of water as an environment of living things, they are a part of ecology. In so far as these subjects are concerned with physical or chemical features such as depth, waves, currents or types of bottom, or with the chemical composition of the water, as items of interest in themselves, they have a relation to ecology similar to that of soil science or physiography on land or of meteorology for the world in general.

The history of the earliest knowledge concerning animal life in water coincides with much of the early development of biology in general, and its relation to the early history of ecology has already been traced (p. 14 ff). Attention was focussed on the larger aquatic animals, especially on the fishes of relatively shallow waters. The gradual accumulation of information regarding these animals in relation to their surroundings came mainly from the expanding lore of the fisherman. Larger aspects of oceanography, and to some extent of limnology, too, were developed from the needs of navigation.

Study of the smaller organisms in water dates from Leeuwenhoek's improvement of the microscope (1632–1723). He himself discovered rotifers and Protista. During the century and more immediately after Leeuwenhoek a motley assortment of men with diverse backgrounds devoted themselves to the study of the taxonomy and natural history of small aquatic organisms. Many of these students of aquatic microscopy seem to have been curious about the Infusoria, much as we are today about aquatic bacteria.

This exploratory period reached a noteworthy stage in the work of Ehrenberg, who, among his other contributions, began a transition to aspects of microbiology more closely related to modern interests. Murray (1895, p. 77) says of him:

"In 1836 Ehrenberg produced his first works.* His name will remain inseparably connected with the discoveries relating to the microscopic organisms of the sea. . . . One salient point may be dwelt on, viz., the connection he established between certain classes of living microscopic organisms and the part they played in geological times. . . . His observations exercised a great influence on the study of micro-organisms, whose role in nature is in an inverse ratio to their size."

Johannes Müller started the next advance when, about 1845, he began to use a tow net to obtain samples of small marine organisms from the North Sea. It remained for Lilljeborg and Sars to recognize for the first time the existence of a pelagic fauna. Needham and Lloyd (1916) make the following comment concerning this discovery:

"Lilljeborg and Sars . . . found a whole fauna and flora, mostly microscopic—a well adjusted society of organisms, with its producing class of synthetic [sic] plant forms and its consuming class of animals; and among the animals, all the usual social groups, herbivors and carnivors, parasites and scavengers. Later, this assemblage of minute free-swimming organisms was named plancton. After its discovery the seas could no longer be regarded as 'barren wastes of water;' for they had been found teeming with life."

Lohmann (1912, p. 22) states that during the 1840's Ehrenberg, the English botanist Hooker, and the Danish naturalist Örstedt, taken together, recognized the role of diatoms and desmids in the nutrition of marine animals. They also found that these plants and the radiolarian protozoans are important in the formation of deposits on the ocean floor (cf. Coker, 1947).

Lampert (1910) cites numerous papers by each of these pioneers, the earliest of which was published by Lilljeborg in 1853. Hensen (1887) proposed the modern term "plankton" for this assemblage of floating organisms; his development of quantitative plankton studies has already been discussed (p. 36).

OCEANOGRAPHY†

According to Edward Forbes (1844), the naturalist's dredge is a modification of the

---

* Ehrenberg had actually published in 1830 and 1832.

† More detailed discussion of the history of oceanography is given by Murray (1895), Murray and Hjort (1912), Herdman (1923), and Coker (1947).

fisherman's oyster dredge and was first used in biological research by the Italians, Marsili and Donati, and after them by Soldani, about the middle of the eighteenth century. These men "sought to explain the arrangement and disposition of organic remains in the strata of their country by an examination of the distribution of living beings on the bed of the Adriatic Sea." The dredge was introduced in more northern waters by a Dane, O. F. Müller, in 1799 as a means for general exploration of the sea bottom (Herdman, 1923).

Reports on the presence of animals in the bottom deposits of the deeper waters of the ocean appear to date from the records of Sir John Ross (1819), who reported on four deep-sea "soundings" made during his voyage to Baffin's Bay in 1817–18. Samples were obtained with a device of his own invention that brought up a quantity of the bottom deposits. Worms were taken at depths of 6000 feet, and both worms and other forms were secured from depths of 2700 feet and more. He also found a starfish attached to his line at least 2400 feet below the surface. A few years later Risso (1826) described a "bathybial" fish fauna that extended to 350 fathoms (2100 feet) in the Gulf of Genoa. Such information did not become widely distributed, since the announcement by James Clark Ross (1847) of animals taken at a depth of 2400 feet and even at 6000 feet during his Antarctic expedition of 1839–40 was hailed as a new and important discovery.

In 1839 the British Association for the Advancement of Science appointed a committee to encourage dredging operations. Edward Forbes was a leading spirit. His "provinces of depth" have already been outlined (p. 34)). Among the other conclusions given by Forbes (1844), the following are pertinent here:

"The number of species is much less in the lower zones than in the upper. Vegetables disappear below a certain depth, and the diminution in the number of animal species indicates a zero not far distant. . . .

"The greater part of the sea is far deeper than the point zero; consequently, the greater part of deposits forming, will be void of organic remains.

"Animals having the greatest ranges in depth have usually a great geographical, or else a great geological range, or both."

The conclusion concerning the existence of a depth zero of life became a matter of controversy. Often the zero point was located at about 300 fathoms (1800 feet), and, as we have already seen, it was discredited as a generalization for animal life before it was first announced. This did not prevent the matter from becoming a focal point for exploration of the deeper waters of the oceans. Mistaken observations or interpretations, if not overweighted with authority, may be stimulating. A dramatic history of scientific progress could be written in terms of known human errors and their final correction. The existence of a universal azoic zone was not disproved until the dredgings of the *Challenger* expedition (1873–76) brought up bottom-dwelling animals from the greatest depths reached. For plankton, as we shall see, the doctrine lingered still longer.

Many factors contributed to a strong movement for oceanographic research from the 1830's to 1900 and beyond. This was the great era of oceanographic expeditions, motivated in part by the kind of general scientific curiosity that provides support for astronomical observatories. A recurrent specific curiosity that runs through much of the history we are tracing focusses on the relation between present day submarine deposits and the fossiliferous strata in terrestrial rocks. These more abstract interests were reenforced by the need for practical information in connection with laying and maintaining transoceanic cables, by the continued and growing interest in fisheries, and in the problems concerned with navigation. After certain initial success, there was added the drive of strong nationalistic competition, shared by most of the great maritime nations.

Among the most prominent of the naturalists closely connected with expeditions wholly or in part concerned with oceanography, we may name Charles Darwin on the *Beagle* (1831–36), J. D. Dana on the *Porpoise* (1836–39), Joseph Hooker with the *Erebus* and *Terror* (1839–43) and T. H. Huxley on the *Rattlesnake* (1846–50). This incomplete list serves to call attention to the high quality of men who, early in their scientific careers, were exposed to the opportunities for work and reflection afforded by such expeditions. Experience gained on these voyages left a strong mark on the later thinking of these men, and their own high quality exerted a profound influence on the further development of biological oceanography.

M. F. Maury, an important pioneer in oceanic research, especially as concerns the meteorological problems of navigation, was also interested in marine biology. He published the first bathymetrical map of the North Atlantic in the 1854 edition of his book, *Explanations and Sailing Directions to Accompany the Wind and Current Charts.* In this map he drew contour lines for 1000, 2000, 3000 and 4000 fathoms. He correctly thought that most of the bottom deposits away from land came from the skeletons of animals that live near the sea surface, but was mistaken in thinking that the conditions in the deep sea made life impossible in ocean depths. A paragraph from his writings will give some of his reasoning (1858, p. 174):

"Does any portion of the shells which Brooke's sounding rod brings up from the bottom of the deep sea live there; or are they all the remains of those that lived near the surface in the light and heat of sun, and were buried at the bottom of the deep after death? . . . The facts, as far as they go, seem to favor the one conjecture nearly as well as the other. Under these circumstances I am inclined, however, to the anti-biotic hypothesis, and chiefly because it would seem to conform better with the Mosaic account of creation. The sun and the moon were set in the firmament before the waters were commanded to bring forth the living creature; and hence we infer that light and heat are necessary to the creation and preservation of marine life, and since the light and heat of the sun cannot reach to the bottom of the deep sea, my own conclusion, in the absence of positive evidence upon the subject, has been the *habitat* of these mites of things hauled up from the bottom of the great deep is at and near the surface. On the contrary, others maintain, and perhaps with equal reason, the biotic side of the question. Professor Ehrenberg, of Berlin, is of this latter class."

Maury then gives an exchange of letters between Ehrenberg and himself in which the pros and cons of the matter are stated fairly and without heat.

G. C. Wallich, naturalist on the *Bulldog*, summarized the opposite point of view in 1862 in statements that Murray thought sufficiently significant to quote in the historical pages of his summary for the *Chal-*

lenger reports (1895, p. 95). He begins the list with the assertion that

"The conditions prevailing at great depths, although differing materially from those which prevail near the surface of the ocean, are not incompatible with the maintenance of animal life"

and concludes that

"The discovery of even a single species living normally at great depths warrants the inference that the deep sea has its own special fauna, and that it has always had it in ages past, and hence that many fossiliferous strata, heretofore regarded as having been deposited in comparatively shallow water, have been deposited at great depths "

Herdman (1923) devoted separate chapters to the following men as founders of oceanography: Edward Forbes, Wyville Thompson, John Murray, Louis and Alexander Agassiz, Albert Honoré Charles, Prince of Monaco, and Anton Dohrn of the Zoological Station at Naples. The work of Edward Forbes has already been discussed, and Murray has been repeatedly mentioned.

Thompson was the active leader of the *Challenger* expedition (1873–76), the object of which was the scientific exploration of the sea with regard to physical, chemical, geological, and biological conditions. The scientific results were published in fifty large quarto volumes, prepared mainly under the editorship of John Murray, himself one of the naturalists of the expedition. The reports were written by notable specialists; Murray later singled out the work of Haeckel on the Radiolaria as being especially outstanding. It is difficult even yet to evaluate the full importance of the contributions made by this great voyage of oceanographic exploration. The reports remain a half-forgotten mine of information.

Among his many other activities, Louis Agassiz made dredgings and soundings off the coast of Florida and came to some significant conclusions on the permanence of the ocean basins. This matter is still the center of a warm controversy, and a quotation from Agassiz (1869, p. 368) is helpful in giving historical perspective:

"From what I have seen of the deep-sea bottom, I am already led to infer that among the rocks forming the bulk of the stratified crust of our globe, from the oldest to the youngest formation, there are probably none which have been formed in very deep waters. If this be so, we shall have to admit that the areas now respectively occupied by our continents, as circumscribed by the two hundred fathom curve or thereabout, and the oceans, at greater depth, have from the beginning retained their relative outline and position; the continents having at all times been areas of gradual upheaval with comparatively slight oscillations of rise and subsidence, and the oceans at all times areas of gradual depression with equally slight oscillations."

Alexander Agassiz, son of Louis, is much more closely identified with oceanographic expeditions and with oceanography in general than is his more famous father. His work is associated with the cruises of the *Blake* and the *Albatross*. His active connection with oceanography extended from 1877 to 1905 and included both general exploration by dredges and nets and much study of the coral reef problem. The conclusions reached by Alexander Agassiz concerning the origin of coral reefs were directly opposed to the subsidence theory of Charles Darwin. After a great deal of search, the younger Agassiz could not find an atoll or barrier reef the formation of which, he thought, could be adequately explained by Darwin's subsidence theory. He also concluded as a result of extensive dredging that the benthic animals of the Caribbean Sea are more closely related to the deep-sea animals of the Gulf of Panama than to those of the deep Atlantic, a conclusion that has stood the test of time to date. His book (1888) deserves especial mention.

As a result of working with a tow net that could be opened and closed under water at any depth, Alexander Agassiz modified somewhat the old idea of an azoic depth zone. He thought that there were practically no plankton organisms in the vast intermediate waters of the ocean below a depth of about 200 fathoms until one came near the bottom. Murray and others disagreed, and on this note of friendly difference of opinion the nineteenth century closed with the azoic zone problem considerably modified, but still alive. We may properly overstep the time limit for the present chapter and bring this particular matter down to 1934 by a quotation from Krogh (p. 430):

"The number and total mass of organisms decreases very rapidly with the depth. This has been established again and again both for net-plankton and for nannoplankton organisms and is well illustrated by the figures given by Hentschel for the number of nannoplankton organisms present in 1 liter of ocean water in the area 0–10° S and 10–20° W in the Atlantic: Surface, 10,100; 50m., 9400; 100m., 2700; 400m., 260; 1000m., 90; 2000m., 50; 3000m., 18; 5000m., 15."

While the plankton population is much reduced, there is no completely azoic region indicated by these data.

Herdman (1923, p. 111) quotes John Murray's estimate of Alexander Agassiz's influence on oceanography as follows:

"If we can say that we now know the physical and biological conditions of the great ocean basins in their broad general outline—and I believe we can do so—the present state of our knowledge is due to the combined work and observations of a great many men belonging to many nationalities, but most probably more to the work and inspiration of Alexander Agassiz than to any other single man."

This estimate, which has the approval of two excellent students of the subject, may help rescue the son from the comparative obscurity produced by the shadow of his father. Alexander Agassiz's last studies and his last expedition in the *Albatross* came in the early years of the present century; hence we have reached the end of the period to be covered in the present chapter. The ecological problems of the ocean had been outlined before 1900, and many of them were well advanced toward solution. With some notable exceptions, such as Möbius' recognition of the oyster bed as a biocoenosis, the possible ecological implications of these studies had not been emphasized.

LIMNOLOGY*

The development of limnology lagged behind that of oceanography, as shown by the fact that Forel (1892), in the first volume of his monograph on Le Léman (Lake Geneva, Switzerland), defined limnology as the oceanography of lakes. Despite much good work on the taxonomy and natural history of fresh-water organisms, it remained for P. E. Müller (1870), a Dane, to recognize the existence of a pelagic planktonic fauna in lakes, such as Lilljeborg

* Short historical sketches of limnology are given by Lampert (1910) and Welch (1935).

and Sars had found in the Baltic Sea (p. 37). This advance was based on a trip to the Swiss lakes in 1868. Beginning analyses of physical conditions in lakes preceded Müller's announcement. Simony was a pioneer in such studies; as early as 1850 he had reported in some detail concerning thermal stratification in lakes.

Forel is regarded as the founder of limnology, not because his work was chronologically first, but because of its long-continued significance. His paper of 1869 dealing with the bottom fauna of Le Léman, though not his initial publication, set the stage for his life work. His prolonged study of Swiss lakes reached a peak with the appearance of the three successive volumes of his monograph *Le Léman* (1892, 1895, 1904). Forel's generalizations, in the form of the first comprehensive discussion of limnology, were published just after the close of the period covered by the present chapter and are specifically noted in the following one (p. 47).

The contributions of Forel include the first demonstration of a deep-water community in lakes, the setting up of the first complete limnological plan for the study of a lake, and, what is more important, its practical realization. Welch, in the index to his 1935 textbook of limnology, cites the work of only three men more frequently than that of Forel: Juday, Birge, and Shelford, in that order.

Lampert's summary (1910, p. 13) of Forel's historical status in limnology gives some interesting comparisons. In free translation he says: Without reducing the merit of the lesser investigators, who like Forel recognized the significance of systematic fresh-water research and of whom especially Weismann [August Weismann of germ plasm fame], Du Plessis-Gouret, and Fritsch must be mentioned, we may still date the beginnings of limnology as a science from Forel's 1869 paper.

Weismann's contributions to limnology began in 1877. Du Plessis-Gouret, who had already published jointly with Forel, wrote in 1885 of the profundal fauna of Swiss lakes, and Anton Fritsch, among other contributions, established in 1888 the first fresh-water biological station. This was a portable laboratory with at first some 12 square meters of floor space. The laboratory was set up on the shores of three different lakes in the Bohemian Forest before 1899.[*]

The dredging operations in Lake Superior, made by S. I. Smith in 1871 and reported at length in 1874, deserve mention. He applied to Lake Superior many of the methods used by Verrill and Smith in their work on the invertebrate life of Vineyard Sound (p. 35) and reports, among other data, a table showing the bathymetrical distribution of the species taken. This promising opening of limnological studies on the Great Lakes has not yet been adequately developed.

Limnological work, once begun, flourished greatly in Europe and on the smaller lakes and rivers in the United States. Such investigations were in full swing in the last decade of the nineteenth century. Early quantitative studies in this field have already been discussed. Kofoid's investigations of plankton in the Illinois River (1903) were carried on from 1894 to 1899 and again deserve mention.

A number of comprehensive bibliographies of limnological work have appeared, two notable ones before 1900. Lampert's first edition of his *Das Leben der Binnengewässer* (1899) contained a fairly comprehensive bibliography. In the same year there appeared a workman-like review by H. B. Ward of advances during the years from 1893 to 1898. This review contains a bibliography of thirty-eight closely printed pages of citations to work published during this brief interval. Its pages remind us that the relict fauna of Tanganyika and of Baikal were being studied, as were also problems concerning the origin and dispersal of fresh-water animals. Cave life was receiving attention, and Ward states (1899, p. 332) that "Lorenzi, Packard, and Lendenfeld have given summaries of our knowledge regarding cave animals with frequent references both morphological and ecological [*sic*] to the freshwater fauna of such localities."

From this bibliography of Ward's we find that the veterans were busy during the half-decade under consideration. They are represented by men like Sars and Forel. Many of the stalwarts of twentieth century limnology had also begun work. Birge was

---

[*] Fritsch's "portable laboratory" was made in eighty sections so that it could be dismantled in an hour and a half, moved to another lake and set up again in two and a half hours. It weighed about 1000 kg. (*personal communication from Chancey Juday*).

writing about Cladocera, about limnetic Crustacea of Lake Mendota, and about the relation of areas of inland lakes and the temperature of the water. Juday, who had not yet established his productive scientific partnership with Birge, reported in 1896 on the plankton of Turkey Lake in Indiana. Reighard of Michigan; Wesenberg-Lund, student of Danish lakes; Zschokke, who studied Alpine lakes of Switzerland; and Apstein, prominent for his work on the plankton of the Holstein lakes, are all cited by Ward. Zacharias, founder of the enduring biological station at Plön, Germany, was especially prolific during these years of the 1890's, while Whipple, and Ward himself, contributed extensively.

The development of limnology, far from being at the end of a period, was in full and active growth in 1900. Limnology had already made direct contact with ecology, notably in Forbes' essay *The Lake as a Microcosm*. Although the subjects had by no means fused, the development of modern, self-conscious ecology owes much to the groundwork laid by the pioneers in limnology and oceanography, that is, to the sound development of knowledge concerning hydrobiology before 1900.

THE RISE OF SELF-CONSCIOUS ECOLOGY

The foregoing pages give in some detail samples of the substrata on which self-conscious ecology developed. Certain of the persons mentioned were directly important in the early growth of the subject in the strict sense; many were not. It is customary to begin the schematized textbook sketches of the history of ecology with the writings of Buffon, who lived from 1707 to 1788 and emphasized, among many other interests, the interrelations of organisms. Saint Hilaire (1859) clearly outlined the scope of such relationships under the name of "ethology," which he conceived of as including "the study of the relations of the organism within the family and society in the aggregate and in the community." John Stuart Mill (1848) in his *Logic* antedated St. Hilaire in using the word "ethology," by which he meant the science of human character. It has been argued that since the character of an organism is revealed only through its reaction to the environment, there is no essential difference between human and other aspects of "ethology."

Haeckel (1869) coined the term "Oekologie," from which the modern "ecology" has been derived. He defined the content of his Oekologie as "comprising the relation of the animal to its organic as well as its inorganic environment, particularly its friendly or hostile relations to those animals or plants with which it comes in contact." Semper (1881) distinguished between the physiology of organs and that of organisms; the latter is concerned, he says, with the "reciprocal relations which adjust the balance between the existence of any species and the natural, external conditions of its existence, in the widest sense of the term."

Lankester (1889) under the term bionomics included a miscellany that contained the lore of the hunter and herdsman, the science of breeding, and the study of organic adaptation. A few other terms have been suggested for these or related phases of biology, but none is important, except the tendency, which still continues, to designate much of ecology as "biology." We read of the "biology" of a snail or of a "biological" survey, when the treatment is mainly ecological. This usage is to be deplored.

Subdivisions of the subject matter of ecology began at an early date. Schröter and Kirchner (1896, 1902) recognized the ecological relations of the individual as "autecology" and those of communities of organisms as "synecology." As stated earlier, Forbes (1895) formulated a definition of ecology and pointed out that economic entomology is simply applied ecology.

This, then, brings ecology and its forerunners approximately up to 1900. It is clear that the field was ripe for further development, a development that has proceeded with quickening pace. The situation at that time is correctly summed up by Pearse (1939) as follows: "At the beginning of the twentieth century ecology was a young, but an established, science, and such eminent ecologists as Wasmann (1901), Dahl (1901) and Wheeler (1902) were discussing whether Saint-Hilaire's ethology or Haeckel's ecology should be used to designate the science of relations of organisms to environments."

Ecology was even more firmly established as a special field of botany, for Cowles (1901) began his important report on physiographic ecology with the statement that: "Within the last few years the subject of ecology has come to find a place of more or less importance wherever botany is studied in its general aspects." Cowles indirectly documents his point by his literature citations for 1896 to 1900.

The end of the nineteenth century is a convenient, though not a logical, division between the early history of ecology and its more recent development. Unlike the modern subject of genetics, which has developed mainly from the spectacular rediscovery of Mendelian heredity in 1900, we can now see that for ecology the years connecting the centuries mark a time of relatively smooth progress. Ecologists of the early 1900's gave praise to Semper for his recognition of the physiology of organisms in relation to "natural conditions of existence," and researches in this field proceeded steadily. Work on ecological aspects of animal behavior was active. Population studies

were moving at an increasing rate. Evolutionary thought was in gradual transition, with the theory of natural selection, known by some even then to be largely ecological, still holding the attention of biologists. Ideas concerning natural cooperation were growing. Natural history had passed its peak of activity in university circles, but was directly and broadly related to the preceding years. The same is true for oceanography; the related subject of limnology was in the midst of a notable advance. In self-conscious ecology, the community concept had been clearly expressed, and there was active research in animal and particularly plant ecology. Scientific attention in general was focussed on nonecological phases of biology, and the science of ecology, now well and firmly rooted, could continue to develop outside the distorting influences often accompanying high popularity.

3. FIRST FOUR DECADES OF THE TWENTIETH CENTURY

INTRODUCTION

At this point let us take stock of what has already been said of the historical antecedents and background of ecology. We have covered in considerable detail some 2200 years of ecological history. From the viewpoint of ecology, four general chronological periods have been recognized: (1) the contributions of the Greeks and Romans; (2) the subsequent thousand or so years of stagnation; (3) the developments of the sixteenth, seventeenth and eighteenth centuries that led into (4) the nineteenth century studies. It has been suggested that since the Renaissance the major contributions to the growth of ecology occurred along four channels: developmental physiology, response physiology, relation of species to their environment, and organic evolution.

Enough of a background has been presented to show that ecology had multiple origins. It was descended neither from a single idea nor from isolated facts. The task now confronting us is that of showing how "modern" or twentieth century animal ecology has come into being and how it is practiced today. There are many ways of approaching this problem. For our purposes

it seems best to adopt a chronological treatment based roughly on the first four decades of the twentieth century. It will be necessary, particularly in discussing the later decades, to appreciate that even present day ecology is not so clearly delimited as are, for example, modern genetics or many other biological disciplines. This means that we are compelled to discuss and consider certain borderline fields. The point is emphasized by examining the "Ecology" section of a recent (1940) issue of *Biological Abstracts;* the following subheadings are listed: "General Animal Ecology;" "General Plant Ecology;" "Hydrobiology" (Oceanography, Limnology); "Ecology of Wildlife Management—Aquatic and Terrestrial," and "Bioclimatology, Biometeorology."

It is advisable to discuss briefly certain aspects of the history of plant ecology during the twentieth century before attention is focussed on animal ecology. Plant ecology got off to a faster start at the turn of the century. Thus, as will be shown later, it had a great impact on the thinking and research of certain pioneer animal ecologists. The development of plant ecology has been reviewed by Conard (1939).

Our responsibility is not to linger on

plant ecology *per se,* but to appraise this field as it has provided fact and catalyst for zoological developments. Specific relationships will be pointed out further on, but these generalizations emerge:

1. The investigations of early plant ecologists were favored somewhat by the fact that plants are essentially fixed geographically and not greatly subject to rapid dispersal.

2. Plant ecology, naturally enough, developed regionally according to the local resources that could be exploited and studied.

3. Plant ecology gave an early and significant orientation to animal ecology in several ways: (a) It stressed the fact that communities or complex natural populations exist over the face of the earth and are subject to analysis. This gave a telling impetus to animal synecology. (b) It crystallized certain comprehensive ecological concepts such as succession and thus sent animal ecologists out into the field to see if animals also furnished data to support the concept. (c) It developed certain techniques of field study that could be used with but minor modification by the zoologist. (d) It emphasized in an ecological sense the fact that plants stand in an important relation to animals in terms of nutrition, breeding, and shelter niches. And, perhaps most important, (e) it gave psychological stimulus around the turn of the century by showing the zoologist that first-rate botanists were investigating ecological problems and getting results. In short, the animal ecologist owes much to the plant ecologist in a historical sense, and, on land, he is still dependent on plant ecology for much of his zoogeographic description.

Our task now is to discuss the growth of twentieth century animal ecology. We find that by dividing the years from 1900 to 1940 into their four component decades, we can consider each of these decades both as a unit and as an interrelated part of the whole pattern. This is not a completely arbitrary treatment. A case can be made for the point that, during this span, ten years seemed to be about the actual interval for certain types of work to materialize and certain ideas to be synthesized. Thus, there is nothing really different between, say, the years 1910 and 1911 or 1930 and 1931, but there does appear to be a real historical difference between 1900 and 1910 or 1911 and 1920 in terms of the development of animal ecology.

Our treatment varies somewhat according to the individuality of the decade in question, but in general we hope to ask, and so far as possible to answer, the following four questions for each:

1. What were the research focal points?
2. Who were some of the leaders in the research fields discussed?
3. What was the historical impact of the work of these men?
4. What grew out of the decade that seemed significant?

The reader should keep in mind that the absence of a favored name or citation in the following pages does not necessarily signify that it has been overlooked or deemed unimportant. It may mean just that, or, contrariwise, it may mean merely that there is not enough space for its inclusion. It is necessary to emphasize that in dealing with the foregoing questions we are *sampling* historical data, and that our sample is not a random one, but is selected. Accordingly, our cases are subject to bias, as, for example, our overemphasis on American historical illustrations. From one point of view this is poor technique with obvious limitations. But from another aspect it is sound, since it does permit us to present *our* notions of what is significant and thereby evaluate ecological history as we see it. With these preliminaries we turn to the first decade of the twentieth century.

1900–1910

During this period of ecological growth, ecological investigations seem to have fallen into the following categories: response physiology, developmental and toleration physiology, natural history, hydrobiology, succession, and general synecology. These did not originate *de novo* with the turn of the century. Most of them had antecedents in earlier work, as we have shown.

Response physiology, or ecological aspects of behavior, was studied actively during this period. Davenport's "Experimental Morphology," the second edition of which appeared in 1908, was still shaping ideas and new researches. This was the period when "trial and error" behavior was much in the scientific headlines. Jenning's classic *Behavior of the Lower Organisms* (1906) had a firm impact on ecological thinking. It showed that environmental stimuli, even if of subtle character, could control an animal's orientation and pattern of movement. Also, it had a significant influence on the thinking of biologists generally. The first edition of *The Animal Mind* by Washburn (1908), to be followed by several further editions, laid certain foundations for the study of animal behavior.

There was much writing during the decade on the behavior of a single species. This is well typified by the study by Raymond Pearl, whose excellent and original monograph on the behavior of *Planaria* summarized the state of things at that time in these words (1903, p. 511):

" . . . Aside from the researches of a few investigators on a small number of forms, we have little detailed knowledge of the behaviour of lower organisms. It is coming to be realised, too, that knowledge of what an animal does is just as important in the general study of life phenomena as a knowledge of how it is constructed, or how it develops."

There are also some writings on social behavior. Wheeler's classical book on "Ants" appeared in 1910 (reprinted, 1926) and, through its emphasis on ant behavior, did much to stimulate behavior studies on the social insects and to provoke comparisons, sometimes invidious, between insect and human responses. A paper by Craig (1908) on pigeons suggested that the vocalization of these birds had some function in the social control of the flock.

The field of developmental physiology was equally active. It also received impetus from Davenport's summary. Mention of several studies will suffice to show the nature of the research of this period. Among others, the works of Bachmetjew (1901, 1901a, 1907) stand out. He not only summarized a wealth of literature, but presented as well many original observations and interpretations. Bachmetjew was concerned largely with the effect of light and temperature on various phases of the development and distribution of insects. Probably one of his more significant contributions was his summary of the effect of low temperature on insect protoplasm. Chapman (1931, p. 61) states this in concise form as follows: "The insect may be cooled below the freezing point without being injured. The freezing point may be past, and the insect may exist in an undercooled condition. When it does freeze, the

heat of crystallization will be equal to the undercooling temperature, and the body temperature will rebound to the freezing point. Cooling will again proceed; and when the insect reaches the undercooling point the second time, death follows, according to Bachmetjew's conception." More modern views do not completely agree with this interpretation, but in 1901 it was an important pronouncement with cogent ecological implications. Bachmetjew also discoursed on light and temperature in relation to zoogeography.

Branching off from developmental physiology is a phase of research that some ecologists designate "toleration physiology" or "toleration ecology." In such work the concern lies with the limits of toleration for organisms exposed to various intensities of environmental factors or combinations of these factors. During the decade 1900 to 1910 there were some studies of this type, and an example or so may be cited. Packard (1905, p. 33) published a paper on the effect of low oxygen tension on survival of certain marine fishes and invertebrates of the Woods Hole (Massachusetts) area. In addition, he showed that if the blood alkalinity of *Fundulus heteroclitus* was increased, there was a corresponding increase in the tolerance of the fish to lack of oxygen. Contrariwise, increasing the acidity of the blood made the fish less tolerant of low oxygen tensions. Bachmetjew (1907) recognized this general problem for insects and published a list of extremes of temperature that various insects have been known to tolerate. Another such list appeared in Davenport (1908).

Natural history has always been inextricably interwoven with ecology. In fact, ecology has been called "scientific natural history." Much of the content of ecology is natural history, and the ecologist usually experiences a certain pleasure in observing and recording the "history of nature." But natural history is not a closely definable entity. It may range from superficial and even misleading nature study, to excellent, precise investigation. Earlier in this section we saw how this phase of ecology contributed to the rise of the science.

During the decade 1900 to 1910 examples can be chosen that run the gamut of type. There were books such as that of Chapman (1900), designed largely for the nature student and amateur. It is hard to evaluate the influence of works like this on ecological development. Then there were books such as Seton's *Life Histories of Northern Animals* (1909). These contributed much that was useful to the ecologist. Seton's book combined a wealth of information about life histories and habits with an extensive bibliography. Von Neumayer (1906) published his two volume compendium on exploration. Adams (1913 p. 63) says of this study: "A very important work, particularly for the traveling naturalist. Chapters by specialists, valuable references on collecting natural history specimens, and other phases of scientific exploration are included." More technical natural history studies of this period are typified by the papers of Reighard (1903), Andrews (1904), and Forbes (1907).

Reighard's paper, on the "Natural History of *Amia calva*," published as a tribute to the Harvard zoologist Edward Laurens Mark, is an excellent case in point. This author, who worked for four seasons in the millponds of the Huron River, records a wealth of careful observation about this fish. He discusses such aspects as secondary sexual characters, habits not peculiar to the breeding season, nest-building, guarding of the empty nests by males, guarding the eggs, protective colors of males, history of the eggs and young in the nest, history of the young outside the nest, and the behavior of the male while with the school. In a historical chapter one need hardly make the point that sound data such as these, multiplied many times to include many different animals, are of profound importance both during the decade of their publication and for years afterwards as well. Reighard's paper on *Amia* drives the point home!

The paper of E. A. Andrews on the breeding habits of *Cambarus affinis* was as thorough a study of an arthropod as that just described was for a vertebrate. Andrews covered much the same sort of observation as did Reighard. In addition, he added some simple biometric linear measurements of the whole animal and certain of its parts that did much to embellish his work. Biometry was already making its influence felt on ecology and natural history. In England, Karl Pearson was in the midst of his dynamic career, and in America, Raymond Pearl and C. B. Davenport, to be followed soon by J. A. Harris, were applying statistical methods to many kinds

of data. Studies such as these had the vital importance of forcing ecologists to think in a more analytical fashion about *group* characteristics.

The latter point is even better made by looking at two 1907 papers of S. A. Forbes. This excellent naturalist of Wheeler's "corn and saleratus" belt did much for ecology starting with his estimable essay, *The Lake as a Microcosm* (p. 36). In the 1907 studies Forbes discussed the local distribution of Illinois fishes and the bird population of Illinois in autumn. In both papers the reader detects careful observation, appreciation of the natural history of the forms studied and an insistence that *numbers* as well as names should be listed. In the fish paper Forbes (1907a) develops what he calls the "Coefficient of Association," designed to show the frequency with which one species is found associated with another in nature. This statement took the following form:

$$\text{C.A.} = \frac{ad}{bc}$$

where *a* equals the total number of collections to be used in the computations; *b*, the number of collections containing the more abundant of two species to be compared with another; *c*, the number of collections containing the less abundant of these species, and *d*, the number of collections each of which actually contains both species together. Despite the fact that Forbes' coefficient is imperfect and is not used by modern workers, it did serve the important function of stating a real problem and suggesting a solution.

In a very real sense, *hydrobiology* (both oceanography and limnology) has developed as a subscience in its own right. However, since we shall be referring continually in this book to ecological principles derived from the data of hydrobiology, and since its early historical development is one and the same with ecology proper, we must examine its contribution to our historical analysis. During the decade 1900 to 1910 many investigations of aquatic ecology were published. We shall sample a few representative studies.

From the marine aspect Johnstone's book (1908) and the papers of Östenfeld (1908) and Sumner (1910) are characteristic. Johnstone's book was a competent summary of modern oceanography. In the first part he discussed the North Atlantic ocean, types of life in the sea, including notes on fishes and fishing; in the second part he stressed the quantitative method as applied to plankton census and productivity; and in the last part he dealt with the "metabolism of the sea"—food relationships, bacteria, and nitrogen circulation. Even to a modern worker the book is a sound contribution. It is safe to assume that its impact on aquatic ecology was considerable.

Ostenfeld's paper was important, since it showed clearly " . . . the controlling relation of marine vegetation upon animal associations and particularly the fish of the coast of Denmark" (Adams, 1913, p. 89). Work of this type indubitably helped to draw together plant and animal ecology. Sumner's paper is an excellent example of a certain type of field study. The bottom fauna and flora of an area around Woods Hole, Massachusetts (namely, Buzzards Bay and Vineyard Sound), were studied in relation to temperature, character of bottom, depth, salinity, and density. The local distribution of each species was carefully determined and mapped. Conclusions were drawn as to which factors were most important in shaping the observed distributions. In addition, the author formulated some opinion about the geographical origin of the fauna of the region.

Fresh-water ecologists or limnologists also were making rapid strides during the first decade of the twentieth century. This period prospered under the influence of F. A. Forel (1841–1912), a professor in the University of Lausanne, who has been called the "founder of modern limnology." In 1901 Forel published his *Handbuch der Seenkunde. Allgemeine Limnologie.* The importance of this volume is well indicated by Welch (1935, p. 5) in these words: "This book is the first general presentation of limnology from the modern standpoint. In fact, it might well be termed the first textbook of limnology. In brief, limnology is indebted to Forel for the first knowledge concerning the profundal fauna of fresh-water lakes, for the first program for *limnological* investigations of such waters, and for the execution of such a program, resulting in 'Le Léman,' which was long a model for subsequent work."

A first-rate paper by Kofoid (1903) on the plankton of the Illinois river was a detailed, meticulous study with a definitely ecological point of view. In 1904 E. A. Birge published a paper in which he clearly demonstrated thermal stratification in inland lakes and formulated a standard method of expressing it. In a historical discussion one is tempted to pause over the names of Birge and his colleague Juday to pay tribute to their cogent contributions to aquatic biology. Another book that seems to have been important during this decade was that by Knauthe (1907).

There is some point in dealing specifically with ecological succession. This was the era when plant ecologists were interested in the phenomenon. The animal ecologist was starting his investigations on succession, to be followed actively in the next ten years. Cowles published his "Sand Dunes" paper in 1899. This stimulated the zoologists V. E. Shelford and C. C. Adams, who were ecologically inclined from their association with Davenport at the University of Chicago, to examine the concept from a zoological aspect. In 1907 Shelford reported on the succession of tiger beetles (*Cicindela*) in the same dunes region where Cowles had studied. He " . . . traced the relation of Cicindela to the succession of plant communities. The distribution of eight species of tiger beetles was in close correspondence with the zoned habitats and communities, and the conclusion was reached that a similar harmony existed with respect to the fauna in general" (Clements and Shelford, 1939, p. 8).

Adams' 1909 paper shows even more respect for the concept of succession than does Shelford's. It starts with this interesting quotation from John Stuart Mill:

"Of all truths relating to phenomena, the most valuable to us are those which relate to their order of succession. On a knowledge of these is founded every reasonable anticipation of future facts, and whatever power we possess of influencing those facts to our advantage."

Adams reviews much of the background for ecological succession current at that time. He discusses general principles as well as specific avian illustrations. From his studies of the latter he reaches this conclusion (p. 134):

" . . . Bird succession means a change from the dominance of certain species or associations to that of others. Thus in the beginning a slight change in abundance of a species may be noted, with a corresponding decrease in another; and this proportion may continue to change until the intruder becomes dominant and the rival form may disappear entirely. The process of change, as a rule, is not limited to a single species, but usually involves several or all of the members of the association, as when a dune invades a swamp and the swamp birds are completely replaced by those frequenting the sand dunes."

Later we shall have more to say of the impact of succession on the rise of ecology.

The term "synecology" apparently was coined by the botanists Schröter and Kirchner in 1902 from the Greek prefix *syn*, meaning "together." Since that time ecologists have used synecology in a general sense to imply the association of individuals in contradistinction to the ecology of an isolated organism ("autecology").* There have been attempts to define the term with more precision. Thus there is the definition of Turesson "the ecology of communities;" of Rübel, "the relation between the community and its habitat;" of Braun-Blanquet, "the study of the dependence of communities upon one another and upon the environment," and of the Third International Botanical Congress, "the study of conditions of the environment and adaptation of species taken in association." For our present purposes we shall use synecology in a broad fashion only and select several early twentieth century studies that depict the state of the science at that time. Obviously, many of the papers already reviewed are synecological in part, but a few cases *per se* are in order.

In 1903 Davenport published a paper on the ecology of a Cold Spring Harbor (New York) sand spit. This was a solid study that stressed the local distribution of animals with respect to local habitat zones. The spit was divided into two areas, the periodically submerged zone and the beach zone, and the fauna of these two was studied. Davenport stressed those adaptations of the fauna particularly adjusted to these two niches. Another representative study was that of Ruthven (1906) on an ecological survey of the Porcupine Mountains in Michigan. This was interesting in that the author placed the faunas in a framework of biotic associations and, as Adams puts it, "treated them

* Autecology is frequently used to mean the environmental relations of a single species instead of a single individual. It is not so used in this book.

from the dynamic and genetic standpoint." The monograph of Eigenmann (1909) on "Cave Vertebrates of America" deserves mention here. Although this work has not stood the test of time so far as its interpretations are concerned, it did serve a real function in placing on record many data on the adjustment between cave forms and their habitats and the phylogenetic regression associated with that adjustment.

Under the heading of quantitative synecology the 1907 note of McAtee deserves mention primarily because it illustrates the use of the quadrat method for sampling surface flora and fauna. McAtee presented in some detail census data of four square feet of forest and meadow floor at several times of the year. The data are then enumerated relative to species, and an attempt is made to show how the nutritional resources of the floor are utilized by the bird population. The latter is important because it stresses the community as a whole rather than isolated habitat niches.

The ingenious Forbes in 1909 had a novel idea and approach. He studied the Indian corn plant in relation to its insect infestation. Using as his biological focus the fact that corn is both introduced and under "the constant supervision of a guardian and the services of a nurse," he develops the argument that this species is ecologically maladjusted and vulnerable to a disproportionate amount of insect competition. His analysis of this corn-insect nexus is an interesting study in synecology.

This concludes our treatment of the 1900 to 1910 period. We shall return briefly to this decade later when we try to draw some generalizations.

One other point must be raised. The reader may ask with justification: Why have there not been reviewed works on evolution as they contribute to ecological growth?*

* One book that appeared during the decade and focussed attention on evolutionary processes was *Darwin and Modern Science*, edited by A. C. Seward (1909). This volume contained twenty-nine essays written by eminent contributors in commemoration of the fiftieth anniversary of the publication of *The Origin of Species*. Certain of these essays were distinctly ecological and should be mentioned: "The Selection Theory," by August Weismann; "Geographical Distribution of Animals," by Hans Gadow; "Experimental Study of the Influence of Environment on Animals," by Jacques Loeb; and "The Value of Colour in the Struggle for Life," by E. B. Poulton.

The answer is that, during this period, the growth of ecology and evolution were so inextricably woven together that it seems artificial to separate the two. Many of the studies we have mentioned in foregoing pages contain data, conclusions, or concepts that bear on evolution or speciation. In other words, certain ecologists of these times had a lively interest in such matters. This is as it should be, and it epitomizes the viewpoint of this book and its authors.[*]

1911–1920

As we survey the second decade of the twentieth century from the viewpoint of ecological history, these items impress us:

1. There was no *major* readjustment of focus between this decade and the first.

2. Not much theoretical synthesis of the material of ecology was attempted.

3. More work was done in the sense that there were more investigators.

4. Technical advances in other fields—physics, chemistry, physiography, climatology, physiology, biometry, and so on—reflect upon ecological research largely through refinement of methods and mensuration.

5. Some books (both text and reference) of use to the ecologist were published.

6. The British Ecological Society and The Ecological Society of America were founded in 1913 and 1916, respectively, to aid ecologists and their enterprises.

In short, this seems to be *primarily* a decade of sure, gradual growth without much reorientation.

Since the literature of this decade is more extensive than that of the 1900 to 1910 era, there is a temptation to devote more space to it. This we cannot do. We can only sample as before and trust that our samples are sufficiently representative to be meaningful.

Some of the books that appeared should be mentioned. Books are valuable in a historical survey because they indicate what was considered important at the time and how the subject matter was studied. Two physiological texts were published that ecologists found useful: Pütter's *Vergleich-*

[*] For the sake of accuracy, however, it should be mentioned that certain ecologists were veering away from an evolutionary viewpoint in the first decade. A good example, perhaps, was V. E. Shelford, who, during that period, was crystallizing his ideas on "physiological animal geography" in contradistinction to historical or faunal animal geography.

ende Physiologie (1911) and Bayliss *Principles of General Physiology* (second edition, 1918). In 1913 C. C. Adams published his *Guide to the Study of Animal Ecology*. This served the useful purpose of classifying the diverse literature of ecology and outlined a reading program for students. Probably the most valuable book of the decade was Shelford's *Animal Communities in Temperate America* (1913). Here was a summary of much original field research organized around a number of habitats within a restricted area (Chicago). The author gave due weight to physiography, the nonbiotic and the biotic environment, and to the quantitative enumeration of animals. Although it is out of date in some respects, teachers and students to this day turn to it for ecological guidance. It was reprinted without essential alteration in 1937.

Several books on hydrobiology appeared and served a real need. Murray and Hjort's *The Depths of the Ocean* (1912) became rapidly a standard treatise on oceanography, and the compendium *Fresh-Water Biology* (1918), edited by Ward and Whipple, facilitated the study of limnology, particularly through its emphasis on taxonomy. In 1916 Needham and Lloyd published *The Life of Inland Waters,* "an elementary textbook of freshwater biology" that served a useful purpose in field zoology and beginning ecology courses. In 1913 L. J. Henderson published *The Fitness of the Environment.* While not an ecological study in the restricted sense, this book was a provocative statement on the relation of the environment to its organism. It forced ecologists to think in new and somewhat theoretical terms and thereby exerted a healthy influence both on them and on the development of their subject. We shall return specifically to this book in a later section (p. 76).

In 1915 Jordan and Kellogg brought forth their *Evolution and Animal Life*, which contained many correlations between ecology and evolution and thus deserves mention in this place. In the preface the authors state: " . . . the writers have tried to give a lucid elementary account, in limited space, of the processes of evolution as they are so far understood." The chapters with particular ecological flavor are "Natural Selection and Struggle for Existence;" "Geographic Isolation and Species-Forming;" "Geographical Distribution;" "Adaptations;" "Mutual Aid and Communal Life among Animals;" and

"Color and Pattern in Animals." This was a useful book which, in the second decade, emphasized the close connection between ecology and organic evolution.

These, then, are some of the books that ecologists were reading during the decade 1911 to 1920. Of course there were others, but the ones mentioned should suffice as a sample. It is our task now to survey briefly certain specific papers as we did in the preceding section. We use the same headings as before: viz., natural history; response, developmental and toleration physiology; hydrobiology; succession; and synecology. In addition, we shall have a word to say about the growth of quantitative methods.

Since ecology is always based in the final analysis on natural history, we find that subject constantly present and to be accounted for. During the decade 1911 to 1920 many first-rate natural history papers were published. These ranged from such popularized reports as Brunner's Tracks and Tracking (1912), which was an "illustrated guide for the identification of mammal and bird tracks or footprints," to such comprehensive studies as those of Herrick (1911), Belding and Lane (1911), Needham (1920), and Pearse and Achtenberg (1920).

Response physiology was an active phase of ecology during the second decade. While the investigations ranged considerably in type, there was a drive towards expressing animal behavior in as precise terms as possible. Frequently, this led the study into experimentation as distinguished from uncontrolled observation. The ecological contributions were made largely through knowledge acquired of the way a single environmental factor induced an organismic response. Review of several studies will clarify these points.

A paper that was interesting from both the behavioristic and ecological points of view was that of Severin and Severin (1911) on death feigning in two aquatic bugs, Belostoma and Nepa. These investigators were concerned with three aspects of the problem: careful description of the death-feigning attitudes, environmental factors inducing death feigning, and the possible significance of this response when expressed in terms of survival value. For example, it was found that while Belostoma assumed either of two attitudes, Nepa

"froze" in the position it held at the time the stimulus was presented. The authors noted that dryness decreases and moisture increases the duration of the death feint in Belostoma and that high air temperature shortens the duration for both species. Their general conclusion about the character of the response is that " . . . the death feint in arthropods is simply a non-intelligent instinctive act" (p. 39).

Dawson (1911), in "The Biology of Physa," approached this topic with a behavior emphasis, but reported much that was ecological, particularly in two sections of the paper: "The Relation of Physa to Its Natural Environment; Including a Comprehensive Analysis of the Habits of Physa in the Ann Arbor Region," and "The Food and Feeding Activities of Physa." The section on "Psychic Phenomena" contains an interesting and ecologically pertinent discussion of the "source of stimuli received by Physa in field habitats." Present day ecological work would profit by careful analyses of the latter type! In 1911 S. O. Mast published Light and the Behavior of Organisms. This was a valuable stimulus to comparative psychology, and it also synthesized much that was instructive to the ecologist. Also during the decade Jacques Loeb (1918) published his well-known and polemic book on a mechanistic interpretation of behavior, Forced Movements, Tropisms and Animal Conduct.

Developmental physiology underwent more specialization during the decade. It also linked itself closely with embryology. Nevertheless, many papers were published that contributed to the growth of ecology. LeFevre and Curtis (1912) reported at length on the reproduction of fresh-water mussels. Much of their work had distinct ecological and parasitological emphasis. Thus they discussed the development of the embryonic mussels in the gills ("marsupium") of the mother. They studied breeding seasons and recognized "summer breeders" and "winter breeders." They described the development and behavior of the glochidia, including the parasitization of the fish by these larvae. Finally, they dealt with the establishment of the young mussel on the bottom and its subsequent maturation.

During this decade there was a growing focus, later to reach fuller clarity, on the effect of the physical environment upon developmental rates. Usually, either temperature or humidity was the variable studied. Headlee's 1917 paper is a representative example. In this he analyzed the effect of humidity on duration of metamorphosis in the bean weevil, *Bruchus obtectus*. For a paper published during the decade, but dealing with temperature rather than with humidity, the reader is referred to Krafka (1920).

Earlier, we called attention to the publication in 1918 of the second edition of Bayliss' *Physiology*. This magnificent volume immediately became a source book for physiologically minded ecologists (as it did for many other biologists) and did much for the field. It was useful especially in the area of developmental physiology.

Not many publications were concerned directly with toleration physiology between 1911 and 1920, although this phase was touched on incidentally in numerous places. A good example of this approach *per se* is the paper of Shelford and Allee (1913), "The Reactions of Fishes to Gradients of Dissolved Atmospheric Gases." For example, they studied the ability of various species of fish to tolerate low oxygen tensions. One of their suggestive findings was this: Species of fish die (in the presence of reduced oxygen supply) in the order of their relation to this factor in nature. Thus, just to make the point, *Notropis*, a swift-water form, starts to die after 376 minutes' exposure, while *Ameiurus*, typically a sluggish-water form, does not start to die until after 1080 minutes.

A number of excellent investigations on hydrobiology were published during this decade. There was perhaps a growing divergence between oceanography and limnology, but the essential viewpoints of these two fields retained much in common. The treatise, already mentioned, by Murray and Hjort, *The Depths of the Ocean*, appeared in 1912 and helped to establish modern oceanography on a firmer foundation. A representative research report was that of Petersen and Jensen (1911), who published a comprehensive monograph on the fauna of the ocean floor both from the quantitative and nutritional aspects. This paper discussed the techniques of bottom study and also presented many significant biological data. Adams in 1913 considered it "a very important paper."

In addition to recognizing the importance of Petersen and Jensen's paper, a word should be said of Petersen himself. It is not always recognized that this man is among the great in the history of ecology and hydrobiology. We should fail in our survey if we overlooked the point. Professor E. S. Russell, himself a distinguished hydrobiologist, in his *The Overfishing Problem* (1942, pp. 68–69) pays tribute to Petersen in these words:

"In introducing a biological and ecological note into this discussion . . . I shall follow the lead of a remarkable man, the late C. G. Joh. Petersen, a pioneer in fishery research and marine ecology, whose work is unfortunately not widely known outside fishery circles. I had the privilege of his friendship, and the opportunity of discussing with him fishery questions and problems of general biology—and I take this occasion to pay a tribute to his memory.

"Petersen was for many years Director of the Danish Biological Station, a State institution devoted to the investigation of fishery problems, and it was his great merit that he regarded these as being essentially problems of ecology. He realised more vividly than anyone else that fish must be studied, not in isolation from their environment, or purely from a statistical point of view, but in close relation to all the factors, including the effect of fishing, that influence their abundance, their rate of growth, and their reproduction."

Fresh-water investigations were also contributing to the growth of ecology during the decade. Birge and Juday were in the midst of their long personal and scholarly association. A representative illustration of their then current work was the still-quoted 1911 paper, "The Dissolved Gases of the Water and Their Biological Significance."

In 1918 Muttkowski published a sound report covering work conducted at Lake Mendota (Wisconsin). This paper was a thorough treatment, with considerable tabular documentation, of the following points: (1) qualitative survey of the macrofauna; (2) quantitative survey of the commoner macrofauna; (3) ecological distribution of the fauna; (4) breeding habits; and (5) food relations, especially insects as food for the fish population. In 1918 there also appeared *Fresh-water Biology*, edited by Ward and Whipple. We have already suggested that this source book had a firm impact on aquatic ecology.

Forbes and Richardson (1919) published a study of the Illinois River that not only contained much of ecological importance, but also utilized physiography as an approach to ecology and presented something of the impact of human society on a natural environment. Their interest centered around the Illinois River as it had been affected by (a) the opening of the Chicago drainage canal into the river; (b) the consequent increase in sewage; (c) the reclamation of river bottoms for agricultural use; and (d) the introduction into the stream of the European carp.

An appreciation of the amount of published research on limnology through the first decade can be had by examination of the "Bibliography of Limnological Literature" compiled in the "Challenger" office and assembled by James Chumley (1910). The reference list contains over 2500 citations.

In discussing some of the developments of synecology during this decade, it is well to remind the reader that many of the papers already cited in other connections contain much of synecological interest. Thus, the reports of Pearse and Achtenberg, of Petersen and Jensen, of Embody and of Muttkowski all have direct bearing and could be cited properly in this section. However, we shall extend our remarks somewhat by reviewing a few more papers selected for the purpose.

During this decade synecological studies were varied in character and in method of analysis. They were dominated largely by successional emphasis and ranged from such papers as that of Gates (1911), describing the distribution of summer Illinois bird life in relation to the local plant communities, to Wheeler's (1911) philosophical essay, "The Ant-Colony as an Organism," in which he pointed out some of the analogies between such a complex, integrated population of organisms and a complex, integrated population of cells.

In 1912 Pierce, Cushman, and Hood published an important paper on "The Insect Enemies of the Cotton Boll Weevil." Although this investigation was motivated by economic considerations, it is a thoroughly sound and stimulating analysis of biological control, i.e., control of the boll weevil population by predatory and parasitic competition. In an attempt to evaluate these predatory and parasitic pressures, the authors reach these major conclusions (pp. 94, 95):

1. "The control of the boll weevil by insect enemies is sufficiently great to give it a high rank in the struggle against the pest. A considerable portion of the insect control would not be accomplished by any other factor; hence it is by no means to be neglected."

2. "The amount of control due to the various factors at work in any given place should be increased if possible. Parasites can be introduced into new fields."

3. "The parasites and predators which attack the boll weevil are native insects, already present in a given territory before the weevil arrives."

The synecological distinction of this paper lies in the authors' constant emphasis on interspecies relationships, whatever the type. This is climaxed in an interesting diagram that attempts to put in simple form all the major relationships unearthed. Because of the novelty of this figure and because it presages much that is to come later in this book, it is reproduced on page 53 (Fig. 1).

The microfauna was not neglected during the decade 1911 to 1920. Waksman (1916) wrote cogently of it in a paper entitled "Studies on Soil Protozoa." He discussed three aspects: (1) active protozoan fauna in the soil; (2) numbers and types of Protozoa in different soils at different depths; and (3) the effect of Protozoa on bacterial numbers and their decomposition of organic matter in the soil. His two major conclusions were that moisture, humus content and soil structure are the most important factors to which soil Protozoa react, and that soil Protozoa reduce bacterial numbers. In reference to the latter statement, Waksman makes the point that, when conditions become favorable for the Protozoa, the bacteria decrease. Presumably, this effect is competitive in character, although Waksman did not analyze it in any detail.

At this point attention should be called to a considerable, early twentieth century "Cornell School" of naturalists, including A. A. Allen (Ornithology), A. H. Wright (Vertebrate Zoology), and James G. Needham (Entomology and Limnology), with their students, and with the addition of W. J. Hamilton (Mammalogy) in 1926. Cornell had become the center of entomological research and education under the influence of John Henry Comstock (1849–1931), and of interest in vertebrate zoology under Burt G. Wilder (1841–1926). "Field Zoology" flourished at Cornell in the varied biotic environments afforded by the Finger Lakes region, with a small limnological station and even with an occasional nocturnal class.

For a certain group of ecologists—a group

presented certain antecedents for this. The chief worker was Shelford, whose writings stress the successional development of the animal community. Shelford's student, W. C. Allee, also showed some interest in

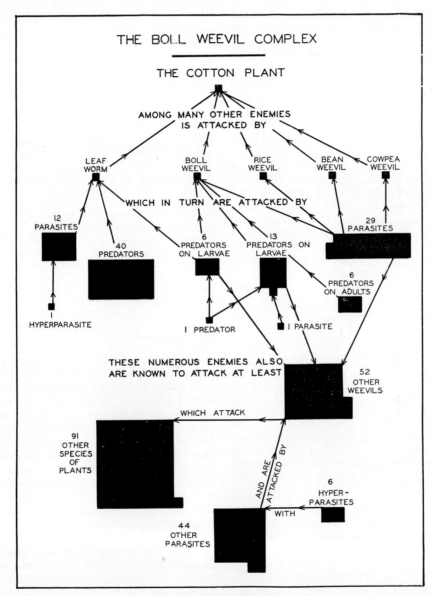

Fig. 1. The boll weevil complex. (From Pierce, Cushman, and Hood, U. S. Department of Agriculture, Bur. Entom. Bull., *100*.)

largely stimulated by the botanist H. C. Cowles at the University of Chicago—the major synecological investigations of the decade centered around ecological succession. In this historical section we have already

the problem both as a junior collaborator and as an independent investigator. In 1911 Allee published a short paper entitled "Seasonal Succession in Old Forest Ponds." C. C. Adams had worked with the problem, and his 1913 book, *Guide to the Study of Animal Ecology,* frequently makes the point by implication that *this* is ecology!

A word is in order about Shelford's then current studies (1911, 1911a, 1911b, 1912, 1912a). We shall return to some of these in a professional sense later. Historically, they had great influence on the growth of ecology. They were climaxed, integrated, and summarized in the 1913 book, *Animal Communities in Temperate America.* From the viewpoint of succession Shelford's greatest contribution was his interpretation of fish succession in streams as contrasted with that in ponds. In the former he showed that physiographic erosion was the important factor. In the latter, the succession was conditioned largely by biotic factors that gradually made over the habitat so that new forms could move in.

One of Shelford's more important theoretical discussions was his "Physiological Animal Geography" (1911c). This paper showed Shelford's reaction away from evolution as an interpretative factor in ecology and towards physiology and function. He discusses briefly the point of view of the historical or faunistic zoogeographers and then proceeds to develop, with case examples, the alternative or physiological aspect. Of the latter he says (p. 554):

"There are two distinct points of view for biological investigation. One is that of *evolution;* the other, that of *physiology,* or the explanation of the organism in terms of physics and chemistry. One may make a physiological explanation of the behavior or structure of an organism and in no wise explain its evolution. On the other hand, one may make an evolutionary explanation of an organism without making any contribution to its physiology. The study of physiological animal geography may be conducted independently of the problems of evolution. It does not need to be concerned with centers of origin, or paths of dispersal, or with other problems of faunistic animal geography. In this paper we are concerned with the *physiological relations of animals to natural environments.*"

It is only fair to state that in concluding paragraphs Shelford does make the point that biological science will be best served by the wedding of these two viewpoints. But the strong feature of his paper is its synthesis of the ecological approach to problems of dispersion.

In present day ecology succession no longer occupies so prominent a place. It is studied, but the emphasis is on the total community, with succession essentially a developmental phase of that total unit. However, during the first two decades of the twentieth century the concept was a vital one in the historical sense; it stimulated much work and provided a rational approach for field analyses.

In 1915 C. C. Adams published his extensive monograph on "The Variations and Ecological Distribution of the Snails of the Genus *Io.*" This gastropod is a river form and was studied primarily in the southeastern and southern states. Adams states the central theme of his study by quoting, with patent approval, W. K. Brooks, who wrote (Adams, p. 7):

"Inheritance and variation are not two things, but two imperfect views of a single process, for the difference between them is neither in living beings nor in any external standard of extermination, but in the reciprocal interaction between each living being and its competitors and enemies and the sources of food and the other conditions of life . . . You will note that it is as great an error to locate species in the external world as it is to locate it in germ cells or in chromatin. It neither exists in the organisms nor in the environment, because it is in the reciprocal interaction between the two."

In this historical survey Adams' paper makes an important point. Here was an investigation by an ecologist, utilizing ecological techniques, that made a sincere attempt to coordinate and interpret the findings as they were related to heredity and evolution. In short, we use Adams' paper as evidence to show that, historically, ecology was not divorced from evolution in the minds of many workers in the field.

Before closing this 1911 to 1920 survey, we wish to draw attention to the point that biometry was growing and its influence on biologists and biology was gradually increasing. The ecologist can not ignore the importance of this fact. Much of modern ecology is statistical and seems destined to become more so. We have mentioned in our review the names of Malthus, Quetelet, Farr, Galton, Weldon, Pearson, Davenport, Harris, and Pearl, names inextricably woven into the history of ecology. Although statistical methods *per se* did not contribute greatly to ecology between 1911 and 1920, they were available and were beginning to be used. The then contemporary situation was well stated by Raymond Pearl in a 1914 (pp. 47–48) address before the American Statistical Association. He said:

"Statistical science has brought to biology three fundamentally important things which it had previously lacked. These are: first, a method of describing a *group* of individuals in terms, not of its component individuals, but in terms of its (the group's) own attributes and qualities; second, the concept of 'probable error,' which makes possible an estimate of the probable accuracy of a series of observations; and third, a method of measuring the degree of association or correlation between the variations in a series of characters or events. . . . By turning to statistical science for aid the biologist has greatly augmented his powers of analysis in the domain of his own particular problems. While this branch of science, which has been called into being by this coalition, is yet too young to have shown its full capabilities, yet I think its achievements have been sufficient in quality and amount to justify the belief that its position is secure and its promise bright. Biometry seems destined to become a permanent and important branch, at once of biological investigation and of statistical inquiry."

These were prophetic and true words, both for biology and for ecology.

1921–1930

During the decade 1921 to 1930 ecology was expanding and maturing; expanding in the sense that more ecological studies were published; maturing in the sense that the field was attaining greater focus. Whereas the second decade of the twentieth century was considerably like the first, the third decade was somewhat different, even though much of the specific research was similar. Ecologists were still conducting research on, say, response physiology, or food relations or succession, but now their work seemed to have more of a common denominator that took form as a "self-conscious" science. Thus, in studies on animal responses or succession there was greater interest in interpreting these phenomena in broad ecological terms. We do not imply that ecology became a closely unified science during the third decade. It is not that today. We suggest only that it was collecting certain varying ends, rearranging its emphases and starting thereby on a newly oriented course. It is our task to examine further these trends.

Certain books published between 1921

and 1930 reflect the temper of the times. At the outset, two textbooks appeared designed for the use of ecologists in university classes: *Animal Ecology* (1926) by A. S. Pearse, and *Animal Ecology* (1927) by Charles Elton. We shall return to these directly. There were other books basically ecological in character. Borradaile's *The Animal and Its Environment* (1923) gave "an elementary treatment of animal ecology including general descriptive matter from natural history, and relatively little quantitative analysis of the environment" (Chapman, 1931, p. 2). In 1922 the third edition of Folsom's *Entomology* was published. It is significant to note that the author added to this edition the subtitle "with special reference to its ecological aspects" and included a new chapter on "Insect Ecology" prepared under the guidance of V. E. Shelford. While this book made no great impact on *ecological* science, its revised publication suggests that the ecological developments of the first and second decades had been sufficient to cause an entomologist to present his subject basically from that point of view.

In 1929 Shelford published *Laboratory and Field Ecology*, which was largely a "methods" book. Although it was to serve ecologists, it did not have anything like the influence on ecological history enjoyed by the author's earlier *Animal Communities in Temperate America*. Elton (1930) brought forth a small book entitled *Animal Ecology and Evolution*, which centered around three chief topics: "The Regulation of Numbers," "The Significance of Migration," and "The Real Life of Animals." In 1927 *Social Life in the Animal World* by Alverdes appeared.

From the dignified viewpoint of scholarship, probably the really significant book of the decade was R. Hesse's *Tiergeographie auf oekologischer Grundlage*, which appeared in 1924. This treatise recognized that there was an approach to zoogeography other than the classical, faunal one. Hesse's conception of the subject is well stated in this translated excerpt from his preface:

"Ecological animal geography is a young science . . . In this new field the fundamental questions are yet to be formulated in order that a rich phase of biology may be opened for further work. I hope this book may be thought of as such an attempt; it deals largely with problems which are taken up separately and arranged in order, and but relatively little space is given to presenting satisfactory solutions. Such treatment does show that the problems of ecological animal geography are capable of exact solution and indicates further in what direction, through observation and experimentation, the solution is to be sought. I hope that this treatment will stimulate further expeditionary researches in this field. We have had an over-supply of travel which yielded animal pelts and alcoholic material; we need rather observations on the relations between animals and their environment."

It is fair to state that Hesse attained these desiderata. A tribute to his book came in the next decade when, in 1937, W. C. Allee and Karl P. Schmidt prepared a revised edition in English and thereby made the volume more immediately available to American and English biologists. In their introduction the translators said, "The appearance of Professor Richard Hesse's book in 1924 marked the beginning of a new phase in the development both of ecology and of animal geography. In the latter field it made the first serious attempt to apply ecological methods, principles and facts to the study of animal distribution on a world-wide scale."

Another book on biogeography was Willis' *Age and Area*, (1922). This study did not have the weight carried by Hesse, but it was extremely provocative and polemic. In a historical survey these characteristics, rather than its scientific validity, may be the significant features of a work. Another important volume of the decade was *Tier und Pflanze in Symbiose*, by P. Buchner, which appeared in second edition in 1930. Buchner and his students carried out extensive studies on the importance and mode of transmission of symbionts (p. 248).

There were other books published between 1921 and 1930 that ecologists found useful. Some of these should be mentioned. *The Determination of Hydrogen Ions* by Clark (1928) and Harvey's *Biological Chemistry and Physics of Sea Water* (1928) presented information about the abiotic environment.[*] Robertson in 1923 published *The Chemical Basis of Growth and Senescence* which contained a good deal about the environment in a biochemi-

cal sense. An important German book on hydrobiology was Hentschel's *Grundzüge der Hydrobiologie* (1923). Three limnological books in German that appeared during the decade should be mentioned: Thienemann's (1926) *Limnologie*, Lenz's (1928) *Einführung in die Biologie der Süsswasserseen* and Brehm's (1930) *Einführung in die Limnologie*. Entomologists were active during the period. W. M. Wheeler wrote several books, among them *Social Life among the Insects* (1923), which summarized this subject with characteristic vigor and scholarship. Wardle and Buckle (1923) and Wardle (1929) covered certain aspects of economic entomology that had a distinct ecological flavor.

At this point we should mention the book by Grinnell, Dixon, and Linsdale (1930) *Vertebrate Natural History of A Section of Northern California through the Lassen Peak Region*. This monograph is an excellent example of modern natural history. Also, its mention permits us to pay tribute to the late Joseph Grinnell, who was, perhaps more than any other, the epitome of the modern natural historian. So far as we can judge from his writings and lectures, Grinnell was not sympathetic to analysis of ecological problems by the methods of instrumentation and mensuration. Apparently, it was his idea that the organism and its responses were a far better criterion of environmental reaction than any measurement. Once, in correspondence with one of us, he said, "The animal is more sensitive than any thermometer or atmometer."

The "Lassen Peak" study was antedated by *Animal Life in the Yosemite*, by Grinnell and T. I. Storer (1924). This work was equally comprehensive, although it may not be cited so much as the former. In the "Yosemite" volume one finds "an account of the mammals, birds, reptiles and amphibians in a cross-section of the Sierra Nevada." Historically this study is significant, not only because of its wealth of natural history, but also because it shows how a public preserve such as a national park can be utilized for field research.

In the population field in a strict sense, Raymond Pearl published four provocative books: *The Rate of Living* (1928), dealing with laboratory populations; *The Biology of Population Growth* (1925), dealing with both laboratory and human pop-

---

[*] Harvey further contributed to this topic through publication in 1945 of a small book entitled *Recent Advances in the Chemistry and Biology of Sea Water*.

ulations; *The Biology of Death* (1922) and *Studies in Human Biology* (1924), dealing with human populations. Lotka's *Elements of Physical Biology* (1925) covered certain phases of biotic interactions from a rational, theoretical viewpoint, and, as its meaning is slowly assimilated, becomes an increasingly distinguished contribution.

In the field of human ecology, straddling the fence between biology and sociology, two books by Ellsworth Huntington came out (*Principles of Human Geography*, 1921, with Cushing; *Civilization and Climate*, 1924), along with *The Population Problem*, by Carr-Saunders in 1922, and *Der Gang der Kultur über die Erde*, by Hettner in 1923.

A rapidly advancing field during the twenties was paleo-ecology. Although the plant ecologists were most concerned, there were enough general principles emerging to warrant the attention of animal workers. Paleo-ecology may lack the quantitative methods of modern ecology, but it is a necessary approach if evolutionary views are to be applied outside taxonomic and phylogenetic studies. A direct way to study this subject by means of modern geological structures was carried out by Professor Richter and his associates in the Senckenberg Museum in Frankfurt. A convenient English summary of this method was published by Bucher in 1938. Other significant publications were F. Clements' (1924) *Methods and Principles of Palaeo-ecology;* O. Abel's (1929) *Paläobiologie und Stammesgeschichte,* and a summarizing paper in the next decade (1935) by C. L. Fenton entitled "Viewpoints and Objects of Paleoecology." In 1928 a journal, "Palaeobiologica," edited by Abel, was founded and published in Vienna.

The general ecology texts by Pearse and Elton warrant further examination. They show how two specialists organized ecology during the third decade. Pearse had the following chapter headings:

i. Introduction. ii. Physical and chemical ecological factors. iii. Biological factors. iv. Succession. v. Animals of the ocean. vi. Freshwater animals. vii. Terrestrial animals. viii. The relations of animals to plants. ix. The relations of animals to color. x. Intraspecific relations. xi. The economic relations of ecology.

He thus laid a general background of physical and biotic factors and then classified animals ecologically according to their major habitats. The treatment was primarily descriptive.

Elton's book appeared under the sponsorship of Julian S. Huxley, who said in the Foreword (p. xiii):

"Finally, there remain subjects which are of such recent growth that their principles have never yet been treated in a comprehensive way. Such, for instance, are developmental and comparative physiology, animal behaviour and ecology. From the point of view of the rapid growth and expansion of general biology, it is these subjects which it is at the present moment most important to summarise in brief text-books, since otherwise the multifarious knowledge which we have already attained regarding them remains locked up in scattered papers, the property of the specialist alone. The present volume deals with a much misunderstood and often underrated subject."

The emphasis that Elton placed on ecology was different from that of Pearse, as was the manner of treatment. This can be seen from the following table of contents:

i. Introduction. ii. The distribution of animal communities. iii. Ecological succession. iv. Environmental factors. v. The animal community. vi. Parasites. vii. Time and animal communities. viii. The numbers of animals. ix. Variations in the numbers of animals. x. Ecological methods. xi. Ecology and evolution.

Elton was concerned more with organizing ecology around principles, and most of his principles centered around the animal community and the natural population. Unlike Pearse, he was interested, not so much in whether an animal was found in a desert or a lake, but rather in the environmental factors limiting the distribution of such a form. Elton stressed also the quantitative aspects, particularly in connection with the number of animals that occupy any community and the impact that these numbers make on their total environment. He viewed food chains as the most important integrating factor of the community, and his treatment of this subject is outstanding.

As we view the growing organization of ecology during the period 1921 to 1930, it looks something like this. There was a rough dichotomy between the physical-chemical environment and the biotic environment. The former was broken down into a series of factors of greater or lesser ecological significance that were studied as "conditions of existence." This was a phrase, apparently tracing back to Karl Semper

(1881, "Animal Life as Affected by the Natural *Conditions of Existence*" [italics ours]) (see p. 22), that Shelford had used in 1918 to describe such environmental factors which, he said, "are of importance only in so far as they affect the life and death processes of organisms." The physico-chemical conditions of existence most studied through this decade were water, temperature, humidity, hydrogen ion concentration,* oxygen and carbon dioxide tensions, salinity, specific gravity, molar agents such as wind, current, and waves, tide, substratum, and altitude. If space permitted, and if it were essential for our historical survey, we could discuss papers that dealt with any or all of these factors. This we cannot do. The major point is that ecologists had recognized the abiotic environment both as a total unit and in terms of its components and were analyzing it from those vantage points. The organism's response, its growth and development, and its toleration of these conditions of existence remained the essential subjects of analysis.

The organization centering around the biotic environment is more difficult to summarize. In part, this means merely that biotic relations tend to be more complex than do the abiotic. In part, it means that ecologists themselves had not crystallized

---

* The biologists of the twenties were amusingly "*p*H-minded." *Here* was a technique, both physiological and ecological, easily applied, far-reaching in its implications, and so respectable! The point is well made in anecdotal (and true) fashion.

A well-known ecologist was setting out from the wharf at the Marine Biological Laboratory (Massachusetts) to collect data about the local distribution of certain marine organisms, particularly those factors correlated with distribution. In true ecologist-fashion his dory was loaded with apparatus and impedimenta of all sorts. On the rear seat there lay a *p*H kit. At the wharf to see him off was a friend, one of America's most distinguished zoological scholars, who asked,

"Where are you going?"
He got his answer.
"What is your problem?"
Again, an answer.
"Why do you take so much equipment?"
The ecologist tried to justify his boat load.
"Well," said the savant, pointing to the *p*H kit, "*that* is all you'll need. Leave the rest at home!"

Thus *p*H in the twenties!

---

this phase of their science at that time. It is possible, however, to recognize certain general categories into which the biotic aspects fall. These are:

1. The animal community:
   (*a*) Distribution
   (*b*) Food and feeding relationships within the community
   (*c*) Successional and other developmental aspects
2. The problem of aggregation
3. The population:
   (*a*) The natural population
   (*b*) The laboratory population
4. Parasitic-symbiotic-social relationships (in a specific sense and distinct from the animal community)
5. Miscellaneous:
   (*a*) Rhythmic phenomena
   (*b*) Dispersal phenomena
   (*c*) Human ecology
   (*d*) Aspects of economic zoology

We cannot take time to document this outline in any detail, but it does seem wise to extend our remarks by discussing briefly the community, the aggregation, and the population. These aspects of ecology were developing rapidly between 1921 and 1930, and are much studied by ecologists today.

Since Elton's treatment of communities seems without question the best of the decade, we can do no better than examine the state of this phase of ecology as seen through his eyes. As mentioned earlier, Elton viewed ecology as essentially the study of populations and communities.

Judging from Elton and the published papers of the decade 1921 to 1930, ecologists were interested in the animal community from these aspects: its distribution in both a geographical and a local sense; its structure and organization; and its temporal development and change. There was not much emphasis on the community as a "social organism," although Elton, among others, recognized the point, nor on the problem of biotic equilibrium. These phases were to come later.

Under the influence of Hesse, Shelford, and others, ecologists were examining communities on a geographical scale and were working on the pattern of their distribution. This did not stop with mere description, for certain of the studies insisted that there were basic analogies between the communities of one area and those of another. These analogies seem to have convinced students that the community was a real biological entity, irrespective of its global location.

The "structural" studies had two major focal points, both of which are aspects of the same problem. On the one hand, there were extensive studies on food and feeding relations within the community, such as those of Sanders and Shelford (1922) and Summerhays and Elton (1923) on terrestrial communities; of Needham, Juday, Moore, Sibley, and Titcomb (1922) on a fresh-water community; and of Hardy (1924) on a marine community. On the other hand, there was a growing interest in "how many" animals occupied a certain niche in a community and the effect of this quantitative relation on the community as a whole. This aspect was really that encompassed by the natural population studies, and we shall return to it shortly.

After studying a series of papers on animal communities and working actively on the problem himself, Elton concluded that (p. 55):

" . . . Animals are organised into a complex society, as complex and as fascinating to study as human society. At first sight we might despair of discovering any general principles regulating animal communities. But careful study of simple communities shows that there are several principles which enable us to analyse an animal community into its parts, and in the light of which much of the apparent complication disappears. These principles are food-chains and the food-cycle; size of food; niches; the pyramid of numbers."

It is not our task here to discuss these problems in a technical sense. That will come in later chapters. We are concerned only with the historical point that the study of natural groups or communities had advanced to such a stage in the third decade that it was possible to conclude: (a) that communities are integrated to a large degree by the sum total of their feeding relations, and (b) that these relations, although they may be completely different in detail, are the common property of all communities, whatever the type and wherever located. Several other studies that appeared during the period and which should be cited are those of Weese (1924), Smith (1928), and Shackleford (1929).

Ecologists were well aware of the significance of temporal factors in the organization of the community. Succession was firmly ensconced in ecological thought as a time factor that brought about eventual community equilibrium when the climax was attained. We have now enough of a background for this point to make unnecessary its further discussion. Other temporal aspects were recognized. Some of these were (1) day-night rhythms; (2) migrations on a vertical axis that occurred at certain intervals as, for example, plankton migration in the sea or vertical migration in a forest; (3) tidal rhythms; (4) climatic rhythms of various types, including the seasons; and (5) extramundane rhythms. Many ecologists of the 1921 to 1930 period were doing more than recognizing these rhythms. They were analyzing them in relation to the community constituents.

Throughout this book we shall have much to say about the phenomenon of animal aggregations and its significance for ecological theory. This is a phase of ecology studied with much intellectual profit. As such, it needs to be considered briefly in this historical review. It is brought in at this point in the third decade, not because the subject "originated" then, but because it was summarized and evaluated in a paper by Allee (1927a) and thus given impetus for further growth. Certain phases of the general problem had been considered earlier by botanists (especially Clements), zoologists, and philosophers, and their contributions must not be underestimated. But to Allee goes the credit for a clear statement of the problem in terms of animal ecology and "general sociology." In his review Allee discussed the method of formation of aggregations; general factors conditioning aggregations; single-species, as contrasted with mixed-species, aggregations; integrative phenomena within aggregations; and the social significance of aggregations.

Despite the existence in the 1921 to 1930 period of considerable knowledge about the physical-chemical environment, the animal community, the phenomenon of aggregation, and, as we shall see in a moment, the population, ecologists did not coordinate these various phases to any degree. When Allee wrote his paper in 1927 he outlined the field of animal aggregations as he viewed it. But this did not mean that, over night, the subject flowered and matured.

In the third decade there was fact finding; there was speculation; there were some attempts at a synthesis of ecological principles. But there was not much synthesis, and, by that token, not much development of ecology as a unified science. It would be incorrect to say that this unification exists today, although some notable steps were to be made during the decade 1931 to 1940.

When the zoologist started to ask himself the quantitative question "How many?" in addition to the qualitative question "What kind?", natural population studies began to emerge from natural history and community investigations. Many ecologists felt that community analyses with their many variables were too complex to be feasible methodologically. Accordingly, they sought to better the situation by counting certain species of animals that lived within the framework of the total community and were of enough ecological importance to warrant such careful scrutiny. These counts were population censuses.

It is inaccurate to suggest that such studies appeared *de novo* in the third decade. There were several historical precedents for them. One important precedent lay in earlier ecological work itself, both botanical and zoological. A basis for population studies had been established in the literature before 1900 (see p. 24). In fact, we mentioned earlier a number of papers that could be cited appropriately. Another precedent came from the work of biologists with a flair for biometry and an interest in biological groups *as such*. Many of these men have already been mentioned. Still another precedent stemmed from the development of statistics as a method for handling biological data, as a technique for rationalizing and formulating biological interactions (e.g., Lotka, 1925; Volterra, 1926), and as a basis for the philosophical interpretation of scientific evidence. These various fields in one way or another were forcing themselves into the ecologist's thinking. From them the population approach, as did many other approaches, began to crystallize.

The early work on natural populations frequently had an economic focus and motivation, as, to a large degree, is still true today. The investigators were concerned with certain species, frequently an insect, that as populations in nature had a significant relation to some problem of human disease, diseases of other animals, or agriculture. Analysis of the former problem yielded data on epidemiology, actually an excellent example of quantitative ecology. The distinguished British sanitarian, Major Greenwood (1932), says of this subject:

"Epidemiology displays the general factors which operate upon populations or aggregates, and lead to the outbreak of a sickness affecting several organisms within a short time. The unit of the epidemiologist is the population . . . "

Thus many of the natural population studies were epidemiological in character and stressed the statistics of host-parasite interaction. A masterly summary of the principles underlying this science was written by Wade Hampden Frost in 1927.

Analyses of insect pest populations frequently yielded many data on the abundance of such forms in relation to climatic cycles and to predation and parasitization pressures. Some representative studies of the decade were those of Cook (1924) on cutworm populations, Bodenheimer (1925) on the Mediterranean fruit fly, Shelford (1927) on the codling moth, and Swynnerton (1921) on tsetse fly populations as a vector for trypanosomes.

Natural population studies also were concerned with cycles of abundance of mammals and birds. In the literature of the period we find studies on lemmings, mice, rabbits and hares, marmots, muskrats, and certain ungulates and birds. While the factors controlling these cycles were not analyzed critically in many cases, the information in the literature suggests that the common causes are epidemics, variation in quality and quantity of food, and sunspot or climatic influences. Elton was much taken with this research, as evidenced by his own papers (1924, 1925) and Chapter 9 in his text. Other representative publications are those by Hewitt (1921) on the wolf, hare, lynx, and red fox; Soper (1921) on hares; and Brooks (1926) on deer.

Experimental or laboratory population studies had their essential inception in the decade 1921 to 1930 and grew out of two groups of investigators. On the one hand, ecologists with a traditional background turned their attention, in part at least, to such studies. On the other hand, general biologists and biometricians interested in the experimental approach to growth of groups became interested in such population studies without the impetus or motivation furnished by earlier ecological training. These two origins were wedded later, particularly in the fourth decade. Perhaps a brief elaboration of this subject is in order.

Approaching these studies through the ecological door were men like W. C. Allee and Royal N. Chapman, both feeling apparently that there was much to be desired in terms of environmental control even for natural populations. The method of such men was to bring into the laboratory an animal that could be cultured there successfully and study its various *group* responses under reasonably controlled conditions.* Chapman transferred his attention to the flour beetle, *Tribolium confusum,* and in this organism found an answer to his problem. His most important paper appeared in 1928, in which he set forth the concepts of "biotic potential" and "environmental resistance" and substantiated them with empirical evidence. We shall return to these ideas in later sections of the book and discuss them carefully (p. 303).

Allee continued his work on communities and natural populations, but brought certain phases of these problems into the laboratory for solution. Particularly was this true of his investigations on aggregations. An examination of his writings shows that between 1921 and 1930 he studied, as experimental populations, isopods, the brittle starfish (*Ophioderma*), the marine flatworm (*Procerodes*) and planarian worms. Unlike Chapman, Allee's interest was not so much in the total analysis of the population as in studying in the laboratory certain responses largely protective in character that arose as a consequence of aggregation or population density.

The other approach through experimental population studies is typified by the work of Raymond Pearl and his colleagues. Between 1921 and 1930 Pearl and his group published an astounding amount of material in journal, lecture, and book form on experimental populations of *Drosophila melanogaster.* It is not our province here

* A somewhat idealized definition of an experimental population would be: a group of inbred organisms cultured under controlled, yet manipulatory, environmental conditions for which repeated censuses of all stages can be readily taken. Extensions and modifications of this definition will appear in the section on Populations.

to evaluate these studies. It *is* our responsibility to indicate the aspects of the subject covered by them and attempt to weigh their impact on third decade ecology.

Pearl was interested in experimental populations from the following five viewpoints:

1. The form of population growth. This work was largely the demonstration that various populations (e.g., yeast, *Paramecium, Drosophila,* man) followed a sigmoid growth curve (the "logistic").

2. The analysis of population density and its end effects. Pearl was thoroughly convinced of the biological importance of this matter. In 1930 he said, "In general there can be no question that this whole matter of influence of density of population, in all senses, upon biological phenomena, deserves a great deal more investigation than it has had. The indications all are that it is one of the most significant elements in the biological, as distinguished from the physical, environment of organisms" (p. 145). Population density was analyzed primarily as it affected reproduction and mortality.

3. The problem of longevity and those factors, both genetic and ecologic, that influence it. These studies were actuarial in character, and the data were summarized to good advantage in life tables.

4. The possible growth analogies between experimental and human populations.

5. An illustration of the applicability of quantitative methods to biological research.

In sum, experimental population studies appealed to the workers of the decade (as well as in the 1931 to 1940 period) for these major reasons:

1. The results can be expressed in quantitative terms.

2. The end responses that can be studied include such variables of patent biological importance as:

  (a) The factors contributing to population growth—fecundity, fertility, fission rate, success and rate of development.
  (b) The factors contributing to population decline—differential morbidity and mortality.
  (c) The factors concerned with selection pressure.

3. There is an absence of terminology in these studies.

4. The studies are theoretically important, especially in relation to the natural population, the community, statistics of host-parasite interactions (epidemiology), social origins and social facilitation, and evolution and speciation.

A final development needs mention: Cleveland's work (1924) on the symbiotic relationship between wood-feeding termites and their intestinal flagellates. Here it was demonstrated that the latter, by secreting a cellulose-digesting enzyme, made wood available as food for the termite colony. In turn, the termite gut furnished a micro-niche for the Protozoa. This study was significant in that it placed symbiosis on an analytical basis and furnished impetus for excellent research in the next decade. Cleveland himself, in collaboration with Hall, Sanders, and Collier, brought forth in 1934 a comprehensive monograph on the symbiosis between the roach *Cryptocercus* and its intestinal Protozoa.

This concludes our survey of the active third decade. We have examined the trends and developments in ecology that centered both around the physical and the biotic environment. We have seen that this was an era when ideas were just starting to emerge into a broader ecological framework and when ecological research ceased being helter-skelter and started to acquire focus.

1931–1942

In discussing this period we shall extend the interval beyond a decade (to 1942) in order to include several significant trends that appeared in the last several years. In this section it is our plan to make these points:

1. Ecology was exceedingly active, both in terms of volume of work and in quality of ecological effort.

2. Ecology gave signs of maturation. It began to develop, crystallize, and coordinate principles of its own.

3. There was a newborn interest in an ecological framework of theory—a theory based, not on speculation, but largely on empirical evidence.

4. By 1942 ecology, with notable exceptions, was in a healthy and lusty state and was looking forward to the decades to come.

It is not feasible to survey the progress of this decade by the methods used in the preceding pages of citing research papers and suggesting their influence on the growth of the subject. As a more mature science, ecology in the thirties gave birth to many sorts of activities, which index and epitomize its growth. We shall try to indicate what these activities were and then discuss them in enough detail to delineate the contribution that was theirs.* This should serve also as a sort of summary for the entire historical treatment in the sense that it will show the state of the science in its most modern dress. To our minds, these activities fall into the following larger categories: first, books; second, journals available to and used by ecologists both for recording research and surveying segments of the field; third, review articles in review journals; fourth, symposia; and last, articles of particular significance in the synthesis of ecological theory.

Books

In discussing the books of the decade we stress the point, as we have done for all the historical treatment, that the list is a sample and not a complete tabulation. It is, however, comprehensive enough to cover the field thoroughly. The books published between 1931 and 1942 fall into these eight categories:

(a) General texts or reference works primarily ecological in character;

(b) Books emphasizing the population primarily;

(c) Books dealing with sociality and social organization;

(d) Books stressing the ecological aspects of zoogeography and dispersal;

(e) Books dealing with evolutionary and speciation aspects and containing an ecological (as well as genetic) treatment;

(f) Books on ecological aspects of behavior;

(g) Books on applied ecology;

(h) Books on theoretical and philosophical aspects that are difficult to place in the foregoing categories.

A list of books according to this classification and in the order of their publication dates is given at the end of this chapter.

At this place a word of emphasis is in order about the Clements and Shelford *Bio-Ecology* (1939) and the movement it rep-

---

* It is obvious, of course, that the account of all these "activities" is reflected in final analysis in the publication of research data.

resents. This book assisted in drawing together the ecological researches of zoologists and botanists under a common denominator. It stressed the obvious point that, typically, there is no such thing as a plant community devoid of animals, or conversely, an animal community devoid of plants. The "bio-ecologists" work with an ecological unit which they designate the "biome."*

The population books deal with the experimental, the natural, and the human population. We include several books on human populations because they contribute in a real way to the ecologist's thinking and methodology. From certain angles the demographers have had a more scholarly approach to the problem than the ecologists. The books on sociality and social organization are written essentially as population studies from which special results are derived. The zoogeography books focus on distribution and dispersion in the Hesse sense; i.e., as they are controlled by environmental factors.

Later we shall show that during the thirties the ecologist turned much of his attention to ecological aspects of evolution. His concern lay with such matters as geographic variation, isolating mechanisms, natural selection, protective coloration, regressive evolution, and so on.

The list of books on behavior is purposely short. Despite its inextricable relation to any ecological analysis or venture, animal behavior studies *per se* were maturing as a separate field ("comparative psychology") and thus making notable contributions in their own right.

During the decade economic biologists became interested in ecology as a solution for their problems. Also, certain ecologists got interested in economic biology. Some of this effort yielded first-rate ecological research, particularly in the field of biological control, host-parasite relations, and fisheries investigation. The books listed document this point, although a survey of the literature suggests that the papers published in journals are more impressive in terms of intellectual content than are the books.

The interest in theoretical ecology was acute during the thirties, but discussion of this point is best postponed until later.

* Their usage of biome is by no means uniform, and is only in part that of the present work.

Journals

With each decade the number of national and international journals available for the publication of ecological data and/or theory increased. This is well illustrated by the journals available to the ecologist during the 1931 to 1942 period. The majority of these journals contain many articles that are not ecological. Of the forty-one listed (p. 70) only four are exclusively ecological: *Ecology, Ecological Monographs,* the *Journal of Animal Ecology,* and the *Journal of Ecology.* The *Journal of Animal Ecology* was started in England in 1932 and has been a successful medium for original research articles. It grew out of the *Journal of Ecology,* in which many first-rate articles on animal ecology had appeared before 1932. In addition to research publication, the *Journal of Animal Ecology* has helped the ecologist to keep abreast of British publications in the several fields of ecology.* The Foreword to the first issue is of some historical interest. There the editor, Charles Elton, said (p. 1):

"The number of ecological papers dealing with animals is increasing, and will undoubtedly increase even more rapidly in the near future. It therefore appeared to the British Ecological Society that steps ought to be taken now to make adequate provision both for centralising to some extent the widely scattered papers on animal ecology that are now being produced, and also, by planning well ahead, to anticipate the future development of the subject, which runs a real risk of becoming split unnaturally into isolated compartments of knowledge attached to specific scientific and economic spheres, and therefore losing the advantages which come from the pooling of ideas and knowledge in a central journal."

More or less concomitant with the founding of the *Journal of Animal Ecology* was the establishment at Oxford University in 1932 of the "Bureau of Animal Population"

* These "fields" as defined in the *Journal of Animal Ecology* are: (1) "Ecological surveys and habitat notes;" (2) "General reports and taxonomic studies of use to ecologists;" (3) "Animal behaviour and the action of environmental factors;" (4) "Parasites;" (5) "Food and food-habits;" (6) "Populations;" (7) "Migration, dispersal, and introductions;" (8) "Reports of organizations." In this connection it is interesting to note that *Biological Abstracts* also covers the several fields of ecological literature (see p. 43), from a less provincial point of view.

under the directorship of Charles Elton. An initial grant from the New York Zoological Society helped make this possible. Its objects were to conduct research on mammal and game-bird populations, and at the same time to act as a world clearinghouse for literature and other information about animal populations and animal ecology generally. The Bureau has continued and expanded up to the present time and has been a thoroughly useful institution.

Ecology (founded in 1920) continued to serve American needs both in plant and animal fields by furnishing a place for publication of research data and by acting as the official organ of the Ecological Society of America. In the Foreword to Volume 1 this statement appeared:

"This journal is issued to meet the demand for the collective publication of articles on ecology. Its pages are open to all who have material of ecological interest from whatever field of biology. While the variety of fields may cause diversity of treatment, yet the ecological significance of the papers will make them of general interest. Specialization is inevitable, but makes more urgent the need for cooperation. To approach different subjects from similar points of view is to lay the foundations of cooperation."

This is followed by an introductory statement by Barrington Moore, the first editor, on "The Scope of Ecology."

Ecological Monographs was founded in 1931 to provide a publication medium for longer manuscripts covering extensive studies on both plants and animals, particularly those written from the community point of view.

Biological science was characterized generally during the fourth decade by the publication of many review articles, numerous symposia, and critical syntheses of theory. These efforts helped scientists keep up with current trends. We can learn much of the growth of ecology during the period by brief examination of these three activities.

Review Journals

The two English language biological review journals of greatest circulation appearing during the period 1931 to 1942 were the *Quarterly Review of Biology*, edited at Johns Hopkins University, and *Biological Reviews*, edited at Cambridge, England. If we tabulate for the former the frequency of ecological articles relative to the total frequency, the data for ten volumes look like this:

Table 2. *Frequency of Ecological Articles to the Total Number of Articles Appearing in the* Quarterly Review of Biology *(1931–40)*

Year	Volume Number	Number of Articles per Volume	Number of Ecological Articles per Volume	Percentage of Ecological Articles per Volume
1931	6	20	3	15.0
1932	7	22	6	27.3
1933	8	23	5	21.7
1934	9	16	5	31.2
1935	10	17	2	11.8
1936	11	17	2	11.8
1937	12	21	6	28.6
1938	13	22	2	9.1
1939	14	16	4	25.0
1940	15	14	5	35.7
For the ten volumes..		188	40	21.3

Thus it is apparent, for this journal at least, that a good deal of the review and survey writing of the decade was ecological when broadly interpreted. The comparable mean percentage for *Biological Reviews* is lower, 11.5 per cent. It is not clear whether this means that English students were not so much concerned with ecological studies as were the Americans, whether the high percentage of the *Quar-*

Table 3. American Ecological Symposia, 1930–42

Title of Symposium	Date of Presentation or Publication	Sponsorship	Published	Central *Ecological* Theme
'Hydrogen-ion Concentration"	1930	Ecol. Soc. America	Am. Nat., *69*	Determination of and effect on animals and plants
"Conditions of Existence of Aquatic Animals"	1933	Chicago "Century of Progress" Exposition	Ecol. Mon., *4*	Lectures on the physical and biotic environment in oceans and lakes
"Oceanography"	1933	A.A.A.S.	Ecol. Mon., *4*	Lectures on ocean bacteria, copepods and marine communities
"The Species Problem"	1936	Am. Soc. Zoologists, Genetics Soc. America	Am. Nat., *70*	Factors in the distribution of natural populations
'Symposium on Experimental Populations"	1937	Ecol. Soc. America, Am. Soc. Zoologists	Am. Nat., *71*	The nature and data of laboratory population analyses
'Plant and Animal Communities"	1939	Cold Spring Harbor Biological Laboratory	Book: Univ. of Notre Dame Press	Aspects of plant and animal communities and animal populations
'Symposium on Insect Populations"	1939	Ecol. Soc. America, Entom. Soc. America, Econom. Entom.	Ecol. Mon., *9*	Aspects of insect natural populations, including control
"Determination of Natural Population Size"	1940	Ecol. Soc. America, Am. Statis. Assoc.	. . . .	Census methods and their evaluation
"Relation of Ecology to Human Welfare"	1940	Ecol. Soc. America	Ecol. Mon., *10*	Ecology as a technique and point of view for human problems
'Symposium on Speciation"	1941	Am. Soc. Zoologists, Genetics Soc. America	Biological Symposia, *2*	Ecological factors affecting speciation in several groups
"Symposium on the Biological Basis of Social Problems"	1941	Western Soc. Nat., A.A.A.S.	Biological Symposia, *2*	Social integration
"Symposium on Population Problems in Protozoa"	1941	Ecol. Soc. America, Am. Soc. Zoologists	Biological Symposia, *4*	Protozoan populations
'Symposium on the Species Concept"	1941	Western Soc. Nat., A.A.A.S.	Biological Symposia, *4*	Discussion of natural selection and insect speciation

Table 3. American Ecological Symposia, 1930–42 (Continued)

Title of Symposium	Date of Presentation or Publication	Sponsorship	Published	Central *Ecological* Theme
"Symposium on Temperature"	1941	Am. Soc. Zoologists, A.A.A.S.	Biological Symposia, *6*	Temperature in relation to evolution
"Symposium on Isolating Mechanisms"	1941	A.A.A.S.	Biological Symposia, *6*	Isolation in toads, gall wasps and *Drosophila*
"The Development of Quantitative and Experimental Work in Ecology"	1941	Ecol. Soc. America, Soc. Amer. Foresters	Ecology, *22*	Summarizing papers using analytical methods
"A Symposium on Hydro-biology"	1941	Univ. of Wisconsin	Book: Univ. of Wis. Press	32 papers on many phases
"Symposium on Animal Populations"	1941	American Soc. Mammalogists, Field Museum	. . . .	Census methods and ranges of mammal populations
"Levels of Integration in Biological and Social Systems"	1942	Univ. of Chicago A.A.A.S.	Biological Symposia, *8*	Integration in populations and societies
"Dynamics of Production in Aquatic Populations"	1946	Am. Soc. Zoologists, Ecol. Soc. America, Limnological Soc. America	Ecol. Mon., *16*	Population productivity

terly Review reflected the positive bias of the editor (Pearl), or whether other factors are involved.

Symposia

During the decade, particularly the latter part, the symposium became a more popular and important medium for the exchange of ideas. It allowed specialists to meet, to discuss a topic of current interest, and, in many cases, to publish the entire record of the proceedings. From the historical view the symposia are excellent criteria of the temper of the times. They are data on subject matter and personalities. In this light we present the following tabulation of those American symposia held between 1930 and 1942 (including one held in 1946) that contributed more or less directly to ecological thought (Table 3).

The following generalizations seem war-ranted from an examination of the table:

1. There was an active interest in ecological problems *per se*.

2. There was also a keen interest in coordinating ecologic with other phases of biology.

3. The two topics most frequently discussed were ecological relations of populations and ecological aspects of evolution and speciation.

4. A variety of societies and many investigators cooperated in the enterprises.

5. Apparently, no great difficulties were encountered in getting such symposia published.

Synthesis Articles

Our final method of appraising the ecological trends of the period is to examine certain articles that were concerned with synthesizing an aspect of ecological theory.

These articles are not necessarily review articles. They may merely collate certain segments of information without any interpretation. During the 1931 to 1942 period the areas of ecology most frequently subjected to such synthesis were (a) the community; (b) population problems, both intraspecific and interspecific; (c) society and social integration; and (d) other aspects.

There is not time, nor is this the place, to discuss the contributions of these articles, and others like them, to ecological theory. That will come later when attention is focussed on specific principles. In general terms the point can be made that ecologists were trying to find a natural pattern into which the data of ecology could be apportioned. This was true whether the individual, the population, the society, or the community was studied. This led theoretically minded students to the question of integration—the mechanism by which an ecological unit maintains that unity in the face of continual environmental impact. Some of the analyses were mathematical, some experimental, and some observational. But they were all concerned with this pregnant question, and all seemed to suggest that when ecology attains a greater theoretical orientation, it will emerge as a science of greater stature. As pointed out in the Introduction, this is a perspective shared by the authors of the present book.*

CONCLUSION

This concludes our treatment of the growth of twentieth century animal ecology. Before closing this chapter, however, a brief review of the forty years considered as a whole seems appropriate. It is our wish here to point out certain of the major historical trends in ecology as well as to draw some parallels between the growth of that science and historical phenomena generally.

In 1900 the basic ecological emphasis was relatively simple. Most biologists were aware of the fact that an organism lived in

an exploitable environment, and now and then this environment-organism nexus was subjected to analysis. However, the analysis was concerned with that problem as an *individual* instance. There was not much interest in generalization or theory. We pointed out this fact in the Introduction to this book. The early workers, through intelligent and enthusiastic labor, unearthed many significant data, and it would be stupid to underestimate their contributions. As the years wore on, a need arose for the integration of facts and concepts. This had a salubrious effect on the development of ecology. It sharpened the awareness of workers to the existence of new and unsolved problems. It brought younger investigators into the field. It demanded the adoption of new techniques developed by other sciences and technologies. It increased the outlets for discussion, publication, review, criticism, and intellectual intercourse generally.

The twentieth century now can be considered briefly in a more specific way. In the early nineteen hundreds the prime emphasis was on autecology. Investigators followed either the path of natural history, in which case they were interested, say, in the life cycle of an organism or in its habitat or adaptational morphology, or they entered by the physiological route and studied the behavior, the development, or the toleration of an organism in relation to its immediate environment. With the passing years, work of this type appropriated some of the skills perfected in other sciences, with the result that environmental measurements became more precise and refined. This seems to be the status of autecology somewhere in the early twenties. Thereafter, ecologists became interested in "conditions of existence," and there arose a more comprehensive autecology with emphasis on the analysis of a wide variety of organism-environment relations. This had a final effect of incorporating a large body of autecological facts in text and reference books, many of which have been mentioned.

Synecological studies lagged behind autecological. There is an obvious explanation for this. The former are inherently more difficult and require a greater background of fact and theory. In the early part of the century there were some sound data on group relations both for aquatic and ter-

---

* An interesting ecological development of the fourth decade that deserves special mention was the organization of field classes to study nocturnal animal communities. Although this was not a completely new venture, its routine adoption did not occur until the early thirties. A note by Orlando Park and H. F. Strohecker (1936) pointed out the potentialities of such night study.

restrial forms, but the data were relatively few, and, as we pointed out, there was little attempt to see common denominators between the operations of one group and those of another. Ecological succession also furnished an important impetus for the growth of synecology. It caused ecologists to view groups from the long-time vantage point of development and maturation In fact, the early workers spoke of this approach as "genetic."

Early in the century certain botanists and zoologists began to conceive of biotic groupings as integrated wholes. These they designated "communities." The community concept flourished from then on and, for a time, was identified by some as synonymous with ecology. It reached a mode perhaps in the late twenties, when overenthusiastic workers began manufacturing names for ecological phenomena at a rate that exceeded knowledge and denied wisdom. Fortunately, this trend is abating, and today community studies are assuming saner proportions and are emerging as a significant phase of ecology. It is clear that they owe their origin to natural history and early synecology of the type discussed. It is equally clear that this phase of ecology is bringing the botanist and zoologist into closer cooperation.

An interest in animal aggregations grew up along with and slightly later than community studies. This interest dates far back into ecological history as a descriptive phase, but it did not attain more precise treatment until the last two decades. We have shown already how this trend is currently merging into a general sociology.

Our review of ecological history also uncovers an urge toward quantification. At the turn of the century research was essentially descriptive and qualitative, with certain notable exceptions particularly prevalent among the marine biologists. Later publications became increasingly numerical. This was true both for autecology and synecology. The former introduced simple algebra, geometry, and graphic techniques borrowed largely from traditional physiology and the physical sciences. The latter took over the tool of statistical methods already well developed and applied in other areas by the biometrician. The adoption of these methods in synecology not only improved the rigor of the evidence, but increased as well the ecologist's awareness of the essential nature of groups and their properties.

We attribute in part the rise of interest in natural and experimental populations during the third decade to this quantification. Ecologists apparently realized that many environmental phenomena can be stated numerically. They then found out that upon analysis these numbers yielded conclusions more searching than those based upon observation alone. Such methodology naturally became part and parcel of population research (see Thomas Park, 1946).

Another trend worthy of emphasis is the growth of applied ecology. Early in the century economic problems were largely those of insect control and fisheries biology. These problems were usually tackled in a restricted way. Later, as the economic zoologist and the ecologist built bodies of knowledge, we see the two turning to each other for suggestions and advice. This now reaches a point among the best modern workers where data collected by one group are directly usable by the other. This rapprochement is excellent.

In mentioning applied ecology, it should be recorded here that the activities now known as "game management" and "wildlife conservation" have appropriated, in increasing measure and to their advantage, a more circumscribed ecological flavor. These fields were foreshadowed by the splendid book entitled *The Grouse in Health and in Disease*, edited by A. S. Leslie and A. E. Shipley (1912), and, latterly, by such volumes as *Game Management* by Aldo Leopold (1933) and H. L. Stoddard's *The Bobwhite Quail: Its Habits, Preservation and Increase* (1932). Then, too, the work of agronomists, particularly those associated with public agencies both here and abroad, has yielded knowledge valuable not only for the ecologist (see chap. 16), but for the general problem of conservation as well. In fact, we are tempted to remark that the ecologist, given the opportunity, has something to say, both scientific and constructive, about the urgent and gloomy problem of conservation and about the establishment of "nature reserves."

Although other trends could be pointed out, enough has been said to give the reader the major features. In closing, we are impressed once more by the fact that a historical development in science parallels closely the growth of a culture or a civilization. For both, there are fads, fancies, and cycles. For all, there are good works and poor works, and occasionally an outstanding contribution identifies itself. We can spot ingenuous scholars, plodders, sluggards, the industrious, and, frequently, those who are more noted for what they did not do or say than for their positive accomplishments. Such cross currents as these obfuscate the story and make it hard to decipher. But they *do* give it color and even humor. It is thus that man-made things develop, and the history of animal ecology is no exception to the rule.

APPENDIX

A. *Books* published between 1931 and 1942, arranged according to their classification.

1. GENERAL TEXTS OR REFERENCE WORKS

Chapman, R. N.: Animal Ecology with Especial Reference to Insects, 1931.
Uvarov, B. P.: Insects and Climate (monograph), 1931.
Elton, C.: The Ecology of Animals, 1933.
Stork, J. W., and Renouf, L. P. W.: Plant and Animal Ecology, 1933.
Bews, J. W.: Human Ecology, 1935.
Elton, C.: Animal Ecology (2nd edition), 1935.
Hesse, R., and Doflein, F.: Tierbau und Tierleben in ihrem Zusammenhang betrachtet, 1935–1943 (2nd ed. by R. Hesse).
Welch, P. S.: Limnology, 1935.
Needham, J. G. (editor): Culture Methods for Invertebrate Animals (compendium), 1937.
Bodenheimer, F. S.: Problems of Animal Ecology, 1938.
Carpenter, J. R.: An Ecological Glossary, 1938.
Clements, F. E., and Shelford, V. E.: Bioecology, 1939.
Just, T. (editor): Plant and Animal Communities (compendium), 1939.
Morgan, A. H.: Fieldbook of Animals in Winter, 1939.
Moulton, F. R. (editor): Problems of Lake Biology (compendium), 1939a.
Park, O., Allee, W. C. and Shelford, V. E.: A Laboratory Introduction to Animal Ecology and Taxonomy, 1939.
Pearse, A. S.: Animal Ecology (2nd edition), 1939.
Calkins, G. N., and Summer, F. M. (editors): Protozoa in Biological Research (compendium), 1941.
Needham, J. G., et al. (editor): A Symposium on Hydrobiology (compendium), 1941.

Sverdrup, H. U., Johnson, M. W., and Fleming, R. H.: The Oceans: Their Physics, Chemistry and General Biology, 1942.

2. THE POPULATION

Allee, W. C.: Animal Aggregations. A study in General Sociology, 1931.
Hjort, J. (editor): Essays on Population (compendium), 1933.
Gause, G. F. The Struggle for Existence, 1934.
Lorimer, F., and Osborn, F.: Dynamics of Population, 1934.
Gause, G. F.: Vérifications expérimentales de la théorie mathématique de la lutte pour la vie (monograph), 1935.
Greenwood, M.: Epidemics and Crowd-Diseases. An Introduction to the Study of Epidemiology, 1935.
Dublin, L. I., and Lotka, A. J.: Length of Life; An Introduction to the Study of the Life-Table, 1936.
Pearl, R.: The Natural History of Populations, 1939.
Simpson, G. G., and Roe, A.: Quantitative Zoölogy, 1939.
Elton, C.: Voles, Mice and Lemmings. Problems in Population Dynamics, 1942.
Russell, E. S.: The Overfishing Problems, 1942.

3. SOCIALITY AND SOCIAL ORGANIZATION

Allee, W. C.: Animal Life and Social Growth, 1932.
Kostitzin, V. A.: Symbiose, parasitisme et évolution, 1934.
Darling, F. F.: A Herd of Red Deer. A Study in Animal Behaviour, 1937.
Allee, W. C.: The Social Life of Animals, 1938.
Darling, F. F.: Bird Flocks and the Breeding Cycle; A Contribution to the Study of Avian Sociality, 1938.
Jennings, H. S.: The Beginnings of Social behavior in Multicellular Organisms, 1940.

4. ZOOGEOGRAPHY AND DISPERSAL

Rowan, W.: The Riddle of Migration, 1931.
Heape, W.: Emigration, Migration and Nomadism, 1932.
Ekman, S.: Tiergeographie des Meeres, 1935.
Pearse, A. S.: The Migrations of Animals from Sea to Land, 1936.
Hesse, R., Allee, W. C., and Schmidt, K. P.: Ecological Animal Geography, 1937.
Moulton, F. R. (editor): The Migration and Conservation of Salmon (compendium), 1939.

5. EVOLUTIONARY AND SPECIATION ASPECTS

Sumner, F. B.: Genetic, Distributional and Evolutionary Studies of the Subspecies of Deermice (*Peromyscus*) (monograph), 1932.

Harms, J. W.: Wandlung des Artgefüges unter natürlichen und künstlichen Umweltsbedingungen, 1934.

Prenant, M.: Adaptation, écologie et biocoenotique, 1934.

Kinsey, A. C.: The Origin of Higher Categories in Cynips, 1936.

Robson, G. C., and Richards, O. W.: The Variation of Animals in Nature, 1936.

Shull, A. F.: Evolution, 1936.

Dobzhansky, T.: Genetics and the Origin of Species, 1937.

DeBeer, G. R. (editor): Evolution; Essays on Aspects of Evolutionary Biology (compendium), 1938.

Banta, A. M., et al.: Studies on the Physiology, Genetics and Evolution of Some Cladocera (monograph), 1939.

Cott, H. B.: Adaptive Coloration in Animals, 1940.

Huxley, J. (editor): The New Systematics (compendium), 1940.

Walls, G.: The Vertebrate Eye and Its Adaptive Radiation, 1942.

Huxley, J.: Evolution, 1942.

Mayr, E.: Systematics and the Origin of Species, 1942.

6. BEHAVIOR ASPECTS

Russell, E. S.: The Behavior of Animals; An Introduction to Its Study, 1934.

Fraenkel, G., and Gunn, D. L.: The Orientation of Animals, 1940.

Warden, C. J., Jenkins, T. N., and Warner, L. H.: Comparative Psychology. Vol. 1, Principles and Methods; vol. 2, Plants and Invertebrates; vol. 3, Vertebrates, 1935–40.

7. APPLIED AND ECONOMIC ASPECTS OF ECOLOGY

Stoddard, H. L.: The Bobwhite Quail: Its Habits, Preservation and Increase, 1932.

Leopold, Aldo.: Game Management, 1933.

Sweetman, H. L.: The Biological Control of Insects, 1936.

Swynnerton, C. F. M.: The Tsetse Flies of East Africa (monograph), 1936.

Riley, W. A., and Johannsen, O. A.: Medical Entomology, 1938.

Herms, W. B.: Medical Entomology, 1939.

Metcalf, C. L., and Flint, W. P.: Destructive and Useful Insects: Their Habits and Control, 1939.

Clausen, C. P.: Entomophagous Insects, 1940.

Dunham, G. C.: Military Preventive Medicine, 1940.

Gabrielson, I. N.: Wildlife Conservation, 1941.

8. PHILOSOPHICAL AND THEORETICAL ASPECTS

Lotka, A. J.: Théorie analytique des associations biologiques, 1934.

Kostitzin, V. A.: Biologie mathématique, 1937.

Hjort, J.: The Human value of Biology, 1938.

Wheeler, W. M.: Essays in Philosophical Biology (a collection edited by G. H. Parker), 1939.

Several comments are in order about this list. The reader may ask: Are there treatises on physical conditions or on communities? The former is covered in two places: in technical sources such as handbooks on physiology, biochemisty, meteorology, and so on, and particularly in the general texts and references. Thus Chapman, Uvarov, Welch, Bodenheimer, and Pearse all enter into such matters in considerable detail. Likewise, the community studies are covered primarily in the general texts. Elton (1935), Clements and Shelford, and Just stressed this problem.

B. Journals containing ecological articles published between 1931 and 1942. The list excludes provincial and governmental bulletins, weeklies and semipopular periodicals. It is patently biassed in favor of English-writing scientists. The figure following each title is the number of the *1935* volume.

Acta Biotheoretica (vol. 1, 1937).

American Midland Naturalist, 16.

American Naturalist, 65.

Annals of Applied Biology, 22.

Archiv für Hydrobiologie, 32.

Archiv für Protistenkunde, 89.

The Auk, 52.

Biologia Generalis, 11.

Biological Bulletin, 68.

Bulletin of Entomological Research, 26.

Condor, 37.

Copeia (founded in 1913; no volume numbers).

Die Binnengewässer, 4.

Ecological Monographs, 5.

Ecology, 16.

Entomological Society of America, Annals, 28.

Human Biology, 7.

Hvalrådets Skrifter. Scientific results of marine biological research (founded 1931; no volume numbers).

Internationale Revue der gesamten Hydrobiologie und Hydrographie.

Journal du Conseil. Counseil permanent international pour l'exploration de la mer, 10.

Journal of Agricultural Research, 58.

Journal of Animal Ecology, 4.

Journal of Ecology, 23.

Journal of Economic Entomology, 28.

Journal of Experimental Biology, 12.

Journal of Experimental Zoology, 71.

Journal of Mammalogy, 16.

Journal of Wildlife Management (volume 1, 1936).

Marine Biological Association, Journal, 19.

Parasitology, 27.

Physiological Zoology, 8.

Population (founded 1933; irregular volumes).

Quarterly Review of Biology, 10.
Revista de entomologia, 6.
Royal Society, Proceedings (series B), 119.
Scientia, 29.
Zeitschrift für Morphologie und Ökologie der Tiere, 12.
Zoögeographica (founded 1932; irregular volumes).
Zoogeographica Argentina (founded 1942).
Zoological Society of London, Proceedings, 105.
Zoologische Jahrbücher. Abteilung für Systematik, Ökologie und Geographie der Tiere, 67.

C. *Review articles* of ecological interest published between 1931 and 1942 in the *Quarterly Review of Biology*.

Johnson, G. E.: Hibernation in Mammals, 1931.
Gause, G. F.: Ecology of Populations, 1932.
Gulick, A.: Biological Peculiarities of Oceanic Islands, 1932.
Allen, W. E.: The Primary Food Supply of the Sea, 1934.
Crawford, S. C.: The Habits and Characteristics of Nocturnal Animals, 1934.
Higgins, E.: Fishery Biology. Its Scope, Development and Applications, 1934.
Severtzoff, S. A.: On the Dynamics of Populations of Vertebrates, 1934.
Pearl, R., and Miner, J. R.: The Comparative Mortality of Certain Lower Organisms, 1935.
Taylor, W. P.: Significance of the Biotic Community in Ecological Studies, 1935a.
Gause, G. F.: The Principles of Biocoenology, 1936.
Bodenheimer, F. S.: Seasonal Population Trends of the Honey-Bee, 1937a.
McAtee, W. L.: Survival of the Ordinary, 1937.
Clarke, G. L.: The Relation between Diatoms and Copepods as a Factor in the Productivity of the Sea, 1939b.
Hammond, E. C.: Biological Effects of Population Density in Lower Organisms, Part 1, 1938; Part 2, 1939.
Galt, W.: The Principle of Cooperation in Behavior, 1940.
Lindsey, A. A.: Recent Advances in Antarctic Bio-geography, 1940.
Park, T.: The Laboratory Population as a Test of a Comprehensive Ecological System, 1941.
Davis, D. E.: The Phylogeny of Social Nesting Habits in the Crotophaginae, 1942.

D. *Synthesis articles* representative of the several fields of ecology published between 1931 and 1942. These papers seem to us to be contributions to *thinking* as well as to fact finding. They are arranged according to the four categories listed on page 67, full citation is given in the Bibliography.

1. THE COMMUNITY

Taylor, W. P.: Significance of the Biotic Community in Ecological Studies, 1935.
Gause, G. F.: The Principles of Biocoenology, 1936.
Lucas, C. E.: Some Aspects of Integration in Plankton Communities, 1938.
Carpenter, J. R.: Recent Russian Work on Community Ecology, 1939.*
Gleason, H. A.: The Individualistic Concept of the Plant Association, 1939.
Park, O.: Nocturnalism—The Development of a Problem, 1940.

2. POPULATION PROBLEMS

Hogben, L.: Some Biological Aspects of the Population Problem, 1931.
Chapman, R. N.: The Cause of Fluctuations of Populations of Insects, 1933.
Hjort, J., Jahn G., and Ottestad, P.: The Optimum Catch, 1933.
Nicholson, A. J.: The Balance of Animal Populations, 1933.
Ottestad, P.: A Mathematical Method for the Study of Growth, 1933.
Allee, W. C.: Recent Studies in Mass Physiology, 1934a.
Smith, H. S.: The Role of Biotic Factors in the Determination of Population Densities, 1935.
Errington, P. L.: What Is the Meaning of Predation? 1937a.
Ford, J.: Research on Populations of *Tribolium confusum* and Its Bearing on Ecological Theory: A Summary, 1937.
MacLulich, D. A.: Fluctuations in the Numbers of the Varying Hare, *Lepus americanus,* 1937.
McAtee, W. L.: Survival of the Ordinary, 1937.
Pearl, R.: On Biological Principles Affecting Populations: Human and Other, 1937.

* There has been much Russian work in ecology published during the last ten years or so. Unfortunately, and because of language difficulties, this is essentially inaccessible to American ecologists. This is a pity. All concerned would benefit if the data and conclusions of such books, papers, and journals could be studied. Elton recognized the point for English ecologists in his 1942 book (p. 69) when he said, "Few scientists outside Russia seem to be aware of the phenomenal growth of ecological research under the auspices of the U.S.S.R., especially during the last ten years. Even considered only as a scheme of organization on paper, these new developments take one's breath away. A whole generation of well-trained workers is growing up and beginning to produce research of a high order. Carpenter's paper forms a very useful guide to the organization of this work."

Hammond, E. C.: Biological Effects of Population Density in Lower Organisms, 1938.

Park, T.: Analytical Population Studies in Relation to General Ecology, 1939.

Thompson, W. R.: Biological Control and Theories of Population Interaction, 1939.

Rhodes, E. C.: Population Mathematics. I, II, and III, 1940.

Wright, S.: Breeding Structure of Populations in Relation to Speciation, 1940.

Allee, W. C.: Integration of Problems Concerning Protozoan Populations, 1941.

Park, T.: The Laboratory Population as a Test of a Comprehensive Ecological System, 1941.

3. SOCIETY AND SOCIAL INTEGRATION

Phillips, J. F. V.: Succession, Development, the Climax, and the Complex Organism: An Analysis of Concepts, 1934–35.

Emerson, A. E.: Social Co-ordination and the Superorganism, 1939.

Allee, W. C.: Concerning the Origin of Sociality in Animals, 1940.

Child, C. M.: Social Integration as a Biological Process, 1940.

Galt, W.: The Principle of Cooperation in Behavior, 1940.

Gerard, R. W.: Organism, Society and Science, 1940.

Park, O.: Concerning Community Symmetry, 1941a.

4. OTHER ASPECTS

Klaauw, C. J. van der: Zur Aufteilung der Ökologie in Autökologie und Synökologie, im Lichte der Ideen als Grundlage der Systematik der zoologischen Disziplinen, 1936.

Daubenmire, R. F.: Merriam's Life Zones of North America, 1938.

Hjort, J.: The Human Value of Biology, 1938.

Allee, W. C., and Park, T.: Concerning Ecological Principles, 1939.

Note: Certain of the quotations used in this chapter have been slightly altered without change of meaning in the interest of brevity.

SECTION II. ANALYSIS OF THE ENVIRONMENT

4. THE GENERAL ENVIRONMENT

FITNESS OF ENVIRONMENT

We are not here concerned with an imaginary ecology based upon a hypothetical environment inhabited by fancied organisms evolved in some vaguely conceived system of life. Such a complex may exist, for all we know, with a different chemical and physical basis from the one we have on the earth. It is sometimes amusing to speculate on the possibilities of living systems that may have developed under conditions of low temperature that obtain, for example, on the outer planets of our solar system. If such life exists, its environment might conceivably be based upon and largely determined by the properties of ammonia. This substance boils at −33.5° C.* and has many fitnesses for being the controlling element in an environment-organism complex which, in many features, would not be too far removed from that on the earth. There is also the more remote possibility of metabolizing, reproducing organisms that live at temperatures well above the upper limits of life here. The organic chemistry of such systems might perhaps be based on silicon rather than on carbon.

Instead of dealing with imaginary situations, we are confronted by the ecology of the earth as we know it, populated by organisms that have evolved here from the basis furnished principally by water, carbon dioxide, and their elements, together with nitrogen (Henderson, 1913). These substances tend strongly to dominate and control both the earth's environment and the life which inhabits it. They are aided by many other elements; at least thirty-six (Fearon, 1933) and probably forty-six (Hutchinson, 1943, p. 342) of the ninety-six elements that are believed to constitute the universe are major or minor constituents of protoplasm. There is suggestive evidence that the chemical elements essential for life are not a random lot, but are correlated with atomic structure (Steinberg, 1938).

On the earth, life requires the following environmental conditions (Lafleur, 1941):

1. An available set of chemicals that will allow variation and reproduction and will carry on the complex processes of metabolism.

2. A suitable temperature; the high temperature on the average star excludes the possibility of the organization of molecules of sufficient complexity to serve as the basis of life. Cold slows down chemical processes, so that near absolute zero life is as impossible as it would be at some hundreds of degrees higher temperature. Life in general occurs much nearer the lowest possible than the highest known temperatures; it is essentially limited to relatively cold environments. Living protoplasm in latent stages has survived temperatures as low as about −270° C. and as high as 150° C. (see Fig. 2). Practically, life is limited to the temperatures at which water is a relatively warm solid or a cool to warm liquid, and exists only in a narrow range of temperatures far below the upper limit for inorganic matter that reaches some thousands or even millions of degrees (Huntington 1945). Molten lava aside, life in some form can exist at most earth temperatures.

3. The proper range of density and pressure; the pressure of a cool "white dwarf" star makes molecular organization impossible. At the other extreme in the slight density of a diffuse nebula, it is impossible for a molecule to collect and align needed chemical units.

From the preceding three paragraphs it

* Unless otherwise stated, all temperatures are given in degrees Centigrade.

follows that a viscous state is necessary which is not too near an ideal solid or an ideal liquid; in the intermediate colloidal gel and sol we find sufficient solidity to permit organization and enough liquidity to allow change. Life, as we know it, is a matter of the colloidal state.*

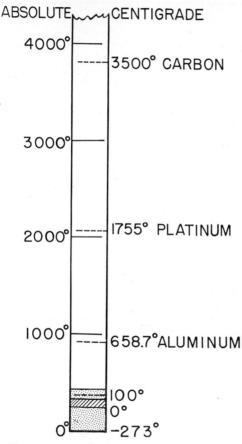

Fig. 2. Lower end of the temperature scale, showing melting points of carbon, platinum, and aluminum. The cross hatched space indicates the biokinetic temperature zone; dotted spaces show temperatures tolerated by some dry protoplasms. (Modified from Bĕlehrádek.)

4. There must be a source or sources of energy and of new materials; there is also a need for controlled reaction rates. Thus in the liberation of metabolic energy, food stuffs are burned by oxygen at controlled rates to supply the body needs. If these reactions occurred spontaneously, without special enzymes regulating the rates, this

* We reserve judgment concerning the relation of crystalline virus to life in general.

control would be impossible, the burning would get out of hand, and no sugar or other food reserves could exist.* Limited but renewable amounts of all needed materials and energy must be locally available to permit living processes to continue. Thus the sun's radiation is a source of energy that reaches the earth in limited amounts, but which so far has been endlessly renewed and shows no sign of becoming exhausted in the near future.

We have gained a much better understanding of energy generation in the sun in the last few decades. The present age of the sun is now estimated to approximate two thousand million years. "During the next ten-thousand-million years the sun is expected to increase about a hundred-fold in luminosity, after which all of its hydrogen will have been converted to helium. It will then rapidly decline and disappear as a star of the so-called 'main-sequence.' "†

5. The absorption of lethal ultraviolet rays of the atmosphere is of great importance. Life, again as we know it, could not occur on the earth today if these shorter abiotic rays were not screened out. Such rays are produced by the sun, which acts in this respect as a black-body radiator with a surface temperature of 6000° C. and an internal temperature of several million degrees. Oxygen absorbs wavelengths shorter than about 200 angstrom units (Å), but is somewhat less effective in screening out those up to 2530 Å. The absorption causes oxygen to become ozone, which absorbs waves shorter than 3000 Å, though it does not completely eliminate those longer than 2860 Å. Today radiations shorter than 2830 Å fail to reach the earth's surface.

This fifth consideration raises some interesting matters that deserve brief attention immediately. The question whether the present day type of atmospheric screening has always existed cannot be answered with certainty. One set of students think that oxygen was present in the atmosphere while the earth was cooling; others postulate a primeval atmosphere without oxygen. According to the latter point of view, the condensation of water vapor from the primitive atmosphere made a shallow sea and

* Gerard, R. W., personal communication, 1942.
† Personal communication from Otto Struve, who cites Gamow (1940).

left a relatively rarefied atmosphere that was probably free from oxygen and, therefore, from ozone.

There is a fair possibility that the early atmosphere did lack oxygen and that the gases then present did not act as effective screens for ultraviolet radiation. If the sun's full ultraviolet spectrum did reach the primeval earth, some possible effects include the following:

1. Under the influence of photochemically active radiations, the relatively inert chemicals dissolved in the oceans might well have formed increasingly complex organic compounds with varied colloidal structures until, finally, living substance itself was synthesized. This photochemical hypothesis avoids certain difficulties imposed by the more usual postulation of a thermal activation of the beginning of life. It is pertinent that ultraviolet radiation is reported to effect the synthesis of carbohydrates from carbon dioxide and water without the aid of chlorophyll (Baly, 1929). Radiations of comparable wavelength acting on modern genes accelerate the rate of mutation. Hence, perhaps, we could expect more rapid evolution in an environment in which they were effectively present in graded intensities.

2. If the initial living material so formed was similar to present day protoplasm, it could have remained alive only in or near the shadows cast by objects like rocks that are opaque to these shorter solar radiations, or in other niches where the newly formed life would not have been exposed for the whole day to the action of the lethal rays. Water could have furnished suitable protection only where it was very deep. It follows that the presence of such abiotic rays above the protecting umbrella of the earth's atmosphere would probably, then as now, kill cysts and spores that might be drifting through interplanetary space. It may be recalled that the theory of the extramundane origin of the ancestors of all life now found on the earth has been supported by various outstanding scientists, the chemist Arrhenius among them. Photochemical considerations are strongly opposed to such a possibility.

The change in the ultraviolet spectrum, after the production of the oxygen-ozone atmospheric screen, would account for the apparent absence of spontaneous generation of life on the earth today when theory apparently demands such an origin at some time in the remote past. This whole line of speculation assumes that the oxygen now in our atmosphere has been largely produced by photosynthetic activity of plants and, hence, that life itself has played an important role in establishing its modern environment. These particular speculations are developed further by Hutchinson (1944) and Giese (1945), who cite many key references.

Oparin (1938) marshalls the evidence indicating that life evolved on the earth from simple inorganic materials. According to his reconstruction, the slightly cooled earth had a central molten core containing metals acquired originally from the sun. The core was surrounded by "a membrane of primary igneous rocks" and enveloped in an atmosphere made up in the main of superheated steam. Oxygen and carbon dioxide were not present in the original atmosphere, but developed secondarily. Carbon itself first appeared as carbide of iron and other metals, all coming from the parent sun. According to these views, hydrocarbons arose from the action of water on the metallic carbides. Nitrogen also appeared on the earth in the reduced state, probably as ammonia.

Oparin summarized the essence of his argument as follows (p. 126):

"Hydrocarbon derivatives such as alcohols, aldehydes, organic acids, amines, amides, etc., undergo important transformations when their aqueous solutions are allowed to stand. In these solutions the dissolved substances undergo reactions of condensation and polymerization, as well as oxidation-reduction reactions; in other words, every type of change occurring in the living cell. As a result, numerous high molecular compounds, similar to those present in living cells, may appear in aqueous solutions of hydrocarbon derivatives on long standing."

From these, given more time, comes the origin of primary colloidal systems and finally of organisms.

Living protoplasm is not adjusted to meet the extreme conditions known to exist within our solar system. Environmental extremes must not be too great, and the transition from one extreme to another must not be too sudden. With life based primarily on water as ours is, the temperature for active metabolism can range only a few degrees below to a few tens of degrees C.

above zero These conditions are furnished by the earth, which rotates on an axis while revolving about an energy-shedding sun.

In general terms, the earth is a dense, crusted body of sufficient size to have strong enough gravitational attraction to hold an extensive gaseous atmosphere, but not strong enough to hold more than a trace of free hydrogen. The presence of water and carbon dioxide in the atmosphere seems to be a normal result of the physical and chemical properties of water and carbon dioxide that have much to do with regulating the general environment of living things on the earth. There is good reason to believe that "water is the substance whose movement in the organic and in the inorganic world constitutes the first, the most fundamentally important activity in the world that we live in" (Henderson, 1922).

Water has a number of remarkable qualities that make it an important factor in the environment of living things as well as the major ingredient of living protoplasm. It is a stable chemical compound that passes readily through solid, liquid, and gaseous states at what we call ordinary temperatures. The thermal properties of water, added to its abundance and wide distribution, make it an important temperature regulator. Its great power as a solvent, especially of electrolytes, and its inertness, which allows many chemicals to pass into and out of solution readily and without change, make it an important bearer of chemical supplies. The property of expansion before freezing has important effects upon life in bodies of water that freeze over. The high surface tension of water, among other things, accounts for the rise of soil water through capillary attraction, and is important in adsorption, which, with other properties of water, makes it of high value in the formation of colloids. There is also a relatively high order of transparency, mobility, and incompressibility. In a different field, water has a markedly high dielectric constant and great ionizing power. Water furnishes the basic environmental division into aquatic and terrestrial habitats.

Another compound that, with water, is of greatest importance in life processes is carbon dioxide. The environment-controlling properties of carbon dioxide are less important than those of water. Carbon dioxide enters and leaves water freely; at ordinary temperatures its absorption coefficient approaches unity; hence carbon dioxide can never be wholly washed from air into water or taken from water into the air. In water, carbon dioxide forms a weak acid that adds to the solvent power of water, and since the acid is dibasic, it has marked power as a chemical buffer and so helps maintain a near neutrality in the acid-base relations of the environment.

Since carbon dioxide is present as a gas in the atmosphere and in solution in water, and since it can readily be extracted from both sources and also readily enters into chemical combinations, it forms an important nutrient for plants. Under the synthesizing processes, particularly those of photosynthesis, carbon becomes the center of a whole class of chemical compounds that are so important chemically that they make up the content of a distinct phase of chemistry, so-called organic chemistry, which consists of the chemistry of the carbon compounds. Carbon has the remarkable ability of combining with itself to form the basis of complex molecules which, when combined particularly with hydrogen, oxygen, nitrogen, phosphorous, and calcium, to mention those that, respectively, compose 1 per cent or more of the organism (Fearon, 1933), make a peculiarly fit system of chemical compounds for use by living organisms as sources of matter and energy for the processes of metabolism.

We are accustomed to the idea that organisms show adaptations of fitnesses to the environment in which they live, and also to the more general view that, everything considered, life in the large is well adapted to its generalized environment. Despite the fact that the idea is no longer new, many do not yet appreciate the basic ecological principle that, given matter and energy and the resulting probability that life when and where it develops will be a mechanism (a complex mechanism, to be sure), the surface of a solid body such as the earth—placed as it is in relation to a central energy-giving sun—does actually provide an excellent general environment for the living organism as we know it. It is possible for the biochemist Henderson (1913, p. 273) to maintain without successful contradiction to date that this is actually "the best of all possible environments for life."

Certainly the fitness of the organisms, which, as the idea of adaptation, Claude Bernard urged should be the basal principle for all physiology, is only one phase of the relationship. The environment is also relatively a fit place for life. Reflection indicates that both phases of this reciprocal fitness are inherently imperative. The environment must have been more than passively favorable; otherwise life would probably not have originated and persisted. This is the primary fitness. The general adaptation of organisms to their environment follows as a necessary corollary.

The developing reciprocity of environment and organism has produced fundamental and far-reaching results. At one time, probably, the atmosphere of the earth consisted chiefly of water vapor and carbon dioxide. Cooling caused the condensation of most of the water, and geological processes, aided in recent geological time by the action of vegetation and the fixation of carbon in coal and peat, have removed nearly all the carbon dioxide. This has resulted in the evolution of an atmosphere in which inert nitrogen forms the greatest bulk and in which oxygen is the most important active chemical element.

As a further evidence of reciprocity between living and nonliving nature, Vernadsky (1929) suggests that all the free oxygen of the earth (1.5×10^{21} gm.) is produced by life alone. Hence, not only are organisms acted on by the environment, but they also react upon it to produce noteworthy changes to which, in turn, evolving life must adapt itself or perish.

In discussing the general principle of the fitness of the earth's environment as the basis of life, certain deficiencies must not be overlooked that make it less than ideally fit.[*] Because of the relatively high opacity of water, anabolic life is confined to a relatively thin film near the surface, while the intermediate reaches and the vast ocean bottom are sparsely inhabited by saprophytes and scavengers, predators and parasites.

The atmosphere, as a result of its low degree of buoyancy, cannot be used as a permanent habitat by organisms, and even its lower reaches can be used as a passageway only by accident or by highly specialized forms. The entire ocean of air supports only a sparse and transient population near its lower phase boundary. On account of the same lack of buoyancy and also because of the usually strong drying power of the air, even earth-supported life is limited to a biosphere which, as a permanent habitat for living things, never rises more than a few tens of meters above the earth's surface. Because of seasonal and regional variations in distribution of heat and water vapor, approximately half of the terrestrial surface of the earth is an impossible environment except for a sparse population of specially adapted organisms. These environmental deficiencies would not have had their present values during much of geological time (p. 8). Cold alone closes almost all of the interior of one whole continent, Antarctica, to endemic life. The sparseness of water vapor results in large areas being inhabited but slightly; the Sahara desert is an excellent example. Yet, while recognizing such difficulties with the earth as an environment for life, we are reminded by Henderson (1917) that water is more widely distributed over the face of the earth than is any other known compound.

To continue with the disadvantages: The relative stability of many carbon compounds and their insolubility in water have resulted in a gradual piling up of carbon in coal and peat deposits, with a resulting reduction in the availability of this substance as a plant nutrient. The stability of nitrogen closes most of the great atmospheric store to use by organisms. Such facts indicate that despite many niceties of fit, the properties of matter can hardly be said to be generously above the minimum required for the origin and maintenance of living systems.

Realizing the importance of these weaknesses in the Hendersonian argument we can still conclude this phase of the present discussion with another quotation from Henderson (1914, p. 527):

"Just because life must manifest itself in and through mechanism, just because, being in this world, it must inhabit a more or less durable, more or less active physico-chemical system of more or less complexity in its phases, components and concentrations, it is conditioned. The inorganic, such as it is, imposes certain conditions on the organic. Accordingly, our conclusion is this: *The special characteristics of the inorganic are the fittest for those general characteristics of the organic which the general characteristics of the inorganic impose upon the organic.* This is the one side of reciprocal

---

[*] The discussion is based on a personal communication from Dr. William Etkin.

biological fitness. The other side may be similarly stated: through adaptation the special characteristics of the organic come to fit the special characteristics of a particular environment, to fit, not any planet, but a little corner of the earth."

VARIATIONS IN SPACE

The division into aquatic and terrestrial organisms or habitats is primary for ecology. The distribution of large bodies of water is important, not alone in determining the general outlines of the biogeography of the world, but also in the regulation of temperature and rainfall. Biogeographically, the oceans provide highways for the dispersal of marine organisms; at the same time they are barriers for animals of the land, of fresh waters, and even for many inhabitants of the shallow, inshore waters of the sea. The present day distribution of plants and animals depends both on the existing configuration of bodies of land and of water and upon the past history of these configurations.

Here we come squarely upon an active controversy that centers about the possible existence of oceanic land bridges. In their more extreme forms, the geological principles of the relative permanence of the present ocean basins, based especially on the principle of isotasy, are sharply opposed to theories of transoceanic land connections or to Wegener's idea of continental drift. The issues involve such matters as continental and insular isolation, the location and duration of routes of travel, and the methods of dispersal of organisms in general and in particular.

The distribution of salts in water is fundamental for large-scale distinctions in the distribution of aquatic organisms. The highly saline lakes or lagoons, the oceans, and the fresh waters of the world form a series of distinct environments. Gradual transitions occur, and brackish water makes a well-known transition between marine and fresh-water environments.

The general principles and facts concerning the broad temperature zones of the world are well known. It is not so generally appreciated that the present zonal climate is a recurrent, relatively transitory phase of climatic history. Throughout much of the time that the earth has been inhabited, the continents have stood lower in relation to sea level than they are at present, and

relatively mild temperatures have extended into subpolar regions. In other words, the strong zonal provincialism of present day temperature belts has usually been replaced by a broad uniformity. One of the unsolved problems of modern world climate is whether we are now in another interglacial period or are moving toward the general amelioration of world climates.

The phases of temperature zonation concerned with life zones will be considered in more detail later (p. 114). Meantime, it should be recalled that many regional or local factors act to modify the temperature in a given region from that to be expected on an idealized globe. Distance from the ocean is one of the modifying factors. The ocean is the great temperature regulator of the world. Islands and coastal areas, in general, undergo relatively slight temperature fluctuations as contrasted with the extremes found in the midcontinental climates at the same latitude. This effect is quite apart from a second important temperature modification brought about by ocean currents. The ameliorating action of the Gulf Stream upon the temperature of northern Europe contrasts with the chilling produced by the Labrador Current at similar latitudes along the northeastern coast of America. Winds exert important effects on the temperature and rainfall of a given region. Thus, the prevailing westerly winds accentuate the ameliorating effect of the Gulf Stream on the climate of northwestern Europe.

Tropical and subtropical temperatures are much more restricted along the western coasts of the continental land masses than they are on the eastern side. This restriction is brought about either by an upwelling of deeper, cold ocean water or by polar currents, or by both acting together. Tropical littoral animals are found, for example, only from the northern coast of Peru, 5 degrees or less south of the equator, northward to northern Mexico or southern California, a total distance of about 33 to 39 geographic degree (Ekman, 1935) (see Fig. 3). On the eastern side of the Americas, the comparable littoral formation extends from Cape Hatteras and the Bermudas at 35 degrees north latitude to Rio de Janeiro or even to the mouth of the Plata river at 35 degrees south latitude. The situation is similar on the two coasts of the African-Eurasian land mass and on those of

Australia, although here it is less dramatic.

Another exception to the diagrammatic expression of global temperature zones is related to the slope of the land. Effects of slope and exposure are more obvious on mountains or hills than on the plains. Even in level regions in the tundra, however, an almost imperceptible slope toward the south may make the difference between a rela-

The world maps of rainfall or vegetation show a fairly definite moisture zonation superimposed on that of temperature. From the equatorial regions northward, with certain known exceptions, the distribution shows the following schematized pattern:

1. A belt of heavy tropical rains with accompanying rain forests lies near the equator.

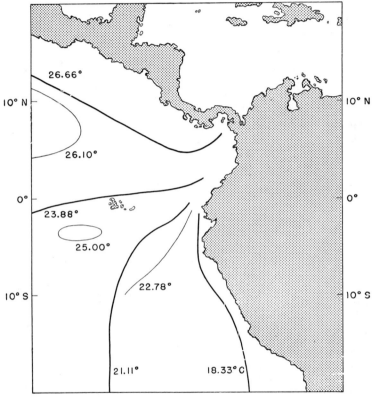

Fig. 3. The temperature zones become narrower near the west coast of tropical America. (Redrawn from Agassiz.)

tively abundant summer biota and a sparse community of hardier forms that live on a similarly slight neighboring slope to the north.

The character of the soil also affects local temperatures. Heavy clay soil warms up much more slowly than does loose, sandy loam. Alkaline soils tend to be heat accumulators, and warmth-limited organisms which grow only on calcareous subsoil in northern Germany and the British Isles are not necessarily so restricted in milder climates.

2. A region of smaller annual rainfall, with more marked rainy and dry seasons, supports tropical savannah or tropical grassland; these formations lie on both sides of the tropical rain forest.

3. Northward over much of the world, there is an area of decreasing rainfall that culminates in the great arid belt that contains the Sonoran Desert of North America, the Sahara, the Arabian, and Persian deserts. Their southern equivalents occur in South America, Africa, and Australia.

4. Generally, the desert gives way to a

northern semidesert which, in California and around the Mediterranean, is an area of winter rain and summer drought.

5. To the north lies a region of moderate rainfall that supports either deciduous forests or grasslands in its southern phases and a round-the-world belt of coniferous forests at the north.

6. Farther north there is the tundra, where the rainfall is characteristically scanty and where even the small amount that does fall is physiologically unavailable during the greater part of the year.

7. Finally, as far as land is concerned, there are the well-developed polar ice caps in Greenland and Antarctica.

A similar set of conditions can be recognized in the southern hemisphere, although, associated with the smaller size of the continental land masses, the rainfall zonation is not so diagrammatically developed except for the polar ice cap in Antarctica.

The distribution of rainfall is strongly affected by mountain ranges. When these extend east and west, as do the Himalayas, the combined rainfall and temperature zonation is accentuated. When the mountains extend north and south, as do the Rocky and the Andes Mountains, a secondary pattern of rainfall distribution is established which, as will be discussed in more detail later (p. 145), runs at right angles to the global temperature zones.

The geography of temperature and rainfall and of associated factors exerts a strong influence upon the distribution of species of plants and animals and of biotic communities that is strikingly shown on the land. Temperature also exerts a strong primary influence on the distribution of marine organisms. The effect of rainfall on marine life is mainly indirect and acts through modification of salinity. Areas of dilution occur along shores and particularly near the mouths of the large tropical and subtropical rivers where the great influx of fresh water, together with the silt it carries, inhibits the growth of coral reefs. The opposite effect may be noted near desert areas, most strikingly in the Red Sea, which shows the effect of its location in the great northern desert belt by the high salinity of its waters, 46.5 per mille, as contrasted with the 35 per mille characteristic of the surface waters of the open ocean.

The surface salinity in the three major oceans, and for these combined, varies from a standard value in direct proportion to the difference between evaporation and precipitation in the area under consideration. Although modified by mixing with water from 400 to 600 meters down, the difference between evaporation and precipitation is of primary importance (Sverdrup, Johnson, and Fleming, 1942, p. 124).

Especially on land, other environmental factors are also differentially distributed and are important in ecological geography and physiology. They are usually subsidiary to the temperature-rainfall complex. Some of the more important ones include the length of day and the environmental conditions associated with altitude and substrate.

The distribution of soil types forms an important basis of endemism in continental areas, while the presence or absence of traces of copper, cobalt, or selenium, to name no more, in the soil may have important ecological effects (p. 221) (Godden, 1939).

VARIATIONS IN TIME

Some major variations in time have been outlined in the preceding pages, especially those changes that have accompanied the evolving fitness of the physical world to support life. The present discussion will center about (a) changes in climate on the earth during geological time and (b) more recent and present day periodicities.

Geological Climates

Physical and biological evidence both indicate that climate during historical times is a poor key to the more usual world climates of the past. Probably less than 1 per cent of geological time has approximated the essentially glacial climatic pattern that is familiar to us. Other aspects of the late Cenozoic and Recent epochs are abnormal. Mountains are more numerous and stand higher; continents are larger; there are more volcanoes; and earthquakes come more frequently than they did during the great stretches of geologic time. We are living in a period of geological revolution, of crustal unrest, such as occurred on a full scale between the Proterozoic and the Paleozoic eras and was repeated between the Paleozoic and Mesozoic eras (Brooks, 1926; Russell, 1941).

Generally speaking, crustal stability,

low average level of land masses, and wide-spread mild temperatures have character-ized the earth during most of geological time. Seas were more extensive and some-what warmer, and the Arctic Ocean was ice-free even in winter. Precipitation was probably less, but thanks to the higher tem-perature of the greater proportion of water

The Pleistocene ice age is of more direct importance for present day ecology than are the several major glaciations of long-past geological eras. The absence of a Pleistocene "continental" glacier from Siberia and much of Alaska not only af-fected biotic distribution at the time, but has had important influence upon the loca-

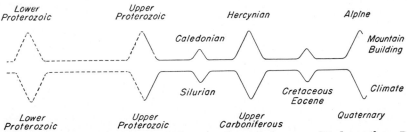

Fig. 4. Periods of mountain building and glaciation through the ages. (Redrawn from Brooks.)

surface, the humidity of the air was higher. If we can trust the generalizations based on a correlation of red soil and salt deposits with aridity, extensive midcontinental des-erts were also characteristic. On this point there is a controversy, and perhaps we may think of these early deserts as being of a ra-ther mild variety. The intense aridity of modern deserts seems to be associated with the high-standing land masses and the zonal climate to be found in periods of geological revolutions.

During the more usual conditions the land areas of the earth probably had a cli-mate much like that of present day tropical lowlands, with forests along the coasts and tropical grasslands in the interior. Toward the poles, that is, above 55 to 60 degrees north latitude, climatic zones became evi-dent, but the shores of the perennially open Arctic and Antarctic Oceans experienced only mild winters.

The change from a normal geologic cli-mate to a glacial one is marked for prac-tical purposes by the formation of a polar ice cap. An increase on the order of 1.1° C. in the general temperature of the earth to-day would eventually make the whole Arctic ice mass unstable in summer, and, if long continued, would probably clear the Arctic seas of ice. Brooks has calculated that an initial change of about 3° C. at the critical temperature at latitude 50 de-grees north would make the difference be-tween a nonglacial and glacial climate (Fig. 5).

tion of many plants and animals today. This last glaciation was marked by four or five main advances of the ice with intervening interglacial periods. In the 30,000 to 40,000 years since the last ice retreated from low-lying regions in the middle lati-tudes of North America and Europe, the climate of the northern hemisphere has not shown a steady trend toward amelioration.

The record is read, in part, from the an-

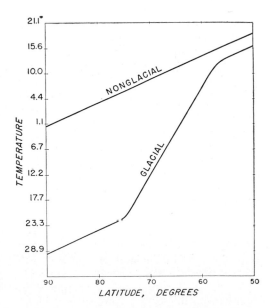

Fig. 5. Temperature difference between non-glacial and glacial climates. (Redrawn from Brooks.)

nual layers of clay interspersed with coarser materials deposited on the bottom of lakes. These are called varves. The finer clays settle slowly in the quiet water under the ice in winter, while coarser stuff is held back until spring and summer. The varves in the Scandinavian lakes have been followed for some 13,700 years.

Tree rings have also been studied for the light they throw on climatic history. As yet, tree ring analysis covers a much shorter period of time. Tree rings must be interpreted with care, since they represent, not annual rings necessarily, but merely alternating periods of rapid and slow growth. A severe midseason drought following a good growing period would produce a good growth ring; another good growing season in the same year would produce another supposed annual ring. Also, we know that damage caused by insects, lightning, fire, frost, intense heat, excessive snow, sleet, wind, and so forth, as well as drought, may affect the rate of growth of trees and so tend to modify the width of the rings of growth (Antevs, 1938).

Past climates can also be reconstructed in part from the succession of plant types in peat, from ecological evidence of the shifting position of the tree line in mountains or in the far north, from the recovery of resistant pollen grains in bogs, from the study of tools, weapons, bones, and kitchen middens of men. Finally, there is the brief period covered by more or less trustworthy human documents.

Humphreys (1942) has a brief word to say about one cause of long-time climatic changes. At present the earth is nearest the sun during the first week in January and farthest away during the first week in July. The difference in distance, if long continued, would modify the temperature on the earth about 4 degrees. If conditions were reversed, as they actually were about 10,500 years ago and will be again in about that period of time, the temperature contrast between summer and winter would be definitely greater than it now is, especially in the northern hemisphere, which contains most of the land mass of the earth. Under present conditions of this long cycle, winters in the northern hemisphere are shorter and milder and summers are longer and also milder, and the climate in general is more equitable in our part of the globe than would be so in any other earth posi-

tion with respect to this motion of the perihelion and precession of the equinoxes.

The study of climatic history since the last glacial retreat, the Recent epoch of geologists, has been most pursued in Europe. A frequently accepted summary of the existing evidence, the so-called Blytt-Sernander hypothesis, follows: The retreat of the ice begun some thirty to forty thousand years ago and continued fairly steadily until about 12,000 B.C.* This time of glacial recession was followed by a sub-Arctic period that lasted about 4000 years until near 8000 B.C., when the ice had retreated sufficiently to allow sea water to enter the then fresh-water Baltic lake.

Then came a warmer Boreal period characterized in the Baltic area by the development of the so-called *Yoldia* fauna (or community), in which the bivalve mollusk *Yoldia arctica* was prominent (today this species is restricted to salt waters that have a temperature of 0° C. or lower). On land the Boreal period was marked by a northward movement of forests. About 5000 B.C. the Baltic began to support animals that live today in waters warmer than those we now find in the Baltic Sea. This is called the *Littorina* period, so named for the snail that is prominent in the deposits of the place and time; several species of this genus now inhabit the shores of the north temperate ocean. This Atlantic period lasted until about 3000 B.C. The climate was generally warm and moist; all the mountain glaciers disappeared from Europe and from much of North America. The Atlantic period marks the climax in amelioration to date since the last glacial retreat.

A drier sub-Boreal period followed that came down to about 1000 B.C., but was interrupted by floods some 300 years earlier. It is supposed, according to the Blytt-Sernander hypothesis, to have given way to a milder sub-Atlantic period, which was in typical development between about 850 and 300 B.C. The existence of the sub-Atlantic period is questioned by some who think that there has been a general deterioration of climate from the Atlantic period to the present, which, however, has been interrupted by relatively small swings in temperature and rainfall (Sears, 1935; Trewartha, 1940).

* Deevey (1944) follows DeGeer in giving a somewhat different time scale.

Minor fluctuations of climate continued. In the first century A.D., climatic conditions were similar to those found today. From near the end of the second to the middle of the fourth centuries, the climate was wet. The fifth century was dry, and the seventh was both dry and warm, so that passes in the Alps were in use that are now closed by glaciers. Heavier rainfall came in Europe near the start of the ninth century, but Nile floods were low until about 1000 A.D.

Warmer, drier conditions returned to Europe during the tenth and eleventh centuries. Greenland was settled in 984 A.D. and was abandoned at the beginning of the fifteenth century. During that period its climate is generally thought to have been milder than it is today. In Europe, the thirteenth and fourteenth centuries were cold and wet. Amelioration must have set in, for the glaciers of Chamonix were small in 1580, but advanced rapidly until the middle of the seventeenth century; then a retreat began that lasted until 1770, when they again advanced up until the middle of the last century. Since that time the glaciers have retreated approximately to the positions held in the sixteenth century (Brooks, 1926; Russell, 1941).

The latter part of this somewhat detailed summary is often condensed as follows:

1. The Boreal period: warm, dry, continental climate; birch and pine were dominant trees.
2. The Atlantic period: warmer, moist, oceanic climate; oaks were dominant trees.
3. The sub-Boreal period: warm, dry continental climate; oaks continuing dominant.
4. The sub-Atlantic period: cool, very wet, oceanic climate; beech and spruce were dominant trees (Clements and Chaney, 1936).

The scheme may be still more simplified to give only three stages (von Post's hypothesis) of postglacial climates, namely:

1. A period of increasing warmth,
2. A period of maximum temperature, and
3. A period of fluctuating, but, on the whole, decreasing temperature.

Climates in other parts of the world may or may not follow the European pattern. The climatic sequence in eastern North America can be correlated in a general way with that of Europe. The correlation is as close as could well be expected, since eastern North America gets its climate from the interior, while, in contrast, western Europe is under strong marine influence. In addition, European climates have been much affected by the complicated history of the Baltic Sea. The three stages of the relatively simple von Post's hypothesis correspond fairly well on the two sides of the North Atlantic, and perhaps a still closer correlation exists, as shown in depth profiles of pollen preserved in bogs; this is outlined in Table 4.

Table 4. Possible Climatic Correlation between Western Europe and Eastern North America (From Deevey, 1944, after Sears)

European Periods	Vegetation, Eastern North America	Climate
Sub-Atlantic	Oak-chestnut-spruce (Oak-beech)	Cool, wet
Sub-Boreal	Oak-hickory	Warm, dry
Atlantic	Oak-hemlock (Oak-beech)	Warm, moist
Boreal	Pine	Warm, dry
Pre-Boreal	Spruce-fir	Warm, dry
Arctic Sub-Arctic Arctic	Missing in North American diagrams	

Shifts in the location of the tree line to the south of the tundra and in mountains also gives evidence of general climatic trends. According to this criterion, there seems to be evidence that, at present, trees are advancing in Alaska, retreating in southeastern Mackenzie, and apparently retreating in eastern Canada. The resulting picture of current trends is by no means clear (Raup, 1941).

Two generalizations stand out as a result of this hasty review of past climates. The first is the reiterated statement that the present zonal climate, which our experience and records indicate is normal, is highly unusual when viewed with geological perspective. Through long geological eras there has been climatic cosmopolitanism rather than present day climatic provincialism. The second generalization, a corollary of the first, is to the effect that modern climates are unstable and have varied much even in recent millennia and centuries.

Periodicities

Many local environmental variations recur with regular rhythms, while others are arrhythmic. The most obvious of the rhythmic variations, that of day and night, is beginning to attract the attention from ecologists that it deserves. The day represents a period of increased heat and convection currents, as well as of increased light; there is also typically a decrease in relative humidity. Frequently, there are associated phenomena such as the local changes in wind velocity and direction that occur especially near the seashore, in mountains, and near forest margins. Many of these daytime changes markedly increase the evaporating power of the air. Important consequences of diurnal rhythms will be discussed later.

Tides run on a shorter period. They are periodic variations in the water level produced by the response of water particles to the attraction of the moon and sun. Tidal streams result that may attain considerable velocity in the shallow waters over shoals such as those of the Newfoundland Banks or in the neighborhood of land. The tidal currents usually follow the direction furnished by natural channnels, if any are present; they become more rapid and the tide rises higher near the head of V-shaped arms of the sea. The length of the ebb usually equals that of the flow of the tide, and the currents near land are in the opposite direction during the two tidal phases. In the open sea, the height of the tide is much reduced, the rate of movement is slower, and the general direction may be rotary.

The oscillatory tidal movement of the water has a normal period of 12.5 hours (Harvey, 1928). Longer tidal rhythms also exist. The simplest of these is the occurrence of a lunar cycle in tidal amplitude in which the high spring tides occur each fortnight when the sun and moon are exerting supplementary influences. Between the periods of spring tides, there are the lower neap tides that come when the two governing bodies are working more or less in opposition to each other. The grunion, *Laurestes tenuis*, a small smelt of the California coast, exhibits an annual breeding cycle that is related to this longer tidal

rhythm (p. 544; Thompson and Thompson, 1919; Clark, 1925).

Many animals of the marine littoral region have lunar periodicities in their breeding activities that are less obviously related to the forces operating during a lunar cycle. Corals, various mollusks and marine polychaete worms, among others, show such relationship. Two types of these lunar periodicities have been described for annelid worms. In one, successive breeding periods occur during the summer season, and each lunar cycle shows two peaks of abundance. Thus, *Nereis limbata* at Woods Hole, Massachusetts, ordinarily live as elongate worms in burrows; they emerge during their breeding period as short, compact, actively swimming forms that are only a fraction of their usual length. Each so-called run begins near the time of the full moon, increases to a maximum on successive nights, falls to a low point about the third quarter of the moon, increases to another maximum, and finally all swimming worms disappear shortly after the new moon. A new run starts about the time of the next full moon, and this double cycle is normally repeated four times during the summer (Lillie and Just, 1913; Townsend, 1939).

A second type of lunar periodicity occurs when a single annual breeding swarm makes its appearance in accordance with some phase or phases of the lunar cycle. The Atlantic palolo, *Leodice fucata*, of Bermuda and the West Indies inhabits coral reefs and spawns most abundantly during late June and July at about the third quarter of the moon, less commonly about the first quarter. There is thus good evidence of an internal or annual rhythm, and yet the time of spawning is partially under direct environmental control. It is delayed by water turbulence and by lunar influence. The causal factors are still obscure; neither changing nutritive conditions, such as may be associated with the tidal cycle, nor changing hydrostatic pressures are important. There seems to be a direct effect of moonlight (Clark, 1941, 1941a).

When the average duration of illumination is increased, spawning is hastened; it is retarded when the duration of exposure to moonlight is decreased. If the length of exposure to moonlight were the only factor involved, spawning would increase to a maximum near the time of the full moon and then decrease. As we have seen, however, the lunar periodicity of spawning in *L. fucata* is bimodal, and the maxima lie about the first and last quarters, when the duration of illumination is first increasing and later decreasing. Something more than a simple quantitative relationship is involved. One factor that varies as does swarming is the rate of change in the duration of moonlight. This reaches a maximum near the time of the new and the full moon and a minimum at the first and the third quarters. Descriptively, then, for the Atlantic palolo, the effectiveness of moonlight seems to be correlated with some aspect of the daily rate of change of duration. The swarming of other annelids may be initiated by other factors, such as a variation in the intensity of moonlight or a change in some direct effect of the tidal cycle. At this point, as in many other aspects of ecology, we await further field and laboratory analyses.

The angles made by the moon and sun with the plane running through the earth's equator vary independently, and so does the distance of each from the earth. The resultant forces exerted by the two bodies on the waters of the earth vary in a complex fashion, one result of which is that in addition to the daily and lunar tidal cycles, seasonal high tides also exist that have their due effect on organisms. Other tidal complications may be important locally or along long reaches of the seacoast; discussion of these does not fit into our crowded outline (Harvey, 1928). Some of the complications, as well as the fundamentals, are treated simply and with insight by Coker (1947).

Seasonal cycles in tidal amplitude and their effects on littoral marine communities are insignificant in comparison with the seasonal changes on terrestrial communities. As stated in Chapter 2, the study of phenomena associated with seasonal appearance, or phenology, has a long history. In much of the tropics, the annual changes are governed by rainfall and associated factors rather than by temperature, which exerts a controlling influence in higher latitudes. An intermediate climate, dominated by winter rains and summer drought, occurs typically around the Mediterranean Sea and in much of California. Many other seasonal variations in climate produce distinctive effects upon biotic communities.

Seasonal appearance does not necessarily follow the four conventional seasons even in a region where temperature is a major element in the annual cycle. In woodlands associated with the prairie peninsula in Illinois, it is often possible to recognize six seasonal subdivisions of the biotic community; these are outlined on page 53. On the south side of the equator, in cut-over and primeval mountain forests in the state of Rio de Janeiro, Brazil, Davis (1945, p. 294) also found the year divided into six comparable seasons. The time limits in such subdivisions are only approximate and may vary widely in different years. The exact number of seasonal subdivisions may also differ according to the community, the geographic and physiographic location of the community, according to the organisms used as index species and according to individual judgment as to the time limits (Clements and Shelford, 1939; Williams, 1936).

Other Cycles

More than fifty environmental periodicities had been listed by 1925; these varied in length from a few days to nearly two centuries. Others have been added since that time. Cycles of solar radiation are frequently discussed and are highly variable in duration and intensity. Among others, they include recurring periods of seven, eight, eleven, twenty-one, twenty-five, forty-five, and sixty-eight months' duration. The last-mentioned runs for about 5.7 years and is approximately half the length of the sunspot cycle of eleven + years. All may be regarded as submultiples of the cycle of magnetic change on the sun that has a periodicity of 276 months, or twenty-three years. A still longer cycle, that of Brückner, lasts from seventeen to fifty years, with a mean length of about thirty-five years. This may be thought of as a threefold multiple of eleven + years or as an effect of interference between this particular sunspot cycle and another of somewhat shorter duration.

The literature on such cycles continues rich in quantity and varied in quality. There seems to be some evidence of mind-set in discussing these problems, and judgments differ concerning the ecological importance of many of them. Clements and Shelford (1939), Elton (1942) and Huntington (1945), to mention only a few mature students, are usually more or less favorable. On the other side, Russell (1941, p. 92) wrote: "Though firm advocates of climatic cycles will sharply disagree, such facts as we possess today neither definitely demonstrate nor disprove the existence of any real cycle. Such climatic variability as has been observed may be explained as resulting from random fluctuations."

The sunspot cycle of slightly more than eleven years has attracted much attention from ecologists and others. The underlying causation of this cycle is still unknown. The cycle itself consists of the periodic variation in numbers of sunspots and is characterized, in part, by the tendency to remain at one length of period during a number of repetitions and then to shift to some other value that is again repeated for a time. Since 1750 the periods have varied from approximately eight to sixteen years. Even average values vary between 11.13 and 11.6 years, and a period of 10.2 years is seriously advanced for the sunspot series between 1615 and 1788 A.D. (Douglass, 1936). The variation reflects the continuing inexactness of the basic data regarding weather and climate (as well as population density), combined at times with the acceptance of indications as a substitute for rigorous proof.

Solar radiation appears to be less when there are few (or many) sunspots; a maximum of radiation is reached when the sunspot number is about 100. It appears that the temperature at the earth's surface tends to be highest when the actual solar radiation is least during this particular cycle of radiation. The reasons for this paradox are not yet wholly clear. Shifts on the order of 1 or 2 per cent in intensity of radiation are matters of record. If other conditions remained constant, as they would not do, an increase of 1 per cent in solar radiation would produce a rise of about 0.75° C. in the mean temperature at the earth's surface, since this temperature varies essentially as the fourth root of the intensity of the radiant energy received from the sun. The reasoning that other conditions would not remain stationary while the intensity of solar heat varies is based, in part, on the knowledge that resulting variations in temperature bring about important changes in atmospheric pressure, and the final effect is to decrease temperature in areas cold for their latitude, while those

warm for their latitude have increased warmth (Brooks, 1926).

It has been estimated that temperature on the earth might vary about 0.6° C. during a sunspot cycle. Small as this amount is, it represents an appreciable fraction of the lowering of temperature that would bring about an ice age. A more recent test of the correspondence between sunspot cycles was made by using temperature records from six scattered tropical stations, covering a period of fifty-eight years. Tropical stations were chosen, since many writers have stated that the closest correlation between sunspots and weather is to be found in the tropics. When the available records were combined in cycles equal to the sunspot cycle of eleven years, a mean temperature amplitude of 0.22° C. was found. The correlation between sunspot number and the annual temperature was found to be −0.37, a correlation which, although low, probably indicates statistical validity (Elton, 1924; Adams and Nicholson, 1933).

Brooks (1926, p. 409) summed up the situation about sunspot cycles as follows: "The most perfect example of a solar relationship hitherto found in purely meteorological data is shown by the level of equatorial Lake Victoria. Generally speaking the eleven-year cycle is characteristic of equatorial regions while the thirty-five year Brückner cycle is characteristic of higher latitudes. The amplitude and regularity of the eleven-year cycle decreases toward the poles, those of the Brückner cycle increase from the equator toward the North Pole at least."

The most discussed biotic cycles include (1) the lemming and mouse cycle of three to four years; (2) the varying hare and lynx cycle of somewhat less than ten years; (3) a cycle corresponding to the sunspot cycle of somewhat more than eleven years which we have been discussing; and (4) another cycle corresponding to the Brückner cycle of about thirty-five years.

As critical studies accumulate, it becomes difficult to discover biological phenomena exactly coinciding with the last two cycles, even as it is difficult to find a sound environmental periodicity that corresponds with the first two cycles just listed. Goldie's (1936) suggestion of maxima as related to the mean cycle of annual air drift over the northern part of the British Isles that recurs at an interval of somewhat less than four years remains for the present a suggestion only. Clements and Shelford (1939), although they are, in general, favorable to the idea of a correlation between the eleven-year sunspot cycle and biological events, are able to cite few well authenticated cases, and they emphasize, rather, cycles that are near or under ten years in length. Elton (1942), following MacLuiich (1937) and his own unpublished data, has definitely abandoned the suggestion that the rabbit cycle of the Canadian forests corresponds to the eleven-year sunspot cycle. Even the oft-cited cycles in tree rings of the giant sequoias of California were reported by Huntington (1932) to supply "another type of evidence of this same cycle of about ten years." Douglass (1936) records cycles in tree rings of 5.7, 8.5, 10, 14, 17, 19 or 20, and 23 years and "certain

cycles close to 12 years in length." It is perhaps worth noting that the much-discussed eleven-year cycle is not listed in this latest summary. This point seems to trouble Douglass (1936, p. 132), who remarks that "the disturbing feature in all comparisons between solar and terrestrial cycles has been the presence of other cycles on the earth of very different lengths and only rarely one of 11 years." Because of his hypothesis of a cycle complex, he concludes, however, that "We feel justified in assuming the hypothesis that there is a physical relationship between our climatic conditions and the sun." Elton (1942) records his belief that we will eventually be led "back to very curious meteorological and perhaps astronomical processes as well as to new relations between climate, physiology, and disease."

5. RADIATION: A GENERAL INTRODUCTION

The effective environment is holocoenotic; it is a whole composed of many parts as a rope is made of many strands. For the next several chapters holocoenotic aspects will be mainly disregarded, and the approach will be frankly analytical; near the end of the discussion, however, an attempt will be made to bring the strands together again into a unit. For the moment we will focus on one factor or on one set of factors at a time.

RADIATION

Radiation that reaches the earth from the sun as heat and light has obvious importance for living things. All functional ecology is closely related, directly or indirectly, to the capture of radiant energy that originates in the sun. Radiations are transmitted in straight lines and are usually thought of as consisting of waves or pulsations which although of different lengths, travel at a velocity of about 3×10^{10} cm./sec. Some phases of the physics of radiation are most readily explained on the assumption that the radiating units are corpuscles rather than waves. This phase of the matter can be left to the physicists, since ecological aspects can be stated with approximate accuracy in terms of the wave theory.

The lengths of the waves, or pulsations, differ tremendously. They extend from the

long waves of radio, thousands of meters in length, to the x-rays, gamma rays, and cosmic rays only a small fraction of an angstrom unit long (an angstrom unit (Å) equals 1×10^{-8} cm.). Those of known ecological significance are (a) the infra-red rays that are important for the heat they carry and that range from about 0.1 mm. (100 μ) or somewhat longer to 7700 Å (1 μ = 10,000 Å) and are not visible to the human eye. Then (b) comes the narrow octave that we know as light; this extends from 7700 to 3900–4000 Å and transmits heat as well as light. The exact limits of visible light vary from person to person and from one species of animal to another. Beyond these are (c) the ultraviolet rays, which, like those of the infra-red region, are invisible to man. Solar radiation received at the earth's surface extends from about 135,000 to about 2860 Å and lies mainly within the wave lengths of 30,000 and 3000 Å. There is a sharp maximum at 4700 Å. The earth radiates as well as receives radiations. Coming from a cool body, these lie mainly between 40,000 and 500,000 Å (4–50 μ), with a maximum at 95,000 Å.

Water vapor absorbs solar radiation differentially, with the absorption mainly taking place in wave lengths of 8000 Å or longer, a region that lies well beyond the point of maximum intensity of incident radiation. The absorption on a clear humid day rarely amounts to more than 15 per cent of the incident energy. Thus 85 per cent of radiations from the sun that are not stopped by other causes pass the water barrier in such an atmosphere. In contrast, water vapor absorbs almost all the terrestrial radiation. If the atmosphere holds only the equivalent corresponding to 1 cm. precipitation, it absorbs 72 per cent of the

TOTAL RADIANT ENERGY

The mean value of the amount of radiation received from the sun at the upper level of the earth's atmosphere is 1.94 gm. calories per square centimeter per minute. This is called the solar constant. If this amount of heat could be absorbed and retained, it would warm a layer of cool water 1 cm. deep at the rate of 1.94° C. per minute. The atmosphere screens out inci-

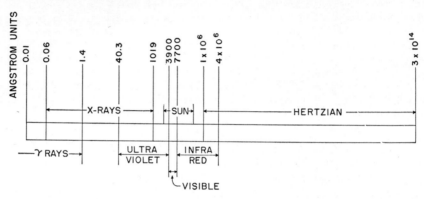

Fig. 6. The electromagnetic spectrum. (Redrawn with slight changes from Heyroth's revision of Ellis and Wells.)

earth's radiation. This phenomenon is called the "greenhouse effect" and acts so that solar radiation is transmitted and the earth's radiation is retained. The effect is still strong in a relatively dry atmosphere.

Scattering and reflection brought about by dust particles in the atmosphere produce an "inverse greenhouse effect." The sun's radiation is screened out by such particles, and the earth's radiation is not affected. The "greenhouse effect" results in a warmed earth, and the "antigreenhouse effect" produces a lowering of the surface temperature (Laurens, 1933). The portion of the sun's ultraviolet radiation that passes through the earth's atmosphere approximately coincides with the so-called near ultraviolet. The middle and extreme ultraviolet rays have many biological effects and great theoretical value, but so far as we now know they are not important in outdoor ecology. The parts of the whole radiation spectrum that are ecologically significant will be considered in the following chapters in the order of their decreasing wavelengths.

dent energy the more, the greater the distance of air mass that is traversed, the greater the amount of water vapor in the air, and the more dust (Brooks, 1926). The amount of energy that reaches the earth's surface is also affected by the distance of the earth from the sun and by variations in the energy radiated by the sun. Other conditions being equal, the solar radiation received in early January is about 7 per cent greater than that of early July, since the earth is nearer the sun in January (see p. 82).

The amount of water vapor in the atmosphere decreases, in general, with latitude and distance from the ocean, and increases with temperature. Radiation intensity is decreased on the order of 2 per cent by an increase of 1 mm. in water vapor pressure.

The intensity of solar radiation differs greatly at different points on the earth and, at the same point, at different hours of the day or night. At Washington, D. C., 127 meters above sea level, the amount of energy received at noon is on the order of 60 per cent of the mean solar constant.

The value falls to about 10 per cent of this constant when the sun stands just above the horizon (Kimball and Hand, 1936). Then the rays pass through 14.5 times the air mass that they have to traverse at noon. These radiations were measured at right angles to the rays of the sun. For many ecological purposes, the total amount of radiation, both direct and indirect, is more important. This is better approximated by using the vertical component of the total solar radiation that falls on a given point.

for a given interval of time can be calculated from the formula:

$$Q_s = Q_0[a + (1.00 - a)S]$$

in which S is the percentage of possible hours of sunshine; Q_o is the radiation received from a clear sky, and Q_s is the amount received from a more or less overcast sky; a is a so-called constant the value of which varies with the character of the clouds, with dust in the atmosphere,

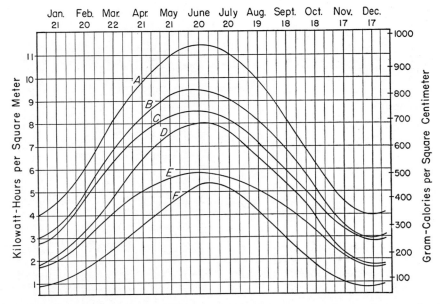

Fig. 7. Smoothed annual variation in the total radiation received on a horizontal surface.
A, Outside the atmosphere at the latitude of Washington.
Cloudless sky: B, Twin Falls, Idaho; C, Washington.
Average cloud conditions: D, Twin Falls; E, Washington; F, Chicago. (Redrawn with modifications from Kimball and Hand.)

The radiation received may consist of (a) direct sunlight, (b) diffuse sky radiation, skylight, and (c) radiation from trees or other objects of the environment.

The distribution of solar insolation is such that only two-fifths as much heat is received per unit surface at the poles as at the equator, and the polar ice and snow cap may reduce the effective insolation still more (Willett, 1931).

All solar radiation is much affected by the amount of cloudiness in the earth's atmosphere. In general, the proportion of direct sunlight varies inversely with the amount of skylight. The effect of cloudiness on the vertical component of incident light

and also perhaps with surface conditions. A commonly accepted value for a in the eastern United States is 0.22, and the basic equation becomes:

$$Q_s = Q_0(0.22 + 0.78S)$$

The maximum amount of sunlight received at the latitude of Washington is 1.5 gm. cal./min./cm.²; this is equivalent to an intensity of about 10,000 foot candles. On Mt. Whitney, at an altitude of 4420 meters, the amount may reach 1.67 gm. cal./min./cm.², or approximately 11,000 foot candles. The distribution of total radiation from the sun at the earth's surface is as follows: The radiation in the remote infra-red supplies an insignificant amount of energy. On some days the infra-red energy between about 20,000 to 30,000 Å and 7700 Å, the beginning of visibility, may be greater than that carried by visible light. In general, 50 to 58 per cent of radiant energy lies in the visible range, and 1 to 5 per cent lies in the ultraviolet region, with less than 0.1 per cent

tive solar energy is such that the entire field of the ultraviolet gives only a small fraction of the caloric energy to reach the earth, while the nonvisible, infra-red rays carry about one-half of the heat received. Data from the latitude of Cleveland, Ohio, are summarized in Figure 8. The maximum intensity of the sun's energy as it reaches the earth lies at 4700 to 5000 Å. with the sun

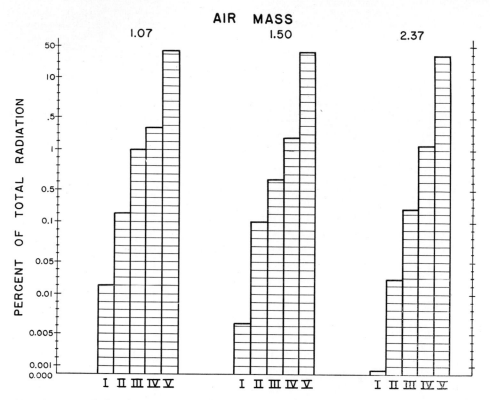

Fig. 8. Spectral distribution in percentage of total solar radiation at the latitude of Cleveland, Ohio. I, Below 3100 Å; II, below 3250 Å; III, below 3500 Å; IV, below 4000 Å; V, 4000 to 7000 Å. (Drawn from data reported by Forsythe and Christison.)

in wave lengths shorter than 3130 Å (Bracket, 1936; Kimball, 1924; Ellis and Wells, 1941).

Figure 7 gives the annual variations and total radiation received on a horizontal surface with a clear sky or with average cloud conditions for three widely separated stations in the United States. The record for Washington, D. C., which is also given, shows weekly variations as great as 50 per cent of the normal values and from 30 to 40 per cent of the mean solar constant.

Spectral distribution of ecologically effec-

near the zenith. The region of the greatest intensity is displaced toward the longer wavelengths with decreasing altitude of the sun and is located at about 7000 Å at 80° incidence when the rays are passing through nearly six air masses; the shortwave limit is similarly shifted toward the red under these conditions (Forsythe and Christison, 1930; Bundesen, Lemon, et al., 1927).

Approximations are sometimes more revealing than exact statements. Roughly one-third of the radiation reaching the earth's atmosphere is thrown off into outer space again without making any change either on the earth or in its atmosphere. Roughly another third is absorbed by the atmosphere, and the final third is absorbed by the earth itself. These are average figures for the earth as a unit when all seasons are considered.

On a clear day, when the sun stands overhead at the zenith, approximately 92 per cent of the radiation at sea level comes from the sun directly; the other 8 per cent comes from the sky. The relative differences decrease until they are equal, though both are much less, when the sun is some 8 degrees above the horizon. The intensity of direct radiation from the sun increases with an increase of height above sea level; conversely, the intensity of sky radiation decreases with altitude. When the sun is overhead in an overcast sky, if the cloud layer is uniform, the brightness is surprisingly uniform; brightness decreases about 10 per cent 45 degrees from the zenith and about half of that at a point almost at the horizon (Humphreys, 1942).

ECOLOGICAL RADIATION UNIT

Under many conditions, the amount of radiation received in a given biotic community, or a fraction thereof, can be summarized by the ecological radiation unit that may be stated in terms of energy or of light intensity (O. Park, 1931). This unit represents a summation of (1) the intensity (a) under the open sky, (b) under different degrees of shade, and (c) in sunflecks under a canopy of vegetation; (2) the area in the community which receives radiation of each of the recognized intensities. In a representative case, the ecological radiation unit of the forest floor can be calculated as follows:

Let $A =$ unit area
$P =$ portion of unobstructed radiation
$Sh_1 =$ shaded portion of density 1
$Sh_2 =$ shaded portion of density 2
$S =$ portion covered by sunflecks
$Q =$ intensity of unobstructed radiation
$Q_1 =$ mean intensity in sunflecks
$q_1 =$ mean intensity in Sh_1
$q_2 =$ mean intensity in Sh_2

When $P + S + Sh_1 + Sh_2 = A$, the following simple formulation can be stated:

$$\frac{PQ + SQ_1 + Sh_1q_1 + Sh_2q_2}{AQ} = \text{Ecological radiation unit.}$$

The ecological radiation unit may summarize all radiation, or it may be broken into different fractions, as, for example, the originally proposed ecological light unit (O. Park, 1931; Strohecker, 1938). The latter has distinctly different values in the several stages of the dune-forest succession.

6. HEAT

EFFECTS OF HEAT ON THE PHYSICAL ENVIRONMENT

Heat is a form of energy, of which two important ecological factors may be recognized. There is (1) the intensity factor, temperature, and (2) a capacity factor, heat capacity. Temperature is measured in degrees on some temperature scale; in this book the centigrade scale will be used unless otherwise stated. The capacity for heat is defined as the quantity of heat taken to raise the temperature of the given substance through $1°$ C. The standard unit, the calorie, is the quantity of heat required to raise 1 gm. of water from $15°$ to $16°$ C.; this is a gram-calorie and represents a relatively small amount of energy. When large quantities are involved, the kilogram-calorie is often used as the basic unit, especially in human nutrition; this is 1000 times larger than the gram-calorie.

Ecologists, and biologists in general, frequently use the words "heat" and "temperature" as though they were synonyms; often they are. A familiar phenomenon will illustrate one basic difference. Much heat energy must be spent to melt ice, yet, until it is melted, the temperature remains constant. It requires 3500 gram-calories per square centimeter of surface to change the ice on Lake Mendota at Madison, Wisconsin, to water; an amount equal to the heat from some 195,000 tons of anthracite coal is necessary to melt the ice on the whole lake, yet the temperature of the water is unchanged by the process. This high latent heat of fusion of water is one of the properties that make it a remarkably fit substance for life and, therefore, a major environmental factor (see p. 76).

The amount of heat present affects both living organisms and their environment. While much of the space available for this discussion will be devoted to the more direct effects of temperature on plants and animals, it is useful to remember that the heat relations of the environment are also important ecologically. For example, surface layers of suddenly warmed rocks flake off from the cooler inner layers; the flaking is often produced by the heat expanding trapped water into steam. Winter cold also disintegrates solid structures, primarily as a result of the force exerted by expanding ice. These matters are commonly treated in physiography. Other aspects of the effect of heat on the physical environment can be effectively summarized and possibilities can be suggested by considering the temperature relations of lakes. A lake affords a rather neat environmental unit, many phases of which, temperature included, have been studied intensively. Good summaries of the literature should be consulted for interesting general features and for details.*

THE HEAT BUDGET

Outside the tropics, the water of a lake accumulates heat during one portion of the year and gives it off at another. Although the processes involved are complex, they can be summarized in terms of the annual energy budget of the lake. This may be considered as being composed of the energy received from the sun and sky each year and is substantially balanced by the outgo of energy from the lake water. In simplest terms, the annual heat budget of the lake is based upon the amount of energy in gram-calories required to raise the temperature of the water, including the energy used in melting the ice, from the winter minimum to summer maximum.

Different lakes vary greatly in heat budgets. The general principles involved can be

*Birge and Juday, 1911, 1912; Birge, 1915, 1916; Needham, Juday, Moore, Sibley, and Titcomb, 1922; Welch, 1935; Hesse, Allee, and Schmidt, 1937, and Juday, 1940.

illustrated from the data concerning the well-studied Lake Mendota. This lake has an area of about 40 square kilometers, a maximum depth of 25 meters, and a mean depth approximately half of that. The minimum balance occurs late in December, when the lake freezes over, near enough to the end of the year so that, for practical purposes, the fiscal year for Lake Mendota corresponds with the calendar year. The mean energy receipts from sun and sky radiation from April, 1911, to March, 1939, inclusive, are shown in Figure 9. The average total of annual receipts is 118,872 gram-calories per square centimeter of surface, expended as indicated in Table 5.

Table 5. Estimates of Energy Expenditure of Lake Mendota (see Juday, 1940)

	Gram-calories per Square Centimeter of Surface
For raising temperature under ice	1800
For melting ice in spring	3500
For raising water to summer temperature	22,400
For raising temperature of bottom, net	1500
For evaporation	29,500
For energy used by organisms, maximum	1000
For surface loss*	28,500
For loss by conduction, convection and radiation	30,000
Total	118,500

* Types of surface losses include reflection, upward scattering by particles in suspension, and absorption by snow and ice.

The bottom of the lake has a heat budget of its own. At four different stations where the depth of the water ranged from 8.0 to 23.5 meters, the budget ranged from about 3000 gram-calories at the shallower station to about 1100 for the deeper. The mean for the lake is near 2000 gram-calories per square centimeter of surface, of which some 500 are used in heating the water under the ice in winter.

In general, lakes in eastern North America that do not present unusual features and that lie between 40 and 60 degrees north latitude have similar heat budgets. When lakes are about 10 kilometers long, 2 kilometers wide, and have a mean depth of 30 meters and a maximum of 50 meters or more, the annual heat budget of the *water*, rather than of the lake as a whole, is between 30,000 and 40,000 gram-calories per square centimeter of surface.

Different types of soils also have characteristic heat budgets, and supposedly rivers do, too, although knowledge concerning the heat budgets of rivers is remarkably scanty.

THERMAL STRATIFICATION

One important relationship between fresh water and temperature is outstanding. As

Deeper lakes, if covered with winter ice for some weeks and not exposed to unusually strong or direct wind action, show an annual cycle that is closely associated with the four seasons of the year. The sequence is: (1) Under the ice in winter, the lake is stratified inversely with the colder, lighter water at the surface floating on the denser water, which has a uniform temperature of about 4° C. (2) There is an overturning and a circulation of water throughout the entire lake in the spring that results from the surface water becoming warmed to 4° C. when it has the same density as

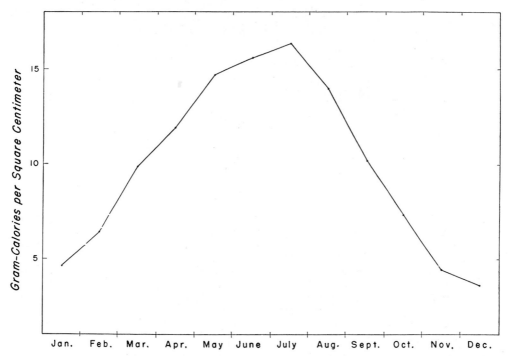

Fig. 9. Mean annual energy receipt at Lake Mendota. Ordinates are in thousands. (Data from Juday.)

the temperature approaches 4° C. from either direction, the density, but not the viscosity, of the water increases. With further cooling or warming, the density falls. This point of maximum density of fresh water at 4° C. has an importance in the temperature relations of a lake that is somewhat comparable, when broad implications are considered, with the fact that the freezing point of such water lies where it does on the absolute temperature scale.

the deeper water. It is then easy for the spring winds to produce the spring overturn. (3) With rising temperature, the surface water is soon warmed above the point of maximum density and floats upon the colder, denser water below (Fig. 10). The spring warming takes place mainly in the water near the upper surface, since from two-thirds to nine-tenths of the incident radiation is cut off, either by surface reflection or by absorption by the first meter of water. As the summer temperature continues to rise, since water is a poor conductor of heat, a direct stratification is established in which the warm upper layer of water, the epilimnion, now considerably expanded, passes by a narrow transition stratum, the thermocline, to the cold lower

the drop in temperature is at least 1° C. per meter of depth. Above and below, the rate of decrease is less. Within the thermocline it may be much greater. The depth of water down to the thermocline and the depth of this zone of rapid change may vary in the same lake at a given time, both in thick-

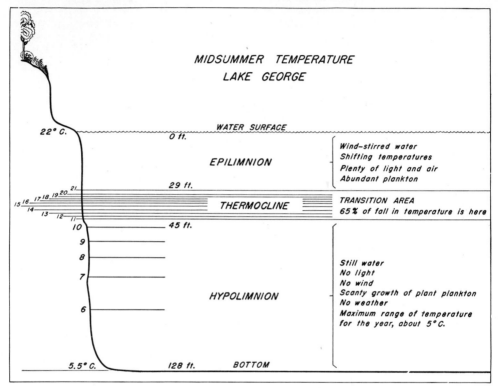

Fig. 10. Summer stratification in Lake George, New York. (Redrawn from Needham, Juday, Moore, et al.)

water, the hypolimnion. The temperature of the epilimnion lags somewhat behind the seasonal march of the temperature of the air. Its waters are kept in a fairly homogeneous condition by wind action. Their oxygen content is high. The water of the hypolimnion is seldom disturbed by summer winds, and it, too, becomes fairly homogeneous, but with lower oxygen content, frequently very low indeed.

As becomes a transition zone, the thermocline is not sharply marked off from the region above and below, though the transition is usually more abrupt from the epilimnion than from the hypolimnion (Fig. 11). Birge's arbitrary rule for the location of the thermocline limits it to the region in which

ness and in depth with seasonal changes. A thermocline to physical oceanographers means the layer of water in which the temperature shows maximum change with depth. They carry this practice over to studies in lakes. Thus, Church (1942, p. 14) speaks of a thermocline in Lake Michigan in which the mean temperature change was 2.5° C. in 20 meters. This double usage is unfortunate.

To return to the outline of the seasonal cycle in lakes: The fourth stage comes with autumnal cooling, followed by a complete circulation of the water until shortly before the lake becomes covered with ice. The vernal and autumnal overturns not only equalize the temperature relations throughout the lake, but also serve to distribute oxygen and other dissolved materials uniformly from top to bottom in decided contrast to the conditions found during winter and especially during summer stratification.

The usual geographic classification of lakes of the world is based on these relationships. It was originally suggested by Forel

Order 3. Temperature of bottom water similar to that of surface water; circulation tends to be continuous except when surface is frozen

II. Temperate lakes: surface temperatures vary above and below 4° C.
   Order 1. Temperature of bottom water at 4° C. throughout the year;

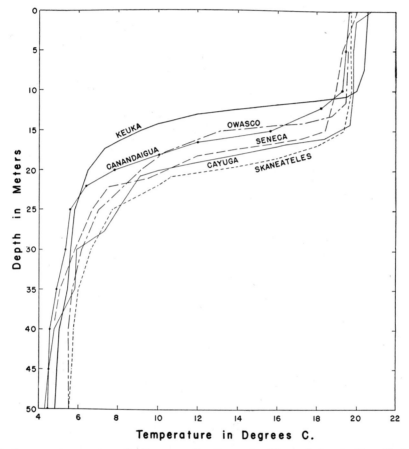

Fig. 11. Summer temperature-depth curves for the major Finger Lakes in New York, shown to the depth of 50 meters. (Redrawn from Birge and Juday.)

(1901), and, after being modified by Whipple (1927) and Welch (1935), is as follows:

I. Polar lakes: surface temperatures never above 4° C.
   Order 1. Bottom water 4° C. throughout the year; one circulation period possible in summer, generally none
   Order 2. Temperature of bottom water varies, but not far from 4° C.; one circulation period in summer

two circulation periods possible (one in spring and one in autumn), but generally none
   Order 2. Temperature of bottom water varies, but not too far from 4° C.; two circulation periods (one in spring and one in autumn)
   Order 3. Temperature of bottom water similar to that of surface water; circulation more or less continuous except when surface is frozen

III. Tropical lakes: surface temperature always above 4° C.

    Order 1. Temperature of bottom water near 4° C. throughout the year; one circulation period possible in winter, but generally none

    Order 2. Temperature of bottom water varies, but not far from 4° C.; one circulation period in winter

    Order 3. Temperature of bottom water similar to that of surface water; circulation at all seasons

From this classification, which sums up in a general way a great deal of limnological research, it is clear that temperate lakes, especially of the second order, are regularly stratified with respect to temperature. Third order lakes generally are too shallow to allow such stratification. In tropical lakes, where the temperature never falls to 4° C., if other conditions are favorable, there is always a direct thermal stratification. Polar lakes, where the temperature is always below 4° C., show an inverse stratification.

These essentials of thermal stratification must be kept in mind when considering the stratification of lake communities (p. 443), and in many phases of the physical environment as well, notably as regards dissolved chemicals (p. 202) and dissolved atmospheric gases (p. 193). Despite earlier suggestions by others (p. 41), we owe much of the background to Birge, whose ecological studies have extended over some fifty years. He introduced the term "thermocline" in 1897 and the terms "epilimnion" and "hypolimnion" in 1910; the amounts of heat acquired and lost by a lake over a year's time were organized and presented by him (1916) as the heat budget. The study of heat budgets should be of great use in the comparison of thermal stratification in different lakes, but has been little used (Rawson, 1939).

Seasonal variation in the progress of thermal stratification has been considered for numerous lakes sufficiently to establish its generality for second-order temperate lakes over the world. A paired example must suffice: Lake Waskesiu, Saskatchewan, and Lake Mendota, Wisconsin, among others, were compared seasonally. In the order listed, vernal overturn began in middle May, as opposed to middle April; summer stagnation with thermocline formation

began the first week of June in the northern lake, as against the end of May for the more southern one; winter stagnation with ice cover and reversed gradient became established in middle November in Lake Waskesiu and in middle December at Lake Mendota (Rawson, 1939). These general thermal cycles vary as much as one or two months for the same lake in different years. The lake cycle also varies with bottom characteristics, altitude, and latitude, but the process itself is universal for suitable lakes and plays a major role in community development both directly and indirectly.

The rate of change of water temperature may prove important in the organization of the lake community. This has been studied in Linsley Pond and Lake Quassapaug, Connecticut, and derived for Lake Mendota, Wisconsin, from Birge's table of mean temperatures, by Hutchinson (1941). Such data indicate that the hypolimnion can be divided into an upper clinolimnion, in which the rate of heating falls exponentially with increasing depth, and a lower bathylimnion, in which the rate of heating approaches a constant value independent of depth.

Not only is there a vertical gradient in thermal stratification, but there is a horizontal gradient as well, at least in large lakes such as Lake Michigan (Church, 1942). Many factors are involved in establishing such gradients; for example, radiation, evaporation, conduction, mixing, chilling by snow, hail or sleet, and condensation. Sea water, unlike fresh water, continues to become denser with cold until it freezes at about −1.9° C., when the salt content is 35 °/$_{oo}$. As the surface water evaporates, it becomes more salty and therefore more dense. Even though warmer than underlying water, it sinks until its density matches that of the colder, deeper water. At such a depth there is a zone of rapid temperature change that may approach the abruptness of Birge's thermocline; this is usually found at depths between 50 and 150 meters. Since ocean water does not show a change in density at 4° C., but continues to increase in density until the freezing point is reached, the abyssal waters of the oceans are cooler than those of lakes and range from about −1° C., in regions of cold currents to slightly above zero elsewhere.

Thermal stratification also occurs on land with depth in the soil, and it is particularly important in deserts and other hot, dry lands, where the animals by burrowing can escape midday heat and the great fluctuations that characterize desert conditions (p. 219). Temperature stratification is found also in the air, especially in regions covered by relatively dense vegetation; such stratification is well developed in forests. There the daytime temperature gradient is largely a result of differential insolation and tends to disappear on heavily overcast days, especially if there is little air movement.

Vertical gradients of other environmental factors also exist under the forest canopy as well as in lake or soil. For the forest, the more notable ones include differential distribution of intensity of sunlight, of wind velocity and of evaporating power of the air. These matters are considered in some detail in dealing with biotic factors of the environment (p. 228) and especially in stratification in communities, as discussed in Chapter 28.

EFFECTS OF HEAT ON ORGANISMS

The relation of animals to temperature supplies another basic ecological division, that between the animals whose body temperature approximates the temperature of their environment, the poikilothermous animals, as contrasted with the so-called warm-blooded or homoiothermous birds and mammals. The body temperature of the homoiotherms may be independent of that of the environment within rather wide limits. Of the million or so known species of animals, all but about 20,000 are poikilothermal. Homoiothermal mechanisms are not required or fully acquired before hatching or birth. The ability to maintain a given temperature normally improves to a steady state with early development. In seasonally variable climates, many species of birds and mammals hatch or are born near a time of optimal temperature, but there are so many exceptions that it is questionable whether this involves a definite adaptation or is merely a tendency. The degree of approximation between the body temperature of cold-blooded animals and their immediate environment may be close; the earthworm *Lumbricus agricola*, for example, when immersed in water, becomes adjusted to a change of 10 degrees within two minutes with an accuracy of 0.05 degrees (Rogers and Lewis, 1914, 1916).

Small aquatic animals, especially if their muscular activity is low, have a body temperature that closely approximates that of the surrounding water. Active fishes, however, may show temperatures some 10 degrees above their environment, and with passivity the temperature of the surrounding water is approached slowly. Under many conditions the body temperature of fishes is about that of the surrounding water (Clausen, 1934).

Terrestrial poikilotherms, especially insects and other similarly active forms, may have their body temperatures raised above that of the surrounding air as a result either of their own activity or of insolation. Within a period of ten minutes, the air temperature remaining constant at 28° C., the internal temperature rose from 27.9° in the shade to 42.7° C. when a third instar grasshopper nymph (*Locusta migratoria*) was directly exposed to sunrays that had an intensity of 1.07 gram-calories (Strel'nikov, 1936). As might be expected, the body temperature of black-brown locusts exposed to the sun is higher than that of green ones. The amount of air movement in the micro-habitat is an important agent in lowering the temperature of insects and other animals. This becomes more effective when combined with the evaporation of water from the exposed body surface. Thus, land amphibians usually maintain a body temperature below that of the surrounding air as a result of constant water loss.

Aggregations of insects may have temperatures within the aggregations decidedly higher than the surrounding air even when there is little integration between the members of the aggregation. Social insects, notably the honeybees in their winter clusters, are much more independent of environmental temperature. As a result of the heat produced by muscles in vibrating the wings and as a further result of the insulation furnished by the covering shell of bees, such a cluster may maintain a temperature decidedly higher than that outside the cluster. At high temperatures honeybees are able to lower their temperature slightly, probably by increased evaporation. Such social insects show partial control over their immediate microclimate and have become facultative homoiotherms as a result of social activities (Pirsch, 1923; Phillips and Demuth, 1914).

The distinction between cold-blooded

and warm-blooded animals tends to break down, also, when approached from the homoiothermal side of the division line. Monotremes afford an example of forms essentially transitional between poikilothermy and homoiothermy. The body temperature of *Echidna* varies from 26.5° to 34° C. without correlation with air temperature (Semon, 1894). Nestling birds may start as poikilothermous animals and, later in ontogeny, develop the ability to regulate their temperature. Hibernating mammals become essentially poikilothermic during hiberna-

tures near maximum toleration; the safety factor is much greater at the lower than at the upper end of the tolerated temperature range. This relationship is illustrated in a generalized fashion in Figure 12; it holds for the majority of aquatic as well as for terrestrial forms.

As with several other environmental factors, the temperature extremes that an animal can tolerate depend on a complex series of relationships. Some of these are: (1) the species or other taxonomic subdivision; (2) the external temperature at which the spe-

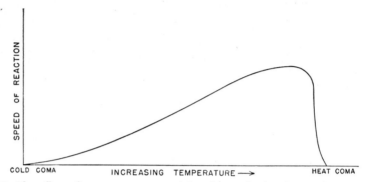

Fig. 12. The effect of temperature on activity of animals. (Redrawn after Verworn.)

tion. The temperature of the extremities of homoiothermal animals fluctuates somewhat with the environment (see p. 120), and the body temperatures of small birds and mammals are independent of the environmental temperature within a narrow range only (Kendeigh and Baldwin, 1928; Rasmussen, 1916; Chevillard, 1935; Gerstell, 1939). Thus, adult passerine birds have a normal body temperature between 38.9° and 44.6° C. The environmental temperature can carry body temperatures of these birds down to about 23.9° and up almost to 46.7° C. for short periods without being necessarily fatal for the birds. The lower margin of safety is rather large, some 15 degrees; this is not the extreme limit of tolerance, for the tiny house wren (*Troglodytes aedai parkmani*) has survived after its body temperature was lowered to 16.7° C. for a short time. The upper margin of safety between the highest normal and the lethal body temperature is much less; it is only 2.1 degrees for adult passerines. This condition seems to be general (Kendeigh, 1934). Most animals, cold-blooded as well as warm-blooded, operate most efficiently in many ways at tempera-

cies normally lives and that in which the given individuals have lived recently; (3) the length of exposure; (4) the internal body temperature; (5) the rate of change of internal temperature as extremes are approached; (6) for low temperatures, the presence or absence of internal ice; (7) the general condition of the individuals as regards items like water content and thermal insulation (cf. Luyet and Gehenio, 1938).

Roughly stated, most poikilothermous organisms are active at temperatures between 6' and 35° C. Numerous exceptions are known, and even the more generous limits from about −37° to +64° C.,* such as have been found on the surface of the Lake Michigan dunes, do not reach the extremes of endurance of active animals. Entire life histories are passed both above and below the usual temperature limits.

* Higher surface temperatures are known. Geiger (1927) cites 71.5° at Tucson, Arizona, and 69° C. at Agra, India. Johnson and Davies (1927) estimate that it is unlikely that the surface temperature of the soil will ever exceed 200° F. (93.3° C.), and the highest soil temperature that may be expected is about 180° F. (82.2° C.).

COLD HARDINESS

We shall first consider relations of organisms to lower temperatures. A cave silphid beetle (*Astagobius angustatus*) is known to carry on its life cycle in ice grottoes where the temperature range is between $-1.7°$ and $+1.0°$ C., and the marine bivalve mollusk, *Yoldia arctica,* is confined to ocean water with a temperature of $0.0°$ C. or lower (see p. 82).

Organisms from the north temperate region can be divided into three main groups on the basis of their resistance to low temperatures. These are:

1. Those that can survive exposure to temperatures that approach absolute zero $(-273°$ C.).

2. Those that are killed at or near their freezing point, usually relatively near the freezing point of water.

3. Those that die when chilled to some point above freezing.

The first assemblage includes plants and animals that, at some stage in their life history, can withstand desiccation and, when dried, become tolerant of extremely low temperatures. This group includes, among others, plant spores and seeds, protozoan cysts, rotifers, tardigrades, and nematodes. The last three, if refrigerated slowly without preliminary desiccation, can survive a temperature of $-253°$ C. (Rahm, 1922); certain bacteria, yeasts, and other fungi can live similarly in extremely low temperatures.

The majority of plants and poikilothermous animals of our latitudes belong to the second group and are killed at temperatures somewhat below, but still relatively near, zero Centigrade. Two general subdivisions of these cold-tolerant forms are known: First, those that can live until their body temperatures fall some 10 to 30 degrees below zero, often they can survive the formation of much ice within their bodies. They can recover after being frozen hard and brittle with the cold, and apparently die from cold only when the last of their cellular liquids solidify. Cold-hardy insect larvae and many woody plants react in this way. This more or less artificial ecological class passes, by continuous gradation, into the second category, which includes a larger assemblage of forms that are killed at or near the freezing point of water.

The third group, killed at some point above freezing, is illustrated by some of the higher plants, by most mammals (except certain hibernating ones) (see p. 105), and by certain poikilothermal animals. Some cladocerans—*Moina macrocopa,* for example—become chilled and cease swimming movements after continued exposure to $10°$ C.; they settle to the bottom and die, since the gill chambers become clogged with mud and debris (Brown, 1929). Long-continued exposure to low temperatures well above freezing may cause death even when the animals can withstand shorter exposure to cold of the same intensity (Leeson, 1941). From the little that is known about cold death of poikilothermous tropical animals, it appears that they are probably killed by only relatively low temperatures; fish near subtropical Bermuda were killed in numbers by winter temperatures when the air did not go below $7°$ C. (Verrill, 1901), and breeders of tropical fishes know that death occurs from cold at temperatures at which more northern fishes thrive. In freezing weather along the Florida coast there is differential killing of the tropical element of the fish fauna.

It is probably not an overstatement to summarize our knowledge of cold death by saying (cf. Luyet and Gehenio, 1938, p. 88) that, with the exception of a few organisms that are killed at temperatures above zero, plants and animals of the temperate latitudes either die when chilled relatively near to their respective freezing points or are not killed by any low temperature to which they may be subjected in nature.

Winter's cold may be escaped by migration or hibernation, or it may be resisted by the development of protective coverings of fat, fur, or feathers, by the seasonal elimination of activities that consume much energy, such as those concerned with reproduction, or by the development of individual or racial cold hardiness. Frequently there are effective combinations of these methods for successful overwintering.

The problems differ for warm-blooded and for cold-blooded animals. Unlike birds, even highly motile terrestrial insects seldom execute geographic migrations. Butterflies do so more than most insects, and even with them, periodic seasonal migrations on a geographic scale are rare. The massed autumnal migrations of the monarch butterfly (*Danaus plexippus*) to the south, and their less conspicuous northward migrations in the spring, are noteworthy, since only in this species are the same individual butterflies known to make the return journey (Williams, 1930, p. 323; 1938; Beall, 1941). Usually, as winter approaches, insects of the tree tops or other exposed places migrate, a short distance to less exposed niches where they escape full exposure to the cold.

The phenomenon of supercooling apparently plays an important role in the cold-hardiness of insects. The body temperature of the adult or juvenile insect, or of eggs, falls, with that of the environment to a critical point at which the temperature rebounds to a brief equilibrium between the heat of fusion and the radiation of heat into the immediate environment, and remains there until the heat released by freezing

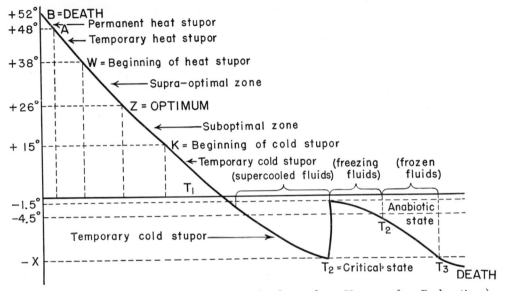

Fig. 13. Temperature relations of an insect. (Redrawn from Uvarov, after Bachmetjew.)

The overwintering of insects has been much studied both by ecologists and by physiologists. Here, as elsewhere, it is hard to separate the work and interests of these two groups. Usually, insects from exposed positions, such as those of tree tops, migrate a short distance to protected micro-habitats and so escape from the full impact of winter conditions. A number of adaptive processes take place as temperature falls: (1) The activity of the insects decreases; (2) production of metabolic water lessens; (3) the percentage of salts and colloids in body liquids increases; (4) other colloidal relations with water may change. From the integration of insect behavior with biophysical and biochemical processes, most insects pass the winter without being frozen, even though they are living in a continental climate in the middle latitudes.

The temperature relations of insects in such climates are summarized in Figure 13.

becomes dissipated; then the temperature drifts downward again to stable equilibrium with the environment. The freezing temperature in insect bodies is not closely related either to the limit of liquid undercooling or to what is sometimes called the rebound temperature. In insects, supercooling before ice formation starts within the body and carries down from a few degrees below zero to $-40°$ or $-50°$ C. (Salt and Mail, 1943).

It is difficult even to approximate the true freezing temperature of an insect. The rebound point is often taken as the freezing point, a concept now known to be erroneous, since the two may differ by as much as 25 degrees. Water in bulk undercools several degrees; it undercools still more in an emulsion, and when subdivided, as a fog, it has been undercooled to $-155°$ C., in the laboratory. Natural fogs occur with temperatures of $-25°$ C. to

−50° C. (Salt and Mail, 1943). Some determinations made in the light of these considerations by puncturing the insects with a thermocouple are given in Table 6.

For the great group of insects of the temperate regions that do not survive undercooling and subsequent freezing, the largest class of insects in temperate North America, the undercooling temperatures appear to be more important than the freezing temperatures. The other two classes of in-

artificial dehydration, and others are not so affected. *Lepticoris* may lose a fifth of its weight by artificial drying without showing any change in the critical supercooling temperature. The converse is also true: an increase in water content by natural means may, or may not, alter the ability to undergo supercooling.

Animals exposed annually to seasonal decreases in temperature typically show seasonal variation in the location of their

Table 6. *Mean Undercooling and Corrected Freezing Temperatures Based on Ten Insects of Each Species (Data from Ditman, Voght, and Smith, 1943)*

Hibernating	Undercooling Mean	Freezing
Carpocapsa pomonella larvae	8.9	1.8
Pyrausta nubilalis larvae	10.4	3.1
Diatraea crambidoides larvae	6.4	1.3
Heliothis armigera pupae	4.2	0.9
Active		
Anasa tristis female adults	7.5	1.1
Anasa tristis male adults	8.9	1.3
Pyrausta nubilalis larvae	6.8	1.3

sects with relation to cold hardiness are: (1) those that are extremely cold hardy and survive undercooling and freezing and are killed only by long exposure to low temperatures or by one or more sudden changes in temperature; and (2) the noncold-hardy nonhibernating insects that succumb to low temperatures even without freezing.

The development of ice crystals within the body is much more harmful than is a lower temperature when ice formation is avoided as a result of supercooling. An increase in the degree to which supercooling occurs in connection with cold hardiness is usually associated with dehydration, but the whole set of relations is far from simple. For example, full-grown larvae that are still feeding, prepupae, and pupae of the moth *Ephestia* all have nearly the same percentage of water, yet they show critical supercooling points of −5.8°, −8.0°, and −21.3° C., respectively. Some animals may have their critical temperature lowered by

critical supercooling temperature. Beetle larvae that bore in oak wood, for example, showed a supercooling point of −22° and a reported freezing point of −12.8° C. in February. In July, similar larvae supercooled only to −2° and froze at −0.8° C. Insects from stored grains that are not ordinarily exposed to temperature extremes do not exhibit this seasonal periodicity, although they show much variation in cold hardiness.

The physiological explanations of these complex phenomena are obscure. Although supercooling presents certain resemblances to the physical supercooling of distilled water, the phenomena associated with cold hardiness are much more complicated. Wigglesworth (1939, p. 366) sums up the physiological situation thus:

" . . . Ice crystals forming in solutions rich in hydrophyllic colloids are liable to become covered with a sheath of dehydrated colloid and thus fail to 'seed' the entire solution; the quantity of such colloids may be a factor in super-cooling. It has been suggested that the water which remains unfrozen at −20° is 'bound' to the tissue proteins; but there is at present no way of distinguishing 'bound' water from water which is supercooled from some other cause."

Not all insects undergo a decrease in percentage of body water in winter. The mound-building ant, *Formica exsectoides,* of which many individuals retire to points near the water line of the soil before hibernating, has practically the same percentage of body water at all times during the year. In fact, hibernation is often associated with a retreat into a more protected situation. The more protected micro-habitats do not reach the freezing points of supercooled

for long periods are least likely to be immobilized by chilling to zero degree Centigrade. Even acclimatization to higher temperatures of stages in the life history that are normally exposed to low temperatures for long periods may not raise the temperature at which chill coma sets in. Later stages of the same insects, stages that ordinarily live at higher temperatures, are more easily affected by cold and have the temperature at which they pass into coma raised by exposure to warmth (Mellanby, 1940). Many poikilothermal animals of the higher latitudes are able to withstand being frozen. Normally, both freezing and thawing take place slowly, and this seems to be important so far as thawing is concerned. There is laboratory evidence that quick

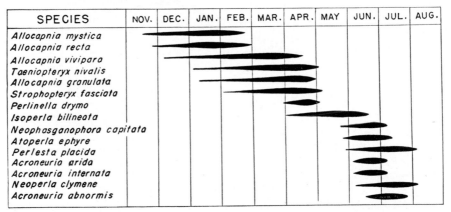

Fig. 14. Seasonal succession in stone flies of Illinois. The width of the spindle suggests abundance. (Redrawn from Frison.)

body liquids, and the most protected niches of soil and forest do not normally reach the freezing point of water even in climates such as those of northern Illinois (Bachmetjew, 1907; Payne, 1926; Holmquist, 1926, 1931; Dreyer, 1938).

The development of cold hardiness in insects has a species as well as an individual basis. This is illustrated by the seasonal succession of stone flies. About one-third of the species of the order Plecoptera in Illinois emerge as adults, mate, feed, and carry on all essential activities during the coldest months of the year (Frison, 1929, 1935). Certain of these seasonal relations are shown in Figure 14. The racial character of cold hardiness is further illustrated by the fact that those stages of arctic insects that are normally exposed to low temperatures

freezing at low temperatures is less harmful than is the slower process; but such freezing is presumably rare in nature (Uvarov, 1931; Parker, 1930; Zeuthen, 1939).

Animals frequently develop structures that aid in overwintering. The gemmules of sponges give an illustration. Fresh-water sponges usually form large numbers of resistant gemmules in the autumn and then disintegrate. The gemmules can withstand freezing and drying and begin growth anew under favorable conditions. In nature, they normally start to develop in the spring when temperatures rise. Freezing and drying are not always necessary; gemmules of *Spongilla* have hatched out after two week's exposure to a temperature of 22° C. in the autumn. The accelerating effect of exposure

to cold, perhaps combined with maturation phenomena, is shown by the fact that similar gemmules hatched after three days in similarly favorable temperatures in the spring. After extended hibernation, development of this sponge takes place at temperatures as low as 2° to 5° C.

The accelerating effect of exposure to low temperatures, freezing included, is also shown, among others, by grasshopper eggs in the middle latitudes. These develop more rapidly if placed at low, even freezing, temperature and later transferred to a higher one, and the process appears to be related, superficially at least, to the so-called vernalization of plants. Seeds of winter cereals can be "vernalized" by adding water until the seeds barely sprout and then chilling them to 3° or 5° C. or even freezing for an average length of thirty-five to forty-five days or over winter. When planted in the spring, such seeds develop as though they belonged to spring varieties (Miller, 1938). From naturalistic evidence, Darling (1937, 1938) has suggested that cold, as such, may act on the gonads of birds and mammals as a stimulating agent alternative to the well-authenticated stimulation produced by light (p. 121), and that low temperatures may be responsible for the marked development of the gonads of hibernating mammals before they emerge from hibernation. C. R. Moore and his co-workers (1934) had already tested this point with the ground squirrel, *Citellus*. The reproductive system of this rodent undergoes a marked regression after the annual spring breeding season. Experiments with diet, darkness, constant warm or cool temperatures, brief transfer from hibernation to warm surroundings, and similar manipulations have yielded essentially negative results so far as the induction of development of the male reproductive system is concerned during seasons when such development is unusual in the ground squirrel. In the female, however, with constant cold and darkness, periods of oestrum have been induced and maintained for many months at times in the year when the animals are ordinarily sexually inactive.

In medial latitudes, cold-hardy animals that emerge in early spring frequently have northern affinities or a northern origin, while forms that appear in late summer tend to have a southern origin or southern affinities.

HEAT HARDINESS

Hot springs furnish the warmest environments known to be inhabited by active organisms. The blue-green algae *Phormidium bijahense* and *Oscillaria filiformis* apparently hold the record for multicellular plants. They live in the thermal waters of Yellowstone National Park at a temperature of 85.2° C. Living bacteria have been found in even hotter water at 88° C. (Copeland, 1936).

Brues (1939) discounts, pending more evidence, certain reports that larvae of brine flies (Ephydridae) live at temperatures of 55° and even at 65° C. and that rhizopod protozoans have been taken from water at 58° C. He regards 50° to 52° C. as the highest temperature compatible with the life of plants other than those just mentioned, and of active animals. Encysted animals and plant seeds resist much higher temperatures. An examination of the temperatures at which animals have been taken in thermal waters indicates that the majority of these heat-tolerant animals live in water below 40° C. As the temperature departs more and more from the usual optimum, the number of species that can tolerate such a temperature becomes reduced. This is a phase of a much more general principle that can be stated as follows: Wherever and whenever conditions approach a pessimum (see p. 213), the biota becomes impoverished, the more so, the closer the approach to the limits of toleration. In East Indian thermal springs, Brues records fifty-seven species from 36 to 40°; twelve, from 41 to 45°; four, from 46 to 50°; and four from above 50° C.

Deaths from heat may occur at much lower temperatures. Some one-celled, snow-dwelling algae cannot resist temperatures higher than 4° C. (Luyet and Gehenio, 1938). The alga *Phacocystis poucheti* dies at 11.0° C., and, despite little exact work on the subject, it is known that many sorts of animals are killed by heat before the temperature reaches 20° C. In general, fishes and marine invertebrates are less resistant to heat than are terrestrial insects or mammals, and animals from streams are less resistant than are related animals from small ponds. Such differential resistance is probably a result of natural selection. One reason for the lack of more data concerning the point at which heat deaths occur is that in the lower ranges of lethal temperatures, the effect of heat is a function of the duration of exposure as well as the absolute temperature. No satisfactory generalized formulation of these time-temperature relations has been worked out.

There is a large, though somewhat confused, literature dealing with heat death; much of it has been summarized by Heilbrunn (1943, 1946). Death from heat does not necessarily occur during or immediately after exposure and, if deferred, is not evenly distributed through the passing hours. Rather, as the life history develops, death may be restricted mainly to times of greatest physiological activity when there is need for the closest interaction between crucial processes (Larsen, 1943).

Attention has been paid to heat hardiness as distinct from heat death. Adaptive processes that make for heat hardiness include, among others, evaporation of water from skin or lungs (p. 183), evaporation of water from the nests of social bees or wasps (p. 215), and aestivation in some more or less completely quiescent stage (p. 185). Many animals emigrate, burrow, or become nocturnal, and so escape more extreme heat. Others apparently acclimate themselves by synthesizing lipoids with a higher melting point. As with cold hardiness, for many organisms, heat hardiness is favored by a decrease in the amount of the water content of the organism (Heilbrunn, 1943).

Ecology, like genetics and evolution, can gain much sound knowledge from the study of domestic animals. Not only do the breeds of cattle with a smaller body size tend to have greater heat hardiness (Davidson, 1927), as called for by Bergmann's rule (p. 119), but a tentative scale of heat hardiness has been worked out by Rhoad (1941) as follows:

$$100 - 10(\mathrm{Tb} - 101) = \mathrm{Ht}$$

The formula is based on 101.0° F. as the normal body temperature for cattle: 100 represents perfect efficiency in maintaining body temperature at 101° F.; 10 is a factor to convert degrees of deviation in body temperature from the temperature scale to a convenient unit basis; Tb is the observed body temperature under conditions of a "severe" test such as would be furnished by exposure under field conditions to a temperature of 95° F.; r. h. of 72 per cent with a wind velocity of only 4.5 miles per hour; Ht is the heat tolerance index. A group of cattle with a mean body temperature of 104.3° F. would have an indicated heat tolerance of

$$100 - 10(104.3 - 101) = 100 - 33 = 67$$

Using this scale, Rhoad reports that cattle tested under comparable conditions on a Texas farm showed the heat tolerance as follows: Brahman cows, 93; Jersey cows, 86; Hereford steers, 73; and Aberdeen Angus cows, 56. These indexes of heat tolerance are approximate and tentative. The method is promising and can be applied widely.

HIBERNATION, AESTIVATION, AND DORMANCY OF VERTEBRATES

Considered in a broad sense, hibernation and aestivation are related phenomena and are united under the concept of dormancy. A period of dormancy under conditions of heat and drought is much more familiar in invertebrates than in mammals (p. 185). The passage of a dry season in summer (and by extension, of any dry season) is commonly referred to as aestivation, which bears directly on the water relations of animals (pp. 183–189). Over wintering in a dormant state is commonly referred to as hibernation.

Poikilotherms

The overwintering of cold-blooded vertebrates in temperate and northern latitudes is much like that of insects and other invertebrates. Most fishes, amphibians, and reptiles are killed by complete freezing, but not by freezing of the extremities. Permanently frozen subsoil accordingly limits their northward spread. The Alaska blackfish (*Dallia pectoralis*) is said to survive being frozen solid. In some fresh-water fishes of the temperate zone there appears to be a tendency to suspend feeding and to form loose or even compact aggregations, sometimes in the water, sometimes in the bottom mud (Norman, 1931, p. 243; Anonymous, 1943, p. 129). Many fresh-water fishes are, of course, active throughout the winter. Marine fishes are not known to exhibit any suspension of activity in the cold season.

An aestivation period becomes a fixed part of the life cycle of many tropical freshwater fishes in regions with a sharply defined alternation of wet and dry seasons. This is especially exemplified by the African and South American lungfishes, which remain in the mud of the drying ponds or marshes and form mucous-lined individual cells in which they stay until the rising water level again frees them. This life-history cycle is essentially like that of fresh-water animals in general in temporary ponds, illustrated among North American fishes by the mud minnow (*Umbra limi*).

Overwintering of both frogs and salamanders frequently involves aggregation in large numbers in a moist terrestrial situation (like a large rotten log), in the bottom mud of marshes and ponds, or in springs. In springs partially torpid frogs may be seen swimming in exaggerated slow motion in midwinter. Toads and the more terrestrial types of frogs may pass the winter in solitary burrows on land (Noble, 1931). Aestivation of frogs during a dry season is reported. The Central Australian *Chiroleptes platycephalus* is said to fill its urinary bladder, lymph spaces, and the body cavity with water and to pass the dry season in this condition in a mud cell much like that of a lung fish (Spencer 1896, p. 164). Holzapfel (1937), by experiment, demonstrated a relation between the hibernation of the common leopard frog in North America and the seasonal cycle, independent of actual temperatures, since the normal dormant condition was readily assumed during the winter months, while frogs subjected to low temperatures in the summer months did not become dormant, and died in a relatively short time. The latitudinal gradient of hibernation in frogs has not been studied. The relation between hibernation and the sexual cycle varies geographically; thus the leopard frog may breed in the fall in the southwestern United States.

The more terrestrial reptiles accomplish overwintering mainly by retreat into rock crevices or burrows, often in considerable aggregations; such aggregations may include several species. More aquatic turtles spend the winter buried in mud beneath ponds and stream borders. Hibernation of solitary individuals has been observed in an American lizard, the anole.

Duration of the period of dormancy is proportional to the length of the winter or dry season. It is evident also that there is no period of dormancy in the life cycle of fishes, frogs, and reptiles in tropical regions without an extended dry season, and that the latitudinal gradient with respect to winter dormancy deserves further examination.

Hibernation of Mammals

Hibernation of warm-blooded animals, i.e., of mammals, differs conspicuously from overwintering of poikilotherms. Observation, study, and experiment combined have disclosed further problems and have led to a great diversity of opinion and hypothesis as to the immediate causes of hibernation, i.e., the factors that induce its deathlike torpor in individuals. Such studies frequently disregard evolutionary and ecological causes and relations. The fact that the temperature of the mammal drops below the normal level in aestivation as well as in hibernation points to the functional relation of lowered metabolic rate for surviving an unfavorable season. (Rasmussen, 1916; Johnson, 1931; Benedict and Lee, 1938; Hamilton, 1939).

Factors that have been thought to induce the torpor of hibernation are low temperature, especially gradually decreasing temperatures; inadequacy of heat-regulating mechanisms; lack of food; dryness of food; concentration of carbon dioxide in hibernacula; accumulation of fat; and glandular disturbance. The operation of special hibernating glands has been postulated, but the supposed glands (in the marmot) prove to be merely masses of fat. Freedom from external stimuli appears to contribute to maintenance of deep torpor, since under experimental conditions activities of the experimenters have been observed to arouse animals from dormancy. The most remarkable feature of hibernation physiology in mammals is the low internal temperature reached, which approximates that of the environment and falls as low as 1° C.; body temperatures of dormant mammals average about 1 degree above that of the environment. Death appears to ensue if temperature falls to freezing; such a fall may arouse the animal and thus save its life, a reaction with obvious survival value, especially for mammals that hibernate in relatively exposed situations. Where the soil is permanently frozen beneath the level reached by summer thaws, hibernation of burrowing mammals can not take place, and hence is absent in polar regions.

Among the characteristics of torpor in mammals are the reduced rate of breathing, with complete suspension of breathing for several minutes at a time; lowered body temperature; and persistence of the heart beat, as in cold-blooded vertebrates, when the animal is decapitated.

Relations between hibernation and sleep have been investigated somewhat. Sleep of mammals in which heat regulation is imperfect, and in which hibernation can develop, differs conspicuously from sleep of the normally winter-active mammal. Relation of the period of hibernation to the sexual cycle is far from clear, but there may be active development of the gonads during hibernation. This is especially conspicuous in Columbian ground squirrels, in which the long period of aestivation and hibernation concentrates active life into about five months. The remarkable interruption of early stages of embryonic development in various mammals exhibits no correlation with hibernation, since it occurs in nonhibernating mammals as well as in hibernating forms.

The zoological dispersion of hibernation among mammals is not especially illuminating, since closely allied forms (e.g., the true squirrels and the ground squirrels) may differ radically in this respect. Hibernation is reported for the orders Monotremata, Marsupialia, Insectivora, Chiroptera, Rodentia, and Carnivora. Hibernation of carnivores appears to differ in important respects from that of other orders and might be referred to as pseudohibernation. The tenrec of Madagascar, a remote relative of the hibernating hedgehog, is often cited as an aestivating mammal. Various ground squirrels of western North America have a well-defined period of aestivation combined with hibernation, since they disappear into their burrows early in August and do not appear until the following March. Ground squirrels in Turkestan have the same habit.

Among gradients connecting the hibernation habit with more normal life histories, there may be mentioned storage of food by nonhibernating rodents, the storage of considerable supplies by some that hibernate, and of small amounts, perhaps as bedding rather than food, by those in which the hibernating habit is fully developed. Aggregation associated with hibernation is widespread among tropical bats as well as those of temperate regions. Aggregation of hibernating mammals is otherwise rare. It is reported for family parties of skunks.

Great differences exist in the extent to which the hibernating animal withdraws from the effects of the environment. Some bats merely enter crevices beneath loose bark, while others congregate into vast winter colonies in caves, where the temperature is constant. Burrows of more familiar hibernating rodents extend well below the frost line into relatively constant temperature, while pseudohibernation of carnivores may occur in hollow logs, in snow-covered depressions, or even on level ground beneath trees.

We do not find an ecological study of the north-south gradient in the hibernation of mammals with a considerable latitudinal range, but it is obvious from scattered information that such behavior clines must exist, though less directly correlated with environmental climatic factors than are similar clinal gradients in overwintering behavior of poikilothermic animals.

In general, it appears that several environmental factors combine with internal factors (which in turn have been modified in evolutionary adaptation to hibernation) to induce dormancy in mammals. Hibernation and aestivation are to be compared with seasonal migration or with food storage as evolutionary adjustments for the passage of an unfavorable season. According to this view, the partial poikilothermy of homoiotherms with the hibernating habit is secondary and, at least in higher orders, is a degeneration.

ENVIRONMENTAL TEMPERATURE AND THE RATE OF BIOLOGICAL PROCESSES

Metabolic rates increase almost to the upper temperature limits at which the organism is normally active.* The possibility that such ecological accelerations are fundamentally similar to the effect of heat upon the speed of chemical and physical reactions has attracted much attention. Chemical reactions in a laboratory test tube, and rate of living of adult organisms, speed of embryonic, larval, or pupal development, rate of living of adult organisms, speed of locomotion, and other behavioristic reactions, are all accelerated with higher temperatures. These results are more obvious in poikilothermal organisms than in

* For exceptions, see Barnes, (1937).

homoiotherms, and they affect such important ecological phenomena as the time span of the life history or the length of any given stage.

A number of mathematical formulae have been used in attempts to express accurately the relation between temperature and the velocity of biological processes. These are of two main types; the first type is based on the chemical "law of mass action," which, in its simplest form, states that the rate at which any chemical reaction proceeds is directly proportional to the concentration of substances actually taking part in the reaction. According to this law, temperature influences can be expressed by an exponential curve. This means that the ve-

whatever the location on the effective temperature scale.*

Réaumur suggested in 1735 (see p. 18) that the sum of average daily temperatures during the growing season bears relation to the time at which fruits ripen. This idea can be expressed by the equation

$$yt = \frac{1}{k}$$

in which y represents time, t, temperature, and k is a constant. The velocity (v) of the process in question can be calculated, since $v = \frac{1}{y}$; therefore, $v = tk$. As stated previously, the ecological zero (see p. 110) of a given process usually fails to coincide with

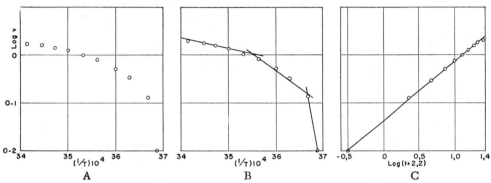

Fig. 15. Velocity of ameboid movement in relation to temperature. A, Log of velocity plotted against inverse of absolute temperature. B, Three straight lines fitted to the same points. C, Log of velocity plotted against log of temperature. (Redrawn from Bělehrádek, after Pantin.)

locity constant is an exponential function of effective temperature, which, in turn, means that the effect of an increase of 1 degree in temperature differs, depending upon the location of the increase on the temperature scale. Van't Hoff's rule (1884) and the formula of Arrhenius (1915) are exponential expressions of this type, while the more empirical catenary formula of Janisch (1932) and the equally empirical one of Bělehrádek (1935) are also exponential. In the second type, the relationship is based on the observation that in many biological processes, the product of temperature and time to a given end point is a constant. Sanderson and Peairs (1914) state this generalization, and the formula of Krogh (1914) gives the usual form of expression. According to this idea, the effect of an increase in temperature of 1 degree is similar.

the freezing point of water. It is a variable quantity and depends on the process and the organism. The last equation must, therefore, be modified by the parameter c, which, practically speaking, shows the location of the intercept of the straight-line portion of the velocity curve on the temperature axis (Bělehrádek, 1935; Powsner,

* Roughly approximated, the overworked Van't Hoff rule, often known as the Q_{10} rule, states that the rate of reaction is often doubled, or more, for each 10° C. increase in temperature in the median range. The use of these temperature coefficients is not a subject for the unwary. Accounts by Shelford (1929) and Chapman (1931) contain helpful discussions of general temperature relations. Readers with stronger physiological inclinations can consult such references as Kanitz (1915), Bělehrádek (1935), Barnes (1937), and Heilbrunn (1943).

1935; Krogh, 1914a) (see Fig. 16), so that the expression becomes:

$$v = tk + c$$

If graphed, the equation $yt = \frac{1}{k}$ gives a rectangular hyperbola, the reciprocal of which is a straight line that theoretically intercepts the temperature axis at zero; the value of c in the modified formula shows the shift of the intercept.

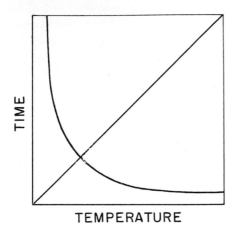

TEMPERATURE

Fig. 16. A generalized time-temperature hyperbola and its straight-line reciprocal. (Redrawn from Bĕlehrádek.)

This statement of the case means that the velocity of the process under consideration is a linear function of temperature, a relationship that has been found to hold for many physiological events that have ecological significance. This is by no means a perfect working tool. It is most useful when few measurements are available at temperatures some distance apart. This makes the Sanderson-Peairs-Krogh formula serviceable for field workers who need to make an approximation of the length of various developmental stages at different times of the year.

When the effects of temperatures closely spaced along the whole range of effective temperatures are examined, the resulting velocity curve remains linear only at intermediate points. Near the ecological zero for the reaction(s), the effect of a degree rise in temperature is greater, and near the upper temperature limit it is less than at the intermediate points. A more or less sigmoidal curve results (see Fig. 17), the form of which is not given by the equation.

In summary, we are forced to the conclusion that, despite a great mass of work by ecologists and physiologists, there is as yet no generalized expression for the known relations throughout the range of effective temperatures that is solidly based on theory. A new approach may be necessary in order to express mathematically the subtility of the effect of temperature on the rate of living processes. Even an approximate solution of the problem may depend on accumulation of more complete knowledge of temperature relations of enzyme systems. The difficulties involved are increased by the readiness with which organisms acclimate to temperature, and acclimatization has ecological implications with both ontogenetic and evolutionary values. For example: There are five species of *Rana* in the eastern United States and Canada. The species whose range extends farthest north, *R. sylvatica*, tolerates lower temperatures, breeds earlier in the season, and has the most rapid rate of development at a given temperature. Similar relations hold with regard to the rate of development of *Ambystoma* (Moore, 1939) and various other aquatic animals, both fresh-water and marine. It follows that the rate of metabolism in animals of the colder waters is not necessarily retarded as would be inferred from temperature formulae.

The different chemo-biological temperature formulae have received attention from ecologists and others out of proportion to their proved usefulness; even so, they are suggestive. The known importance of temperature upon such processes as the rate of egg laying, of development, and of death of insects, among others, indicates that velocities dependent on temperature affect population ecology as well as the ecology of individuals. The probable significance of favorable temperatures in relation to outbreaks of insect plagues and the usefulness, here as elsewhere in ecology, of an approach to mathematical formulations are reasons for continued preoccupation with these problems.

VARYING TEMPERATURES

The most densely inhabited portions of the earth's biosphere have daily or seasonal fluctuations in temperature or both. Many well-occupied habitats, on the other hand, have nearly or quite constant temperatures the year around. Even under arid conditions, soil temperature is nearly constant at a depth of 2 meters, although the soil surface may vary more than 56 degrees in one day (p. 219). This state can be reached much nearer the surface under less extreme conditions, and in steadily shaded portions of tropical rain forests, where even sunflecks are absent, temperature on the forest floor may show little variation from one year's end to another. Deeper parts of caves characteristically have constant temperatures.

the Bay of Biscay is one example of such a situation (Sverdrup, Johnson, and Fleming, 1942).

At the surface of the sea, diurnal temperature changes average not more than 0.3° C.; hence, short-lived populations in surface waters often live out their life cycle without great temperature fluctuation. In deeper waters, according to records taken at fifteen stations in the Atlantic and Atlantic-Antarctic oceans, the mean temperature variation between depths of 4000 and 2000

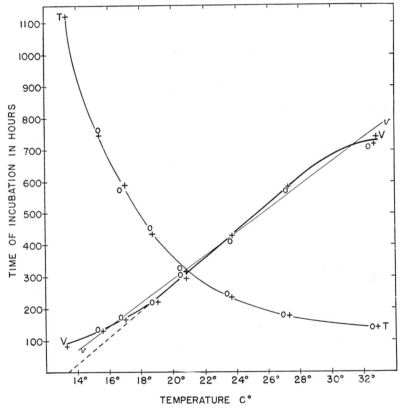

Fig. 17. Duration of incubation of chrysalids of *Tenebrio molitor* in hours (T); V is its reciprocal and shows velocity of development; it approximates straight line (v). (Redrawn from Krogh.)

The bottom waters of lakes of the first and second order (p. 95), whether arctic, temperate, or tropical, do not vary much from 4° C. at any season. Similarly, animals that live in the ocean, the upper part of the lighted zone alone excepted, meet little if any temperature variation. Even well within the lighted region, at a depth of 100 meters in many temperate locations, annual variations are on the order of 1° or 2° C.;

meters averaged only 1.3° C., with extreme ranges from 0.3° to 2.3° C. At these depths a great many generations must live under temperature conditions that approach or equal those we call constant in experimental laboratories. We do not know what would be the effect of subjecting animals from such steady environments to the controlled constant or variable conditions that characterize studies in experimental ecology. This leaves a large gap in fundamental knowledge concerning temperature relations of animals.

It is not fair to compare the biological effects produced by constant temperature with those obtained under the variable conditions found in nature, since, for many animals, laboratory life at its best is highly artificial. In the laboratory, organisms exposed to variable temperatures frequently, perhaps usually, show accelerated development as compared with those held at a constant temperature of the same mean value, if other conditions remain equal. This generalization might not hold true for animals that live in the steady temperatures such as obtain in even the upper layers of the soil of the tropical rain forests or at some depth in lakes or oceans. Exceptions have been recorded for terrestrial animals from the middle latitudes (Headlee, 1914; Ludwig, 1928).

The amount of acceleration varies with different stages in the life history, with different species, and with the combinations of temperatures that are used. When the range is held between the minimum effective temperature and the maximum for the given process, blowfly larvae and pupae showed acceleration (Peairs, 1927). The codling moth (*Carpocapsa pomonella*) was accelerated between 7 and 8 per cent for egg, larval, and pupal stages. Grasshopper eggs held at 22° C. for sixteen hours and 5, 10, or 15 degrees higher for eight hours daily showed an average acceleration for *Melanoplus mexicanus* of 38.6 per cent and for *Camnula pellucida* of 30.5 per cent, as compared with the rate of development at comparable constant temperatures. Grasshopper nymphs reared in such alternating conditions were accelerated some 12 per cent over expectation based on results from constant temperatures (Parker, 1930).

Certain complexities involved are illustrated by relations reported for the flour beetle, *Tribolium confusum*. The eggs develop more rapidly in constant temperatures than in comparable variable ones without reference to the position of mean temperatures, except when the upper temperature lies below the optimum and the lower temperature is at the developmental zero. In the pupae, if the mean of the combination lies above or at the optimum with symmetrical alternating temperature, development is delayed; if the mean lies below the optimum, development is accelerated. With *Tribolium,* the most rapid acceleration comes with an alternating amplitude of 5 degrees. The thermal optimum in the action of alternating temperatures may be different from the optimum for constant temperatures.

Alternating temperatures may affect survival as well as the rate of development. *Tribolium* shows increased longevity with alternating temperatures, especially in the lower part of its favorable thermal range. The range of constant temperatures, with a survival greater than 50 per cent, is narrower than the range of mean alternating temperatures that produce the same result.

Relations between effects produced by variable as contrasted with constant temperature of the same mean value depend, among other things, upon the species, the process measured, the location of the temperatures used in relation to the effective temperature range, and the length and amplitude of the thermal cycle. It is unfortunate that the majority of the experimental work has been done with terrestrial insects and plants that are sensitive to changes in humidity and under conditions that at times leave doubt concerning the exactness of the control of the latter factor (Mikulski, 1936, 1936a).

From an entirely different approach, there is much evidence that man thrives best and works most efficiently when exposed to daily or weekly changes of weather rather than in the same locality in periods of relative constancy. Further, changeable temperate climates are more stimulating to man than are relatively constant tropical regions (Huntington, 1924; Taylor, 1927).

ECOLOGICAL TEMPERATURE ZERO

The lowest temperature at which a given physiological process, or development through a given stage in the life history can be carried through to completion is the effective temperature threshold for the function under consideration. In the lower temperature range, the highest externally imposed temperature at which such a functional unit *cannot* be successfully completed is its ecological temperature zero. This is a new name for an old idea. The concept of an ecological zero of development is a general one; the ecological temperature zero represents only one of its many components (see below). In studies related to life histories and behavior, the first temperature just given is often referred to as the "threshold of development" and the second approaches the "developmental zero." Actually, some development frequently takes place at temperatures that will not allow the successful completion of a given stage or process; hence the ecological zero represents a somewhat higher temperature than the developmental zero (Parker, 1930; Bělehrádek, 1935; Powsner, 1935). The biological zero of Bělehrádek denotes "the temperature at which a given protoplasmic action is arrested by cold without formation of ice." Its precise relation to the ecological zero has not been determined; presumably it approximates the developmental zero. Bělehrádek (pp. 139–145) lists the biological zero for diverse processes in different organisms. These "zeros" and "thresholds" may be affected by time of exposure as well as by temperature and such physiological factors as age, previous conditions, and temperature adaptation.

The location of the ecological temperature zero for a given process or stage in development can be determined only by experimentation. Its position can be approximated rather closely at times by plotting the point at which the straight-line reciprocal of the temperature hyperbola crosses the temperature axis (see Fig. 17). This is the so-called *alpha* point for the curve; it has theoretical rather than ecological significance. Usually the true ecological zero lies at some lower temperature than is indicated by this intercept, a fact that has already been considered in connection with the correction of the simple equation for the hyperbolic temperature curve (see p. 107).

The effects of exposing organisms to temperatures between the ecological zero and the complete stoppage indicated by the developmental zero and then returning them to higher temperatures are not uniform. In some instances, acceleration up to 80 per cent occurs (Parker, 1930; for grasshopper eggs). In other cases there is retardation (cf. Ludwig, 1928; Powsner, 1935). This discrepancy may be interpreted as follows: Some processes always continue at temperatures at which the organism is not killed by cold. The effect of low temperature is probably differential, and some

processes are slowed down more than others. If not pronounced, this may well have an accelerating influence when the organisms are placed in medial temperatures. The "disorganization" that results from chilling increases with time; if the temperatures again become favorable, a lag period follows before metabolic processes become sufficiently well correlated to proceed normally. If the "disorganization" has gone too far (and this depends on the length of exposure as well as on low temperature), the process cannot be completed or completion will follow only at a retarded rate.

SUMMATION OF HEAT

The useful ecological practice of summation of temperature represents in reality an attempt to find an index for a summation of the heat energy required to complete a given stage in the life history of an animal or plant. As such it has a theoretical basis in the "law of constant heat summation" of thermochemistry. This generalization states that the quantity of heat involved in a chemical process is the same whether it takes place in one or in several steps (Getman and Daniels, 1931). Actually, summation of the capacity aspect of heat (see p. 91) has not been practiced by ecologists in connection with life histories; they have used temperatures instead.

Modern ecological summation of temperature developed from the extended experience of the phenologists that the accumulation of a given daily excess of temperature above some convenient base will approximately coincide with the completion of a given stage in development. This amount is usually found by summing so-called day-degrees. In present usage, a day-degree represents 1 degree of mean temperature above the ecological zero lasting for one day. The needed accumulation to a selected end point is called the thermal constant for that set of processes. In more refined usage, especially for shorter life histories, hour-degrees are used for summation, and attention may be turned from such environmental units to reciprocal values called developmental units. A developmental unit is defined as the amount of organismic development produced in a given amount of time, frequently one hour, by an increase of 1 degree of medial temperature. Developmental units are obtained by dividing the whole developmental period by the number of days (or hours) taken for its completion; they represent the reciprocal of the fraction of the whole development that takes place in a day (or an hour). Practically, the medial temperatures are those at which the increase in rate of development is directly proportional to the rise in temperature, i.e., to the region expressed by a straight line in the temperature velocity curves shown in Figure 17. Developmental units can be used to demonstrate that the rate of development under variable

environmental or in organismic units, temperature summation, in the present sense, finds its mathematical formulation in the equations of Sanderson and Peairs and of Krogh, and their modifications.

Supporting evidence for the validity of the concept of temperature summation is to be found in the work of many biologists who have studied a wide variety of organisms, both under natural conditions and in the laboratory; special attention has been paid to the length of life histories of insects. The straight-line portions of the preceding

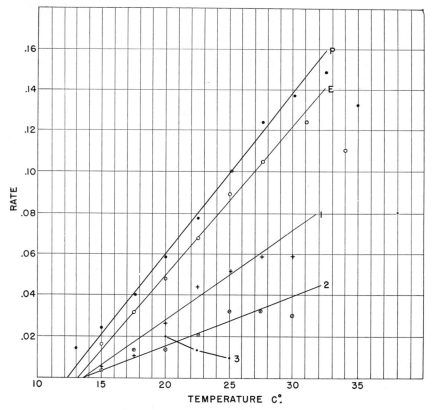

Fig. 18. Comparison of the rates of development of each stage of the Japanese beetle: *P*, Pupa; *E*, egg; 1, 2, and 3 represent respective larval instars. (Redrawn from Ludwig.)

field conditions approaches expectations based on the theory of temperature summation and on laboratory experience with controlled temperatures. When summed for a given process, the total number of such units for completion of the process in question is a more refined expression than that given by the thermal constant obtained from the summation of day-degrees (Shelford, 1929, p. 368). Whether measured in

temperature-velocity curves all imply that temperature summation is relatively accurate within the indicated medial temperatures. Similar data from one more set of experiments are summarized in Figure 18, for the developing Japanese beetle, *Popillia japonica*. This is a good final test case for several reasons. Data for eggs and pupae fit the theory rather well. Those for larval stages show irregularities produced, in part by variations in food and presence of a resting stage in the first instar. The third instar runs contrary to expectation; this indicates correctly that laws governing heat summation for biological processes are imperfectly known.

Experience suggests, however, that summed temperatures are frequently related to the development of many animals and plants in a fairly exact manner. The closeness of fit is readily disturbed and is particularly faulty when resting stages occur during one of the developmental stages. The relation between summed calories as contrasted with summed temperatures awaits appropriate experimentation.

among poikilothermal animals is correlated with Rubner's hypothesis that within a given genetic combination, longevity is inversely proportional to the intensity of living. In other words, this hypothesis states that a definite sum of living action determines the physiological end of life. Although originally advanced as a result of studies with mammals, this hypothesis is now generally restricted to cold-blooded forms in medial ecological conditions. For

Table 7. *Evidence That, for Many Processes, the Total Amount of Work Done Is Relatively Constant at Medial Temperatures, Regardless of the Velocity Imposed by Temperature*

| Observer | Organism | Process | Temperatures | | | | Temperature Range |
			Low a	b	c	High d	
Rubner (1908)	*Proteus*	Days until gills disappear. Coefficient, N_2 utilization	30 0.75	22 0.73	20 0.75	8 0.75	8°–21° C.
Krogh (1914a)	*Tenebrio molitor*	Total CO_2 produced in liters per kilo.	59.6	59.1	58.0	59.3	20.9°–32.3° C.
MacArthur and Baillie (1929)	*Daphnia magna*	Days duration of life. Days of life times mean heart rate per sec.	108.2 182.5	41.7 177.5	25.6 175.0	. . . .	8°–28° C
Parker (1930)	*Melanoplus atlantis*	Days duration nymphal stage. Mg. dry wt., consumed food	94 4079	54 4311	27 4098	25 3988	22°–37° C.
Filinger (1931)	*Phlyctaenia ferrugalis*	Days to 50% prepupae. Food consumed, mg.	58 868	22 870	12.5 815	11 735	15°–30° C.

RUBNER'S HYPOTHESIS

The existence of a "developmental total" or "thermal constant" for many processes

example, at medial temperatures, such forms live longer at low temperatures than at higher ones, and various types of measurements indicate that total energy transformation is approximately the same regardless of the length of natural life. Some of the supporting evidence for this generalization is given in Table 7.

Rubner's hypothesis finds general support

in many other data that suggest that animals with a higher rate of metabolism tend to live for a shorter time than do others of the same species with lower metabolic rates. Frequently these data are not carefully quantitative. It is, for example, rather general experience that the rate of metabolism of males is higher than that of females and that the latter live longer. Fairly exact information has been collected on this subject for the cladoceran, *Daphnia magna*. The rate of heart beat gives a rough indication of the rate of metabolism of this organism (Table 8).

15° than at 26° or 30° C. and much greater in light than in darkness (Northrup 1926; MacArthur and Baillie, 1926).

THE LIFE ZONE CONCEPT

Merriam's so-called temperature laws on which his life-zone system for North America is based, were stated in 1894. They grew out of the idea of temperature summation and find their modern basis, in part, in the hyperbolic temperature equations. The forerunners of the scheme included the system of faunal areas worked out by American naturalists and Merriam's own

Table 8. *The Mean Age in Days and the Average Number of Heart Beats per Second, Times the Average Age for Males and Females of* D. magna
(Data from MacArthur and Baillie, 1926, 1929)

Sex	Length of Life in Days		Heart Beats per Second × Days of Life	
	1926	1929	1926	1929[*]
Male....................	37.8	38.6	161.5	178.4
Female..................	43.8	44.7	162.1	174.5

[*] Data for 1929 taken at 18° C.

In these tests the females lived approximately six days longer than the males, yet the product obtained by multiplying the average life-time rate of heart beat by the duration of life in days is of the same order of magnitude for the two sexes in each test. The greatest discrepancy given here is that for 1929; the males lived 13 per cent shorter time than did the accompanying females and showed a life-time heart beat of 2 per cent more; unfortunately, we cannot give a statistical evaluation of these results. Regardless of differences produced by temperature or sex, the average total number of heart beats for this race of *Daphnia* was estimated to be on the order of 15.4×10^5.

Not all the tests of Rubner's hypothesis have given positive results. In one set of experiments, aseptic cultures of *Drosophila* were reared under controlled conditions. and their total carbon dioxide was measured as an indication of total metabolism. The amount produced was not constant, as required by the hypothesis; it was greater at

sound field studies on vertical zonation of animals and plants in the Rocky Mountains (Merriam, 1890, 1892, 1894, 1899, 1899a; Allen, 1892; Daubenmire, 1938).

When isotherms were drawn through localities said to have equal sums of effective temperatures, certain of these coincided suggestively with the northern boundaries of distributions of certain animals and plants. This is summarized in Merriam's first temperature "law," which states: "Animals and plants are restricted in northward distribution by the total quantity of heat during the season of growth and reproduction." A similar study of the mean temperature for the six hottest weeks of summer led to the second "law," which is: "Animals and plants are restricted in southward distribution by the mean temperature of a brief period covering the hottest part of the year."

The division lines ran roughly east and west over the plains and prairies, but made a sharp dip southward in the mountains. Along the western mountain and coastal country, the different zones made a complex system. The zones and their supposed temperature limits are listed in Table 9.

The transition zone and the two zones south of it were later divided into a dryer western and a moister eastern region at the 20 inch line of equal annual rainfall (isohyet) which, in these latitudes, happens to approximate the 100th meridian. Merriam planned to use 6 degrees as the base for temperature summation. Through a misunderstanding, the temperatures were summed with zero Centigrade as a base, although only for those days on which the mean temperature was above 6° C. The values for summed temperature are therefore much too high, and the agreement between Merriam's isotherms and the boundaries of his life zones becomes a proof of the incorrectness of his use of temperature in setting up the scheme. Corrected tables have never been published.

at what purports to be the root of Merriam's life zone concept have actually affected its usefulness very little. This paradoxical situation results from the fact that, from the very beginning, the life zones have been mainly delimited by the observed distribution of life-zone indicators rather than by temperatures. The life-zone concept owes its considerable vitality to the soundness of the work of the early naturalists on which it was really based. The weakness of the false façade of temperature relations has been a factor in preventing ecologists generally from taking the life zones seriously. Also, their studies of the distribution of biotic communities have shown that, south of the Canadian forests, temperature is only one of a number of environmental factors that regulate biotic distribution (Sanderson, 1908; Shreve, 1914; Allee, 1923; Kendeigh, 1932; and Shelford, 1932).

Table 9. The Temperature Values in Degrees Centigrade Assigned to Merriam's Life Zones

Zone	Northern Limit in Accumulated Day-Degrees	Southern Limit; Mean Temp. of 6° C. Hottest Summer Weeks in Degrees, Latitude
Arctic*	......	10
Hudsonian	......	14
Canadian	......	18
Transition	5500	22
Upper austral or upper Sonoran	6400	26
Lower austral or lower Sonoran	10,000	
Tropical†	14,500	

* Northward, ground never thaws.
† Southward, no freezing.

This application of temperature "laws" to latitudinal distribution zones overlooks entirely the phenomenon of winter killing and cold hardiness, an oversight that biologists soon emphasized. Further, in hot weather, daily maxima are more important limiting factors than are daily means, and still further, high temperatures may be an effective limiting agent for the distribution of organisms at other times besides the six hottest weeks of summer.

These inadequacies and others that strike

Students of the distribution of birds and mammals in the Rocky Mountains and westward in North America continue to find this scheme of life zones useful in a descriptive sense. The distribution of vertebrates in the Yosemite region of California is given in Figure 19 in terms of the local life zones. Even in these vertical distributions, the temperature implications of the life-zone system present an oversimplified picture. In northern California, for example, the following environmental factors are

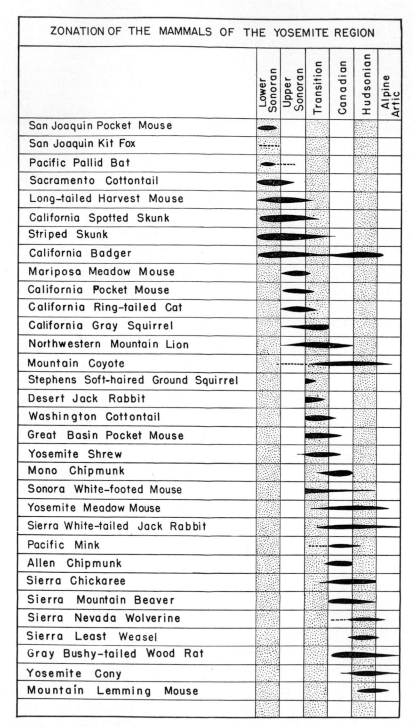

Fig. 19. Distribution of vertebrates in the Yosemite region of California in terms of Merriam's life zones. (Rearranged from Grinnell and Storer.)

known to affect the distribution of animals (Grinnell and Storer, 1924; Grinnell, Dixon and Linsdale, 1930): vegetation, food, rain, humidity, soil moisture, pH of soil, temperature, altitude, atmospheric density, available breeding niches, available refuge niches, light, cloudiness and competition.

The distribution of animals in many parts of the world is more or less closely tied up with temperature. For instance, temperature races of the fruit fly, *Drosophila funebris,* exist in Europe. Northwestern populations are more resistant to cold; southwestern ones, to heat. All eastern populations, whether from the northeast or the southeast,

ture of their respective habitats. Doubtless their distribution is also affected by other environmental factors.

THE BIOCLIMATIC RULE

In spring and early summer in temperate latitudes, periodic phenomena, such as beginning of blossoming for a given species, ripening of fruit, or appearance of active insects, usually come three or four days later for each higher degree of latitude and for each 100 to 130 meters of latitude from any given base. In late summer and autumn, similar relations can be recognized, but in the reverse direction. In certain regions tem-

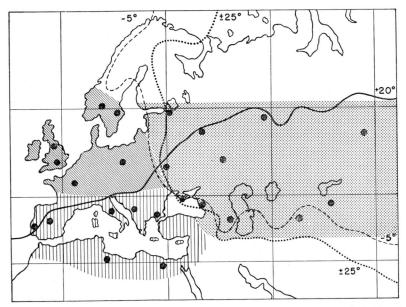

Fig. 20. Approximate distribution of three "temperature races" of *Drosophila funebris.* (Redrawn from Timoféeff-Ressovsky, in Huxley.)

show high tolerance to both heat and cold. These differential resistances are correlated with the respective temperatures of the regions under consideration. Figure 20 shows that the January isotherm of −5 degrees runs from northern Norway to southeastern Russia. The July isotherm of 20 degrees runs from Lisbon on the Atlantic eastward and then northward up to about 63 degrees latitude in Russia. The spread between these isotherms in the east encloses an area with a seasonal difference of 25 degrees and reveals the continental climate of this inland region. Thus, even a coarse analysis of these temperature races of *D. funebris* shows a high correlation with the tempera-

perature relations vary also along a given set of meridians. Thus Hopkins, who definitely formulated the bioclimatic relations for the United States as a "law" of nature, added that there was a seasonal retardation of four days from west to east for each 5 degrees of longitude. This rule was originally worked out on the basis of observations on North American and European phenology.

The speed of migration of birds gives a convenient test for the application of this rule to one prominent periodic phenomenon in animal life. From New Orleans to southern Minnesota, the average speed of migration for all species of birds is close to 23 miles a day. The speed for individual migrants or for a given twenty-four hours may be much greater or much less, but the average holds, and this average brings the mean rate of migration within the rule as stated. Northward, the rate of migration is faster, probably because some of the slower species have stopped to nest, and so the average rate is increased, and because, once started, the season develops faster in northern latitudes.[*]

In China, the bioclimatic rule was followed, in whole or in part, by eleven species of Lepidoptera (41 per cent of those studied). Three of these species have one annual generation only and overwinter as pupae. Of the sixteen species (59 per cent) that did not conform, six overwintered as larvae. The rule seems, in general, to be a useful summarizing statement of a situation that holds for some, though by no means for all, seasonal events. It must be remembered that seasonal changes are affected by differences in length of day and frequently by rainfall and other conditions as well as by changes in temperature.

STRUCTURAL MODIFICATION INDUCED BY TEMPERATURE

It is easy to produce changes in metabolism in response to changes in temperature. Such functional modifications, important as they are at times, are usually reversible and transitory. Those modifications of function that result in phenotypic changes in structure attract more attention because they are both rarer and more obvious. Changes in temperature are known to produce structural modifications, and numerous instances can be cited with the well-studied *Drosophila melanogaster* alone, in which, among other structures, temperature affects the number of facets in the eyes, the size of vestigial eyes, and the presence or absence of supernumerary legs (Goldschmidt, 1938).

Cyclomorphosis

A most striking instance of a relation between body form and seasonal change in temperature is the phenomenon of cyclomorphosis in some small aquatic organisms,

[*] Selected references include Cooke (1917), Hopkins (1918, 1920), Clarke, Margerie, and Marshall (1924), Chapman (1934), and Mell (1935).

including Cladocera, some simplified aspects of which are illustrated in Figure 21. The facts as collected from observations in nature are: In Danish waters, at least, a change of form in whole populations of wild *Daphnia* follows a rise in temperature to between 12° and 16° C. (or to above 19° in Connecticut; Brooks, 1946). The head projections or helmets become fully developed in a few weeks and thereafter remain at their summer size; hence, there is little

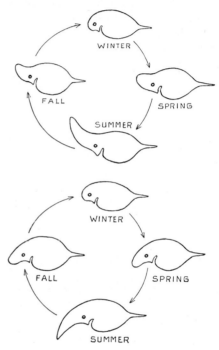

Fig. 21. Cyclomorphosis in Cladocera, showing identical winter forms, but contrasting summer forms. (Redrawn from Coker.)

correlation between the degree of warmth of the water and the size of the helmet. A gradual reversion to the round-headed winter form may occur in the autumn; in summer, perhaps after the formation of ephippial eggs, the daphnia may disappear to reappear in autumn as ephippial round heads. Correlation of helmets with abundance of food, if indeed it exists, is only partial, and all size relations, both with temperature and food, fail when populations from different waters are compared. There is a rough, partial correlation between the size of the body of water and degree of helmet development, with larger helmets in larger bodies of water and their almost complete absence in laboratory dishes. In different locations and despite individual variations, the general form of the helmet is characteristic for the several populations.

Two main theories have been advanced to explain the phenomenon of cyclomorphosis in cladocerans (Coker, 1939). The first, the buoyancy theory, is based on the related species from warmer waters. The low temperatures retard the rate of growth and delay the appearance of sexual activity; this delay tends to produce larger forms. In marine copepods, for example, there is an inverse correlation between body size and temperature. The relation to temperature may be more indirect, since the viscosity of warm water is so much lower than that of

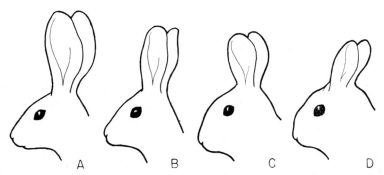

Fig. 22. The decreasing size of ears of *Lepus* from south to north. *A,* Arizona, jack rabbit (*L. alleni*); *B,* jack rabbit from Oregon (*L. californicus*); *C,* varying hare from northern Minnesota (*L. americanus*); *D,* Arctic hare from the Barren Grounds (*L. arcticus*). (Redrawn from Hamilton.)

fact that the floating power of warm water is much less than that of cold water, and there is the suggestion that protuberances, whether spines or helmets, will aid the flotation process in summer. The other theory holds that the protuberances are directive and stabilizing surfaces that function as do rudders or keels.

Jordan's Rule

Jordan's rule that fishes in low temperatures tend to have more vertebrae than do those in warmer waters holds true in general; however, this is not the only factor that affects the number of vertebrae of closely related fish. One of the exceptions is illustrated by the observation that the average number of vertebrae of young coalfish, *Gadus viens,* is lower for small fish than it is for large ones of the same year class. A possible, though unproved, explanation for the relations found in coalfish may be that small eggs produce smaller fish larvae than do larger eggs and that such effects persist in later life. In such an instance, temperature is involved only indirectly (Dannevig, 1933).

Cold-water forms of many sorts are frequently larger than are individuals or cold water that the larger forms would be handicapped in their efforts to maintain position in warmer seas (Hesse, Allee, and Schmidt, 1937; Coker, 1934).

Bergmann's Rule and Allen's Rule

Homoiothermal animals from colder climates tend to be larger in size and hence to have less surface in proportion to body weight than do their relatives from warmer regions. This phenomenon occurs widely even though not universally among birds and mammals and is usually interpreted in relation to heat conservation in the north and to heat radiation in the south. This is Bergmann's rule. Allen's rule is correlated with it and is concerned with the marked tendency toward the lessening of extremities in colder climates (see Fig. 22.) Allen based his conclusions on measurements of animals killed in nature. His observations have many confirmations both from field and laboratory studies, especially when rather large differences in temperature are considered. For example, mice reared at 31 to 33.5° C. have longer tails than those of the same strain reared at 15.5 to 20° (Allen's rule), and the latter have larger and stockier bodies and hence are decidedly heavier (Bergmann's rule) (Allen, 1905; Ogle, 1934). Similarly, the young of the common domestic fowl kept at 6° C. during their third and fourth months of life were shorter in body length, gained more weight, and had shorter tarsi and tails than did their former flock mates, which were kept throughout at 21 to 24.5°. The birds from the lower temperature also had larger hearts, as has been reported for birds in nature (Hesse, 1921; Hesse, Allee, and Schmidt, 1937; Allee and Lutherman, 1940).

An interesting sidelight on the relation between internal and external temperatures with respect to extremities throws important light on phenomena such as those that doubtless underlie Allen's rule. Red bone marrow, ordinarily absent from the distal regions of the tail in many animals, will form if the intact tail tip is inserted into and retained in the warm body cavity by a simple surgical operation (Huggins and Blocksom, Jr., 1936). Conversely, spermatozoa of certain animals with pendant testes, such as sheep, will not develop if the temperature is raised to that normally found within the body cavity (Moore and Quick, 1924).

Poikilothermous terrestrial animals tend to have their species and individuals with largest size in warmer, rather than in colder, climates. In this, a main trend in their surface-mass geographic relations differs from the general rule for homoiotherms. Terrestrial lizards, snakes, and many insects have their larger species, or individuals within a species, in the warmer parts of their range.

Exceptions occur to both the homoiothermal and poikilothermal phases of this rule. Among mammals, there are many, of which racoons (*Procyon*) afford an example, in which the body size becomes smaller toward the north. The reduction in body size corresponds with an invasion of a less suitable climate. Hibernating mammals and migrating birds escape the full rigors of winter cold and may show no relation between body size and environmental temperatures. Small birds have difficulty in maintaining an even, high body temperature in a variable climate and may be lim-

ited to the tropics except for summer migrations; the hummingbirds give an example. An exception to the usual rule that in terrestrial, cold-blooded forms the body size is largest toward the tropics is furnished by bumblebees, which are fuzzier and larger in the northern part of their range. These are evidently adjustments that conserve the body heat generated by the action of large wing muscles. Here we have another example of the frequent experience of ecologists. When different principles come into conflict, only a direct inquiry can determine which will be followed in any given instance. It is worth repeating that while we can discern and outline many broad general ecological principles with confidence, their application in a given situation is frequently a matter for empirical research.

CONCLUDING STATEMENT

Temperature is an important factor in the physical environment of organisms. Its relative value must not be judged by the length of the present chapter as compared with others in this section. Neither has the available information about the temperature relations of animals been summarized in overgreat detail. It is easy to measure temperature with a high degree of accuracy even under field conditions, (unfortunately without necessarily identifying the critical temperatures involved). Sturdy recording thermometers are available that require a minimum amount of attention. Also, temperatures are relatively easy to control in the laboratory. Finally, in addition to its known general importance, man has long been much interested in temperature on his own account, and this subjective factor, combined with ease of measurement, has led to the accumulation of a vast amount of seasoned information about temperature as an ecological factor, not all of which has been surveyed here. The interested student is referred to the bibliography for work done to date and to *Biological Abstracts* for the steady flow of new data dealing with temperature.

7. LIGHT

Visible light represents a small fraction of the whole gamut of radiation. As might be expected, this fraction shares many of the properties of other wave lengths, especially of those just longer or just shorter than the visible band. Although it is a restricted part of radiation, light is a complicated environmental factor. Organisms are affected directly by energy values, intensity, and wavelength, including associated aspects of color. Certain of these factors vary in a regular way in different parts of the spectrum; heat energy is relatively greater at the red end, and photo-chemical activity is greater at the violet end. To the normal human eye, brightness is greatest in the orange for high and in the green for low intensities. As a result, the effect produced varies greatly for different organisms and for different processes.

Photonegative animals are frequently not disturbed by exposure to red light and will collect at the red end of an experimentally imposed spectrum. The opposite tendency is exhibited by those light-positive animals that react primarily to photochemically active wavelengths of light. These collect near the blue end of the spectrum. Animals that respond primarily to brightness frequently collect in the yellow-green. Photosynthesis of carbohydrates by green plants, the most important chemical synthesis of the world through long geological ages, proceeds most rapidly under red light, although with heat-energy values equalized, it goes forward at the same rate in violet light.

Light may be important in development and toleration as well as in response physiology. The fundamental polarity of the egg of the marine alga *Fucus* is environmentally determined, and light is one of a number of potent determining agencies. Other things being equal, the lighted end of the algal egg becomes the growing apical point of the plant, while the shaded end develops into a holdfast (Hurd, 1920; Whitaker, 1931).

It has long been known that light retards the rate of elongation of green plants. Bachmetjew (1907) reviewed critically the effect of light on the rate of development of insects and decided that the absence of light retards the development of insect larvae that normally live in the light, while the presence of light has a retarding effect for those that normally live in darkness. This generalization can be extended to population physiology since marine surface plankton are likely to contain light-resistant forms, while those from the deeper waters may all be light-sensitive. Tested animals include lobster larvae, a northern coral, amphipods, ascidians and shrimps (Huntsman, 1924). With temperature controlled, animals as diverse as the marine mussel *Mytilus* and certain salmon larvae in their early stages grow larger in darkness than in light. On the other hand, lighted salmon larvae show earlier differentiation and slightly better survival (Smith, 1916).

PHOTOPERIODICITY IN ANIMALS

The literature concerning the effect of length of day upon animals is large, complex, and rapidly growing. The relation between increased length of illumination and egg laying of birds or their seasonal migration has a long history (Chapter 2), but has flowered, so to speak, since the work of Garner and Allard (1920) on photoperiodicity in plants. We now know of short-day, long-day and indifferent day-lengths processes among animals as well as among plants. These include:

Gonadal Activation

Some sheep, deer, and goats correspond to short-day plants and may be brought to sexual activity by a decrease in the length of exposure to daylight. Spring-breeding birds and mammals—ferrets, starling, juncos, turkeys—and many others become sexually active with lengthening days; they correspond to long-day plants. Brook trout show a similar reaction. Stickleback fish, ground squirrels, guinea pigs, and guinea fowl are little or not at all affected by the length of exposure to daylight, and house sparrows breed both with increasing and decreasing length of day. (Bissonnette, 1936, 1936a).

Migration

The evidence collected by Rowan (1931) and others, including Wolfson (1945), though incomplete, supports the suggestion that certain birds migrate toward the north when their glands associated with sex are aroused by longer days and toward the south when the sex glands are showing short-day, autumnal regression. Rowan states his argument thus (p. 116):

"Nearly all animal activities are related in one way or another, directly or indirectly, to the influence of the sun. If a species leaves Alberta habitually in the first week of September it may leave (in different years) with the barometer either high or low; the earth may be sunbaked or the very gopher holes may be

its of its influence cannot be estimated at present.

Pelage and Plumage

The varying hare, *Lepus americanus,* is one of the numerous mammals that bear brown fur in summer and white fur in winter. The color change in the hare can be prevented by exposure to light for eighteen hours daily in the autumn, regardless of temperature, while the change from white to brown can be brought about in

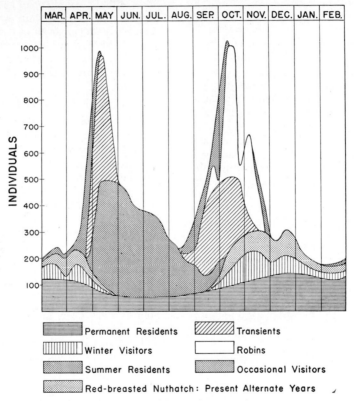

Fig. 23. Seasonal changes in the bird population of the beech-maple climax community in Ohio. (Redrawn from Williams.)

spouting water; the leaves may be golden or they may have fallen weeks before; the food supply may be abundant or it may have failed or be completely covered by a fall of snow. Only one factor of the environment would be certainly constant—the length of day. Its dependability suggests it as the inaugurating principle."

Length of day appears to be one important factor in the complex ecology of periodic migration. The full extent and lim-

January by a sudden increase to eighteen hours' illumination each day. The brown color will be retained throughout the year, despite occasional moults, provided the hares are exposed to an eighteen-hour day, and reduction to nine hours of light will bring a moult to white winter pelage even though the temperature remains at 21° C. (Lyman, 1943).

The pelt cycle of the ferret, *Putorius vulgaris,* of the mink, *Lutreola vison* (Bissonnette and Wilson, 1939), and of two weasels[*] can also be controlled by manipulating the daily light-dark ratio. For weasels, prime winter pelts can be produced in summer, despite high temperature, by reducing the length or the intensity of the lighted period. Thermo-induction is at most a minor factor in this reaction. With birds, it was shown before the modern period that moulting of the scarlet tanager and bobolink could be controlled in part by reducing illumination and that, even in midwinter, the males could be made to break out in their spring songs if gradually brought into the light for a week or two and meal worms were added to the diet (Beebe, 1908). More recently, Höst (1942) has controlled plumage color in the willow ptarmigan (*Lagopus lagopus*) by changes in the photoperiod, irrespective of temperature.

The length of day and night is approximately equal at the equator throughout the year. At 6 degrees from the equator annual differences may amount to forty minutes, and at 10 degrees the differences may be as much as seventy minutes. Small weaver finches, *Euplectes* (=*Pyromelana*) *franciscana* among them, were transferred to north latitude 42 degrees from near Senegambi in tropical Africa. In the experimental laboratory, the birds showed an annual rhythm in color pattern that could be controlled by varying the length of the lighted period. Fifteen or sixteen hours of light daily were more effective than fourteen hours or less. *E. f. pusilla* is in plainer plumage in southern Ethiopia from December to February; in the Sudan, the same species (typical *franciscana*) is in *nuptial* plumage from August to January. The two populations are geographically distinct. They are physiologically isolated by differences in their respective breeding seasons, yet the scanty evidence available suggests that each might assume the breeding habits of the other if transplanted to its habitat. The ability to respond to difference in length of days is apparently inherent in these tropical birds (Brown and Rollo, 1940; Friedmann, 1937).

Wings and Sexual Reproduction in Aphids

The marked and regular autumnal shortening of length of day is apparently a major

[*] *Mustela frenata noveborecensis* and *M. cicognanii cicognanii* (Bissonnette and Bailey, 1944).

factor in the production of bisexuality in the root louse, *Aphis forbesi,* of the strawberry. The change from parthenogenetic forms normally occurs in November, but was brought about in May by subjecting aphids to only 7.5 or eight hours of daylight during twenty four hours. The aphids were kept in a ventilated dark chamber out of doors. Temperature was not a factor, although wing formation for some aphids is suppressed by high temperatures. Shortening days may also produce alate forms reminding one of short-day plants. In the rosy apple aphid, *Aphis sorbi,* in which alate migrants appear in any generation after the third one in spring, they can be produced by experimentally lengthening the daily exposure to light; such changes suggest the reactions shown by long-day plants (Marcovitch, 1923; Shull, 1942). Other environmental controls of wing production in aphids are known; one of these, the effect of crowding, is discussed on page 347.

General Considerations

It must be emphasized that many other factors affect seasonal periodicities of animals. Stickleback fish respond to changes in temperature, but not to light. Vitamins, proteins, fats, and salts as elements of diet are frequently important. With field mice, light, food, temperature, rainfall, and locality all affect the seasonal cycles, and temperature, as well as lighting, is important for hedgehogs (Baker and Ransom, 1933; Allanson and Deansley, 1934). While our knowledge of the ecology of seasonal activities of animals is far from complete, we now know that photoperiodicity is a factor of major importance. Many of the cycles formerly thought to be under the control of temperature, or of an unanalyzed internal rhythm, have since been shown to be primarily controlled by the length of day. In evaluating these advances in knowledge, we need to remember that the changes produced by experimental manipulation modify times of expression of inherent potentialities rather than change the potentialities themselves.

The evidence indicates that the eyes are the chief receptors for the stimulation that produces photoperiodicity among animals. As with plants, low intensities are effective; an increase of as little as 1.7 foot candles can produce an increase in the activity and size of the testes in the starling, *Sturnus vul-*

garis. The speed of reaction of the testes is increased with higher intensities.

With the starling, red light is more effective than white and green in stimulating gonadal activity, and green light may actually be inhibiting when the relative heat energy reaching the birds is 10:1:2.5 for the three types of light (Bissonnette and Wadlund, 1931, 1932). Supporting evidence of the differential effects of different wavelengths on the breeding cycle is found among mammals. The winter anoestrus period of ferrets can be broken by increasing the length of day. The activating radiation extends from the red (6500 A) to the near ultraviolet (3640 A). The fairly sharp threshold at the red end, 7500 A, is barely effective even when its intensity is high; this indicates that the effect is produced by visible light rather than by heat.

An interesting geographical experiment is furnished by the shifting of animals from the northern to the southern hemisphere, or *vice versa*. When ferrets are transferred from the north during the period of lengthening or long days in spring or summer to the similar period well south of the equator, a change-over occurs in their breeding period corresponding to that induced by a comparable experimental change in the length of day among laboratory ferrets in the north. This tendency is not shown by bird migrants that penetrate deep into the southern hemisphere during our northern winter (the golden plover is an example). For such birds the annual rhythm may have become sufficiently stabilized so that it is not susceptible to alternation by the exposure gained in a single season. There is some evidence that storks, if held well south of the equator, will in time adopt the rhythm imposed by the southern environment. Deciduous trees transplanted into southern latitudes may show a similar lag of a few years before they become adapted to the changed conditions (Bissonnette, 1935; Rowan, 1931).

PENETRATION OF LIGHT INTO WATER

Most solid objects in nature are opaque to light—ice is an exception. The transparency of water is affected by many factors, among which are the following: (1) angle of incidence of the sun's rays that varies with the time of day, the season of the year (except at low latitudes), and latitude itself; (2) reflection from the surface (this is related to the angle of incidence, and reflection increases when the surface is ruffled, as it usually is); (3) thickness of the layer through which the light must pass; (4) clearness of the water as regards color and turbidity; (5) the wavelength of the light; and (6) the intensity of the incident light.

Measurements summarized by Welch (1935, p. 75) indicate that, in midnorthern latitudes, surface loss may run from 5 to 70 per cent. Of the light that enters the water, about one-third is lost in the first meter, about three-fourths in the upper 5 meters, and only about one-tenth remains at 10 meters' depth. These figures give orders of magnitude for relatively clear salt or fresh waters. From the surface downwards, light intensity is reduced according to the following equation (Clarke, 1939):

$$\frac{I}{I_0} = e^{-kL}$$

where I_0 is the initial intensity; I is the final intensity; k is the coefficient of extinction; L is the depth in meters, corrected to give the mean path of the light, since this is usually greater than the vertical depth; and e is 2.7. When reduction of light intensity and water depth are plotted semilogarithmically a straight line is obtained, the slope of which is determined by the extinction coefficient k, which becomes an index of transparency.

Light may penetrate a thousand meters or more in the open, subtropical ocean; photographic plates are darkened at 1500 meters in mid-Atlantic. At a thousand meters the amount of light is reduced to 3×10^{-6} of that 1 meter below the surface. The euphotic stratum in the open ocean reaches a depth roughly of 80 meters (30 to 100 meters) and is succeeded by a dysphotic stratum, sometimes called the twilight zone, that extends to the effective limit of light, a limit that often occurs at some 200 to 600 meters. On an exceedingly brilliant day, Beebe, in a "bathysphere dive," found light still visible to his eye at 571 meters; at 610 meters all visible daylight had vanished. In an earlier descent he found the lower limit of visibly detected light at 511 meters (Beebe, 1932, 1934).

The higher the latitude, the narrower is the lighted stratum, and marine organisms, accordingly, are more concentrated near the surface. Similarly, when the sun is near the horizon, the lighted zone is more shallow. Under all conditions and at all latitudes, the length of day decreases with depth.

Something of the degree of variation of the penetration of light is shown by the fact that, in Wisconsin lakes, the depth at which light is reduced to 1 per cent of that at the surface varies from 1.5 to 29 meters. Similar values for sea water are: 8 meters for the harbor at Woods Hole (Mass.); 32 meters for the Gulf of Maine and 149 meters in the Sargasso Sea. The last value indicates nearly or quite the most transparent water yet measured and is to be compared directly with the value of 29 meters for Crystal Lake, Wisconsin, which is the most transparent body of fresh water that has yet been studied with comparable methods. In Crater Lake, Oregon, thick green mats of green mosses, *Fontinalis* and *Drepanocladus,* grow over the bottom at a depth of 18 to 60 meters and are found at 120 meters. These two genera of mosses have been reported at a depth of 20 meters in Crystal Lake (Hasler, 1938).

Different wavelengths of light show differential penetration with depth. The usual rule of clear water is that light from the blue end of the spectrum is more penetrating. In strongly colored waters, the longer wavelengths of the red end penetrate more readily. In such waters, below 1 meter's depth, there is little light present with a wavelength of less than 6000 Å. With moderate transparency, such as is found in many lakes and inshore waters of the ocean, maximum penetration shifts to the yellow (about 5500 Å).

Such physical facts are meaningless ecologically until they have been considered in relation to living things. It can readily be understood that both the quantity and the quality of light is important in the energy-storing processes connected with photosynthesis. Some of the other biological relations will be considered immediately.

Bioluminescence

As the sunlight fades in the deeper waters of the ocean, bioluminescence increases. This ability to produce animal light is found among a variety of plankton forms in surface waters, including protozoans, jelly fish, ctenophores, copepods, and tunicates. A few burrowing animals of the littoral region also are photogenic—the annelid *Chaetopterus,* for example. A glowworm, *Arachnocampa luminosa,* excepted (Blakeslee, 1948), the ability is lacking among cave dwellers and in animals from fresh water, although a number of terrestrial forms are bioluminescent, of which the lampyrid beetles are outstanding examples.

In his bathysphere dives, Beebe saw the first animal bioluminescence at 207 meters; below that point there was a slow increase in the number of such forms, down to the greatest depth reached at 924 meters. Light is produced most efficiently by fishes, crustaceans, and cephalopods, some of which have highly specialized light-producing devices. Other animals give off light from diffuse organs scattered over the surface of the body (Harvey, 1940).

Coloration

The relatively rapid absorption of light with increasing depth, combined with the distribution of animal life from the lighted surface to the abyssal depths, allows a test of the possible relationship between intensity and quality of illumination and the coloration of animals. In the lighted benthal regions, coloration of animals is varied and, at times, related to the colors of the background; flounders, for example, may change their color intensity and pattern and match that of their background. Surface pelagic animals tend to be transparent, or they have blue, greenish, or brown backs with silvery sides and bellies. The pattern may be broken by wavy dark lines as in the mackerel. At some distance below the surface, in the so-called mesopelagic region, there is a preponderance of reds of various shades shown by a great variety of animals. The red spectral rays have been screened out, and these red animals must appear as though they were black. Almost all decapod crustaceans below 750 meters in the tropics, 500 meters in middle latitudes, or 200 meters in polar seas are red in color. Black and violet predominate as deep-sea colors. Some other animals become pale or colorless, and color patterns may or may not be present. Again, there is a marked contrast between these varied colors and the faded-out, white animals from caves.

Relation to Size of Eyes

The ratio of eye to head in crustaceans and fishes is called normal in surface-dwelling forms, but as the upper limit of the lightless zone is approached, the eyes increase in size and diminish again in the deeper sunless water. The deep-sea contains many species of fish with vestigial eyes; benthal fishes with eyes, apparently using animal light, are also present. Some pelagic cephalopods have large eyes, but their habits of life are not sufficiently known for us to be certain of the suggested correlation. In the twilight stratum of the sea, the increase in size of eyes suggests comparison with the similarly large eyes found in terrestrial geckos, owls, and tarsiers, for example, that are among the twilight or nocturnal animals of the land.

The enlargement of the eyes in the twilight zone of the sea may involve the whole organ or may be limited to an overgrowth of the lens to form the so-called telescopic eyes of small fishes; such telescopic eyes have evolved in five different orders and in eight different suborders. Further, the retinas of deep-sea fishes contain only the more light-sensitive rods; the cones are largely or entirely absent, and the sensitivity to light is much increased.

Vision

Light is important in photosynthesis, in growth and differentiation, in toleration, and, for many animals, in the initiation of annual breeding activities that may include migrations on a geographical scale. Even so, the most significant aspect of light for men and for other animals that, like man, live primarily in a world of visual shapes, lies in the fact of its visibility. The limits of visibility vary with different animals. Many vertebrates react as though their visual limits closely approach those of man. The limits of sensitivity of insects to light may differ widely from the human standard; some react to red light as they do to darkness, and others respond to ultraviolet patterns that are invisible to man.

With this approach we have another opportunity to appraise the biological significance of the penetration of light into water. Many fish depend on eyesight to locate their food. Consideration of numerous exceptions belongs elsewhere. As a result of the work of physiologists and experimental biophysicists, we are able to make an approximation of the relations of certain fish to visible light. Analysis of the visual power

of a sunfish, *Lepomis,* show that its maximal visual sensitivity has a sharp peak in the yellowish-green (5300 to 5500 Å), which is the part of the spectrum of daylight that penetrates most effectively into the waters of lakes and coastal regions where there is medium transparency. These are the waters in which fishes are most numerous. By extrapolation from the ascertained minimum of effective illumination for *Lepomis,* it follows that fishes with similar visual sensitivity would be able to see objects at the bottom of such waters and down to about 430 meters in the Sargasso Sea (Clarke, 1936; Bigelow and Welsh, 1924).

For such fish the effect of light on photosynthesis of plant planters, while fundamental for their existence, lacks the immediate importance of the visible qualities of light. The reflection of much incident light from the surface of water and its rapid differential absorption with depth are vital to the fish because of the effect on the depth at which food can be seen. Similarly, the long days of the Arctic summer permit birds to feed for long hours during the season of rapid growth of their helpless young. On the other hand, the short winter days may not give birds time enough to find sufficient food to maintain their high internal temperatures, despite their effective insulation by feather-bound air and fat.

Many animals can change their color patterns, and for these the stimulus for chromophoral changes often is picked up by the eye. Frequently, the ratio between the intensity of direct light from above, as contrasted with that reflected from the bottom, determines the shade that will be assumed. Some of these animals—the flounder, for example—when disturbed from a background to which they have been long adapted, will come to rest, if convenient, on a background with a color pattern like that to which they are already adjusted.

The response may be more complicated; apparently, toads, like men, can react to a patch of shade as a sign of associated factors, coolness or increased humidity, perhaps. Responses to what are essentially patterns of light and shade, especially when the patterns are in motion, bring visually motivated animals to their food and help them escape their enemies. In many instances these also involve the reaction to a sign, such as when waving grass discloses the presence of a mouse to the hunting hawk or the flight of a group of birds gives warning to a fox or coyote. It is a far cry from such reactions to patterns of light as a sign of unseen things to the gleaning of ideas from a printed page, yet the two reactions are not altogether dissimilar.

ULTRAVIOLET RADIATION

Even under optimum conditions, the atmosphere is opaque to ultraviolet rays shorter than about 2900 Å. Hence we are concerned here with the ecology of the small fraction of radiant energy that lies between the shortest visible wavelengths of

and the situation in Chicago is shown in Figure 24. The floor of the beech-maple forest under the full canopy of summer receives less than 1 per cent of the ultraviolet radiation to be found in direct sunlight (Strohecker, 1938).

The lethal action of ultraviolet radiation from the sun is important. The bactericidal effect begins at about 3650 Å and is stronger in the shorter wavelengths. The energy necessary to kill bacteria at wavelengths of 3650 Å is 10,000 times that needed to kill at wavelengths shorter than 3000 Å. Enzyme action may be destroyed by 3300 Å (lipase) or shorter wavelengths.

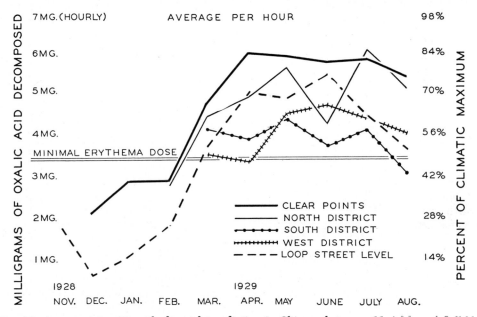

Fig. 24. Average intensities of ultraviolet radiation in Chicago between 11 A.M. and 3 P.M. (Redrawn from Tonney and DeYoung.)

violet light (3900 Å) and the limit of atmospheric transmission. This band contains about 1 to 5 per cent of the total radiation from the sun that is received at the surface of the earth. Often the atmospheric cut-off comes at longer wavelengths; when the December sun in Chicago stands about 20 degrees above the horizon, transmission stops at 3050 to 3100 Å. The smoke pall that hangs over many cities acts as do the forest leaves in nature to eliminate much of the ultraviolet that would otherwise be received at ground level. Baltimore is estimated to lose half of its potential supply,

Bacteria, fungi, nematode eggs, and viruses can be inactivated by radiation between 3400 and 4400 Å, a region in which sunlight is intense. This lethal action of visible light, as well as the similar effect of ultraviolet radiation, is an important factor in the low survival of infective agents in nature. The mechanism of inactivation differs; the bactericidal influence of white or blue light depends on the presence of oxygen, while ultraviolet kills *Staphylococcus albus* equally effectively in air and in high vacua (Duggar, 1936; Buchbinder, 1942; Hollaender, 1942).

The presence of ultraviolet rays increases the photopositive reaction of *Drosophila melanogaster* and causes *Paramecium,* which is indifferent to white light, to become photonegative. The stingless bee, *Trigona,* can be trained to respond to ultraviolet patterns invisible to the human eye (Warden, Jenkins, and Warner, 1940). These instances indicate that animals may detect and react to ultraviolet radiation to which man is totally blind. Flowers have patterns in the ultraviolet, as well as the familiar ones in the visible range. The extent to which these shorter wavelengths are important to nonhuman animals, insects particularly, in such matters as protective coloration, mimicry, and sex recognition in dimorphic species, is still an open question.

Certain chemical syntheses appear to be related to the photochemical effect of radiations of short wavelength. More nitric acid is found in the atmosphere at high altitudes than would be expected from amounts present nearer the earth. Irradiation of moist air by ultraviolet greatly increases the amount of oxides of nitrogen present, perhaps as a result of oxidation of ammonia. Formaldehyde can be detected in rain water, which presumably obtains it from the air, and may be produced from carbon dioxide and water in the stratosphere by irradiation with a wavelength of 2550 Å at altitudes where ozone absorption has not eliminated this wavelength (Ellis and Wells, 1941).

Ultraviolet radiation is closely associated with production of the antirachitic vitamin D that is accomplished by irradiation of certain sterols. This vitamin rarely occurs in living plants, although it may be rapidly formed by irradiation of dead plant material. It is abundant in certain oils of fishes and occurs widely among animals. We do not yet know the source of the rich supply in fishes. It has been suggested that vitamin D is formed by insolation of plankton, which makes up the food of many small fishes, which in turn contribute their supply to the larger fishes that devour them. We do know that ultraviolet rays may penetrate a considerable distance in sea water.

The alga, *Nitzschia closterium,* synthesizes vitamin A, but not D. Zooplankters contain ergosterol, but no vitamin D in the spring; in midsummer they may also contain this vitamin. If the fish get their rich supply from irradiated animal plankters, they must concentrate it with high efficiency. At least a part of their supply may be synthesized by the fishes themselves. Irradiation of birds and mammals is the source of much of their supply of vitamin D. Irradiation of fishes, on the other hand, whether done experimentally or naturally, does not seem to be similarly effective. The basking shark, *Cetorhinus maximus,* for example, suns at the surface for hours at a time, yet the vitamin D content of its liver oil is low, although some of its non-basking relatives have an unusually large amount.

Higher vertebrates lack the ability to synthesize vitamin D; they must ingest their supply or obtain it by the insolation of fats on the integumentary surface. The skin of many animals has a fairly good supply of sterols, and all animal fats contain them. Irradiated skin or fur or feathers, if oily, are antirachitic; even the irradiation of the feet is curative for rickety chickens that have their preen glands removed. The feathers and skin of the birds without preen glands have little antirachitic power. In licking fur, or in preening feathers, mammals and birds secure irradiated oil. Carnivores apparently acquire their needed supply by eating the feathers and fur of their prey, for the young of certain carnivores in captivity require such material as a part of their diet if they are to develop successfully.

Carotinoids are widely distributed among plants, and those found in phytoplankton in general have vitamin A activity. The carotene synthesized by algae is taken up by animal microplankters, including minute crustaceans. It can be used by animals as a source of vitamin A that they can make for themselves. Many mammals obtain vitamins from the symbiotic bacteria present in the alimentary tract. Thus, the cow does not need pyridoxine (vitamin B_6) in its food, since its supply can be obtained from the bacteria present in its extensive stomach (Heilbrunn, 1943).

Knowledge of the ecology of vitamins is inadequate, and is based largely upon observations on man and certain laboratory vertebrates. Such information is by no means final. Earthworms, snails, and other invertebrates contain substances with properties like those of provitamin D, and it is possible that this vitamin may be important for many invertebrates as well as for vertebrates (Giese, 1945).

SUMMARY

Light is a complex environmental factor that produces diverse ecological effects. First of all, it supplies energy for the photosynthesis of carbohydrates by green plants. Although this food synthesis is fundamental for the existence of animals, the whole process is largely taken for granted in the present account. Many organisms, plants as well as animals, react definitely to photic stimulation. Vision is important in the life of the majority of higher animals, whether insects or vertebrates. The direct effects of light on growth, development, and survival are mentioned, but not discussed at length.

Animals as well as plants may be affected by seasonal (or experimental) changes in the length of the daily period of illumination. Examples of both show long-day and short-day effects that express themselves in animals, by gonadal activation or regression among many seasonal breeding forms, by migration as in birds, and by pelage or plumage changes, including marked alteration in color. In certain aphids, the appearance of winged forms and the change from parthenogenetic to sexual reproduction may depend, among other influences, on the relative length of day (p. 123). Although other environmental factors, such as temperature, may control seasonal changes in plants or animals, photoperiodicity is frequently of prime importance. The precise significance of its influence can be determined only by direct tests for the given kind of organism. As might be expected, the eyes are the chief receptors concerned in the photoperiodicity of animals.

In a much different field, there is the matter of the penetration of light into aquatic habitats. Extinction occurs in slight depths in fresh waters, along sandy or muddy marine coasts, and, for a different set of reasons, in polar parts of the oceans exposed to the more slanting rays from the sun.

So far as vision is concerned, sunlight is replaced to a slight degree by bioluminescence in the otherwise aphotic depths of the sea. The animal inhabitants of different depths show fairly regular differences in color. The eyes are larger in the zone of perpetual daytime twilight, and are smaller or even lacking in forms from still deeper water.

Finally there is the matter of ultraviolet radiation from the sun, which never reaches the earth's surface at wavelengths shorter than 2900 Å; the atmospheric cut-off is usually effective at somewhat longer wavelengths. Lethal effects of ultraviolet rays on viruses, bacteria, fungi, and eggs of animal parasites are important for many animals, as are also the vitamin syntheses produced under exposure to such radiation.

8. GRAVITY, PRESSURE, AND SOUND

The mechanical forces in the environment of animals consist primarily of gravity and pressure, currents of air and of water, and sudden jars that provide mechanical shock. These constitute the molar forces. Sound is a closely related environmental factor, but will be discussed separately. Mechanical forces may impinge on the animal with great uniformity, as does gravity, or they may vary dramatically, as winds that range from dead calm to hurricane force. Running water also ranges from a gentle, steady flow that is almost imperceptible to the full turbulence of waters in flood. Waves vary enormously in pounding power. The less spectacular of these forces are not necessarily the less important.

GRAVITY

The direction of pull of gravity is invariable, and the intensity is also constant for any given location. The force of gravity varies with the distance from the center of the earth. This variation is not great enough to effect even those animals that by swimming or flight, by mountain climbing, or by being carried in currents, travel from equator to pole or move vertically from sea level to the height of Mt. Everest. For a given animal, change in relation to other environmental factors as a result of such vertical translocations dwarfs the effects produced by a variation in the pull of gravity.

The constancy of gravity makes analytical

experimentation difficult, and it is hard to determine the ecological effects that can be ascribed solely to its action. As yet, it is impossible to free an animal from gravity, although the pull can be equalized by rotation on a wheel or klinostat. A certain amount of experimentation is possible, because, within limits, animals react to centrifugal forces as they do to gravity. Since gravity is always acting on the animal while it is in the centrifuge, this method is mainly effective for centrifugal forces somewhat stronger than gravity. Difficulties in analysis are increased by the presence in nature of many vertical gradients such as those of light intensity, pressure, temperature, and related viscosity, or of oxygen or carbon dioxide content. These vertical intensity gradients are frequently steeper in water than in air; in either medium, some animals may react to environmental stratifications much as other organisms do to gravity itself.

THE EFFECT OF GRAVITY ON THE ENVIRONMENT

Isostasy

Probably the most far-reaching ecological effect of gravity is in relation to the principle of isostasy. According to this principle, the distribution of the continental platforms and the deep ocean basins is, in the main, a result of isostatic balance. Determinations of the pull of gravity show that this force is weaker over the continents than over the ocean, furnishing a strong indication that the materials underlying the oceans are heavier than are those in or under the continental protuberances.

If the earth originated largely according to the postulations of the planetesimal hypothesis, as it now seems reasonable to believe, differential distribution of densities in the earth's crust can be explained, as it was by T. C. Chamberlin, in terms of selective ingathering of planetesimal debris combined with selective placement of the products of weathering (Mather, 1939). Under any conditions, isostasy strongly suggests that the great continental platforms are relatively fixed and stable in location; hence gravity, working to establish and maintain isostatic balance, has been of fundamental importance in setting up the primary division of world habitats.

The principle of isostasy is related to the evolution of habitats rather than to that of individuals; like certain other environmental principles, isostasy is more closely concerned with community ecology than with the ecology of individuals.

Earthquakes

Earthquakes are of decidedly smaller importance than is the general isostasy or the planet. They are not rare. Including the slight tremors, earthquakes may well run to about 30,000 in a year. Those strong enough to destroy towns come much less often and averaged between one and four a year during the nineteenth century.

The majority of earthquakes take place in two relatively narrow bands that lie along the Alpine-Italian-Caucasian-Himalayan great circle and along the giant horseshoe made by the Pacific coast line. These two belts meet in eastern Asia. Of 160,000 earthquakes, 53 per cent were recorded from the Mediterranean-Himalayan circle and 38 per cent from the Malayan-Japanese-Andean horseshoe. Were the study of these two regions equally careful, these percentages would probably be different. In any event, 68 per cent of earthquakes strong enough to affect a tenth of the earth's surface originated near the borders of the Pacific Ocean. In contrast, earthquakes are rare in the great continental lowlands of central Russia, Brazil, and in mid-North America. The general rule is that of two adjoining regions, the one with the greater average slope is the more unstable.

Many earthquakes occur near volcanoes, particularly preceding eruption, or near those that are nearly or quite extinct. Such tremors cover a relatively small area of 100 to 200 square miles, have shallow foci that are usually less than a mile in depth, and show great intensity near the focus. General tectonic earthquakes have deeper foci, often ranging from 6 to 20 or more miles below the surface. Still deeper ones are known that have an estimated depth of from 125 to 375 miles or even more. The really large earthquakes cover areas up to two million square miles.

Earthquakes commonly result from displacement along a fault line. At times the disturbance follows a warping of the earth's crust with no visible fault. The amount of slipping ranges from a fraction of an inch to several feet and may be local or extend for a few hundred miles.

Submarine or coastal disturbances set up so-called tidal waves that arc not really tidal at all (Macdonald, Shephard, and Cox, 1947). These range up to some 90 feet in height and may travel even the 10,000 miles from South America to Japan. Such sea waves frequently cause changes along the shore line with accompanying destruction of the existing biota. On land, earthquakes may produce avalanches of snow or earth in mountains that may sweep away whole forests and may alter river courses or dam them to form lakes. Level land has been thrown into mild undulations, and the underground water level may be disturbed. These and other community effects will be mentioned in a later section (p. 578).

Finer Stratification of the Environment

Gravity continues to produce stratification in the environment. In regions where carbon dioxide escapes from the earth, its greater density causes it to displace the lower air, as in the death valley on the Dieng plateau in Java (Hesse, Allee, and Schmidt, 1937). Animal life is impossible in such areas. Not all the stratification in the atmosphere can be accounted for by gravity. Thus ozone is heavier than either oxygen or nitrogen, and yet, perhaps because it originates as an ionization product in the increased light intensity and decreased pressure of high altitudes, it is found mainly in the stratosphere. There is little ozone below an altitude of 52,000 feet, and 75 per cent of the total ozone is above 72,000 feet (Ellis, and Wells, 1941).

Stratification also occurs in aquatic environments. As was shown earlier (p. 93) in discussing thermal stratification, warmer, lighter water floats on colder strata, often with a fairly sharp boundary between the two. Fresh water is lighter than salt water. The fresh water released by melting glaciers and ice floes in summer overlies the denser cold water of the colder oceans, where surface layers may have only half the salinity of the deeper waters. Similar conditions prevail in regions of brackish waters. In the Baltic Sea, the surface waters tend to be less salt than is water from the depths. In the western Baltic, the salinity at the surface may be 8 to 12 *per mille* where the underlying water is 27 °/$_{oo}$, as opposed to about 35 °/$_{oo}$ for the water of the open ocean. The surface waters are diluted for

miles off shore near the mouths of large rivers. Depth-tolerant marine communities can exist in deeper, saltier waters even though overlaid by less dense brackish water, which they cannot tolerate, provided that the stratification on the basis of density does not restrict the oxygen supply too greatly.

Mechanical sorting of solid particles is of common occurrence. The heavier materials settle out of a watery or aerial suspension most rapidly and hence are found nearer their source, while the light dust or detritus may be carried much farther. Thus, coarser gravels are deposited near the mouth of a river, while the finer mud settles slowly far out in the lake or ocean. The annual formation of varves on the bottoms of the lakes in the temperate zone also results from selective settling. Coarser materials that accumulate on the ice or are brought in by spring freshets sink rapidly and become overlaid by finer stuff that settles more slowly; the finest particles are finally drawn down in the quiet water under ice in winter (see p. 82). Stratified rocks are a more permanent expression of these same tendencies. The bottom ooze of the oceans at a distance from coast lines is characteristically fine.

The pull of gravity provides food for the animals in the deeper waters of the ocean where food supplies come only from the drifting down of whole or disintegrating bodies, or excreta from above. Similarly, gravity produces the autumnal fall of forest leaves as well as occasional crashing of the trees themselves. The pull of gravity brings rain down to the earth and causes water to run toward lower levels. All the work of running water, which produces much of the dissection of physiographically young landscapes and causes the peneplain formation characteristic of older ones, results from the force of gravity. Few environmental forces are more important, more difficult to control experimentally, or more neglected in modern ecological study.

DIRECT EFFECT OF GRAVITY ON ANIMALS

Animal Structure

An animal's bulk cannot exceed certain structural and functional limits without endangering its life. The body weight must be adequately supported. Principles of physics indicate that there are natural limits to the size of land vertebrates, since the Weight increases by cubes, while strength length, the so-called cube rule, while the strength of a leg, as of any other structural support, is related to its cross section. Weight increases by cubes, while strength of support increases by squares. In large land animals, the bulk of the leg must increase out of proportion to the increase in weight of the remainder of the body.

The size that skeletal animals may attain with safety varies with structural mechanics and with the surrounding medium. Water has more power to support the weight of organisms than does air. Largely as a result of this relationship among animals in which skeletal support is important, aquatic forms may be larger than their terrestrial relatives when both follow a similar structural pattern. The Hercules beetle (*Dynastes*), which reaches 15 cm. in length, or giant grasshoppers (*Palophus*) that may attain a length of 30 cm., or, for that matter, the larger land crabs, are much smaller than the lobster (*Homarus*), which may be 60 cm. long, or the really giant crab (*Kampfferia*), whose appendages may reach a spread of more than 10 feet. The giant eurypterids of Paleozoic seas were far larger than their descendants, the terrestrial scorpions.

Similar conditions hold among the vertebrates. Modern whales, 30 meters in length and weighing up to 108,000 kilograms, dwarf living elephants, 3.5 meters in length and weighing only 4000 kilograms. The extinct reptile, *Brontosaurus*, which was 20 meters long and weighed perhaps 38,000 kilograms, is also dwarfed by modern whales. It was smaller than the similarly extinct, water-dwelling *Brachiosaurus*, whose periscope-like neck could easily have looked over a three-story building, if such had been present. It may have had a living weight of 45,000 kilograms (Romer, 1933).

Another effect of increasing weight of body brings in an application of Euler's principle that the capacity of a column to support weight varies inversely as the square of its length. In accordance with this principle, the leg bones of a heavy vertebrate tend to be shorter than those of related lighter species.

The various mechanical principles that are illustrated by the vertebrate skeleton, particularly for terrestrial forms, are closely comparable to many of those used in building houses or bridges. Considered from this point of view, functional osteology is closely related to ecology. This theme is well developed by D'Arcy Thompson (1917; see also Böker, 1935).

Among terrestrial animals, birds have a different ratio between supporting bones and body bulk from that found in mammals. They are able to carry more weight per unit of the supporting skeleton. Their supporting bones are excellent examples of the strength to be found in paper-thin structures formed into cylinders or with stiffened ridges. The frigate bird, with a wing expanse of 7 feet, weighs in all about 2 pounds; the skeleton weighs 4 ounces, somewhat less than the feathers.

The hollow tubular bones of birds contain air cavities connected with the lungs. Other air sacs, in addition to the relatively large lungs, are found in the body, and all are filled with air which, the lungs excepted, is usually warmer than that in the surrounding atmosphere. Often the inner air is much warmer than that outside; and the greater the difference, the greater is its lifting power. A considerable amount of somewhat warmer air is also trapped within the feathery covering of the body. All these mechanisms help lower the specific gravity of the whole bird.

The weight-saving mechanisms that reduce the specific gravity of birds are related to their powers of flight. The supporting planes formed by wings and tail also assist birds to maintain themselves in the air against the pull of gravity. The various devices are sufficiently effective so that large birds can maintain or gain altitude in soaring flight in uprising currents of air of such slight power that they will barely support dust particles or tiny winged insects.

Gravity exerts its persistent pull on aquatic animals. Other things being equal, these tend to be slightly heavier than sea water; most recorded values for the specific gravity of different types of cells lie between 1.02 and 1.08. Aquatic organisms have evolved certain flotation devices which, acting with the supporting power of the water, help to offset the tendency to sink. More than one device may be present in a given organism, and those of diverse evolutionary relationships may show convergent adaptations for floating.

Some of the flotation mechanisms are:

1. Reduction in skeleton or shell as compared with bottom-dwelling relatives—pelagic Foraminifera, for example.

2. The incorporation of large amounts of water in jelly-like matter, as in jelly fish. The excess weight of living protoplasm is thus spread and made to displace a larger amount of water.

3. The storage of light materials:

    (a) Water of lower specific gravity, as in the ctenophore, *Beroe*

    (b) The accumulation of fat; for example, the sunfish, *Mola mola*

    (c) The storage of oil droplets, as in the radiolarian protozoa or in the floating eggs of many fish

    (d) The inclusion of air in the float of siphonophores or in the air bladder of bony fish or in the air cells of the eggs of anopheline mosquitoes

    (e) Carbon dioxide secretion as a tissue-enclosed gas

4. Flattening of the body, as in most jellyfish, in which the oral aboral axis is usually shorter than the radial axis.

5. Suspensory projections. These are effective only among small or very small organisms; for example, the foraminiferan *Globigerina;* also many copepods, the tropical forms of which have a greater development of plumose extensions than do those of colder waters. This is in keeping with the reduced viscosity of warm water.

6. Suspensory projections increase the surface area. This is closely related to a general principle; the rate of sinking of a body heavier than water is directly correlated with the ratio between friction and the difference between the specific gravity of the body in comparison with that of the surrounding water. A relatively large surface area is associated with small size, and this is probably one of the important reasons why plankton organisms are usually small.

Animals with structures that aid in floating also frequently show behavior patterns that serve the same end. Swimming is one of the most common of these reactions. This may be either directly against the pull of gravity or a component of the normal forward movement. *Daphnia*, for example, show more or less rhythmic alternations of quiet, passive sinking and active, vertical swimming. The shark is an excellent example of an animal that avoids sinking by forward swimming, a component of which is devoted to maintaining level in the water.

The problem of keeping afloat is greater for animals that live in fresh water than for marine organisms. Similar antisinking mechanisms are employed. The relative wealth of the minute nannoplankton in lakes, as compared with marine habitats, is in part related to the greater difficulty of the larger, coarser animals in keeping afloat. (Nannoplankton is too small to be caught in a fine-meshed plankton net.) Often the nannoplankton has five times the biomass of the net plankton for a given body of fresh water. Further, the practical absence in lakes and rivers of large plankton organisms, such as are fairly common in the sea, is a testimony to the lesser support offered by the less dense and less viscous medium (see also p. 165).

Structures Produced by Animals

Constructed nests, unlike excavated ones, need adequate support, as do the roofs of excavated burrows or tunnels. Nests placed flat on the ground present a minimal problem in this connection; those built above ground, where, incidentally, they are safer from predation, must be constructed on, or against, or suspended from some solid support. The frequent nicety of the instinctive solution of the engineering problems should focus attention upon, rather than divert it from, the fact that it is the steady pull of gravity, as well as stresses from wind and rain, which is being built against. Covered and bridging roadways of ants or termites illustrate the same point. Even in subterranean nests, the frequent construction of a water drain is, indirectly to be sure, a response to gravity. It is a matter of some interest that termites may excavate wood until a paper-thin shell is left, but they do not excavate to the point of immediate collapse of the wood under its own weight.

Orientation to Gravity

In their reactions to gravity, animals may either orient and move in response to gravitational force, or they may merely maintain position or body equilibrium. They are geo-negative if the orientation is away from the earth's center of gravity, geopositive if toward that center, and transverse if at right angles to the pull of gravity.

The transverse reaction to gravity has resemblance to equilibrium responses, and both may be related to what is called the "ventral-earth reaction." In the ventral-earth reaction, the animal keeps an accustomed part of its body, usually the ventral side, oriented toward the ground or other effective substrate. This may be a complex response that is only partially, if at all, controlled by gravity. It has elements of a so-called dorsal-light reflex, of reaction to touch, and is also related to "righting behavior." It may be given to vertical planes and even to the roof of a cave, by climbing animals.

Distribution

Gravity, among other factors, contributes to the differential vertical distribution of animals. The supporting power of water, which is primarily a function of its density and viscosity, aids organisms in resisting sinking. In the ocean, such support becomes steadily greater at lower temperatures, as in polar seas or in ocean depths; in fresh water, the density component increases as the temperature falls to 4° C. and then rises somewhat with further chilling of the water. Salinity decidedly increases both density and viscosity. Equivalent organisms sink less readily in the sea under the pull of gravity than do those in fresh water (see p. 133).

Radiolarians, for example, of the family Challengeridae, show a vertical distribution apparently determined by the interaction of the pull of gravity and the support given by water. Those in the upper 400 meters tend to be smaller, 0.11 to 0.28 mm. in diameter; in intermediate depths, the radiolarian size tends to be intermediate, 0.21 to 0.28 mm. for the group under consideration; the largest ones sink to depths at which they can float, and below 1500 meters they range from 0.33 to 0.58 mm. Sagitta, the arrow worm, is larger and more mature in deeper water. The relation of buoyancy of water to cyclomorphosis in Cladocera has already been mentioned (p. 118).

The vertical distribution of both marine and fresh-water animals allows a generalization that approaches the dignity of an ecological rule: The younger stages in the life cycle occur nearer the surface than do the older, more mature forms. This applies both to animal plankton and to the more actively swimming nekton; the smallest leptocephali of eels furnish one exception to this rule. Newly hatched cladocerans (*Daphnia*) sink more slowly than do adults and so require less energy to keep afloat in the surface waters of lakes and ponds. In the ocean, active swimmers, such as sharks or fat-laden floaters like the ocean sunfish, *Mola mola*, are found in the surface waters. Such adults give other exceptions to the general rule that surface-dwelling marine fishes tend to be juveniles.

A geographic test of the ecological application of the interaction of principles concerned with flotation, despite the pull of gravity, comes from a diverse lot of organisms. Thus *Clione*, a pteropod (Gastropoda), the marine copepod, *Calanus*, and jellyfish, *Aglantha*, live in the surface waters off the Norwegian coast. They are absent in the warmer Atlantic, but live at a depth of 750 to 1000 meters. The support offered by the water is similar throughout this distribution (Hesse, Allee, and Schmidt, 1937).

Adaptive Behavior

Animals show adaptive responses to gravity other than those that are primarily concerned with the maintenance of level. The geonegative reaction of the caterpillars of the monarch butterfly (*Danaus plexippus*) and of other insects, aids them in finding their natural food. When fully fed, or in environmental stress, the organisms often become geopositive. The Colorado potato beetle (*Leptinotarsa*) becomes geopositive with desiccation. A final, familiar instance of the adaptive behavior of animals in relation to gravity must suffice. Juvenile spiders frequently travel to some vantage point where the air flow is little interrupted. They then spin a gossamer thread that is carried by the wind until at length the tiny spinner balloons away, at the mercy of the currents of air, to some new, wholly unchosen spot. Death, or a new lease on life, lies at the end of this aerial journey. Many spiders are broadcast so, although each individual organism is heavier than air and each is always being pulled toward the earth by the persistent, powerful force of gravity. The other side of this story, the distributing power of air currents, will be considered in the following chapter.

PRESSURE

Pressure acts as a mechanical process and as an osmotic phenomenon. Although these two forms of pressure have much in common, it is convenient, and probably logical, to consider the former in close connection with gravity and to treat osmotic pressure as one phase of the physicochemical environment.

Mechanical pressure may impinge locally on a small part of an animal, or the whole body may be subjected to altered pressure. Organisms that live at sea level are exposed to a pressure of approximately 15 pounds to the square inch. This constitutes a pressure of one atmosphere; it decreases with altitude and increases with increasing depth of water. The pressure to which organisms are exposed ranges approximately from half an atmosphere at an altitude of about 5800 meters to 1000 atmospheres at a depth of 10,000 meters in the ocean.

Animals are sensitive to uneven pressure on their bodies. The whole set of responses to touch illustrates this general statement. A moving ameba, for example, stops motion if subjected to a slight local pressure. Yet amebae are relatively insensitive to increased pressure equally applied to all parts of the body surface. For many animals, touch reactions are important in orientation. Many animals normally respond to touch so that some accustomed region, usually the ventral side, is in contact with the substratum, while other body surfaces are more or less free from local pressure. This is an important part of the so-called ventral-earth reaction, which was discussed in connection with responses to gravity; touch may often be more important than gravity in initiating righting behavior patterns.

There is space only for mention of the whole field of thigmotaxis, as the automatic response of nonsessile animals to tactile stimuli is now called. In general, many animals respond positively to slight local pressures and give a strong negative reaction to more intense ones. Touch is especially important for animals that live in weak light or in darkness and may be quite potent even for animals in lighted habitats. It is also an important element in sex recognition for many animals (Warden, Jenkins and Warner, 1940).

ATMOSPHERIC OR SUBATMOSPHERIC PRESSURE

At sea level at 0° C. the mean atmospheric pressure is 1033 gm. per square centimeter; this equals 1.1033×10^6 dynes /cm². It amounts to about 14.7 pounds per square inch and is sufficient to support a column of mercury 760 mm. high. For rapid approximations, 15 pounds per square inch or 1 kg./cm². may be said to equal one atmosphere's pressure. Ecologists, in common with many meteorologists, usually speak of pressures of less than an atmosphere in terms of the millimeters (or inches) of mercury that would be supported. Increases in hydrostatic pressure with depth are often recorded in terms of the standard atmosphere as a unit.

Ecological interest in variations of the total air pressure revolves about phenomena that accompany storms and those concerned with higher altitudes, whether encountered by mountain-climbing or by airborne organisms. Day-to-day variations in atmospheric pressures differ in different latitudes. In the belt of the trade winds, the mean barometric pressure is almost constant from month to month, although there is a small diurnal fluctuation of approximately the same amplitude day after day. In higher latitudes, more or less periodic variations occur during part of the year, and still larger and more sudden changes take place in connection with tornadoes and hurricanes.

It is not yet clear to what extent the variations in pressure are themselves important for animals, although there is no doubt that the winds and rains that accompany large scale fluctuations in atmospheric pressure have real ecological significance; these will be discussed later. Although there has been a considerable amount of experimentation, here, as elsewhere in researches that deal with the effect of pressure on animals, the better analytic experiments have seldom been concerned with the range of values normally found in nature. Aside from some good observation and experiments by Bert (1878), experimenters from Boyle (see p. 16) to the present have been primarily interested in subjecting animals to vacua or near vacua or to extremely high pressures, wholly impossible even on the highest mountains or in the deepest ocean. Such experiments test the physiological limits of protoplasmic possibilities without yielding clear indications of ecological properties. They illustrate a significant difference between physiological and ecological approaches to many problems.

A small amount of evidence connects emergence of pupae with change in barometric pressure. Chapman (1931) reports that "adult insects are said to emerge during times of high barometric pressure." In direct opposition, Uvarov (1931) cites evidence from Pictet that for the cabbage butterfly, *Pieris rapae*, "in nature the emergence of adults in the majority of cases does not take place except on the fall of the barometer, a reduction of one millimeter being sufficient to cause the emergence of all adults which are ready for it." If a pupa is about to transform when the pressure rises, emergence is said to be retarded until there is a new fall. The completion of pupation with a falling barometer, Pictet thought, may be a result of the greater ease with which the pupal cases may be broken with lowered external pressure. In view of all the other known variables and granting that the facts may be as stated, the explanation is too simple. Recent evidence indicates that hormones influence such phenomena (Wigglesworth, 1939; Scharrer, 1948).

There are many reports of a correlation between animal activity and change in barometric pressure. Again decreased activity has been recorded both for increased and for decreased pressures, particularly for the latter. While recognizing the possibilities, we conclude in general, as does Uvarov (1931) for insects, that the influence of normal variations of atmospheric pressure acting alone on the activities of animals has not as yet been critically studied. The relation to humidity is a particularly important matter which has not been properly separated from pressure changes.

Much greater pressure changes occur with altitude; the limits extend from about 800 mm. of mercury for land valleys below sea level to about 300 mm. in the highest mountains. It is extremely difficult to separate effects properly attributed to reduced pressures in nature from those produced by other environmental factors at higher altitudes. As altitude increases and atmospheric pressure decreases, the partial pressures of atmospheric gases also decrease. The fall in partial pressure of oxygen and carbon dioxide is particularly important; in fact, for man, the decrease in the supply of atmospheric oxygen becomes the most important factor in the study of the effects of high altitudes. There is also a lowering of temperature with altitude, and increases occur in the rate of evaporation, in light intensity, and in products of gaseous ionization. In the biotic environment, food supply is greatly reduced. These associated factors are sufficiently important to make it doubtful whether most of the ecological effects found in connection with low atmospheric pressures in high altitudes are to be attributed to low pressures as such. Birds are handicapped in their flight by thinness of the air as well as by the reduced supply of oxygen. Soaring flight is possible for certain birds in high altitudes, but even these have difficulty in taking off. Birds have been recorded as high as 27,000 feet. Hingston (1925, p. 194) saw a chough, a crowlike bird, at that altitude on Mt. Everest. It could take off down hill, but did not fly far. It is worth noting that the Andean condor nests at altitudes up to 16,000 feet.

INCREASED (*Hydrostatic*) PRESSURE

Unlike mountain climbing, or even aeroplane ascents, pressures change rapidly and dramatically with increasing depth of water; an added depth of 10 meters (10.07 meters at average density) adds another atmosphere of pressure. The ocean bottom has an average depth of about 3800 meters, and hence the pressure there is about 380 times greater than that at the surface; in the real "deeps," pressures approximate 1000 atmospheres. Such pressures acting alone produce important changes on the environment and on the animals living therein. Physical oceanographers use the "bar" as their unit for hydrostatic pressure; this corresponds to one million dynes/cm.^{2} Their working unit is the decibar (0.1 bar), which approximates the increase in pressure with each meter's added depth.

EFFECTS OF PRESSURE ON THE
ENVIRONMENT

Compressibility of Water

Within the ecological range, water is only slightly compressible. Johnstone (1923) writes that if water were wholly incompressible, the volume of the sea would be increased some 11 millions of cubic kilometers and its level would be raised almost 30 meters. Such a rise of mean sea level of 15 fathoms would alter the outlines of the land surface to a noticeable degree. Despite these superficially impressive totals, the buoyancy of water is little changed with depth, and an incompressible body which falls readily through the upper levels will continue to fall to the bottom; an easily compressible body, one that contains air encased in a more or less readily collapsible shell, will fall more rapidly with increasing depth. Cork and wood, because of the air contained in their cells, are good floats at the surface, but not at great depths, because the walls have collapsed under heavy pressure (Murray and Hjort, 1912; Johnstone, 1923).

The rate of falling of animal bodies and of animal excreta is important, because they are the external source of food for bathypelagic and benthic animals. A sinking velocity of 100 meters an hour will bring a body to the bottom in most places in less than two days (Krogh, 1934).

Pressure alters solubility, ionic dissociation, and surface tension in complex fashions even for inorganic solutions. As a general rule, pressure increases dissociation in weak solutions and, in theory, increases the surface tension. Change in solubility depends on the solvent and solute that are exposed to pressure (Cattell, 1936).

The effect of increased pressure upon the velocity of chemical reactions of liquids has been investigated for a number of organic chemicals, and some data are available for the pressures within the ecological range; more often the experimental pressures greatly exceed 1000 atmospheres. In general, the following rules appear to hold:

1. Reactions that proceed slowly in the absence of catalysts at a pressure of one atmosphere show an increased velocity at the same temperature under higher pressure. Rates of reaction may be increased from five to ten times by an increase of 3000 atmospheres.

2. Reactions that do not proceed at a pressure of one atmosphere in the absence of catalysts, similarly do not proceed at pressures up to 3000 atmospheres.

There is less evidence concerning the effect of increased pressures in aqueous solutions. Such reactions may be accelerated or retarded by pressure, depending on the catalyst concerned. Acid inversion of cane sugar is decreased in velocity by about 5 per cent when subjected to a pressure of 500 atmospheres (Fawcett and Gibson, 1934).

The influence of pressure on viscosity varies with the liquid tested; viscosity usually increases with pressure. Water is an exception since, at low temperatures and within the ecological pressure range, it shows a decreased viscosity under pressure. When salinity and temperature are disregarded, the probable difference between viscosity at the surface and at a depth of 10,000 meters is so slight as to be negligible; hence pressure exerts no significant influence on viscosity in the oceans (Sverdrup, Johnson, and Fleming, 1942).

EFFECTS OF PRESSURE ON ORGANISMS*

It is even harder to summarize the results that pressures, such as occur in the ocean, produce on animal life than it is to outline the physical changes such pressures make on the ocean. It is interesting and probably a significant comment on the current lack of information on the possible ecological effect of pressure in the ocean, that Sverdrup, Johnson, and Fleming (1942) do not discuss pressure in their chapter on "Animals in Relation to Physical-Chemical Properties of the Environment." Knowledge is particularly lacking of the ecological effects produced by high pressures acting over long periods of time. There are indications that many physiological processes continue unchanged in pressures no greater than those found in the ocean. Gastric and pancreatic juices, for example, retain their activity throughout this range. The action of some bacteriophages is retarded by exposure to 1000 atmospheres pressure for forty-five minutes, that for staphylococcus being thus affected. Others are unchanged by this pressure range even when they are sensitive to super-normal pressures such as are readily applied in the laboratory. Some yeasts fail to carry on fermentation at 600 atmospheres, although they recover complete activity after decompression, even after exposure to 1000 atmospheres. Similarly, the prolonged application of 700 atmospheres retards putrefaction of a variety of organic substances well contaminated with putrefactive bacteria; many bacteria are unaffected by brief exposure to much greater pressure.

Increased pressure has no effect on the activity of many protozoans until approximately 250 atmospheres are reached. This pressure causes a cessation of movement in

* The ecological literature in this field is not extensive. Regnard's summary (1891) is still useful. Hill's monograph (1912) covers a part of the field, and Cattell (1936) gave a scholarly view of some ecological and certain more narrowly physiological aspects.

Amoeba proteus, for example. The pseudopodia remain extended until about 450 atmospheres, at which point amebae round up and are likely to die if kept under pressure of this magnitude for an hour. Ameba gives evidence of increased fluidity under pressure. Some, though not all, of the individual protozoans, of such genera as *Chlamydomonas, Paramecium, Vorticella,* and *Euplotes,* survive pressures of 500 atmospheres for twenty-four to forty-eight hours.

Many invertebrate metazoans are inactivated by exposure to from 400 to 600 atmospheres. This group includes the mollusk, *Cardium;* the annelid, *Nereis;* the crustacean, *Gammarus;* and others. Some echinoderms (*Asterias*) and coelenterates (*Alcyonium* and *Actinia*) are more resistant and have survived pressures of 1000 atmospheres for an hour.

Surface fishes without swim bladders, or with emptied swim bladders, are not affected by 100 atmospheres, but lose mobility at double that pressure and are killed at 300 atmospheres. Small flatfish (*Pleuronectes*) consume oxygen at a decidedly increased rate up to pressures of 125 kg/cm². Fish eggs (Salmonidae) from surface waters will develop and hatch at the normal time up to 200 atmospheres. Eggs in 300 atmospheres are retarded about 10 per cent in time to hatching. Higher pressures kill the developing embryos, more rapidly, the higher the pressure; 650 atmospheres brought death in two days' exposure. Early cleavages of eggs of the common minnow, *Fundulus,* are retarded by 100 to 130 atmospheres when applied for from 0.5 to 3.0 hours. Such pressures produce abnormalities in developed embryos even though no significant changes can be observed during or immediately after the onset of treatment (Draper and Edwards, 1932).

The statement is common that the tissues of many deep-sea fishes have a loose texture when examined at the surface, and the assumption has been that the enormous pressure under which they normally live would make their flesh firmer. Such assumptions have not been confirmed. Pressure acts on fish tissues as it does on water, whieh (p. 136) shows a reduction of less than 2 per cent at 4000 meters' depth; fish tissues under similar stress should increase in firmness by about that amount (Krogh, 1934).

Pressures, such as obtain in the ocean, tend to increase the hydration of colloidal systems. Gels in water take up more water when compressed. "According to the theorem of Le Chatelier, pressure, which causes a decrease in volume, should promote the imbibition of water" (Cattell, 1936). Bayliss (1931) states Le Chatelier's theorem as follows: "When any tendency or factor capable of changing the equilibrium of a system is altered, the system tends to change in such a way as to oppose and annul the alteration of this factor." If a reversible reaction involves a change in volume, the application of pressure will shift the position of equilibrium to the side of lesser volume, and if the number of molecules differs in two aspects of a reacting system, increased pressure will shift equilibrium towards the side with fewer molecules. This principle is widely exhibited among animals experimentally exposed to pressures such as obtain in oceanic mid-depths; characteristically, such animals show great swelling. Animals accustomed to such pressures must acclimate to this as well as to the other peculiarities of their deep-sea environment.

Fishes with air bladders, diving mammals, and diving birds introduce a complication. The increasing pressures produce important changes in the tension of the gases dissolved in blood and other protoplasm. A sudden release of pressure often permits gas bubbles to form in the blood (gas embolism) with harmful or fatal results. The invasion rate of nitrogen is an important determining factor in gas embolism. Men can stand exposure to about 9 atmospheres if unaided by a rigid suit and if compression and decompression are slow. Small mammals have successfully withstood pressures up to 25 atmospheres, again if decompression comes slowly. Whales dive into higher pressures than these and may go below the level of alveolar collapse, after which nitrogen invasion of the blood must be slow. Gas embolism occurred in a seal after an experimental dive to a pressure of 30 atmospheres; it probably occurs exceptionally in whales, which, when harpooned, may dive to 800 meters. Sperm whales must be able to withstand large changes in pressure, since they feed mainly on giant squid that live pelagically at depths of 500 mm. (Krogh, 1934; Scholander, 1940; Sverdrup, Johnson, and Fleming, 1942).

Most fishes maintain an internal density about equal to that of the surrounding water. For those with air bladders, this is done by appropriate exchange of gases between the swim bladder and the blood. When such a fish descends to a deeper position in the water, the increased hydrostatic pressure compresses the gases in the bladder to a point at which the swim bladder no longer helps support the fish. Under these conditions, fishes adapt themselves by putting more gases into the bladder. As fishes rise in the water and pressure is released, the bladder is overbuoyant, and some of the gases are absorbed. The mechanisms whereby these changes are brought about have not yet been demonstrated (von Ledebur, 1937; Brown, 1939).

The present summary indicates clearly that the ecology of the deep sea is not yet understood. There is a need for precise observations and experimental studies, particularly of the effects produced by continued exposure to different pressures within the ecological range. It is clear that we cannot understand the ecological complex in the depths of the ocean on the basis furnished by our more extensive knowledge of relationships at the surface even when reenforced by principles derived from physical, chemical, and physiological research on the physiology of high pressures. We do know that hydrostatic pressures within the ecological range may affect such basic matters as the velocity of chemical reactions, the viscosity of certain fluids, the imbibition of water, and the physiological activity of some bacteria and bacteriophages. Pressures greater than the ecological range bring about irreversible changes in proteins; they inactivate most enzyme systems and strongly affect the bacterial toxins and the viruses.

The simpler forms of life—bacteria and Protozoa, for example—are more sensitive to pressure than are nonliving systems, and the sensitivity increases in general with increasing complexity of organization. Most aquatic invertebrates are less sensitive to pressure than are fishes, and fishes lacking an air bladder are much less sensitive than are birds and mammals. The latter relationship may be stated more generally as follows: Animals are much more resistant to marked changes in environmental pressure in the absence of free air or gas within the body.

Many instances have been recorded in which small increases in pressure are stimulating; and although apparent exceptions occur, this, too, may prove to be a general condition. Greater pressure is uniformly depressing and becomes lethal if sufficiently increased. The changes produced are reversible in the lower ranges, and high pressures are less likely to be harmful if compression is relatively slow and particularly if decompression is gradual.

Eurybathic animals exist that have a wide vertical range; Anthozoa (Coelenterata) furnishes examples. Many plankton and nekton organisms move vertically through great pressure changes in the daily routine of their existence; malacostracan crustaceans, for example, make diurnal migrations of 200 and possibly of 600 meters (Waterman, Nunnemacher, Chace, and Clarke, 1939). Other animals are restricted in vertical range; that is, they are stenobathic. Air-breathing animals or fishes with air bladders are surface, stenobathic forms, and fishes of the *Macrurus* type are stenobathic animals of the ocean depths.

SOUND, SUBSTRATAL VIBRATIONS, AND MECHANICAL SHOCK

Sounds are produced and conveyed by mechanical vibrations. Although they may be caried through fluid or solid media, sounds of ecological importance are best known as vibrations transmitted through air. They vary primarily in pitch and intensity. Those of low pitch, which result from vibrations of low frequency, grade into vibrations that are detected by touch rather than by an auditory organ. At certain relatively low frequencies, both methods of detection may be used. Mechanical vibrations with too low frequencies to produce physiological sound may be carried as substratal vibrations, and these are reacted to by a variety of animals. When such vibrations are sudden and intense, they produce mechanical shock, a stimulus to which a wide range of animals react. These three physical phenomena—sound, substratal vibrations, and mechanical shock—are closely and inextricably interconnected.

All three types of vibrations are produced by nonliving forces in nature. Waves lap gently on the beach or crash heavily in storms. Winds whistle through rock crevices. There is the sharp crash and roll of thunder, and the swish and patter of rain. Rocks, displaced by frost heaves, may roll noisily down a mountainside, and the sound of a mountain avalanche or of a major earthquake carries still farther. The roar of a waterfall or of a river in flood is fairly distinctive. Despite such physically produced vibrations to which many animals may react, especially birds and mammals, it is the substratal vibrations and sounds of biotic origin that are of prime importance in ecology, and their discussion is not directly appropriate in connection with the physical environment.

Hearing is much more important for man than for most other animals, especially because of the use of sound in intercommunication in our species. This holds true in human society even though our sense of hearing is less keen than that of certain other animals and although our ear muscles are undergoing evolutionary retrogression. In general, sight, the chemical senses, and touch have decidedly greater significance for animals than does phonoreception. The importance of sounds is further limited since they are primarily restricted to the terrestrial environment or, at most, to the surface regions of bodies of water.

One of the most dramatic uses of aerial vibrations with regard to the relation between animals and their physical environment is their employment by bats in flight as a means of avoiding obstacles. The method by which these dusk or night-flying forms are able to fly successfully through dark forests or in and out of long tortuous caves without injury has long been a matter of controversy. Spallanzani is said to have found in 1794 that blinded bats could fly as skillfully as those with full vision and

that they could even successfully avoid silk threads hung about the room. Jurine (1798) discovered that stopping the ears of bats lessened their ability to avoid objects, an observation that Spallanzani confirmed (Allen, 1939; Jurine, 1798). The fact that a few wires stretched over a watering trough at night form a good collecting device for many bats is only apparently in contradiction to these observations, since experiments by Griffin and Galambos show a minority percentage of contacts made by bats flying through a barrier of wires.

It now appears that bats emit sound near the upper range of human hearing (between 20,000 and 30,000 cycles per second) (Best and Taylor, 1943) and also give out short bursts of supersonic vibrations of from 45,000 to 50,000 vibrations per second. These can be made audible to man and recorded by modern sound-detecting and amplifying systems. Flying bats detect obstacles in their path by emitting supersonic notes that appear to be reflected back and form what may be called sound shapes and shadows. These are detected by the bilaterally placed ears. A small, active, alert bat, by appropriate maneuvering in full flight, can avoid wires only a millimeter in diameter. Ability to avoid such small objects varies from species to species. It is greater in the smaller insect-catching species than in larger forms. Different individuals within the same species show varying degrees of this power, and the same individual loses its precision of performance with increasing fatigue. Do night-flying insectivorous bats find their often minute particles of food by the same device (cf. Allen, 1939, p. 136; Griffin and Galambos, 1941; and Galambos and Griffin, 1942)?

9. CURRENTS OF AIR AND OF WATER*

Currents in air or water are a direct expression of the pushing power of pressure, which, in turn, results from the pull of gravity. Other things being equal, such currents run from regions of greater to those of lower density; and the rate of flow is faster, the steeper the density gradient. Temperature differences produce density differences that have great ecological effects in setting up and maintaining currents of either air or

water. Heated fluids become lighter and tend to rise and flow over cooler parts of the same mass. Contrariwise, chilled fluids become denser and sink until they are in

* For an extension of this discussion, the interested reader is referred to the following: Byers (1944), Humphreys (1942), Kendrew (1938), Sverdrup, Johnson, and Fleming (1942), Wenstrom (1942), and Willett (1931, 1944).

equilibrium with the surrounding mass or until they meet a denser substratum. Then, if the supply of dense material continues, they flow under the lighter medium that has been pushed aside in sinking. These forces, acting on a global scale, whether in the atmosphere or in the hydrosphere, tend to set up planetary circulation in which air (or water) rises in the tropics and sinks at the cold poles. The currents of air are known as winds; those of water are called currents.

currents of air or water can be stated simply: If one faces down stream, or down wind, this force causes currents that are free to do so, to bend to the right in the northern and to the left in the southern hemisphere. Winds blowing toward the equator, if they persist over long distances, tend to blow from east to west, that is to become east winds. Conversely, winds blowing toward the poles, if similarly persistent, tend to become west winds such as prevail in middle latitudes.

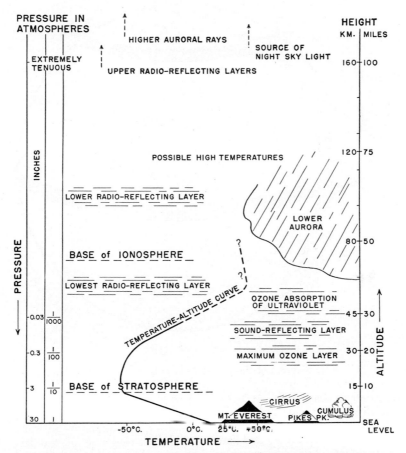

Fig. 25. General structure of the atmosphere. (Modified from Wenstrom.)

The simplified global system just outlined is complicated by another potent world force that acts similarly on wind and on water currents and is called the deflecting force of the earth's rotation. It is sometimes referred to as Corioli's force, after the French physicist who first gave a mathematical expression for it. The effect produced by the force of the earth's rotation on

As a result of the interaction of these two general sets of forces, a global system of currents is established and maintained both in the atmosphere and in the oceans. The schematic systems are complicated by various other factors. For ocean currents, some of the complications are furnished by the containing continents, by differences in salinity, and by the configuration of the bottom, particularly in the higher latitudes. The distribution of the masses of land and water and the topography of the land, among other things, also disturb the simple working of the diagrammatic planetary pattern for winds especially in the lower atmosphere and more especially over the continents. The world systems of winds and of ocean currents have much in common

in which the air is mixed by convection currents and in which temperature decreases with increasing height. Above the troposphere is the stratosphere, in which convection currents are lacking and in which temperature, when not independent of altitude, becomes higher with increasing distance above the earth. Above the stratosphere, at an altitude of almost 50 miles,

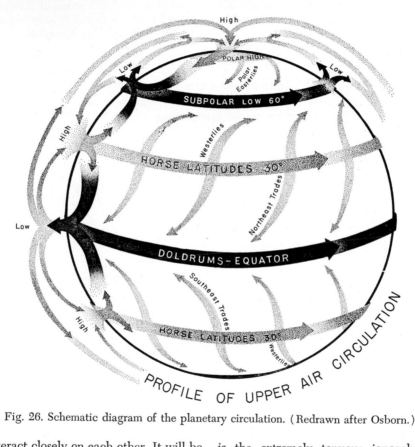

Fig. 26. Schematic diagram of the planetary circulation. (Redrawn after Osborn.)

and interact closely on each other. It will be helpful to consider the winds first, not as entities in themselves, as meteorologists do, but in their ecological relations, and later to turn to a similar, brief discussion of ocean currents.

THE ATMOSPHERE

The atmosphere has a more or less definite structure that is schematically summarized in Figure 25. The portion nearest the earth is called the troposphere. It extends some 6 or 7 miles above sea level in temperate latitudes and usually goes up 8 or 10 miles in the tropics. This is the region

is the extremely tenuous ionosphere. Although the atmosphere is composed of "thin air," it weighs in all some $56,328 \times 10^{11}$ tons, and one of the large cyclonic storms, characteristic of the temperate region, may cause the physical translocation of five million-million tons of atmosphere.

THE PLANETARY PATTERN OF THE WINDS

If the earth's surface were relatively homogeneous and smooth, we would expect to find an average planetary wind system like that outlined in Figure 26. Some distance up, say about two and a half miles, still well within the troposphere, the move-

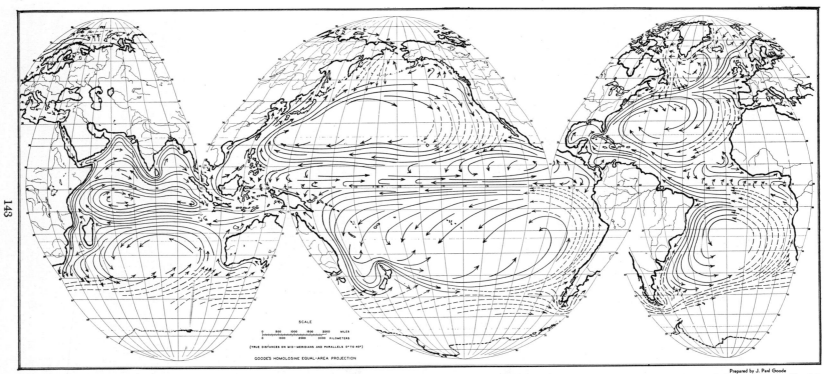

SCALE

0   500   1000   1500   2000   MILES

0   1000   2000   3000   KILOMETERS

(TRUE DISTANCES ON MID-MERIDIANS AND PARALLELS 0° TO 40°)

GOODE'S HOMOLOSINE EQUAL-AREA PROJECTION

Prepared by J. Paul Goode
Published by the University of Chicago Press, Chicago, Illinois
Copyright 1917 by the University of Chicago

Fig. 27. Oceanic winds in July. (Redrawn from Goode and Kendrew.)

ment is much simpler. The actual wind system of the lower atmosphere is more complex, especially over the continents. The winds that blow over the oceans during the northern midsummer season are shown somewhat realistically schematized in Figure 27. In July the sun shines vertically some distance north of the equator, and the global wind system is then shifted to the north of its average position. Northeast trade winds occur in the Atlantic and eastern Pacific, and southeast trades are typically developed in all three oceans of the southern tropics. The polar easterlies blow sparingly at the latitudes that are clearly shown in Figure 27. The southern westerlies are charted as the winds that blow around the world, and characteristic cyclonic whorls occur in the corresponding regions of the northern hemisphere. The Indian monsoon is well developed.

We cannot examine the climatic effects produced by these winds in detail. In general, the situation is as follows: The ascending moist air in the equatorial region, when chilled, furnishes the downpour of tropical rain characteristic of the area. The seasonal shift of the heat equator with the position of the sun gives the simplest cause of rainy and dry seasons that are characteristic of the north and south borders of this tropical rainy belt. On both sides of these equatorial doldrums are the descending, dry, easterly trade winds. When they develop over land they tend strongly to help produce the circumtropical arid regions; the Sahara Desert is a notable example. As the trade winds pass over extensive bodies of water they pick up moisture that is precipitated as rain on the windward side of any mountains occurring in the trade wind belt. In India, the onshore monsoon brings the rains, and the offshore monsoon of winter establishes the dry season.

Poleward from the dry trade winds, the prevailing westerlies bring much rain, particularly to the western side of the continents or islands in their path. They are not a steady current, especially in the northern hemisphere, and the accompanying rains are usually intermittent. The great north-to-south mountain ranges—the American coastal ranges or Rockies, for example—cast a decidedly dry "wind shadow" to the east. Precipitation is relatively slight in the cold polar regions. This analysis of global conditions reinforces an earlier, more generalized account of world rainfall (p. 79).

The Prevailing Westerlies and Air-Mass Analysis

The conditions over the continents in the region of the northern prevailing westerlies are of especial interest to ecologists, both because of their complexity and because much of the more detailed ecological study has been done in this world belt. Here, particularly in winter, large cyclonic storms move eastward in almost regular weekly progression. The rate of translocation of the whole storm system is about 15 miles per hour in summer and about 25 miles per hour in other seasons. According to air-mass analysis, this succession of weather is based on five relatively simple relationships. These are summarized here in somewhat simplified form from an already overschematized statement by Wenstrom (1942); they may well be compared with a more generalized account by Willett (1944).

1. Air masses that remain for some time in a given region become air conditioned in temperature and humidity relations and can be identified by temperature-humidity characteristics.

2. These large masses tend strongly to retain their characteristics even when they move to wholly different conditions. Changes begin near their contact with the ground and only gradually affect the upper parts of a given air mass. These masses are moved about by various forces that, in the large, are under the control of the planetary wind system.

3. When two dissimilar air masses come in contact, they do not mix immediately, but retain a more or less definite boundary or "front" where mixing takes place. Warmer, lighter air flows up and over a sloping mass of colder air as it would over sloping land, or the cooler air underruns the warmer mass.

4. The contact and mixing of air masses along a "front" produce clouds, rain, and other types of weather, often in fairly rapid succession.

5. Weather changes can occur within the air masses either as a result of the internal characteristics of the mass itself or because of the movement of the mass to a new location.

Air masses become modified as they travel across the continent so that they lose their originally distinct characters just outlined; for example, a polar air mass is much changed by passing over one or more of the Great Lakes. Other things also happen. Thus a tropical Gulf air mass may be in contact with the ground for the first few hundred miles up the Mississippi valley; it may then flow up and over one cold mass and have another push in under it from the west and so occlude the warm air from contact with the ground. Even with such complications, this concept of air masses gives a framework on which much of our knowledge of the winds and the weather in the zone of prevailing westerlies may be arranged in manageable form.

The cyclonic and anticylonic air circulations, which are typical of the middle latitudes, especially in the northern hemisphere, are extremely complicated phenomena, and, despite recent, rapid advances in knowledge, summarized by Byers (1944) and Willett (1944), they have not yet been adequately analyzed by meteorologists to allow us to make a simple, truthful summary. Much more is known about them than we have indicated, but the interactions of mechanical and thermodynamic forces are not yet understood completely, even qualitatively. Meterological explanations remain, as Willett stated in 1931 (p. 211), "at best only roughly qualitative and in parts entirely hypothetical."

It must not be forgotten that the weather is a matter of prime importance in the lives of many animals other than man.

Monsoons and Local Winds

A monsoon is a large-scale, periodic wind circulation that has a direct thermal origin and is characterized by a seasonal change of direction. It is closely associated with sizable land masses and affects neighboring parts of the sea. Although recognized in other continents by meteorologists, monsoons are best developed in Asia, where they blow out over coastal waters of the Pacific and even extend far across the northern Indian Ocean. A high pressure area exists in central Asia during the winter with a resulting steady outflow of air over much of the continent; this becomes distinctly dry south of the Himalayan barrier. Conversely, in summer, a strong monsoon area of low pressure exists north of the southern mountain chain, causing an inflow of air the effects of which reach beyond the equator. The resulting summer monsoon in India brings in much moisture and produces the well-known monsoon rains. These rains

are heaviest on the southern slopes of the Himalaya Mountains, where precipitation in the Khasi Hills of Assam reaches an annual average of more than 35 feet of rain, most of which is brought in by the summer monsoon.

Although the Indian monsoon is the best-known one in the world, actually the screening mountains prevent a typical winter monsoon from reaching the Indian plains as it does those of southeastern China. The monsoon circulations dominate the climate of India. The rain-bearing summer monsoon may arrive early or late and may be strong or weak, resulting in heavy or light crops or in complete crop failure. Similar effects are produced on vegetation in general with the result that animal life, including man, is exposed now to plenty and again to severe starvation (Willett, 1944; Byers, 1944).

In many ways the Indian monsoon is a local wind on a subcontinental scale. Much smaller versions develop on a diurnal basis along most coasts where onshore breezes prevail during the day, when the land warms more rapidly than the neighboring water; these turn to offshore breezes in the late evening as the land radiates its heat more rapidly than does water. A large lake, like a miniature ocean, has its own set of shore breezes, and forests show a similar, though still fainter, set of air currents—outward on warm, sunny days, and inward on clear nights. Among mountains, the warmed valley air creeps up the mountainside during the day, and the chilled air of the upper altitude flows down the mountain slopes at night. Long, canyon-like valleys may channel these flows into near-gale force.

The Chinook wind of the eastern, leeward side of the Rocky Mountains, which is similar to the foehn wind of the Alps, deserves special mention. A moist air mass, saturated and rainy, ascends the western slope of the Rockies. It cools relatively little despite its increase in altitude, since it is warmed by the latent heat of vaporization of the water released by condensation to form rain or snow. On the east slope of the mountains the air mass, now dry, becomes compressed as it flows down into regions of greater pressure and is warmed by the compression to a temperature well above that it had before crossing the mountains. The altered mass flows out onto the northern plains as a warm, dry Chinook wind that may raise the temperature some 10° C.

in fifteen minutes and evaporates snow in dramatic fashion.

A somewhat related phenomenon is the location of a "frostless belt" or "orchard zone" near, but not at the foot of, a mountain slope. The belt is located low enough for the descending night air to be warmed by condensation, and higher than the point reached by nightly accumulations of cold, dense valley air. The "frostless belt" is warmer than are the adjacent higher or lower levels, and this relationship is especially important during the clear cold nights, when frosts occur, in spring or autumn. Its significance in animal ecology has not been analyzed adequately.

Wind Storms of Great Violence

The high transport value of tropical hurricanes, called typhoons in the Far East, and temperate tornadoes, together with their effects on the distribution of land life, calls for a brief mention of these powerful storms (cf. Darlington, 1938a). Tropical hurricanes arise near the doldrums, where convection regularly carries much water vapor aloft. Latent heat released by condensation of water, if great enough, induces an increased inflow of moist air; the condensation of this new moisture releases still more heat energy, and so the storm gets the enormous energy that keeps it going. The force of the earth's rotation spins the hundred-mile wide disk of activity off on a course that may run a few thousand miles over the oceans before subsiding. Speed of translocation of the whole revolving mass of air is ordinarily about 10 or 12 miles an hour. The section of the storm to the right of the general track is the more dangerous half, since to the speed of the circular hurricane is added the speed of translocation of the whole. On the left of the hurricane track, speed of general movement is subtracted from the circular wind velocity, and this becomes the less dangerous part of the storm, though it still has potent force. On land, much of the damage is done by the left half, especially near the hurricane center, where there is a rapid reversal of wind direction. Objects somewhat adjusted to stress from one side may break when quickly exposed to reversed stress. Hurricane winds frequently blow at the rate of 150 miles per hour, and smaller gusts within the larger mass may have a velocity of a hundred miles more. The great

hurricane belts of the world include the West Indies and Florida, the Philippine Islands, China Sea, and the southern margin of Asia. Hurricanes do not persist long over land.

Since every animal is a member of an ecological community, the effect of a hurricane and accompanying rainstorms may be complex. A colony of aphids is at the center of a fairly simple biocoenose that includes ladybird beetles, syrphid flies, and many more forms. A hurricane in Florida reduced a given aphid population by 80 per cent, destroyed syrphus fly larvae, ladybird larvae and all other aphid predators except adult coccinellid beetles. The storm swept away all aphids infected by the fungus, *Empusa*. Within a fortnight after the catastrophe, the local population of selected aphids increased some two-and-a-half times and was about half as numerous as it was before the storm struck it (Thompson, 1928). The disruption of ecological routine in littoral and forest communities is often great, and the ecological balance, normal for the local situation even when occupied by a climatic climax, may be delayed for years.

Hurricanes sometimes move out of their usual storm tracks, as did the great New England hurricane of September, 1938. This storm carried with it birds from three ecological habitats:

1. Sea birds, normally found off the coast of North Atlantic states, including Leach's petrel, red phalerope, and the parasitic jaeger.
2. One species from tropical seas, the sooty tern.
3. Birds from the Carolina coasts, especially the snowy egret, Wilson's plover, gull-billed and royal terns, and the black skimmer. The last mentioned species was brought into New England in large numbers. On its way north, the hurricane swung inside Cape Hatteras, where black skimmers were abundant, and carried off large numbers.

The storm had two other marked effects. It picked up migrating birds, carried them back north, and caused much loss of life among land birds, especially of Cape Cod (Hill, 1945). Other examples of aerial transport will be discussed within the next few pages.

Tornadoes are intense, smaller storms of great power that typically arise in the midlatitudes in the warm southern sector of an otherwise routine and moderate cyclone. They are especially abundant in the North

American midwest and midsouth. Tornadoes may uproot stands of large forest trees with catastrophic destruction of the whole biotic community. A tornado in Western Iowa during July, 1940, killed an estimated 1000 birds in a tract of about 100 acres (McClure, 1945; see p. 339).

More Routine Results of Wind Action

In addition to the large-scale climatic effects produced by winds, such as have already been suggested, air currents exert important controls on the micro-climates of habitat niches. For example, winds modify temperature both directly by transport of air of changed temperature and by influencing the evaporating power of the air. The strength of the wind in the habitat niches in which most small animals carry on the major part of their life activities is greatly reduced as compared with that in the open air a few inches, feet, or yards above. The wind intensity to which most insects are exposed is on the order of 10 per cent or less of the air movement measured by the meteorologist. Air drift near the floor of a Panama rain forest is known to average only 1 mile a day at a time when the winter trades speed over the forest roof at a rate 575 times greater. Geiger (1927) gives a brief generalized discussion of the effect of forests on air movement.

The wind creates major as well as minor habitats. It is responsible for the formation of the sand dunes of the world, whether of the desert or long shore lines. The capture of dunes by vegetation and animals is one of the well-worked chapters in successional ecology (p. 566). The formation by wind action of the great, fertile loess beds of China and of central North America is even more important. The sheet erosion by winds in deserts, in semiarid and drought-stricken dust bowls of the world, fills, in part, the other side of the picture. Wind dissection of regions characterized by stronger relief, as in the arid southwestern United States, yields picturesque landscapes, often of great beauty and of marked poverty of animal life.

Animal Habits Affected by Wind

The strong winds in exposed habitats are a special handicap, particularly for animals with weak powers of flight. Habits of life are frequently changed from those shown by related forms in less windy regions. Birds hide behind wind-breaking ledges of rock or more casual stones. In the windy desert in high Tibet, as in other deserts, some birds build a rampart of pebbles on the side of the nest that is usually to windward; various larks in Algeria, Palestine and Iraq, and Tibet show this behavior pattern.

Insects meet such conditions in various ways. Some are confined to sheltered niches and show a relatively increased tendency to burrow in the ground. Certain butterflies and moths flatten themselves on the ground and attempt flight only in relatively calm air; others make rapid darts from shelter to shelter, while some insects—*Pseudabris* beetles, for example—show a death-feigning reaction as the wind shakes their food plants. They fall to the ground, only to "revive" when the wind slackens, and the beetles then run over the ground to a nearby food plant (Meinertzhagen, 1927; Hingston, 1925).

Animal Structure in Relation to Wind

A much-discussed relation between body form and wind action is found in the observation that, for many insects, regions of strong winds and of circumscribed habitats, such as are found in islands and mountains, have an unduly large proportion of wingless forms. Wollaston (1854) reported that a third of the native species of beetles of Madeira were flightless, and Hingston (1925) emphasized a similar condition among the grasshoppers of the high, windy plains of Tibet, although winged forms occur at lower levels. Darwin, in the *Origin of Species*, advanced an explanation for such relationships. He thought that reduced wings and the tendency toward being flightless in exposed habitats results from natural selection. The winged forms were supposed to be blown away and perish. This explanation has only recently been seriously questioned, and then, directly, only for restricted groups.

It now appears that in the family of ground beetles (Carabidae), the relations between reduced wings, or winglessness, and a given habitat are much more complex than was suggested by Darwin's theory. The evidence and argument are given by Darlington (1943). In summary: carabid beetles with reduced wings not suitable for flight (hereafter called flightless) occur on continents in habitats in which flight tends to lose its usefulness without necessarily being harmful. Flightless ground beetles occur on mountains in sheltered as well as in exposed habitats. On islands, flightlessness is correlated with the presence of mountains and with coolness rather than with exposure to winds. Everywhere Carabidae tend toward flightless forms, not by selection against flight, but mainly by the selection of the inherently simpler, more viable, flightless beetles when flight itself is not useful. In scattered habitats, where the population density fluctuates widely, flight has selection value, since it allows the beetles to occupy a large number of the suitable niches and to keep them occupied. In small areas, where populations of these species are relatively dense, flight is not essential, and selection hinges on other factors, whether the animals live on islands, or mountains, or in continental areas. The whole situation as regards even these ground beetles is too complex to be compressed into a single paragraph; Darlington's more complete statement should be consulted.

This information concerning flightlessness among carabid beetles does not demonstrate the absence of a simple negative selection against winged forms of other types of animals that have flightless representatives in exposed, windy habitats. There are many indications that such selection may occur. The demonstration for the Carabidae does show the necessity for a reexamination of the evidence.

Animal Distribution by Wind

Ballooning spiders (p. 134) are but one of a large number of organisms that are regularly or sporadically carried aloft and distributed by mild currents of air definitely lacking storm force. Among other organisms, pollens, plant spores, bacteria, sponge gemmules, statoblasts of Bryozoa, encysted rotifers, and various insects may be airborne for miles. Bacteria from sea water are blown into the air surrounded by droplets of water not much larger than the bacteria themselves. A steady wind with a velocity of but 10 miles an hour could carry such a bacterium some 3000 miles before it could fall from a height of only 100 feet. A slight updraft would enable such a particle to remain in the air almost indefinitely. Currents of air are also important as scent

carriers, and odors are much more readily detected down wind from their source. These are matters of importance in predator-prey relations among mammals and in the sex life of many animals, notably of saturnid moths.

In season there are millions of insects, often including hairy larvae as well as adults, above each square mile of suitable land surface, and many are carried out to sea. They are sometimes called aerial plankton, but none pass complete life histories in the air as do many plankton organisms in water. One of the rich collecting grounds for insects in the Chicago area is the drift line along Lake Michigan (see p. 534). Insects flying at any given season are carried out over the Lake; many fall into the water and drift ashore, to be thrown up by the waves in long and often dense rows near the edge of the beach.

Many air-borne organisms are killed by desiccation, by sunlight, by ozone, and by other adverse conditions. Despite such hazards, aphids and syrphus flies have been taken alive on Spitzbergen after an estimated wind drift of some 800 miles (Elton, 1925). Diverse small animals are so carried. In the air over Louisiana, spiders and mites and representatives of eighteen orders of insects were collected from aeroplanes well above ground level. Diptera were most abundant, with beetles next. Homoptera and Hymenoptera were taken at 14,000 feet and a spider was trapped a thousand feet higher (Glick, 1939). These altitudes probably represent approximate rather than extreme upper limits of the biosphere for such forms under more usual air conditions.

Even tiny snails may well be transported by wind for considerable distances. If a landfall of such snails becomes established, it can undergo adaptive radiation and produce larger forms. Many groups of snails have minute representatives. Such considerations make one less certain that land connections between regions now separated by deep ocean water are necessarily required in order to account for the known distribution of land snails and other small animals (Gulick, 1932). As a final bit of evidence of the potency of winds of more usual velocity in animal distribution, attention may be called to the greater number of aerial waifs among American birds that make landfalls on European shores, as compared with the relatively few European birds that make their way to North America against the prevailing westerly winds.

As we have seen (p. 146), hurricanes are potent possible forces for over-water transport of organisms. The inner cyclonic wind closest to the hurricane center angles rather sharply upward, and the rate of ascent probably increases when the cloud zone is reached. The central updraft carries some thousands of feet into the air. The main hurricane wind probably has relatively little lifting power, but it carries along gusts, in the form of small secondary whirls, that may pick up live shrimp, for example, along with masses of sea water and carry them aloft until the slackening force of the wind releases them to fall back into the sea, sometimes still alive. These secondary whirls lift and carry palm leaves and other heavy debris for long distances.

Zoologists usually underestimate the lifting and carrying power of winds, partly because, until relatively recent times, men were confined to the ground level and, further, because men are large animals not readily swept literally from their feet. Small animals have a much higher ratio of surface to weight than do larger ones. This relationship has already been noted in connection with the radiation of heat (Bergmann's rule, p. 119) and with the flotation of plankton (p. 133). Weight increases in proportion to the cube of the length, modified by an appropriate factor, and surface similarly increases as its square. An animal that weighs an ounce—an adult house mouse, for example—has about fourteen times the ratio of surface to weight as does man.

Another phase of these possible comparisons is important: The pressure exerted against a given object varies as the square of the wind's velocity. A gale of 100 miles per hour exerts sixteen times the force of a wind that is blowing one-fourth that rate. These values pyramid upon each other in a formidable fashion. A mouse exposed to the full force of a gale of the strength just given would have to meet 14 times 16 or 224 times the amount of carrying power as would a man in a wind of 25 miles per hour. The smaller the animal to be compared with man, the higher the ratio. It is difficult for those who are not accustomed to handling aeroplanes in strong winds to appreciate the force such winds exert. Relatively heavy smaller animals such as earthworms, tadpoles, frogs, salamanders,

small fishes, and mollusks are known to have been carried to new locations by wind storms (McAtee, 1917; Gudger, 1921; Darlington, 1938a).

"Dust devils" of the dry lands are small whirlwinds, with the conelike apex near the ground, that are made visible by the dust they carry. They also pick up plants and animals such as mice, and even those as big as a kangaroo rat (*Dipydomys*). The vertical component of large "dust devils" exceeds a speed of 25 miles per hour (Ives, 1947).

Darlington (1938a) summarizes evidence indicating that the foundation stock of many animals of the Greater Antilles (Cuba, Hispaniola, Jamaica, and Puerto Rico) may have been transported by air from Central America. To be sure, the majority of these storms pass from the islands, to Florida, but there are enough that move from Central America to the islands to satisfy the requirements made by the observed distribution. Three further considerations support this possibility: (1) The more violent, more efficient right-hand half of the hurricane flows from Central America toward the Antilles. (2) This may carry plant debris of considerable size which could, in turn, carry many different kinds of animals, even those that cannot withstand long exposure to sea water—for example, mites from the forest floor. (3) The geological evidence suggests that the water gap was once narrower than at present, although it does not present conclusive evidence of a former land-bridge connection. Certainly the known evidence is not notably inconsistent with the theory that the land animals of these larger islands of the West Indies have descended from waifs deposited after aerial or, in some instances, raft transport from Central America.

OCEAN CURRENTS

Temperature relations in the oceans are one of the significant influences in establishing and maintaining ocean currents. These relations can be specifically related to oceanic conditions by an application of the theorem of Bjerknes, which Sverdrup, Johnson, and Fleming (1942) state as follows: "If within a thermal circulation, heat shall be transformed into mechanical energy, the heating must take place at a greater depth (and therefore at a greater pressure) than the cooling." This theorem has been successfully tested in experimental models. Its application to oceanic circulation presents some difficulties, since on first inspection it would appear that heating and cooling of ocean water both occur at the same level, that is, at the surface. Closer study reveals that the heating actually takes place, in part, at some distance below the surface.

The heated, lighter water spreads from the tropical regions over the surface of the ocean toward high latitudes, where it gives off heat and becomes denser. The water then sinks and flows back toward the equatorial region at some depth below the surface. So far, the conditions realize the generalized scheme presented earlier (p. 141). The returning water is heated by conduction before it actually reaches the surface in the tropics; hence heating does occur at a greater depth than cooling and so accords with the theorem of Bjerknes. The depth scale is not great when contrasted with the long north and south expanse of the oceans. When the surface water near Spitzbergen at 80 degrees north latitude has a temperature of 3.3° C., the vertical lowering of the warming point of water for the North Atlantic cannot be more than about one and a quarter miles in contrast to something over 5000 miles of horizontal distance. The warming of deeper water by conduction is not efficient, since water is a poor conductor of heat, hence the direct thermal component underlying oceanic circulation of water is not an effective driving force.

Density differences related to salinity also play a role in these large-scale, oceanic currents. Surface water evaporates, especially in the warm, dry regions, and leaves an increased concentration of salt. Such water sinks. The density-salinity component of the global circulation of sea water has been fitted into an extension of the theorem of Bjerknes by Sverdrup, Johnson, and Fleming (1942) as follows: "If a thermohaline circulation shall produce energy, the expansion must take place at a greater depth than the contraction."

Again, let us examine the situation in the Atlantic Ocean. Thanks to tropical rains, the equatorial region tends to have diluted surface water which, moreover, is warm. Both factors make for lowered density. Heating is less intense on both sides of the equatorial belt, and the dry, subtropical trade winds cause surface evaporation. The expansion does take place at a greater depth than the contraction, and the density-dilution gradients in this part of the ocean tend to reenforce the thermal circulation. Poleward, the conditions are reversed, the density relations tend to run counter to the thermal component, and circulation is retarded. The final result is a compromise.

Winds exert a strong force on water underlying them. The driving power is exerted by the frictional contacts between air and water and is greatest when winds blow steadily over the water from the same direction. The correlation of orientation of flow of winds and of ocean currents is high in the open sea and may entirely override the primary density relations within the sea water itself.

Coastlines are a disturbing influence. In the northern hemisphere, along coasts that lie to the right of the direction of wind flow, the warmer surface water tends to be piled up on the coast, and replacing, colder water wells up at some distance out from shore. In seas that approach being landlocked, wind-driven water piles up on the lee shore under conditions that closely resemble seiches in lakes, and small seiches are also known, even under usual wind conditions, along coasts that are practically open to the sea. Larger masses of wind-driven water are all too well known because of their destruction of human life and property.

If the coast lies to the left of the wind direction in the northern hemisphere, lighter water is carried out to sea, and the colder, denser water wells up near the shore. The upwelling is usually from moderate depths. Similar phenomena occur in the southern hemisphere, only there, in keeping with the effect of the rotational force of the earth (Corioli's force), the directional relations are reversed, and the lighter water is carried to the left of a person who is facing down wind.

The same winds that produce an upwelling of deeper water near shores also aid in setting up currents that flow parallel with the shore line and in the same general direction as the prevailing wind.

Other forces act to bring deeper water up to the surface; the steady flow of offshore winds has this effect. Thus, off the African coast in the South Atlantic, the northward-blowing winds throw the lighter water out to sea and cause deeper water to rise inshore. In addition, the southeast trades that blow out from over the continent reinforce this circulation. A similar combination of winds produces the upwelling of water off the coast of Peru in the eastern Pacific.

The climate of both sea and land is affected as a result of cooler water being brought to the surface near shore. The biota of both is also influenced, often strongly, by changes in the food chain. The upwelling water brings mineral nutrients to the lighted zone of the sea, where they become available for phytoplankton, and a rich growth of sea life usually develops. Man is affected by the more productive fisheries of such regions and frequently even more so by the guano deposits from the dense populations of sea birds that congregate around the rich supply of food. The islands off the coast of Peru afford a notable example.

The climatic changes produced by the transport of large masses of warm water into Arctic latitudes or the opposite transport of Arctic water into midlatitudes are too well known to need more than passing mention. The effect of the warm Gulf Stream on the climate of northern Europe and the chilling produced by the cold Labrador current at similar latitudes on the American side of the Atlantic make the point. Their action can be duplicated in many parts of the world, and such currents control the geographic limits of whole biomes.

Tides and tidal currents have been discussed earlier (p. 84). These water movements in the relatively fertile waters of the continental shelf make possible, among other things, an extensive development of the sessile habit of divergent groups of animals, including protozoans, sponges, hydroids, sea anemones and corals, bryozoans, barnacles, urochordates, and many mollusks. The communities of which such animals are prominent members, together with associated worms, snails, crustaceans, and the like, have their basic food supply carried to them primarily by tidal and other local currents. Many burrowing organisms are similarly served. The notable absence of the sessile habit among land animals bears witness to the relative paucity of air-borne life as contrasted with aquatic plankton.

Oceanic currents have been much studied both by physical and by biotic oceanographers. The well-documented information on the subject is too extensive and too complex to have even its basic principles fully outlined here. The established principles, especially of physical oceanography, have been expressed mathematically in many cases, but to consider them further now would take us adrift from our main course. The interested student is referred to Sverdrup, Johnson, and Fleming's book (1942).

WATER MASSES

Density differences set up by thermosaline forces produce vertical convection currents. These are important in the vertical migration of plankton organisms that may show diurnal depth movements of considerable extent (p. 139). Convection is even more important in establishing a homogeneous layer of surface water, the depth of which depends on the strength of the convection currents. The existence of surface, as distinct from deeper, waters serves to introduce the present day concept that the ocean, like the atmosphere, is composed of a set of recognizable masses. The water masses of the sea are identified by their temperature-salinity characteristics, just as air masses are known by temperature-humidity differences.

Figure 29 shows schematically the distribution of the oceanic upper water masses. Typically, the oceans have a relatively shallow surface layer extending down about 100 to 200 meters. The temperature-salinity values vary greatly within this layer, and great seasonal variations occur in areas with variable climates. Other water masses have relatively stable temperature-salinity values. In many ways the Antarctic Ocean furnishes a helpful introduction. In the subantarctic region five vertically arranged water masses can usually be distinguished as follows: (1) subantarctic upper water, (2) subantarctic intermediate water, (3) upper deeper water, (4) lower deeper water, and (5) bottom water.

The subantarctic mass of upper water extends northward far into each bordering ocean, taking its place, according to density relations, between the given central water and the deep water. In the Atlantic, but not in other oceans, the intermediate water mass originating in antiboreal regions extends beyond the equator and reaches as far as 20 degrees north latitude.

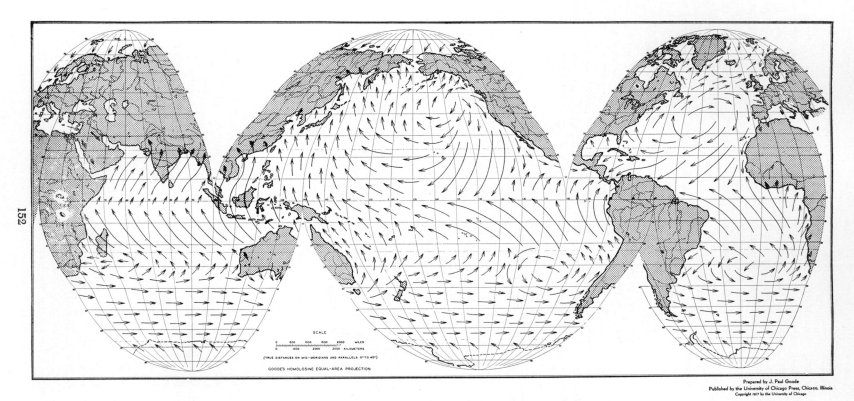

SCALE

0   500   1000   1500   2000   MILES

0   1000   2000   3000   KILOMETERS

(TRUE DISTANCES ON MID-MERIDIANS AND PARALLELS 0° TO 40°)

GOODE'S HOMOLOSINE EQUAL-AREA PROJECTION

Prepared by J. Paul Goode
Published by the University of Chicago Press, Chicago, Illinois
Copyright 1917 by the University of Chicago

Fig. 28. Oceanic currents in July. (Redrawn from Goode.)

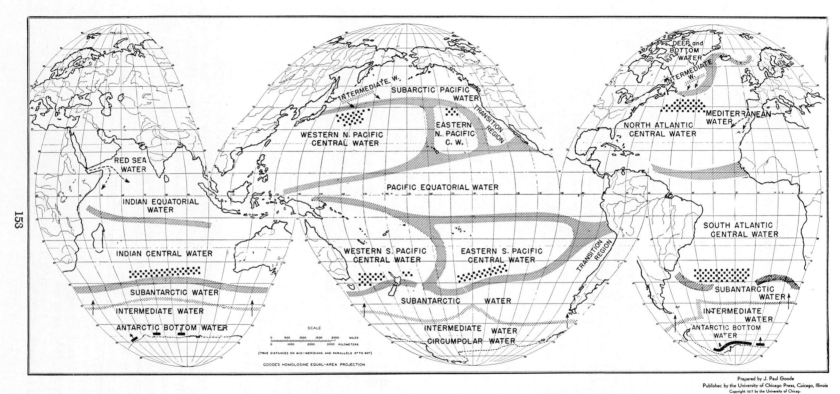

Fig. 29. Surface water masses of the oceans. Squares indicate areas of formation of central masses. Regions of sinking polar water are shown by narrow dotted areas. (Redrawn from Sverdrup, Johnson, and Fleming.)

As a rule, subsurface water masses originate at the surface; they sink and spread in accordance with differential density relations. Two major exceptions to this rule are furnished by the equatorial masses of the Pacific and Indian Oceans that are formed by subsurface mixing. The place of origin of a given water mass is indicated by the area in which, at least for a part of the year, the vertical temperature-salinity relations of the given mass are present as horizontal surface characteristics.

Another general rule is that subsurface water masses are not regularly formed at the surface of the oceans in low latitudes. Again two important exceptions are known: the intermediate masses originating in the Mediterranean and in the Red Sea. Both are composed of dense water with high salinity that underlies the polar intermediate water masses in the Atlantic and Indian Oceans, respectively.

FLOWING FRESH WATER

The modification of the physical environment by running water on land consists primarily in dissection and degradation of physiographically young areas. These processes continue until peneplain formation is reached. The shift of masses of continental material into the great delta regions of the world helps produce stresses that in time lead to crustal readjustments. These in turn lead to re-elevation of the continental blocks, or of some parts of them, and the cycle continues. Aggradation, as well as degradation, may occur by direct action of running water. When the bed of a river comes to lie below base level for that stream, the current slackens, mud is deposited, and aggradation occurs.

Running water carries fine particles in suspension and sweeps coarse matter along the channel bed as a so-called tractional or bed load. The stream often acts as a sorting agency. When the current is reduced in velocity and turbulence, a part of the bed load is deposited on the bottom, and some of the suspended material settles into the bed load. The heavier objects are deposited first and, other things being equal, are found upstream from deposits of lighter stuffs.

The suspended load consists in part of colloidal particles that carry an electrical charge; fine clays may be so carried. These charged particles are less affected by current velocity than if they were mechanically suspended. They aggregate and become flocculent when brought into contact with electrolytes in solution or with colloidal particles of the opposite electrical sign. Contacts of this kind may occur below the junction of two streams or where fresh water flows into the sea (Meinzer, 1942; Twenhofel, 1942).

The capacity of a stream to carry a bed or traction load varies as the third or fourth power of the velocity of its current. The variation is in relation to such factors as slope and total discharge of the stream and with the form and fineness of the transported material. The erosive power of a stream is related to the forces that determine its load-carrying capacity (Gilbert, 1914).

Flowing fresh waters are sometimes referred to as composing a lotic environment for plants and animals, as contrasted with the so-called lentic environment in lakes and ponds. Lotic waters have greater geographical continuity, both because of connections through the oceans into which they flow and because of the not infrequent pirating of the head waters of one stream by another. Because the current flows in one direction only, streams tend to carry plankton organisms out to sea or into lakes or larger streams and so retard the development of an autochthonic plankton in the main current of the given stream. River plankton develops rather in lakes, bogs, and marshes, which are drained by the streams, or in the stagnant backwaters of river bayous. The more rapid the current of the river, the sparser is the plankton, both because such organisms are more speedily swept from the river and because of the active destruction of plankton in the quickened flow of river rapids. Here, as elsewhere, the rule holds that, other things being equal, the more plankton, the more fish. Hence the clearing currents of rivers act to decrease the size of the fish population without necessarily carrying healthy fish downstream.

Nonplanktonic stream animals, such as fresh-water isopods and amphipods, may fly nymphs, various beetles, and dipterous larvae, to name no more, are also carried downstream. Under almost ideal field conditions, such animals settle to the bottom of a lake near the outer limit of the slackened inflowing current and may live there for weeks. Directly or indirectly, wave action is the usual cause of death (Dendy, 1944).

The current produces other effects on river systems. The chemical content of the water tends to become generalized in the lower reaches, even though the different tributaries receive drainage from diverse types of soils. Currents of fresh water, with their dissolved salts, suspended matter and warmth, produce profound changes in the marine environments into which they eventually flow. There is usually an absence of a distinct, deep-water stratum even in the largest and deepest rivers.

Floods introduce special complications in the way of an increased rate of flow, in increased volume of water that overflows the usual channel to cover the flood plain, and in the increased turbidity of the river water. Many rivers are always turbid; the mud-carrying Missouri is such a stream. Among other effects of turbidity, the lessened penetration of light is important.

The velocity of the current of a stream seems to be one of its most significant ecological features. Velocity is more important than the division based on size into permanent brooks, creeks, and rivers proper, and more important than the distinction between upper, middle, and lower river. Rapid water tends to contain a somewhat similar community of animals, whether in the upper reaches of a stream, in mid-course, or near the mouth. The velocity of flow depends mainly on three factors: (1) the steepness of the basic gradient; (2) the roughness of the stream bed; and (3) the hydraulic radius. The hydraulic radius is found by dividing the area of the cross section of a stream by its wetted perimeter, and stream velocity itself is determined by the following formula:

$$V = c \sqrt{Rs}$$

V represents velocity; *c* is a coefficient based on type of bottom; *R* is the hydraulic radius; and *s* gives the slope or gradient (Galtsoff, 1924).

The more rapid the flow, other conditions being equal, the higher the oxygen content of river water. The rate of flow also affects the temperature relations. The daily and yearly range of temperature is less in rapidly flowing streams, even though they are often shallow, than in the sluggish portions of a stream in the same latitude. Temper-

ature tends to be uniform at all depths, even in a large river such as the Mississippi. Source waters often excepted, small streams tend to fluctuate with the temperature of the air more than do larger ones, and the latter are more sensitive to changes in air temperatures than are large ponds or lakes. Thermal stratification, especially that associated with thermocline formation, occurs but rarely in streams, and then for limited periods and only in deep, slow-flowing rivers.

As a stream erodes its way back into hitherto ungullied land, it first flows only when there is a run-off of rainwater. As the gullies cut by such occasional currents become deeper, the duration of flow increases. At length the level of fairly permanent ground water is reached, and durable pools occur in the more deeply eroded pockets. With further erosion, these finally become connected by permanent rapids, and the stream enters a pool and rapids phase that is frequently of long duration. With further erosion, the stream bed becomes eroded to more nearly uniform level and finally reaches the sluggish stage of a meandering, base-leveled river.

Each of these phases in the physiographical history of a stream is typically reached first in the region near the mouth, and each tends to move farther and farther upcountry as the stream lengthens. This is a schematic, oversimplified history of stream development. Local variations of gradient or substrate may hasten or retard the aging of a given stream or of portions of it. Each characteristic part tends to be inhabited by an appropriate community of organisms, and these, too, move with the change in position of their typical habitat. This whole set of processes is known as physiographical succession in streams. Its ecological significance was perceived by Woodworth (1894) and developed by Adams (1901) and Shelford (1911). Terrestrial aspects from the point of view of plant ecology were outlined by Cowles (1901). The standard description of this phenomenon is based on the work of Shelford (1913); some of the distribution relations found by him are shown in Figure 30.

An entirely different stream history is presented by mountain streams, especially when the mountains extend above the snowline. The headwaters of such streams may be composed of rivulets in tundra-like alpine meadows or of the cascade type of violently descending waters. This general subject is discussed again in the chapter on Succession (p. 572).

Streams frequently show a transverse as well as a longitudinal asymmetry. This is especially noticeable in eroding streams where one bank, the outer bank in a bend, is being under-cut and material is being deposited on the opposite margin.

Adaptations to Stream Life

Animals that live in rapid currents usually are adapted by structure or habit, or hand, propel, and on the other resist its passage down the oviduct. The streamlining of the bodies of birds and fishes is brought about, not by direct action of the environment, but by evolutionary processes. Evolution has also affected the form of the eggs of many species of birds.

In the hen's egg, the foremost part becomes the broad end, and the cross section of greatest width lies well forward as the plastic egg is moved down the oviduct; the posterior part tapers over a longer distance. The same relations are further developed in the streamlined bodies of fishes, although

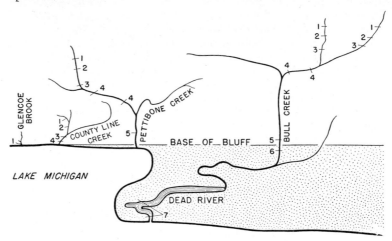

Fig. 30. Diagrammatic arrangement of streams entering Lake Michigan north of Chicago. The numbers show progressive stages in succession. (Redrawn from Shelford.)

both, to maintaining their position against the sweep of the current. Some of the structural devices include suckers of various sorts, attachment threads, and gripping appendages and surfaces. Adaptations in habit include the darting movement of certain fishes that is often combined with the tendency to take shelter below or under projecting stones or among vegetation when that is present.

A more universal adaptation to life in a current or to active movement through water or air is the development of a streamlined form. A form is said to be streamlined when air or water flows around it so smoothly that resistance is reduced to a minimum. A hen's egg is automatically streamlined by the direct action of the combination of pressures that, on the one with them the motive force is internal and only the environmental resistance is furnished by the surrounding water. The rounded head parts the water with a minimum of eddy formation; the parted medium closes in on the elongated, gently sloping posterior body and so tends to restore some of the energy expended in making the original separation of the water. The gradual slope of the posterior body also avoids the retarding water eddies that result from flow past a more angular figure.

Study of the resistance of models to movement through water dates back at least to 1775. The celebrated physicist, Clerk Maxwell, explained certain of the laws in 1854. Clemens (1917) used models of equal weight, made in each case by using the same wax, and found the pull needed to keep the model in position in a steady current. Care was not taken to maintain a constant cross section in the different models, and hence the data obtained are only approximate. It is worth noting that sharp edges increased the pull.

Bottom-dwelling animals in rapid currents or in similarly disturbed coastal waters of lakes or oceans often have flat perhaps sucker-like ventral sides and streamlined dorsal halves. An interesting example of streamlining and a test of the whole set of relations we are discussing is furnished by black fly larvae of the genus *Simulium*. These larvae are found only in running water, where each is attached by a self-spun thread in such a manner that the posterior end is upstream while the head end dangles with the current. Despite the reversed orientation, here, as usual in streamlined forms, the widest bulge is near the rounded upstream portion of the body, and the head lies at the end of the tapering "after-body." Streamlining remains, but the usual morphological relations are reversed. D'Arcy Thompson (1942) gives a more

head and long, gently sloping posterior body of the heterogeneous lot of bottom-dwelling fishes, known collectively as the darters (*Boleosoma nigrum* is an example), emphasizes the multiple adaptation of these animals to the turbulent waters that are their characteristic habitat. Rather than being strictly bottom-dwellers, as are flounders in the sea, the darters live in the current close to the bottom and between stones, where the velocity of the current is reduced.

Bottom-dwelling animals in rapidly flowing streams, whether brooks or rivers, particularly forms such as the darting fishes, may fly nymphs, and damsel fly nymphs, tend to be more or less automatically oriented to face upstream. Their organs of attachment, the large pectoral fins for the fishes and the thoracic legs for the nymphs, are placed well forward. The current acts on the long posterior body, as wind does on the after-body of a weather vane, to turn the animal with its head upstream. Similar morphological relations are also found in related nymphs that live in ponds, hence, as with many other adaptations, the auto-

Table 10. *The Effect of Streamlining on Resistance to Flowing Water*
(*Data from Clemens, 1917*)

Form	Orientation	Pull in Grams
Cone, rounded edges	Base upstream	12
Cone, rounded edges	Base downstream	50
Sunfish	Head upstream	15
Trout	Head upstream	6
Trout	Head downstream	10
Chirotonetes { May fly	Head upstream	9
Chirotonetes { nymph	Head downstream	16

complete, interesting discussion of these problems.

In addition to being streamlined, fishes of rapidly flowing streams have rounded, muscular bodies that contrast strikingly with the flattened and often shorter body form of those that live in less pronounced currents. The contrast between brook trout and the common sunfish (*Lepomis*) makes the point. The darting habit is also characteristic of many fishes that live in rapidly flowing waters, and this is normally correlated with the possession of enlarged pectoral fins that serve to help anchor the fish to the bottom. The streamlining shown by the blunt

matic orientation in a rapid current is probably secondary rather than primary.[*]

* A short chapter on electricity as an environmental factor has been eliminated to save space. The interested reader is referred to the series of essays edited by Fleming (1939). The chapter included a brief summary concerning atmospheric electricity (Gish, 1939; Schonland, 1939; Wenstrom, 1942); the electrical fixation of nitrogen (Clarke, 1924; Ernst, 1928); fires started by lightning (Heyward, 1939); terrestrial magnetism (Fleming, 1939); earth currents (Rooney, 1939); and the possible effect on homing and migration in birds (Warden, Jenkins, and Warner, 1936, 1940).

10. THE SUBSTRATUM

The atmosphere, in its lower reaches, is a much used medium for active locomotion by flying animals or for passive transport, especially for smaller plants and animals and their disseminules. Unlike water, which is denser and therefore more suitable for buoyant support, the air is too tenuous a substratum to furnish the physical base in which an animal can pass its entire life history. The biosphere is a relatively thin shell over the earth. It extends down to the greatest depths of the sea, and, on land, bacteria have been reported from coal at depths of up to 1089 meters (ZoBell, 1946).

The regions of contact between the atmosphere, hydrosphere, and lithosphere make the great interphases in the physical environment. The surface of water, the air-water interphase, is a sharply defined film. The surface of the harder rocks, whether covered by air or by water, also is a precise, definite boundary. The meeting of earth and air, or of lithosphere and hydrosphere, usually furnishes a transition zone of some depth that provides a series of habitats related to the degree to which subterranean air penetrates the soil, or to which water penetrates the underlying lithosphere to form a "terraqueous" zone.

The surface of water is an important substrate for life, though not nearly so important as the surface of land. Both water and the upper layers of the lithosphere, whether covered by water or air, furnish important mechanical substrata for plants and animals at the surface and for some distance below it. The extent to which these surfaces are occupied by organisms depends on other conditions in addition to fitness for physical support. The limiting action of other factors can be illustrated by relations to light. Even in the presence of a suitable substrate, green plants grow only on the lighted areas on the surface of the land and in a thicker but still relatively shallow region in aquatic environments.

In this whole general section we are discussing the relation of animals to their nonliving physical environment, and here we come squarely upon an essential artificiality of our basis for classification of the environment of animals. Living organisms are important substrates for surface-dwelling forms and for internal symbionts and parasites, and the bodies of dead plants and animals also support varied small biotic communities. In many instances, animals appear to react to certain other animals and to many plants as they do to similarly solid, nonliving objects in comparable positions. The carapace of a mature horseshoe crab (*Limulus*) on a tide flat may carry about the snail, *Crepidula*, a common barnacle, and some hydroids and other animals characteristic of neighboring rocks, and on land a puma may lie in wait for its prey in the lower branches of a tree as it might atop an advantageously placed rock. The prehensile tail of American monkeys and other animals of the tropical forest are understandable in relation to the hard, round branches of trees as a type of physical substrate. At present we shall restrict ourselves to the non-living environment.

WATER SURFACE

The air-water interphase is characterized by a surface-tension film, both sides of which are important for animals. A whole ecological assemblage of birds, the so-called water birds, if not in flight, typically float or swim on the water. Many float relatively high, as do swans, while others are nearly submerged, like the cormorant. In addition to such flotation, many small objects are supported directly by the surface film of water, which is a transparent false bottom of considerable strength. The classical and easy demonstration is made by floating a slightly oiled needle on the surface film. The needle does not sink in quiet water despite its high specific gravity. The uppermost film of water has a tensile strength of from 10,700 to 25,000 atmospheres resulting from intermolecular attraction (Terzaghi, 1942). Such a film can support real weight, whether it impinges from above or is attached from below.

The organisms associated intimately with the surface film of water have been called the neuston, as contrasted with the plankton immersed in the water and mainly at the mercy of water currents, and with the more efficiently swimming nekton. The organisms of the neuston may be microscopic or macroscopic; its animals and plants, associated at the surface film of fresh water, include many insects such as water striders, whirligig beetles, springtails, and a variety of spiders, all of which run about on the surface without breaking through to the water below. Many of the organisms of this supraneuston, those above the surface film, are also at home in the water itself. The surface-dwelling habit has persisted for a long time, long enough, apparently, for the gyrinid beetles to have evolved divided eyes, with the upper part suitable for vision in air and the lower part adapted to vision under water. One of the few marine insects is a water strider that runs about on the surface film.

Grasshoppers and other heavy-bodied terrestrial insects may be partially or wholly supported by the surface film for a time. The presence of such land-dwelling insects, helpless on the surface of the water, supplies a source of food for predaceous aquatic animals and may be related to the life history of such parasites as *Gordius*.

A glance at the lower side of the surface film in a well-stocked aquarium gives some appreciation of the possible richness of life that may hang there. Some soldier fly larvae (Stratiomyidae) and mosquito larvae and pupae, among others, are suspended with their spiracles exposed to the outer air. Even fairly large pulmonate snails may also cling so while breathing and may anchor the upper end of a mucus thread to the surface film; by this thread they make periodic trips up and down in the water. The common hydra can move along the under side of the film or hang suspended from it, and planarian worms glide along its under surface.

In addition to pulmonate snails, animals in varied assortment make periodic excursions to the surface film to breathe. They may attach momentarily while replenishing their supply of stored oxygen, or the surface film may be significant only as a phase boundary between water and the air above. Large animals, frogs, crocodiles, and hippopotami float just below the surface with only their protuberant eyes and nostrils exposed to the air. These animals obviously are not members of the neuston, even though they occur in ludicrously close juxtaposition. Some ecological associations may indeed seem ludicrous; different mechanisms may keep different organisms in the same general region, and many different ecological relations may be illustrated by animals that live alongside each other. A community of interests may usually be discerned even among widely different animals thus brought into the same habitat.

WATER-LITHOSPHERE INTERPHASE

It is common usage to call the water-air interphase the top or surface of the water and to regard the zone of contact between water and the underlying lithosphere as its bottom. The water itself is a substratum for many pelagic organisms that rarely make physical contact with either surface or bottom phase boundary and for bottom-dwelling forms that may spend much of their life swimming or floating freely in the water. Honoring present interests, we pass directly from top to bottom to discuss the physical relations of bottom-dwelling forms. These compose the benthos of the sea and the pedon of fresh waters.

Pedonic or benthic animals are closely related to the physical character of the bottom. They are roughly divided into (a) those that live much of their lives in the water and descend to the bottom for breeding, feeding, or resting, as contrasted (b) with animals that spend most of their lives on the bottom; and finally, (c) the burrowers. These categories are not mutually exclusive.

The solid bottom characteristic of rocky shores makes one extreme type contrasting with the soft mud or sand that lies at or near the other extreme of physical consistency. Hard rocks provide secure places for attachment and are difficult to penetrate; on the other hand, sand and mud furnish insecure attachment and easy burrowing. Each of the many variants supports a more or less characteristic animal community, the composition of which depends also on many other factors, such as geographical location, extent of the given habitat, depth, temperature, salinity and other chemical conditions, including biotic pollution, turbidity, lighting, currents, and associated organisms. In final analysis, even closely knit biocoenoses —the oyster-bed, for example—depend on the relations between key organisms and their physical substrate.

It is difficult to judge the relative importance of the independent conditions of existence in a given habitat. In a study of the factors controlling the distribution of communities of littoral invertebrates in shallow water near Woods Hole, Massachusetts,

Allee (1923, 1934) decided that the character of the sea bottom was the single environmental factor most closely associated with community distribution. With the details still freshly in mind, he concluded (1923, p. 246): "The character of the sea bottom . . . . the most obvious, the longest used, is still the least treacherous single-factor index of littoral distribution in this region. It should be used with discretion

(1922), for the bottom-dwelling fishes near Tortugas, and MacGinitie (1939), particularly for the coast of California, also emphasized the importance of the physical character of the bottom in animal distribution. On the other hand, Shelford and his associates (1935), in discussing the distribution of some biotic communities on the Pacific coast of North America, concluded that "the general hy-

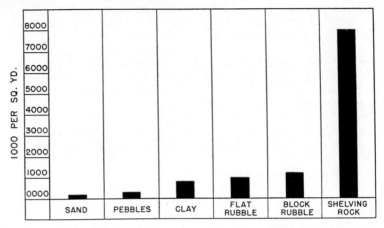

Fig. 31. Total population in thousands per square yard in relation to the type of substratum in Lake Erie. (Redrawn from Krecker and Lancaster.)

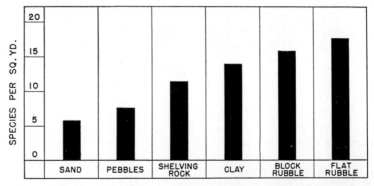

Fig. 32. Number of species of animals per square yard in relation to different kinds of substrata. (Redrawn from Krecker and Lancaster.)

since a rock well back on a (tidal) flat supports a different set of animals from one on an exposed point, but the corrections are obvious and easily applied." The small community on such a rock differs decidedly from those on the surrounding sand or mud. Among others, Petersen (1913, 1915), for the bottom communities of the coast of Denmark, Longley

drographic conditions (submarine climate) are more important than kind of bottom materials in determining the character of benthic communities." Controlling factors may well differ in different situations. It is probable, however, that if the "general hydrographic conditions" were broken down into constituent parts, the character of the bottom, the world over, would be found to stand high in comparison with any other given factor of the inshore littoral environment.

The kind of bottom is also important in lakes where rocky, eroding shores support animal communities that resemble those on rocky bottoms of streams of the same general area. Sandy depositing shores of lakes usually maintain a sparse population, and if the sand is much battered by waves, as at the south end of Lake Michigan, the loose sand tends to be as bare of life as is a sandy desert during the heat of the day.

cated in Figure 33. When mud is mixed with the sand, bottom-dwelling animals, burrowing or otherwise, show a great increase in numbers of species and in population density. On favorable tide flats of New England, the substrate may be completely stippled by the siphon openings of the burrowing clams, *Mya* and *Venus*. On other coasts, thickset colonies of oysters grow on suitable substrata between the tide lines (Fig. 34). Numbers of species and individuals decrease as the bottom becomes almost sandless mud, especially in regions

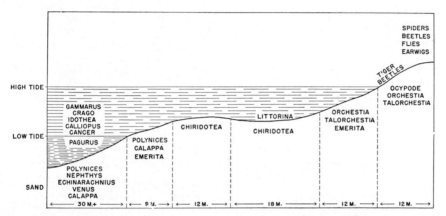

Fig. 33. The usual positions of a number of characteristic animals on the sand beach along the coast of Carolina. (Redrawn from Pearse.)

The relation between population density and the type of substratum within the six-foot contour line in western Lake Erie is summarized in Figures 31 and 32. Sandy beaches and shoals are most sparsely inhabited, with only about 100 macroscopic invertebrates per square yard. Flat shelving bedrock supports the densest population, with an average of some 7700 individuals per square yard. The animals on bedrock were mainly dipterous midge larvae. Sand substrate also supports fewer species, six per square yard; pebbles, shelving rock, clay, block rubble, and flat rubble follow in an ascending series. There were approximately seventeen species of these invertebrates per square yard of flat rubble.

Along sea coasts, loose sand similarly supports relatively little animal life. The Pismo clam of California, mole crabs (*Emerita talpoida*), and "terraqueous" burrowing copepods of the sandy littoral of eastern North America are some of the characteristic inhabitants. Others are indi-

of stagnant water, where, if the mud has a high organic content, hydrogen sulphide develops.

Near land and in the Arctic Ocean, the sea bottom is characterized by rain wash along the coast, and by stream erosion often from far back upcountry. Such eroded debris falls to the bottom mainly on or near the continental shelf. Glaciers carry a heavy load of miscellaneous soil and rock, some of which may be deposited hundreds of miles out at sea, as may also the air-borne dust from wind erosion of arid land or from volcanoes. The "mud line," which marks the seaward limit of terrigenous deposits, usually lies somewhere outside the 200 meter contour.

In deeper water, in 2000 meters or more, gravels, sands, and silts from the land are mainly replaced by pelagic oozes or red clay. In exceptional cases, as in the Arctic Ocean and in a broad strip between Antarctica and South America, terrestrial deposits apparently predominate much beyond the 2000 meter line. On the other hand, organic matter is often mixed in with sand and mud even close to shore (Johnstone, 1923).

Character is given to the organic oozes of the deeper ocean bottom by the skeletal matter that accumulates on the bottom. These skeletons originate mainly from waters in or just below the lighted, surface

deeper than the others. The calcareous oozes cover the major part of the bottom in the Atlantic and Indian oceans.

The important features of these substrates for bottom-dwelling animals are their consistency and the organic matter they contain. The consistency is about that of unchilled butter in summer, and animals living on such a semisolid medium require

Fig. 34. An intertidal oyster bank in South Carolina. (Photograph by Dean; loaned by Fish and Wildlife Service, U. S. Department of Agriculture.)

zone. Bottom oozes are of two kinds: calcareous, characterized by *Globigerina* (Protozoa) and by Pteropod (Gasteropoda) shells; and siliceous oozes, characterized by diatom or radiolarian remains. Red clay, when typically developed, lacks more than a trace of these skeletal remains. It appears to be richer in organic matter than are the calcareous oozes, but not so rich as the diatomaceous ones. Red clay covers some 38 per cent of the ocean bottom beyond the limit of terrigenous deposits, as compared with 14 per cent for the siliceous, and 48 per cent for the calcareous oozes. Red clay is poor in calcareous remains. It occurs in the three main oceans and is most extensive in the Pacific, an ocean that is somewhat

specialized support if they are not to become engulfed. Motile animals of the deep benthos have an enlarged ventral surface— several echinoderms, for example—or long legs with terminal segments expanded by bristles that increase their supporting surface, as in deep-sea crustaceans. Sessile forms are raised above the soft ooze by a stalk with rootlike outgrowths or by brushes or collars of spines. Such structures are typical of deep-sea sponges, hydroid polyps, and a variety of other animals of this extensive community (Hesse, Allee, and Schmidt, 1937).

Marine animals are best known from the littoral region. Benthic littoral animals are abundant on rocky surfaces and on fairly firm mixed sand and mud that is not exposed to the direct pounding of the waves. Animal communities on rock surfaces contain a large number of sessile forms such as sponges, hydroids, and anthozoans, bryozoans, mollusks, and urochordates. Other animals in great variety crawl over these and take refuge in the interstices between their bodies. Many sessile animals also live on the firm physical extension of the bottom furnished by attached or rooted vegetation, and other animals move actively over such plants.

The burrowing habit is more common in muddy sand than in either pure shifting sand or in solid rock, although specialized burrowers occur in both these substrata. The sand burrowers (p. 161) must be able to dig rapidly to keep covered in a substrate that shifts quickly. Some of the diggers in muddy sand—the lugworm (*Arenicola*), for example—also dig rapidly. Solid rock shelters a mixed lot of boring forms: boring sponges, annelid worms, lamellibranchs, sea urchins, barnacles, and isopods. They are usually found in the softer rocks, but the boring sea urchins can penetrate even lava and metamorphic rock. Representatives of some of these also attack wood, notably *Teredo,* the molluskan "shipworm" of the family Pholadidae. Many animals that lack the power to bore for themselves occupy burrows of others, and many more live in the natural furrows furnished by the crevices between stones.

The rock-boring habit appears to be absent in fresh-water communities so far as the firmer rocks are concerned. Certainly, it is even less well developed than in the sea. A wide variety of unrelated forms burrow into softer substrate and use a number of burrowing mechanisms. Perhaps the densest animal community of the fresh water is that formed on and among stones in moderately swift streams where relatively little burrowing occurs. A dense population of tubificid worms may occur in the surface layer of mud with high organic content. These small annelids are shallow burrowers that live in tubes from which they protrude the posterior end and wave it actively back and forth, probably as an aid in respiration.

Water, even shallow water, serves as a protective substratum against the invasion of many land predators. Dwellers in vegetative islands of cattails (*Typha*) and other swamp plants are protected by the surrounding moat of water, the more so the more permanent the water moat.

LAND SURFACE

The physical character of land surface is an important factor in the ecology of land animals. Mammals dwelling on rocky ground tend to have resistant, nonskidding feet that help to make them sure-footed even on difficult terrain. This is the more important, since rocky habitats are frequently associated with the steeper mountain slopes. The feet of nonburrowing animals that live mainly on soil approach the generalized condition characteristic of their group. Specializations occur, among them the tendency of ratite birds (emu, rhea, and ostrich) for a reduction in the number of toes to three or even to two, and among cursorial mammals towards smaller feet, likewise with fewer toes. Heavy animals, living on a soft substrate, tend to develop larger feet than those of closely related forms from firmer ground. The webbed feet of birds function to keep their possessor from sinking in mud as well as to swim. The extended toes of the jacana enable these birds to walk on floating leaves of water plants.

Mammals that live mainly on a habitat with a soft substratum have noticeably large feet, whether they live in marshes (moose) or run on snow, as does the snowshoe rabbit, or on loose sand (*Gazella loderi*). Many different kinds of animals have become adapted to move over loose sand. Tenebrionid beetles of extensive sands are supported by widened tarsi extended by chitinous hairs or have their mesothoracic and metathoracic legs greatly lengthened and so run over loose sand somewhat as water striders do on the surface film of water (Faussek, 1907; Gebien, 1920). Among their sand-dwelling species, four different families of lizards show convergent development of lateral rows of scales or fringes on their toes. Different genera of snakes, living in different parts of the world, have independently become "side winders" as an adaptation to locomotion over loose sand (Fig. 35). The jumping mouse (*Dipus*) has lateral hairs from the soles of its feet and the sand grouse (*Syrrhaptes*) has feathered toes and a web. The toes of some species of grouse are extended during winter months by a curious fringe of horny points that act as snowshoes. These are shown for the spruce grouse in Figure 36, in contrast with the slender toes characteristic of the sharp-tailed grouse. These instances illustrate the convergent adaptations of animals that live on a shifting substratum, whether it is sand or snow.

Fig. 35. The side winder, *Crotalus cerastes,* with tracks on sand (moving from lower right to upper left). (Rephotographed from Mosauer.)

kangaroo and in the various jumping mice and rats of the dry, open plains. Such terrestrial forms are to be contrasted with the long-armed, short-legged apes and monkeys that clamber about on the physical substrate furnished by tropical trees.

The solid ground, whether made of rock fragments or soil, furnishes a medium in which diverse kinds of animals live, as well as being a substratum for varied animal activities. Dense populations of protozoans and of larger, but still small to tiny, soft-bodied animals, and some larger ones, too, are restricted to living within the soil. Others spend significant parts of their lives in burrows, and many more are casual residents or visitors underground. A brief re-

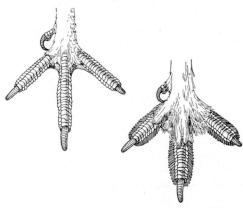

Fig. 36. "Snow-shoe" extensions (right) on the feet of the spruce grouse *(Dendragapus canadiensis)* contrasted with those of the sharp-tailed grouse *(Pediocetes phasianellus)*. (From specimens in the Chicago Museum of Natural History.)

The various structural convergences found in the rapid-running mammals of the usually firm-surfaced plains find a logical extreme in the horse and antelope and, in another direction of development, in the

view of some of the complex relations of these animals to the soil would be suitable here; such a discussion is reserved however, for Chapter 16, dealing with Ecological Relations of the Soil.

11. PHYSICOCHEMICAL AND CHEMICAL PHASES

The emphasis in the last several chapters has been upon environmental physics. Light, heat, gravity, pressure, currents of air and of water, sound, substratal vibrations, mechanical shock, and the substratum in general have been discussed. The extent to which the life and distribution of animals

depends upon the action of the physical forces of the world in which they live may come as a surprise. The great influence of water and of carbon dioxide in controlling the environment (p. 76) is related to the physical as well as to the chemical properties of these important compounds.

It is difficult to distinguish clearly and accurately between modern physics and chemistry. The two meet in the annectent science of physical chemistry. Physicochemical aspects of ecology include such phenomena as diffusion, osmosis, hydrogen ion concentration (acidity and alkalinity), chemical buffering of the environment, other ion effects, and adsorption. Solute relations in aqueous solutions, including the unique colligative properties associated with osmotic pressure—the lowering of the freezing point, the lowering of vapor pressure, the elevation of the boiling point—and surface tension, have been or will be considered in part in connection with other topics rather than directly (see Index). Ecological applications of colloidal chemistry, despite probable importance, have been slightly developed and will be discussed only briefly. All these are, in the main, physicochemical characteristics of the environment, but no attempt will be made to distinguish between physicochemical and more strictly chemical reactions within the nonliving environment. Neither will the line be drawn sharply between possibly biotic effects and those that result from reactions between nonliving systems.

VISCOSITY

Viscosity of water results from cohesion among the water particles, including water molecules. Under appropriate conditions, adhesion to rocks, sand, mud, or other constituents of the shores or bottom affect the expressed viscosity. The greater the viscosity, the more resistance is offered to changes in form and to movement. Under ideal conditions, a streamlined body moving at an appropriate speed parts the water without ripples or eddies and initiates a series of layers gliding smoothly past each other. This provides an example of laminar viscosity such as is rarely realized in nature. Rather, turbulence is produced, at least to some extent, and the resulting confused or smoothly developed system of vortices provides examples of eddy viscosity that is at once much more complex and many times greater than laminar viscosity. The intrinsic difficulty in analysis of eddy viscosity in precise terms is indicated by the mathematical discussion in Sverdrup, Johnson, and Fleming (1942, p. 469).

Viscosity of water is related to cyclomorphoses (p. 118), to flotation in general (p.

132), as well as to the streamlined form of many aquatic animals (p. 156). Viscosity increases decidedly with lowered temperature, increases somewhat with salinity, but is only slightly affected by pressure even in the depths of the ocean (p. 137). The general ecological relations of aquatic animals to the viscosity of water are simply and correctly outlined by Coker (1947). Similar relations with air hold for land animals, except that the viscosity values are less.

DIFFUSION

In aqueous solution and in natural mixtures of gases of ecological importance, as well as in solutions and gases less directly related to ecology, all the molecules or ions present move more or less freely through the whole. The movement is free with gases, less so in liquid solutions, still less free in those solutions that approach solids, and least free when the solvent is a solid. Many essential materials in the environment of organisms owe their tendency toward uniform distribution to diffusion, and diffusion through membranes, called osmosis, places organisms in effective working relations with many aspects of their environment.

The relatively simple but important facts concerning diffusion, uncomplicated by considerations of membrane permeability, may be summarized both for solutions and for gaseous mixtures as follows: All the ions and molecules present as solvent, or dissolved solute, tend to diffuse throughout the whole available space; such diffusion is active and continuous. The diffusion of each kind of ion or molecule is almost independent of other kinds that may be present; thus, within the limits of normal sea water, the rate of diffusion is almost independent of salinity.

While ions or molecules move in random fashion, collision with other similar particles is more frequent toward the region of their greater concentration; hence there is a tendency for net movement to be toward the region of greater dilution of the given ion or molecule regardless of the position of greatest concentration of the sum total of all substances present. This principle applies both to the concentrations of the solvent and of the solute.

The rate of diffusion across any plane at right angles to the direction of diffusion bears a simple, linear, quantitative relation to the concentration gradient. The natural constant so obtained is called the diffusion constant. This is Fick's "law," similar to Newton's "law of cooling," and is one form of the more general "law of velocities." It follows that, as diffusion equilibrium is approached, the rate of diffusion is steadily decreased.

Many of these statements about diffusion eddy coefficient in analyzing diffusion in natural environments. The transport resulting from turbulence may be many times greater and more rapid than that from diffusion, and under many conditions the rapidity and completeness of the intermixture of diffusible substances are primarily dependent on turbulence rather than on diffusion.

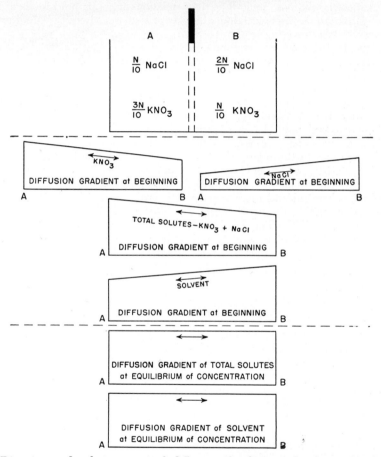

Fig. 37. Direction and relative rates of diffusion of solutes and solvent. (Redrawn from Miller.)

are illustrated in the diagrams shown in Figure 37. For our purpose, the figure is self-explanatory. Diffusion processes are discussed thoroughly for the physiologist in relatively simple, mathematical terms by Jacobs (1935). There is no equally competent monographic presentation of the subject from the ecological point of view. In ecology, turbulence introduces a disturbing relationship in the process of diffusion, and it is often necessary to introduce a so-called

The rate of diffusion stands apart from many chemical and biological processes in that it is little affected by changes in temperature. The velocity of molecular movement in gases, and probably in liquids, is proportional to the square root of the absolute temperature. If the velocity is 1000 at 20° C., it will increase to 1017 at 30°. Thus exponential temperature "laws" (p. 107) do not apply to this process.

The practical results of the operation of

the process of diffusion are such that material scattered almost in "trace" concentrations will steadily diffuse into the environmental niches from which they are being withdrawn by organisms. Sea water contains a number of chemicals in extremely dilute solutions; of these, silicon is normally present in amounts ranging from 0.02 to 4.0 mg. per kilogram of sea water, and is extracted from this dilute concentration by diatoms and various sponges, among other organisms. Glass sponges (Hexactinellida) give interesting examples of animals that form extensive and heavy skeletons from silicon hydrate. These sponges reach their greatest development at the bottom of the ocean in depths from 500 to 1000 meters. They commonly grow to be from 10 to 30 cm. long and may even reach a length of a meter. A museum specimen of *Euplectella,* 23 cm. long weighs 5.3 gm. Diffusion must be an important factor in this large concentration of silicon.

Copper, present in sea water in quantities of between 0.001 to 0.01 mg. per kilogram is concentrated to become an important constituent in hemocyanin, the respiratory pigment of *Limulus* and of many other marine invertebrates. Similarly, iron, an important part of hemoglobin, the respiratory pigment in fishes and other vertebrates and

Table 11. *The Relative Concentration of Different Ions in Pond Water and in* Nitella *in Millimoles**

mM.	Pond Water	*Nitella*
Cl⁻	0.9	90.8
SO⁻⁻	0.3	8.3
$H_2PO_4^-$	0.0002	3.6
NO_3^-	0.55	0.0
Na⁺	0.2	10.0
K⁺	0.05	54.3
Ca⁺⁺	0.78	10.2
Mg⁺⁺	1.69	177.7

* A "mole" or *molar solution* of any substance equals the number of grams corresponding to the molecular weight of the substance, dissolved in distilled water, and made up to a liter of solution. A *normal solution* contains 1 grammolecular weight of solute divided by its hydrogen equivalent and made up to a liter of solution; a normal solution contains 1 gramequivalent of the solute in 1 liter of solution.

in the red-blooded marine invertebrates, must be concentrated from dilutions in sea water of the same order of magnitude as copper. It is not meant that the individual animal necessarily concentrates such dilute materials from the sea directly, but at some stage in the food chain, the concentration is accomplished, and diffusion plays a large and vital role whenever it happens. More striking instances are known.

Nitella is an alga growing in fresh water. The concentrations of different ions in pond water and in *Nitella* are shown in Table 11. *Nitella* concentrates Cl⁻ some 100 times and $H_2PO_4^-$ 1800 times the density found in pond water. It is able to do so because the ions continue to diffuse toward the point of reduced density produced by the action of the alga (data from Krogh, 1939). These concentrations are carried on directly by *Nitella;* they are not automatic, since NO_3^- is excluded, and the other ions are taken up in differing proportions.

OSMOSIS

Living organisms are surrounded and subdivided by membranes through which substances must pass when there is an effective exchange of materials between organism and environment. Diffusion through membranes is known as osmosis, though usually in osmosis membranes are thought of as being somewhat semipermeable. It is, in part, an ecological process (cf. Shelford, 1929; Pearse, 1939). Various other phases of osmosis are treated extensively in books on physical chemistry and on general physiology, and these should be consulted for many details and refinements that cannot be included here.

A given membrane or set of membranes (forming the surface of an organism) may be impermeable or almost completely permeable, or there may be one or more combinations of a great variety of partial permeabilities. When a membrane is permeable to water and approximately impermeable to solutes, it is said to be semipermeable. Completely semipermeable membranes probably exist only in theory. If the concentration of solutes is unequal on the two sides of a so-called semipermeable membrane, water passes through to the more concentrated solution (the one in which there is less water per unit volume) until equilibrium is established. The pressure that results from this osmotic process is called osmotic pressure; it may be defined as the difference in pressure on solution and solvent that establishes an equilibrium such that there is no longer a tendency for the solvent to flow in either direction. Organisms with a higher concentration of solutes within the body than is found outside tend strongly to take in water and exhibit turgor. Some of the physiological adaptations to counteract such processes will be outlined on page 169.

The outer covering of *Ascaris megalocephala,* a nematode intestinal parasite, is practically impermeable to digestive fluids of the host and even to 10 per cent formalin. The vitelline membrane of trout eggs becomes impermeable to water when placed in contact with fresh water. Such egg membranes are permeable to oxygen and to carbon dioxide, and respiratory exchanges can take place between the developing egg and the surrounding fresh water.

Membrane permeability for water is measured by a "minute number" which is the time taken for 1 cc. of water to pass through 1 square cm. of membrane under a pressure of 1 atmosphere. It approximates one minute for certain filters, but for many animal membranes the "minute number" varies from a few thousand minutes (a few days) to several years. In general, membranes with relatively low permeability for water are only slightly permeable for some associated ions. For those substances for which the membrane is readily permeable, osmosis follows the rule applicable to simple diffusion. The passage of electrically charged particles through a membrane is more complicated, and more specialized accounts should be consulted for details; see especially Krogh (1939), who gives a useful guide to the complicated literature of this whole phase of physiological ecology.

Living organisms are not simple osmotic machines. They can maintain differences in salt concentration across a membrane despite its semipermeability. Animals and plants in fresh water, even when water-permeable, keep a much higher total concentration within the body than exists in the surrounding water. To do so requires a continuous expenditure of energy. With such organisms, there is no true osmotic equilibrium between the internal fluids and environment. Rather, they are said to maintain a "steady state," and steady states may apply either to the distribution of water or of ions, or both.

Animals may be either poikilosmotic or homoiosmotic. A poikilosmotic animal is in osmotic equilibrium with its environment; the equilibrium shifts through rather wide degrees, depending on the dilution or concentration of the environment. Marine invertebrates are frequently poikilosmotic. A homoiosmotic animal steadily maintains a total internal concentration of body fluids unlike that of the environment. Fresh water animals and most marine fishes belong in this category. This division on the basis of osmotic characteristics suggests the better-known division into poikilothermy and homoiothermy. All homoiothermal animals are also homoiosmotic, but poikilothermal animals may be either poikilosmotic or homoiosmotic.

The body fluids of many poikilosmotic invertebrates of the sea have an ionic composition closely approximating that in sea water. In this they are unlike the poikilosmotic marine vertebrates whose body fluids may differ decidedly in ionic constitution from their environment. Homoiosmotic animals, especially those of the fresh water, have ionic concentrations that differ widely from those found in the surrounding medium.

The poikilosmotic character of marine invertebrates is shown by the almost isotonic relation between their body fluids and the sea water in which they live. The invertebrates of the Mediterranean, in keeping with its higher salinity, have a higher concentration of salts than those of the North Sea or the open Atlantic. These invertebrates do not require osmotically protective structures or processes in skin, gills or gut or other specialized devices for maintaining osmotic balance or keeping the internal osmotic pressure within the bounds of toleration.

The invertebrates in fresh water maintain much higher salt concentrations in body fluids than those in the water around them. Some large groups are excluded from the fresh waters because they have not evolved effective mechanisms to control or counteract osmotic exchanges of water and ions; among others, these include the entire phylum of Echinodermata. On the other hand, successful groups in fresh water, notably the amphibians and insects, have been almost unable successfully to invade marine environments. Animals adapted to life in fresh water overcome the constant tendency for a strong inflow of water in one or more of the following ways:

1. Most commonly there is an increased activity of the excretory system, and the surplus water is ejected. The contractile vacuoles of fresh-water protozoans have this as their main function. Marine Protozoa may, or may not, have a contractile vacuole; if present, its rate of pulsation is slow and serves to eliminate water engulfed with food. The nephridial systems of fresh-water metazoans, whether flame cells or nephidia proper, are all active in eliminating excess water. The mechanism whereby fresh-water sponges and coelenterates rid themselves of water that enters osmotically is unknown (Krogh, 1939, p. 31).

2. Eurysaline animals have some power of adjusting skin permeability in keeping with the concentration of the surrounding medium. Calcium reduces permeability of membranes, as is shown almost diagrammatically by exposing the marine planarian *Procerodes* (= *Gunda*) to fresh water with and without calcium (Oesting and Allee, 1935). The presence of calcium in quantity is important for the invasion of brackish water by marine organisms (Breder, 1934).

3. The possession of naturally impermeable body walls reaches a logical extreme in the water spider, *Argyroneta*, which carries its own supply of oxygen below the surface and avoids all osmotic exchange with the fresh water in which it lives. Air-breathing insects, like the dytiscid beetles, are similarly independent of osmosis. Small aquatic arthropods, whether crustaceans, arachnids, or insects, if the adults are small, or in the egg stage, or in early instars of larger forms may carry on respiration by exchange through an outer membrane impermeable to water. The same exoskeleton that, as a water-conserving mechanism, makes life possible for insects in a dry atmosphere, permits them to invade fresh water habitats and allows some to invade the waters of salt lakes. Larger insect nymphs with gills excrete water that enters by osmosis, as do many other animals of the fresh water.

4. A vitelline membrane, impermeable to water, has been described for trout eggs and is probably common among eggs of fresh-water animals. The eggs of *Hydra* and of crayfish have a dense covering, and fresh-water planarian eggs, among others, are enclosed in a thick-walled case.

5. A heavy coating of mucous apparently slows down the ingress of water into many aquatic plants and animals, including the eel (Hesse, Allee, and Schmidt, 1937, p. 35).

Bony fishes from fresh water have a concentration of body fluids which is much higher than that of their environment and approaches the concentration in marine fishes. The exposed membranes, including gills, skin, and mucous membranes, are permeable to water, and there is a large inflow of water through these structures. Even fresh-water fishes drink water (Allee and Frank, 1948). Osmotic balance is maintained, as with invertebrates, largely by the active excretion of dilute urine; water intake and excretion are more nearly proportional to surface area than to weight.

Marine fishes have evolved two methods of meeting the osmotic situation presented by the salt concentration found in sea water. Elasmobranch fishes, the sharks and rays, are nearly isotonic with their environment as a result of the urea found in their blood and body fluids. Actually, the osmotically active internal concentration is somewhat higher than that of sea water in the open ocean or in the higher salinity of the Mediterranean. The internal concentration does not fall to a point approaching equilibrium when these fishes invade fresh water habitats. The usual slight inward flow is increased among the invaders of fresh waters. In both instances, the excess is eliminated by the kidneys; the fresh-water forms have a large output of quite dilute urine (Smith, 1936).

The bony fishes of the sea have a lower concentration of osmotically active substances in their body fluids than that of sea water; hence, unlike fresh-water animals they face a steady loss of water by osmosis unless their integument and gills are impermeable to water. This is usually not the case. Actually, marine fishes drink large quantities of sea water, and both water and salts are absorbed from the alimentary tract, the latter somewhat selectively (Smith, 1930), and excess ions are disposed of apparently by extrarenal excretion.

Anadromous and catadromous fishes provide an interesting check on the ways in which fishes adjust to the salt concentration of their environment. Anadromous fishes breed in fresh water, and the young migrate to the sea, where they live until sexual maturity; catadromous fishes exhibit converse migration. The anadromous chinook salmon, *Oncorhynchus*, shows a somewhat greater salt concentration of the blood

abruptly from salt to fresh water, or *vice versa*. The equally severe tests of knowledge concerning osmoregulatory mechanisms furnished by inhabitants of brine cannot be met at present. *Artemia*, the brine shrimp shows eurysalinity in an extreme form; it can live in fresh water and in salt lakes with a concentration of 222 *per mille* and more. The permeability of the surface is

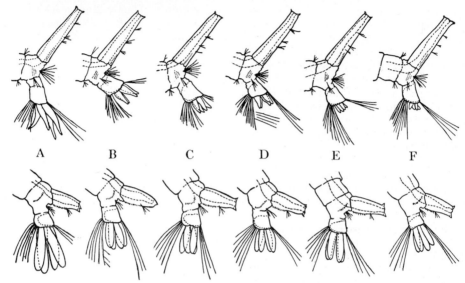

Fig. 38. Posterior segments of *Aedes* larvae (lower row) and *Culex* larvae (upper row), showing size of anal papillae, from media with different concentrations of sodium chloride. *A*, Distilled water; *B*, tap water (0.006 per cent of sodium chloride); *C*, 0.075 per cent; *D*, 0.34 per cent; *E*, 0.65 per cent; *F*, 0.90 per cent. (From Wigglesworth.)

when in the sea than after the spawning invasion of fresh water. The measured depression of freezing point of the blood of marine specimens ranges from 0.7° to 0.8°, that for spawning fish from 0.61° to 0.67° C. The indications are that these salmon swallow sea water while in the ocean as do other marine teleosts, and that they decrease the amount swallowed while in their long, nonfeeding existence in fresh water. They apparently have the mechanisms of marine animals for osmotic regulation while in the sea, and those of fresh-water animals, including lowered permeability of gill membranes, while in fresh water.

The eel, a catadromous fish, shows a similar set of behavioral and physiological adjustments, including the remarkably low permeability of the skin and gills (Krogh, *op. cit.*, p. 150). Known principles meet the tests furnished by these fishes that can pass

low, but it is permeable to water, and the method of osmotic regulation is unknown (Krogh, 1939).

IONIC EXCHANGE

The other side of the osmotic picture, the diffusion of ions, is more obscure than the diffusion of water. Animal membranes, weakly permeable to water, are also permeable to many ions. The precise mechanisms whereby ionic transfers through a membrane occur scarcely concern us here. Marine invertebrates approach ionic balance with sea water; hence their membranes must be permeable to ions as well as to water. With marine teleost fishes, the problem is to secrete ions engulfed when sea water is swallowed, and there is evidence that at least Cl^- is excreted actively through the gills, and Krogh (1939, p. 145), who has done much to formulate the problem clearly, believes that marine fishes generally excrete chlorine and sodium independently. The process is reversed in fresh-water organisms. In them there is a steady inflow of water and a steady loss of ions. Both processes must be counteracted. As we have already seen, the excess water is characteristically controlled by secretion of a dilute watery urine. The inner concentration of electrolytes is maintained by an active ionic absorption. This interpretation is supported by a considerable body of evidence and includes that presented by Wigglesworth (1938), summarized in Figure 38. As the figures show, the size of anal papillae of mosquito larvae is correlated with the concentration of chloride solutions in the media in which they live, supposedly because these act in absorbing ions from the surrounding solution. Papillae that may function similarly are found in various parts of many insect larvae that live in fresh water.

One of the primary ecological divisions, the separation of aquatic animals into the communities associated with marine and those associated with fresh waters, is not only a matter of permeability to water and of methods of supplying water or of eliminating excess water intake by osmosis, there is also the equally important matter of the maintenance of an appropriate concentration of necessary ions. Both aspects of osmoregulation are also highly important for inhabitants of brackish water. The permeability of skin, gill, and gut membranes, the functioning and even the structure of contractile vacuoles of the Protozoa, of nephridia of invertebrates, and the kidneys of vertebrates, and the structure and processes associated with extrarenal transport of ions through membranes are among the important morphological and physiological adjustments associated with the distribution of aquatic animals into waters of various salinities. It is interesting to find the nephridial system, usually located deep in the internal anatomy of animals and, in many ways, well insulated from the outside environment, directly associated with animal ecology.

As for many other ecological processes, a study of osmotic relations throughout the life history shows that habitats suitable for reproductive processes are frequently more restricted than those that can be tolerated by adult animals. Many aquatic animals shed eggs and spermatozoa into the water, and fertilization takes place externally. Sea water is a fairly favorable medium for external fertilization; fresh water is much less so. Fish spermatozoa retain their activity for but a minute or two in fresh water, and in this medium, artificial insemination at the hands of fish culturists is often more efficient than is natural fertilization, because the spermatozoa can be so placed that they are exposed to water for a shorter period before reaching the eggs. About 10 per cent of British trout eggs are fertilized on the natural breeding grounds; 90 per cent can be fertilized by artificial methods (Gray, 1920). Spermatozoa of fresh-water trout remain active for ten or twenty minutes in brackish water in which the fish do not breed, although, so far as longevity of spermatozoa is concerned, brackish water is ten to twenty times more favorable than the fresh water in which trout do breed. Other maladjustments to salinity are known; shad spawn in fresh water, but the optimum for egg development is about 1 per cent salinity.

Evidence from optimum salinity, such as has just been reviewed, points to the sea as the ancestral home of fishes. This conclusion goes against much evidence from the osmoregulatory processes and the kidney structures of adult teleosts. Homer Smith (1932) was much impressed by the latter evidence and argues that it points to a fresh-water origin for all fishes. Others have been struck by the resemblance between the salt concentration and ionic balance in the blood and other body fluids of many aquatic and even of land vertebrates with that supposed to have existed in the ocean at the time of the evolution of the early representatives of present day classes of animals. Rogers (1938), from the point of view of comparative physiology, and Pearse (1939), from that of ecology, review these ideas sympathetically, and Beadle (1943) also is friendly to them. Available comparisons are stimulating to the imagination without being definitely convincing. The subject of osmotic regulation in nature will be extensively developed in future books on ecological physiology.

IONS AS ENVIRONMENTAL FACTORS

The influence of ions in the environment of animals is best shown in the ocean. Sea water is nearly a physiologically balanced solution of salts, particularly for marine invertebrates. In the concentration in which they occur in sea water, salts are about 90 per cent ionized. There are four principal electropositive ions (cations), Ca^{++}, Mg^{++}, K^+ and Na^+, and four main electronegative ones (anions) CO_3^{--}, SO_4^{--}, Cl^- and Br^-. Forty chemical elements, gases excluded, are dissolved in sea water in smaller amounts; many of those in trace concentrations probably are completely ionized (Sverdrup, Johnson, and Fleming, 1942). Water itself is slightly dissociated into H^+ and OH, ions (10^{-7} normal).

The ions present exert a joint force in affecting the osmosis of water through a semipermeable membrane; in addition, they often act also to produce characteristic effects on living organisms. Even ions closely related in their physicochemical

HYDROGEN ION CONCENTRATION (pH)

Hydrogen ion concentration as measured on the pH scale runs from normal acid to normal base. Some of the pertinent relations between different pH values are illustrated in Table 12, which makes the reciprocal relations between positive H ions and negative OH ions apparent at a glance.

Many pH measurements have been taken in environments fairly free from biotic conditioning as well as in those influenced by plants and animals. We shall limit attention to the former. Differences in the use of physicochemical constants, in methods of measurement, and frequent disregard of errors resulting from different salinities, especially with colorimetric methods, prevent a close comparison of results reported

Table 12. The pH Scale and Some of Its Equivalents

pH	Acid Normality	Alkaline Normality
1	0.1	0.0000000000001
2	0.01	0.000000000001
3	0.001	0.00000000001
4	0.0001	0.0000000001
5	0.00001	0.000000001
6	0.000001	0.00000001
7*	0.0000001	0.0000001
8	0.00000001	0.000001
9	0.000000001	0.00001
10	0.0000000001	0.0001
11	0.00000000001	0.001
12	0.000000000001	0.01
13	0.0000000000001	0.1

* Neutrality.

properties may affect certain living processes differently, and quite unlike ions may yield closely similar results. The relations between cations and organisms are much better known than are those of anions, and both antagonistic and synergistic effects exist (Heilbrunn, 1943).

The end result is that the physiological balance of ions in sea water, together with the isotonicity of this medium for most marine invertebrates, helps strongly to make sea water an excellent aquatic environment for many diverse plants and animals. It is true that these organisms have evolved in adjustment to this environment.

by the many different people who have made pH determinations.

The pH of sea water in free contact with the atmosphere varies between about 8.1 and 8.3. There is, in general, a decrease with depth to about the region of minimum dissolved oxygen (p. 192), and then an increase in deeper water. The pH is not greatly changed even in intermediate depths; it reaches about 7.5 in the north Pacific at a level at which the oxygen content of the water is reduced to some tenths of a cubic centimeter per liter (Sverdrup, Johnson, and Fleming, 1942). In inshore waters, particularly those of the tide pools, bays, and estuaries, the range may be much greater. Near Woods Hole, Massachusetts, over deep muck at low tide, the pH was 7.3; at the surface of the water in a mat of eel grass and in the bright sunlight, the pH was 9.0; only 30 inches of well-buffered sea water separated the two locations. These differences practically disappear at high tide (Allee, 1923). At the same time, the dissolved oxygen ranged from a trace at the bottom near the muck to the supersaturated value of 12.97 cc./L. at the surface. Other things being equal, regions of relatively low pH (high H ion concentration) are frequently also regions of reduced oxygen content. The pH of marine bottom deposits may fall below 7.0 or stand above 8.5 (ZoBell, 1946).

The pH of fresh waters, unmodified by man, range from 3.2 (or perhaps 2.2) to 10.5 or thereabouts, although most streams and lakes have a range of from 6.5 to 8.5, inclusive. The moss, *Sphagnum,* and some other plants secrete acid, and the water in sphagnum mats approaches the lower recorded limit. Bogs in general, whether sphagnum or otherwise, usually have acid water. Streams and the water from the surface strata of lakes in limestone areas usually have about the same pH as does the ocean.

CHEMICAL BUFFERS

The H ion concentration is kept from large fluctuations in most animal environments by the presence of chemical buffers. Buffers are largely absent in rain water and in water from recently melted ice or snow; there is a high concentration of them in hard waters that are rich in carbonates. The effectiveness of chemical buffers as a neutrality mechanism can be understood by a brief consideration of a buffer system based on carbon dioxide, which closely accompanies water in nature in the following forms:

Free carbon dioxide, CO_2

Carbonic acid, $\dfrac{H}{H} \Big> CO_3$

Bicarbonate or alkali-acid carbonate or "half bound" carbonate, $\dfrac{H}{Base} \Big> CO_3$

Alakali or "bound" carbonate, $\dfrac{Base}{Base} \Big> CO_3$

If a strong acid is added, the dynamic equilibrium shifts rapidly. Simply put,

some of the acid combines with the alkali, let us say from the bound carbonate, and the nearly neutral bicarbonate is increased. If more acid is added, some of the bicarbonate may be converted to carbonic acid; this may break into water and carbon dioxide, and any excess of the latter will escape into the air. The neutrality of the medium is not greatly changed until the alkali reserve approaches exhaustion. The alkali reserve or buffer value is sometimes referred to merely as "alkalinity," a term that in this connection has no relation to the hydroxyl ion concentration for the given medium. Conversely, if a strong alkali is added, it reacts with carbonic acid to form bicarbonate or, if in larger amount, to form a "bound" carbonate that is more nearly neutral than the alkali originally added.

Phosphoric acid, with three hydrogen ions bound to the acid radicle, makes an even better buffer. The principle is the same, and though phosphates are less abundant in aquatic environments than are the carbonates, they may be an effective buffer for soils. The common use of phosphates for buffering water in physiological experimentation is open to serious objection, since the phosphate ion often produces a situation quite different in ion content from that found in nature and therefore ecologically unsound.

pH AND ANIMAL LIFE

The expectation that the hydrogen ion concentration of the environment might prove to be of outstanding importance (p. 58) has not been realized. The hypothesis was based on observations that enzyme activity is often closely related to the pH of the medium and that respiratory rate in vertebrates is controlled by the pH of the blood. Also, there was early evidence of the importance of pH in the culturing of bacteria. It is now known that some bacteria, as with animals, grow only in a narrow pH range and may be restricted to less than a pH unit, and that others can tolerate a range of six or even of nine such units (Buchanan and Fulmer, 1930).

Among Protozoa, *Euglena mutabilis* occurs in pools and streams with acidities as high as pH 1.8 produced by acid drainage from mines. In pure cultures, free from bacteria and fungi, they tolerate pH 1.4 for twelve days and have a similar resistance to pH 7.9. They grow in concentrations from pH 2.1 to 7.7, inclusive (von Dach, 1943). Tapeworms adjust to changes in hydrogen ion concentration from pH 4 to 11, the range to which they are normally exposed; their optimum is at pH 10. Other animals are much more limited; the ciliate, *Stentor coeruleus*, is reported to be adjusted to only pH 7.7 to 8.0. (Hetherington, 1932), and *Spirostomum ambiguum* is apparently limited in nature by pH above 7.8 (Hutchinson, 1941a).

Some striking correlations between pH and community distribution have been reported. In one instance, in southern Canada, a pool located in a granitic outcrop was separated from one in limestone by only a few hundred yards. The pH of the former ranged between 6.2 and 6.8; that of the latter between 7.6 and 9.2. Each pool had its characteristic biota; none of the species of algae, protozoans, and entomostracans recorded from either pool were found in the other (Reed and Klugh, 1924). Since this is approximately all we know about the case, one can only wonder about the role played by pH in controlling the distribution. No analysis was given of the water of the two pools, and it is almost a certainty that the lime content was decidedly different. The determining factors could be settled by simple toleration experiments.

Shelford (1925) suggested that pH may be a guiding factor in the return of spawning salmon of northwestern North America to their natal streams. Some mosquito larvae are killed by acid water; a pH of 5 is the threshold for development of the first instar of *Anopheles maculipennis* (Sebenzow and Adova, 1929); tree-hole mosquito larvae can live in much more acid water. In their extensive studies, Jewell and Brown (1929) found snails limited to water with a pH of 6.1 or more and the fingernail clam *Pisidium* to those of 5.8 or more. This last value approximates the acidity at which the deposition of lime becomes theoretically impossible.

From experience with ecological factors associated with the distribution of communities of marine invertebrates near Woods Hole, Massachusetts, Allee (1923) concluded that while a combination of the average pH, the extent of range, and the relative positions of extremes of pH does allow one to place the communities studied in their natural order with considerable

exactness, such data do not classify the communities with the precision necessary for a successful single-factor index. Salinity changes were more accurately associated with the observed distribution of these communities, and the character of the substratum was still more closely correlated.

Present evidence bearing on the relation between pH and species distribution indicates that in general a close correlation can no longer be expected. The limits of pH toleration differ more or less for different species, and yet Jewell and Brown (1929) summarized a considerable amount of first-hand experience with distribution of fresh-water fishes and pH as follows: "While most of the species are found in waters having a pH value between 7.2 and 8.6, yet inasmuch as most fresh waters have pH values within these limits, the only indication is that the fish are where the water is." The longer these authors worked on this subject, the more convinced they became that pH, as such, is rarely a limiting factor in the distribution of fresh-water fishes in natural waters. Behre (1928) came to a similar conclusion from her studies of fish distribution and the pH of fresh-water habitats in Panama.

Observations such as these show the need for caution concerning conclusions about the degree to which pH determinations can be correlated with distribution in nature. Perhaps the correlation is as close as can well be expected, considering the complexity of the interactions between pH and other phases of the physical environment. In the main, discussion of the interrelations of different environmental factors is reserved for separate treatment; but with pH, the interplay of various factors has a large importance in comparison with the effectiveness of hydrogen ion concentration considered alone and some joint effects need to be considered at once.

The pH of lake water is low under the ice in late winter. It rises with the spring overturn and then becomes progressively higher in the epilimnion and progressively lower in the hypolimnion as summer stratification develops. These changes are associated with the consumption of carbon dioxide in photosynthesis; that in deeper water, with the accumulation of carbon dioxide and the leaching out of acids from the substratum. There are valid reasons for the use of pH as an indicator of stagnation, or lack of it, in lakes subject to thermal stratification. Diurnal changes in hydrogen ion concentration sometimes come with dramatic suddenness (see p. 343); seasonal changes take place more slowly. The limits in certain well-studied Wisconsin lakes (Juday *et al.,* 1935) seldom pass three whole units. Stated thus, the variation seems small, but this is misleading on the pH or any other logarithmic scale. Actually, as shown in Table 12, a change of three such units indicates a thousandfold variation.

The conditions just outlined indicate that the hydrogen ion concentration of the water is often correlated with the carbon dioxide content. The relationship is imperfect, and pH alone may reveal little or nothing about the amount of carbon dioxide present, since carbon dioxide and carbonates in general are but one of a number of factors known to affect environmental pH. Even so, under many conditions it is the carbon dioxide content of water, together with the alkali reserve, rather than pH, that is of primary importance. This conclusion was reached both on the basis of field and of laboratory studies (Powers, 1939). In the laboratory, the most convincing evidence comes from removing all carbonates by bubbling air through water acidified to pH 4 and then establishing the needed pH by treatment with alkali (Clowes and Smith, 1923; Hyman, 1925). For the planarian, *Dugesia,* Hyman found that the acidification of natural waters was followed by a decrease in oxygen consumption in all cases where the pH fell below 7.0 and usually when it was reduced from pH 7.8; this effect disappeared when pH changes were made in water free from carbonates, except when the acidity was produced by adding carbon dioxide.

Photosynthesis, with its active removal of carbon dioxide and the giving off of oxygen, helps explain the inverse correlation that often exists between hydrogen ion concentration and oxygen content of water, whether salt or fresh. Other conditions work to the same end; thus bottom deposits rich in organic matter contribute acid to the water above them and absorb oxygen. With fishes, and many other animals, the reciprocal distribution of hydrogen ions and oxygen produces two important ecological effects. In the first place, many aquatic organisms are less able to tolerate low oxygen tensions in acid waters, and, in the second place, many

fishes turn back from water of low pH more readily than they do from water that merely has a low content of dissolved oxygen. They turn away from the combination of low oxygen and high hydrogen ion concentration still more readily. Such reactions have survival value.

Another type of interaction between pH and other environmental factors is shown by the relation of heat resistance to the hydrogen ion concentration of the medium. Often this is not a straight-line relationship. When paramecia are transferred from room temperature to 40° C., death occurs within a few minutes before there has been time for acclimatization. Greater resistance to heat is found at about pH 6.8 and 7.8, and definitely lowered heat resistance occurs at about pH 5.7, 7.2, and 8.3 (Chalkley, 1930; Garner, 1934). Chalkley suggests that the results arise from changes in permeability of the cell membrane induced by the different hydrogen ion concentrations.

Environmental pH has neither the real importance it frequently has within the organism, the duplication of which was expected by enthusiastic ecological students in the 1920's, nor the lack of importance sometimes expressed and often implied later. The large amount of evidence available amply supports the following relatively simple generalizations:

1. Some organisms tolerate a wide range of pH, others only a narrow range, and still others are intermediate.

2. Some organisms flourish best in acid, others in alkaline environments, and others find their optimum at or near neutrality.

3. The reactions may be to the hydrogen ion concentration directly or to changes produced by or related to changes in pH, as is the carbon dioxide concentration in a carbonate-rich water or soil.

4. When effective, the relationship between ecological processes and pH is not necessarily represented by a straight line graph, but may be much more complex.

5. Hydrogen ion concentration is no more important than many other environmental factors and is usually less significant than water (in its various forms), sunlight, heat, the character of the substratum, and some of the other conditions of existence.

The conclusion is that the hydrogen ion concentration has real, though limited, value as a factor in the environmental complex of animals.

ADSORPTION

Much that has been written about adsorption has indirect rather than direct application to ecology. This subject is discussed at length in physical and colloidal chemistry, and the interested student must consult such sources to get a general view of the subject. Adsorption has been little studied from the ecological point of view; here again general physiology is much in advance of ecology.

Any process that diminishes the free energy at the boundary between a solid or immiscible or slowly miscible fluid, and an aqueous solution, tends to proceed toward an equilibrium, whatever may be the energy involved—chemical, mechanical, or electrical. A process that diminishes the surface electrical charge is an example. The concentration of a substance in an aqueous solution on the surface of another phase of matter is called adsorption. The relation between adsorption and the surface energy is known as the principle of Gibbs. In addition to stating that the concentration of a substance will be increased if it lowers surface energy, Gibbs' principle implies the opposite process: If a substance raises surface energy, its interphase concentration will be decreased, a process that has been called negative adsorption.

Finely divided materials—powdered charcoal, suspensions of clay in water, or colloids in general—present large amounts of surface per unit of solid matter and are likely to be potent adsorbing agents. Charcoal in water carries a negative surface charge and adsorbs positively charged colloidal particles or the cations of dissociated chemicals; the surface of most solids, insoluble in water, have a negative charge when immersed in it. Clay is an electronegative colloid; egg albumin carries an opposite charge. Electrical charges opposite in sign diminish, neutralize, or even reverse the surface charge. Alkalies and acids acting through OH^- and H^+ ions affect the surface charge so that the same substance may adsorb now anions and later cations from the same solution, depending on its pH. Among the ecological effects produced by adsorption, we may mention the following:

The adsorption of water on dust or salt particles is the basis of condensation of water droplets in the atmosphere.

Inorganic salts raise the surface tension at the water-air interphase and produce negative adsorption there.

Gases are adsorbed by solids; the action of charcoal is well known in this respect and may have ecological importance in the soil atmosphere of burned-over areas. Charcoal may also reduce the free cations in soil water and, if present in sufficient amount, may affect the reaction of the soil.

Clay suspensions in water also adsorb cations and tend to lower the pH. Such suspensions are common in the muddy waters of flooded streams. The aluminum content of clay is high, and aluminum is a particularly effective adsorbing agent. In keeping with its positive charge, unlike clay, it adsorbs negative ions. Its effectiveness as an adsorbent illustrates the rule that adsorbing power increases rapidly with valence, and aluminum has a valence of three. General information concerning adsorption in relation to valence is not easily come by beyond the fact that trivalent ions are more potent adsorbing agents than are ions with a valence of two or one. Recent books on surface chemistry should be consulted for further pertinent details.

To continue with the general ecological effects of adsorption:

The solutes present in a mixed solution, and the solvent as well, are adsorbed in definite proportions.

Adsorbed material may be eluded either by changing the electrical charge on the interface or by the presence of another substance with greater ability to lower surface energy. In the latter instance, the more potent substance tends to replace the less potent.

Many soil characteristics are determined by the adsorbing power of soil particles; for example, adsorption allows the soil to retain soluble mineral nutrients so that they are not all carried away by percolating water.

Micro-organisms may be poisoned in proportion to the amount of adsorption of certain poisons on their body surfaces, and cell processes in general can be strongly affected by substances that remain on the surface. In ecology, such processes have direct and obvious importance with micro-organisms. Bacteria may themselves be adsorbed on soil particles and so rendered inactive.

Adsorption plays an intimate role in

enzyme action, and extracellular enzymes and other catalysts have an importance in ecology the extent of which has not yet been measured.

Ordinary chemical reactions may follow surface adsorption.

Adsorption on the external body surface is especially important in the life of bacteria, protozoans, and of small metazoans. It may also produce significant effects in gilled animals generally, especially in those such as the lamellibranch mollusks that have much surface in relation to bulk.

Our discussion of adsorption is inadequate and must remain so, pending basic advances in surface chemistry and the appearance of monographic studies of adsorption as a physiological and finally as an ecological process.

The bacteria of the sea and, to a certain extent, those of fresh water are adsorbed on, or attached to surfaces, usually to the surfaces furnished by larger planktonic forms. Aquatic bacteria are relatively rare as free-floating organisms; they may be classed as only pseudoplanktonic. Even the cleanest surface of almost any kind promotes the growth of bacteria in dilute solutions, especially in dilute solutions of some 10 mg. per liter or less. The surfaces act (a) by adsorbing organic nutrients, especially colloids or poorly dissolved solutes, and (b) by retarding the diffusion of exoenzymes and of nutrients that must be hydrolyzed extracellularly before ingestion by the bacteria. The surface thus acts as a concentrator of nutrients from the extremely dilute solutions found in most waters. Particles larger than the bacteria themselves are most effective concentrators; in fact, particles smaller than the bacteria, adsorbed on the bacteria, may retard or accelerate the work of the latter organisms (ZoBell, 1943).

12. WATER

The hydrological cycle consists of the varied events happening to a particle of water from the time it is a bit of vapor in the atmosphere until it is again evaporated. Water enters the atmosphere from the surface of bodies of water and from the soil, from plants in transpiration or in drying, and, in smaller amounts, from animals. It is disseminated through the atmosphere by winds, precipitated as liquid or frozen rain, or as snow. Once precipitated, there may be immediate evaporation, or this may be delayed until after a run-off in streams or a slow creep-off as seepage or in glaciers. The water may be stored in soil, swamps, lakes, or oceans before re-evaporation takes it back to the beginning of the cycle. Plants and animals take water out of the inorganic hydrological cycle and make a subsidiary organic one from which the water returns sooner or later by diffusion, excretion, or as a result of organic decomposition. The main features of the cycle are suggested diagrammatically in Figure 39. The hydrological cycle is the central concept of the subscience of hydrology.

The oceans are the great reservoirs of water. They occupy 70.8 per cent of the 510.1×10^6 square kilometers of the earth's surface and have an average depth of 3795 meters. Their total volume is about 1370×10^6 cubic kilometers. The amount of water frozen into the ice of glaciers and ice sheets equals some 9.3 per cent (9.3×10^{-2}) of this amount. That found in the air as vapor is only about 9×10^{-6} of that in the sea. In more direct terms, if all moisture in the air were precipitated and collected in the ocean, the sea level would be raised only 3.5 cm. The best available estimate suggests that the amount of fresh water is about thirty-three times that in the atmosphere (Wildt, 1942).

Estimates vary widely as to the total amount of free water in the earth's crust. They range from less than 1 per cent to a quarter or even a half of the total amount in the oceans. Meinzer and Wenzel, commenting on these estimates (1942), regard both extremes as erroneous. They indicate that "the quantity of water in the rocks is much less than the quantity in the ocean but many times as great as the quantity in lakes, streams and the atmosphere." About half of this underground water is held in molecular attraction; the remainder is free to flow out into springs and wells. There is no available estimate of the quantity of water bound in chemical combination within the lithosphere or any knowledge about its possible occurrence in molecular or dissociated form in the interior of the earth.

In considering these estimates* and their implications, one is struck by the importance of the role played by the relatively

ICE

Pure ice is somewhat lighter than pure water. It has a density of 0.92 and floats even without the presence of air bubbles that are often enclosed. It forms a solid covering for the unfrozen liquid below and so preserves the liquid habitat of most

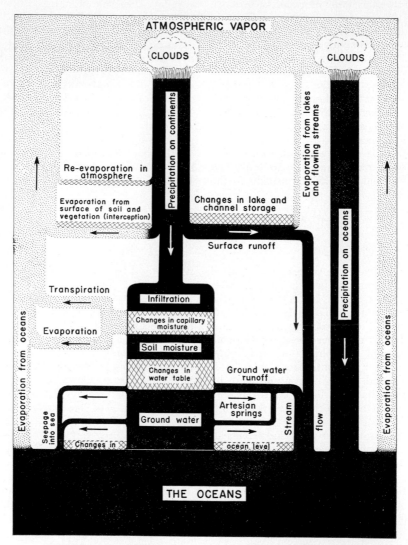

Fig. 39. The hydrological cycle. (Modified from Meinzer.)

insignificant amount (in proportion to the whole) of water carried by the atmosphere. In one way the smallness of the amount of atmospheric water enhances its importance, since its distribution frequently acts as a limiting factor in the distribution of plants and animals.

aquatic animals, even in cold climates. Ice provides an extension of the solid sub-

* The estimates given are based on data given by Bernard, 1942; Mathes, 1942; Sverdrup, Johnson, and Fleming, 1942: Meinzer and Wenzel, 1942; Fuller, 1906; and Wildt, 1942.

stratum of the land and is used as such by many land animals that are active in winter; witness the excursion of arctic foxes over sea ice far from shore. Ice is more or less transparent to both heat and light; it is not readily permeable to gases. As a result, ice-covered lakes may be lighted sufficiently to make some photosynthesis possible, and their waters are warmed by sunlight that penetrates through unmelted ice. Such lakes become stagnant if long frozen over, with an accompanying decrease in dissolved oxygen and an increase in carbon dioxide.

Ice expands and contracts with temperature changes and often forms pressure ridges along weak points; these may pile high in Arctic seas, especially near land where tidal pressures vary. Expansion of warming ice may exert strong outward pressure against banks of frozen rivers or shores of lakes. The entire frozen area of a river bank may thus be broken free from the unfrozen subsoil and piled in ridges parallel to the channel. Similar action may bring sand bars above water, even though they are usually submerged and are surrounded by deeper water. Ice has little tensile strength and readily cracks from contraction with falling temperature.

The presence of salt lowers the freezing point of sea water so that it remains liquid to $-1.91°$ C. When sea water does freeze, the ice crystals themselves are probably salt free; they form a matrix that encloses enough somewhat concentrated sea water so that the ice crystals, together with the enclosed sea brine, if melted together, will approximate the same composition and concentration of ions found in the sea water before it was frozen. If freezing occurs slowly, there may be a marked reduction in the salinity of the melted sea ice. In one instance sea water with a salinity of 30 $°/_{oo}$ frozen at $-16°$ C. yielded brackish water with a salinity of 5.6 $°/_{oo}$. As the temperature rises, the sea ice surrounding the entrapped brine melts, and small pores appear through which the brine in the upper ice can trickle down to lower levels. Old sea ice, exposed above the water level, may come to yield practically fresh, potable water unless it is contaminated by salt spray. When large amounts of such old ice thaw with some rapidity, a layer of water with lowered salinity spreads over the surface of the surrounding sea.

Being frozen in ice is not necessarily fatal for many animals (see p. 99). Whole resistant communities, such as the bryocoles of the tundra and of bogs, are frozen each winter. Some hardy forms among groups like the protozoans, tardigrades, and rotifers exist, although they are frozen during most of the year or perhaps for several years at a time (Murphy, 1928). Shallow lakes in high latitudes freeze to the bottom each winter and still support a fairly rich animal life. So-called anchor ice may form on the bottom during the night in cold weather or even in daytime when cloudy winter skies keep back the heat of the sun. Anchor ice is especially likely to form over dark rocks that rapidly radiate their heat to the water above. Typically, the ice melts with the return of direct radiation (Church, 1942). Anchor ice may be destructive to sensitive, bottom-dwelling animals.

The grinding of small bits of ice or of large masses of it breaks down living things exposed to its action and may be quite destructive even with short exposure. Such wave-driven ice also exerts strong eroding force along shore lines. It is one of the reasons why winter-killing is more extensive in intertidal or adtidal communities along the sea shore than it is in somewhat deeper water (Allee, 1919).

SNOW

Snow is an integral factor in the physical environment. It is important particularly in the higher latitudes and on the higher parts of mountains where the snow cover may last through the year. Its significance is increased by the large amount of land surface in northern Eurasia and North America. The limits of snow to the south and in lower latitudes vary with the general climate and with local conditions. Snow extends farther south in continental climates than in those characterized by marine influences, although this general rule is modified by humidity, wind direction, topography, other local regional considerations, and by ocean currents. The snow line is pushed northward by the Gulf Stream on the European coast and by the Kuroshio in the western and northern Pacific Ocean. It extends farther south along the shores of Canada and New England under the influence of the Laborador Current, and the cold Oyashio Current has a similiar effect in Japan and in adjacent parts of Asia. The snow line in mountains stands much higher in the tropics, at 16,000 to 18,000 feet, descending gradually to sea level in higher latitudes. The snow level in mountains is also affected by such other conditions as moisture content of the air, exposure, and the general wind pattern.

In any serious attempt to evaluate the ecological significance of snow as such, it is important to keep its ecological relations as distinct as possible from those of low temperatures, storms, and glaciers, with all of which it has obvious relationships. Snowfall is usually heavier in forested country than in the more open grasslands. It is not so great as might be expected in polar regions, since these tend toward dryness, but enough snow is usually present in the tundras in winter so that these may be characterized as regions of snow dunes.

The quality of snow varies from the wet, heavy snow of warmer weather to the granular or even powdery snow characteristic of more intense cold. The surface ranges from the extreme softness found in forests to the hard sleet or the icy slickness of frozen rain, and the depth may reach several feet of even undrifted snow. Thawing and freezing produce a hard crust over the surface that is frequently strong enough to bear the weight of large animals, including man. The crust hinders, or even prevents, entrance or escape from the snow by the animals that retire under its protecting cover. Snow is a poor conductor of heat, partly because of the air held within its mass, and thus provides protection for many small forms that penetrate or are covered by it. Snow is frequently an aid to hibernating animals and acts as a protective mulch for many plants. In deciduous forest, at latitude 45 degrees north, for example, the ground beneath the snow may remain entirely unfrozen through a severe winter. A good snow cover prevents frost heaving of the soil and so retards spring erosion, and practically or completely prevents wind erosion. Precipitation falling as snow on unfrozen ground frequently melts slowly enough to avoid a direct run-off and permits much of the moisture to penetrate the soil.

Large drifts in mountains or open country may have decided local effects on vegetation and associated animal life, since they persist as snow cover long after the snow has disappeared elsewhere. Thus in the Steens Mountains, in Oregon, areas of twisted and dwarfed poplar are sharply set off from the surrounding sage brush; these areas are confined to the lee of mountain crests, and are obviously conditioned by long-persistent snowdrifts.

Snow covers much of the available food for many animals and is a factor causing migration, both of birds and of mammals, toward areas that are somewhat or entirely free from its direct influence. The autumnal migrations move away from the snow-covered regions near the polar zones, especially in the north; or there may be much shorter migrations down from the higher country in mountains.

An assemblage of small mammals, notably small rodents, tunnel through the snow among or near the underlying mosses or grasses and so get access to buried food and obtain protection from winter cold. Snow not only covers much food, it also serves somewhat as a natural ladder for those animals capable of using it, enabling gnawers, such as snowshoe rabbits, to browse in winter on otherwise unavailable twigs and woody stems. Snow can also be used as a cold-weather substitute for drinking water, although its low mineral content presents a special condition. In the tundra, the nonhibernating collared lemmings (*Dicrostonyx*) breed during winter beneath the snow.

Snow impedes or prevents the locomotion of mammals and of running birds; even mammals with long legs, such as deer or moose, can not travel through overdeep snow. A common adaptation is the evolution of relatively large feet that act as natural snowshoes. Thus ptarmigan and grouse have feathered feet or develop elastic extensions (Fig. 36); the Siberian ptarmigan, *Lagopus lagopus*, has a body weight of about 15 gm. per square centimeter of foot surface, in contrast with *Perdix perdix* of the steppes, in which this ratio is about 40 gm. per square centimeter (Formosov, 1946). The snowshoe rabbit of North America (*Lepus americanus*), like *Lepus timidus* of northern Eurasia, has widened feet that enable it to run over the surface of the snow. The feet of this snowshoe hare are more than double the size of those of a Kansas jack rabbit, which weighs over twice as much (Seton, 1909). The corresponding relation appears between the size of the feet of the Canada lynx and bobcat (cf. p. 163). A factor of some ecological importance appears when the snow crust is strong enough to bear the lighter predators, like lynx and wolf, but will not support a caribou or deer, placing the herbivorous prey at an extreme disadvantage.

Other means of meeting the snow hazard include trail making and the formation of restricted winter "yards" in which the snow can be kept packed down wholly or in part. Canadian moose may be restricted to a yard less than 300 feet in radius (Seton, 1909). Ungulates frequently paw through the snow to underlying vegetation and are often accompanied by feeding symbiotes that are able to obtain otherwise unavailable food from the partially cleared areas. The willow ptarmigan (*Lagopus albus*) may keep near a reindeer herd during the winter months and so get food that is often deeply buried under the snow (Sdobnikov, 1935).

A series of polar birds and mammals have a predominately white color. Others, even in cold-temperate areas, show seasonal color changes well exemplified by the varying hare and by the common weasel of Canada; the summer brown upper parts of the latter turn pure white in winter, only the black tail tip remaining unchanged. The color changes of both the varying hare and weasels have been experimentally controlled by manipulating the length of day (p. 122). Theories about protective or cryptic coloration of such changes need not be abandoned in all cases. The ptarmigan tends to keep to lingering snow patches until the birds lose their white winter plumage. Although white coloration is proportionately more frequent towards both poles, the explanation of inconspicuous coloration cannot well be the only operating causation, since the importance of color concealment in the short dull days of the polar winter appears to be small (Hesse, Allee, and Schmidt, 1937).

MOISTURE IN THE ATMOSPHERE

Water exists in air in three forms: (1) as solid hail, sleet, or snow; (2) as liquid droplets suspended in fog or cloud or as rain drops; and (3) as invisible water vapor. We shall neglect the first two for the present and focus attention on water vapor. This acts as do other gases in the atmosphere; it exerts pressure, called vapor pressure, and has definite heat relations. Unlike the associated atmospheric gases, it varies in partial pressure both with time and with location, whereas each of the other gases of the troposphere makes up a remarkably constant part of the whole. The amount of water vapor the air can hold changes with the temperature, and the amount of possible variation is greater than that for any other vapor (Henderson, 1922, p. 413).

Some definitions are needed. The *absolute humidity* of the air is the amount of water vapor in a given amount of air; it may be expressed as grams of water vapor per kilogram of air. *Specific humidity* is the ratio of the weight of water vapor to the weight of humid air containing it. *Relative humidity* is the amount of water vapor present in comparison with the amount required to produce saturation at the same temperature and atmospheric pressure; it is expressed as the percentage of saturation. *Vapor pressure* is the partial pressure of the water vapor measured in millimeters of mercury or by other appropriate standards. The *vapor pressure deficit* or *saturation deficit* is the converse of relative humidity; it measures the difference between the vapor pressure at saturation at a given location (E_1) and the actual vapor pressure (e_1) at the same spot; the saturation deficit is the difference $E_1 - e_1$ and should not be used, as it has been at times, to represent the difference between saturation of an evaporating surface (E_0) and the observed vapor pressure in some other location (e_1) (Leighly, 1937; Thornthwaite, 1940). The *dew point* is the temperature of saturation of the air by water vapor; with falling temperature, condensation begins at the dew point.

Evaporation is a dynamic physical process; practically speaking, it occurs when the number of molecules of water leaving a surface in a unit of time is greater than the number entering it. The converse process is called condensation. Evaporation is determined more by energy at a water surface than by the humidity above the surface. Boiling water sends off vapor into saturated air, and dew may form from air that is not saturated except in the micro-niche formed by the cooler air next to the surface where condensation actually takes place. The vapor pressure at the surface is lowered by dissolved salts. This is one of the associated colligative properties of solutions that include also osmotic pressure, freezing point depression, and boiling point elevation. If one of these is known, the others can be computed for the given conditions (see p. 165). Under ordinary ecological conditions, the rate of evaporation depends upon the steepness of the gradient between the vapor tension at the evaporation surface (E_0) and the air above (e_1, e_2, and so on), as well as upon energy regulations at E_0 (Fig. 40). This part of the process is affected by the relative humidity (or saturation deficit) of the air and by its turbulence.

morning temperature of 50°F. and a relative humidity of 100 per cent, the vapor pressure of the air would be .3626 inches of mercury. If the temperature of the surface of a water body were also 50°F. the vapor pressures would be the same and there would be no net addition of water molecules to the air or the water surface, and consequently neither evaporation nor condensation. As the air temperature rises to 60°F., if moisture is neither added nor abstracted, the vapor pressure will remain at .3626 inches, the relative humidity will drop

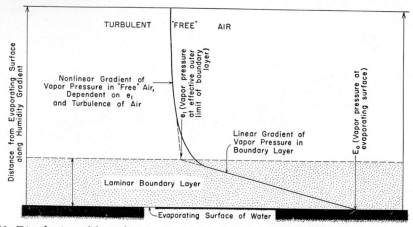

Fig. 40. Distribution of humidity in the laminar boundary layer and in adjacent turbulent air over an evaporating surface. (Adapted from Leighly.)

Whenever the relative humidity and temperature of the air produce a vapor pressure that exceeds the vapor pressure at the exposed water surface, condensation occurs and water is added. Whenever the relative humidity and temperature result in a vapor pressure less than that at the evaporating surface, evaporation results. The gradient of vapor pressure is important both in its steepness and its direction. It appears that a more or less thin laminar layer of air exists next to the evaporating surface in which water movement occurs by diffusion only; above that comes a layer, or a series of layers, of turbulent air. The degree of turbulence affects the rate of evaporation and is in turn affected by wind action and by convection currents produced by differences in heat. The mathematical relations are developed by Leighly (1937).

An illustration from Thornthwaite (1940, p. 21) will help at this point.

"There is a daily march of relative humidity which accompanies the diurnal march of temperature. On a summer day, with an early

to 70 per cent, and a vapor pressure deficit of .1594 inches will have developed. As the air temperature rises to 70°F., 80°F., and 90°F., the relative humidity will fall to 49, 35, and 26 per cent, and the vapor pressure deficit will decrease to .3743, .6708, and 1.0608 inches respectively. But as long as the water temperature remains at 50°F., the vapor pressure of the air and the water surface are the same and there can be no evaporation.

"Evaporation will occur only when the vapor pressure of the water surface exceeds that of the air. With a rise in air temperature or with direct absorption of radiant energy, the water temperature will rise and the vapor pressure of the water will become greater than that of the air, more water molecules are emitted from the water surface than are returned to it and evaporation occurs. Also the moisture concentration and consequently the vapor pressure of the air may be reduced. As the air increases in temperature, turbulence due to convection may set up, causing mixture of surface layers with drier air from aloft. Similar dissipation of moisture into the upper levels of the atmosphere may be caused by mechanical turbulence due to wind movements. Wind therefore affects evaporation simply through lowering the vapor pressure of the air in relation to that of the evaporating surface. Generally speaking, the greater the intensity of turbulent mixing, the drier will the surface of the air become, the larger will be the vapor pressure gradient, and the greater the evaporation."

RELATION OF ANIMALS TO MOISTURE

Water makes up a large proportion of the bodies of plants and animals, whether they live on land or in the water. Active protoplasm holds about 70 to 90 per cent of water. Measured values for active animals lie between 50 per cent for meal worms (tenebrionid beetle larvae) (Hall, 1922) and 98 per cent for medusae from brackish water (Hyman, 1940). Animal tissues tend to lose water with age; man, for example, has about 72.5 per cent at birth and 66 per cent when adult. The water content of various insects is given in Table 13.

The difficulties encountered in maintaining the proper water balance by aquatic animals (p. 169) become much greater for terrestrial forms. This was one of the obstacles to the invasion of land habitats by plants and animals. The internal supply of water must be maintained; loss of one-third of the water present produces death in taxonomically widely separated forms such as land isopods and the house mouse, though other animals can lose much more and live. Despite the danger of desiccation, an intimate contact must be maintained between actively respiring cells with a high water content and the surrounding atmosphere, which may be relatively dry. Plants face these difficulties as well as animals. In relatively dry continental climates, 99.9 per cent of the water taken from the soil passes through the plant and is dispersed into the atmosphere in transpiration; in many moister climates, the percentage falls only to 99.7 (Klages, 1942). Evaporation of this water helps control the temperature, and its passage though the plant performs other valuable functions.

The evaporation of water is the one important means of dissipation of body heat in hot climates or on hot days in any climate. The humidity of the air has a large effect in determining how high a temperature can be endured. In desert heat, a decrease of 1 per cent in relative humidity is almost as effective as lowering the temperature 1° F. (Adolph, 1943). Water has high heat capacity and high heat of vaporization. The animal or plant body consists so largely of water that it approaches the heat capacity of the latter and so is well buffered against temperature fluctuations. Dill (1938) reports that a resting man kept in thermal equilibrium with his environment would increase in body temperature at the rate of 2° C. an hour as a result of his own metabolism. If he were made of steel and could still carry on the same metabolism as at present, his rise in temperature in an hour would be about eight times as fast as it is at present.

The blood is largely water and so has high heat capacity that enables it to transfer heat from the deeper parts of the body to the skin and respiratory tracts, where it is dissipated by evaporation of water or by heat radiation. The vaporization of 1 liter of water at 33° C. requires 580 kilogram-calories (Dill, 1938). Much water is lost in respiration. Air is taken into the lungs of man in quantities of from 5 to 100 liters per minute. The inspired air may be warm or cold, saturated or almost entirely dry. On expiration it is practically saturated with water vapor at 33° C. About 400 cc. of water are lost daily in this way by the average man. So-called insensible perspiration increases water loss by 300 per cent, and man in the desert can sweat at the rate of a liter or more an hour or even roughly three times that amount. Vaporization of this amount of water would remove over ten times the heat produced in basal metabolism of man and over four times that of hard physical labor (Brody, 1945). Human sweating varies greatly with different individuals and is much affected by acclimatization. It also varies still more widely between species. The loss of water in heat regulation is closely associated with salt losses, and both are correlated with the quality and quantity of urinary secretion.[*]

Brody (1945) states that up to about 29° C., water vaporization in man shows an irregular increase and dissipates as much as 35 per cent of the heat. There is a steep and orderly rise above this point, and a balanced heat budget for the body is at-

[*] Dill (1938) gives a readable, accurate summary of heat and water regulation of man and several other animals under a variety of climatic conditions, especially those of hot climates, both arid and humid. He is interested in the physiological and ecological aspects of the subject; see also Brody (1945).

tained at about 35° or 36° C.; at 40°, twice as much heat is dissipated as is produced. There are numerous contrasts in heat regulation between the sweating and nonsweating mammals. Among other differences, the sweating species increase their pulse rate as they become hot; their blood is routed to the cooled surface layers, and the respiration rate may decrease. In contrast, nonsweating animals show a decreased pulse rate when hot; the blood is routed away from the hot surface, and the rate of respiration increases to the well-known heat panting. Both types avoid long exposure to the hot sun.

Acclimatization to heat is striking and important, both in direct connection with efficiency in living and as an illustration of the general principle of acclimatization. In becoming accustomed to the desert, high altitudes, or other environmental extremes, a warm-blooded animal shows physiological changes that promote maintenance, for example, of suitable body temperature, of salt, and of water content. Acclimatization to changed conditions seems to be an expression of a latent capacity that develops under appropriate stimulation. The range of environments is so great that even a euryökous organism, such as man, cannot be ready at any one time to cope with all to the optimum extent.

Different degrees of water saving are at the basis of an ecological classification comparable in importance to that based on tolerance of salinity among aquatic forms or on temperature relations for all organisms. Plants that grow only in water or wet places, such as swamps or wet meadows, are called *hydrophytes*. Plants of forests or prairies that grow in regions where there is neither an excess nor a deficiency of water are *mesophytes*. Those that live in dry situations subjected to high evaporation stresses are *xerophytes* (Weaver and Clements, 1929).* Animals with similar habitat relations are *hydrocoles* if they live in water (*hygrocoles* if living in moist places), *mesocoles*, and *xerocoles*, respectively. Both plants and animals develop certain structures related to the amount of moisture they normally encounter and so show hydromorphic, mesomorphic, and xeromorphic fea-

---

* The suffix *phyte* refers definitely to plants; hence it is not appropriate to speak of *xerophytic* animals or even of *xerophytic* habitats.

tures. Differences in physiology and in habits also allow animals to adjust their water requirements to the available supply.

Animals obtain water (*a*) by drinking, (*b*) by absorbing it through their skin from contact with some damp object, as toads or frogs get water from damp ground (Adolph, 1932), (*c*) directly from their food, or (*d*) from water produced by metabolism, as do most terrestrial insects that feed on dry food materials. The method of securing water and the relation to the supply of liquid water, as well as resistance to the drying effects of the surrounding atmosphere, are important in determining the distribution of animals. It may be doubted whether animals absorb water from an atmosphere saturated with water vapor except under special conditions when the vapor tension of the surrounding air is greater than that of the water-permeable surface of the animal.

A consideration of the preceding discussion about the vapor tension, together with Adolph's observations on the water relations of frogs (1932, 1933), shows the reason for this inability. When Adolph exposed frogs to

" . . . Saturated atmospheres under rigidly uniform temperatures it was found that evaporation still went on. Hence, under no steady conditions could a frog gain water from the atmosphere. The reason for this is one that holds for all organisms and tissues; it is that the frog is continually producing heat, thus raising its temperature above that of its surroundings, hence enabling it to evaporate water by raising the dew-point of the air in contact with its surface."

Contrariwise, Ludwig (1937) holds that grasshoppers are hygroscopic and can absorb water from air with a high moisture content. The difference, if real, may be related to the relative impermeability of the grasshopper's exoskeleton.

The adjustments that permit animals to live surrounded by a drying atmosphere include, among others, the following adaptive features:

1. A more or less impervious integument
2. Internal lungs or tracheal system
3. Water saving:
   (*a*) By the secretion of concentrated and even of crystalline nitrogenous waste
   (*b*) By depositing dry feces
4. Suspended animation

5. Burrowing and nocturnal habits
6. Humidity control
7. Migration
8. Obtaining water from food and from metabolism

1. Impervious Integument

Only those animals that have a relatively or completely impermeable body covering can invade the drier habitats. Reptiles, birds, mammals, and many insects have such an integument. Some mammals, notably men, apes, and horses, lose much water (and salt) through sweat glands in heat regulation. Most rodents and some ruminants—antelopes, for example—nearly or completely lack sweat glands. Moist-skinned animals, certain mites, soft-bodied insects, earthworms, and amphibians are terrestrial hygrocoles restricted to swamps, stream margins, moist soil, and other similarly damp places, or they must be able to retire readily to such niches. These are frequently crepuscular, nocturnal, or shade-living creatures. The dry-skinned insects, reptiles, birds, and the nonsweating mammals are adapted to live in drier habitats, but even among them further adaptations are needed before the comparatively dry regions can be successfully occupied.

2. Internal Lungs or Tracheal System

The mode of respiration also is important. The scaly body covering of a fish may be practically impermeable to water, and exchanges may be limited to gills and gut. Some few fishes, like the mudskipper, *Periophthalmus,* can venture out of water into moist ad-aqueous habitats. Crustacea, with their gills covered by a water-retaining carapace, carry with them a liquid environment for their gills. Though more terrestrial than the mud-skipping fishes, land-dwelling crayfishes burrow to water, and the more terrestrial land crabs are not successful invaders of dry habitats far from waters. Internal lungs, whether in pulmonate snails, land isopods, spiders, or higher vertebrates, together with the internal tracheal system of insects, are water-saving. Much water is lost in breathing, even by animals equipped with internal lungs. The loss in insects and in many gastropods is less than might be expected, since in these animals the external openings close under excessively dry conditions.

3. Dry Excretions

A further water-saving device is the excretion of concentrated, relatively dry nitrogenous and fecal waste material. Again, as in the osmotic relations of aquatic animals, we are reminded that the organs secreting nitrogenous wastes, whether malpighian tubules of insects or kidneys of vertebrates, have important ecological relations. Even the land mammals least dependent on water conservation concentrate their urine by active transfer of water into the blood stream against the osmotic gradient. Water-saving insects, reptiles, and birds dispose of their nitrogenous wastes as solid uric acid; the ostrich, though a bird of dry regions, is an exception and secretes liquid urea. The deposition of dry feces is common among water-saving animals; the dry fecal deposits of rodents and antelope contrast strikingly with the more liquid feces of cattle. Insects, reptiles, and birds typically deposit fairly dry feces.

4. Suspended Animation

Some animals with simpler organization, especially the bryocoles—such as tardigrades, rotifers, and nematode worms—can retain their vitality in long-continued drying in direct sunlight and regain activity when water is again available. Desert snails also are resistant to drying (p. 20). These animals are not completely desiccated, although they approach that condition. Other animals aestivate during droughts, and are active only in the moister seasons of the year.

5. Burrowing and Nocturnal Habits and Modes of Humidity Control

A simple form of aestivation is closely associated with burrowing down to continually moist earth and there remaining dormant until the rains come. Various types of frogs and toads have this habit, as do some aquatic forms that live in lakes, ponds, or streams that often become dry—the African lungfish, for example. Still other animals die off, leaving resistant eggs that are often protected by impervious egg cases. Related desiccation-resistant devices include the gemmules of fresh-water sponges and the statoblasts of bryozoans. Nocturnal animals are exposed to lowered temperature and lower relative humidity, conditions that tend to reduce the rate of water loss. Many soft-bodied animals are active at night and burrow or remain in other protective niches during the day.

6. Humidity Control

The building of enclosed nests and covered runways, as exhibited by termites and ants, is a possible development from burrowing behavior. This serves, among other things, to help these social insects gain control of the humidity to which they are normally exposed.

7. Migration, Emigration and Nomadism

Many birds and mammals of arid regions migrate when water becomes scarce or, as a result of drought or for other reasons, the food supply is low. Mammals in such areas

be available comes with the power to live without drinking. A common adaptation is the ability to live on the moisture obtained with food, as shown by herbivores and carnivores. Even domestic cats can exist for long periods with no moisture intake other than that from the flesh and blood of recently killed animals (Caldwell, 1931). Many herbivores utilize the high water content of plants in this manner, the insects especially. Some precise data for insects are given in Table 13.

Inspection of this table indicates that a number of insects, like the granary weevil, contain water greatly in excess of that found in their food. This seems to be the usual situation even when food material is relatively rich in water. Thus, the larva of

Table 13. *Water Content of Insects and Their Food (From Uvarov, 1931, after Robinson)*

Insect	Food	Percentage of Water in Food	Percentage of Water in Insects
Granary weevil, adult *Sitophilus granarius*	Stored wheat	9–11	46–47
Rice weevil, adult *S. oryzae*	Stored wheat	15–16	48–50
Locust borer, adult *Cyllene robiniae*	Locust tree trunk	30–32	56–60
Colorado potato beetle, adult *Leptinotarsa decemlineata*	Potato plant	70–74	62–66
White grub, larva *Phyllophaga*	Wheat shoots and roots	64–67	73–82
Mourning cloak, larva *Vanessa antiopa*	Willow leaves	70–73	77–79
Willow sawfly, larva *Cimbex americana*	Willow leaves	70–73	79–82
Army worm, larva *Cirphis unipuncta*	Corn plant	77–78	87–89
Imported cabbage worm *Pieris rapae*	Cabbage	88–89	83–84
Polyphemus moth, larva *Telea polyphemus*	Hazel leaves	71–73	90–92

are particularly given to irregular roaming without definite return to a given place, a type of activity aptly called nomadism. Droughts may also produce the eruptive types of emigration that are associated with the movement of swarms of grasshoppers characteristic of extensive arid lands.

8. Water from Food and from Metabolism

Another adjustment to life in regions of low humidity where liquid water may not

the mourning cloak butterfly feeding on willow leaves maintains a water content slightly higher than that of the leaves on which it feeds. Succulent green plants, such as cabbage, may furnish a higher concentration of water in their tissues than is found in the bodies of insects feeding on them. Watermelons and other plants store water that is often used by animals. In addition, most animals make more or less use of so-called water of metabolism, meaning thereby the water released by the breaking down of sugars or other carbohydrates and also that produced by the oxidation of hydrogen or carbon in the body of the animal. Fat is rich in hydrogen as well as carbon and is poor in oxygen, and so is a potent source of this last-mentioned kind of water of metabolism.

Certain insects, including *Tribolium confusum* and *Dermestes vulpinus,* eat more food at lower humidities to produce a given unit of body weight; the length of the larval period increases, and the weight of the pupae decreases. With such insects at such humidities, the greater part of the body water is derived from the oxidation of food (Fraenkel and Blewett, 1944).

Some animals are able to live indefinitely without water beyond that furnished by air-dry food. Forms like the drywood termites (*Cryptotermes*) and powder-post beetles are examples. Others combine the use of metabolic water with other kinds of water supply; the ability of the desert-adapted camel to go eleven or more days without drinking comes from its being able to use water of metabolism obtained, in part, from the oxidation of the fat in its hump, as well as to store water in special compartments of its stomach.

As a result of combinations of these different water-producing and water-conserving abilities, desert mammals, such as antelopes and many rodents, can exist for months without taking liquid water other than the often copious desert dew. The combination of a dry, impervious integument, internal lungs or tracheal tubes, dry feces, and the excretion of crystalline uric acid, often combined with burrowing and nocturnal habits, make reptiles, birds, and many insects well fitted to withstand life in dry habitats.

Color may be affected by humidity, or by humidity and heat. The correlations are summarized as Gloger's rule (Hesse, Allee, and Schmidt, 1937; Dobzhansky, 1941). Exceptions aside, races of birds or mammals living in cool, dry regions are lighter in color (have less melanin pigment) than races of the same species living in warm, humid areas. The same rule holds among insects, except that pigmentation increases in humid cool climates and becomes less in hot, dry ones. Appropriate changes frequently follow rearing under controlled experimental conditions and seem more affected by the humidity than by temperature.

Insects and Moisture

In many ways insects present a special case in their relation to environmental moisture, especially in relation to atmospheric humidity. Insects are all small when judged by vertebrate standards, and many of them are tiny even when considered in relation to their fellows. Once again we have to deal with the principle that the bulk of an animal increases as the cube, and the surface increases as the square of the length. The ratio of surface to body bulk is large in the small to tiny insects, and this has vital importance in the water conservation of the more minute insects that have only a thin chitinous covering. For these, the loss of water quickly becomes acute. Kennedy (1927) recognized this relationship for insects and concluded that the most outstanding adaptation to equalize the chance of survival of such an insect in a drying environment lies in its sensitiveness to changes in the humidity of its surroundings, particularly when the minimum toleration point is approached. Such sensitiveness cannot save insects in marginal habitats; a series of dry years decreases the area inhabited by the pale western cutworm (*Porosagrotis*) by hundreds of square miles (Cook, 1924).

The rate of development of some insects varies with the vapor pressure of the atmosphere—that is, with absolute, rather than with relative, humidity. The "cotton stainer" insect, *Dysdercus howardi,* shows such a relationship fairly well for the egg stage (Fig. 41).

There is factual support (Headlee, 1917, 1921) for the commonsense suggestion that an optimum humidity exists for each species and varies from stage to stage of the life history. The optimum humidity depends apparently on the concentration of the body fluids and on the energy relations at evaporating surfaces. The latter have never been measured for any animal, and, according to Adolph (1932), the vapor tension of the skin of the living frog cannot be measured. This is the more important, technically, since the frog is a good experimental animal for such purposes; size alone makes it much more favorable than are most insects. Until methods are available to approximate, at least, the vapor tension of living evaporating surfaces, knowledge of humidity relations of organisms will remain in an unsatisfactory condition. This does not mean that the humidity of the air is unimportant. Although humidity exerts a secondary, rather than a primary, influence on the dynamics of evaporation, certain correlations with ecological events are apparent in temperature relations (p. 207), as a component of the complex that is summarized as the evaporating power of the air (p. 206). Even when humidity is considered as relative humidity and as a separate environmental factor, it still has certain ecological importance.

the number of alighting mosquitoes remains practically constant; activity declines sharply as the saturation point is approached more closely. The feeding of *Culex fatigans* ceases when the daily mean relative humidity is under 40 per cent; 50 per cent is favorable for feeding (Uvarov, 1931). Clothes moths can complete their life history under experimental conditions at the lowest relative humidity tested (20 per cent) when their food contained 5.8 per cent of moisture. Even so, with optimum temperature, their life cycles were shorter and the adults lived longer at 75 per cent relative humidity, when the food contained

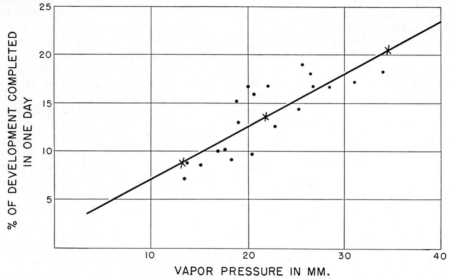

Fig. 41. Velocity of development of the egg of the "cotton stainer" insect, *Dysdercus howardi*. (Redrawn after MacGill.)

Some of the observed relations are: Tree frogs react to humidity gradients, even though the vapor tension of their skin cannot be measured. Many insects come to a lighted screen in vastly greater numbers during rain as compared with clear days or nights. Although certain workers find no correlation between the flight of moths and humidity, others report that the capture of night-flying noctuid moths is correlated with the relative humidity (r.h.), with maximum flight at an evening value of 54 per cent relative humidity (Cook, 1921). The number of mosquitoes alighting on man increases almost directly with an increase in relative humidity up to 85 per cent; from 85 to 95 per cent relative humidity

12.2 per cent moisture, than at lower or higher values (Griswold and Crowell, 1936).

The subsocial, log-inhabiting beetle (*Passalus cornutus*) shows relatively low activity when the relative humidity is high. As the relative humidity decreases from near saturation, there is a definite gradual increase in activity down to 20 per cent relative humidity, the lowest point measured. When the log in which such beetles burrow is broken open, the beetles are exposed to decreased humidity, and the resulting increase in activity has adaptive value in finding another suitable habitat (O. Park, 1937). The probability that arthropods react to humidity is emphasized by the demonstration of humidity receptors in the tarsi of spiders (Blumenthal, 1935) and in the antennae of the beetle, *Tenebrio molitor* (Pielou and Gunn, 1940). When ant lions, which characteristically construct their pit traps in dry sand or soil, are placed in a humidity gradient, they react by trial and error and finally collect and remain quietly in the dry end of the gradient.*

Relative humidity is readily determined with fair exactitude even in the field. As

* A. E. Emerson, unpublished material.

with pH, this is not necessarily a sound reason for the amount of study devoted to it. The analysis of Leighly (1937) and Thornthwaite (1940) show that much of the work will need to be repeated when suitable methods are developed for approximating the vapor tension of evaporating surfaces, whether living or nonliving. Pending the development of gross methods suitable for larger habitats and for larger organisms, micro-methods that will reveal the intimate relations of small organisms in their habitat niches must wait.

13. THE ATMOSPHERIC GASES

The total atmosphere of the earth consists of an estimated $56,328 \times 10^{11}$ tons of matter, of which an average of about $14,615 \times 10^9$ tons are water vapor. Since the water vapor varies, it is customary to disregard it and base the analysis of gases on air that is theoretically dry. If the total amount of dry air is regarded as 100 volume per cent and as making a total pressure of 760 mm. of mercury, then the different constituent gases are present in the amounts indicated in Table 14.

duces no confusion if one remembers that both carbon dioxide and ozone are highly important elements of the environment of living organisms, even though each represents but a small percentage of the whole. Carbon dioxide, drawn largely from the air, is a basic ingredient in the process of the photosynthesis of carbohydrates by green plants (p. 199), and ozone screens out ultraviolet radiation from the sun that otherwise might destroy nearly all the life we know (p. 74).

Table 14. *Gases Present in the Atmosphere (Data from Humphreys, 1931, and Sverdrup, Johnson, and Fleming, 1942)*

Gas	Volume %	Partial Pressure in mm. Mercury
Nitrogen	78.03	593.02
Oxygen	20.99	159.52
Argon	0.9323	7.144
Carbon dioxide	0.03	0.228
Hydrogen	0.01	
Neon	0.0018	0.088
Helium	0.0005	
Krypton	0.0001	
Ozone	0.00006	
Xenon	0.000009	

Xenon, with the lowest percentage, has a total estimated mass in the atmosphere of 21×10^8 tons. Nitrogen and argon are combined in common usage and regarded as forming 79 per cent of the atmosphere, and oxygen is then said to make up the other 21 per cent. Such a simplifying assumption has much justification and intro-

The percentages of the gases in the lower atmosphere are practically constant, except for rare death valleys and where carbon dioxide accumulates as it escapes from some underground source. One such valley occurs on the Dieng plateau in Java (Hesse, Allee, and Schmidt, 1937). The chemically unstable ozone is more abundant in the higher atmosphere near its region of origin (p. 131), though it is a relatively heavy gas like carbon dioxide.

In addition to the gases listed in Table 14, various amounts of different trace concentrations appear in the air. These include heavy water, ammonia, nitrous and nitric acid and their compounds, sulfurous and sulfuric acids and their compounds, and oxides of nitrogen. Droplets and frozen particles of water condense about dust particles or minute bits of sea salt evaporated from spray. These tiny particles, together with pollen grains and spores of many kinds, are carried aloft from the earth, and, in the reversed direction, outer space contributes an invisible shower of cosmic dust. Radioactive products of radium and other elements continually enter the air and make up a part of its electrified particles (Humphreys, 1931). Certain of the environmental roles of these atmospheric gases and impurities have already been suggested (see Index). We need to discuss primarily the ecological relations of the nitrogen complex, oxygen, and carbon dioxide, both in the atmosphere and when dissolved in water.

NITROGEN

Nitrogen is chemically inert. It is difficult to get atmospheric nitrogen into stable chemical combination, and it often escapes from artificial compounds with explosive violence. The great reservoir of nitrogen in the air acts as a diluent of the chemically active oxygen and of carbon dioxide. Atmospheric nitrogen may be "fixed" as nitrites or nitrates by electric discharges, and the products are washed to earth by rain or snow in small but measurable amounts.

Nitrogen-fixing bacteria are important agents in the nitrogen cycle (p. 497), especially those that live symbiotically with legumes. Some evidence suggests the possibility of the fixation of free nitrogen by green plants, though this is still highly debatable. There is also evidence that the aerial parts of plants absorb significant amounts of nitrogenous compounds from rain and dew. E. C. Miller (1938) reviews both these points critically.

OXYGEN

Oxygen is present in the atmosphere in sufficient amounts so that it does not become a limiting factor for animal or plant life except in the carbon dioxide-rich death valleys and at the low partial pressures prevailing in higher altitudes. For some processes, the normal partial pressure of oxygen in the atmosphere is not optimal. The early growth of the chick embryo is accelerated by exposure for five days to concentrations of oxygen above normal; fastest growth occurs at an initial concentration of about 30 per cent, though continuous exposure during the whole period of incubation gives the highest percentage of hatching at 21 per cent (Cruz and Romanoff, 1944; Barott, 1937). Animals can use oxygen taken directly from the atmosphere or that obtained as a by-product of photosynthesis carried on by indwelling symbionts. Animals having anaerobic respiration either obtain their oxygen or otherwise carry on oxidative processes without the use of free oxygen (von Brand, 1946). Normal oxygen pressure is a limiting factor for many anaerobic organisms.

CARBON DIOXIDE

The general contribution of carbon dioxide to environmental control has been discussed in earlier pages (76 and 173). Now we are interested in its role as the main source of carbon in the tissue of plants and animals, obtained through photosynthesis, in the function of this gas in regulation of the respiratory activity of vertebrates and insects, and in its relation to other biological processes. The percentage of carbon dioxide in the atmosphere, 0.03 per cent, is remarkably constant over land and sea. It is increased near certain escape vents from the lithosphere, near industrial plants, and in cities where it is released in large amounts. The partial pressure of carbon dioxide may also be increased somewhat near decaying matter or just above well-fertilized soil, especially if the soil surface is loosely pulverized, as in land under good cultivation. A gradient from 0.053 to 0.28 volume per cent at the surface, to 0.04 to 0.067 just above the leaves, has been found in a well-cultivated beet field. The partial pressure of the carbon dioxide in soil atmosphere is always relatively greater than that above ground.

Within the effective range of other factors, such as light, temperature, and moisture, green plants in greenhouses and even in fields can increase their rate of photosynthesis if they are supplied with an atmosphere enriched by additional carbon dioxide. Such acceleration throws light upon the supposed more rapid rate of the growth of plants in earlier geological epochs, when, presumably, the carbon dioxide content of the atmosphere was greater than it is at present. The volume of atmospheric carbon dioxide represents a balance between the amount fixed in photosynthesis and as chemical carbonates or bicarbonates, on the one hand, and the amount released by respiration, decay, and by geological or industrial processes, on the other.

The respiratory nerve centers of man and other vertebrates and of insects are sensitive to variations in the concentration of carbon dioxide. Addition of this gas to inspired air produces an increase in the volume of respiration in man that corresponds directly, in lower ranges, to the amount of carbon dioxide introduced. Likewise, a decrease in carbon dioxide concentration, such as may be brought about by repeated deep breathing while otherwise at rest, retards later respiration, until the normal internal atmosphere of some 5 to 6 per cent is reestablished (Dill, 1938).

DISSOLVED ATMOSPHERIC GASES

Atmospheric gases dissolve in water in accordance with certain well-established principles of which the following are important:

1. Given time and physical contact, a gas soluble in water dissolves in it until equilibrium is established.

2. The solubility of a gas in water increases with lowering of the temperature of the water and decreases with increasing salt content.

3. Bohr's invasion coefficient approximates the rate at which gas enters at a water-gas interface. This coefficient may be calculated for a given temperature from the following relations:

$$\frac{\text{(Volume of gas entering surface in one minute)} \times 760}{\text{(Gas pressure in air)} - \text{(Gas pressure in water)} \times \text{(area of interface)}}$$

The relation between small gas bubbles in water can be stated in terms of Bohr's coefficient: at 37° C., when water flows past a small bubble, the invasion coefficient equals 0.07. The value is smaller for large bubbles, and Bohr's formula is approximated only when both air and water at the interface are steadily and rapidly renewed (Harvey, 1928).

4. The rate of solution is greater (a) for dry gas than for one holding water vapor; (b) the greater the partial pressure of the gas in the atmosphere or the greater undersaturation of that gas in water (these factors are combined in the statement that the rate of solution is greater, the steeper the concentration gradient between air and water); (c) the greater the exposed surface; and (d) the greater the agitation of the water by waves or otherwise.

Oxygen diffuses slowly through the surface of placid water. At 10° C., it would require about a million years for Lake Constance, Switzerland, to be saturated to its greatest depth of 250 meters if the water remained quiet and the oxygen entered by diffusion alone. Conversely, water that has much surface agitation, whether by waves, by waterfalls or rapids, or by any other agency, tends strongly to become supersaturated with atmospheric gases.

5. The concentration of a saturated solution of a gas is proportional to the pressure at which the gas is supplied (Henry's "law").

6. The pressure exerted by each component of a gaseous mixture is proportional to its partial pressure in the mixture; the total pressure of the gaseous mixture is the sum of the partial pressures of its components (Dalton's "law"). Each gas dissolves irrespective of the solution of other gases.

7. Solubilities differ for different gases. With distilled water at 0° C. and with 760 mm. pressure for each designated gas, each liter of water contains, at equilibrium, 49.24 cc. of oxygen, 23 cc. of nitrogen, and 1715 cc. of carbon dioxide. That is, for equal pressures and with other conditions similar, oxygen is something over twice as soluble as nitrogen, and carbon dioxide is approximately 35 times as soluble as oxygen.

As shown in Table 14, the atmospheric gases meet the surface of water with widely different partial pressures; hence, in place of the 21 volume per cent of oxygen found in the atmosphere, the air dissolved in water is almost 35 per cent oxygen, and the percentage of nitrogen is correspondingly reduced. Further, as a result of the differential effect of salinity on the solubility of these two gases, the oxygen-nitrogen ratio in a given volume of sea water is slightly higher than in fresh water. Oxygen is about 17 per cent less soluble in sea water than in fresh water. The decrease in solubility with an increase of temperature from zero to 25° C., a common enough change in nature, is about 41 per cent for fresh water.

The partial pressure of the gas at the water's surface, and the solubility of the gas, together with the salinity and temperature of the water, determine the amount of gas dissolved at equilibrium. The effect of hydrostatic pressure of the water is negligible; water at any depth of the ocean contains the amount of dissolved oxygen it would have at surface-equilibrium, plus or minus (always minus, in lightless depths) the amount contributed or removed by organic matter, living or dead. Comparable relations exist for dissolved nitrogen.

NITROGEN

The nitrogen dissolved in water comes mainly from the atmosphere. Some is brought in by ground water that is fully saturated at low temperature and so becomes supersaturated when the temperature rises. The liberation of nitrogen in water by the action of denitrifying bacteria has been reported. It now appears that, at least under conditions found in the sea, which have been much studied, there is little or no loss of fixed nitrogen (Sverdrup, Johnson, and Fleming, 1942; ZoBell, 1946). In a lake with a thermocline (p. 94), the nitrogen content of the epilimnion tends to be in equilibrium with the air, as is the entire lake during spring and autumn overturns. The water of the hypolimnion becomes and remains supersaturated with nitrogen as it gets warmer in summer. Ventilation by convection is lacking, and the diffusion rate is low. Water may become warmed so rapidly that nitrogen and oxygen escape as bubbles. Fishes in such water are subject to gas embolism from the gases that pass out of solution in their blood and collect in veins and sinuses as gas bubbles.

OXYGEN

Oxygen exists in chemical combination with hydrogen to form water. Such oxygen is effectively removed from the oxygen environment of animals and when we speak in ecology of the oxygen content of water, we refer only to the oxygen dissolved in water.

Certain generalizations regarding the amount of dissolved oxygen in aquatic habitats have already been stated. We know that during the summer stagnation, the hypolimnion of thermally stratified lakes may have a low oxygen content (p. 94); that there tends to be an inverse relationship between the oxygen and carbon dioxide content of water and frequently, therefore, between the oxygen content of water and its pH (p. 173). Water obtains its dissolved oxygen both from the air and from the oxygen released in photosynthesis by green plants. Within the lighted surface region, water is often supersaturated with oxygen during daylight. There is an oxygen pulse that reaches its peak in the afternoon of sunny days and is at a minimum near dawn. In lower levels of the lighted zone, the organisms present consume more oxygen than is produced by photosynthesis. The depth at which intake and consumption of oxygen are in balance is called the compensation level. Normally this lies near the surface at night and normally sinks up to the time of maximum light penetration during the day; seasonally, the compensation level lies lower in summer and, geographically, descends in depth toward the equator.

Below the compensation level, the fairly large animal population that feeds on organisms drifting down from above, together with the decay of these dead forms, serves to reduce the oxygen content often far below the saturation point characteristic of surface waters. The deeper waters of the ocean obtain their oxygen supply primarily from the drift of sinking cold water from polar seas and have a larger oxygen content than that at intermediate depths. The oxygen profile with depth is shown for a few stations in Figure 42.

Oxygen is lost from water as a result of the respiration of living organisms and through the oxidation of organic matter and of dead bodies; bacteria probably consume more oxygen in sea water and bottom deposits than all other organisms taken together (ZoBell, 1946). Oxygen is also extracted from water and carried to the upper air by the bubbling of other gases like methane, appropriately called marsh gas. Water near the surface may become warmed and itself give off its dissolved gas in bubbles. Dissolved oxygen is also lost in the oxidation of iron and perhaps of other inorganic material. The amount of oxygen present in a lake may be significantly diluted by the inflow of ground water, which is typically deficient in dissolved oxygen and usually carries a heavy load of nitrogen and of carbon dioxide. Much of the hypolimnial deficit in lakes is a result of the oxidation of bottom deposits (Alsterberg, 1927), though bacterial oxidation of methane and hydrogen may help account for the oxygen deficit in some lakes (Rossolimo and Kusnezowa, 1934).

have large amounts of hydrogen sulfide and are devoid of animal life.

STRATIFICATION OF DISSOLVED GASES IN LAKES

The presence of gradients of concentration of dissolved gases, especially of oxygen, has been indicated in the pages just preceding. The emphasis to be placed upon stratification in the analysis of communities (Chapter 26) requires a brief summary of this phase of environmental

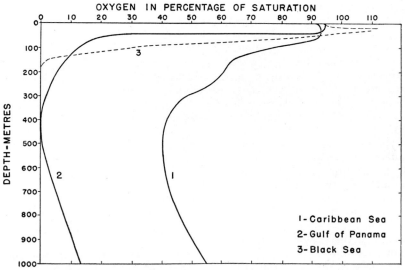

Fig. 42. Depth profiles of dissolved oxygen in sea water. (Redrawn from Schmidt.)

Water above mats of algae or dense growths of such plants as *Chara* or *Elodea* is frequently supersaturated with oxygen during the daylight hours and yet supports a reduced population of animals. Experiments show that, as compared with appropriate control groups, mosquito larvae have a high rate of mortality when reared in aquaria containing dense growth of these water plants (Matheson, 1930). The toxicity may be a result of the presence of nascent oxygen; at least nascent oxygen when it is released from ozone, is toxic to fishes in concentrations of only one part in six to twelve and a half, and even to 33 million parts of water (Hubbs, 1930).

The lack of sufficient dissolved oxygen frequently becomes a limiting factor in the distribution of aquatic organisms. The mass of water in the Black Sea below 200 meters or at the bottom of deep, narrow fjords, contains no dissolved oxygen; such waters

stratification. Dissolved gases, inorganic compounds of many kinds, innumerable organic substances, and suspended particles are all directly and indirectly involved in the vertical environmental gradients of lakes. All residents must adjust to or tolerate these gradients that, in turn, are affected by the processes and by-products of metabolism as well as by decomposing dead bodies. It is not surprising that, despite much limnological and oceanographic research, a great deal remains unaccomplished in this broad, complex field.

Dissolved oxygen and carbon dioxide are important in lake biology. As we have already seen (p. 94), in lakes with a summer thermocline the oxygen and carbon dioxide content is largely equalized during the vernal overturn. With the appearance of the thermocline, the supply of oxygen in the hypolimnion begins to diminish and may disappear from this stratum, although a relatively high oxygen concentration remains in the epilimnion. In the autumnal overturn, hypolimnial oxygen is replaced, but this vital gas may be again depleted during winter stagnation under ice. Summer depletion of dissolved oxygen in the hypolimnion is of greatest significance in lake metabolism (Rawson, 1939), and the hypolimnial deficit may well be expressed in terms of area (Strom, 1931). Hypolimnial deficits may then be calculated, combining area and time factors (Hutchinson, 1938).

The lack of oxygen keeps many animals away from the hypolimnion, and yet this region is not devoid of life even in summer; in fact, a large number of organisms may be present. Fishes from the epilimnion "dive" through the thermocline to feed and ascend to oxygenated water as a diver rises to air (Pearse, 1920). *Chaoborus* (=*Corethra*) larvae, phantom-like in their transparency, migrate to the epilimnion at night and back into the deeper hypolimnion during the day, a type of depth migration widespread in waters that are almost uniform in oxygen and temperature relations. These larvae have air sacs that probably help them to live in oxygenless water below the thermocline. Other forms live constantly in the profundal zone. The source of oxygen for such animals in the stagnant waters of the hypolimnion is unknown. Suggestions include: (1) *oxygen storage,* but this is inadequate for animals that do not invade oxygenated waters during the entire summer; (2) *anaerobic respiration* by a splitting of oxygen-rich carbohydrates; and (3) the use of *atomic oxygen* from decaying tissues (Welch, 1935). Facultative anaerobes are known among animals; some protozoans, nematodes, mollusks, and even fishes have this ability to a more or less limited extent. Some animals can survive the absence of oxygen for several days, and the more resistant may live for much longer periods, even though they carry on many activities.

In extreme stagnation, with low oxygen and high carbon dioxide concentration in the hypolimnion, many of the usual deepwater residents move out (trout) or at least show a decrease in population size (Oligochaeta, chironomid larvae, and fingernail clams). This was demonstrated for Lake Pinantan (British Columbia) by Rawson (1934). He suggests that hydrogen sulfide present in a gradient from relatively high concentration in the terraqueous bottom upward through the hypolimnion is an additional limiting factor in this biological desert.

Three types of relationship are known between the rate of respiration of aquatic animals and the oxygen content of the surrounding water. Some are nearly independent of the oxygen tension over a wide range; paramecium is an example, and many fishes show this relationship. Others use oxygen at a constant rate over an intermediate range, with the rate of use increasing above and decreasing below that range. Many, perhaps most, aquatic animals that use dissolved oxygen belong in this category; *Dugesia dorotocephala,* a flatworm, is a well-studied example (Hyman 1929). The fishes that we have tested maintain a constant rate of oxygen use in ordinary intermediate tensions and show a decided reduction in rate below 1.5 to 2.0 cc./L. The third type has a rate of oxygen consumption that is highly dependent on the oxygen content of the surrounding medium; the echinoderms, *Patira* and *Strongylocentrotus,* and the common lobster, *Homarus,* are examples (Hyman, 1929).

The clam worm, *Nereis virens,* provides an interesting example, not alone of the point under discussion, but also of the necessity for approximating normal conditions in laboratory tests, if natural reactions are to be observed. When *Nereis* is placed in a clean bare flask under excellent conditions for a standard laboratory determination of oxygen consumption, the rate is closely affected by the amount of dissolved oxygen in the water throughout the normal range of its concentration. When allowed to crawl into a glass tube, a rough approximation of their normal tube-dwelling existence in nature, these worms respond as does the second type of animals and are able to keep constant their rate of oxygen use down to 3 or 4 cc./L, the lowest tension tested (Hyman, 1932).

RESPIRATION FROM GAS BUBBLES

A number of aquatic insects, including corixid hemipterans and dytiscid and hydrophylid beetles, are air-breathing, although they spend much of their life surrounded by water. They obtain bubbles of air at the surface and have special adaptations for carrying them down as they dive. The bubbles are used as a direct source of oxygen for respiration, and also act as collectors of dissolved oxygen from the surrounding water and, in so doing, illustrate several physical principles. The oxygen-collecting mechanism works as follows: When first captured, the bubble holds 21 per cent oxygen, the partial pressure of the atmosphere. As the insect consumes oxygen, the partial pressure of this gas falls, and the partial pressure of nitrogen is relatively increased. Under many conditions this eventually results in a diffusion of oxygen from the water into the bubble and a diffusion of nitrogen out into the surrounding water. The carbon dioxide given off into the bubble diffuses out into water so rapidly that we need take no serious account of it. The bubble continues to act as an oxygen collector until its gases are dissolved, and loses its functional significance as an oxygen-collecting device only after the use of oxygen by the insect sufficiently exceeds the rate of its diffusion from water. Considering solubilities and partial pressures (p. 191), oxygen will diffuse into the bubble about three times as fast as the nitrogen diffuses out, and the underwater bubble may finally yield some thirteen times the amount of oxygen it originally contained (Ege, 1918).

Some mammals trapped below ice make use of a variant of this device. They exhale air just below the surface of the ice to form a flat bubble with a large air-water surface, and after a short time they inhale. As with the insects, such a bubble collects oxygen, disposes quickly of carbon dioxide, and so enables the trapped animals to swim under ice for relatively long distances.

OXIDATION-REDUCTION POTENTIALS

Oxidizing and reducing substances exist in the environment and in the organism, often in close proximity to each other. Oxidation in chemistry means not only reactions in which free oxygen actually is used up, or even the transfer of combined oxygen from one substance to another, but may mean the introduction or increase of one or more electronegative elements or, conversely, the reduction or removal of one or more electropositive elements. In simplest terms, oxidation is the process of removing electrons. Reduction is the opposite of oxidation, and hence it consists primarily in the addition of electrons (Kendall, 1923). One and the same substance can give up electrons (oxidation) or accept them (reduction), de-

pending on its relative position on the oxidation-reduction scale in comparison with other available reacting systems. Position on this scale indicates the oxidation-reduction potential (redox potential) of the given material. The position is expressed as an electric potential in terms of E_h recorded in volts. A system with a high potential can oxidize one that stands lower in the scale and itself undergoes reduction in the process.

The oxidation-reduction potential of the physical environment offers a promising field of study that has received relatively little attention. The redox-potential of sea water is correlated with the amount of dissolved oxygen and with the pH of the water. When there is little dissolved oxygen, or in the presence of hydrogen sulfide, dissolved organic substances apparently need to be considered also.

Oxidation-reduction relations have two aspects: intensity, as measured directly by the potential, and the buffering of the system. Buffering in this sense refers to the ability to carry on a given amount of oxidation (or reduction) without a significant change of potential; it is sometimes called the capacity of the oxidation-reduction system.

The importance of the oxidation-reduction potential of the environment is most obvious for microorganisms. Aerobic bacteria require a high potential and cannot live long in the low one supplied by stagnant waters or muds where oxygen is absent. They tolerate an E_h of from $+0.4$ to -0.2 volts. Anaerobic bacteria are limited to oxygen-free waters and bottom sediments. They live in microhabitats where the E_h may go below -0.42 with a pH of 7.0. As a general rule, the E_h of the bottom sediments decreases with depth, with a zone of rapid change in a few upper centimeters. Active aerobic bacteria are consequently limited to or near the upper surface of such sediments; below come the facultative and obligate anaerobes (Sverdrup, Johnson, and Fleming, 1942).

The presence of electrical potentials has been demonstrated in fresh water and soil surveys as well as in sea water and bottom mud (Burrows and Cordon, 1936; Allgeier, Hafford, and Juday, 1941), and it is believed that such potentials are oxidation-reduction (redox) potentials. If this is true, such readings are destined to play an increasing part in hydrobiology and soil science, since the gradient of oxidation-reduction from top to bottom of a body of water should be of value in relating such factors as pH, oxygen, carbon dioxide, hydrogen sulfide, and ferrous and ferric iron.

This is not to suggest such a prominent role for redox potentials as was once claimed for pH, but simply to greet with satisfaction another index of organization of the environmental background and its effect on the organization of the community. According to expectation, stratified lakes have a stratification in oxidation-reduction potentials.[*] A low content of dissolved oxygen seems not to be the only factor involved in decreasing the redox potential in the hypolimnion; ferrous iron, hydrogen sulfide, and organic reducing systems are also involved. In oligotrophic lakes (those with relatively poor nutritive supply) there was either no decrease or only a slight decrease in redox potential of hypolimnial water; in eutrophic lakes (those rich in nutritive materials) the decrease in oxidation-reduction potential was greater (Allgeier, Hafford, and Juday, 1941).

The quantity of ferrous iron in solution has been shown to determine the value of the redox potential for certain lakes in Connecticut and New York (Hutchinson, 1938). Redox potentials and ferrous iron are in close correlation with the occurrence of larvae of several genera of Chironomidae, often used as indicators of the trophic conditions in the hypolimnial region, and Rawson (1939) believes that the redox potential will provide a useful index for the habitability of hypolimnial and benthic environments.

HYDROGEN SULFIDE

The deeper waters of lakes or ponds or of isolated lagoons, bays, and fiords may contain enough hydrogen sulfide to exclude all life except anaerobic bacteria. Small ponds with a bottom of deep muck that has a high organic content may also contain much hydrogen sulfide in, or just above, the bottom material. This poisonous compound may also accumulate under ice in winter, in the hypolimnion of thermally

[*] Methods for measuring oxidation-reduction potentials, matters of general theory in this field, and general applications are discussed in Michaelis (1930) and Hewitt (1937).

stratified lakes or fiords in summer, and in streams that are heavily contaminated by sewage. Hydrogen sulfide is likely to occur in ponds, lakes, or embayments of the sea in which stagnant water underlies a rich surface biota. The accumulations may be local or may be geographic in extent, as in the Black Sea (p. 193), where a shallow "sill," provided by the Bosphorus Ridge, that reaches to within some 40 meters of the surface, prevents the renewal of the deeper salt water by cutting off the Mediterranean circulation. Inflowing water tends to float near the surface, and the lower 1900 meters have their dissolved oxygen replaced by dissolved hydrogen sulfide; only the upper 200 meters are aerated.

Water rich in hydrogen sulfide has a low redox potential. Not only are aerobic organisms excluded from such waters, but changes are produced in the physical environment. For example, iron, if present, is precipitated as ferrous sulfide, and may eventually become the relatively stable mineral known as pyrite or fool's gold.

CARBON DIOXIDE

Carbon dioxide is dissolved in water as a free gas, as are oxygen and nitrogen. Unlike these associated gases, carbon dioxide also enters into chemical combination with water to form the weak carbonic acid, H_2CO_3, and by chemical reactions with available alkalis, it forms half-bound and bound carbonates, hence its solution in lime-rich fresh water and in sea water does not follow the usual gas "laws." The role of these carbonates in buffering water against rapid changes in pH has been discussed (p. 173), and other general effects of the carbon dioxide content of water have also been indicated (p. 76).

Carbon dioxide enters water from the air, from the ground, especially by means of inflowing ground water, from the decomposition of organic matter, from the respiration of animals at all times and of plants in the absence of light, and from the action of acids on bound and half-bound carbonates dissolved in the water. In lighted waters this gas is removed by green plants in photosynthesis, in which process it is a basic ingredient. The carbonates may be deposited as marl, as the remains of calcareous algae or as shells, especially of foraminiferans, corals, and mollusks. All these relations often set up and maintain a vertical gradient in carbon dioxide concentration especially in thermally stratified lake waters.

It is difficult to give briefly, clearly, and fully an indication of the role of carbon dioxide in animal ecology. It is one of the major environmental factors (Chaps. 4, 11) and acts as a chemical buffer to help maintain the neutrality of aquatic habitats. In addition, carbon dioxide affects varied important aspects of animal (and plant) ecology. It acts as a retarding agent for many biological reactions even if present in fairly low concentrations. On the other other gill-breathing animals. Finally, in this brief list, many aquatic animals, fishes among them, react fairly definitely to an increased amount of carbon dioxide. This may be important, since regions of low oxygen tension often have an increased supply of carbon dioxide.

An optimum concentration of carbon dioxide often exists, below which some measurable rate of activity is decreased; optimum concentrations have been found both for organisms exposed to the atmosphere and for those in aquatic environ-

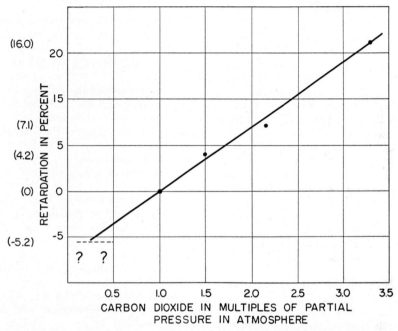

Fig. 43. Relation between carbon dioxide tension and retardation of early cleavages in frog's eggs. Cleavage rate at a partial pressure of 1 atmosphere is placed at zero. (Redrawn from Merwin and Allee.)

hand, an increase in carbon dioxide up to an optimum accelerates the photosynthesis of green plants, hastens germination of mold spores, speeds the growth rate of populations of certain bacteria and some protozoa, and heightens the rate of respiration in higher invertebrates and in vertebrates. Certain echinoderm plutei grow larger with increased carbon dioxide tension, perhaps because carbonates are used in the formation of their spicules (Merwin and Allee, 1943). If present in some quantity, carbon dioxide raises the threshold of availability of oxygen, a process that is especially likely to be important for fishes and ments. In addition to the processes just summarized, early in incubation, the hen's egg develops faster at concentrations of carbon dioxide somewhat above those found normally in the atmosphere. On the other hand, there are equally vital processes, the early cleavage of the frog's egg being an example, that become steadily more rapid the lower the carbon dioxide tension. The latter effect is illustrated in Figure 43. It is impossible with present knowledge to suggest a general rule as to which processes will be stimulated and which inhibited by a slight increase above the carbon dioxide tension normally encountered in nature.

14. DISSOLVED SALTS AS LIMITING FACTORS

An environmental factor exerts a limiting influence when, despite the favorable nature of the remainder of the environment, it comes to control the habitat because of scarcity or overabundance. The amount of available moisture in arid regions is an example of a limiting factor; in many places, after irrigation, the xerocole biota of the typical desert is replaced by a much more abundant biota of mesocoles. Accumulated water in swamps, bogs, ponds, or streams is also a limiting factor for obligate xerocoles or mesocoles. Low temperature acts as a limiting factor in winter in the higher latitudes or altitudes, as does heat toward the equator. Oxygen is a limiting factor in the hypolimnion of thermally stratified lakes and in higher altitudes on mountains.

Historically, this field was first crystallized around the principle of the minimum that was brought into prominence as Liebig's "law of the minimum" (1840) and was later restated by Blackman (1905) as his "law of limiting factors." The reaction of organisms to these limiting influences is sufficiently regular and widespread to be summarized by Shelford's "law of toleration" (1911c). This generalization considers the reaction to both minimal and maximal quantities of different environmental factors.

The principle of the minimum is well illustrated by the effect of certain nutrient salts upon the density of basic plant populations, such as those of the plant plankters in water, that form the broad foundation for the food pyramid (p. 501) for aquatic animals. The use of dissolved chemicals to illustrate and test this principle is appropriate, since Liebig originally worked with the relations of mineral nutrients, especially those in the soil, to plant growth. A statement of this principle by Johnstone (1908, p. 234) is a convenient point of departure for the present brief discussion.

"A plant requires a certain number of foodstuffs if it is to continue to live and grow, and each of these food-substances must be present in a certain proportion. If one of them is absent the plant will die; and if it is present in minimal proportion the growth will also be minimal. This will be the case no matter how abundant the other food-stuffs may be. Thus the growth of a plant is dependent on the amount of the food-stuff which is presented to it in minimum quantity. Marine plants require certain things—carbonic acid, nitrogen compounds, silica, phosphoric acid, and certain mineral salts. The carbonic acid and the mineral salts are present in relatively large amounts, but the proportions of nitrogen compounds, silica, and phosphoric acid in the water of the sea are very small. The density of the marine plants will therefore fluctuate according to the proportions of these indispensable food-stuffs."

It is not easy to recognize a supposedly limiting factor in nature. Whether the limitation is imposed by the scarcity of energy or substance, the needed information includes:

1. The amount of the limiting factor regularly present and the limits of its normal and its occasional variations.

2. The rate of input of the limiting factor into the ecological system under consideration and its variations.

3. The rate of consumption of the limiting factor.

4. The degree to which some vital activity, such as rate of population growth, is affected by the low concentration of the limiting factor.

5. The time relations; usually observations must be continued for a considerable period of time in order to understand the causal relations underlying the observed sequences of pulse of increase and decrease of the limiting factor in relation to the process limited.

Information concerning the amount of a limiting factor that is regularly present is relatively easy to secure within the limits of accuracy of approved quantitative methods. Estimates of the rate of use are characteristically based on measurements and calculations dealing with accumulations in the biota or in some part of it. Input of radiant energy excepted, trustworthy data about the rate of input are usually hard to come by.

The rate of use may be so closely related to the rate of input that the amount of the limiting factor present in the eco-system may remain constant or almost constant. Sometimes, as with the amount of carbon dioxide in the atmosphere, the small supply regularly present—0.03 per cent, or a total of 1700×10^9 tons—compared with the

in the sea as largely unsolved. It is his belief that, besides the soil-like nitrifiers that are commonly found in bottom deposits and near land, "there are other marine nitrifying organisms which have escaped detection."

PHOSPHORUS

Phosphates, like nitrates, are brought by rivers to the sea in large amounts. The Mississippi River carries enough combined from the Mississippi River (Riley, 1937).

Phosphates show much the same distribution in depth as do nitrates, and, in broad outline, their seasonal and geographical variation approaches that of the nitrates. The depth profile is shown in Figure 46. Phosphates are present in much smaller concentration than the nitrates and appear to be of high importance as limiting factors in the development of populations of plant plankton. One milligram of phosphate-phosphorus in a M^3 of sea water is enough,

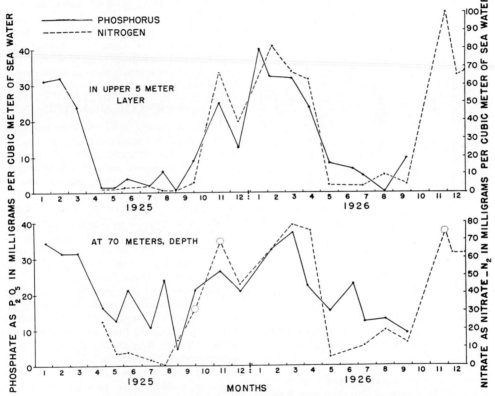

Fig. 45. The seasonal cycle of dissolved nitrates and phosphates in the English Channel. (Redrawn from Harvey.)

phosphorus to contribute 1 mg./M^3 daily to an area of 1000 square kilometers near its mouth and to a depth of 50 meters. Growth of phytoplankton is measurably affected in a relatively narrow coastal zone for at least four geographic degrees along the neighboring Gulf coast. Although it is not certain that phosphorus here acts as a limiting factor under usual conditions, the zone of greater density of phytoplankton approximates the area of increased phosphate content of the water produced by the inflow other things being equal, to allow the production of a large population of diatoms. The ratio of nitrate nitrogen to phosphate-phosphorus present in the sea roughly approaches a constant value of about 15:1 in milligram-atoms and is approximately 7:1 in weight (Cooper, 1938; Sverdrup, Johnson, and Fleming, 1942). Many variations occur from any given mean value, but still the idea of a rough ratio of about this order of magnitude helps fix in mind their relative abundance. The proportion of these two elements in marine plankton approximates the same ratio.[*]

The negative correlation that was noted for the amount of nitrates and the quantity of dissolved oxygen in sea water becomes more pronounced when phosphates and

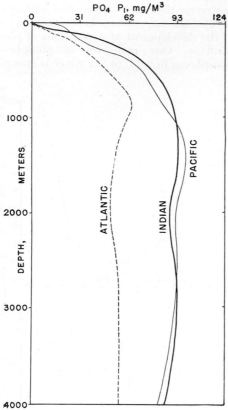

Fig. 46. Depth profiles of phosphate-phosphorus. (Redrawn from Sverdrup, Johnson, and Fleming.)

nitrates together are compared with oxygen content. The seasonal distribution of phosphates resembles that of nitrates (Fig. 45), except that the "regeneration" of phosphates in surface waters takes less time; hence the autumnal upswing starts earlier than does that of nitrates in the same waters. This may mean simply that the release of dissolved phosphates from dead organisms is a relatively simple process, whereas the similar nitrate release represents an end stage in a longer series of changes (Harvey, 1928).

[*] The nitrogen:phosphorus ratio in fresh water is not necessarily the same as that in the sea (Hutchinson, 1941a).

There exist for restricted locations quantitative data concerning cycles of abundance of carbonates and silicates as well as phosphates and nitrogen compounds, both as mineral nutrients and at the organic level. Often the peaks and depressions are correlated with utilization of the given substance by organisms or with their release after death and decay, and these changes tend to be associated with the local annual climatic cycle.

Although the amounts of nitrates and phosphates, taken together, seem to be the principal limiting mineral nutrients in the sea, at times the growth of populations of unicellular algal cells, like diatoms, are at a minimum when these two mineral constituents are relatively plentiful, and there must be other limiting factors in addition to these two important ones.

LIMNOLOGICAL ASPECTS

In fresh waters both nitrogen and phosphorus occur in small amounts and are subject to marked changes seasonally and vertically. Phosphorus averages 0.05 mg./L. or less; inorganic nitrates are usually less than 0.5 mg./L., and nitrites less than 0.1 mg./L. Ammonia is equally scarce. There is usually a seasonal maximum toward the end of winter stagnation in ice-covered ponds and lakes, followed by redistribution in the vernal overturn that results in uniformity. With the formation of the thermocline and summer stagnation, uniform distribution is again lost, since the flowering out of epilimnial phytoplankton makes demands on these salts in the surface waters. There is a steady drizzle of dead, decomposing organisms down into the hypolimnion, with a resulting increase of the raw materials for protein synthesis in these deeper waters. By the middle of summer stagnation, since the thermocline tends to retard the free distribution of nitrogen and phosphorus, these latter may be several times more abundant in the hypolimnion than at the surface. In fact, diminishing amounts of these elements may act as limiting factors and retard diatom production, although light intensity, temperature, and other conditions are favorable. The autumnal overturn after the thermocline disappears redistributes these vital elements, particularly by currents. During winter stagnation, with low light intensity, photosynthesis is notably reduced, and the water is being continuously enriched by the death of many organisms. This results in the seasonal maximum. Such annual cycles are basic in thermally stratified lakes and, as we have seen, have their counterpart, but on a much vaster scale, in open ocean (Russell and Yonge, 1928; Park, Allee, and Shelford, 1939). (Attention is directed to the Chap. 27, on Community Metabolism, for a fuller integration with the ecology of communities.) The actual limiting influence of nitrogen and phosphorus on the production of lake plankton is not yet thoroughly understood; investigations demonstrate a correlation in some cases and none in others. In general, oligotrophic lakes are low and eutrophic lakes are high in nitrogen content. In the former, the dominant phytoplankters are desmids; as a rule, such lakes have bottom sediments poor in organic content. This partially explains the small amount of nitrogen present. In eutrophic lakes, phytoplankton is relatively rich in quantity, and diatoms flourish. Prescott (1939) found a direct correlation between nitrogen content and the quantity of plankton. He concludes that nitrogen is an important determiner of both abundance and distribution of phytoplankton and suggests that the nitrogen demand by many blue-green algae is so strong that their presence may be used as an index of high nitrogen concentration and organic wastes.

Opposed, we have the work of Atkins (1926), who found no evidence of correlation between nitrogen deficiency and phytoplankton limitation in Wisconsin lakes. Additional support for either view can be found in the literature.

To conclude the present discussion, Juday (1942) records that phosphorus and nitrogen are thought to be limiting factors in fresh waters. The growth of fish populations in European ponds seems to be limited by the concentration of these two sets of mineral nutrients. Although their role in limiting the growth of fresh-water populations is not yet fully known, greater emphasis is usually placed on the limiting action of the more dilute phosphorus salts alone than on nitrogen salts alone (Welch, 1935; Ketchum, 1939).

CALCIUM AND MAGNESIUM

Calcium itself, or calcium plus magnesium, may be a limiting factor in lakes. The summer standing crop of phytoplankton and rooted vegetation in two calcium-poor, soft-water lakes of Wisconsin (0.7 to 2.3 mg. Ca/L.) differs decidedly in quantity and in species from that in two hard-water lakes in the southern part of the same state (21.2 to 22.4 mg. Ca/L.). Most of the rooted plants in the soft-water lakes are limited to that type of water. Lakes with hard water were more productive per unit area than were those with soft water. The total plant crop weighs three to five times, and the animal population, excluding fish, two to three times, that of the soft-water lakes. As might be expected from these figures, the dissolved organic matter, largely a degradation product, is also much larger in the hard-water lakes (Juday, 1942).

The amount of bound carbonates gives a good measure of the hardness of water. In fresh waters the carbonates are mainly combined ("bound") with calcium and magnesium. For practical purposes the quantity of calcium may be taken as a measure of the "hardness" of lake water. Ohle (1934) suggested that lakes with 9 mg. or less per liter of water are to be regarded as poor in calcium and may be known as soft-water lakes; those with 10 to 25 mg. per liter are intermediate; those with 26 mg. or more are hard-water lakes. In general, soft-water lakes show little calcium stratification (Juday, Birge, and Meloche, 1938), but a slight increase occurs in the deep hypolimnial area; intermediate calcium lakes have a decided increase in the hypolimnial calcium. This is a generalization to which exceptions are known, but its basic application is important.

Calcium is circulated through thermally stratified lakes during vernal and autumnal overturns. This redistribution is the more needed since this substance enters into intimate relations with plants and animals in many ways. Besides being much used in shell formation, it is essential in plant and animal metabolism and helps regulate permeability to water. Calcium has important general relations, as we have seen, with carbon dioxide and, through its carbonates, with the H ion concentration.

The effectiveness of hardness of water as a limiting factor in distribution can be tested by its correlations with environmental relations of mollusks. Of the bivalve mollusks, all members of the family Unionidae found in an extensive study of Wisconsin waters were restricted to habitats with nearly neutral or alkaline water and usually with 12 or more parts per million (ppm) of bound carbonates. Two of the species of *Anodonta* range into water with as little as 3.2 ppm, and one of these lives in even softer water. The little fingernail clam *Pisidium* can live in lakes that have a *p*H of 5.8 and as little as 1.5 ppm of bound carbonates; shells of bivalves are thin and may be quite flexible in such soft waters. A few species of snails, both gilled and pulmonate, thrive in exceedingly soft waters, and the gilled snail *Campeloma* builds a fairly large thick shell in lakes with a *p*H of 5.8 and fixed carbonates of as little as 1.1 ppm. This *p*H approaches the degree of acidity at which it is theoretically impossible for animals to deposit lime shells (Jewell and Brown, 1929), and it is puzzling that mollusks can withdraw sufficient calcium from such lime-poor, acid waters to build their shells. It may be that they live in habitat niches where conditions are more favorable and so escape the full rigors of the generalized habitat. The Wisconsin lakes that are intermediate in hardness (10 to 20 ppm of bound carbonates) harbor the greatest number of species, and the lakes with the hardest waters (over 30 ppm), in the region studied have the greatest abundance of individuals (see also p. 341).

SILICON, COPPER, AND OTHER ELEMENTS

Silicon occurs in fresh water and in the ocean in some form of soluble silicate. It may be present in colloidal form, especially in river waters. The silicon content of lakes may be a limiting factor in the growth and distribution of fresh-water sponges, Spongillidae. Some species, like *Spongilla ingloviformis,* are restricted to waters low in mineral content, but are largely indifferent to the amount of silicon present. Others, like *Ephydatia everetti,* are restricted to waters low in silicon as well as in general mineral content. Others require waters fairly rich in minerals; *Ephydatia mulleri* is an example. Some species of sponges can live in a wide range of mineral content, although their skeletal development may be much affected by the quantity of available silicon. Jewell (1935) reports:

"In waters of SiO$_2$ content below 0.4 mgms. per liter and of low conductivity and solids,

Spongilla lacustris shows a progressive attenuation of its spicules, eventually losing its microspinal spicules (an important species character). These skeleton-poor forms appear no less vigorous and thrifty than heavy-spiculed specimens from more highly mineralized waters. Similarly *Tubella pennsylvanica* shows marked variations correlated with the degree of mineralization of the water. These entirely normal variations, in some cases, abrogate accepted generic criteria."

Silicates of lakes and ocean have been suggested as one of the limiting factors in the growth of marine and freshwater diatoms and of other organisms that have a siliceous skeleton. Silicates are present in amounts ranging from a spring maximum in the surface waters of the English Channel of 60 to 70 gm./M^3 silicate-silicon to a summer minimum of 12 gm./M^3. There are larger amounts in the unlighted depths. Harvey (1928) did not believe that silicon acted as a limiting factor in the sea in any of the cases observed to that date. Sverdrup, Johnson, and Fleming (1942, p. 769) comment that areas rich in silicon show a degree of utilization of this element by diatoms that exceeds the total supply available in areas poor in silicon.

In lakes, silicon is present in epilimnial waters in quantities that are usually less than 10 mg./L. Ricker (1937) determined that silica at 6 mg./L. per liter in Cultus Lake was about twenty-five times the amount required by resident diatoms at their maximum abundance. The indications are that lake silicon is not a limiting factor for diatom populations either in vernal or autumnal peaks of density. Since silicon, like so many other environmental factors in lakes, is usually stratified, its gradient of abundance may have indirect effects that are not now apparent.

Iron acts at times as a limiting factor (Gran, 1931), as does also manganese (Harvey, 1939).

In addition to its effect upon oxidation-reduction potentials (p. 196), iron is thought to act as a catalyst in chlorophyll formation and to be involved in respiratory activities, as well as being a possible limiting factor in phytoplankton growth. Iron is usually stratified in lakes with a thermocline; it is less than 2.0 mg./L. in the epilimnion and usually increases in the hypolimnion. Manganese may or may not serve as a substitute for iron in lakes and usually occurs in lower concentrations; it is more abundant than iron in humus lakes (Ohle, 1934).

The extent to which other elements present in the sea in trace concentrations—copper, manganese, cobalt, and vanadium, for example—are limiting factors remains largely for future investigations. There is little doubt that these elements exert influences on the distribution and other ecological relations of at least some organisms.

Though the ecology* of trace concentrations is still largely an untouched field of study, the effect of minute amounts of copper on the ecology of some marine organisms has already been established. The settling and attachment ("setting") of oyster veliger larvae (*Ostrea virginica*) in Connecticut are most pronounced at the stage of the tide when the copper content of littoral

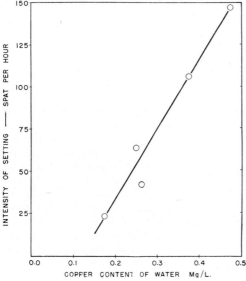

Fig. 47. At Milford Harbor, Connecticut, the more copper present within the effective range, the greater the rate of attachment of oyster larvae. (Redrawn from Prytherch.)

waters is highest and within the range of 0.05 to 0.5 mg./L. At this concentration the number of oyster larvae that respond to copper stimulation is directly proportional to the amount of copper present (Fig. 47). Copper is leached from the land and brought to the littoral region of the sea by

* For a discussion of the physiology of trace elements, see the review of Pirschle (1938).

surface and underground waters (Prytherch, 1934), and occurs near Woods Hole at a concentration of between 0.01 and 0.02 mg./L. (Galtsoff, 1943).

Another phase of the ecology of trace elements should be mentioned. Granted that little of such substances as copper or cobalt is needed by the organism, does the environment furnish even these small amounts? Sometimes it does not; often it does. A rough calculation indicates that in sea urchin eggs stimulated by 10^{-13} molar solution of copper salt (Finkel, Allee, and Garner, 1942), the copper is some twenty-five times more concentrated in the eggs than in the surrounding sea water. Other cells are known to make concentration of this order of magnitude (cf. p. 167). The capture of ions of the heavy metals should be no more difficult than that of lighter metals such as magnesium and sodium and may well be easier, since heavy metals are readily adsorbed by organic surfaces.

The density of a species population that spends its life history in one habitat niche depends on the most unfavorable environmental factors in that niche during the part of the life history when resistance is lowest. Low resistance frequently accompanies some phase of the breeding cycle or comes during early development. The same generalization holds when emigration and periodic migrations are considered, except that then the habitat includes the geographic range occupied by migrating individuals of the population in question.

The discussion of Liebig's "law of the minimum" and its various extensions, like the treatment of different environmental factors throughout this whole section, has been on the assumption that each of these factors acts independently of the others. This assumption has been a matter of convenience known to be contrary to the facts (p. 87). It has become increasingly difficult to maintain the fiction of the independence of the different environmental factors, and the need to do so no longer exists even for pedagogical reasons. The limiting action of one of the dissolved mineral nutrients may be strongly affected by the amount of others present. The application of an incomplete fertilizer deficient in potassium, nitrogen, or phosphorus, for land plants, leads to an increased use of the other two and may actually result in a decreased absorption of the omitted element from the already deficient soil. Similarly the absence of potassium salts from a nutrient solution may produce an increased absorption of nitrogen and phosphorus (E. C. Miller, 1938), and there is much other evidence that, with plants, the "law of the minimum," though finally effective in extremes, is much influenced in its action by the combination of environmental influences operating at the time.

Vitamins also act as limiting factors. Although little work has been done upon the action of vitamins in nature, there is evidence that growth-promoting accessories are necessary for the growth of certain diatoms (Harvey, 1939) and that these become limiting in their action only when the quantity present is very small. Hutchinson (1943) reported that the thiamine (vita-min B_1) content of unfiltered water from certain ponds or small lakes in Connecticut lay between 0.03 micrograms (γ) and 1.2 γ per liter. In Linsley Pond he could remove from 61 to 93 per cent by filtration. Even half the amount of thiamine present might be ecologically significant for promoting growth of planktonic algae. Although seasonal variations occur, no accumulation of thiamine was found in the hypolimnion at the end of stagnation. Unconsolidated mud contained 2 to 3 γ per gram of dry mud. A variety of plankters, both plant and animals, living in these waters were rich in thiamine. Growth accessories are produced by other organisms and are, therefore, derivatives of the biotic environment and should be included in a complete discussion of biotic factors.

15. COMBINATIONS OF ENVIRONMENTAL FACTORS

Only when a given aspect of the environment approaches maximum or minimum toleration limits for an individual, a population, or a community does it become sufficiently important to assume virtual control of the ecological situation. Normally, as we have just said, each environmental factor is only one of a number of influences in a given habitat, and organisms react to the whole rather than to parts hypothetically dissected out of it. Even the limits of toleration for a given factor are partially set by the extent to which the remainder of the environment is favorable.

A number of important interactions exist between pairs or groups of environmental factors. Heat and light are often closely associated; in fact, unequivocal separation of them as regulators of seasonal succession does not seem to have been demonstrated (Hutchinson, 1941). Heat and humidity effects are also closely intermingled, and heat, relative humidity, and wind combine to form the environmental complex often called "the evaporating power of the air." This complex unit would be more significant if it could include also the vapor pressure of water both at the evaporating surface and in the air above (p. 182).

A less expected temperature relationship is found in the strong evidence that the shells of marine organisms from warm habitats tend to have a higher proportion of magnesium to calcium carbonate than do those of the same general taxonomic groups from colder waters. The analyses by Clarke and Wheeler (1922) show this correlation for crinoids and alcyonarians and suggest it for foraminiferans, crustaceans, and calcareous algae. They comment that the facts are definite but unexplained.

Reaction to a vertical gradient in the environment is easily oversimplified and regarded as a response to gravity. It may be just that, or it may be a reaction to any other stimulus, or to some combination of stimuli, possessing a vertical differential. Vertical gradients in light, heat, substratum, turbulence, or pressure, may affect or control the reaction. In air, these may include also an evaporation gradient; and in water, vertical differences in density, viscosity, mineral nutrients, and dissolved gases are readily recognized. It requires direct investigation to find which one of these, or what combination of them, is responsible for observed reactions toward or against the pull of gravity and for the distributions that result from these reactions.

Diurnal depth migrations, such as are common among aquatic animals and are made by some forest invertebrates like the hemipteran *Menecles* (Park and Strohecker, 1936) and other land animals, may result from the interaction of change in light intensity, or other diurnal changes, with the pull of gravity. They may also be given as an active response to one or more of the wide variety of physical gradients just listed or to these plus various biotic influences. Vertical migrations also result from passive conveyance by convection currents in water or air and from equally passive relations to changes in density or viscosity that are closely associated with daily temperature rhythms.

TEMPERATURE AND MOISTURE

Temperature and moisture acting together make a much-studied environmental team. Each affects the potency of the other under many conditions, and both together are influenced by other phases of the environmental complex, notably by light and by mineral nutrients. The relations of moisture and temperature to plants have been summarized by a hydrothermal index (Livingston, 1916) based on the following formula:

$$I_{mt} = I_t \frac{I_p}{I_e}$$

I_{mt} is the moisture-temperature (hydrothermal) index; I_t represents an index of temperature efficiency (Klages, 1942); I_p and I_e give indices based on precipitation and on evaporating power of the air respectively. As in most other work in which the evaporating power of the air is considered, this index is weak in that vapor tension relations are not yet known (p. 189). It also has a number of other defects, one of the more important of which is the failure to consider the effects of soil moisture stored during the nongrowing season and used later. Even with these handicaps, maps showing hydrothermal zones of the United States differentiate fairly well between southern regions of warm-weather crops and northern ones with cool-weather plants, and also serve to separate in a general way the eastern moist from western more arid regions. The correlation coefficient for 112 stations between the hydrothermal index and the length of the growing season is reasonably conclusive, with r = 0.63 ± 0.04. The relation of this index to animal life has not yet been critically evaluated. Maps based on data calculated from the hydrothermal formula show some correlations with broad generalities of animal distribution in the United States.

Moisture and temperature are two important elements in comparative climatology (Taylor, 1918). These are graphically shown in temperature-rainfall or temperature-humidity charts in which mean monthly temperature and mean monthly moisture values are indicated by a single dot properly entered on a grid that indicates temperature on the vertical and moisture on the horizontal axis. The twelve dots for a year may then be connected to form a polygon that may be irregular in form. Temperature is recorded in Centigrade or Fahrenheit degrees for dry-bulb or wet-bulb readings. The moisture record is usually based on precipitation or relative humidity. Judging which of these is to be used should depend on knowledge of which is more important for the ecological relations under consideration. Soil animals in general are more likely to be sensitive to precipitation, and fresh-water animals may be decidedly under the influence of temperature and rainfall, especially in streams, ponds, and the smaller lakes. On the other hand, many animals that live above ground are more affected by humidity, especially insects with thin exoskeletons (p. 187). It is not always easy to know the relative value of humidity and rainfall in the ecology of insects; both are often important, as in the ecological life history of the codling moth and the chinch bug (Shelford, 1927, 1932).

Selected examples of temperature-moisture graphs are shown in Figures 48 to 52. Wet-bulb temperatures are plotted against relative humidities in Figure 48, because these correlate more closely with subjective human estimates of discomfort. Dry-bulb temperatures for Jhansi (India) average 95° F. in May in place of 75° for the wet bulb; the whole graph for Jhansi would be moved up the temperature axis if dry-bulb temperatures were used. Different types of climates are illustrated in this figure by using data from selected regions. They are to be compared with each other and with the shaded region that is based on the climates of twelve large cities of the world in which the population is predominately white. No graphs are given for combinations of low temperatures and low relative humidities; such climates are rare. Tropical climates usually show a small range in mean monthly temperature and a large variation in relative humidity; their graphs tend to extend along a humidity axis, as does that of humid Batavia in Java. The range both in temperature and in humidity is frequently much less than that shown for Jhansi and Simla with their monsoon climates.

Tropical climates, if they show seasonal differences at all, have the main seasons determined by moisture relations. Such

main variation along the temperature axis.

Human death and insect mortality are among the important phenomena that may well be affected by temperature and humidity (Huntington, 1919). Eggs of the desert locust (*Schistocerca gregaria*) have a much more restricted temperature tolerance at 20 per cent relative humidity than at complete saturation (Fig. 49).

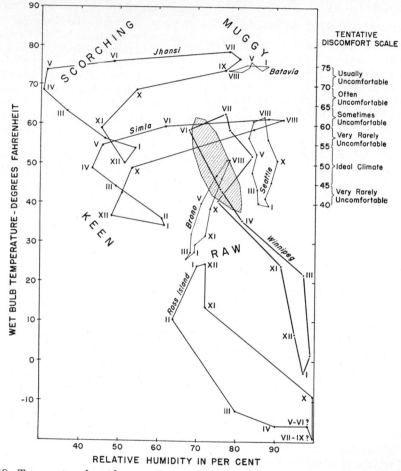

Fig. 48. Temperature-humidity graphs of some important climatic types. The shaded figure shows the composite climate of twelve large cities inhabited mainly by white people. (Simplified from Taylor.)

climates are in striking contrast with those of coastal regions in the temperate latitudes, as illustrated by Seattle and still more so with a continental climate such as exists in Winnipeg. Apes and monkeys characteristically live in warm climates where the seasonal differences in rainfall or humidity, or both, may be large; the white man thrives best in temperate climates with the

Extensive studies of the rate of development and of mortality of the codling moth (*Carpocapsa pomonella*) and the chinch bug (*Blissus leucopterus*) similarly have reduced ranges of temperature tolerance with lower relative humidity (Shelford, 1927, 1932). Many insects have an optimum combination of temperature and humidity, both for survival and for development. Often this lies near the maximum temperature limit and above 50 per cent relative humidity. Optimum conditions for human health are placed by Huntington (1919) at a mean temperature of 64° F. and a relative humidity of 80 per cent.

The closeness with which temperature-humidity means or extremes of a given habitat approximate the optimum requirements and tolerations of a species is an

other factors being equal, in a year like 1927 than in one like 1932. Ecological requirements being known, prospective population levels can be predicted with some accuracy.

The other localities whose temperature-humidity graphs are shown in Figure 50 were selected to test the favorability of their climatic condition for the development of the Mediterranean fruit fly. Paris presents

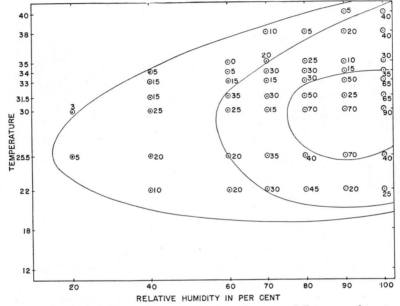

Fig. 49. Percentage of mortality of eggs of the desert locust at different combinations of temperature and humidity. (Rearranged from Bodenheimer.)

important factor helping to determine population density both for a given year and for many years together. The Mediterranean fruit fly (*Ceratitis capitata*) thrives best in temperatures that range from 16° to 32° C. and in relative humidities between 65 and 75 per cent. The combined range of optimum temperature-humidity relations are indicated in Figure 50 by the smallest quadrangle. Conditions are favorable for the development of this fruit fly in the wider range shown by the middle quadrangle, and the limits of toleration are outlined by the largest one. In Tel Aviv, Palestine, these climatic factors are favorable the year around and may be optimal during the major part of the year. As is usual in many parts of the world, there is a considerable variation from one year to another, and a much larger population could be expected,

relatively adverse conditions during the cooler six months of the year without transgressing the limits of toleration. Ankara has an intolerable climate for three months, and Kartoum for nine months each year. Hawaii is favorable, as is Tampa, Florida, (not shown on the chart). Some danger of important outbreaks could be expected if the fly gained a foothold at Los Angeles, California, where there are nine favorable months. Large populations could not be expected in California's dry interior, irrigated regions aside, because of a sequence of four months of extremely low humidity.

This introduces the concept of bonitation (Bodenheimer, 1938). Bonitation may be regarded as the state of well-being of a species or community as shown by its population density. Estimates of climatic control of bonitation were originally based primarily on temperature and humidity corrected for rainfall, and for biotic associates. Bonitation may depend on temperature-rainfall conditions; the intensity of the attack of wilt disease on plants of the cucumber family gives an illustration (Fig. 51). Heavy rainfall kills many kinds of insects, chinch bugs

occupied by animals may be different from the general meteorological conditions; this is especially obvious for irrigated lands.

Fire is an environmental factor to which forest and grassland animals have been exposed spasmodically from time immemorial. The fire hazard depends on the combina-

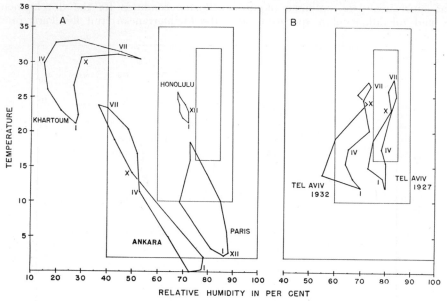

Fig. 50. Temperature-humidity relations of the Mediterranean fruit fly. (Based mainly on Bodenheimer.)

among them. Temperature-rainfall graphs may show whether a given season is favorable or unfavorable for the development of large population of such insects. Under the weather conditions diagrammed in Figure 52, A, crop damage by chinch bugs in Illinois was severe. By contrast, Figure 52, B shows average conditions for years in which crop damage was light. The difference in rainfall during the warm growing season of May, June, and July is the important factor.

We cannot overemphasize the fact that estimates of bonitation based climatic factors must be seasoned with sound common sense. A large amount of rain in a month with favorable growing temperature is not necessarily fatal to rain-sensitive insects. Much gentle rain may not be harmful even though an impressive total amount falls during critical periods, and heavy localized showers do not necessarily prevent disastrous outbreaks of chinch bugs. The temperature-moisture relations in the habitat

tion of a number of variables. Given combustible material and an igniting spark such as might be furnished by a stroke of lightning, the danger of fire depends on wind velocity, temperature, and fuel humidity, both directly and in terms of the time since the last precipitation. These elements can be combined rather simply into an index of fire danger that is used in practical fire control work in forestry.[*]

Enough selected detail has been given to document the generalization that the physical factors of the environment can work in effective combination in pairs or other groups of factors as well as singly. It is now useful to consider some of the relations of many elements of the environment considered together and of the environment as a whole.

[*] Anonymous, 1939a, Fire Control Handbook, Region Two, Forest Service, U. S. Department of Agriculture.

MACROCLIMATES AND MICROCLIMATES

The abstraction called climate is a more or less formalized integration of environmental elements such as temperature, humidity, insolation, and time. Its structure may be visualized by the relations outlined in Table 15.

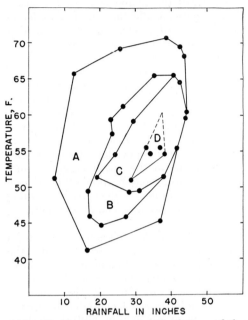

Fig. 51. Temperature-rainfall relations of the wilt disease of cucubit plants; severity increases from *A* to *D*. (Redrawn from Tehon.)

Table 15. *The Anatomy of Climate (After Trewartha, 1937)*

Climatic Controls	Climatic Elements	End Results

Sun
Latitude
Land and water
Winds
Ocean currents
Altitude
Mountains
Semipermanent
  low and high
  pressure centers
Storms
	Temperature
	Humidity
	Precipitation
	Air pressure
	Winds
		Varieties of weather and climate

A climate may be either regional or general, and both have macroclimatic or microclimatic aspects. Knowledge about macroclimates is based on records taken at networks of observing stations that are placed at a height of 1.5 sometimes 2 or more, meters above the ground surface. This is the climate to which man is most exposed; it may, in fact, be designated as human climate.

The lowest few feet of the atmosphere are sufficiently different in climate as to be properly called a microclimate or plant climate. The vertical reach of the plant climate varies with the height of the vegetational cover; over bare, or practically bare, ground it reaches to a height of about 1.5 meters. The considerable, though still relatively scanty, body of early knowledge dealing directly with plant climates was summarized in 1927 by Geiger.

Another and smaller climate can also be recognized; it may be called an insect climate and is, relatively speaking, a micro-microclimate. Little is known with certainty about the characteristics of the thin layer of air, only a few millimeters thick, that impinges on the surface of the ground and penetrates the small superficial nooks and crannies where many insects spend the major portion of their lives.

Among others, Uvarov (1931) emphasized the importance of the ecoclimate, which is the name he proposed for the sum

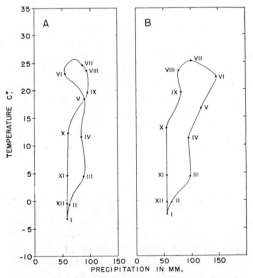

Fig. 52. Rainfall-temperature graphs for years of heavy damage to Illinois crops from chinch bugs (*A*), contrasted with years in which the damage was light (*B*). (Rearranged from Shelford.)

total of meteorological factors within a habitat. In this connection, a habitat means a forest, a marsh, a sand dune, and the like.

Plant climates have been studied primarily in western Europe and in the middle reaches of North America, both relatively humid regions. A given plant climate in these areas is determined primarily by the nature of the surface, that is, by the various kinds of bare ground or of vegetation, by slope, by exposure, and by such meteorological phenomena as cloudiness, dew formation, and evaporation.

In the macroclimate, temperature decreases by 0.2° to 1.0° per 100 meters above ground, and temperature inversions are relatively rare. The temperature gradient is normally much steeper in the plant climate in general, and it may become especially steep in the climate of crawling insects. Inversions are much more common in microclimates than in macroclimates.

Two patterns of plant climates are clearly distinguished: the *radiational* type, characteristically developed on clear nights and (Fig. 53), the *insolational* type, diagram-

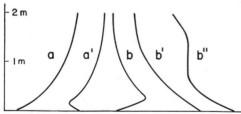

Fig. 53. Types of vertical distribution of temperature in the zone of plant climate. For each graph, distance to the right represents the higher temperature. (Modified from Geiger.)

matically developed on warm sunny days in summer. As these graphs indicate, the surface of the ground (the insect climate) is the point of greatest interest in plant climates. In sunny daytime, it is the location of highest temperature with a sharp temperature decrease in the air above and the soil below. Even in humid, temperate climates, the atmosphere above the soil surface in bright sunlight may show a drop of 3° in the first 8 mm. of air, and insects readily escape to cooler air even by low flights. At night, the surface becomes cooler than the air in the soil, but the gradients are less steep. These and other temperature gradients of aerial microclimates are

shown in Figure 53. Graph *a* gives conditions at the time of minimum temperature in early morning, when outward radiation is dominant. When dew is being formed (graph *a'*), heat of condensation of water vapor raises the temperature of the insect climate without affecting the remainder of the plant climate; the air may be warmed at the ground level as much as 0.6°. As the sun rises and becomes effective, the layer in the insect climate is warmed first, and conditions can again be summarized by graph *a*, although the causal relations are different. With increasing insolation, the temperature profile of the plant climate changes to the insolation type shown in graph *b* after a heavy dew; the thin layer of chilled air in the insect climate comes from the rapid consumption of heat used in the evaporation of dew; early morning warming may produce conditions shown in graph *b'*.

An insolation plant climate in pure form (graph *b'*) is often disturbed during the midday hours by the formation of a layer of air, about a meter above ground, in which the temperature may actually rise somewhat and certainly does not continue the steady fall that again sets in at an altitude of about 1.5 meters (graph *b''*). This upper limit sets a convenient, and perhaps a natural, upper limit for the microclimate (plant climate). The causes of these phenomena are unknown.

Other environmental conditions show special development in the zone of microclimates. Humidity relations differ near the ground from those higher in the air. Except when dew is forming, there is nearly always a maximum in absolute humidity just above the ground surface as compared with higher levels of the plant climate. Maximum absolute humidity varies between day and night, and relative humidity is normally decidedly greater at night. Wind velocity is much reduced near the ground, even in level country lacking vegetational cover. There are more hours of absolute calm in the zone of insect climate than a few centimeters higher, and wind movement is still more constant above the limits of plant climates. The rate of air movement to which ground-dwelling insects are normally exposed probably does not normally exceed one-tenth that which man experiences (cf. p. 147). A few of the other relations between macroclimates and microclimates have been worked out; we know, for example, that the determination of the length of the frostless season at 1.5 meters above the ground does not necessarily approximate the frostless season for small seedlings or for insects. Meteorological data accumulated at standard weather bureau stations can be applied to the plant climate in a given locality only with caution, and to the climate of crawling insects with still less certainty.

ECOLOGICAL OPTIMA AND RELATED MATTERS

In the discussion of ecological optima and related phenomena and principles, it is possible to make much the same points either by considering the ecological relations of some process or set of processes, such as those concerned with development or respiration, or by dealing with the ecology of a recognizable ecological unit. Ecological units, whether individuals, populations or communities, can be treated as entities, since each is sufficiently integrated to react in a more or less unitary fashion. Populations and communities will be discussed at some length in Sections III and IV. We are primarily concerned just now with ecological relations of individuals.

Most environmental factors normally present a graded series of influences. The *minimum* concentration (p. 198) constitutes the ecological threshold for the ecological unit or process; below this there is an ecological zero so far as the given factor has a final limiting effect on toleration. A *maximum* concentration exists at the other extreme, with an *optimum* at some intermediate point. An absolute *pessimum* can be recognized as representing the existing condition furthest from the optimum. These values shift with different stages in the life history, with individual or population differences within the species, and with species or seral difference within the community. The whole gamut of relationships may be diagrammatically developed from below the ecological minimum through the optimum to the maximum and above, as with temperature, or the series may be open at either end. The absence of a solid substratum makes no difference to many fishes, although, at the other extreme, its presence may mark a sharply defined limit to distribution. Water can scarcely be too abundant

for many organisms; beyond some limit, a further increase in the amount present does not directly increase the ease of living for the individual, though it may increase the area available for occupancy by the population.

Minimum, maximum, optimum, and pessimum apply also to the whole environmental complex, except that the interrelations are much more complex since all forces in the effective environment must be evaluated. The general ecological optimum for the physical environment, considered as a unit, may not coincide with that for any single factor and may be far from the optimum of one or more of them. Yet the optimum may be a reality and provide the general conditions of radiant energy, moisture, medium, and substrate, in short, of the chemical and physical conditions at which life is most successful for the ecological unit under consideration. To be final, biotic factors must also be considered; these usually complicate still more an already highly complex situation. Moist land in the middle latitudes appears to provide the nearest approach we know to the ecological optimum for temperate deciduous forests and for the white man. Contrariwise, the humid tropics give the ecological optimum for tropical rain forests and for many monkeys.

We are familiar with the fact that some ecological units can live in a wide range of temperature and are, therefore, eurythermal rather than stenothermal. Similarly, we know of wide and of narrow tolerances for many phases of the environmental complex. The same concepts can be applied to the environment as a whole, and we recognize ecological units that are euryokous, with wide tolerances for many factors, and others that are stenokous. The moss-dwelling bryocoles show highly developed euroky, and coral reef communities are stenokous.

Euroky and stenoky may or may not be closely associated with the ability of an ecological unit to cross barriers, that is, with its *vagility*. Forms carried by air usually have high vagility, whether they are flying birds or passively transported spores. On the other hand, Hawaiian achatinellid snails, with special subspecies in each mountain valley, are conspicuous examples of low vagility. Local taxonomic races are likely to be evolved in species with low vagility even when the forms concerned are not closely stenokous; mere distance is a separating factor, although there may be an entire absence of other physical or biotic barriers. Euryokous ecological units with only relatively high vagility tend to be cosmopolitan, as shown by the wide distribution of many fresh-water organisms and communities. One must avoid easy generalizations, and reef corals provide an interesting test case. As an ecological community, coral reefs are tropicopolitan. They are stenokous, and their primary constituents, the reef-building corals, have low vagility. The active dissemules are tiny, ciliated, weak-swimming larvae that have only a brief interlude of activity, during which, however, they may be carried by ocean currents.

The use of reef corals to test the operation of the principles under discussion has an important handicap: the taxonomy of corals presents difficulties. Differences between described species may result from ecological rather than from hereditary influences (Hickson, 1906). Accepting the species as described, Verrill's account (1902) indicates that the corals of the West Indies spread with good uniformity from the Bahamas and Florida to Colon in Panama. They can be traced down the Lesser Antilles to Venezuela and are directly related to the corals of Brazil. Bermuda has an impoverished coral fauna derived from the Atlantic region of tropical America. Verrill found the absence of *Acropora muricata* from Bermuda especially noteworthy, since this is among the most important and abundant of West Indian forms. He suggests that the larval period of this and other missing species from Bermudian waters is too brief to allow them to make the journey of rather more than 700 miles even with the aid of the Gulf Stream. Vaughan (1912) advanced a similar suggestion to account for the scarcity of *Acropora* and the absence of whole families of corals from Hawaii. Although abundant in the other coral reefs of the world, the acroporas are entirely absent from the Pacific coast of the Americas. A related genus, *Montipora,* is found in tropical waters, except those of the Atlantic. There are few coral genera in the West Indies that do not occur in Indopacific waters, although, conversely, a number of important genera from the latter region are unknown among West Indian reefs. The fungiid corals are represented by some five genera and some forty-six species in the Indo-West-Pacific reefs. The entire family is absent from Atlantic coasts, and there is but one species (*Fungia elegans*) on the west coast of North America (Ekman, 1935). The low vagility of the coral larvae evidently limits the distribution of many forms.

Environmental conditions are seldom static. In addition to the diurnal, seasonal, and longer cycles, there are the great climatic trends (p. 80) that have made a marked impress on the distribution of plants, animals, and communities. As conditions change either in a short-run or more enduring pattern, ecological units exposed to them may meet the changed conditions by dying off. This is the probable reaction of stenokous organisms with weak vagility if the environmental change is relatively sudden and extreme. An unusually early and heavy frost or a sudden flood takes a heavy toll, as do the more unusual drastic changes, such as tidal waves, tornadoes, or volcanic eruptions. Slower changes often result in a local dying-out of many organisms and communities. The more euryokous forms may survive the changed conditions, thanks to their greater toleration, and may even increase in numbers as a result of slackened competition. Given time, even some of the less tolerant units may acclimate and survive. Frequent changes in conditions often result in the selection of various escape mechanisms: encystment, burrowing, movement into the burrows made by others, and emigration sometimes on a spectacular scale as with lemming.

There are also physiological escapes, the ecological aspects of whose evolution will be discussed in a later section (p. 705). Homoiothermy is such a partial escape that has been achieved at the individual level by birds and mammals only. Homoiothermal animals are free from many of the limitations imposed by temperature on poikilothermal forms. A few other animals have found partial freedom from temperature restrictions, often by cumbersome methods. Solitary wasps can excavate in sand that has a wasp-numbing temperature by flying in sunlight until thoroughly warmed and then digging briefly in the cold earth before another warming flight. Similarly, by appropriate alternations of digging and flying in cooler air, bembioid wasps can dig through a sandy surface that is hot enough to kill them if they are confined thereon (Chapman, 1931).

In addition to the partial freedom from the environment allowed by homiothermy or by the possession of a dry, impervious body covering and other similar devices, man and some other animals have partial control over their immediate surroundings primarily as a result of group behavior. The closed nests of termites control the immediate moisture relations of the colony, exclude air currents, and retard temperature changes. The winter clusters of honeybees allow the inner bees to escape the full impact of low temperature, and their own activity within the insulating shell of their fellows exerts a temperature control unless the outside cold becomes too great. Bees and wasps cool their nests in summer by self-fanned ventilation and by evaporation of transported water. Beavers secure a partial freedom from several limitations by building dams and lodges. Social animals tend towards securing greater control over their environment than that possessed by more solitary forms. A forest, a coral reef, and similar ecological biocoenoses are environment-controlling mechanisms in which the dominant forms meet the full impact of the habitat and so modify it that sensitive elements of the community can live in regions that they could not otherwise occupy. Freedom from physical surroundings is never complete. Even the impressive freedom achieved by man often leaves him at the mercy of common phenomena such as fogs, winds, and rainstorms, except as they can be walled out of restricted spaces.

The range of an ecological unit is a practical expression of the distribution of the habitat niches it can tolerate and of its ability to reach them. Range provides a concrete test of ecological valence and vagility. A stenokous community, like that of the hot springs, may be cosmopolitan in distribution, although the habitable niches are restricted in size. The physical factor of time plays an important role at this point, as well as the biotic factor of aggressive vigor. New habitats may open faster than they can be entered. This is strikingly illustrated by the lag between the appearance of new man-modified areas and their invasion by forms well suited to the changed conditions. In North America, the gray ground squirrel (*Citellus franklini*) is still extending its range from the western plains into the new grasslands of the recently cleared forest areas to the east of the climatic prairies. Similarly, in Western Europe, the hamster (*Cricetus cricetus*), a postglacial relic, is also actively expanding its range into the grasslands created by man. Neither species has as yet had time to reach equilibrium with its environment. Similar instances that do not involve the human biotic factor form the factual basis for the much-disputed age-and-area hypothesis of Willis (1922, 1940); the limited application of this concept should not prevent due appreciation of its validity under some conditions. Time is a factor in ecology.

Extent of a tolerable habitat, its geographic position, together with present and past relations to surrounding physiographic and biotic features, are often effective in determining occupancy. An island, whether of land surrounded by water, of forest surrounded by grassland, or of mountain meadow surrounded by peaks, or of some other sort, normally supports a different biota than that found in a similar habitat with a more extensive range. The southern part of a grassland that extends far to the north supports different animal communities as compared with the northern portion of a south-extending grassland, even though both are in the same latitude and are subject to generally similar conditions, provided only that the two are fairly well separated from each other and from other grassland communities. These are as truly physical aspects of the environment as are direction and degree of slope, type of substrate, or temperature and rainfall.

16. ECOLOGICAL RELATIONS OF SOIL*

Consideration of soil as a habitat of animals and plants brings together many of the principles presented throughout this long section, and helps serve as a transition to the discussion of biotic aspects of the environment (p. 227) and to the consideration of some phases of the biota itself (p. 225). Soil is a highly generalized name for the shallow upper layers of the land surface of the earth that by weathering of underlying rocks, intimate association with organic matter and with living organisms, has become a suitable habitat for the root systems of plants and for many burrowing or permanently indwelling animals.

Soil science is a meeting ground for physiography (and geology in general) and the physics and chemistry of an involved colloidal system. Its relations are complicated by constant ecological interactions with a complex biota that forms a normal, integral part of the soil. This soil complex in itself is a bridge between the inorganic, organic, and living worlds. It is a dynamic system and is a unit of such inherent strength that the artificial character of the dissection of nonliving nature into the separate factors is again strongly emphasized.

SOIL CYCLES

Soil pulsates with many rhythms ranging from fairly simple daily changes in superficial temperature, through the deeper, slower-moving seasonal temperature variations, to longer temperature and rainfall cycles (p. 85) and to geophysical-chemical rhythms that may extend through geological epochs. A long-run calcium cycle will illustrate the last. Calcium compounds are

* It is difficult to summarize the role of soil as an element in the environment of animals, in part because so much is known on the subject. Of books devoted to soils, we have consulted Lyon and Buckman (1927), Waksman (1932), Paul Emerson (1930), Robinson (1936), Russell, (1937), and *Soils and Men,* the 1938 yearbook of agriculture of the U. S. Department of Agriculture. We have profited particularly from reading the treatment of soil in Weaver and Clements (1929), in Newbigin (1936), and Nikiforoff's summarizing essay in the Sigma Xi Quarterly for 1942. The interested student of ecology will need to consult these and many more to secure full information on the role of soil in ecology.

weathered from underlying bedrock limestone and, either *in situ* or after transport by glacier or travelling water, or both, become a part of the soil. As such, they may pass in and out of plant and animal bodies again and again. Finally, the calcium is carried to the sea, where, after possible exposure to other biological cycles, it is fixed by marine animals, perhaps as coral reef or bottom deposit. In either case it may again be consolidated to limestone and remain as such until diastrophism elevates the shallow sea bottom and starts the calcium on another geological cycle. Carbon, nitrogen, phosphorus, and silicon, to name no more, may also exhibit these long geological soil cycles as well as shorter ones, and all those mentioned here exhibit biological phases in which the different elements are intimately bound in with living organisms.

Cycles of abundance of the more important plant-nutrient salts occur in both sea and soil. The cycles of carbon, nitrogen, phosphorus, and sulfur are primarily biochemical and show decided similarities in the hydrosphere and pedosphere (the soil) despite the physical difference between these two great storehouses of the nonliving environment. Cycles of hydrolysate elements, like iron and manganese, are less easily compared. These substances are not very soluble in water, and plants can secure them more readily from the soil than from sea water. The alkalies—sodium, potassium, rubidium, and caesium—and the alkali earths—magnesium, calcium, strontium, and barium—show highly individual differences in their behavior in the ocean as compared with that in the soil. There is a tendency toward a reciprocity of behavior in these two media, shown especially by calcium and barium in one group and by sodium and potassium in the other. The reciprocity is related to the relative solubility of the substances in water and their relative energy of adsorption, or other fixation, on soil colloids. These relations are outlined at greater length by Hutchinson (1943, p. 388).

SOIL FORMATION

Soil-forming (pedogenic) processes are initiated and continued primarily by energy from the sun and secondarily by the potential energy bound up in crystals, molecules, and atoms. This latter energy may be stored deep in the earth or may be more superficial. Such energy is liberated in the weathering of rocks, to an extent that is suggested when we know that the transformation of 1 gm. of granite to clay liberates about 120 calories.

The mechanics of the decomposition of primary rocks in nature are not fully known.

The depth of soil developed *in situ* varies from a few millimeters to several meters; it is usually not more than 3 meters deep. Its thickness reflects the climate, the topographic relief, nature of the source rocks, vegetation, the animals actively present, and the length of time the particular soil has been evolving. Soil equilibrium, when achieved, is dynamic rather than static.

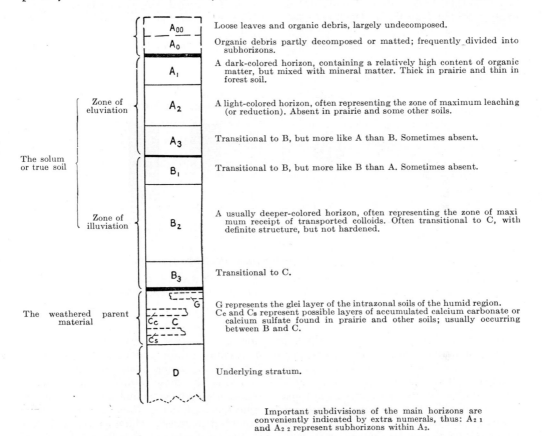

Fig. 54. Schematic arrangement and nomenclature of horizons in the soil profile. (Redrawn from the U. S. Department of Agriculture Yearbook of Agriculture, 1938.)

Even igneous rocks, if divided finely enough, can be decomposed by water that contains acid. The acid may be furnished by suspended hydrogen clays, acidic organic colloids, or dissolved carbon dioxide. Surface waters receive their acidic organic colloids from biological sources, as they usually do their carbon dioxide. It follows that one of the basic decompositions in the biosphere is now being produced, as it has been during much of geological history, by the reaction of organisms on their nonliving environment (Hutchinson, 1943).

THE SOIL PROFILE

Soil consists of several horizons, some of which are illustrated in Figures 54, 55 and 57. A part of a soil that develops characteristic physical and chemical properties is called a soil horizon; taken together in natural sequence from the surface downward, the soil horizons in a given place make a soil profile. Regardless of their distinctness, the soil horizons in a profile develop together as a more or less harmonious system. They may have come directly from the same parental material, or some may have been transported and deposited after a partial evolution elsewhere. The soil horizons in a given profile are in continual interrelations with each other; even the petrified hardpans, almost impervious to water and to animals, are a fossilized end product of soil dynamics.

The different horizons are in direct contact with their immediate neighbors and are easily influenced by them. They are affected by those at a greater distance (a) by the processes associated with growth and decay

loess may settle on water-deposited sand or gravel that in turn rests on unstratified glacial till, and this finally may have been superimposed on soil that evolved *in situ* or on bedrock. These different materials have certain "inherited" values, as contrasted with others acquired as a result of pedogenic processes.

The most concentrated human populations of the earth live on fertile deltas near the mouths of the larger rivers. The soils that support these dense populations were first and in the main air-deposited collec-

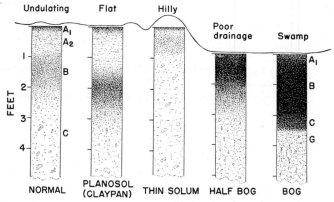

Fig. 55. Soil profiles from similar parental materials, but developed in regions of different surface relief (see legends in Figure 54). (Redrawn from Byers, Kellogg, Anderson, and Thorp.)

of penetrating root systems, (b) by the burrowing of animals, and, most significantly, (c) by water transport of dissolved or suspended matter. This last process is called eluviation, especially as concerns the transport of colloids. Eluvial horizons have lost material; illuvial ones have gained it. The water transport may be downward or sidewise, depending on the direction of water movement through the soil.

The soil profile in part reflects features of surface relief as well as parental material. As Figure 55 shows, shallow soils develop in hilly regions with accompanying excessive run-off and erosion. Flat land has little or no erosion and favors the development of leached upper soil and a dense claypan. Low-lying regions with poor drainage favor accumulations of humus.

The soil profile evolves from different layers of stratified or unstratified material mechanically superimposed one on another, as well as from underlying rock. Air-borne

tions of loess. They were then eroded away by running water and carried along until they became water-deposited deltas. Other rich soils like those of Iowa and the pampas of northern Argentina are air-deposited collections of loess formed from water-deposited materials. Much of the rich soil in the 'granaries of the world' has been transported and deposited by wind (Hobbs, 1943).

Soil has solid, aqueous, and gaseous phases. Soil solids form the skeletal framework composed of bits of rocks and of minerals and their decomposition products; they range in size down to ultramicroscopic colloidal particles. The solid phase has much to do with determining soil texture, which, in turn, is closely related to porosity, a factor that is structurally determined by the ratio of pores to soil solids. Soil fluids, both aqueous solutions and gases, flow through the interconnected pores, whether these are relatively large or capillary in size. The relation of noncapillary to capillary porosity is important, since it determines the ease of circulation of soil fluids. Widely different patterns of soil textures may present similar porosities.

Porosity and texture are the major items that determine soil consistency, a soil attribute that depends on the pattern of pore space, the mechanical units, and the composition of the material present. Soil consistency is not constant for a given soil; rather, it represents the condition at the moment and is especially influenced by moisture. Viscosity and plasticity of the soil are also closely related to its water content. Fine soil texture makes for a high degree of

sulting alteration in color, and changes in all the other physical and many chemical attributes of the soil. Heat conductivity is changed, water percolates more slowly, adsorptive powers increase, and the associated biota is altered; the whole character of the soil is made different as a result of an increased rate of hydrolysis.

THE SOIL CLIMATE

In sunlight, temperature at the soil surface varies more than in the air above or in the soil below. Daily fluctuations penetrate the upper layers, and seasonal variations go deeper. The depth penetrated depends on insolation, on atmospheric conditions, and

Table 16. Soil Temperature Gradient at Tucson, Arizona (From Sinclair, 1922)

Depth	June 21, 1915		Annual Temperature		Daily Range	Annual Range
	° Max.	° Min.	° Max.	° Min.	°	°
Air in standard shelter...	42.5	11.0	42.5	0.3	31.5	42.2
Soil 0.4 cm..........	71.5	15.0	71.5	....	56.5	
2.0 cm..........	62.1	22.0	62.5	....	40.1	
4.0 cm..........	48.1	23.5	50.2	....	24.6	
7.0 cm..........	44.1	25.2	46.1	....	18.9	
10.0 cm..........	40.1	26.3	42.2	....	13.8	
15.0 cm..........	35.6	28.1	37.0	3.0	7.5	34.0
20.0 cm..........	33.4	29.0	35.0	....	4.4	
30.0 cm..........	29.8	27.8	31.6	9.0	2.0	22.6
45.0 cm..........	27.9	27.8	29.7	....	0.1	
60.0 cm..........	26.4	26.4	20.0	15.0	0.0	14.0
100.0 cm..........	24.5	24.5	27.0	18.0	0.0	9.0
200.0 cm..........	Nearly constant temperature, about 20°					

plasticity; coarser soils are more friable. Like soil consistency, soil structure refers to its condition and is shown most diagrammatically when the soil is air-dry. Soil structure depends largely on the presence of aggregates of soil particles; these tend to disappear with increased moisture, and in the presence of sufficient water, soil structure almost vanishes.

The most obvious physical characters that differentiate the soil horizons are structure, consistency, porosity, texture, and color. These affect and are affected by chemical processes—by hydrolysis, for example. Active and continued hydrolysis increases the proportion of clay with a re-

on the local soil characteristics. As would be expected, dark exposed soils absorb heat more rapidly than do somewhat similar ones of lighter color. Decided changes are especially characteristic of the surface and upper layers of the soil in deserts. Table 16 gives an indication of the magnitude and steepness of the daily and annual temperature gradient in the upper 2 meters of arid soil. The resulting soil climate is closely related to and derived from the atmospheric climate; even so, microclimatic conditions in soil may bear only a distant relation to the ecoclimate above its surface.

Movement of moisture through the soil and its storage there are affected by the attributes of the soil and by the physical forces that make for capillary attraction, adsorption, vaporization, condensation, and evaporation, and for transpiration from plants. Capillary attraction is itself a function of pore size in the soil taken together with the surface tension of water. The pull of gravity also exerts a strong influence over water, the passage of which in quantity through the soil, as after a rain, drives out the older, modified soil atmosphere and allows an inflow of fresher air. Hence the flow of water under compulsion of gravity tends to increase the usually low oxygen content and to lower the usually high partial pressure of carbon dioxide in air-filled soil spaces, thus promoting oxidation.

In areas with poor drainage, soil may become so water-logged as to drown out many inhabitants seasonally or permanently and allow the invasion of burrowing hydrocoles, such as the crayfishes of temperate latitudes. In dryer soils, the amount of moisture that a given organism can remove, rather than the total amount present, determines whether the soil is too dry. The proportion of soil moisture that remains after a plant has taken all the water it can from the given soil and has wilted beyond recovery is called the wilting coefficient, and is expressed as the percentage of dry weight of the soil. The wilting coefficient varies widely with different plants and with different soils; it is much higher in the moisture-holding clays than in sand or sandy loam. Similar values are important for soft-bodied soil animals, but far less is known about the basic water relations of such organisms.

The subject of wilting coefficients is discussed in plant ecology (Weaver and Clements, 1929), soil science (Russell, 1937), and in plant physiology (E. C. Miller, 1938). The reasons for giving this subject more space in plant physiology than in plant ecology appear to be historical rather than logical and are perhaps related to the greater interest of the physiologists in precision measurements, a situation that happily is changing rapidly in some aspects of ecology.

Soil water exists in the following categories: (Bouyoucos, 1921):

1. Freely moving gravitational water; often ecologically unavailable or superavailable
2. Water held in soil interstices and freezing

at −1.5° C.; so-called free water; ecologically readily available.
3. Water adsorbed on soil particles and freezing when supercooled to −4°; so-called capillary adsorbed water; ecologically slightly available
4. Water of hydration of soil colloids that does not freeze; so-called bound water; ecologically unavailable
5. Water chemically combined as water of crystallization; does not freeze and is ecologically unavailable

The indicated ecological relationships are based primarily on observations on plants; soil-ingesting animals may have somewhat different relations with the more firmly held water. The amount of water in the soil is affected by such diverse factors as slope of surface, nature of organic constituents, soil texture, soil structure, and the amount and type of precipitation. Snow is often important, for it acts as a mulch and prevents surface evaporation from the soil; if it covers unfrozen ground and thaws slowly, there is little run-off. Similarly, prolonged gentle rains provide a much higher percentage of soil-penetrating moisture than does an equal amount of water that falls as torrential rain. Soils with somewhat sandy surfaces allow ready penetrations; the surface then dries and breaks the upward capillary flow. Such soils retain moisture better than do heavier ones that do not readily form a dust mulch. Water can thus be stored in the soil for months, even over winter after a good rainy season. This principle is basic for dry farming in semiarid regions.

Silty loam in good condition to support growth of many plants has about half its volume composed of pores, and the other half is solid. Of the solid substance, about 10 per cent is organic and 90 per cent inorganic material. The pore space in such a soil is approximately half occupied by air and half by water (Lyon and Buckman, 1927). The proportion of organic matter varies with different soils (see p. 224).

SOIL CHEMISTRY

In its passage through soil, subsoil, and underlying superficial layers of the earth's crust, water picks up a highly varied load of dissolved chemicals, while giving up some of those it may bring to the soil from the atmosphere. The variety and quantity of chemicals depend on the character of the substrate through which the water percolates. There is not space here to discuss many of the highly important ecological results of this pertinent relationship; a few significant cases must suffice. In regions with underlying limestone, soils are commonly rich in calcium, and this affects both soil characteristics and the plants and animals associated with such soil. The soil reaction becomes less acid; clays are made more porous; leaching of magnesium and potassium is retarded; bacterial action is increased to the benefit of both the carbon and the nitrogen content. Well-limed soils accumulate heat more readily than do heavier, unlimed clays.

in New Zealand suffer from a cobalt deficiency disease when feeding on natural vegetation from soils with less than 2 or 3 ppm. of cobalt; normal growth occurs with as little as 5 to 10 ppm.

Fluorine is found in soils from practically none up to 8 ppm. or more. Fluorine in drinking water in concentrations over 1 to 3 ppm. produces more or less unsightly, mottled human teeth, although such teeth are resistant to decay (Arnold, 1943) Selenium is present in all soils; it reaches toxic concentrations in semiarid climates in soils evolved from Cretaceous shales. Certain plants concentrate selenium; consump-

Table 17. Relation of "Hardness" of Drinking Water to Soundness of Teeth in German Children (Hesse, 1924)

Mean Degrees of Hardness of Drinking Water (on an arbitrary scale)*	Amount of Investigation		Average Number of Defective Teeth	Percentage of Defective Teeth per Set	Percentage of Wholly Sound Sets of Teeth
	Places	Children			
Under 2.0.................	15	5185	9.1	37.0	1.3
2.0–4.9.................	21	5092	8.3	33.7	3.4
5.0–9.9.................	22	3875	7.4	29.7	4.3
10.0–14.9.................	21	3214	6.9	27.4	6.5
15.0–19.9.................	18	3240	6.6	26.7	6.4
20.0–24.9.................	19	3513	5.9	23.9	9.8
25.0–29.9.................	17	2632	4.7	18.9	14.5
30.0–37.9.................	11	2004	4.2	17.1	17.9
Over 38.................	14	2833	3.8	15.4	20.2

* "German degrees of hardness," in which $1 = 10$ g CaO per m^3 of water.

A few animals (the fire salamander of Germany is one) avoid calcium soils. Contrariwise, many animals, especially many snails and mammals, flourish best on soils rich in calcium. Deer that grow new antlers annually are favorably affected, and the bones of other animals tend to be decidedly heavier in limestone soils than in regions based on igneous rock. Human teeth provide an almost diagrammatic demonstration, as shown in Table 17, where the increasing amount of calcium is indicated by the degree of "hardness" of the water.

Trace concentrations of chemicals may be as important in soils as in aquatic habitats. Cobalt, for example, is present in most soils in concentrations up to some 10 or 15 ppm. Plants do not seem to be affected by the lack of cobalt, but some animals are. Sheep

tion of these by cattle gives rise to "alkali disease," a fairly common disturbance in some of the drier sections of the western United States (McMurtrey and Robinson, 1938).

Other elements more or less important in trace concentrations in soil include boron, iodine, manganese, molybdenum, zinc, arsenic, barium, cadmium, chromium, lithium, rubidium, strontium, vanadium, and perhaps lead (Brenchley, 1943).

At the other extreme, salts may collect in the soil, especially in the surface layer, to such an extent that the soil becomes saline. Roughly speaking, all saline soils are referred to as alkali soils, regardless of their pH. They occur in basin-like areas where water accumulates in soil that is overlaid by a drying atmosphere as in arid or subarid climates. The salts include calcium carbonate, gypsum, and various sodium and potassium salts. These soils are usually neutral in reaction except when impregnated with sodium or potassium carbonate; then they become true alkali soils. The salt accumulation is usually near the surface.

Extremely saline soils such as occur near the Dead Sea or Great Salt Lake are bare of vegetation and almost free of animal life. In such places spiders eke out an existence on insects blown in from more fertile areas. In the Great Basin in western North America, the upper soil contains some 2.5 per cent of salts in salt flats, 0.8 per cent in greasewood, and 0.04 per cent in sagebrush communities (Weaver and Clements, 1929). Thus there is a gradual transition from saline to normal soils.

Irrigation, especially if not accompanied by subsurface drainage, often flushes salts to the surface, where they are left by evaporation of the soil water. Even when this does not happen to a marked extent, calcium may be replaced by sodium with a resulting dispersion of the soil particles, leading, perhaps, to a tough, rubbery soil mass with impaired tilth* and permeability. These modifications produce a decided change both for surface and in-soil biota (Scofield, 1938).

Only eight chemical elements are usually present in soil solids in amounts exceeding 1 per cent each. In their respective approximate percentages, these are: oxygen, 46; silicon, 28; aluminum, 8; iron, 5; calcium, 4; sodium, 3; potassium, 2.6; magnesium, 2 (Emerson, 1930). As with protoplasm itself and with sea salts, the bulk of the soil is composed of common chemical elements. It is the chemical constituents that make up the remaining 1.4 per cent of the soil from which we would normally expect to get those present in limiting, minimal amounts, and actually, in soil as in the sea (Chap. 14), available nitrogen and phosphorus most commonly act as limiting factors.

CONCEPT OF PRIOR PROBABILITY

We come here full upon the concept of prior probability. This matter has been outlined by Jeffreys (1939) and Hutchinson (1943, p. 342). Briefly stated, the concept

* Tilth is a general term used by soil scientists in describing the physical condition of a soil in relation to plant growth, especially crops (see Lyon and Buckman, 1927).

of prior probability, as applied to the ecology of chemical elements, states that one well versed in the physical sciences, especially in geochemistry broadly conceived, might predict with fair accuracy the probable importance of any given element in colloidal systems based on water; living protoplasm is such a system.

The bases for such predictions are largely common sense considerations such as the following:

1. Rare elements would be less likely to occur than would common ones.

2. Highly insoluble elements would be less likely to be important than would the more soluble ones.

3. Elements largely confined to the metallic core of the earth would be less likely to be present in quantity than would those concentrated near the surface.

Using such criteria, other things being equal, it may be seen that hydrogen would have a much higher prior probability than aluminum, and aluminum than a rare element like indium; such expectations are realized. The concept of prior probability, if applied on the basis of present knowledge, would lead to some mistakes. Manganese is more and strontium less significant biologically speaking, than would be indicated on this basis. Prior probability would also underrate the importance of the heavy metals. Despite these weaknesses, as Hutchinson (1943) suggests, prior probability may provide working hypotheses for investigating the biological role of elements not yet identified with biological systems.

SOIL pH

Soils are amphoteric buffers; they show properties of both bases and acids. When the buffering capacity is measured by determining the amount of alkali required to effect a given change in pH, the descending scale of buffering capacity is: raw humus > forest soil, A-horizon > loamy sand > sand (Robinson, 1936). In the presence of a sufficient concentration of organic acids, such as may be produced by decomposition of organic compounds, the soil reaction may become acid. The same result follows the absence of sufficient calcium and magnesium bases; in fact, since calcium provides about 80 per cent of the exchangeable bases in soils, a somewhat close relation frequently exists between pH and the calcium content of the soil (Robinson,

1936). From previous comments regarding some of the effects of calcium on soil structure (p. 221), it is not surprising to find that in acid soil, with reduced calcium content, the flocculation of clay may be destroyed with a consequent increase in contained water and a decrease in aeration. Such soils tend to be in poor physical condition and are heavy and relatively cold. At least a part of the relation of plants and animals to acid soil is not to the H ion concentration as such, but to accompanying

available *p*H range, but those with calcareous shells are limited to the more alkaline soils where calcium is more abundant; available granite and quartzite regions (acid soils) have few species, basaltic soils (intermediate in *p*H) have a richer fauna, and limestone areas (alkaline soils with local acid situations) have most species and individuals. Even for these snails, the correlation between soil *p*H and distribution is imperfect, since within an area of 2

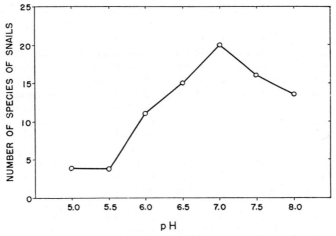

Fig. 56. Number of species of snails in Ireland in relation to soil *p*H. (Redrawn from Atkins and Lebour.)

centration as such, but to accompanying calcium deficiency and altered physical properties.

Recorded *p*H values for soils lie between 2.2 and 9.6, inclusive (Russell, 1937), values below 4.5 and above 8.5 are unusual. Volcanic ash is practically neutral. In the rainy tropics the soil tends to be acid; dry areas are frequently alkaline. The suggested generalization is unsafe, even when purely local variations are disregarded, because of differences in the original soil from one place to another. The soil profile shows differences in reaction that are at least loosely correlated with humidity. In a humid climate the upper layers of the soil tend to be more acid than those below; in arid climates the reverse tends to be true (Arrhenius, 1922). Soil reaction is often a limiting factor in the distribution of land snails. In Ireland, snails were found to be more numerous at *p*H 7 to 8 than at other H ion concentrations, with the number of species greatest at 7.0 (Fig. 56). Irish land snails with hyaline shells occur throughout the

square miles certain species may be absent from one locality, though abundant in others with a similar *p*H, chemical content, and aspect, but differing in exposure to wind (Atkins and Lebour, 1923).

The relation between earthworms and soil reaction is intimate and may be summed up briefly. In Ohio, earthworms live in soils with a *p*H range of 4.5 to 8.4, inclusive; around Chicago the range is from 5.6 to 8.3. The reaction of most soils is from 4.5 to 8.5; hence the H ion evidence indicates that earthworms live in soil—not a startling conclusion. Again, there are some species differences in *p*H toleration, and earthworms usually are most numerous in somewhat alkaline soils; the mode in Ohio is about *p*H 8; near Chicago it is somewhat less, and apparently in England the optimum lies about *p*H 7.2 (Salisbury, 1923).

PRINCIPLE OF PARTIAL EQUIVALENCE

Consideration of the role of soil in the life of plants and animals brings to light an ecological principle of some importance that may be designated as the principle of the partial equivalence of different ecological factors. A physically light soil may be equivalent to a clay soil that contains lime. Dry limestone hills in central Europe have, on their south slopes, a biota characteristic of the Mediterranean region. The warm, dry soil produces edaphically a warmer southern microclimate. Conversely, far out into the North African desert, the vegetation along water courses is affected by the coolness and moisture in the soil and keeps something of the character of a northern mid-European deciduous forest of poplars.

Sandy soils in humid climates may compensate for dryness, and in more arid climates may have the reverse effect. Aridity is introduced into many moist climates by sand dunes. On the other hand, sandy soils have a lowered wilting coefficient, and more of the soil water present is available for use. In the Great Plains of the United States, an annual precipitation of 40 cm. allows the gramma grass community (*Bouteloua oligostachya*) to grow, but not the bunch grass community (*Andropogon scoparius*). Under ordinary conditions, bunch grass requires some 50 to 60 cm. of rainfall. In regions where denser soil is replaced in part by sand, bunch grass grows even when the rainfall does not exceed 40 cm.

Deep soil retains its water supply; its temperature varies less, and even in mid-continent the climate approaches "oceanity." Contrariwise, light soils tend to produce features characteristic of a continental climate, even when they occur near the seashore.

Manure replaces not only most of the natural soil nutrients, but also, to some extent, water. A properly manured meadow, even though relatively dry, supports a vegetation resembling that of a humid unmanured grassland. Human and other animal activities may replace certain environmental factors. A cool, moist climate favors the production of mountain meadows above the timberline, an effect that can be produced by tooth, axe, or sickle under various conditions. The burrowing of many animals —ants, earthworms, or rodents—can be the equivalent of lime in producing a lighter, more porous soil.

The action of the principle of partial equivalence modifies Liebig's fundamental "law of the minimum" (p. 198), since there is always the possibility that a single factor present in minimal concentration in laboratory cultures may, in nature, be partially replaced by some other available influence or influences. The same end result may be reached by different routes, some of which may allow the by-passing of a factor present in subminimal quantites; $2 + 2 + 2 + 2$ and $0 + 1 + 2 + 5$ both give the sum 8 (Rübel, 1935), figuratively as well as literally.

HUMUS

Organic matter in soil is mainly amorphous, dark-colored material (pp. 218, 225). It develops from the decay of vegetation and of animals and the products of both. The profile of organic matter is much affected by the surface and in-soil biota. There is usually an accumulation of humus in the upper soil that is carried into deeper horizons by burrowing earthworms, rodents, and other animals, and in a different way by the root system of plants.

Decay of organic matter may continue in the soil until oxidation leaves only water and carbon dioxide. Often such destructive processes do not proceed to completion and dark, amorphous, relatively resistant humus remains. This arises (1) by anaerobic humification, as in water-logged soils, and, under extreme conditions, results in peat formation. (2) Acid humification takes place in dry or moist soils in the absence of calcium and other bases; it may occur in the presence of good aeration and yields acid peat as an end product. (3) Forest and prairie soil humification is more complicated. It is affected by moisture, as illustrated by the decreasing amount of humus deposited as forest conditions become drier. With still less moisture, when grasslands form, there is a marked increase in humus formation that reaches a peak under conditions of greater aridity than those found at the forest-grassland margin. The nature of the processes involved are not yet understood, but they are thought to be associated with summer drought and its effect on the microbiology of the soil. With still greater aridity, humus formation declines, in part because of the decreased amount of source material.

Peat formation, favored by humid climates, may result in a soil that is almost entirely composed of organic matter. Usually, even grassland soils are 85 per cent or more inorganic and only 15 per cent or less organic. The amount of organic material in English soils varies from 3 to 10 per cent. The organic content of soils is usually low in hot climates and lowest in hot, arid ones.

Humus is typically colloidal in structure and helps to retard erosion. Like lime, increased organic content tends to make heavy soils more granular and make it easier to keep them in good tilth. Humus acts to conserve mineral plant nutrients and to regulate their liberation. It modifies structure, color, consistency, moisture-holding power, and other physical and physico-

varied group spend a part of their life underground, and many of these organisms become an integral part of the soil if the latter is broadly rather than narrowly defined.

Few land animals burrow into rock. A Colorado bee, *Perdita opuntiae*, regularly excavates its own holes in sandstone (Custer, 1928). Many animals burrow among rock slides or live in the natural openings between rocks. These petrocoles include, particularly, snails, spiders and other arthropods, ants, and various small mammals. In favorable locations, lizards are likely to

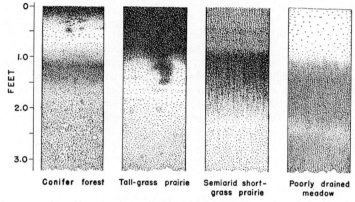

Fig. 57. Selected soil types (see legends in Figure 54 for soil horizons). (Redrawn from Nikiforoff.)

chemical properties of the soil. Like soil itself, humus is not stable, but is in constant change; the older humus decomposes and in part mineralizes. The amount present at any place and time is the algebraic sum of decomposition and formation (Nikiforoff, 1938).

BIOTA OF THE SOIL

The organic matter in the soil supports a complex microflora and fauna and often a complex biota of higher organisms, an adequate discussion of which would require a book in itself. The soil in the root zone of growing plants—the so-called rhizosphere—contains various root excretions, including vitamin-like growth-promoting factors. These permit growth of bacteria that are unable to synthesize such materials. Less specialized bacteria can live outside the rhizosphere (Knight, 1945). Myriads of bacteria, protozoans, worms (especially nematodes and earthworms), crustaceans, a long series of arachnids, insects, and many vertebrates live in the soil. An equally

be found. Flattening is characteristic of petrocole lizards, and even of a turtle that has become adapted to life in rock crevices. Animals are still more numerous under stones that lie somewhat loosely in contact with the earth.

A series of burrowing mammals dig out their dens in ground studded with rocks or make the openings to their burrows among the large roots of trees, particularly those near the forest margin. The common fox, *Vulpes fulva*, has this habit.

Animals of another ecological series dig in moist to wet soil, where the burrows extend to or below water level. These include the ant, *Formica ulkei*, mound-building termites, and numerous crayfish. Still others, like the muskrat, burrow into the banks or dykes of streams, placing the opening of the burrow under water.

Soil may act as a barrier for burrowing animals. Certain north-south distributions of well-drained soils in the Gulf Coast region appear to act as barriers to crayfish dispersal. For example, a lobe of drier soil with good drainage extending across the coastal plain to the Gulf of Mexico somewhat east of Mobile Bay apparently is a western barrier to four Florida species of *Procambarus* and an eastern barrier to three other species. Of the five species known to live on both sides of this soil barrier, three or perhaps four have a present range that extends north of the northern limits of the barrier, which indicates the probable means of transgression Hobbs (1942) describes.

It is in the open country of the grasslands, savannahs, or parklands of the tropics and temperate latitudes that the burrowing habit is most fully developed. Termites and ants may or may not build tunnelled mounds above subterranean nests. In the tropical savannahs of the world, termite mounds may assume the size of hillocks. They are made by cementing together bits of excavated material with a sticky salivary secretion supplemented by pellets of excrement. On the other hand, the nest may be entirely underground, and many intermediate stages are realized.

Reptiles of the open country are great burrowers; land turtles and many lizards and snakes have this habit. Mammals are represented underground by insectivores such as various moles (Talpidae) and particularly by rodents. Moles and pocket gophers (Geomyidae) are the only North American mammals restricted to fossorial life. Prairie dog "towns" of the western United States are duplicated by those of whistling hares in Mongolia, and by the not closely related long-tailed jumping "hare" (*Pedetes*), the Abyssinian spiny squirrel (*Xerus*), and by the octodont rodent (*Ctenomys*), of Patagonia.

The burrowing owls may dig their own burrows or may inhabit abandoned rodent holes, as do a number of insects, smaller rodents, some snakes, and a variety of other animals. Numerous birds, such as kingfishers and bank swallows, make their nests in holes dug in banks, and other birds, the petrel among them, excavate nesting holes in more level ground.

Sand of dunes or deserts is a much-burrowed substratum. Insects like the digger wasp, *Bembex*, make shallow cavities for resting or deeper burrows for their eggs. The tiger beetle larvae (*Cicindela*) have species that burrow only in the moist sand, and other diggers—the burrowing spider, *Geolycosa,* for example—restrain loose sand

by silk webbing. Larval ant lions (Myrmeleonidae) and dipterous worm lions (*Vermileo*) dig conical pits and traps. This habit is possible only on a substratum of dry sand or dust.

The burrowing methods and equipment of animals differ widely. Many forms, both insects and mammals, ranging from digger wasps to dogs, dig with their forelegs and throw the dirt backward between their posterior appendages. The mole cricket, like the mole, pocket gopher, and a whole convergent series of other animals, has strong shovel-like, well-muscled anterior digging feet and claws. In fossorial mammals the shoulder girdle and associated musculature is enlarged, and the pelvic development is relatively weak. Snakes and lizards show other convergent series. Thus, unrelated forms have a specialized digging rostrun. on the snout. Short, flat lizards, such as the "horned toad," *Phrynosoma*, and the not closely related *Phrynocephalus* produce horizontal movements with their bodies that carry them quickly below a sandy surface. Perhaps most extreme of all, some amphibians, lizards, and burrowing snakes have a smooth, cylindrical or annulate, earthworm-like form.

These burrowing animals show structural and color modifications that do not necessarily have positive adaptive value. The elongated tail of ordinary snakes appears to lack survival value among burrowers and may be replaced by a short, abruptly terminated tail, as in the blind snakes or in the shield-tailed snakes of southern India.

In many instances Gloger's rule, that animals in warm, humid regions tend to be more melanic than those in arid or cool climates, holds for burrowing forms as well as for surface dwellers. This may be seen by inspecting a series of burrowing rodents of of the same species from regions, as in California, where moist areas grade into regions of great aridity.

Another principle is illustrated by some burrowing animals of which the coral snake, *Micrurus*, is an example. This poisonous American snake is strongly banded in red, black, and yellow. The two species in the United States, from the southeast and from Arizona, do not show any association of color with humidity. The brilliant colors in burrowing snakes are not readily explain able in terms of prevailing theories concerning cryptic or warning coloration. They are understandable on the assumption that the coral snakes can develop the color patterns called for by their hereditary mechanisms without effective control by selection pressures of either their physical or biotic environment. Here mutation pressures that affect color patterns reign, little controlled by environmental checks.

Related matters will be discussed in Section V.

17. BIOTIC FACTORS IN RELATION TO INDIVIDUALS

It has been objected that the ecology of individual animals, as autecology, is logically a contradiction in terms; but the advantages of preliminary analysis appear to outweigh this consideration. It may be pointed out that a single isopod moving upstream with no other isopod within several yards has relations to its physical environment as an *individual;* this may be an extreme case, but in such instances autecology is logical and real. The difficulties involved in the dissociation from each other of the biotic factors of the environment, and in the analysis of these factors, are obviously much greater than is the case with the inorganic physicochemical conditions. The inorganic factors, indeed, merge with the biotic in the field of organic chemistry; witness our consideration of the organic constituents of soil, water, and air. The overlap of the biotic with the nonliving factors is as follows:

evolutionary origin. The subject matter of the section on "Biotic Factors in Autecology" in Chapman's *Animal Ecology*, which deals with the analysis of the biotic potential, is referred by us to the section on populations (see Chap. 22).

MICROCLIMATES AND THE PLANT MATRIX

The fundamental dichotomy of organisms into plants and animals with only a small persisting overlap in a few types of microorganisms and in the slime-molds, is of basic importance for the consideration of the modification of animal habitats by the biotic environmental factors. Animals live in a plant environment referred to by Clements and Shelford (1939) as the plant matrix, and this forms a logical, though perhaps a somewhat artificial justification for a treatment of animal ecology as distinct from plant ecology. Even the major com-

In the present section the discussion of the biotic factors in the environment must accordingly lean heavily on the organic portion of the preceding section, and in many cases we shall require little more than mention of the topics involved, which either have already been discussed, or are to be treated more extensively in connection with the organization of populations, or with the community, or with evolution.

Our account of the biotic factors in the environment of animals will deal with shelter relations, with the energy relations of the food supply, with the series of relations grouped under symbiosis (including parasitism), and with disease, in so far as these various elements can be dissociated from the community complex and from their

munities of land animals are obviously dominated by the major divisions of the plant environment into forest, grassland, desert, and tundra. The total relations of animals to aquatic plants are much modified, as compared with terrestrial communities, by the importance of the role played by plant plankters. The aquatic plant matrix in aquatic habitats resembles its terrestrial counterpart in stands of rooted vegetation or in the dense, floating mats that characterize some ponds and lakes and attain an acme of development in the oceanic reaches of Sargasso seas. The gigantic rooted algae of the *Laminaria* type may form submarine forests comparable in height with the sequoias.

Modifications of the physicochemical environment, especially the climatic factors, by the biotic elements of the environment are a major influence in setting up micro-climates, the appreciation of which is a relatively recent development[*] (the term "microclimate" has much the same meaning as the so-called plant climates of Geiger, 1927; see page 231). The microclimate is distinguished from the climate in general by the modifications of the component factors within distinguishable zonal or areal formations. These are partly inorganic, as in

tical temperature gradients, measured in two widely separated tropical forests, are illustrated by the data given in Table 18.

The dominant trees of both forests are about 120 to 130 feet high; hence the gradient extends over a considerable vertical distance. Otherwise there is no difference in principle from the temperature stratification to be found under any dense growth of plants. It is noteworthy that the air near the forest floor may have a relatively constant temperature for days in suc-

Table 18. The Vertical Temperature Gradient in the Tropical Forests of Panama and Luzon (Data from Allee, 1926, and Brown, 1919)

Location	Duration of Test	Forest Canopy	Midforest	Air near Ground
Panama............	1 week	24.5–35.3°	23.6–33.0°	25.8–27.4°
Luzon............	2 years	15.9–40.0°	17.0–31.5°	16.6–29.7°

the various inhabited depth zones in soil and broken rock, and partly biotic, as in the grass mat of a prairie or within a forest canopy. The minor niches within major biotic formations have their own distinctive microclimates, with their own seasonal cycles.

Temperature

Plant cover produces a conspicuous biotic modification of the temperature factor by the combination of shade, altered humidity, and lessened wind movement, with an obvious extreme in the forest floor in dense forest. Indeed, in wide areas of forest, the modifications induced by the leaf canopy, the humid air below it, and the root network in the soil combine to affect the macroclimate over great areas in such other major features as rainfall and soil moisture.

Temperatures in a variety of microclimatic niches may be compared with nearby open air temperatures. The steepness of the temperature gradient within the plant matrix and the sharpness of the transition from one temperature to another depend on several factors, of which the height of plant growth, the density of shade, and relative exposure to wind are important. Ver-

cession. During the week's record used in Table 18 to illustrate the forest temperature gradient in Panama, the extreme variation at 9 inches above ground level was only 1.6°; for most of the week the temperature ranged between 26° and 27° C. In the absence of nearby sun flecks, the air at the bottom of the atmosphere of such a forest tends to approach the uniformity of temperature to be found in the water near the bottom of a deep lake, or in the desert soil some distance below the surface.

Recurrent daily variations in the tree tops, in midforest, and near the ground are recorded in Figure 58, together with graphs of the daily variations in water evaporated from a continually moist filter paper in the tree tops and near ground level. The graph at the bottom of this figure shows the customary, slight daily variation in barometric pressure that characterizes the trade-wind belts of the world.

All available records show that the air in March (1924) over Gatun Lake in Panama took up approximately three times as much water as that in the forest canopy and six times as much as that near the forest floor. Sherff (1913) cites evidence and references indicating that the rate of evaporation just above dense stands of tall "sedge vegetation," cattails, and other marsh and swamp plants may run as much as 1500 per cent above that found near their base.

[*] See K. Friederichs (1930) and Uvarov, (1931).

But to come back to temperature: as in forests, the effects produced by low-growing vegetation depend on the height of the vegetation, its density, and on the amount of interference with the penetration of the sun's rays. Thus a stand of a broad-leafed plant like the snapdragon (*Antirrhinum*) has a different effect from that produced by stands of grasses.

Plants with flat, horizontal leaves permit the sun's rays to penetrate only with difficulty, although the air may fall or rise readily with changes in density. The upper surface of the vegetation practically coin-

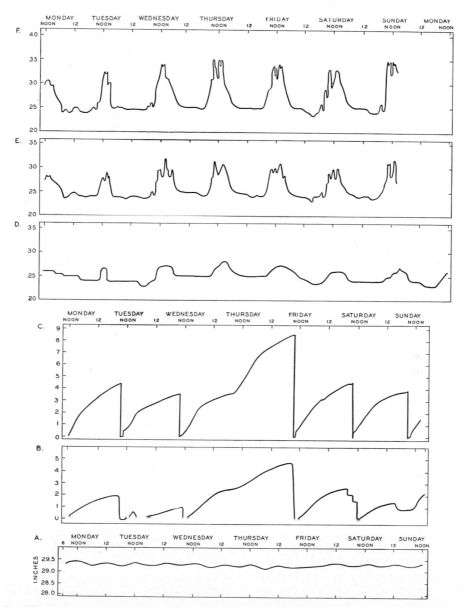

Fig. 58. Temperature record in degrees C. at three levels of the Barro Colorado Island tropical rain forest. *D*, 9 inches above the ground; *E*, 55 feet; and *F*, 86 feet. Graphs *B* and *C* represent the corresponding cycles of evaporation (in artificial units), respectively, from 4 inches above the ground and at 75 feet. Graph *A* shows the barometric pressure in inches. All are for the same week in March. (Redrawn from Allee.)

cides with the active radiating surface. When such plants cast an effective shade, the temperature at the ground level at noon on a midsummer's day is lower than that found 2 meters higher in open exposure to sun and wind. At night the minimum temperature is still located near the ground, and the air becomes steadily cooler until free equilibrium is reached well above the vegetation. The relations are shown in Figure 59.

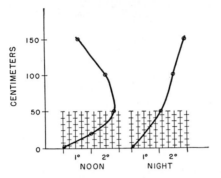

Fig. 59. Temperatures in a snapdragon flower bed in August, in Munich. Height above ground level in centimeters; higher temperatures shown at the right. (Modified from Geiger.)

The contrasting conditions found with close stands of tall grass are illustrated in Figure 60. The maximum absorption by the surface of the stalks lies below the upper surface of the vegetation. Under many conditions, radiation penetrates relatively far,

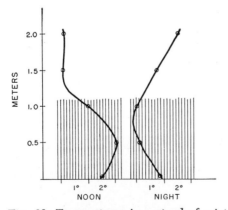

Fig. 60. Temperatures in a stand of winter rye in May, near Munich. Height above ground in meters. The temperature curve bends to the left to show lower temperature. (Modified from Geiger.)

and in short grass or grains like wheat or rye the temperature maximum is at ground level. As the grasses grow taller, the level of maximum temperature also moves upward; the temperature falls in the upper levels of grass or grain until it reaches approximate equilibrium with the air above.

At night, in a rye field, the minimum temperature is found some distance above the ground. The air is cooled about the heads, but as a result of the density of the lower stalks and leaves, the chilled air can sink only part way to the ground so that the minimum lies about midway between the upper surface of the grain (or grass) and the earth.

These examples were selected to show that, without measurements, the height at which maximum or minimum temperatures occur in a given type of vegetation can be only roughly approximated from general rules known at present. The case illustrated by night conditions among coarse vegetation (Fig. 59) shows that a plant matrix of this sort would provide no protection from frost to insects living in it, since cold air sinks through the coarse stand all the way to the ground. Dense stands of grasses would supply protection from frost near ground level. Both these types of vegetation, as well as forests, give considerable protection from direct sunshine.

The control of temperature and of other physical factors by aggregation of both poikilothermous and homoiothermous animals will be discussed under the heading of aggregation (p. 398). The still more intimate biotic modification of the temperature in symbionts (including parasites) is of evident importance.

Wind

The modification of wind by the plant matrix is as obvious as are the temperature relations. Wind velocity is reduced by even a fringe of trees. Witness the familiar "windbreak" of prairie farmsteads. The natural ribbons of timber along the streams of the North American Great Plains constitute effective natural windbreaks. Within dense forest or even in dense growth of shorter vegetation, air movement may be reduced to convection and diffusion and may approximate stagnation.

In the rain forest of Panama, wind movement reaches its highest level during the dry months of January, February, and

March. During parts of the last two months in 1924, air movement 2 meters from the forest floor on the windward side of a large tree measured approximately 1 mile per day (twenty-four hours). Another similar recording anemometer, placed in the forest canopy 75 feet overhead, recorded an average movement of 10 miles per day for the same period. Overhead, over the tops of the highest trees, the wind was blowing some 240 miles per day. The rain forest in this instance reduced air flow to approximately 0.4 per cent of the unobstructed rate (Allee, 1926); the air movement in the so-called insect climate, within a few millimeters of the ground, must have been reduced still further.

Systematic observations of wind velocities in a low cover of vegetation are scarce. Geiger (1927) summarizes evidence that the gradient of wind velocity above cultivated fields is the same as that above bare ground and can be expressed by the equation:

$$v = v_1 \cdot h^a$$

In this expression, v gives the wind velocity at h meters above the ground in meters per second; v_1 signifies the wind velocity at an elevation of 1 meter, and a is a coefficient that varies with changing conditions. In data collected on level ground near Potsdam, a had a value of approximately 0.3.

The surface of vegetation acts as does the surface of the ground when we define the former as the level at which resistance to the wind reduces its velocity so as to approach zero. In dense grass, or other types of plant cover, there is an almost complete calm at the ground level, like that of the lowest level of the tropical rain forest. In a wind-blown field of wheat only the heads are directly moved by the wind; the stalks swing mechanically after them. This effect has been measured among heather where, on a windy, sunny day at a height of 2 centimeters, the air movement was less than 0.008 meter per sec.; among the tops of the heather at 40 cm., it was 1.7 meters per sec., and above the heather at 180 cm., the air was moving at a rate of 5.1 meters per sec. The reduction to 0.15 per cent of the upper velocity is of nearly the same order of magnitude as that measured on a much larger vertical gradient in the tropical rain forest. The velocity of winds is reduced through a considerable height above the vegetation cover. Rooted plants act on the same principle in reducing the rate of flow of water currents.

The calm produced within the plant layer is a feature of great importance in the microclimate, not only as regards animals in the given habitat, but also in relation to the activities of plants themselves. The difference between the plant-produced microclimate and the general climate becomes more important as the latter becomes less favorable. Temperature and humidity are affected as well as air movement. The vegetation of arctic and of alpine regions is able to utilize solar radiation to produce a microclimate suitable for low-growing plants and for many small animals, particularly insects, as a result of the calm maintained even in such vegetation. Documentation and further discussion of these points are furnished by Geiger (1927).

Light

The modification of light by the plant matrix is obvious in the contrast between open terrain and forest floor, and is directly correlated with the temperature relations of the same situations. Light values in various biotically modified situations are as follows:

In the Panama rain forest, a corrected series of readings by Allee (1926) indicates that if a mean light intensity of 18.4 foot candles in shade on the forest floor is taken as representing an index figure of 1, the index for the forest half way between floor and canopy is 5, and for the shade in the upper forest canopy 25, at times when the index for full sunlight is over 500. Similar effects of forest cover are illustrated by Figure 61, and by changes in light intensity resulting from forest succession in the Chicago region (Orlando Park, 1931).

Similar shading is a universal result of plant cover. The grasses and needle-leafed conifers are not nearly so efficient as shade producers as are broad-leaved plants. Measurements by Ångström (1925) show that in a good stand of mixed timothy and orchard grass approximately a meter high, the intensity of incident light is scarcely affected in the upper half of the erect grass stems. Below that point the intensity falls rapidly until only a quarter of the whole penetrates to 10 cm., above the ground, and only a fifth part reaches the base of the plants. With broad-leaved plants in a similarly dense stand, apart from sun flecks, only one-five-hundredths part of incident light reaches ground level.

Water

Vegetation exerts well-known climatic effects on humidity, on precipitation, and wind (Geiger, 1927); it modifies the velocity of winds and of water currents; it causes other changes even in lakes, large rivers, and many arms of the sea. Coral reefs also have a major biological influence and

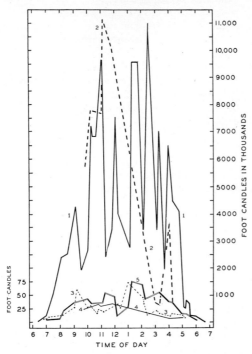

Fig. 61. The effect of forest cover on light intensity in Panama in February (Graphs 1, 3, and 5) and on an Indiana beech-maple forest in September (Graphs 2 and 4). A line connecting the lower points in Graph 1 would summarize light intensities during cloudy periods, and one connecting the upper points would do the same for periods of brightest light. (Redrawn from Allee.)

produce strong physiographic effects. At a much different level, subtle biotic conditioning is important for many plant and animal populations (p. 398). These matters will not be discussed here. There remain the ecological effects associated with the small amounts of water enclosed by pitcher plants, caught at the bases of leaf whorls, as in bromeliads, or held by moss or in tree holes, to name but a few. Such

waters constitute a series of small, distinct environmental niches. We shall comment further only on the liquid found in pitcher plants, studies of which are summarized by Lloyd (1942).

Sarracenia, the widely distributed genus of pitcher plants in eastern North America, contains bacteriologically sterile liquid in the young unopened pitchers. The open pitchers, with captured prey, contain bacteria, but the leading part in the digestion of the captured insects is taken by the protease of the pitcher liquor. In most cases this enzyme acts best in an alkaline medium, but it is also active, in some instances, when the liquid is acid. Water is absorbed by the plant from its pitchers, but not so rapidly as is the nitrogenous material formed by proteolysis of insect bodies in the liquor. Phosphates are also absorbed. A variety of digestive enzymes occur even in the fluid of closed pitchers. In *Nepenthes,* the pitcher plant of the Oriental tropics, proteinase is secreted by the pitchers, and there is little doubt that tryptic digestion occurs over and above that carried on by bacteria.

Some organisms, plants as well as animals, are able to live within the modified water; in fact, this specialized biocoenosis includes animals that live only in pitchers and are not found elsewhere. Thienemann (1932) called these later organisms nepenthebionts in contrast with (*a*) those that are occasionally found in pitchers, but usually live elsewhere, and (*b*) those that regularly pass their aquatic phase in *Nepenthes,* but otherwise live elsewhere. *Sarracenia* also has a number of closely adapted species of animal associates not known apart from the pitchers. The biocoenosis includes mosquito larvae, a small tree toad, and a small iguanid lizard (*Anolis*) that are not obligate inhabitants of this niche.

Habitat Niche

Habitat niches may have a distinctively biotic environment within the major communities of which they form a part.

Major parts of the plant formation in general may be occupied as a shelter environment by animals; the root-mat of forest or grassland, the moss-cushion of the tundra, the leaf canopy of forest, or the grass-stem tangle of the prairie have characteristic animal assemblages. Such large scale "biotic habitat niches" differ profoundly in their influence on the animal components of the community involved, according to population numbers of the dominant plants, e.g., according to purity of stand. It is the relatively pure stands of agricultural crop plants that introduce the ready transmission and increase of plant disease and of plant-eating

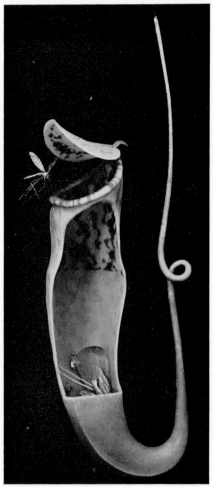

Fig. 62. The pitcher-leaf, *Nepenthes* sp., represents the most elaborate of the pitcher plants. Model of a single "pitcher," with side cutaway to show interior. (Courtesy of Chicago Natural History Museum.)

insects. The less uniform but nevertheless extensive stands of such dominants as cat-tail or white pine in nature contrast radically with the complexity of the community in which a mesophytic hardwood forest forms the matrix.

The bromeliad whorls, pitcher plants, and tree holes afford striking examples of minor niches. Others that immediately suggest themselves are the ripening individual mushroom, the insect-bored leaf or plant stem, the ant-attracting hollow stems and thorns of plants, and the rotting log with its invisible bacterial and mycelial living components. These niches lead us directly to the nest structures of animals, which on one hand constitute a biotic modification of the physical conditions of the environment, and on the other tend to reduce biotic pressure on the nest-building animal and, more especially, upon its young. Nests may be classified naturally into individual, family, and communal types. Nest construction as a response to the abiotic and biotic environment is clearly an evolutionary phenomenon (see pp. 425 and 633). Nests of all kinds, from simple to elaborate, in addition to their primary inhabitants, tend to acquire a more or less specific assemblage of animals, such as those of a meadow mouse nest, a prairie dog burrow, or, in its most elaborate development, a termite or ant nest. An extreme of the biotic environment as such is to be seen in the nest of the army ant, composed of the living workers (p. 431).

Phragmosis

An extreme type of niche adaptation is seen in the hole-closing devices of a great variety of animals, whose principle of operation was termed by Wheeler (1927, p. 30) phragmosis. It is exhibited most notably in certain ants and termites, in which the head of a soldier is modified to fit the openings in woody plants employed by the insects. The device involves a series of adjustments of behavior as well as of structure. Wheeler writes:

"These ants use the head, like the thick door of a safe, to close the entrance of the nest and keep out intruders. The nest which is excavated in hard wood, ligneous galls or the stems of rushes, has a perfectly circular entrance which is guarded by a soldier whose head exactly fits the orifice. When a worker desires to forage she strokes the soldier's abdomen with her antennae and the animated door moves back and as soon as she has passed out of the nest returns at once to its previous position. On returning she knocks with her antennae on the exposed truncated surface of the janitor's head and a similar response permits her to enter. I find this type of head in single exotic species of three other unrelated genera: *Pheidole*, *Crematogaster*, and *Epopostruma*, which, in all probability have much the same habits."

The fact that the truncated hole-closing head or abdomen is found to be independently developed in many different types of burrowing or crevice-inhabiting forms clearly indicates an evolutionary response to biotic pressure. It appears in annelids, insects, arachnids, frogs, snakes, and mammals. The development of an operculum in snails, the rolling up of various beetles and isopods, the closure of the combined openings for the head and tail in the rolled-up shield of the three-banded armadillo by the head and tail shields and the various modes of closure of the shell in turtles, form a related class of protective devices. Wheeler remarks further: "The phragmotic insect, instead of secreting or constructing a stopper, like the operculum or epiphragm of snails and the earthen or

special environments supplied by decaying plant and animal masses are greatly modified in both physical and chemical peculiarities by their organic components.

The conspicuous biotic control of the climatic environment as a whole shown by social insects (p. 425) leads out of the more casual or temporary modifications produced by aggregations of animals in more simply organized groups, like the sessile marine forms. The modifications of currents and wave action produced in the sea by mats of algae and eel grass or by masses of coral correspond to modifications of microclimates on land.

An illustrative example of biotic limiting factors is afforded by the elf owl (*Micropallas whitneyi*), which lives in arid parts of California and Arizona. It nests exclusively

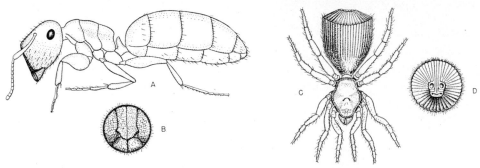

Fig. 63. Phragmosis, illustrated by an ant and a spider. The ant (*Colobopsis etiolatus*) is common in live oak galls in Texas. *A*, Soldier; *B*, head of soldier from in front. The spider (right), *Chorizops loricatus,* of tropical America, shows the truncated end of the abdomen, *C,* and a view from the rear, *D.* (After Wheeler.)

silken barricades or doors erected at the entrances of their burrows by many ants, wasps, and trap-door spiders, actually employs for the purpose a specialized portion of its own body, thus affording proof that no hard and fast line can be drawn between behavioristic activities on the one hand and physiological and morphogenic processes on the other."

The microclimate may be influenced by the animal components of the environmental matrix in various ways. The body warmth of mammals must alter the air and soil temperature in burrows or nests, which become the habitat niche of a considerable number of associated smaller forms. The closely packed herd of musk oxen, in winter, is said to be overhung by a sharply defined fog blanket produced by the rising exhalations of the animals. The important

in holes made by two woodpeckers (*Centurus uropygialis* and *Colaptes chrysoides mearnsi*) in stems of giant cactus (*Cereus giganteus*). The range of the elf owl is limited by the distribution of these two biotic elements of its environment. The woodpeckers, unlike the pigmy owl, are not limited to this one cactus for nesting; they excavate nest holes in other trees and plants. The owl is limited by absence of cactus even though woodpeckers are present, and by absence of woodpeckers even though cactus is present.

BIOTIC MODIFICATION OF THE SUBSTRATE

The concept of habitat niche as a specific type of environment includes the broader concept of habitat (as the total effective environment within which an individual or a species operates) as well as the more specific and limited elements in the larger communities, such as a type of fungus or mouse nest. Niche is not here employed in the sense of a particular role in a food chain or pyramid, though the two concepts may in some senses overlap (see p. 232).

Every modification of the inorganic substrate by a single species of plant or animal is seized upon by a series of successional forms that exploit the gains made by the first, and this successional series tends by increasingly complex interaction toward the organic balance of a climax. Modifications of the organic substrate, and herbivore exploitation of the habitat niches provided by the strata of the plant matrix (soil, humus, dead leaf cover, plant thicket, tree trunk, trunk cavity, forest roof, pp. 478–495), provide corresponding environmental opportunities to animal predators, which may be temporary invaders of these niches or may become completely adjusted to them. The series of elements of the plant matrix has an invading series of larger forms, such as nematodes, earthworms, pine mice (*Pitymys*), cottontail rabbits, squirrels, and the leaf-eating insects, with the secondary series of soil mites, moles, weasels, foxes, martens, and fishers, and the great number of insect-eating birds to prey upon the insect horde.

The basal biotic strata are characterized by vast numbers of microscopic and minute forms. These compose the edaphon of Francé (1914, p. 111). It is such complexes of vast numbers of minute plants and animals that most evidently form the "biotic environment" of larger forms. In the edaphon, as in the plankton, there are larger forms like the gophers and moles and perhaps the badger. The plankton most evidently composes a biotic environment for such forms as the whale-bone whales or the sieve-bearing appendiculates. In the marine environment the balance between inorganic food, microscopic and macroscopic plants and the pyramid of predators in plankton and nekton has reached a perfection that doubtless corresponds with the age of this environment. The much greater variety of terrestrial communities, and their inferior areal extent, may be thought to reflect their relative youth.

Among the terrestrial communities, the blanket of edaphon grades insensibly from its climax of complexity in the moist soil of forests to the minimum of bare rock or rock desert and of the polar ice fields. Chemical factors produce local pessima. The edaphon is not without direct similarity to the fresh-water plankton or even with the plankton of the sea. The concept of a biotic environmental matrix thus logically supplements that of the plant matrix, and leads directly to the concept of the environment as holocoenotic (p. 87). Indeed, the edaphon affords a biotic matrix for the plant societies that draw upon it for support and nourishment.

The edaphon is in turn greatly affected by the mechanical and chemical influences of invaders from higher strata or from other communities, such as burrowers whose excavations are retreats or nests and do not involve the active life of the burrowing animal. Though directly related to the higher plants that root in it, and thus to the whole of the upper communities, the edaphon has perhaps a continuity that may underly many of the more conspicuous successional phases of the whole complex. The independence and complexity of the edaphon reflect great evolutionary age.

BIOTIC MODIFICATION OF MEDIUM

The biotic nature of the environment of the individual animal is intimately affected by adjustment to the biochemistry of its own species and presumably also to that of all the species of its natural communal environment. How delicate the biochemical balance may be is shown by the long series of studies on conditioning of the water medium by aquatic animals in causal relation to aggregation (Allee, 1931, 1938; also p. 398). It seems evident that such conditioning of the environment must extend to the vast aquatic communities in nature and to the edaphon, whose elements are largely dependent on soil moisture.

The complexity of biochemical relations is further exemplified by the "odor environment," to which many animals have made elaborate adjustments.

Biotic Pressure

The concept of biotic pressure within the environment of an animal, made familiar by Chapman (1931) under the name biotic resistance, includes the competition of any given individual with its fellows of the same population, as well as the competition of other animals with similar food habits or with similar shelter requirements (p. 648).

Much the larger segment of biotic pressure is to be seen in the influence of predator animals. The relation of plant evolution to the animals that feed upon plants is evident in the innumerable animal-repellent devices, in the physiological and populational adaptation of the development of a surplus, and finally in animal-attracting devices when a surplus food material exists and some benefit is derived by the plant from the animal members of the association.

The relation of a food animal to its predator environment is equally evident. It may be referred to under the concept of predation pressure, and this relation results even more clearly in varied evolutionary transformations. Broad effects widespread through the animal kingdom that are summarized as responses to predation pressure are, on the passive side: protective resemblance, poisonous or otherwise repellant secretions or qualities (these often associated with conspicuous coloration), armor and defensive spines, and high reproductive potential, i.e., a safety factor in population numbers. Active forms may be adapted in the direction of fleetness, of defensive weapons actively used, of intelligence, or again in the direction of higher reproductive potential. The relation of a host to its parasites falls mainly and necessarily into the passive series, and the only effective responses lie in the development of immunity to toxins produced by the parasite, in the production of countertoxins or in the more or less incidental growth of sufficient surplus of food or food tissue for the parasite. The attempted active avoidance of parasites by host animals, familiar to farmers in the reaction of horses and cattle to their respective botflies, though apparently quite ineffective, shows how such adverse environmental factors may impress the germ plasm with inherited behavior reactions through natural selection.

Only a few plants other than bacteria and certain fungi such as the Laboulbenaceae effectively prey upon living animals (see p. 259). Among those that do, many exhibit elaborate structures in the form of traps or pitfalls, with a wide range of complexity from the simple sticky pads of the sundew to the spring mechanism of Venus' flytrap, and the simple pitcher of *Sarracenia* to the elaborate pitcher-leaf (*Nepenthes*). The abundant aquatic bladderworts (*Utricularia*) tap the supply of minute crusta-

ceans and insect larvae of fresh waters by means of their submerged traps. The tropical fungi of the genus *Cordyceps* parasitize and kill caterpillars and even adult insects (Hingston, 1932). The concept of biotic pressure appears again in subsequent chapters, in connection with population ecology, community metabolism, and evolution (pp. 349 and 648).

Impact of Food Surplus

The principle that animal populations tend to be limited by their food supply involves the corollary that populations tend to expand in the presence of available food. When the Darwinian principle of natural selection is taken into account as a transforming influence, it is evident that the development of new species and of new types is to no small extent an evolution to take advantage of unexploited food surpluses. Such an evolutionary expansion is notable in animals adapted to severe climates, like the Antarctic penguin or the Arctic polar bear, in those adapted to peculiar conditions like those in caves or in the deep sea, and in the return of land animals of various types to fresh-water or marine life. It is our thesis that *evolutionary* exploitation of food surpluses is a far-reaching principle, throwing light on many ecological problems, and especially pointing to the significance of surplus food in contemporary adjustments of animals to their environment.

It appears to be a fundamental attribute of living organisms to tend to use all available food supplies. The vast invasions of new habitats, like the conquest of the land by plants in Devonian time, the expansions of land animals in the late Paleozoic, or the reconquest of vast northern areas after the retreat of the glaciers of the Pleistocene, afford illustrations on a grand scale of the response of living matter to unused food supplies. Further illustrations may be seen in minor expansions into the smaller habitat niches which often exhibit rigidly adapted organisms (e.g., the commensals of ants and termites) and adaptation to specific levels in food chains and food pyramids (e.g., scavengers monophagous types).

The evolution of plants involves a great variety of adjustments for the utilization of inorganic food supplies wherever these come in contact with oxygen, carbon dioxide, and water, with, of course, secondary adjustment to the use of food from organic sources. We may point to the ubiquity of microscopic plants and their evolution of resistant stages whereby their dispersal is accomplished. Exploitation of food supplies seems to be the common factor in such diverse phenomena as the adaptations of the plants of rock surfaces, of desert plants, of epiphytes and parasites, and of the plants of rich soils or especially enriched areas of the sea.

There is a striking and fundamental correlation of density of marine life with continued fertilization from a specific source, like the influx of plant food at a river mouth, or like the tapping of deep water supplies of dissolved substances by an upwelling current. The fertilization of the sea bottom with a rain of dead organisms produced by the interaction of the radically different Labrador Current and the Gulf Stream may be said to produce the cod and halibut fisheries of the Grand Banks.

The density of plant populations on land depends largely on available food (using the term *food* in a broad sense), availability being dependent on water supply. The rich plant cover of the tropical forests reflects the maximum use of the available plant food, and with water in excess, other factors than the food supply may limit its development. Aside from such considerations (see p. 562), the evolutionary diversity of the tropical forest may be thought of in terms of increased utilization of food supplies, on the basic principle of differences in food requirements from the soil as well as in terms of occupation of all possible niches, as by lianas, epiphytes, and parasites.

Succession in temperate climates, in the change from simple transitory communities to complex and stable ones, while based in part on the toxicity of the wastes of the earlier types of the series, reflects improved utilization of food by specific evolutions of plants toward improved use of available food and by the filling of all available niches in which a food surplus develops.

Finally, it may be pointed out that bacteria in general and anaerobic bacteria in particular tap otherwise wholly unavailable food supplies.

In the whole evolutionary development of the plant matrix, the production of an excess of material by the individual plant may be regarded as a factor of safety for the individual. It has been pointed out that trees normally bear something like 50 per cent more leaves than are necessary for growth and survival under normal or average conditions (Clark, 1927). This excess of foliage becomes of vital importance to the plant under the extreme conditions which may arise at longer intervals in the climatic or biotic cycles to which the individual plant is exposed during its life. The excess of foliage, and of other plant substance, is in turn the basic food supply of many animals, and the excess itself may be thought to be further increased by the response of plants to the benefits received from the wastes produced by their animal "enemies" (p. 496).

A still further surplus of plant food is supplied by the vast excess production of spores, pollen, seeds, and of mature individuals necessary for the survival of the *species*. Progressive evolution seems to be in general toward the reduction of this excess in plants as in animals, but there can be no question that plant species face increasing hazards to their survival with reduction of their populations below an optimum level, and that the excess of numbers is in part a factor of safety for the species. The total surplus of food is thus the excess of the surplus of the individual multiplied by the total number of individuals.

The surplus of plant food is reflected in the quite similar derived surplus of animal food. Excess populations of animals further elaborate the various food chains, food webs, and food pyramids. The development of surplus animal food goes hand in hand with the evolution of predaceous controls, which depend on surplus populations, and with the invasion of the niches supplied by the individual animal to parasites, which depend on the individual's surplus of body tissues. Since evolutionary success in the direction of utilization of food supply tends to produce an excess of individuals beyond the capacity of the base of the food pyramid (either plant or animal) to support, predaceous controls become beneficial to the oversuccessful herbivore or intermediate prey, and these benefits afford the foundation for the development of complexity in the community. Evolutionary success of animals in the direction of reduced rates of reproduction can apply only to the final elements of a food pyramid. In a food chain, if the final members (like the guano birds of the Humboldt Current) have few enemies and a vast food supply, the numbers of individuals of the successful species simply breed up to the available food, and the normal death rate returns an appreciable amount of food for plants to the initial elements of the chain. In either food chain or food pyramid, there is still a population level below which the survival of the species is in hazard from external accident or from the longer cycles of the environment, so that in the great excess of normal years there is a food surplus. The correlation of the snowshoe-rabbit and Canada lynx cycles of boreal America (with the lag of a year or more in the lynx cycle) affords an illustration of the influence of surplus animal food. The now familiar fate of the deer in the Kaibab Forest of the north rim of the Grand Canyon in Arizona illustrates the role of predator control in relation to surplus (see p. 706). This whole matter is discussed further in relation to community metabolism and evolution (pp. 370 and 509).

There are notable illustrations of the exploitation of food surplus at the nonevolutionary level. The density of human populations may be traced to food supplies at various levels of society. The riverbank villagers of the Sepik River in New Guinea, dependent on the sago palm (of the lowland swamp area) for a basic starch, supplemented by fish from the river, exhibit a narrow ribbon of dense population following the river and its branches. The density of animal populations of single species is correlated with the surplus of a basic food supply. For herbivores this will be diatoms, grass, browse, or tree-top foliage. For carnivores (in a broad sense) it may be plankton (e.g., as the food environment of baleen whales), rodents, or artiodactyls. It is evident that the distribution of a given species of fish may be analyzed in terms of its centers of population density as well as in its total range, and that such centers are as vitally important to the success of the species as to the fisheries that develop in them (see page 602 for the genetic-evolutionary aspect of this phenomenon).

The modern pattern of bird migration is thought to have originated largely as a response to the opening up of the north temperate zone with the retreat of the Pleistocene glaciers. With the establishment of ice-free summers, with seasonal abundance of food, vernal expansion of the pre-existent types of birds into the northern areas was possible, but could develop only in correlation with autumnal retreat to the south. The various physiological mechanisms by which bird migration is controlled are to be thought of as regulatory rather than as causal. More ancient Tertiary patterns of bird migration may be discerned, for example, in the relation of the North American bird fauna to that of South America (Mayr, 1946). It is evident that the dispersal of birds has been to some degree correlated with the capacity for migration.

In connection with the impact of the food surplus as the food environment of the individual animal, we may point to some of the large-scale evolutionary implications as they have affected the biotic environment. The variety of structural types in the sea seems to be correlated with maximum utilization of food supplies, and in an obscure way the variety of marine phyla may be compared with the variety of species in the tropical forest, which also appears to correspond to the seizure by specifically adapted forms of every possible food supply. In the sea adaptations to the principal types of habitat—sand beach, rock beach, open water, deep sea—evidently correlate with the presence of food otherwise unutilized. Evolution to exploit developing surpluses leads to secondary food specializations for taking special types of food, such as those of the plankton-feeding whales, herrings, and appendiculates.

The evolution of land animals into the major habitats accomplishes the utilization of the otherwise untapped food supplies of the riparian, terrestrial, subterranean, arboreal, and aerial environments. Invasion of more special or peculiar habitats, like the alpine zone of mountains, the desert, the polar regions, or caves, may likewise be thought of in terms of exploitation of a pre-existing surplus, or at least of a surplus developing step by step with its exploitation. The invasion of fresh-water and marine habitats by land animals reflects their attraction to food supplies, as is sufficiently evident in such partially adapted riparian forms as seals and sea lions.

The more extreme specializations of animals to specific foods could scarcely become possible without the marginal excess of living matter. Uniform *kinds* of food, like grass, leaves, leaf-tissue (tapped by leaf miners), nectar, insects of various size levels, herbivorous mammals at various size levels, appear to have afforded the opportunities for adaptational evolution; further steps in the same direction are to be seen in the development of the still more specific monophagy frequent in the insect-plant and parasite-host relation (see p. 614).

The preservation of primitive types of animals may be accomplished by the extremes of food specialization made possible by the very fact that they have had available long periods of time for their evolution. This is especially clear when their adaptations are correlated with an otherwise incompletely tapped food supply, as with sloths and anteaters.

Caenogenesis is partly a response to a food supply available to the separately evolving stage, as is evident in specific food adaptations of such stages. Adaptive radiation into specific environments and for specific foods is as evident among larval insects or tadpoles as in adult animals.

Symbiosis, which we define to include commensalism, mutualism, and parasitism (see p. 243), is a further evolutionary adjustment to more complete utilization of food surplus. Social habits and social organization likewise involve efficient exploitation of food supplies, whether of great variety, as by man, or of extreme uniformity, as by termites.

As was remarked with reference to the sea and the forest, the concept of an organized interlocking community of plants and animals involves the idea of maximum continued utilization of the food supplies available in the given environment. Development of a complex food pyramid or of a food chain depends on a basic food supply and on the preservation of continuity in that food supply by means of controls on the predator superstructure. The evolution of communities in the direction of increasing complexity appears to be a direct correlation with fuller utilization of existent and developing food supplies (Schmidt, 1945).

Basic Nutrient Cycles

A number of chemical cycles exist in which inorganic material becomes a part of living protoplasm and is later returned to the nonliving, perhaps even to the inorganic, world. The return follows release as a result of metabolic processes or decay and occurs either directly or, after transfer from organism to organism, as in a food chain. The water cycle, which in part runs such a course, has been given in some detail (p. 177), and important aspects of other cycles, particularly of the nitrogen cycle, will also be discussed (p. 497). It may be repeated that the nitrogen of the air is largely unavailable either to plants or to animals. A small portion becomes usable when combined under the influence of electric discharges to form ammonia, nitrites, or nitrates (p. 199). Fixation of nitrogen also occurs under the influence of nitrifying bacteria (p. 711); those symbiotically associated with the root nodules or tubercles of clovers and of legumes in general form a particularly intimate part of the biotic environment. Animals are mainly dependent on plants for their nitrogen, although some protozoa lacking chlorophyll can build their own protein from nitrogenous salts without ingesting plant proteins (Heilbrunn, 1943).

The carbon cycle is based primarily on the processes concerned with the photosynthesis of carbohydrates by chlorophyll and the transformations of primary sugars into related substances by plants and by animals. Carbon dioxide is taken from the surrounding air or water, used in photosynthesis, and returned sooner or later to the external environment.

Chemical cycles also include those dealing with oxygen, phosphorus, and sulfur, as well as somewhat similar ones of such substances as iron, calcium, sodium, potassium, iodine, and silicon. In fact, all chemical elements composing the bodies of plants or animals come on last analysis from the inorganic environment. Many become incorporated in animals only or mainly through the mediation of plants. With some substances the cycle may be short and frequently repeated; others are bound for longer periods, perhaps, as with coal, for geological ages (cf. Rogers, 1938).

Impact of Kinds of Food*

The biotic food environment of the individual animal has been of profound evolutionary influence in the direction of specialization, with the result that an animal with a high degree of specialization is rigidly

* Franz Doflein (1914), especially Chapter 2, pages 21 to 326, serves as a general reference.

limited in geographic range and in ecological habitat by its food relations. It may be added that food specialization as a direction of evolution may be quite independent of progressive evolution, in which lack of such specialization may be one of the conditions of progress. Extreme specialization may be thought of as essentially irreversible (see p. 679).

As a preliminary comment on the food environment, it must be stated that we reject the Pütter hypothesis that an important part of the energy-yielding food of aquatic animals consists of dissolved organic materials. We are still uncertain of the extent to which animals make use of particles in colloidal suspension. By way of orientation it may be pointed out further that there is a radical and far-reaching difference between the plant base of the food pyramid in the sea and that on land. In the marine habitat the basic food supply consists of the microscopic plants of the lighted zone of open water, composing the major proportion of the nannoplankton; while for land animals the basic plant food consists of the macroscopic vascular plants. Even the vast beds of the giant kelp plants, that are sometimes as tall as the sequoias, form an insignificant proportion of the total vegetation of the sea. Thus the largest marine organisms are carnivorous, dependent upon plants through a chain of smaller animals, as is the case even with the gigantic plankton-feeding baleen whales. The largest land animals, in contrast, are herbivores, directly dependent

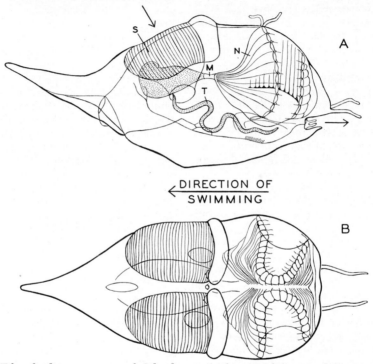

DIRECTION OF SWIMMING

Fig. 64. Filter-feeding apparatus of *Oikopleura*. *A,* The animal (in stipple) in its gelatinous "house," viewed from the side: *S,* sieve; *M,* mouth; *N,* net filaments; *T,* tail. *B,* Cast of the house, viewed from above. The discovery of the marine nannoplankton was largely the result of the examination of the food of *Oikopleura*. (After Hesse and Doflein.)

on vegetation composed of plants of considerable size. The animals of fresh waters include so large an element of secondarily or temporarily aquatic forms that they do not fall readily into the marine-terrestrial dichotomy (Sverdrup, Johnson, and Fleming, 1942).

The marine phytoplankton (mostly as the minute nannoplankton) is fed upon directly by a great number of small but still macroscopic marine animals, among which copepods (*Calanus* spp., for example) and euphausids (*Euphausia pellucida*) are especially noteworthy for their vast numbers, while the appendiculates (e.g., *Oikopleura*) are notable for the extreme elaboration of their filter apparatus. The net-plankton forms the immediate food of some of the largest of the whales, or it may be fed upon by fishes of various size grades, whose enormous schools in turn provide food for larger fishes, or for birds and mammals. Filter feeding leads to extreme structural specialization. It should be noted that among filter feeders the distinction between herbivorous and carnivorous habits is not a sharp one and that availability becomes the only criterion governing the food supply. Specialization in the direction of monophagy, evident among land animals, is essentially excluded by the conditions of plankton feeding.

In general, land animals fall rather sharply into herbivores and carnivores, and omnivorous types are the exception rather than the rule. In some groups, however, like the opossum, there may be no apparent food preference, while in others, like the pig, primarily herbivorous habits readily give way if animal food is available. The categories are in any case not absolute, for extremely well-adapted herbivores may be driven to animal food by scarcity (as the reindeer may take to eating fish), while carnivores, in the absence of suitable prey, may eat a considerable proportion of plant material. The specialization of feeding apparatus in these two principal directions is familiar in the grinding teeth of artiodactyls and the flesh-cutting dentition of carnivores. The more extreme limitation to plant or animal food alone arises in connection with specialization for feeding upon specific parts or types of plants or animals (p. 701).

Such further specialization for more specific types of food leads to some of the most remarkable and extreme adaptations and transformations of animals. Thus, living woody plants supply food to insects that feed exclusively upon sap, such as aphids and scale insects; other insects eat the wood, either of the main stem or of the twigs, and may depend on special layers such as the bark, cambium, or the older wood; still others feed exclusively on leaves, and these are joined by a wide variety of mammals and a few reptiles; minute insects, the leaf miners, live between the surface layers of the leaf, and thus feed only on the softer part of the leaf tissue; hosts of insects, birds, and mammals depend exclu-

sively or primarily on the seeds or fruits; still others are flower eaters, or are minutely specialized for feeding on pollen or nectar; and the subterranean roots may furnish food to burrowing animals.* These adaptations are reflected in the systematic categories of insects.

Nectar feeding by insects, birds, and bats, and occasional other mammals (especially the marsupial *Tarsipes*), is enormously developed in the insect group, hand in hand with the evolutionary expansion of nectar production by plants in correlation with the benefits of cross fertilization. Other glandular secretions of plants are fed upon by insects and may commonly be produced by hypertrophied structures when some benefit to the plant accrues (see p. 248). The browse (twigs and leaves taken together) constitutes a special type of plant food for the larger mammalian herbivores and may be a sufficiently exclusive food to exhibit correlation of the food-taking structures, as in elephants, or in the African black rhinoceros, whose finger-like labial appendage contrasts sharply with the square lips of the grass-eating white rhinoceros.

Herbaceous plants, except for the absence of wood and bark borers and for the greater number of root eaters, exhibit the same series of specialized animal dependents as do trees and shrubs. Ferns and their allies appear to be little preyed upon. Fungi, on the other hand, attract a great variety of animals, including a number primarily dependent upon them. Bacteria as food for land animals are important only in the edaphon, and the only specialists dependent upon them are presumably the most minute of single-celled animals.

A further grade of food specialization appears in the limitation of animals already confined to a single type of plant food to a restricted taxonomic group of plants (e.g., a species, genus, or family). The distributional conditions set by the biotic environment for such monophagous forms are radically different from those set by the plant environment for polyphagous or omnivorous creatures.

The great group of scavengers that depend upon the products of plant decay may be mentioned in this connection, though their food environment, while organic, is essentially nonliving. Decay, however, is so

* The extremes of insect food specialization are discussed by Brues (1946).

essentially a bacterial process that the distinction is perhaps not a valid one. The succession of animal populations, in which insects appear to predominate, that reduces a fallen tree trunk from living tissue to soil is well set forth by Savely (1939). The transition from the freshly fallen leaves to forest soil is accomplished by a quite different series of populations, in which earthworms may be dominant. The decay of dead vegetation in grassland seems to be overshadowed, so far as transition to soil is concerned, by its transformation in the metabolism of larger herbivores, especially mammals, many of which may subsist as well for long periods on dry grass (hay) as on fresh vegetation.

Among air-breathing animals something corresponding to filter-feeding in the sea may be seen in the smaller bats and the nighthawks and swifts, which depend on aerial insects for food. Though their cruising of the air is by no means entirely at random, such forms cannot be specialists beyond the requirement of a specific size-range of their food and its presence in the air. The webs of spiders are likewise in some respects a sieve-feeding device, straining insect food from the air as the net of *Oikopleura* strains nannoplankton from sea water.

Specialization in relation to the nature of animal food does not ordinarily extend to special parts of the animal structures being eaten. Exceptions to this rule are found among certain parasites and blood-sucking animals. Bloodsuckers include vampire bats, leaches, numerous adult insects, and mites and ticks; within this series the special adaptations for securing blood and finding suitable prey are extremely diverse.

The organization of any animal community exhibits much specialization to size-ranges of food, as reflected by the common terms "insectivore" and "carnivore." In this relation the smaller members are the more strictly limited, and the effects on evolution are produced by a preponderance of a special type of food rather than by exclusive food relations. Foxes prey proverbially upon chickens, but do not scorn meadow-mice or even grasshoppers, and the prey of bears ranges from large herbivores to ants. Powers of rapid locomotion in carnivores, with structural mechanisms modified in the same direction as are those of their principal prey, do not produce an exclusive food relation

(cheetah and antelope, red wolf and deer). No more does the correlation of cryptic coloration in the predator with that of the animals preyed upon imply any great degree of food specialization.

Animal food can lead to further specialization, beyond the limitations set by size-grades, only when certain herbivores exist in such numbers as to constitute a constantly available prey, and strict monophagy develops only among insect predators and parasitoids, and among parasites in general (see pp. 258 and 613). Some of the most conspicuous food specializations of air-breathing animals are found in those that return to the sea or to fresh waters for their food (mammals, birds, insects, and so on). Specialization to taxonomic groups among predaceous animals seems to be mainly in correlation with availability. Such a relation may be thought of in the bison-wolf relation of the Great Plains in the days of the great bison herds, or in the feeding of birds on a seasonally abundant species of insect. The possibility of the final step toward monophagy appears to be constantly open through food specialization that reflects originally merely availability.

The scavengers that make use of animal wastes and decaying animal bodies exhibit numerous and remarkable specializations to specific food materials and thus to specific food environments. These food environments are at least as much biotic as are those provided by the decay of plant materials. Familiar examples are seen in the life histories of the dung beetles and in the elaborate three-year succession from vultures and flesh flies to tenebrionid beetles in a sizable animal cadaver (Doflein, 1914, pp. 249–257). In this succession specific adaptation to the stages of decay and to special chemicals—i.e., lipoids, proteins, tendinous tissue, and keratinoids—chemical adaptations for finding the food, and modifications of life history to make use of it and for dispersal, are evident. These specializations exhibit the general trend toward fractionation in adaptive evolution. The only evident explanation for such a trend lies in the more effective exploitation of food materials, the tapping of potential surpluses as they develop. Similarly elaborate specialization for the utilization of animal wastes and remains may be seen in the community of the sea beach, in fresh-water lakes and rivers, and in the animal life of the deep sea. The abyssal community, with no plants other than bacteria, occupies a domain of vastly greater volume than that of the parent community in the lighted zone of the sea (Sverdrup, Johnson, and Fleming, 1942). The bizarre forms of deep sea creatures reflect the necessities of their food-getting devices as well as their difficulties of locomotion and of the finding of individuals of one sex by those of the other, and are perhaps correlated also with absence of predation pressure such as we know in the denser populations of the lighted zone.

SYMBIOSIS

Within the loose bonds of the animal and plant community and among the more sharply defined associations of the component biocoenoses there develop the remarkable cooperative pairings of specific plant with plant, plant with animal, and animal with animal commonly termed symbiosis. Symbiosis is often defined to include only mutually beneficial relations of such partners. The concept of symbiosis is here broadened in accordance with its literal meaning to include the phenomena of commensalism, in which the benefit relation is one-sided, without injury to the host, and parasitism, in which the relation is typically detrimental to the host (Steinhaus, 1946). This broad meaning of symbiosis is the original one of De Bary (1879), and the use of the term in this sense has the support of the American Society of Parasitologists. The term "mutualism" in our usage corresponds exactly to the more limited concept of symbiosis that has been widely current. Quite evidently such relations pertain to the biotic environment at an individual level. Antibiosis is the term applied to the opposite relationship, of mutual antagonism (ZoBell, 1946), familiar, for example, in the Protista.

COMMENSALISM

Van Beneden (1876, p. 1) defined a commensal organism as a messmate that "requires from his neighbor a simple place on board his vessel, and does not partake of his provisions. The messmate does not live at the expense of his host; all he desires is a home or his friend's superfluities." The relation in commensalism is one of individual to individual, and the relation is essentially unequal, active on the part of the commensal partner and passive on the part of the host.

So defined, the concept of commensalism already differs considerably from the simplest implications of being messmates that is, from those collections of diverse sorts of animals about a common food supply. This is a common, well-known type of aggregation (see Aggregation, p. 393). In present usage, commensalism has been expanded to include all those ecological unions in which, although both parties do not benefit, as in mutualism, neither one is harmed, as in parasitism, by the association. Space, substrate, shelter, and transport relations may be involved, as well as food.

The attachment of one animal to another for shelter, support, locomotion, or a food supply (exclusive of feeding on the living tissues of the host) may be either facultative or obligate. "Obligate" commensalism refers on the one hand to the essentiality of the relation for the guest, and on the other to relations with a taxonomically defined special host. In either facultative or obligate commensalism, one of the animals (or plants) is the host, and the animal guest may be expected to be somewhat or considerably smaller. The four main ties of shelter, support, locomotion, and food supply that relate guest to host may be single or variously combined, and loose or specific. Dispersal may obviously be added to this list, as an extension of the usefulness to the guest of the locomotion of the host. The relation may be without taxonomic specialization, as in algae of the same species growing on a turtle shell and on driftwood, or specialization may have developed, as is illustrated by algae found only on turtle shells (*Rhizoclonium* on *Chrysemys*); the extreme is reached in the special barnacles that live only on other barnacles that live only on whales.

A commensal may be quite unattached to its host, living in close and direct association with it; it may live upon the host's body or be sessile upon it; or it may live actually within the body of the host, in the respiratory or alimentary tract or in any other cavity of the body open to the exterior (see p. 254). Many of the organisms living in the water held in pitcher plants are in commensal relations with their host (p. 232)

The size relations of host and guest depend somewhat on whether the host is sessile or mobile, colonial or individual. It may be difficult to distinguish commensalism at its nonspecific level from many of the non-predaceous relations within a biocoenosis. Only when the host-guest relation is recognizably specific, i.e., a particular species (or group) as guest only of a particular species (or group) as host, does commensalism become easily definable. In the support relation, almost any sessile animal or plant with a hard shell or exterior may serve as base for encrusting or other sessile animals. Coral reefs, for example, afford support for a vast assemblage of associated plants and animals, only a part of which is specifically limited to the coral reef community, while still fewer are demonstrably limited to coral itself. Nevertheless, the support relation of the coral in the community is as evident as is the shelter relation of its branched portions (cf. the coral reef, p. 456). In this case the host animal proper is smaller than many of its supported or sheltered guests. The opposite size relation is usual, as exemplified by the inhabitants of worm tubes or the nests of various animals (meadow mouse nests), in the shelter relation. In the support relation the supported guest likewise is usually the smaller, as in the encrusting bryozoa and hydroids of sargassum.

When the supporting animal is active, there is evident benefit to the passive guest in the avoidance of stagnation in aquatic habitats. The growth of algae on the backs of the naiads of aquatic insects or on turtles affords an example of facultative commensalism.

Representatives of many different phyla grow as epicoles (epibionts) on the shells or the skin of others without becoming noticeably parasitic and without contributing anything to the well-being of the animals on which they perch. A basically similar, though more intimate, relationship exists when one organism lives within the body of another without otherwise becoming a parasite.

The shelter relation at the facultative level is presumably exemplified by the hosts of micro-organisms that live most of their lives within the intestinal tracts of animals, feeding upon the digesting food or refuse, and necessarily dispersed from animal to animal by an independent stage of the life cycle. Many of these bacteria and protozoans, however, become either obligate commensals or become in-

volved in the process of digestion so as to enter the category of mutualists (p. 247). A whole microcommunity of plants and animals lives in the canal system of sponges, and the intestinal fauna and flora of ruminants and other mammals are largely non-parasitic. The *Pinnotheres,* that lives in the mantle cavity of certain sea mussels, is mainly a commensal; the crab steals food collected by the host mollusk, but does little if any other known injury.

Specialization of the commensal relation apparently begins at the behavioral level —for example, in such beetles as are known primarily or exclusively from the nests of meadow mice, or in the commensal insects, birds, and mammals that have attached themselves to the society of man. These exhibit an often completely obligate relation, without distinctive structural adaptation. Commensal nest beetles are well exemplified by *Leptinus testaceus* (Park, 1929).

Structural specialization is notable in the development of means of attachment to the host by the guest, as of branchiobdellids on crayfishes, or of the remoras on sharks and other large marine animals. The differentiation of species of barnacles found only on whales and pelagic sea turtles suggests that there must be some structural modification of these forms to limit them to a living substrate. Such extremely specialized forms may, however, be obligate only in the broadest sense; i.e., the same species of remora may attach to various species of sharks. A more strictly obligate relation, however, may readily develop in such forms, as is illustrated by the small remora, *Pheirichthys lineatus,* that attaches to barracudas and spear fishes instead of to sharks. Similar direct specialization of commensals is seen in coral-inhabiting gastropods and in the flattened inhabitants of worm tubes.

The commensal relation grades without sharp distinction into external parasitism, since mammals and birds both afford a food supply of epidermal scurf to forms little different from ectoparasites. Even internal parasitism, if the parasitic inhabitants of the alimentary tract of various animals be regarded as "internal," may have one of its origins in the commensal inhabitants that gain access to this tube from either the mouth or anal opening. Gill and lung cavities may have commensal inhabitants as well as parasites. The hydrachnids found on the gills of fresh-water bivalves do not seem to feed upon the tissues of their host; at most they derive nourishment from the mucous secretions (Welsh, 1930).

The transition to obligate commensalism from facultative is illustrated in sessile animals that depend for support on the encrustation of solid or hard objects and avoid soft-bodied animals. This is notably evident in the barnacles, which attach at the close of their free-living larval stage primarily to nonliving solid objects, as well as to corals, crustacean shells, and the like, and not to other types of marine creatures, such as sea anemones, echinoderms, or fishes. Whatever the barrier to the attaching barnacle larva may be, it has been overcome by the evolution of special types adjusted to special hosts, like *Coronula* on whales, *Chelonobia* on sea turtles, and *Alepas* on sharks and on sea snakes. The step from such obligate (perhaps we might write "doubly obligate") commensalism to parasitism is evidently a short one. It is illustrated by the isopods that live as external commensals on fishes; *Ichthyoxenus*, for example, calls forth a gall-like modification of the belly of the host, and *Cymothoa praegustator* lives in the mouth of the sardine-like menhaden (*Brevoortia tyrannus*), stealing a little food as it passes along. Other isopods (Jordan, 1905; Smith, 1909) associated with fishes may be attached to their hosts for only part of their lives, and even perhaps discontinuously.

Commensalism in which the relation between host and guest is limited to the transport of the guest by its larger host has been distinguished as phoresy (Fr. *phoresie*). It appears as a relatively widespread phenomenon. Small diptera are transported by dung beetles to suitable breeding sites for both, larvae and adults of certain beetles are transported to the nest of the host, or from nest to nest, and pseudoscorpions and mites are similarly transported by various insects. Ants appear to be especially given to the role of "porteur." The analogy to the impressment of mammals as agents of dispersal by plants is evident, though only remotely a commensal relation.

Notable obligate commensalism is that of the small fishes attendant upon siphonophores and sea anemones. Such fishes evidently derive shelter and protection from their hosts and may obtain part of their food from the food of the hosts as well. In these, as in the holothurian-inhabiting *Fierasfer*, the relation is extremely intimate, but no benefit to the host is discernible. The little pomacentrid fish, *Amphiprion percula*, with an especially brilliant coloration, is so regular an associate of the large sea anemone *Discosoma* of the East Indian coral reef that some mutual advantage may be suspected, and certainly far-reaching physio-psychological adjustment has been attained by the fish, since it swims freely among the tentacles that paralyze other fishes, and even enters and re-emerges from the stomach cavity of its fish-eating host. The relation between the fishes of the genus *Nomeus* and *Physalia* is similar, but there is some possibility that *Nomeus* feeds on the tentacles and zooids of its host (Kato, 1933).

MUTUALISM

The often obscure relations of host and uninvited guest crystallize into the more sharply defined mutually beneficial relations of partner with partner summarized under the concept of *mutualism* ("symbiosis" of many authors). The origin and development of mutualistic relations is of such great interest in connection with evolution that this subject will receive fuller treatment in Chapter 35, page 710. In a sense, animals as a whole are broadly symbiotic in their relations with the plant kingdom. To some extent herbivorous animals are the commensal guests of plants, feeding on their surplus without doing them vital harm;[*] the reciprocal metabolic relations of the two kingdoms may be thought of as mutualistic; when the animal partner gets out of hand (so to speak), as in overgrazed lands, it may correspond at this level of discussion to a parasite.

At the individual level, the relation of metabolism benefit exchange between particular kinds of plants and special animals may be distinctively mutualistic. The plant partner supplies synthesized carbohydrate food, elaborated proteins, and oxygen by its metabolic processes, while those of the animal produce nitrogenous wastes and carbon dioxide useful to the plant. When the relation is between algae and larger animals, the animal provides support and defense, and a biotic niche in addition. The coloni-

[*] Though they produce on them a selection pressure made evident by its evolutionary effects on many plant structures.

zation of animal bodies, in special forms of Protozoa, Porifera, Coelenterata, Platyhelminthes, Aschelminthes, and Mollusca by green algae—the zoochlorellae—or by the yellow or brown zooxanthellae (flagellates), is well known. Familiar animal hosts are *Amoeba viridis, Chlorohydra viridissima,* and the flatworm *Convoluta roscoffensis* of the European sea coast. The vast extent and biological importance of this type of mutualism are evident when it is recalled that zoochlorellae and zooxanthellae are present in the individual polyps of most reef corals. A high perfection of such metabolic equilibrium between host animal and guest plant is indicated by the long life of *Chlorohydra viridissima,* with its zoochlorellae when it is sealed off in water in a glass tube (Buchner, 1930).

The studies of Yonge and A. G. Nichols (1931) on the relation of zooxanthellae and coral polyp indicate that the host polyp is not dependent for carbohydrates or proteins on its plant associate; but they leave unquestioned the mutual benefit of oxygen supplied to the polyps and carbon dioxide to the zooxanthellae, plus benefit of removal of nitrogenous wastes, in this partnership. Their studies suggest that nutritional aspects of the plant-animal mutualisms recently enumerated require experimental re-examination.

The breadth of the physiological basis for such metabolic mutualism is shown by the ingenious experiments of the Buchsbaums (1934) who showed that when a culture of the green alga *Chlorella* is combined with embryonic chick tissue cells, both are evidently favored, as compared with either algal or tissue culture alone.

These metabolic relations of plant and animal may be as intimate as the mutualistic relations of plants with plants. Algae and fungi associate to form the varied group of lichens, which, from their successional position on bare rock and from their abundance under the severe climatic conditions of the tundra, may be supposed to carry this type of mutualism backward toward the earliest geologic times in which life was present. The equally intimate association of fungi with the roots of higher plants in the mycorrhiza (apparently present in the majority of plant species) are clearly symbiotic and apparently mutualistic. The relation of fungus to higher plant may be either extraorganismic or intraorganismic, without much

significant physiological difference (Weaver and Clements, 1929). The close relation of nitrogen-fixing bacteria with leguminous plants is discussed in Chapter 35 (p. 711).

An extremely intimate type of plant-animal association into mutually beneficial partnership, in which the animal is the dominant partner, is exhibited by the series of fungus-growing beetles, by the fungus-garden ants, and the fungus-growing termites. The relation of man with food plants that no longer are found in the wild state, like wheat or Indian corn, may be thought of as exhibiting essentially the same type of relation. The fungus-growing forms represent sharply definable taxonomic groups, which attests to the fixity of the relation. The corresponding development of fungi specific (as species) to the particular group of beetles engaged in growing them appears to be demonstrated. The agricultural status of the fungi grown by ants and termites resembles that of plants cultivated by man that are not genetically distinct from natural populations, since the ant and termite fungi are believed to occur independently (see p. 714).

Especially notable is a graded series of increasingly complex means of transmitting the fungus to new colonies among the various families of fungus-growing beetles, all of which are wood-boring forms the larvae of which are associated with the adults in burrows in living or at least in sound wood. Thus in certain platypodid beetles, the spores of the fungus and fungus fragments are carried by the adult female beetle in an elaborate external apparatus on her head from the burrow in which she has passed her larval life to the new excavation in which she will establish a new colony. In the Scolytidae the fungus is carried in the midgut and is regurgitated in the new burrow. The females of the beetles of the family Lymexylonidae have an apparatus connected with the ovipositor that effectively smears the egg with fungus spores as it is laid. An even more elaborate apparatus for injecting mycelium and spores into a new excavation is that of the wood-boring wasp *Sirex* (and of closely related forms), in which the whole fungus-insect relation is still under investigation.

The more advanced fungus-growing ants are sometimes referred to as "parasol ants" because of a fancied resemblance of the green leaf fragments being carried into the enormous subterranean nests by the workers streaming back from some tree or other plant that is being stripped of its leaves. The leaf fragments decompose in heaped-up masses in special chambers in the nest to form mushroom beds. The transmission of the fungus to a new colony is accomplished by the virgin queen, who carries with her a pellet of fungus from the old nest in a special pocket situated below the mouth, and after mating deposits it in the new small chamber in which her first eggs are laid.

The fungus-growing termites establish special chambers in their large terrestrial

great variety of other animals is particularly significant in forms with a restricted diet, and especially in those restricted to a diet of cellulose. True mutualism is inferred in many such relations, and is experimentally demonstrated as mutual interdependence in others (see p. 716). Especial attention has focussed on the biological aspects of the protozoan-cockroach and the protozoan relationship with the less highly evolved termites (Fig. 254), in which the essential function of cellulose digestion by the remarkably distinctive protozoans is most clearly developed. A similar, but less accurately definable, mutualistic function and

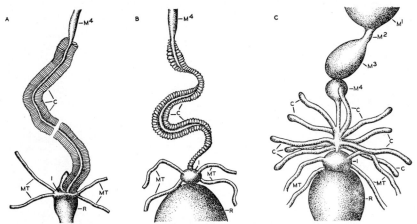

Fig. 65. Intestinal caecae of Hemiptera, showing extreme elaboration of the structures containing the supposedly mutualistic bacteria. A, *Anasa tristis*; B, *Thyrecoris unicolor*; and C, *Blissus leucopterus*. In all figures c designates caecae; *i* is the ileum; M^1, M^2, M^3, and M^4 refer to the first to fourth stomachs; *MT* refers to the malpighian tubes; and *R* is the rectum. (After Galloway.)

nests and grow fungus on a substrate of termite excrement. The mode of establishment of the fungus garden in a new colony is unknown.

In these several types of fungus-cultivating and fungus-eating insects the insect may be said to live in a fungus environment. In these instances the fungus relations differ sharply from those of the varied inhabitants of the fungus niche, in which fungi provide both food and shelter for a whole series of insects, nematodes, and other animals. The step toward growing and controlling the growth of a fungus as an invariable food supply falls into line with other tendencies toward control of the environment that are most notably associated with the development of societies.

The symbiosis of gut-inhabiting bacteria and protozoa with vertebrates and with a

relation to cellulose digestion seems to be the role of a great many bacteria and some protozoa that constitute a part of the flora and fauna of herbivorous animals—especially in the rumen of artiodactyls and the caecum of lagomorphs and rodents. Bacteria inhabiting these organs and other parts of the intestines produce significant quantities of various B vitamins that are utilized by their hosts. Man is one of the many animals showing such relationships with his intestinal flora (Najjar and Barrett, 1945).

The similar phenomena in insects result in elaborate modifications of the gut to provide special structures in which bacteria may be lodged (Fig. 65).

The evolutionary step is not great from the last-mentioned type of organized association to the truly internal nodules and special structures containing bacteria and fungi found in various heteropterous bugs and in all the Homoptera. The inference that these are mutualistic rests on the development by the insects in question of elaborate structural and physiological mechanisms for the transmission of the fungi or bacteria into the maturing egg, thus ensuring the transmission of the symbiont plant from generation to generation of bug.

It is to be further noted that this type of mutualism is associated with the limited diet of plant sap that characterizes the feeding of the Homoptera.

The presence of bacteria-containing structures in the bedbug and in the keratin-eating Mallophaga, again together with struc-

the elaborate and varied structures for the transmission of the bacteria or fungi developed in the host animal seem to exclude the parasitic relation, in which the problem of transmission falls to the parasite and in general depends on chance or is met by multiple host parasitism. For a review of plant-animal mutualism, both external and internal, reference should be made to the comprehensive summaries of the subject by Buchner (1930) and Steinhaus (1946).

A further major type of plant-animal mutualism is represented by the adaptations of flowering plants to attract insect and other animal visitors, and the complementary structures and habits of animals that ensure

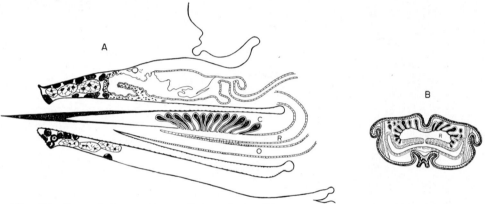

Fig. 66. Transmission apparatus for symbiotic bacteria in the trypetid fly, *Dacus oleae*, shown in sagittal section, *A*, of the ovipositor; *R*, rectum; *O*, oviduct; and *C*, caecae. The caecae are packed with bacteria derived from the gut; the eggs are smeared with bacteria as they pass through a longitudinal slit connecting the rectum and oviduct. Infection of the individual egg takes place through the micropyle. *B*, Cross section through caecal region to show slit connecting the rectum and oviduct. (After Buchner.)

tures for obtaining the transmission of the bacteria via the egg, afford further examples of this somewhat obscure symbiotic relation. Numerous Diptera and Coleoptera likewise exhibit bacterial and saccharomycete-filled organs and have associated structures for transmission of the plant via the egg to the succeeding generation. The subject of internal plant-animal symbiosis, and especially the conclusive demonstration of its mutualistic nature, offers intriguing problems for research (see p. 712). One of the more provocative of these problems, particularly in the present state of knowledge concerning insects and vitamins, springs from the evidence that these contained organisms supply essential vitamins of the B complex for certain insect hosts (Blewett and Fraenkel, 1944). It is to be noted that

cross pollination. Observation of the fact of cross fertilization of plants by insects must long antedate scientific studies of the phenomenon. The whole subject was summarized by Knuth in 1898, after classical studies by Darwin and by Fritz and Herman Müller. The present account leans primarily on Doflein.

The numerous structural arrangements that make difficult or prevent self-fertilization in the monoclinous flowers of the higher plants are evidence of a powerful evolutionary advantage favoring cross fertilization, and from the great variety of adaptive structures of insects it seems equally evident that the food surpluses (p. 236) provided by the excess pollen of plants, with the addition of nectar, have been a dominant factor in insect evolution (p.

715). Conspicuous flowers afford no discernible advantage to plants other than the accomplishment of cross fertilization. The diversity of form and color and especially the species-specificity of these characters appear to be derivable through natural selection only on the hypothesis of benefit from animal associates or partners. The counterbenefit offered by the plant is, in the first place, a food material available in surplus. The development of a large excess of pollen for wind pollination, i.e., chance pollination, in ages antecedent to the evolution of insect pollination, affords a simple explanation of the existence of such a surplus. The surplus pollen is offered entirely without disadvantage to the plant. The insect (or animal) contribution then lies in increased certainty of pollination, or cross pollination, and particularly of transport of the pollen. The capacity for movement in most animals contrasts with the incapacity in this respect of most plants as a major difference between the two kingdoms. By impressing animals into their service for the transport of pollen through the roundabout means of random variation and natural selection and reciprocal evolution, this very contrast between plant and animal becomes fulcrum and lever for mutualistic evolution.

The modern result is that a vast number of insects live (at least in their adult stage) in a flower environment—some with catholic breadth of taste feeding on the nectar and pollen supplied by the seasonal succession of flowers, others sharply limited to the blooming of a single plant species. The most obvious general changes on the part of plants to facilitate animal transmission of their pollen lie in the development of stickiness of pollen; in the development of monoclinous flowers; in the development of structures that prevent self-fertilization; and in structures and additional food supplies specifically adapted to attract animal visitors to the flowers, whether monoclinous or diclinous, monoecious or dioecious. It is to be noted that the mainly carbohydrate food materials supplied by nectar supplement the mainly nitrogenous materials of pollen.

The separate series of structures that fit insects and other animals into the role of nectar and pollen feeders on one hand and on the other into that of the agents of cross pollination, are extremely evident and exhibit numerous instances of parallel evolution.

Several quite distinct orders and families of birds enter the category of flower-feeding and pollen-transporting mutualists. The mainly tropical hummingbirds of the Americas and the sun birds of the Old World provide noteworthy examples and are adapted to nectar feeding by their extraordinary modified whirring flight as well as by their greatly elongated bills. An elaborate brush on the tip of the tongue, found in the honey eaters (Melliphagidae) and in the trichoglossine parrots of the Australian region, serves as an efficient pollen-collecting device. A few species of bats and the Australian marsupial *Tarsipes* are flower visitors, and the effectiveness of bats in securing cross fertilization of certain plants is reasonably attested, especially in night-blooming plants. In general, birds and mammals may frequently be pollen or nectar feeders without performing any function of cross fertilization.

The majority of cross pollinating animals are insects. These exhibit every gradation from the most evidently accidental and generalized relation to flower visiting, to the most precisely adjusted species-specific relations. Knuth (p. 196) summarized the graded series of mutualistic reciprocal adaptation as follows:

"1. The more specialized a flower—i.e., the more complex its structural arrangements and the more deeply seated its nectar—the less are its insect visitors indiscriminately drawn from the entire insect fauna of a district, and the more do they belong to one or several similar species adapted to pollination.

"2. The flatter and more superficial the position of the nectar, the more varied are the visitors in different regions, and the more are they indiscriminately drawn from the entire insect fauna of the region in question."

Nectar-sucking devices characterize whole families and even most of the families of an order—the Lepidoptera—and pollen-collecting or pollen-bearing structures are equally evident. When it is remembered that in a field of alfalfa or clover, or in the sweet clover masses of roadsides and railway embankments, every floweret must be visited if a good crop of seed is to be set, the numbers of insects required to perform this function may be appreciated. The hairbrush structures that ensure the bearing of pollen from flower to flower are quite distinct from the pollen-gathering devices when the pollen is used as food; or they may be neatly combined, as in the honey-bee. The bees, in which the peculiar nectar-pollen food supply (i.e., a "balanced ration") is carried over to the larvae, contrast sharply in this respect with the moths and butterflies. These in their adult flower-visiting stage have completed their growth and can fulfill their energy needs by the carbohydrate nectar alone. The group behavior of honeybees that leads them to exploit a single type of flower at a time obviously tends to extreme efficiency of cross pollination (von Frisch, 1923).

It may be pointed out that insect visitors are abundant at the male flowers of many wind-pollinated plants, feeding on the vast excess of pollen, but that in diclinous plants of this type they do not exhibit the slightest tendency to visit the female flowers (Doflein, p. 93).

The short adult life of many moths and butterflies makes it possible for them to develop close adjustment of an individual species to the short blooming season of a particular flower. Resting places for the slow-moving butterflies appear to be developed in numerous types of day-blooming flowers, but are less frequent among the night flowers visited by the whirring moths.

An extreme of adjustment between specific species of plant and specific animal visitor is presented by the extraordinary length of the nectar-bearing lobe in certain tropical orchids, which is matched by the length of the tongue in the attendant sphingid moth. The extreme length of 250 mm. is reached in the Madagascan *Macrosilia cluentius* (Doflein, p. 109).

To summarize the flower environment of insects: A rich food supply is offered in the form of nectar and excess pollen by the majority of flowering plants, and the animal exploitation of these foods is accomplished by specific and exact adjustments, not only to the securing of the food, but quite certainly for the development of pollen-transferring devices. Double and reciprocal evolution of plants and animals has led to extremes of evolutionary adjustment. That the attraction of the flowers for the insects is in the service of the plant-species for cross pollination is shown by the occasional instances in which the lure for the insects consists of smell only, with no counter benefits of food supplied. The familiar instance of the pollen-and-nectar-feeding bees exhibits complete adjustment of the whole animal

throughout its life history to the balanced diet offered, and strongly indicates that the social evolution of the honey bee was profoundly influenced by the nature of the food supply.

The majority of insects adjusted to nectar or pollen feeding or both belong to the orders Lepidoptera and Hymenoptera and these types function especially in cross pollination. Pollen-feeding beetles present little adjustment either to the special food or to the function of cross pollination (except for the fuzzy coats of certain flower visiting beetles). The Diptera have evolved an illuminating series of graded adjustments for nectar-and-pollen feeding and for cross pollination. The excrement-and-carrion feeding flies are also exploited by certain flowers by means of the development of corresponding bad odors. The elaborate tropical swan flower (*Aristolochia grandiflora*) is a notable example of a "carrion flower."

Extremely close obligate adjustment between insect and pollinated flower, extending beyond the provision of pollen and nectar as food for the visiting insect, is exhibited by the chalcidoid wasps that fertilize the various species of figs. A species of *Blastophaga*, for example, is essential to the commercial production of the familiar cultivated Smyrna fig. These wasps develop in a special series of pistillate flowers referred to as "gall flowers;" the complex life history of the insect, with wingless males and winged females, is accurately adjusted to the development of the successive staminate and fertile pistillate flowers of the fig. Thus a series of flowers is sacrificed by the plant in its rigidly specific association with an insect predator-pollinator.

The reciprocal adjustments of the yuccas of southwestern North America and a tinaeid moth, the yucca moth, are less complex, but involve equally specific adjustment of the moth in both structure and behavior. The moth has a special pollen-gathering apparatus on its maxillae, into which it actively packs a ball of sticky pollen. The moth subsequently turns to egg laying, pierces the wall of the yucca ovary with its ovipositor, and deposits an egg within; after each egg is deposited, the moth climbs to the top of the pistil and rubs part of the sticky pollen into the open end of the stigmatic tubes. About six eggs are laid, and each requires developing fertilized ovules for its growth; but there is a large excess of unmolested ovules that ensures an ample seed supply for the plant. The yucca flower is adjusted to prevent self-fertilization, and the moth is essential to the perpetuation of the species.

The biotic environments supplied by the fig and the yucca are thus extended to the whole life history of the fertilizing agent, as in the social bees.

Seed dispersal appears to have had long range effects on the interrelations of plants and animals, tending toward mutualism, and demonstrating anew that animals living in the plant matrix also provide an animal

Before turning to the further discussion of the mutualism of animal with animal, conspicuous examples of mutualism apparently derived directly from commensalism may be examined. The cowbird *Molothrus*, familiar in North America, and the oxpecker (*Buphaga*), attendant on the buffalo and rhinoceros of Africa, render a considerable service to their hosts by ridding them of external parasites and by reducing the plague of biting and sucking insect predators, and add to these functions the service of watchmen, well known to hunters. The benefits of the constant food supply to the birds is

Fig. 67. The cattle heron, *Bubulcus*, shown with the water buffalo, associates itself with the larger wild and domestic mammals throughout its range, from North Africa to the East Indies. The mutualist relation resembles that of the American cowbird. (Drawing by W. J. Beecher.)

environment to which plants adapt themselves through the processes of evolution. The great number of plants with clinging seeds that become dispersed by mammals and birds exhibit a kind of plant-animal commensalism. The development of edible fruits, in which a readily available food material envelops a hard and resistant seed, suggests that the dispersal of such seeds by the animals feeding on fruits is a mutualistic relation; wild berries, in particular, are most effectively dispersed by birds; but there does not appear to be any development of a strict taxonomic relation like that in so many examples of mutualistically paired species in which pollination is involved. Effective means of dispersal of plants is important in the course of succession and in the maintenance of biotic communities.

evident, and the constancy of the association is attested by the vernacular names of the birds. A great many other birds enter into this loose type of partnership with mammals; one of the most conspicuous and unexpected is that of the little white heron of Africa and the Orient (*Bubulcus*) and the larger hoofed animals, whether wild or domestic. Eight of these birds have been observed perched on the back of an African buffalo and as many as twenty on the back of an elephant.

Marine animals exhibit the most astonishing of partnerships in which mutualism appears to be directly derivable from commensalism. Decapod crustaceans, in particular, tend to have the dorsal shell of certain species covered by a specific type of sponge, hydroid, or sea anemone, deriving benefit from the resulting camouflage or nematocyst defense, while giving benefit to their sessile partners by their locomotion and consequent avoidance of stagnation of the water of the immediate environment, and by their transfer from feeding area to feeding area. The relation of decapod crustacean and sea anemone is facultative in so far as the juvenile animals are concerned, but older individuals seem to be always in partnership, and the obligate nature of the relations is then evident in the evolution of distinct species of hermit crabs. These crabs begin their snail-shell-inhabiting career without the *Sagartia,* and the juvenile *Sagartia* may be found on stones, unassociated with the crabs.

The difficulty presented to the individual crab, when it must exchange its snail shell house for a larger one, of preserving its protective attendant, and equally the danger faced by the sea anemone of being left behind on the old shell are met in other mu-

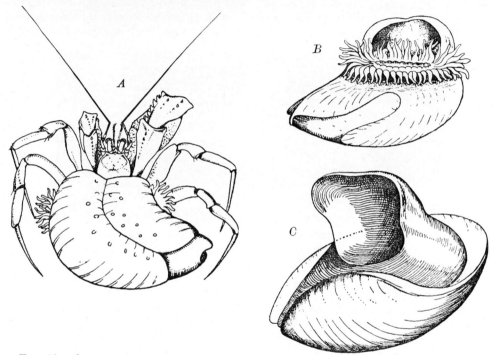

Fig. 68. The mutualist sea anemone, *Adamsia palliata,* associated with the hermit crab, *Eupagurus prideauxi. A,* The hermit crab, its snail-shell house almost concealed by two sea anemones. *B,* The shell and sea anemones abandoned by the crab. *C,* The empty shell, showing the extension of the opening produced by secretion from the foot of the sea anemone. (From Hesse and Doflein.)

species of the attached forms limited to this habit and to a particular species of crab. Each becomes a dominant biotic environmental factor in the life of the other.

The intimacy of this completely external type of mutualism is reenforced by the development of special structures by the sessile partner. In a simple type of sea anemone-hermit crab relation, the crab has been reported to transplant the sessile associates to a new shell when it has outgrown the old one and is forced to change. A single crab may bear several sea anemones. The sea anemone *Sagartia parasitica* is reported from several North Atlantic tualists of the hermit crab-sea anemone series by the modification of the foot of the sea anemone to form an extension of the snail shell house. This reaches an extreme in the relation of *Eupagurus prideauxi* with the sea anemone *Adamsia pileata* (Fig. 68). Still other crabs bear small sea anemones on one of their claws, or hold one in each claw. The effective defense provided by the sea anemone against so formidable a predator of crabs as an octopus is reported from observations made at the Naples Aquarium. The mutualistic actinians have, in fact, extremely well-developed nettle cells, and usually belong to genera in which the nematocyst-bearing acontia (which extend outside the body when its opening is contracted) are especially developed.

The association of the hydroid *Hydractinia sodalis* with *Eupagurus constans* is notable as an independent instance of substitution of a structure formed by the sessile guest for the snail shell house, and is further remarkable for the differential placement of the special defensive polyps at the open edge of the structure.

The crab-sponge association is a common one, exemplified by the hermit crab *Paguristes maculatus* with the sponge *Hircinia variabilis* and by *Dromia vulgaris* with *Suberites dromuncula.*

Mutualism between animal and animal has been mentioned as frequently explainable as a derivation from commensalism. In animal-animal mutualists the size relations vary remarkably. At one extreme are the microscopic protozoa of herbivorous mammals and of certain cellulose-digesting insects, associated with at least macroscopic animal "hosts;" the disparity of size is considerable, though much less when both members of the pair are macroscopic, as in the ox-tickbird relation. In the crustacean-sea anemone or crustacean-sponge relationship, the more passive of the pair of species may actually outweigh the more active partner. There are equally great disparities in the populations of the respective mutualists, greatly in favor of the smaller partner in the case of intestinal protozoa, reducing to approximately the one-one relation as the sizes becomes subequal, except that in social forms, like the ants and termites, mutualist nest-inhabiting beetles and other termitophiles and myrmecophiles are enormously in the minority as compared with the host populations.

The transition from nest commensalism and social parasitism to be found in the nest inhabitants attracted to the organized colonies of ants and termites presents another clear indication of the origin of mutualism from a predatory-prey, a parasite-host, or a host-guest relation. These relations arise in the extremely well-defined and evidently favorable biotic environment afforded by the stabilization of microclimate and food supply in their nests by the societies of ants and termites. The evolutionary trend for the nest inhabitants to offer a counter-benefit to their hosts results in

numerous extreme types of obligate mutualism (see p. 718).

The relation of ant and aphid and of ant and other symbionts has often been compared to that between man and his domestic animals. In general, the development of domestic animals in association with human societies, as well as the relation of man with certain cultivated plants, represents an approach to mutualistic relations. That these are at best loose is shown by the capacity of a great many domestic animals to revert to self-sustenance in feral life, no less than by the capacity of man himself to become "feral."

PARASITISM

At this point in our development of ecological generalizations under the heading of Symbiosis we are concerned with parasites primarily as part of the biotic environment of their hosts and with the hosts as a major part of the total environment of their parasites. The relations between the two are always intimate and may be exact and crucial. Primarily, the operational aspects of these relations need to be considered in the present connection. Population, community, and evolutionary phases of parasitism will be discussed in later sections (pp. 379–386 and 701–704).

Parasitism is a form of symbiosis in which a small organism lives on or in or with and at the expense of a larger animal or plant. The parasite obtains noteworthy aid in the form of food, shelter, protection, or transport. It not only does not give due return, but is more or less harmful to its host. In a narrower usage, parasitism is restricted to those cases in which the parasite lives on or in and at the expense of its host's body.

Parasitism, commensalism, and mutualism, the three main types of symbiosis, are distinguished from each other on the basis of benefits received and harm inflicted; these are relations that often have demonstrable positive or negative survival values. If neither associate is harmed and at best only one benefits, we are dealing with commensalism; if both associates are benefited, the relation is mutualism; if one is harmed, it is parasitism. The distinction of these categories is on the basis of short-run, operational values. Often, in the absence of precise information, judgment must be suspended or estimates must be made that resemble, more or less closely, the value judgments in which philosophers indulge. Since philosophers often contend that science is not concerned with values, it is a matter of some interest that these value determinations or judgments are an integral part of ecology. It may be that evolutionary survival values with real or implied objectivity should be separated rather sharply from subjective value judgments such as will be illustrated in the following paragraph.

The whole parasitic habit is regarded with repugnance by most people, including many biologists. They appear to make informal emotional value judgments to the effect that external predation of a relatively large predator on small prey, as of fox or marsh hawk on meadow mice, is praiseworthy and that, in contrast, internal predation of hookworms on the gut wall of their host is ignoble. An ecological approach is necessarily wholly objective. A pallid endoparasite is rarely a thing of visual beauty, yet the intricacy and delicacy of its adjustments to life in a living environment—often a complex series of such adjustments—delight the initiated student; harmony is the essence of beauty. It must be admitted that the individual parasite, embodying the results of regressive evolution, may be a less obviously harmonious organism than its free-living ancestor. Our subjective judgments are evidently based in part on the obvious harm to ourselves and our commensal domestic animals from the more destructive parasites that attack them and man. Some aspects of the remarkable range of the natural history of parasitic adjustments are outlined by Pearse (1939).

Living organisms, as hosts to parasites, form one of the three major habitats on the earth, comparable to the aquatic and terrestrial habitats in which the hosts themselves dwell. This living habitat presents various niches, many of which are occupied by assemblages of organisms comparable with those of shore lines, abyssal depths, caves, forests, or streams, except on a scale necessarily smaller in actual space, though not necessarily smaller in terms of population numbers. The body surface is a generalized habitat with habitat niches provided by hair follicles, pores, glands, and the various body recesses that have external openings. The alimentary canal is a particularly well-inhabited niche. Air passages, coelom, muscles, internal glands, central nervous system, for example, each may support a varied ecological assemblage of plants and animals (cf. Smith, 1934).

A habitat that is itself alive offers ready food for those equipped to take it, provided the associated physical and chemical conditions can be tolerated. There are internal habitat niches in the bodies of animals that are regions of reduced oxygen tension, inhabited by successful endoparasites able to carry on oxidations wholly or in part by anaerobic metabolism. They must also be immune to diverse protective mechanisms available to the host, including wandering macrophages, specific antibodies, and countermeasures that depend on individual or cooperative behavior adjustments. The ability of the host to alter its habits and habitat may be an important part of its total protective power. The ecological relations of host and parasite, and of both with their biotic and physical environments, are varied and intimate. One is continually reminded that it is a short step from considering the biotic aspects of the environment to dealing with food webs and other phases of the ecological community in all its complexity.

Parasites must manage to retain position, often in opposition to currents and other forces of considerable strength. Particularly, parasites must be able to transport themselves, or secure suitable transport of enough representatives, to insure the continuing existence of populations of parasites in habitats anyone of which at best has only a temporary existence. Except in passive transport, in which a predator eats its prey, parasites and all, and thereby gains an infection, the parasite population periodically is exposed to the rigors of the nonliving environment. Such exposure is often fatal, since in their active stages even the regular dissemules may tolerate only a restricted range of environmental conditions. Encysted stages of parasites, however, may be resistant to environmental conditions. Encysted nematodes have been found alive after twenty years' encystment, and this is by no means the longest case on record.

The understanding of ecological aspects of parasite-host interrelations requires a knowledge of the physiological needs and interactions of both populations. Such information is hard to obtain even for a given parasite in a particular host. Theobald Smith (1934), a distinguished pioneer in this field (p. 29), in his search for underlying relations presented the hypothesis that two factors are characteristic of the behavior of both parasite and host. Both show more or less active offensive and also defensive activities. Active injuries and more passive resistances are often involved for both the invading and the invaded organisms.

The wide variety of parasite-host relations are related to (1) differences in both host and parasite species, populations, and individuals, resulting from diverse influences both hereditary and environmental; (2) differences resulting from the degree of adaptation to the given parasitism, including (3) differential responses to aberrant or unusual invasions.

The various anti-alien reactions of both parasite and host are much influenced by immediate reciprocal stimulation and follow no generally uniform order. The aggressive anti-invasion activities of the cells and tissues of the host are derived from his normal physiology and are, in general, lytic (i.e., dissolving). Among the primary difficulties that affect the parasite-host relation are the serological differences between animals of all kinds. Similarly, the antihost activities of the parasite are related to those in its ancestral, free-living conditions. Until changed in evolution, these effects tend strongly toward being essentially toxic or otherwise destructive.

The self-protective activities of host and parasite similarly include both preadaptation and adjustments evolved in the course of evolution of the parasitic relation. The fairly successful, but still vulnerable, evolving endoparasite has achieved heightened surface resistance, or a new covering substance like that furnished by bacterial capsules, or some degree of immunity to the antigens of the host. The fairly resistant, but still vulnerable, host has met the situation by the formation of a series of specific antibodies and the development of phagocytic cells devoted to either internment or destruction of the invading population.

The development of a more or less balanced condition between host and pathogenetic (or potentially pathogenic) microorganism requires three conditions: prolonged association, opportunity for a high proportion of the host species to become infected, and the absence of any important means by which the pathogen can survive for long periods in the absence of the host. When such conditions prevail, a low grade, widespread infection should exist with little host mortality.

A virus or a bacterial population may be introduced into a new host in which it can flourish with or without killing the host, and be transferred from one individual to another in the newly infected species. If the new host is relatively solitary, the infection may kill an individual or two and go no further; if the new host is gregarious, a new ecological conflict is set going that will eventually be resolved by the elimination of the virus, the death of the infected host population, or the development of a new balance (Burnet, 1945).

The parasitic habit has multiple origins. It can develop from monophagy as well as from commensalism, or from mutualism. It may evolve toward mutualism, but parasites are usually too specialized to be able to move away from the parasitic adjustment. We would expect that external commensals and epicoles (epibionts) of various kinds could become ectoparasites with relative ease. A hint as to how free-living forms may become epicoles is shown by the observation of Mashtaler (1937): When *Hydra* was placed with one of its predators, *Limnaea stagnalis*, only those hydra that happened to fasten themselves to the snail's shell survived. Internal commensals or mutualists could become endoparasites. Certain nematodes, among others, may have begun as saprophytes. Some free living nematodes take only liquid food. The narrow lumen of the gut of *Rhabditis* will admit only solid particles of the size of bacteria, and the food taken consists of material liquefied by bacterial action. It is a short step to the ingestion of food liquefied by the digestive ferments of a living host, as happens with the nematode *Ascaris*. Flesh flies can transfer from laying eggs on dead animals to laying them on decaying flesh still attached to the wound of a living animal; it is then an easy step to laying eggs on the "clean" flesh of an open wound.

Sessile animals are already partially preadapted to parasitism by adaptations for attachment, for example, as are many small species that are negative to light, positive to touch stimuli, and capable of living in habitats with reduced oxygen tension. The parasitic habit has something in common with cave dwelling, and some similar preadaptations appear to be involved.

Whether a parasite finds all the suitable habitats that exist depends on four main relations: (1) The plant or animal host must live in the same geographical region inhabitated by the parasite. (2) The general habits and ecological relations of the two must be such that parasite and host come together when the parasite is infective and the host is open to invasion. Among other considerations this means that (3) the life cycles of the two must be sufficiently synchronized so that the parasite can gain the necessary foothold or entry; (4) population density and mode of dispersal of both parasite and host may be governing factors, as in the relations between many plant-eating insects and their insect parasites (see p. 380). These and other aspects of parasitology are discussed by Hegner, Root, Augustine, and Huff (1938) with some general ecological emphasis.

The organisms that have become established in living habitats belong to two informal series that are more or less distinct. There are those that undergo regressive evolution (p. 676) and become finally, as in the adult stages of the crustacean *Sacculina*, primarily bags enclosing reproductive organs with suitable devices for attachment and for absorbing host tissues as food. At the other extreme are the active, undegenerate trypanosomes such as cause African sleeping sickness in man and rinderpest in many ungulates. Size relations excepted, there is much similarity between the feeding of these internal carnivores and external ones, such as the coyotes or pumas (with which we are more familiar), provided we focus on generalities rather than on details, however important the details may be in other connections.

Elton (1927) stressed the different size relations between predator and prey and parasite and host as one of the outstanding characteristics of parasitic relationships. "The parasite," he states correctly, "cannot exceed a certain size without harming its host too much." Another sentence of Elton's that is much quoted seems to us to be less apt. He says (p. 72): "The difference between the methods of a carnivore and a parasite is simply the difference between living on capital and upon income; between the habits of the beaver, which cuts down a whole tree a hundred years old, and the bark beetle, which takes a daily toll from

the tissues of the tree; between the burglar and the blackmailer."

This whole matter falls into truer perspective when we remember that the beaver is preying on some few individuals annually from a population of trees, just as the bark beetle is taking a toll from the population of cells that together make up an individual tree. Similarly, the marsh hawk is not living on capital when it kills off vulnerable bobwhite quail that have been produced beyond the year-round carrying capacity of the area. Both external predator and internal parasite are normally adjusted to their food supply so that in an ecosystem that approaches balance, the welfare of the populations preyed upon, like that of the species serving as host to parasites, is not disturbed too much. Some of the similarities between herbivore and animal parasite within a plant are even more readily apparent. Grasshoppers are important grass consumers; they also obtain shelter from the dense tufts, especially when near the ground. Nematode worms, parasitic in the grass blade or stem, likewise obtain both food and shelter. Both grasshoppers and nematodes depend on present or former growth processes of the grass; both normally live on income rather than on capital.

The similarity between predatism and parasitism is emphasized when the bloodsucking habit is considered. Are blood-sucking bats, bugs, flies, or leeches predators or parasites? They may or may not remain on the host; lice do; bedbugs do not. They may fly actively and still remain near their food supply, as do even the winged species among the hippoboscid flies, or they may live somewhat apart from their sources of food and hunt it actively, as tabanids fly towards horses and other suitable animals that come near their habitat. Still another variation in the comparison between predatism and parasitism is furnished by the parasitoid insects. The larva of an ichneumon fly slowly devouring a caterpillar from within is scarcely less predatory than is a wolf rapidly devouring a deer from without. In the former case the hunting was done by the preceding generation, but even this may be compared to a wolf hunting prey for its recently weaned cubs. The basic difference lies in the relation to dispersal.

A type of social parasite, the robber, is exemplified by various insects and birds. The bald eagle (*Haliaetus leucocephalus*) on occasion may depend for its fish food upon the osprey (*Pandion haliaetus*). The osprey is the better fisherman, and is victimized by attack in the air when carrying a captured fish. Such habits develop at the individual level, the bald eagle as a species being by no means dependent upon the osprey. The robber-victim relation has become more fixed in various other birds, notably in the frigate bird (*Fregata*), which robs various sea birds, and in the marauding gulls known as skuas and jaegers (*Stercorariinae*), which force their weaker cousins to disgorge already swallowed prey (Knowlton, 1909). It appears that robbery is individually habit-forming, since it is reported as well known in the honeybee, in which individual workers may take to robbing neighboring hives. Such robber bees are regarded as a nuisance by bee keepers, and are repelled and killed by the workers in the invaded hive; the robbing habit seems to be easily established and, once established, not likely to be lost, in spite of the unnecessary life-and-death hazard to which the individual robber bee is exposed (Root *et al.*, 1945). Various predaceous Diptera in the tropics take up positions along the line of march of army ants and driver ants, and rob the worker ants of their prey, and they are joined by various passerine birds that take ants as well as ant-booty (Bequaert, 1922).

There is a difference between parasites and predators in their relation to the pyramid of numbers (see pp. 522, 523). The typical predator-prey pyramid has a broad base of key-industry forms and a restricted apex of relatively large master carnivores. Contrariwise, in the parasite-host pyramid, with each step from the primary host, the parasites become smaller and more numerous. One rat may carry a population of a few tens of fleas, each of which may support a great many herpetomonad flagellates.

After considering all known differences, we agree with Elton (1927, p. 75) that the resemblances between parasite and predator are more important than the differences. From our point of view, successful parasitism may be regarded as a compromise or partial truce between two living populations; the truce may be broken and severe injury result for either parasite or host whenever conditions become especially favorable for one or the other (cf. Smith, 1934).

The types of dichotomies illustrated by parasites include the following:

(*a*) *Location on host:* ectoparasitism or endoparasitism. Numerous transitions from ectoparasitism to endoparasitism are known, such as those shown by series of small mites that live on the skin of various mammals or penetrate it in one way or another. Jigger fleas contrasted with ordinary fleas illustrate another such series, as also do barnacles on whales; certain species of barnacles, apparently originally merely epicoles, now live as internal parasites below the surface of the whale's skin. Consider also the robber-victim relation, in which the parasitism is behavioral.

(*b*) *Duration of parasitism:* temporary or permanent. Tapeworms and many other animals remain parasitic through practically all the stages of their life cycle. In other instances parasitism is limited to one stage in the life history. Often the larvae are free swimming and serve as dissemules, as in the crustacean *Sacculina*, parasitic on the gonads and other tissues of certain crabs; the taxonomic relationship, obscured in the highly degenerate adult, is revealed by the characters of the nauplius larva. Perhaps less often, the larva is parasitic, as in the *Gordius*, the fresh-water "horse-hair snake." The larvae of various species of *Gordius* are parasitic, and the adult is free-living. This is the characteristic situation among the parasitoid insects and in the trombid mites. Often there are complications. The common fresh-water unionid mollusks release their glochidia as free-swimming organisms when a fish is near; a glochidium swims for a brief period and, if lucky, becomes parasitic for a time in the gills or fins of its host and later, after metamorphosis, leaves it and takes up a sedentary bottom-dwelling existence. Many other variations are known.

(*c*) *Necessity:* facultative as contrasted with obligate parasitism. Crabs of the genus *Pinnotheres* may live independently, but both adult and larvae of *P. littoralis*, for example, enter the mantle cavities of certain marine mussels (Wells, 1940). At the other extreme, many tapeworms are obligate parasites at all stages in their life history.

(*d*) *Specificity:* The specificity of parasite-host relationships is a complex subject. One type of host specificity is shown when the parasite transfers directly from one definitive host to another of the same or related kind without living in an intermediate host. This is common but not universal among protozoan parasites. Often the sexually immature stage is spent in an intermediate host, or there may be a succession of intermediate hosts. In a much-cited instance, the broad tapeworm of fish and man (*Diphyllobothrium latum*) passes through at least three hosts. The egg is shed into fresh water and develops into a ciliated, free-swimming coracidium larva. This gains entrance to a copepod and develops into a small procercoid larva. If the infected copepod is eaten by one of several species of fishes, the procercoid develops into an actively migrating plerocercoid stage. This may be found in fish-eating pike and pickerel and sometimes in other predaceous fishes, in the northern United States. The sexually mature, strobilating tapeworm is found in man, or in several other fish-eating mammals (Pearse, 1942; Craig and Faust, 1943).

Another type of specificity is illustrated by many parasites, especially by *Ascaris*, and other worms, or the larvae of the various botflies. Restriction to special habitats within the host is the rule rather than the exception for these and many more. Thus *Ascaris*, when adult, lives in or near the duodenum. The eggs of the horse botfly (*Gasterophilus equinus*) hatch in the stomach, and the larvae attach to its wall, while the eggs of a common botfly of cattle hatch on the limbs; the larvae then penetrate the skin and wander through the body tissues to come to rest along the back, on each side of the midline. This type of specificity holds both for ectoparasitic Mallophaga (Kellogg, 1913) and for endoparasites, including the majority of parasitic bacteria (Smith, 1934).

Host specificity usually refers to the tendency of many parasites to attack a single species or a limited number of taxonomically related species. There appears to be a widespread belief in host specificity of this kind but it is difficult to find a definite statement to that effect in the several generalized books on parasitology that were examined. Chandler (1944) is cautious. "Every parasite," he says, "has at least one species of host, and sometimes several in which it can meet living conditions." Wenrich (1935, pp. 606, 643*) is frankly skeptical. In his three decades of experience in studying protozoan parasitism, he has

* And personal communication in 1944.

matured a conviction that the idea of host specificity has too many exceptions to make it a significant principle in parasitology. The other side of this question will be developed in another section (see p. 628).

Wenrich's account of protozoan parasites indicates "(1) that in many instances the same or nearly related species have invaded many hosts belonging to widely different taxonomic groups; (2) that a number of species of the same genus may be found in the same species of host and (3) that one species of host may harbor many species of parasites belonging to widely different groups."

Insect parasites show both specificity and nonspecificity in their toleration of hosts. An insect may show avoidance of apparently potential hosts, the opposite of host selection (see p. 615). Such avoidance may be to all organisms other than those of a single taxonomic unit, which may be as restricted as a species; more usually the avoidance is related to some higher taxonomic category. Thus the braconid subfamily Aphidiinae shows such "host avoidance" except to aphids. Near the other extreme, the tachinid fly *Compsilura concinnata* has been recorded from more than 200 species of hymenopterous and lepidopterous larvae in the United States and from more than fifty European species (Wardle, 1929).

An interesting footnote to the discussion of host-parasite specificity is furnished by the distinct nonspecificity of the relations between biting bird lice (Mallophaga) and the birds of the Galapagos Islands. The general rule, Kellogg (1913) said, is that the Mallophaga of one host group, such as genus, family, or order, are more or less closely confined to each particular group and tend to be characteristic of it. This rule breaks down for Galapagos birds, because, Kellogg suggests, the land, shore, and sea birds in that region meet in close contact with each other on the shore sand and rocks. The unusual opportunity for transfer from one host to another of widely different taxonomic position and different ecological habitat in other parts of the world helps to account for this particular lack of host specificity.

Other instances of host specificity will be given later in this volume in the section on Evolution (p. 615). We conclude from the evidence at hand that for given stages in the life history, parasites, like free-living animals, exhibit monophagy, various degrees of oligophagy, and of polyphagy. It remains to be discovered which of these tendencies is most frequent.

All theoretical possibilities are met in the interplay of plant and animal parasites with plant and animal hosts. Plants, notably the rusts, parasitize other plants. *Saprolegnia* and many other fungi and bacteria parasitize animals. A great variety of animals,

Fig. 69. Caterpillar parasitized by *Cordyceps militaris*, a fungus belonging to the Sphaeriales. The majority of the 200-odd species of *Cordyceps* parasitize insects. (After Steinhaus.)

notably nematodes, parasitize plants. Most major phyla of animals have representatives parasitic in other animals; the echinoderms do not.

Like free-living animals, parasites of necessity meet the basic needs of (1) ecological position, including food, shelter, transport, or locomotion; and (2) reproduction and dispersal. In the more advanced cases of parasitism, all but reproduction are met within the parasitic relationship. In sexual reproduction there are numerous instances in which a reduced male is parasitic on the more robustly developed female of the species. Parasites as a whole tend strongly to specialize in reproductive activity. They normally have great egg-laying ability to compensate for the high mortality at certain stages, and their complicated life histories abound in instances of alternating

asexual and sexual reproduction. The great development of reproductive power is made necessary by the restricted size, the discreteness, and the short life of the habitats they can tolerate, and by the inefficiency of their means of dispersal and means of reaching their host-habitats. Each host is a small, biological island, more or less completely isolated from other host islands (Kellogg, 1913). The host is furthermore a living organism, and the multiplication of parasites within its tissues frequently sets up immunity reactions such that the parasite population, to survive, must find another host whose tissues are unmodified.

These same characteristics increase the difficulties in establishing contact between

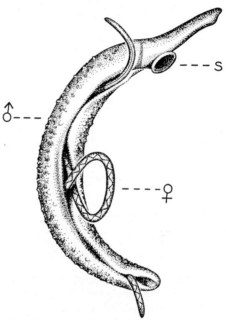

Fig. 70. Association of the sexes in the parasitic trematode, *Schistosomum haematobium*, which lives in the larger blood vessels of man, reaching a length (in the male) of about 15 mm.; S, sucker. (After Hesse and Doflein.)

the sexes. Various devices have been evolved that aid in securing cross fertilization. Many parasites are hermaphroditic, and a part of the elaborate development of the accessory sex organs in trematodes seems best understood as adaptations that help avoid self-fertilization (Borradaile and Potts, 1935). A spectacular adjustment ensuring cross fertilization is that of *Diplozoan*, a trematode parasitic on the gills of minnows, in which two hermaphroditic animals meet and fuse in permanent copulation. The male of another trematode, the blood fluke, *Schistosoma*, carries the female in a fold in his ventral body wall.

Several diverse types of free-living animals that live in sparse populations or have poor powers of sexual "search" have developed sexual parasitism. Perhaps the development of this habit has enabled these forms to persist in sparse populations. In the typical development of this relationship, a minute male becomes parasitic on or in the body of the large female. This situation exists in the echiuroid worm *Bonellia* (an

passive. A common method of transfer is the eating of food contaminated by fecal matter and encysted stages of parasites. Definitive hosts often prey upon intermediate hosts and so receive parasites they are unable to digest. There is normally a close correlation between the successive stages in the life history of a parasite and the food-chain relationship of the successive hosts. Air and water also are well-known avenues of infection. Other parasites gain transfer by close association, as between dog and man.

Insect and other vectors carry many parasites from one host to another, as anophe-

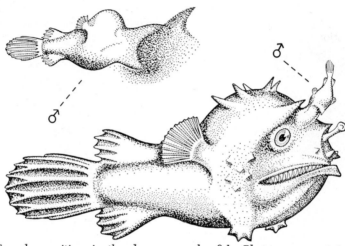

Fig. 71. Sexual parasitism in the deep-sea angler fish, *Photocorynus spiniceps*, in which the difficulty of one sex finding the other is met by permanent attachment of the much smaller male to the female. The union is so complete that the male has no independent existence at all, being nourished by the blood of the female to which he is attached. (After Norman.)

aberrant annelid), in several copepods, and in the deep sea species of the angler fishes (*Photocorynus spiniceps* and others) in which the normal-sized female carries the reduced male attached to her head or some other part of her body. The tiny male fish establishes organic connection with the blood vessels of the female. It seems evident that the difficulties of finding the opposite sex in the adverse, lightless deep sea are correlated with this extreme modification of the sex environment of the individual.

Dispersal of parasite from host to host presents increasing difficulties as the parasite becomes less and less capable of active locomotion. In the parasitoid insects, the free-living adult may be mainly a means of dispersal of the parasitic larvae. In many, perhaps most, parasites, even transfer is

line mosquitoes carry *Plasmodium*, the parasite that produces human malaria. Blood parasites are especially likely to be distributed by blood-sucking insects. Some, like *Plasmodium*, may be as definitely parasitic in the insect host as in their sexual stage in the blood of a vertebrate. Parasites may invade developing ova and so literally grow up with the oncoming generation. Pasteur demonstrated this means of infection in pebrine, a sporozoan disease of silkworms. Some parasites can also pass to the mammalian embryo through the placenta.

Parasites and hosts that have long lived together are often said to develop a mutual toleration such that the two populations are nearly or quite in equilibrium (Chandler, 1944; see also p. 707). Ball (1943) questions this interpretation and attributes pathogenicity to some kind of innate incompatibility between the parasite and certain hosts. Ball's main argument is based on the well-authenticated observation that populations of parasites experimentally introduced into new host species do not necessarily persist, to say nothing of running riot and killing the new host species. This happens even though the parasite is introduced into fairly close relatives of its usual hosts, and is illustrated by experimentally introducing various strains of bird malaria into species of birds that they do not normally inhabit. Whatever the evolutionary background may be, infected populations often form reservoirs of infection that are a potential danger to other possible hosts in which immunity for the parasite in question has not been developed. Various rodents, including the common rat, ground squirrels in certain regions, Mongolian marmots, and others, serve as living reservoirs of *Pasteurella pestis,* the causative organism of bubonic plague. Rat fleas carry the bacteria to man, who notably lacks resistance to its ravages save in the disease called *pestis minor.*

Rocky Mountain spotted fever, a rickettsian disease, is carred by ticks of several species. These in turn feed on small wild rodents such as various ground squirrels, without doing them notable injury. If infected ticks bite men, the resulting human mortality rate is rather high. Hogs and rats are reservoirs of infection of the nematode *Trichinella spiralis,* the organism that produces trichinosis in man.

There is a vast literature on this general subject, especially as related to man and his domestic animals. Hull (1930), Riley and Johansen (1938), Herms (1939), and Chandler (1944) will serve as introductions. The relations between bacteria and animal parasites and the many populations of animals in which man is only slightly interested have, as yet, received relatively little attention. Enough has been done to suggest that the key to many present day ecological puzzles may be found as our knowledge of general host-parasite relations is extended.

Parasites, whether animal, bacterial, or virus, produce diverse kinds of crippling or fatal diseases when they gain entrance to nonimmune hosts. Study of the various types of natural or acquired immunity is a phase of biology that is essentially an aspect of ecology. It is, however, mainly developed in human or veterinary medicine as regards virus, bacterial, and protozoan parasites. Often the immunity reaction is called forth by the presence of a nonlethal population of parasites and hence is a direct reaction of the host organism to its invaders such that the latter are rendered temporarily or permanently impotent or are completely destroyed. Here again the interested reader is referred to the immense medical literature on immunity to which Topley (1933) gives a good introduction. Certain of the direct effects of disease on populations will be discussed in a later section (p. 381). Various students believe that the lack of organization apparently characteristic of viruses marks them as essentially parasitic organisms, the resultants of regressive evolution.

To return to more general matters: It is well to remember that parasitism is difficult to delimit accurately. There are many and varied conditions in which irreciprocal relations occur between members of different species such that one may benefit and the other may be harmed by the association. Examples will illustrate some types of such irreciprocal associations. Thieving ants feed on termite eggs within the termite nest. Staphylinid and pselaphid beetles sometimes prey on the brood of the ant colonies whose nests they inhabit. The organic material of termite nests may be food of nest inquilines such as tineid caterpillars and fungus-gnat larvae. Many different kinds of nests and burrows are inhabited by diverse animals in addition to the forms that build or dig them. Sometimes the relationship is one of casual occupation, and sometimes the invaders receive more than incidental benefits from close association with the original builders.

A bond may be formed directly between the animals themselves and what may be regarded as neighborly groups in which one species finds protection by the proximity to another without occupying any part of its nest, if a nest is present. Thus fishes may be associated with the Portugese man-of-war, with medusae, with sea anemones, or with corals.

A still more intimate relation exists in the various forms of temporary and permanent social parasitism. A fertilized female ant, of a group in which the power of initiating colony formation has been lost, joins herself with the fertilized female of some species that has retained this power. The parasitic queen is able to develop a brood in a mixed colony to which she contributes little or nothing. The nest parasitism of European cuckoos and of American cowbirds illustrates a somewhat similar situation among birds.

Representatives of many different phyla grow as epicoles (epibionts) on the shells or on the skin of others without becoming noticeably parasitic and without contributing anything to the well-being of the animals on which they perch. A basically similar, though more intimate, relationship exists when one organism lives within the body of another without otherwise becoming a parasite: a whole microcommunity of plants and animals lives in the canal system of sponges, and the intestinal fauna and flora of ruminants and other mammals is largely nonparasitic. The *Pinnotheres*, that lives in the mantle cavity of certain sea mussels, has already been cited (p. 244); the crab steals food collected by the host mollusk, but does little if any known injury.

In conclusion, it is important to note that the parasitic habit is a specialized, more or less intimate ecological relationship between two kinds of organisms in which each forms an important, often a critical, portion of the environment of the other symbiont. In the small-scale ecological community of host and its parasites, the host shows many resemblances to the dominant species in large-scale ecological communities in that the host also receives the full impact of the more generalized environment and so modifies it that associated organisms can thrive under conditions that they could not otherwise tolerate.

So many animals support a great variety of species of parasites, and individual metazoans may harbor such great populations of the smaller parasites, as to justify the statement that parasitic animals approach, and perhaps outnumber, the nonparasitic in individuals if not in species. Without examining this proposition more closely, it is evident that the higher animals live in an environment in which parasites and disease-producing organisms form one of the most important of the biotic factors.

SECTION III. POPULATIONS

18. GENERAL PROPERTIES OF POPULATIONS

Up to this point the discussion has focussed largely on what has been called contemporary operational aspects. Under this heading certain principles that concern the physical and biotic environment of organisms have been set forth. These have been largely, although not exclusively, concerned with individual organisms. Our emphasis now shifts. Using the ideas developed earlier as background material, we turn our attention first to the population, and then to the community; and, finally, to the ecological aspects of evolution. The present section deals with the population *per se.* Here it will be our responsibility to show first, that the population, both infrasocial and social, can be studied and interpreted with some rigor; second, that certain ecological principles emerge from such analyses; and third, that these principles are fundamental to the understanding of a more complex ecological group, the community. The material of this section also bears upon the section on Evolution (V), as we shall see.

In developing these points the discussion is organized in the following manner: General Properties of Populations (Chap. 18); Biological Backgrounds for Population Studies (Chap. 19); Certain Demographic Backgrounds for Population Studies (Chap. 20); The Growth-Form of Populations (Chap. 21); Population Factors and Selected Population Problems (Chap. 22); Animal Aggregations (Chap. 23); and The Organization of Insect Societies (Chap. 24).

This treatment has a certain underlying logic. Chapter 18 (the present chapter) is preliminary in the sense that it deals with the broad questions of definition and orientation. Chapters 19 and 20 partially lay the foundation essential to any understanding of population operations, namely: reproduc-

tion, mortality, and dispersion as they relate to group survival. The chapter on Growth-Form (21) is predicated on the idea that change (or stability) of population numbers furnishes the best end criterion of events within that population. Chapter 22 attempts to order and make meaningful certain of the actual factors that produce the observed growth-form; to discuss the interoperation of these factors, or, better put, their integration; and to review selected problems in the field of population ecology. Chapters 23 and 24 discuss populations that have distinct subsocial and social aspects and lead to a treatment of the highly organized societies of social insects.

In this discussion no serious line of distinction will be drawn between experimental (laboratory) and natural populations, or between an aquatic and a terrestrial population. While it will be necessary now and then to point out dissimilarities between these groups, the primary interest centers on their common properties. In other words, this is not a discussion of certain types of populations, but, rather, of general facts and principles common to many populations. This approach is based on the belief that any established population when effectively studied will contribute to a general ecology of populations irrespective of the type of group considered.

POPULATION PROPERTIES

A population has characteristics that it shares with an organism as well as characteristics that are its own unique possession. The former might be called in a loose sense its "biological attributes;" the latter its "unique attributes," which are largely statistical. This is not to say that a population is unique only as a statistical entity. It is to say that the biological features express themselves as statistical functions which

263

emerge at the group level as new biological expressions. These are common property of the group as a whole. The point merits further elaboration. Below are discussed the biological attributes possessed by a population and shared with an organism and certain of the population's unique features. For an extension of this discussion, the papers of Pearl (1937) and of Thomas Park (1939) may be consulted.

At least five general attributes are exhibited by population and organism alike. These are:

1. A definite structure and composition is constant for any moment of time, but fluctuates with age.

2. The population is ontogenetic. It exhibits (as does an organism) growth, differentiation and division of labor, maintenance, senescence, and death.

3. The population has a heredity.

4. The population is integrated by both genetic and ecologic factors that operate as interdependent mechanisms.

5. Like the organism, the population is a unit that meets the impact of its environment. This is a reciprocal phenomenon, since the population is altered as a consequence of this impact, and, in time, it alters its effective environment.

While it does stress the analogies between organism and population, this list fails to indicate certain of the dissimilarities. Pearl (1937, pp. 52–53) spoke to this point when he said:

"A population is a group of living individuals set in a frame that is limited and defined in respect of both time and space. The biology of populations is consequently a division or department of group biology in general. The essential and differentiating feature of group biology is that it considers groups as wholes. It aims to describe the attributes and behavior of a group as such, that is as an entity in itself, and not as the simple sum of the separate attributes and behavior of the single individual organisms that together make up the group. The concept of group attributes, separate and different from the attributes of the component individuals, is a familiar one in other fields. For example, the familiar measures of variation such as the standard deviation and coefficient of variation, are quantitative expressions of a group attribute, namely, the shape of the distribution of frequency of the component individuals in respect of the character measured. Similarly, birth rates and death rates are quantitative expressions of group attributes, meaningless relative to any individual."

These "group attributes" are not limited to birth rates and death rates and should be examined further. Another such character concerns numerical distribution in space and in time—dispersion. The geographic position of an individual organism is hardly a matter of much import. But the dispersion of its group may, and usually does, have great significance both in terms of survival of the group and of its impact on the environment it exploits. Thus dispersion emerges as a population attribute.

Population density is also a group phenomenon. One of the tasks of this section will be to make this point. It is self-evident that density is a numerical concept and a population product. Any density analysis yields data that are directly concerned with population mechanics. Population growth-form and equilibrium are also group attributes, and the fact that populations have functioned as units of selection in evolution adds another convincing argument for the reality of such attributes (p. 684).

Perhaps the point is best made by taking an illustration from the field of genetics. Mr. Doe is a white man living, say, in the town of Richmond, Indiana. In terms of his blood groups he is in group O, which means that he has no isoagglutinogen in his blood cells and has a and b isoagglutinins in his serum. In respect of this character Mr. Doe has the genotype ii, the other possible alleles being I^a and I_b. Although this is a precise description of him as a *person*, it has no validity as a description of the *population* to which he belongs. There, the description has reality only when stated as a frequency; i.e., in population terms. On the basis of a 20,000 sample the genetic description of Mr. Doe's group would be, not ii, but 26 per cent I^a, 7 per cent I^b and 67 per cent i. (For further reference see Strandskov, 1941.)

The ultimate in population attributes is attained in the truly social insects. Termites, for example, have a division of labor fixed by heredity and by coactions with other members of the colony in which certain castes are differentiated functionally and structurally for the survival of the colony as a whole. This special phase of the problem is discussed later and need only be mentioned here (Chap. 24).

Enough has been said about the formal, yet supplementary, biological and statistical attributes of the population. These features are studied shortly as actual cases.

DEFINITIONS, METHODS, AND SCOPE

Definitions

The word "population" is derived from *populus,* meaning "people." It is commonly used in two connotations, one concrete and one abstract. Thus we can speak of a chinch-bug population or the population of the state of Kentucky, or we can refer to the population theory of Malthus or Doubleday. Certain formal definitions met in the literature include:

1. The whole number of people or inhabitants in a country, section or area (Sociology)
2. The organisms, collectively, inhabiting an area or region (Biology)
3. "A group of living individuals set in a frame that is limited and defined in respect of both time and space" (Biology) (Pearl, 1937)
4. The entire group of organisms from which samples are taken for measurement (Biometry)

Although general, these definitions include at least four distinct concepts. These are *number of individuals; likeness of kind enumerated; aliveness;* and *limitation of universe in space and time.* Number of individuals, or enumeration, is an essential theme in all population definitions. As pointed out in the section on History, the first question asked by the population student is "How many?" To have meaning, such a numerical statement must enumerate kinds that have likeness. This gives the statement dimensional homogeneity. It would be absurd to count all the "horses and apples" in the state of Texas. Yet to count the number of persons in Texas (or, possibly, the number of apples) yields a statistic of considerable meaning. Aliveness suggests that any population definition deals with organisms. We do not speak of the "population of nuts and bolts in a factory."[*] Aliveness is also suggested by the

very root, *populus.* Limitation in terms of space and time means only that a population must be defined in terms of a particular date or date-interval and a specific area (or volume) exploited by the population. When we define the population of New York state, we mean the number of persons in the area that is New York at some specified time or during some specified period.

As ecologists, we wish to extend the definition to include more than one species. We speak of such groups as "interspecies" or "mixed populations" in contradistinction to "intraspecies" populations. The geneticist and the student of speciation are primarily concerned with a single species population, since at this level the genes are assorted both quantitatively and qualitatively among the component organisms. The ecologist, however, frequently meets in nature an interacting system in which one species population stands in some immediate and functional relation to some other species population. This, an interspecies phenomenon, then becomes a situation to be analyzed within the *total* ecological system. Some readers may argue with cogency that a mixed species, interacting group is in reality a simple community. To this we can reply only that the point is worth consideration, and that, therefore, the choice of terms may become a matter of arbitrary definition. Personally, we restrict "community" to more complex natural groupings and use "population" for any single or mixed species association in the laboratory or in nature that presents a

---

[*] The term "population" is used frequently by the statistician in two senses: (1) the entire group of items from which a sample is taken; (2) the number of observations in any given

statistical sample, indicated by N (see Kurtz and Edgerton, 1939.) These are connotations not implied in our usage. Simpson and Roe (1939) say, "Zoölogy is, or should be a study of populations . . . The word 'population' in this sense is not only literal, applying to a natural assemblage of animals, but also figurative, applying to all existing phenomena of which a few are observed. Thus when specific characters are determined from a sample, the population is literal, the assemblage of all animals of the species. When an individual's behavior is studied, the population is figurative and twofold: it is (1) the whole of the individual's behavior in this respect, before, during, and after actual observation; and (2) the behavior of all animals in which that behavior follows recognizably similar patterns." (p. 166).

closely interacting system[*] which can be studied and expressed with some quantitative rigor (p. 368).

Populations can be thought of both in the absolute and the relative sense. An *absolute* population is merely a count of individuals stated in integers. *Relative* statements of population are more meaningful in that they include information not present in an absolute statement. Under relative statements we recognize space-relative and time-relative statements.

1. *Space-Relative Population.* This is the number of organisms per unit of space they occupy. It is necessarily a positive number, but it may be a fraction. This is commonly called "density of population" and will be so designated hereafter. The spatial unit may be any suitable measure. It varies both with the organism studied and the judgment of the investigator. Thus, in human populations one meets such units as square miles, acres, cubic feet, beds, and so on, all of which are meaningful when judiciously used. In studies with the flour beetle, *Tribolium*, the favored unit is a gram of flour, i.e., beetles per gram. In protozoan studies the cubic centimeter of culture fluid is a standard of reference. The generalized definition of a space-relative population is

$$_,D = \frac{P}{A} \text{ or}$$

$$\text{Density} = \frac{(\text{Absolute number of organisms in an area})}{(\text{Number of spatial units in that area})}$$

2. *Time-Relative Population.* This can be defined in one form as the difference between the numbers of a population at a particular date, T_2, and an earlier date, T_1, relative to the absolute number at the earlier date, T_1, and averaged to some appropriate figure of time.[†] In human populations for which such indices are best developed, time-relative populations are sometimes denoted in such a form that they may be called "mean annual growth rates

per cent of population." This is defined as follows:

$$\text{M.A.G.R. \%} = \frac{100(P_2 - P_1)}{P_1(T_2 - T_1)},$$

where P_1 is the population size at date T_1; and P_2 the population size at the later date, T_2. M.A.G.R. may be either a positive or a negative number. It measures the annual (or other) average rate of change in size of a population within a defined time interval, relative to the initial magnitude of the changing population. For this rate to have precise meaning the duration of the time interval must be stated. For example, suppose a specified population of 576,872 individuals in 1920 increased to 834,964 individuals in 1930; what is M.A.G.R.? Substituting in the formula

$$\frac{100(834,964 - 576,872)}{(576,872)(10)} = 4.47\%$$

This means that *on the average* the population increased 4.47 per cent over its initial size each year for ten years. This is purely an arithmetical, empirical description of the growth process. But it does have some usefulness as an index.

Methods

The Determination of Population Size.[*] It is immediately apparent that, since the population problem revolves around the question of enumeration, the techniques employed in this enumeration are of vital importance, and require brief mention even in a book devoted to principles, whenever the understanding of a technique is relevant to the evaluation of a principle. In this section we review many of the various ways that population size is determined without any detailed description of the methods themselves. There seem to be seven major methods in common use. These are:

---

[*] Examples of such interactions on a mixed species level are predator-prey relationships; host-parasite relationships; several species competing for a common food supply, and so on.

[†] There are, of course, other ways to state this, but this definition seems simple and arithmetically effective. One of us heard the definition in an unpublished lecture given by the late Raymond Pearl. We are also indebted to this lecture for several other ideas expressed in this chapter.

[*] Animal abundance is usually assayed and reported in terms of the number of individual organisms per unit area or volume. Sometimes it is only possible and in fact desirable to index abundance in terms of weight. This is typically referred to as "biomass" (live weight) and has been used most extensively by students of insect, plankton, and fish populations. Various definitions of biomass appear in a paper by Elton (1932), and applications of these definitions to ant populations are discussed by Pickles (1938).

1. Total count of all individuals of all stages or classes;
2. Total count of all individuals of a certain stage or class;
3. Determination of population size by the registration method;
4. Sampling methods (general statement);
5. The method of marking;
6. Indirect methods; and
7. Combination of several methods.

These will be considered in order.

1. *Total count of all individuals of all stages or classes.* The total count method gives the only precisely accurate census. For any particular spatial unit at any particular moment of time this technique provides a perfect numerical picture of population size. Actually, this is a desideratum rarely attained except in a few laboratory population studies. The total census is used for human populations and is there subject to certain obvious errors. These errors are so minor, however, for most civilized societies that, for all practical purposes, they can be ignored. Pearl concluded that of the 2,069,094,126 persons in the world in 1932,* 97 per cent, or 2,029,608,900 persons, were either counted or computed by extrapolation, while 3 per cent, or 39,485,226, were estimated purely by guessing. The ecological population student owes a debt to the human demographer for setting up a creditable standard in total census methods and demonstrating the importance of such statistics. The first wide-scale census was started in 1666 by Canada and adopted by nineteen other countries between that date and 1897.

2. *Total count of all individuals of a certain stage or class.* Stage or class counts are used in population studies either because they are preferable or because the total count is impracticable. It is often more meaningful to enumerate a certain component group of a population than to enumerate the population as a whole. Thus, in human populations the group can be dissected into such smaller categories as sex, race, age classes, persons exposed to the risk of contracting influenza, and so on. Likewise, this treatment is valuable in natural and experimental populations. In the salmon,

* This figure was derived largely by tabulating census reports given in the "Statesmans' Year Book."

for example, one of the most meaningful statistics is the age-class distribution of the population. In a *Tribolium* (flour beetle) culture it is usually desirable to know, in addition to the total population size, the number of eggs, larvae, pupae, and imagoes comprising that population. When data such as these are available, one stage can be studied relative to another, frequently to the profit of the analysis. On the other hand, there are times when a total count cannot be made. Then a count of a specific stage or class is substituted. Much of the population work with *Drosophila melanogaster* is based on the imagoes and eggs only; the larvae are particularly hard to count.

3. *Determination of population size by the registration method.* The registration method is a theoretically sound, but practically unimportant, method. It requires that, after an initial census has been taken, each birth, death, immigration, and emigration that occurs in a specified population shall be recorded for a stated time interval. These registration data are then treated as follows:

Registration Summary or $X = ($Births + immigrations$) - ($Deaths + emigrations$)$

Population size at the time specified then is computed:

$$\text{Population size} = \text{Initial size} \pm X$$

This method is rarely used because it is frequently difficult to get the observations on dispersion, and in many cases it is obviously easier to census the population a second time than to compute its size by the registration formula. This method is valuable, however, in that it systematically places on record many basic data for the observed population.

4. *Sampling methods (general statement).* The determination of population size by sampling presents these aspects: (a) Commonly this is the only method that can be used; (b) for certain populations this method works well when intelligently applied; (c) there are numerous examples in the literature in which sampling has been inadequately, even foolishly, applied; and (d) the investigator must have some knowledge as to what constitutes a suitable sample, must know whether the census samples are drawn from a distribution that

is essentially normal or, as is frequently true, aggregated or "contagious" (p. 365), and must test his method and his data by appropriate statistical techniques.*

Before sampling, the investigator should ask himself questions something like these:

1. Is this a case (i.e., his study) in which sampling can be used at all? Can the population size be approximated by samples with an error that the investigator is willing to exclude as negligible or unimportant?

2. Can the magnitude of this error be determined objectively? Then, can the decision be reached as to whether the method needs to be refined or, as is sometimes true, to be coarsened? The determination of the magnitude of the error involves statistics; what to do thereafter largely involves good judgment. Defection in either aspect prejudices the entire study.

3. Is enough known of the general ecology and distribution of the species to determine how the samples should be taken both in space and in time?

4. Is it technically feasible to take the required samples both from the point of view of the method and the labor involved? Patently, a sampling method that is too laborious defeats its own purpose.

We stress these obvious points because, in our opinion, the ecologist too frequently derives a datum from inadequate sampling. We appreciate that it is often difficult, if not impossible, to live up to these rubrics. But we do think that population ecology will improve when more serious attention is given to these matters. The problem is particularly vexatious for the student of complex natural populations. It is relatively easy for a protozoologist working with a liter volume of paramecia in a dense culture to stir his population thoroughly, quickly draw off a cubic centimeter of fluid, count the protozoa in this sample, collect, say, thirty such samples, and then compute with considerable accuracy the number of paramecia in the whole volume and per cubic centimeter. But it is harder for a student of forest-floor Collembola to determine the number, density, and time trend of that population for the entire locality. In each case the problem is one of sampling; but the first requires only a simple treatment with a modicum of judgment, while the second demands much knowledge

* An unusually cogent discussion of sampling appears in Simpson and Roe (1939, Chap. IX).

about the form, its habitat, its distribution, and various statistical methods before it can be assured that an adequate sample is obtained. Later in this section, when discussing Contagious Distributions (p. 365), and in the chapters on Communities, we shall return to this subject.

5. *The method of marking.* Marking, a technique of much promise, but containing many pitfalls for the unwary, is being more and more adopted. It has at least two variants: (*a*) In the first, animals such as small mammals are individually marked and turned loose in an area that is extensively and systematically supplied with suitable live-traps. Each time an unmarked animal is caught it is marked. If a marked animal is caught, this fact is recorded. By maintaining this routine for an appropriate time interval the investigator learns much about the density of the species in the study area. Also, he is able to plot territories or "home-ranges" for those forms that have them. There are objections to this technique: one, the animals may become "trap-shy" or "trap addicts"; another, animals may move in or out of the area. These bias the sample somewhat, especially in the case of certain species. On the whole, the data thus collected can be relatively trustworthy. (*b*) The second variation is adaptable to more types of populations. A known number of marked animals is turned loose in the original area (or volume). Since these animals supposedly redistribute themselves in their original population as they were before they were withdrawn, prior knowledge about the pattern of their distribution is not required. Then, after an appropriate interval of time, which must be based on the judgment of the investigator, a sample of the population is taken and the proportion of marked to unmarked forms is computed.

The second variant, sometimes referred to as the "Lincoln Index," may be clarified by an actual case. Green and Evans (1940) worked with snowshoe hares in the Lake Alexander area of Minnesota. They set live-traps for the hares. Those caught were marked before they were released. This was called the "precensus period." In a certain instance they banded 948 hares. At a later trapping, "the census period," they caught 167 marked and 254 unmarked rabbits. The following simple proportion then was set up:

Hares banded in precensus period
Other hares present in precensus period
$$= \frac{\text{Banded hares trapped in census period}}{\text{Other hares trapped in census period}}$$

Applied to the actual case this becomes;

$$\frac{948}{X} = \frac{167}{254}$$

$$X = \frac{(948)(254)}{(167)} = 1442$$

948 + X = Total population
948 + 1442 = 2390 hares; the total population

The authors believe that " . . . by this method we obtained a fairly accurate estimate of the population of the middle of the precensus period; i.e., about February 1."

There are two major sources of error in this method. If the marking incapacitates the animals in any way, they may not redistribute themselves as do unmarked forms. This apparently did not obtain in this case, since the rabbits were marked by small metal bands clipped to the ears. It might hold true, say, in insects if spray paints are employed. The other error is introduced when deaths and migrations occur between samplings. This would be particularly significant in short-lived and highly motile animals. This error is discussed by Jackson (1933, 1936, 1939), who introduces certain corrections that can be used to take it into account.[*]

Dennis Chitty of the Bureau of Animal Population at Oxford University, who has recently worked intensively with the marking method, has kindly given us permission to quote the following statement as an evaluation of this method: "The value of the marking technique is limited by two general considerations: (1) the behaviour of marked animals may not be representative of the whole population and death rates may differ too much between marked samples; (2) even when all theoretical requirements are satisfied, the error of the estimates may be rather considerable and cannot at present be evaluated. Where

* An application of the marking method applied to the determination of population density of sheep blowflies (*Lucilia cuprina*) and including statistical analysis of the findings has been presented by Gilmour, Waterhouse, and McIntyre (1946). The authors conclude that the major error in their method was of the magnitude of 20 per cent.

these limitations can be overcome the technique is simple and useful."

6. *Indirect methods.* Population size is sometimes estimated by using the frequency of some manifestation of the population as a criterion of its size. This is not a census method *sensu stricto*, but, rather, an index of abundance, and its applicability is limited as is its accuracy. Properly, it should be used as a supplement to sampling; i.e., to substantiate or invalidate an estimate of population size gained by another method. This point made, it remains for us to list some of the indirect techniques which have been used without attempting to evaluate them. The list that follows is a summary of certain of these "manifestations:"

1. The number of shed antlers (deer populations).

2. The number of fecal pellets and droppings (derived from "Scatology"). (For discussions of this method, see MacLulich's 1937 work on the varying hare and Scott's 1941 study on the red fox. For a report overenthusiastic to the point of humor, see Seton, 1925.)

3. Pelt records, particularly those of the Hudson's Bay Company of Canada. These yield data for many mammals whose hides are marketable. Difficulties encountered in using such records are discussed ably by Elton (1942).

4. Amount of food consumed.

5. The frequency of prey remains in the stomach contents of predators. (For a deservedly critical discussion see Errington, 1937.)

6. Vocalization frequency; bird calls, mammal noises, and the like. (See discussion of L. Tinbergen's work, p. 374.)

7. The frequency and pattern of tracks and trails.

8. The amount of oxygen consumed or carbon dioxide produced by a defined population (See Howe and Oxley, 1944.)

7. *Combination of several methods.* In those cases in which a total census cannot be taken or in which the sample is not considered adequate, the careful investigator may combine several of the above techniques in getting at population size. The final derived figure is based on the correlation that exists between the several reliable methods. One of the better illustrations of such application is MacLulich's (1937) study of the varying hare. This investigation, centering about population fluctua-

tions, utilizes elaborate and repeated assays of population size. These techniques were used:

1. Records of furs taken by trappers
2. Statements in the literature
3. Questionnaires concerning hare abundance
4. Field work (conducted at nine stations)
   (a) Trapping (both live and dead traps)
   (b) Censuses of various sorts
   (c) Observations on hares seen
   (d) Information derived from scatology

This ends the treatment of the determination of population size. The reader will recognize that, while this problem is technically the central one in population research, it is often a difficult one to put into actual, accurate operation. He will recognize also that some of the applications in the literature are inadequate for one reason or another and that in planning any population venture this whole matter demands prior thoughtful attention.

Scope[*]

Something is gained by examining briefly the practical categories into which modern population studies fall. While these are not necessarily the most logical ones, they show how the entire field is developing. There are at least six of these categories.

1. Studies of natural populations (both intraspecies and interspecies)
2. Studies of experimental laboratory populations (both intraspecies and interspecies)
3. Studies of human populations (intraspecies)
4. Epidemiological studies (interspecies)
5. The approach through theory
6. The approach through experimentation based on theory

A brief discussion of each of these categories is relevant.

1. *Natural Population Studies.* By and large, these studies deal with the distribution, total size, density, territory relations, equilibrium and departures from it, predation and other interspecies competition effects, intraspecies feeding activities, and the relation of the population to its immediate physical environment. Animals that have been most studied as natural populations include insects, fishes and plankton, birds,

[*] Before reading this section the reader is encouraged to re-examine the historical chapters, particularly pages 60 and 61.

and mammals. Each of these groupings may be broken down more specifically (although by no means completely) as follows:

(a) *Insects:* collembola; locusts; chinch bugs; gall midges and other midges; tsetse flies; mosquitoes; *Drosophila* spp.; Mediterranean fruit fly; boll weevil; Japanese beetle; European corn borer; cutworms; codling moth; thrips; bees and ants

(b) *Fishes and Plankton:*[*]
   (1) *Marine fishes:* salmon; European plaice; cod; haddock; herring; mackerel; hake; halibut
   (2) *Fresh-water fishes:* some game fishes; trout; whitefish; carp; *Ameiurus; Gambusia*
   (3) *Plankton:* studied relative to (a) composition, density, and distribution; (b) food for the fish population

(c) *Birds:* pheasants; snowy owl; bobwhite; song sparrow; ringdove; mourning dove; house wren; red-winged blackbird; great horned owl; ducks and geese; gulls and terns; sparrow hawk; starlings; finches; titmice; English robin; swifts

(d) *Mammals:* voles; mice; lemmings; rats; hares and rabbits; chipmunks; squirrels; muskrats; skunks; weasels; shrews; Arctic fox; red fox; lynx; sheep; elk and deer; monkeys and apes

(e) *Miscellaneous:* soil protozoa and bacteria; triclad worms; snails (particularly *Lymnaea* and *Goniobasis*); oysters

2. *Experimental Populations.* The background and development of experimental population studies were discussed in some detail in the historical section. These studies make their prime contribution by a control of the physical and biotic environment not possible in the field. The laboratory studies attempt to analyze a specific group relationship that would be technically difficult, if not impossible, in many natural populations. Thus they are viewed as complementary and supplementary to field work. The general problems most studied in the laboratory are:

(a) Intraspecies
   (1) Population growth-form
   (2) The nature of population density
   (3) The effect of density on reproduction and mortality

[*] This is a logical association. The plankton are often studied as populations purely because, in furnishing food for the fish populations, they occupy a unique place in the food chain of the community.

(b) Interspecies
  (1) Competition of two species for a common niche
  (2) Competition of two species for a common food supply
  (3) Predator-prey interaction

Some of the organisms that have been most used in such laboratory studies are yeast; protozoa (especially *Amoeba, Chilomonas, Euglena, Stylonychia, Oxytricha, Paramecium, Colpoda, Colpidium, Didinium*); the eggs of various aquatic animals (p. 356); insects (especially *Tribolium* and other grain beetles; flour moths; *Drosophila melanogaster;* chalcid-flies; bees and ants), and, among the vertebrates, chickens, wrens, mice, monkeys and apes.

3. *Human Populations.* Before the time of Malthus the student of human populations focussed his attention on overpopulation and underpopulation in relation to the economics of the state (see Duncan, 1929). Malthus was concerned largely with overpopulation, a reflection of conditions in England during his life. His famous "Essay on the Principle of Population as It Affects the Future Improvement of Society" suggested that population growth is a function of the food supply. The impact of Malthus on ecology was reported in the historical section. Modern students of human populations are descendants of Malthus to a certain degree, although they do not, of course, accept wholeheartedly his theory. The ramifying and complex human population studies will not be reviewed here. We can point out that the principal motivations in such studies are medical, economic, and sociologic, and that their techniques are statistical methods. An unusually comprehensive outline of research in this field was published in 1934 by the Population Association of America (in *Human Biology,* 6: 223–239). This outline suggested that the two major subfields are "larithmics," or "factors in the numerical growth of population," and "eugenics and euthenics," or "factors in qualitative determination of population." The ecologist finds population studies valuable for the high technical standards they set in the quantitative analysis of data and for the knowledge that has emerged, particularly about reproduction, mortality, and dispersion.

4. *Epidemiological Studies.* These cover population aspects of host-parasite relationships. They are interspecies as used here, although some workers refer to "epidemics"

of single species populations to suggest unusual abundance. Most of the studies are statistical and medical and deal with such diseases in epidemic form as malaria, sleeping sickness, typhus, typhoid fever, septic sore throat, acute anterior poliomyelitis, influenza, the common cold, diphtheria, and tuberculosis. In these cases *Homo sapiens* is the host population. Then, too, there are some recent and fascinating experimental investigations, set up so that an artificial epidemic is established in a controlled population. The course of the epidemic is studied and the causal factors are analyzed. Some of these studies have rather direct clinical application, like those of Majo. Greenwood on mouse plagues. Others are entomological, rather than medical, like Salt's work on chalcid-fly parasites, H. S. Smith's work on the pupal parasite *Mormoniella* of the housefly, and Varley's (1947) excellent analysis of population balance in the knapweed gall-fly, *Urophora jaceana.* Thus epidemiology lies within the scope of modern ecology (p. 60).

5. *The Approach through Theory.** Theoretical population ecology has not advanced to a great degree in terms of its impact on ecological thinking. There are some significant papers. But the major developments and applications are yet to come. Workers have concentrated at three different levels: (1) mathematical rationalizations; (2) the social origins problem and social facilitation (see pp. 59 and 410); and (3) synthesis of knowledge to build up a concept of population integration. In the first field important contributions center on population growth curves (Pearl and Reed); on interspecies interactions in a "self-contained" system (Lotka and Volterra); and on the concept of population equilibrium, balance or the "steady-state" (Nicholson and Thompson). These matters receive attention in later pages.

6. *Experiment Based on Theory.* The experimental approach based on theory has two aspects: the testing of postulates established by rationalization, and the design of experiments in the light of theoretical suggestions. Experiments based on theory have progressed only far enough to show that the future holds bright promise. (For a pertinent illustration of this approach, see Crombie, 1945, 1946.)

* See the monographic summary by Umberto D'Ancona (1942).

19. BIOLOGICAL BACKGROUNDS FOR POPULATION STUDIES

In any scientific field there are focal points of study. The geneticist stresses the mode of transmission and the biochemistry and physiology of the gene. The cytologist stresses the structure of the cytoplasm and nucleus. The population ecologist is in the final analysis concerned with three composite factors: natality, mortality, and dispersion. These are the forces that shape the course of population growth, the composition of the population, and its distribution in space. In short, they are factors in the statistical sense related to group *survival*. We wish now to discuss these factors in greater detail, for by so doing we develop a partial "biological background" for the population problem.

NATALITY

Natality is the population-increase factor. It can be defined in a general sense as the "force" of total population reproduction. There is some reason, despite their academic character, for recognizing two aspects of this reproduction—*potential* and *realized*. (Other discussions of this point appear in Chapman, 1931; Bodenheimer, 1938; Thomas Park, 1942.)

Potential reproductive capacity is a theoretical concept in the sense that a species potential is probably never realized by a natural population. We recognize *absolute potential* and *partial potential*. Absolute potential is the maximum reproduction possible for a species population. To attain this maximum a species would exist under ideally optimal ecological and genetic conditions. Partial potential is the maximum reproduction possible for the species population under a given set of conditions. This rate would not equal the absolute potential unless the conditions were ideal. Species with a high reproductive potential characteristically have a great toll taken by death, while those with a low potential have a smaller death toll. We shall discuss shortly and at greater length this interaction of reproduction with mortality.

Several examples of high partial potential, or at least of great reproductivity, may be of interest. Galtsoff (1930) reported that an individual oyster can produce 55 to 114 million eggs, while Pearse (1939) estimates

that the blue crab of the Western Atlantic carries 1,750,000 eggs at one time. The capacities of queen ants and termites are also well known. Emerson (1939a) reports that an ant queen has been observed laying 341 eggs per day, while a capacity of 6000 to 7000 eggs per day is not unusual for specialized queen termites. In a period of about three weeks, the housefly (*Musca domestica*), under favorable conditions, can lay six batches of eggs, each batch containing about 140 eggs.

Hart and Tester (see Pearse, 1939) have described the spawning activity of the Pacific herring in the Strait of Georgia. There, on four spawning grounds, a population of 1 to 9 million fishes annually produces 8 to 75 billion eggs. Of these about 0.1 per cent reaches maturity, although 95 per cent may hatch. Chapman (1931) suggests that the shad lays ". . . from 30,000 to 100,000 eggs per season and the carp from two to four million." Raillet (1895) concluded that the parasitic tapeworm *Taenia* produces at least 8800 eggs in a single proglottis and liberates as many as thirteen or fourteen proglottids each twenty four hours.

When graphed by generations, natality potentials typically assume an exponential or "compound interest" form. This is a situation in which increase at any moment is proportional to the size already attained. It is important that we understand the form of such growth curves, since this concept will be needed for later discussions. Bodenheimer (1938) has shown, for example, that an individual *Paramecium* under stated conditions of culture multiplies by fission with a consequent s-shaped or "logistic" population growth-form (see page 301). The early phases of growth coincide closely with an unrestricted or exponential pattern. However, after the fifth filial generation the exponential and observed curves begin to diverge abruptly. The population reaches its maximum possible size ("asymptote") of about 300 paramecia per cubic centimeter after twelve generations. Had the growth for this interval been exponential, there would be 4096 organisms instead of 300. Between the twelfth and fifteenth generations the population remains at the 300 level, although presumably the reproductive potential is as high as earlier.[*] Exponentially, for the same period, the protozoa would have increased from 4096 to 32,768. For organisms with exclusively biparental inheritance the principles are similar, although the details may differ.

Realized reproductive performance is the observed population birth rate. This is the amount of reproduction that actually occurs over a defined time interval. Thus, a population of 2000 organisms of the same species might have a potential of 12,000 offspring per year, but a birth rate of, say 2000.[†] The birth rate is influenced by the potential reproductive capacity, which in turn is affected by both genetic and ecological factors. In addition, mortality of the re-

group, is antithetic to natality. It can be defined loosely as the "force" of total population deaths. The biologist is interested both in why organisms die and why they die at a given age, an interest shared by the population student. The first aspect is significant for us whenever the causes of death can be ascribed to the ecological environment. The second aspect is significant because of the obvious relation between age of death and the birth rate. Under mortality we discuss physiological life expectation, ecological life expectation, and age distribution in populations and its importance. We shall return to certain other considerations of mortality in the chapter on Demography.

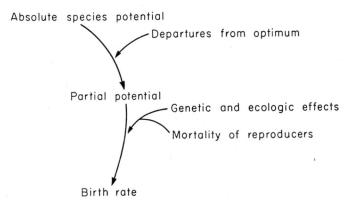

Fig. 72. Schematic relation between species potential and birth rate.

producing members of the population affects (usually lowers) the birth rate. Some of these relations are stylized in Figure 72.

MORTALITY

Mortality is the population-decline factor and thus, in terms of its effect on the

[*] This, an assumption commonly made on mathematical grounds, seems dubious from the biological point of view. See discussion on page 392.

[†] Imagine that 1000 of the 2000 were females, each physiologically capable of producing twelve young per year, or one a month. The population potential for twelve months then would be $1000 \times 12 = 12,000$ under the assumed conditions. Actually, each female during that year might give rise on the average to only two young. Thus the birth rate would be $1000 \times 2 = 2000$. Whether the population as a whole would grow, remain stationary, or decline under these conditions would depend on the mortality and dispersal relations and could not be answered by knowledge of natality taken alone.

Physiological and Ecological Longevity

The population student recognizes two types of longevity—physiological and ecological. The former represents the capacities of the individuals of a species to live out their life span (or their capacities to resist death), while the latter depicts the observed life duration of the members of the population. There is an analogy here with the concepts of potential natality in contradistinction to realized reproduction.

Bodenheimer (1938), on whom we lean considerably in this section, has given a workman-like discussion of this question, and his definitions follow:

1. "Physiological longevity is the average longevity of individuals of a population living under optimal conditions and of genetically homogeneous stock.[*]

[*] This definition seems to imply that all mortality is environmentally produced.

2. "Ecological longevity is the empirical average longevity of the individuals of a population under given conditions."

These two concepts would become most meaningful if we could examine a population under conditions approaching physiological longevity and compare it with another otherwise similar population of the same species under known conditions of ecological longevity. The difference in size between the two (the latter population is always smaller) would give an expression of the intensity of the mortality that can be ascribed to the environmental vicissitudes.

sources of ecological mortality as well as, frequently, of mortality itself. There is an emergent ecological principle here of some validity: The greater the ecological mortality, the greater the reproductive potential of the species. The converse statement, that with decreased ecological mortality the reproductive potential also decreases, is equally true.

Several workers, notably Rubner, Pearl, and Bodenheimer, have concluded that the curve of physiological longevity (number still alive plotted against age) is quite similar in its form for all species. It is departure from the curve owing to ecological

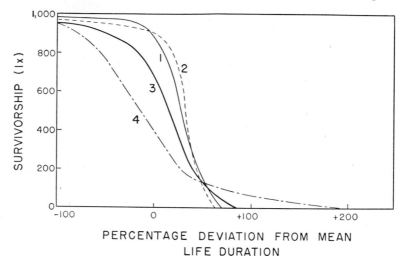

Fig. 73. Survivorship curves for (1) starved, wild-type *Drosophila melanogaster;* (2), starved, vestigial type *Drosophila;* (3), fed, wild-type *Drosophila;* (4) fed, vestigial type *Drosophila.* (From Bodenheimer.)

Knowing this intensity, we then become interested in those ecological factors operating to produce it such as unfavorable climate, excessive crowding, infection, disease and parasitization, predation pressure, accidents, and so on. It stands to reason that there are great differences between species in terms of ecological mortality, some regularly having many deaths from many causes, grading imperceptibly into others with lower death rates from fewer causes. An example of the first would be locust populations living in relatively unprotected situations in the grasslands; an example of the second, honeybees, before they become fieldbees, which live in a highly buffered microniche with a well-organized societal structure. Bodenheimer points out that one of the common attributes of a social population is its reduction, through group activity, of the

mortality that is significant in the population sense. These writers suggest that each species-population attains a maximum lifespan when living under "optimum" ecological conditions and having a genotype that is "healthy" and homogeneous for all the components. A survivorship curve (a curve that graphs age on the abscissa against numbers surviving on the ordinate; see page 296) plotted for a population under these conditions would approach a right angle. Here it is self-evident that the group's members live practically without death until they reach a ripe old age, whereupon they quickly die. In short, they live the life span characteristic of their species without the complications of deleterious heredity or environment. This concept is essentially academic, since its chance of occurrence in natural populations is negligible, although, as we pointed

life cycle, a point stressed by Shelford in 1915. For *Schistocerca gregaria* populations in the outdoor cages the approximate total mortality by stages is:

Egg .... $130^\circ/_{00}$
Nymphal (five instars) .... $675^\circ/_{00}$
Imaginal (total) .... $195^\circ/_{00}$
   Prereproductive .... $73^\circ/_{00}$
   Reproductive .... $87^\circ/_{00}$
   Postreproductive .... $35^\circ/_{00}$

These figures show that in the nymphal stages, especially the first and second in-

It is conventional and meaningful to compute the death rate as well as death cases (see p. 290). This is usually expressed as rate of mortality per 1000, or the number dying in a particular interval of age among 1000 alive at the beginning of that interval. Bodenheimer treated the *Schistocerca* data in this way, and the resulting curve is shown in Figure 78. There is a considerable parallel between Figures 77 and 78 from egg stage through the prereproductive period, for about 150 days. In short, the

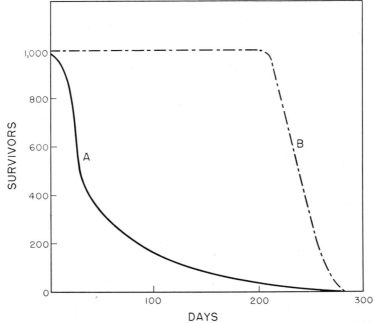

Fig. 76. Approximate survivorship curve for the locust, *Schistocerca gregaria* (*A*), compared with the idealized physiological curve (*B*). (From Bodenheimer.)

stars, as seen from Figure 77, the number of deaths is high. Bodenheimer does not clarify this point. Presumably, it is caused by a combination of factors, among which hazards of postembryonic development, vulnerability to predation, and denser and less motile populations can be discerned. The imaginal mortality is lowest for the postreproductive period and is substantially lower than that of the egg and nymphal stages. Bodenheimer does list certain factors that decimate *Schistocerca* populations in nature. The eggs particularly are subject to insect parasitism and fungus disease, while the nymphs and imagoes are preyed upon by lizards, birds, small mammals, and man.

number of deaths and the death rate per 1000 follow similar patterns. However, the death rate jumps towards the end of reproductive life and becomes extremely high, as would be expected, during old age.

The table listing ecological mortality for the locust *Schistocerca gregaria* is concerned with each stage as a discrete unit. It is obvious that there may exist differential mortality between early or later phases *within* any one stage of development. Birch and Andrewartha (1942) have shown that the susceptibility of the eggs of the grasshopper *Austroicetes cruciata* to dryness varies with the state of development, being greatest for newly laid eggs and least for eggs in the summer diapause. The eggs became progressively more susceptible to desiccation as diapause disappeared during the winter months. Although the eggs are most resistant to desiccation during diapause in labo-

Three further illustrations of ecological mortality are in order. The first is based on the data of Bliss, Cressman, and Broadbent (1935) and Cressman, Bliss, Kessels, and

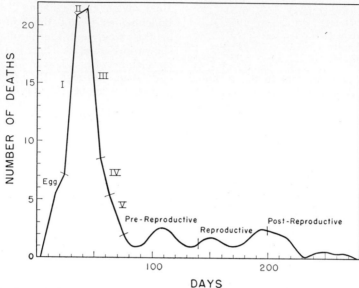

Fig. 77. Number of deaths (approximate) of *Schistocerca gregaria* during egg, nymphal instars, and imaginal stages. (From Bodenheimer.)

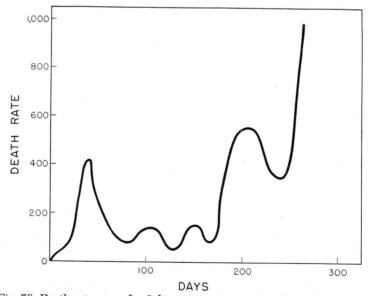

Fig. 78. Death rate curve for *Schistocerca gregaria*. (From Bodenheimer.)

ratory experiments, nevertheless the greatest mortality in the field occurs during the diapause stage, owing to the severity of the drought and heat of the summer months (Birch and Andrewartha, 1944).

Dumestre (1935) on the camphor scale, *Pseudaonida duplex* Ckll. This coccid oviposits beneath the scale of the mother, which is attached to the leaves of camphor trees. The eggs hatch into nymphs known as "crawlers" that wander over the leaves for a short period and then "settle" and begin feeding. The female scales moult twice, yielding two instars; the males moult four times. It is possible to distinguish prereproductive and reproductive phases of imaginal life. Carpenter (*loc. cit.*) constructed a death curve for *Pseudaonida* which is reproduced with slight emendation as Figure 79. This graph brings out certain relationships between mortality and developmental stage. The situation is well summarized by Carpenter as follows:

based on rat populations in the postnursing stage. It is known that there is ecological mortality both *in utero* and during the period of suckling. Bodenheimer (1938) estimated prenatal mortality as 5 per cent of conceptions—a low figure. King (1929), reporting on captive Norway rat colonies (*Rattus norvegicus*), recorded a mean of 0.549 per cent stillbirths, but this figure does not include early miscarriages.

Wiesner and Sheard (*loc. cit.*) observed mortality during "the span of life spent by the rat in greater or lesser dependence on

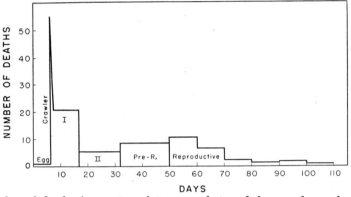

Fig. 79. Number of deaths (approximate) in a population of the camphor scale, *Pseudaonida duplex,* over the entire life cycle.

"These data show a very low mortality in the egg, which is protected by the scale of the female, followed by an overwhelming mortality during the period when the newly hatched nymphs or crawlers wander over the host plant searching for new feeding sites. Under adverse temperatures and wind conditions, probably most of the young perish at this stage. The first and second stadia scales show a comparatively small mortality, the pre-reproductive adults a somewhat higher rate, and the reproductive adults continue this trend to the median day of egg laying. Since adults of most oviparous scale-insects die very shortly after having deposited their eggs, the oviposition records presented by Bliss were taken as indicative of the death trend of the adults after the sixtieth day. The great mortality during the crawler stage and the first stadium leave too few individuals to have the adult death peak very large, but it appears to be associated with the beginning of the egg-laying period."

If now we return to the albino rat population (see page 276 and Figure 75) and examine it from the viewpoint of ecological rather than physiological longevity, we can add to its analysis certain points of interest. It will be recalled that these data were

its mother," a span ending about thirty days after birth. Of a total of 250 litters observed, comprising 1607 births, 492 (241 males, 251 females), or 30.6 per cent, died, and 1115 (571 males, 544 females), or 69.4 per cent, survived. Thus there is a high mortality (30.6 per cent) for this early period. The authors suggest that the possible sources of this ecological mortality are low viability; accidents, such as " . . . squashing of the young by the mother because the latter fails to assume the appropriate 'nursing posture;'" cannibalism on the part of the mother, and size of litter. The entire cycle of mortality over the life span of these rat populations clearly depicts the low mortality *in utero,* and the excessive mortality of the nursing period. The low mortality of the reproductive period accounts for the approach to the physiological curve and the increased mortality of the post-reproductive ages.

Some valuable observations on the ecological mortality of the prereproductive span were obtained by Ranson (1941) on experimental populations of the vole, *Micro-*

tus agrestis, under optimal conditions of light, temperature, and food. This worker, by palpating the embryo in the uterus and then noting the number of live and still-births, could determine the prenatal mortality. This study, along with an earlier paper by Leslie and Ranson (1940) on adult life, covered ninety-six weeks of observation with the following periods represented: conception to birth, zero to twenty-one days; birth to weaning, twenty-one to thirty-five days; and weaning through old age, thirty-five days to ninety-six weeks. The first two periods are described by Ranson in terms of mortality as follows: "The

rion of 'rogueness' is for a vole to have absorbed or killed at birth most of the foetuses in at least 50 per cent of its litters. This may appear to be rather an arbitrary standard, but in point of fact once a vole has shown 'rogue' tendencies it hardly ever returns to normal breeding life, and usually if it is going to be a 'rogue' it will start at the very first litter it produces. It is not known whether 'roughness' in voles is a genetic weakness or a vice which is acquired, but it is possible for either the male or the female to be a rogue, and for a normal parent which has produced normal litters when mated to another normal to produce rogue litters when mated to a rogue. Habitual litter eating is a phenomenon well

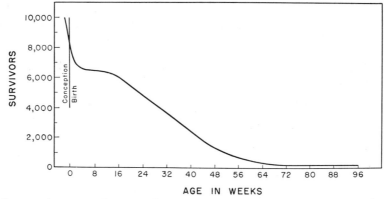

Fig. 80. Survivorship curve for the vole, *Microtus agrestis,* showing the number of survivors out of an original population of 10,000 embryos. (From Ranson.)

results obtained . . . show a [pre-natal] mortality of at least 21.07 per cent. 14.20 per cent of the young born alive die during the 14 days between birth and weaning, giving an accumulated loss of at least 32.28 per cent for the first 35 days of existence. The sex ratio at weaning was 50.89 ± 2.22 males per cent" (p. 57). The mortality of the entire life span is presented in Figure 80. This graph shows that there is an excessive mortality component from conception to weaning. Thereafter, the deaths are relatively few for about fourteen weeks and then increase gradually until about sixty-four weeks of age. The truly old voles live on for something like thirty-two weeks more.

An interesting aspect of Ranson's study is his discussion of "rogue voles" and the relation of this to mortality.

"The parent stock can be divided into two main groups; normals and 'rogues.' The crite-

known to stockbreeders, and has been reported on in laboratory mice . . . and in Norway rats" (p. 47).

This "rogueness" then becomes an intraspecies source of ecological mortality and, as such, is pertinent here. Ranson demonstrated that, while the death rates of normal voles for the conception to birth and birth to weaning periods are 13.3 and 13.6 per cent, respectively, the comparable and much higher percentages of "rogues" are 60.9 and 28.6.

We believe enough examples have been discussed (1) to illustrate the essential difference between physiological and ecological longevity; (2) to evaluate the importance of the latter concept for the student of populations; and (3) to stress the point that different phases of the population's life history have different and characteristic death rates and that this, as Shelford (1915) and many other ecologists have noted, is a most obvious but valid principle of ecology.

AGE DISTRIBUTION IN POPULATIONS

A consequence of ecological mortality in a population is its effect on the age distribution within that population. This, in turn, is significant, since the age of the components is characteristically related to their reproductive performance as well as to their morbidity and mortality. It is a valid principle of ecology and demography that a rapidly growing, vigorous population has a preponderance of young organisms; a stationary population, an intermediate number

tion than in a stationary or declining group. The curves come close together for the age interval thirty to forty years—the class of males most consistently represented in all three populations. After forty years there is an increasing divergence until age seventy is attained. Thereafter, among the few really old members, this divergence decreases until at 100 years of age the three populations are essentially similar. Bodenheimer describes such changes by three geometric figures: (1) a pyramid for the growing population suggesting by its broad base many young and few old components; (2) a bell-shaped structure for a stationary

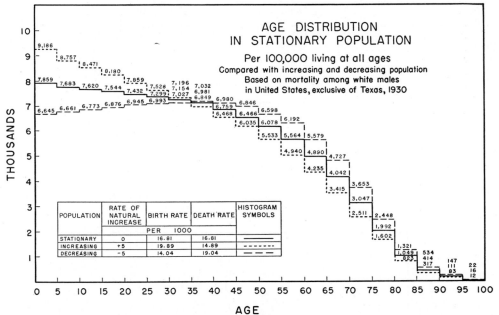

Fig. 81. Age distributions in human populations that are stationary, increasing, and decreasing. (From Dublin and Lotka.)

of young, middle aged and old organisms; and a declining population, a preponderance of the older age groups. Figure 81 expresses this principle. The chart is based on the mortality of United States males (exclusive of Texas) in 1930. It contrasts a "stationary population," in which the rate of natural increase is zero per 1000 per year, with an "increasing population" having a rate of natural increase of five per 1000 per year, with a population decreasing at a rate of five per 1000 per year.

The three curves show clearly the age differences. They start far apart at the zero to ten year age class. This indicates a higher proportion of children in a growing popula-

population suggesting about equal numbers of young and middle-age classes; and (3) an urn-shaped structure for a contracting population depicting the increase in middle-aged and old organisms relative to the young.

These ideas can be expressed in another way, using actual census data, as Dublin and Lotka (1936) did for the United States population from 1850 to 1930 (observed) and from 1940 to 1980 (estimated). Table 19 condenses their data and summarizes for certain years the percentage composition of the population by age classes.

Thus, in 1850 the small but vigorous United States population yields, on random

sampling, over 50 per cent young folk under twenty years and only 2.6 per cent old-
sters sixty-five or over. One hundred years
later, in 1950, the population will have increased by 115 millions, becoming large and
mature, with a predominance of men and

teristic of human population studies are, of
course, not available.

In his 1938 book Bodenheimer includes
a chart, based on his own work, that shows
how age structure within a laboratory population of *Drosophila* varies as the culture

Table 19. Percentage Composition of the United States Population, 1850 to 1980

Year	Total Population (Millions)	Percentage of Population in Age Groups			
		0–19	20–49	50–64	65–
1850.....................	23.2	52.5	38.6	6.3	2.6
1880.....................	50.2	48.1	40.0	8.4	3.4
1910.....................	92.0	42.0	43.9	9.7	4.3
1920.....................	105.7	40.7	43.9	10.7	4.7
1930.....................	122.8	38.8	44.0	11.8	5.4
1940.....................	130.9	33.4	45.6	14.3	6.7
1950.....................	138.3	29.0	45.7	16.2	9.1
1980.....................	153.6	26.9	37.0	19.2	16.9

women in their twenties, thirties, and
forties. In addition, the young will have
decreased relatively and the old increased.
As time goes on we can confidently expect
these trends to continue; either to worsen
or improve, depending on the individual
point of view.

waxes and wanes (Fig. 82). It is apparent
that, as in human populations, there are
many young flies in the early days of
growth and many older ones in the later
days. Although an arithmetical analysis of
the data is not practicable, the figure brings
out well this principle.

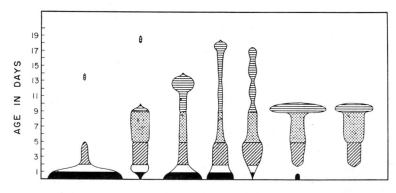

AGE OF CULTURE

Γig. 82. Age distribution in a changing *Drosophila melanogaster* population. (From
Bodenheimer.)

We agree with Bodenheimer's contention
(1938) that investigation of age distribution in populations is " . . . a greatly neglected study in animal ecology." In these
pages we review briefly several illustrations
taken from invertebrate and vertebrate
populations. Data of the scope so charac-

In a paper on the plaice of the Irish Sea,
W. C. Smith (1939) discusses the age-
structure of that natural population relative
to two ecological areas: inshore grounds
and spawning grounds. This is a purely
empirical study based on catching the fish
in trawl-nets and determining their age by

otolith examination. Smith found that for the inshore area, several year-classes are represented in the catch. The distribution of these classes in the entire population is as follows:

Age-group (year)	I	II	III	IV
Frequency	1398	2421	246	5
Percentage	34	60	6	—

Smith says of this table: " . . . Two-year old fish constitute the bulk of the trawl catch . . . and . . . few older plaice are taken. One-year old fish are probably the most abundant on the grounds, but the majority of them are too small to be taken

tory populations of the vole, *Microtus agrestis*. In one table they contrast age-structure in populations that are "stable or Malthusian" with those that are "life-table or stationary." The former type was defined by Dublin and Lotka (1925), for human populations, as " . . . the relative rate at which a population would alternately increase or decrease, if the observed mortality and fertility were to remain constant in a stable and unlimited environment." The latter or life-table population is the form that would be " . . . ultimately established in a population where the birth-rate and death-rate were equal . . . " and in a limited environment. Table 20 shows the com-

Table 20. Age-Structure in Vole Populations

Age Group (Weeks)	Age Distributions	
	Stable or Malthusian	Life-Table or Stationary
0–	577	235
8–	255	212
16–	107	178
24–	41	138
32–	14	97
40–	5	63
48–	1	38
56–		21
64–		10
72–		5
80–		2
88–		1
Total	1000	1000

by the net." The sex ratio of the inshore samples is forty-nine males to fifty-one females.

During the February and March spawning season the ripe fish congregate in an offshore area. This population consists of males two to six years old and females four to twelve years old. These males are three times as numerous as the females. Smith finds that the three-year females are essentially absent from the offshore area catches. For some unknown reason this age-class of females passes its third year presumably in another, and unknown, offshore area. A somewhat similar study is that of Jones (1939) on age-classes of salmon.

Leslie and Ranson (1940) present some observations on age distribution in labora-

puted age-structure in vole populations on the basis of these two assumptions (Leslie and Ranson, 1940).

For the Malthusian distribution, the birth rate is 0.1127, and the death rate 0.0250. "That is to say, taking one week as a unit of time, and given a population of 1000 females of all ages distributed in the stable [Malthusian] form, we should expect 25 of these to die and some 113 daughters to be born." Thus we have additional evidence for the principle that when births exceed deaths a population has a youthful age composition. In the life-table population in which the births are equal to the deaths the range of age is much greater.

Emlen (1940) presents an illustration of age shifts in populations based on actual observations of the California quail (*Lop-hortyx californica*). This study was conducted over three complete years at the University of California Farm. The findings are well illustrated in Figure 83 and by the author's comment:

"The age ratio [of immature to adult birds] in November 1936 was 150:100, indicating a

contrasted with the estimated normal 33%. The population by November, 1937 had dropped to 87, 70% of the 1936 level, and at the same time showed a strong preponderance of immature birds, 235:100. It is evident here that the better than average replacement indicated by the high age ratio was insufficient to make up for the severe loss of adults during the year. Reduced to a numerical basis the summer

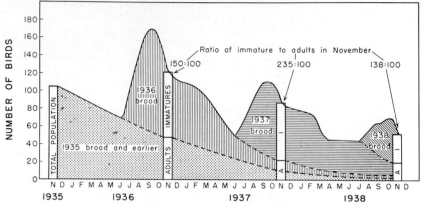

Fig. 83. Changes in quail population at the University of California farm at Davis, 1935 to 1938. Columns show population size and age distribution for four successive Novembers. (From Emlen.)

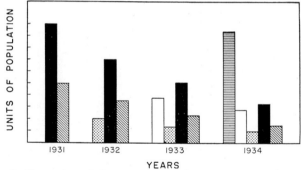

Fig. 84. Schematic illustration of changes in year-class composition of a hypothetical population of marine fishes. All the bars are identifiable in the 1934 group. These are, from right to left, year-classes older than 1930; 1930 classes; 1931, 1932, and 1933 year-classes. (From Sverdrup, Johnson, and Fleming.)

net summer replacement of 60% for 1936; somewhat less than the yearly replacement of 67% estimated to be normal for the area. Despite this subnormal increment of young birds, the population had increased during 1936, and by November was 116% of that of November 1935. A high annual survival was obviously involved. Solving for the equation $S = P(100 - R)^*$, the survival is found to be 46% as

* Where S = the survival, R = the replacement, and P given by the ratio:

$$\frac{\text{(Current population level)}}{\text{(Previous population level)}}$$

replacement was 70% (118% of normal), the total annual survival only 21% (63% of normal). In 1938 the population decreased to 52. The low replacement, indicated by the subnormal age ratio of 138:100 can account for part of this reduction, the rest is a consequence of high adult mortality. The summer replacement was 58% (69% of normal), the annual survival, 25% (75% of normal)" (p. 96).

This discussion is well ended by quoting a passage from *The Oceans* (Sverdrup, Johnson, and Fleming) that illustrates nicely the changes in age-composition from one year to another as they might occur in natural populations of fishes (see Fig. 84).

"For purposes of illustration we may consider a species with a life span of several years in which the age of individuals can be accurately determined and in which adequately large and inclusive samples are obtainable for comparison. Now, assume a highly successful spawning and larval survival in a moderate

and of the successful year 1933. As indicated [Fig. 84], the 1930 and 1933 spawning produced 'dominant year classes.' From such comparative studies of year classes and with a knowledge of the spawning habits and age groups, means are provided for analysis of probable environmental factors that determine the degree of success of spawning or survival of larvae, because the relative number of individuals entering into any year class must depend mainly on these critical periods."

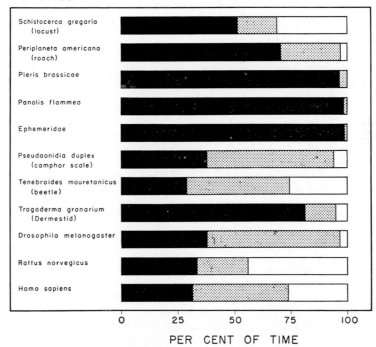

Fig. 85. Percentage of time spent by various animals in the periods of development, reproduction, and postreproduction: black, stippled, and plain bars, respectively.

population of this species in the breeding season of 1930, a very poor spawning season in 1931, an average degree of spawning and survival of larvae in 1932, and then another highly successful year in 1933. The 1930 year class will, upon investigation of the whole population in 1931, show up as a disproportionately great number of small, one-year-old individuals in relation to the other age groups in the population. In the next year (1932) the two-year-old individuals of the 1930 spawning are still conspicuous in the population, but the smaller number of one-year-old individuals is evidence of a poor spawning or survival for the 1931 reproductive season. Thus, in 1933 and subsequent years the downward trend of numerical strength of the 1930 and 1931 classes can be traced and compared with other year classes—for example, that of the average year 1932

AGE DISTRIBUTION AND REPRODUCTION

Earlier we mentioned that age distribution is significant, not only in relation to mortality, but to natality as well. Within the span of reproductive life the rate and success of reproduction are usually influenced by the age of the reproducer. Several illustrations of this fact will suffice.

King (1916) followed the sexual history of seventy-six female rats comprising 585 litters containing 3955 individuals, of whom 2036 were males and 1919 were females. The mean number of young per litter was 6.7. It was found that fertility, as measured by the total number of litters cast, increases with the age of the mother until she is seven months old. After the female is one year old there is a sharp decline in fertility. Typically, the menopause appears at about eighteen months. The mother's age is a factor that affects litter size as well as litter number. Young mothers have small litters, and later litters are large until the female attains an age of seven months. Thereafter the number declines to a point where, for females near the menopause, there are rarely more than three young.

Dublin and Lotka (1936) assembled statistics for human populations that relate the age of the mother to the rate of reproduction. The interpretation of these data is self-evident, the facts being presented in Table 21 (p. 294) in connection with another topic.

Bodenheimer (1938) stresses that, since age distributions in populations are significant in relation to reproduction, the life history of organisms should be studied to emphasize this point. Accordingly, he proposes three "ecological ages" into which all animals fall: the *period of development,* extending from fertilization of the egg to the first birth; the *period of reproduction,* covering the reproductive span; and the *period of postreproduction,* or that time between the end of reproduction and death. Needless to say, these periods vary greatly between species when expressed as percentage components of the total life-span. In addition, the requisite information for most forms is lacking. Bodenheimer presents a table covering certain examples. We have borrowed some of the material from this table, added certain illustrations and graphed the results in Figure 85. From this figure three general points emerge: (1) There seems to be no consistent relation between systematic position and percentage of time spent in the three periods. Thus, the two orthopterans, *Schistocerca* and *Periplaneta,* and the two beetles, *Tenebroides* and *Trogoderma,* are quite different one from the other, while *Tenebroides* happens to be rather similar to man. (2) In general, the postreproductive period is the shortest and the period of development, the longest. (3) It is obvious that a species population of, say the ephemerids, will have a different kind of population dynamics than, say, *Tenebroides.* This is an essential point for the ecologist. It must be considered in any population analysis.

DISPERSION

The ecologist is frequently concerned with population dispersion. This may take the form of small movements or rearrangements within the group or mass movements of the group itself. The extent of the latter depends upon the vagility of the species involved. In most natural populations emigrations and immigrations are constantly taking place. At times these are so slight or extend over so long a time that the population adjusts its growth trend and is not altered in any statistical sense. At other times the dispersion may be excessive and result either in the depopulation or the overpopulation of an area. When this occurs, the compensations by the population are more extreme. We discuss this question of dispersion and migration in various connotations elsewhere in the book (see pp. 363 and 539). Here, our concern lies only in emphasizing that such group movements, along with natality and mortality, form the third set of factors that in final analysis affect the populations' growth form and accordingly must be included in this chapter devoted to "biological backgrounds."

It is self-evident that an immigration temporarily increases population density, while an emigration temporarily decreases it. It is not so self-evident, perhaps, that a population can react to these dispersions in a number of different ways and thus bring about various end results in terms of its size and composition. The reactions, of course, always take place through reproduction and mortality and, occasionally, through additional dispersion. Some of them may be stated in somewhat oversimplified and descriptive fashion in the form of the following rubrics:

1. A population in equilibrium (i.e., numerical stability) may return to that condition rather quickly by increased mortality of the increment added by an immigration. Or, the reproductive rate of the total group may decrease, owing to the increased density, until the equilibrium is reattained. Or, both things may happen. If there is emigration, the population may make up the decrement by lowered mortality and/or increased reproduction.

2. A growing population will have its growth form altered by a dispersion if the latter is of sufficient intensity. Excessive

emigration could result in extinction, although this probably happens but rarely in nature.* A more likely result is that the growth is merely greatly retarded and may, in temperate latitudes, be even postponed for a season. Excessive immigration might either hasten the population's progress towards its equilibrium or exceed the equilibrium position. The latter would result in compensations of the type mentioned in the preceding paragraph.

3. Excluding radical changes in the exploitable resources of an environment or some equally radical biotic maladjustment, a natural population rarely reaches a density so low as to be in danger of extinction. Should either of these events occur along with considerable emigration, the population could die out in that particular ecological area. An immigration would help to re-

* Does not include geological extinction.

store the equilibrium, provided initiating the decline had been r they had not, the immigrants wc die or become emigrants.

We shall make some attempt later to provide some actual illustrations. The literature, although it is rich in descriptive information about dispersion and migration, unfortunately boasts little that can be called truly quantitative and analytical. The illustrative propositions just listed, however, have some value in connection with this chapter: They point out certain of the obvious methods by which a population reacts to dispersion patterns through the medium of mortality and natality; they focus attention on dispersion as a third factor that affects population growth form, and they set the stage for discussions in this and later sections.

20. CERTAIN DEMOGRAPHIC BACKGROUNDS FOR POPULATION STUDIES

Earlier we pointed out that a population has a series of "group attributes" which can be dealt with in numerical terms only (see pp. 263, 264). In short, any analysis of population phenomena requires that the data be subjected to statistical tabulation and treatment. This does not imply that such procedures are necessarily esoteric. In fact, many of the important statistics are obtained by simple arithmetic, graphs, and the elementary operations of classical statistics. Nor does it imply, on the other hand, that population investigations do not profit both in their design and their analysis from the intelligent application of certain of the newer statistical methods such as analysis of variance and co-variance, factor analysis, the method of small samples, the methods of probits, path-coefficient analysis, and so on. Our only point is one of emphasis: that population ecology, as in other phases of ecology and much of biology is, of necessity, quantitative ecology and must be dealt with accordingly.

Statistical methods and biometry obviously fall outside the scope of the present work. We do assume that the reader has a modicum of statistical knowledge, so that commonplace statistics, where used, are not defined.

Certain expressions, however, developed by the population student, especially in connection with human population studies, merit brief attention here. These have some application in the pages that follow and should also form a larger part of the equipment of the modern ecologist than they do now. Our intent is not to develop a coherent treatment of demography, but, rather, to suggest by examples that these techniques have real methodological value. In this chapter we discuss briefly the following: birth rates; death rates; the true rate of natural increase; the life-table; and the logistic curve of growth. This is far from being an exhaustive list, but it will introduce the reader to certain essentials of demography.

THE BIRTH RATE

The demographer recognizes two forms of the birth rate; the *crude* rate and the *specific* rate. The former is expressed merely in terms of population size; the latter is expressed relative to some specific criterion such as age, sex, race, economic status, and so on. The specific rate generally has more meaning in the sense that it has greater analytical value; the crude rate is easy to compute and has the virtue of almost universal adoption by civilized countries.

Crude Birth Rate

The crude birth rate is defined as follows:

$$R_B = \frac{B}{P},$$

where R_B is the crude birth rate; B, the number of births (exclusive of stillbirths) in a given time, as a year; and P, the total living population. The crude birth rate is usually expressed per 1000 or per 10,000 persons. Pearl (1940, p. 194) has this cogent comment about this statistic:

"This rate is obviously a most crude measure of the reproductive capacity of a population. To begin with, not all living persons are exposed to the risk of having a baby. Only females, and those between certain ages (roughly from ten to sixty outside limits) are liable to this occurrence. . . . [Crude birth rates] can be used for comparison of different places only with the utmost caution, because differences in the age and sex constitution of the populations compared, quite regardless of their true forces of natality, may have most profound effects upon the rates."

Several examples of crude birth rates taken from human demography are given below to illustrate the range that this statistic can take. A series of countries is listed along with the respective birth rates computed from the 1931 data. The countries are purposely widely chosen geographically to present both extreme and mean conditions. (The reader should ignore for the time being the right-hand column on death rate. We return to that several pages hence.)

From this tabulation we note that a rate of fifty births per 1000 population *per annum* is excessively high, while a rate below fifteen births is unusually low, and that there is a *tendency* for countries populated with caucasoids to have lower birth rates than those populated by noncaucasoids, although this, of course, does not imply that the differences are caused by genetic factors.

The birth rate is also frequently applied to the long-time history of a population. This furnishes, wherever data are available, an interesting illustration of the trend of natality. One of the best examples is set forth in a paper by Lotka (1936) describing the birth trends for Sweden, England and Wales, and the United States. The Swedish data are particularly exemplary. Since they extend back to 1750, it is possi-

Country	Births per 1000 Population	Deaths per 1000 Population
North America:		
Guatemala	50.8	22.8
Canada	24.5	11.9
United States	18.0	11.1
South America:		
Chile	39.8	24.7
Venezuela	29.6	16.9
Uruguay	24.0	10.5
Europe:		
U.S.S.R.	40.8	21.8
Poland	32.8	15.8
Italy	26.2	13.8
France	18.1	15.7
Germany	17.5	11.1
England and Wales	16.3	11.4
Sweden	15.4	11.7
Asia:		
Formosa	43.2	21.7
India	36.0	26.9
Japan	33.0	20.0
Oceania:		
Philippine Islands	33.5	17.3
Australia	19.9	8.6
New Zealand	18.8	8.6
Africa:		
Egypt	43.7	27.3
Union of South Africa	26.6	9.7

ble to plot a long uninterrupted birth history for this country. The observations on England and Wales start in 1840; the estimates on the United States in 1875; and the actual reports in 1915 (Fig. 86).

Certain conclusions can be drawn from Figure 86. In Sweden, as Lotka points out, the annual birth rate in the middle eighteenth century was in excess of thirty four per thousand. This was maintained until the eighteen-sixties. About 1865 a decrease started that was gradual up to the year 1920, " . . . after which a decline so rapid set in that in the course of a single decade the birth rate fell from over 20 to a little more than 15, a decrease by over 25 per

Specific Birth Rate

The specific birth rate is defined in the same way as the crude rate except that the numerator, B, signifies the births in a specified class of the population, and the denominator, P, those individuals in the total population that are capable of providing the births. Thus, if our interest is in age-specific birth rates, the denominator is the number of women of a given age or within a given age range, and the numerator is the number of infants born per year to those women in the stated age-class. This statistic measures "fertility" rather than "fecundity."*

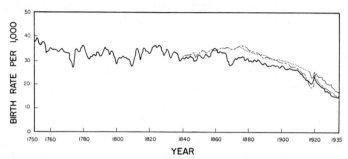

Fig. 86. Birth rates per 1000 for Sweden (heavy line), England and Wales (broken line), and the United States (estimated 1875 to 1914, dotted line; observed from 1914 on, thin line). (From Lotka.)

cent . . . . " The picture presented by Sweden is essentially characteristic of most of the leading civilized countries.* The birth rate of England and Wales and the United States after 1880 dropped about as did that for Sweden. Thus, we emerge with a generalization about many human populations: during the last seventy-five years or so natality has been decreasing. There are probably a number of reasons for this of which some are biological and some socio-economic. In part, it is an expression of a shift in age distribution of the type discussed in the preceding chapter (see p. 281). Modern populations are increasingly characterized by a predominance of middle and old-aged individuals, and this has the statistical consequence of lowering the fertility rate.

* A notable exception is France, where the major decline started *earlier* in its history. From 1920 to 1925 the birth rate was almost stationary. Since then the decline went from 19.0 in 1925 to 15.2 in 1935.

An illustration of age-specific birth rate is presented in Table 21 (p. 294). There the number of births of daughters per 100,-000 mothers relative to nine maternal age categories are set forth. The essential point that arises from this table is that these particular mothers attained their maximum effective fertility rate in the age range twenty-five to twenty-nine years. This is a valuable demographic conclusion. It could not have been reached if the crude rate alone had been computed.

The relation of age to fertility usually follows the general form just described. However, the specific birth rate, when applied to other populations, shows that this is not invariably true. In 1917 Knibbs published a treatise on the population of Australia in which he showed, as later analyses of Pearl (1940) stressed, that there the

* We shall use these two terms frequently: *fecundity* refers to egg production (or sperm production in the male); *fertility* refers to the number of eggs that develop into living young.

youngest mothers (nineteen and under) had the highest fertility or age-specific birth rate and that this rate drops consistently with age. These data, in abbreviated form, follow:

Age of Mothers (Years)	Annual Births per 1000 Married Women of Indicated Age
19 and under	476
20–24	394
25–29	306
30–34	227
35–39	160
40–44	71
45 and over	9

Enough has now been said about specific birth rates to suggest their various advantages and applications for the population student.

THE DEATH RATE

As is true for birth rate, the demographer uses both a *crude* death rate and various *specific* death rates. There is a prodigious literature on these rates as applied to human populations, largely because of the relation of deaths to actuarial, medical, and numerous socio-economic enterprises. The population ecologist can also derive something of value from a knowledge of such statistics, since as mentioned in the last chapter, mortality is one of the great forces underlying population operations and since death rates provide a technique by which this force can be measured. When more complete data are available, birth and death rates will be more fully used in population studies of other organisms, including plants.

Crude Death Rate

The crude death rate is defined as follows:

$$R_e = \frac{D}{P},$$

where R_e is the crude death rate; D, the deaths from all causes; and P, the total population or $D + (P - D)$. This rate is usually expressed "per 1000," "per 10,000" or "per 100,000" individuals. The crude death rate is not a refined statistic, because, as Pearl (1940) puts it, "The deaths are not separated as to cause, and the entire population is assumed to be at risk of death. The annual crude death-rate measures the probability of a person, regardless of age,

sex, race, or occupation, dying within one year, from any cause whatever, in a population constituted in respect of its age, sex, racial and occupational distribution, as the population under discussion happens to be."

On page 288 we listed crude birth rates by countries, and also the corresponding mortality rates. Certain points about the latter can now be made:

1. The birth rate is higher than the death rate for these geographically widely-chosen countries. Thus, although the human population of the world may be declining in some restricted areas, it is in general growing. Although not very valid statistically, the birth rates and death rates of the table can be averaged for purposes of rough comparison. When this is done, the mean birth rate is 28.9 births per 1000, and the mean mortality rate is 16.6 deaths per 1000. Thus, for the year 1931 and on the basis of the twenty-one samples, there were on the average 12.8, or 55.8 per cent, more births for every thousand persons living than there were deaths. This difference would change, of course, with the size and character of the sample and has a large standard deviation and range.

2. In general, a country with a high birth rate has a high death rate. In the table the countries are arranged according to decreasing birth rates. With exceptions, this arrangement follows along fairly well for mortality. Guatemala and Egypt, with birth rates of 50.8 and 43.7, have death rates of 22.8 and 27.3; while England and Sweden, with birth rates of 16.3 and 15.4, have death rates of 11.4 and 11.7.

3. There is a *tendency* for the "industrial caucasoid countries" to have lower death rates, just as there is a tendency for them to have lower birth rates. Again, no biological explanation should be inferred from this suggestion without particular study.

It is equally interesting to examine the trends of death for countries over an extended period of time. In the Middle Ages and early Renaissance, European death rates must have been excessively high, just as those in certain primitive areas are today. In fact, so far as the evidence goes, these rates did not start consistently downward until the middle of the nineteenth century. From that time on, accurate statistics are available for certain countries, and this downward trend can be examined with considerable precision. To document the point we have assembled crude death rates for the United States, England and Wales, Sweden, and Italy, extending for the last four countries from 1871 to 1938 and for the former from 1901 to 1940. These rates are graphed in Figure 87.

Probably the most important point in Figure 87 is the downward trend of the death rate for all four countries over the sixty-odd years of observation. During this interval the curve of ecological mortality steadily approaches (with the exception of the war years) the curve of physiological matters pertaining to health and group living.

Figure 87 also allows some instructive comparisons between countries. It is patent that Italy is in a "curve family" by itself. There is no confluence between its line and those of the other three. Also, it is true that Italy started to control its excessive mortality about 1920; from that time on the trend is consistently downward. In the last quartile of the nineteenth century Sweden had a distinctly lower death rate than did England and Wales. This persisted until

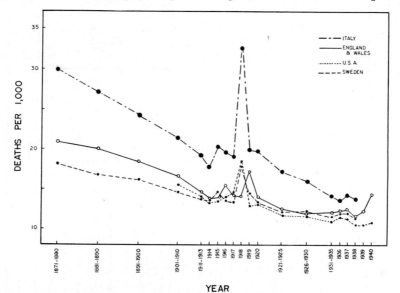

Fig. 87. Deaths per 1000 for Sweden, England and Wales, Italy, and the United States. (From Lotka.)

longevity. Italy, starting with a rate of thirty deaths per 1000 population in the 1871 to 1880 interval, in 1938 had a rate of 13.9—a decrease of about 53 per cent. Sweden drops from 18.3 to 11.5, a 37 per cent decrease. The trends for England and Wales and the United States are essentially similar to those of Sweden as well as to each other. There is no doubt that the decline in mortality is real, although the causal factors are somewhat more obscure. As a general assumption, it seems safe to conclude that the major cause is not a genetic difference between the organisms of 1870 and those of 1940, but, rather, a fundamental betterment of the population ecology. Probably the most important factor-complex is an improvement in the practices of public health and preventive medicine along with a gradual education of the populace about

about 1910, when the two became reasonably similar. The United States also falls into this pattern.

The final point of interest is the striking relation between World War I and the death rate. This holds true for all countries whether belligerent or nonbelligerent. Italy's rate jumped from 19.2 in 1917 to 32.9 in 1918; Sweden's from 13.4 to 18.0; and the United States' from 14.3 to 18.1. England and Wales had two accelerations: one in 1916, when the rate went from 14.0 (1915) to 15.7, and the other in 1919, when it increased from the 1918 figure of 14.3 to 17.3. Again the interpretations are difficult, although the influenza pandemic and a general worsening of living standards consequent on the war come to mind as significant contributing causes. It is interesting to note that Italy, with a past history of high mortality and poor sanitation, had a greater actual and relative rise during the war years than the other countries.

Specific Death Rates

In its various forms the specific death rate is a widely used and useful statistic. It is commonly applied to age, sex, race, occupation, location of dwelling, and as a statistic (Fig. 88). We see that all four curves (1910 males, females; 1930 males, females) have a characteristic form. There is a high death rate under one year of age. representing the infant mortality component; a low death rate between nine years and, say, thirty to forty years, followed thereafter by a rapid increase through middle and old age.

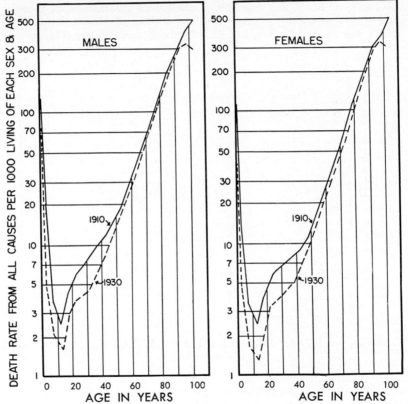

Fig. 88. Age and sex-specific death rates for 1910 and 1930, United States census data. (From Pearl.)

measure of infant mortality. The definition is

$$R_s = \frac{D_e}{E}$$

where R_s is the specific death rate; D_e, the deaths in a specific class of the population; and E, the number exposed to risk of dying in the same specified class of the population from which the deaths came. These rates are usually stated "per 1000."

A case computed by Pearl (1940) on age and sex-specific death rates for twenty states of the United States population in the years 1910 and 1930 will illustrate this

In terms of sexual differences the females as infants may have a higher mortality than do the males, but if they live to be one year old their prospects for long life in the statistical sense are better. Insofar as information is available, this sex differential applies generally to most animals; it is not limited to man (see discussion under the Life-Table, p. 294).

The final point to be made from Figure 88 is that in the twenty years between 1910 and 1930 the mortality decreased for all sexes and for all ages. The greatest reductions occurred from birth through age fifty. There is some, although relatively slight, difference during later life.

This illustration of a specific death rate nicely demonstrates some of the advantages of the statistic, not only for human populations, but for others as well.

We now have discussed birth rates and death rates in enough detail to illustrate certain of their attributes and limitations. That they are the basic statistics of human populations is incontestable, and that ecological population students can utilize them with profit should be equally clear. In short, some knowledge of these rates should be part of the equipment of the modern ecologist. Nevertheless, from the point of view of population growth trends, it is meaningless to consider a birth rate independent of a death rate or a death rate independent of a birth rate. As was stressed in the last chapter, the interaction between the two is significant. We now wish to discuss an index, the true rate of natural increase, that expresses this interaction.

THE TRUE RATE OF NATURAL INCREASE*

The "true rate of natural increase" is a statistic that has been championed by A. J. Lotka. Since it has much to recommend it and since an understanding of the underlying principles clears up a number of points about birth rates and deaths, we consider it advisable to discuss it in some detail. We follow closely the excellent treatment, as well as the example, presented in Dublin and Lotka (1936, pp. 242–247).

In 1920 the observed birth rate for the white population of the United States was 23.40; the death rate, 12.41. The difference between these two, 10.99, is frequently called the "rate of natural increase." Dublin and Lotka question the validity of this index and propose instead the "*true* rate of natural increase," now to be discussed. True natural increase takes into account the age distribution of the population. This is

* In earlier years demographers frequently used a statistic known as the "vital-index" or birth-death ratio to express the interaction of natality with mortality. This index is defined as 100 births divided by deaths, and, upon solution, yields the number of births per each 100 deaths per designated time interval. When the index exceeds 100, the population is growing; at less than 100, it is declining. The vital index finds little adoption today because it is "open to misinterpretation as a measure of population reproductivity since it is partly determined by the age composition of the population" (Linder and Grove, 1943).

sound procedure for two reasons: (1) because the death rate, as we have seen, varies with the age-class composition of the group, and (2) because, in the human population, reproduction is concentrated essentially between the female ages fifteen to fifty years. For these reasons, Lotka rightly believes that a measure of population increase that does not evaluate the particular age distribution is not so accurate as it should be.

Age distribution itself is not a random distribution; it has a pattern of its own. It has been shown (Sharpe and Lotka, 1911) that if the fertility of females at each age (i.e., the average number of children born in a particular year of life) and the mortality at each age remain constant, the age distribution eventually assumes a form that can be predicted by calculation. From this distribution the birth rate, death rate, and true rate of natural increase characteristic of this population can be computed. These rates "represent more correctly the inherent power for growth of the population."

The ultimate course of events in a population rests on the ratio of total births in two consecutive generations. Dublin and Lotka illustrate these data for twenty-three states in 1920 as contrasted with 1930. Their basic figures appear in Table 21.

In 1920 the total white female births by women twenty to twenty-four years old was 186,302. The total number of white women in the population was 2,548,435. Their reproductive rate, as shown in Table 21, was 7310 daughters per 100,000 (i.e., 186,302: 2,548,435 = X:100,000). We now follow the history of a cohort of 100,000 female babies, assuming they are subjected to the mortality characteristic of 1920. As they mature their number is reduced by deaths. At twenty-two years of age the table shows 85,509 surviving. These reproduce at a rate of 7310 girls per 100,000, or give rise to 6251 per annum. Thus, in five years there are 31,255 girl births (5 × 6251). After the fifty-fifth year the cohort will have produced 116,635 girls. This means that for the age schedule operative in 1920, the ratio of total female births in two successive generations would have been 1.166. Dublin and Lotka comment on this point as follows:

"Evidently, we have here the requisite conditions for a growing population, each generation exceeding its predecessor in the

Table 21. Computation Schedule: Ratio of Total Births in Two Consecutive Generations According to Fertility and Mortality in 1920 (White Females only) (From Dublin and Lotka)

Age Group	Annual Births of Daughters per 100,000 Females	Fraction of Births Surviving to Center of Age Group	Product (2) × (3)
(1)	(2)	(3)	(4)
10–14...	9	0.88567	8
15–19...	2,202	0.87438	1,925
20–24...	7,310	0.85509	6,251
25–29...	7,481	0.82960	6,206
30–34...	5,780	0.80181	4,634
35–39...	3,898	0.77417	3,081
40–44...	1,552	0.74664	1,159
45–49...	172	0.71610	123
50–54...	5	0.67860	3
			23,327
			×5
Total...	.....	....	116,635

ratio of 1.166 to 1. Furthermore, our data determine a definite rate of growth per generation, and hence, if we know the mean length of one generation in years, they determine a rate of growth per annum. This mean length of one generation is found, in close approximation, as the mean age of the mothers in a cohort, at the time of the births of their children. This mean age is . . . 28.5 years. The net result, so far, is that the conditions of fertility and mortality prevailing in 1920, if continued unchanged, would have resulted in an increase of births in successive generations at such a rate that a cohort of 1,000 newborn girls would, by the end of their reproductive period, have given rise to 1,166 daughters. This corresponds to an increase in total births at a rate of 166 per 1,000 per generation. It can be shown that this is also the ultimate rate of increase of the population as a whole, after the stable form of the age distribution has become established."

This rate of increase of 166 per 1000 per generation can be converted into a rate of increase per year. This is the *true rate of natural increase*, and, for our example, is 5.41 per 1000 per annum.* If now we compare this figure, 5.41, with the crude rate of natural increase, 10.99 (i.e., crude birth rate minus crude death rate),

* To convert rate per generation to rate per year, Dublin and Lotka present the following algebraic solution:

$$e^{28.5r} = 1.166$$

$$r = \frac{1}{28.5} \log_e 1.166 = 0.00541$$

we see that the latter has a spurious optimism about it. By taking into account the age distribution with its consequent effects on mortality and natality, the true rate is only half the magnitude of the crude rate.*

THE LIFE TABLE

One of the most useful of all numerical aids for the population student is the life table, a device that records in systematic fashion those facts basic to the age distribution of mortality. In short, a life table "keeps the books on death."

In this discussion we wish to show briefly what a simple life table is and then present several illustrations taken from the literature of human and other population studies. Since the life table underlies actuarial matters and "life insurance," it has, of course, a voluminous bibliography. For our purposes the two best general treatments are those of Dublin and Lotka (1936) and Pearl's (1940) biometry text. Deevey (1947) has published a most useful review of the life table as a tool in the study of *natural* populations.

Structure of the Life Table

Conventionally, a life table is a series of columns each of which describes something

* After the above was written, a first-rate discussion of this method as applied to insect populations was published by Birch (1948). This paper not only interprets the index, but shows clearly the steps in its computation. See also Leslie and Park, 1949.

about the mortality relations within a population when ages of the components are taken into account. Conventionally also a life table starts with a certain sized group, usually 100,000 or 1000, at its time of birth and tabulates the events to which that cohort is subjected, although it may have other variants. This tabulation takes the following form (adapted from Pearl, 1940):

is based on the mortality statistics for white males in continental United States, 1929 to 1931.

Several obvious points can be derived from Table 22 about the age distribution of mortality. The death rate, or more specifically the infant mortality rate, is high during the first year of life. As shown in the q_x column, the probability is that of each

x	l_x	d_x	q_x	e_x
Age in appropriate units, stated as an interval	The number surviving at the beginning of the age interval stated in the x column	The number dying *within* the age interval stated in the x column	The number dying in the age interval divided by the number of survivors at the beginning of the interval. *The rate of mortality*	Life expectation. Mean length of life remaining to each organism alive at the beginning of the age interval

Other columns are sometimes used, but these are by and large the ones of greatest applicability. The plan seems self-explanatory. The x column first states age; l_x tabulates the survivors remaining after death takes its toll; d_x shows the actual number of deaths; q_x is the rate at which the deaths occur and is usually expressed as a rate per 1000 population, or $1000q_x$, and e_x denotes the life expectation, mean "after lifetime," remaining once an organism has attained a certain age.* The computations, although tedious in an extended table, have the virtue of essential simplicity.

Illustrations

Human Population. There is in the literature a profusion of life tables for human populations for many countries and other political units and under many socio-economic conditions. An unabridged life table is a formidable creation in terms of length. For our own illustration we have chosen a table reported *in extenso* in Pearl (1940), which we have considerably condensed. This condensation is effected by reporting, after the first ten years of life which are taken up year by year, only the last year of a five year span; e.g., 14 to 15, 19 to 20, and so on. This table (Table 22), originally taken from Hill's (1936) study of the United States Bureau of the Census data,

* These items, especially l_x and d_x, were dealt with in a somewhat different connotation in the discussion of physiological and ecological longevity (p. 273).

1000 births, 62.32 will die before the first birthday. After this initial and rigorous elimination, with its selective significance (p. 640), there is a consistent drop in the death rate until the age interval ten to eleven years is attained. At this time q_x is at its lowest (1.47). Thereafter it rises, at first slowly and later with increasing rapidity. After age fifty the rate accelerates.

A life table for females from the same sample shows that their mortality relative to age is lower, or, conversely, their longevity greater, than that of the males. The e_x figure for baby girls (0 to one year) is 62.67 years, as contrasted with 59.12 years for the males. In their fifteenth year of life the females had a life expectancy of 53.92 years; the males, 51.29 years. In the fiftieth year the figures are 24.19 and 22.25 for females and males, respectively. This is almost universally true for the human species. It is just as real a sexual difference in population terms as, say, secondary sexual characteristics are in terms of an individual organism. Nor is it limited to *Homo sapiens.* As the data accumulate, it seems to hold equally true for other animal populations.

One of the most useful features of the life table is that its columns lend themselves readily to graphic representation. Conventionally, three graphs are derived from the table: the l_x curve, the d_x curve and the $1000q_x$ curve. These are plotted on the ordinate against age on the abscissa. The graphs are illustrated in Figures 89, 90, and 91, which are based on the data of Table 22.

The survivorship curve shows clearly the initial drop owing to an infant mortality component; the gradual decrease for about

gevity and ecological mortality were developed (see page 273).

The curve of deaths, or d_x describes in reverse the survivorship graph. It has the pictorial value, however, of an accentuated

Table 22. *Abridged Life Table for White Males in Continental United States, 1929 to 1931 (Adapted from Pearl, 1940; originally from Hill, 1936)*

Age Interval	Of 100,000 Males Born Alive		Mortality Rate	Complete Expectation of Life
	Number Alive at Beginning of Year of Age	Number Dying During Year of Age	Number Dying per 1000 Alive at Beginning of Year	Average Number of Years of Life Remaining at Beginning of Year of Age
x	l_x	d_x	$1000q_x$	$\overset{\circ}{e}_x$
0– 1	100,000	6232	62.32	59.12
1– 2	93,768	931	9.93	62.04
2– 3	92,837	483	5.20	61.65
3– 4	92,354	331	3.59	60.97
4– 5	92,023	285	3.09	60.19
5– 6	91,738	243	2.66	59.38
6– 7	91,495	208	2.27	58.53
7– 8	91,287	179	1.96	57.67
8– 9	91,108	156	1.72	56.78
9– 10	90,952	142	1.55	55.87
14– 15	90,246	172	1.90	51.29
19– 20	89,172	268	3.01	46.88
24– 25	87,692	321	3.66	42.62
29– 30	86,053	346	4.02	38.39
34– 35	84,222	410	4.86	34.17
39– 40	81,979	522	6.36	30.03
44– 45	79,036	691	8.74	26.05
49– 50	75,188	900	11.98	22.25
54– 55	70,165	1184	16.87	18.66
59– 60	63,496	1563	24.61	15.34
64– 65	54,924	1960	35.68	12.33
69– 70	44,253	2373	53.62	9.68
74– 75	31,986	2515	78.61	7.43
79– 80	19,565	2344	119.83	5.57
84– 85	9,159	1587	173.33	4.21
89– 90	3,068	712	232.11	3.21
94– 95	672	211	313.32	2.35
99–100	72	32	438.79	1.62
104–105	2	1	621.87	1.05
105–106	1	1	666.56	.96

fifty years, followed by the rapid decrease in later life. The reader will recognize that these l_x curves based on life table data are similar in construction and principle to those we discussed in the last chapter, in which the concepts of physiological lon-

ordinate scale. This emphasizes the relations between age and mortality. For example, the high incidence of deaths during the first year of life is excellently displayed in the figure.

The death rate, or $1000q_x$, curve plots for

curves, reproduced in Figure 92 along with comparable curves for the human species. The latter are added because, as Pearl, Park, and Miner pointed out, there is, coincidentally, more confluence between the mortality of *Tribolium* and man than for population. The number of deaths attains its maximum during the middle period; the death rate is highest in old age. To quote from the paper cited, "The fundamental similarity in form of the *Tribolium* life curves and those for man is evident. The

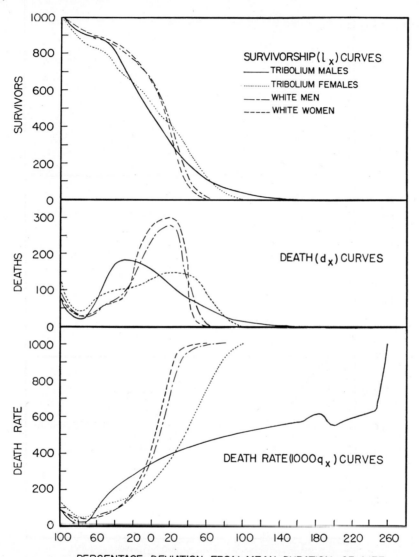

Fig. 92. Survivorship, death, and death rate curves for the flour beetle, *Tribolium confusum*, compared with those for man. (From Pearl, Park, and Miner.)

any other species for which actuarial data exist.

In the *Tribolium* curves proper we see that there is a drop in survivors, or an increase in deaths, during the early days of life, a slow tapering off during middle life, and then a long and gradual decline of the only important difference between them is found in the much greater variation exhibited by the death (d_x) curves in *Tribolium* as compared with the human. The *Tribolium* d_x curves not only have a greater *range* of variation, but are much flatter over the major portion of their course. *Tribolium* has a wide ratio of total life span to mean duration of life. In the males this ratio is about 304:100, and in the females 219:100. For the human life table the corre-

In the chapter on Biological Backgrounds certain illustrations were presented that made use of life table data, particularly in terms of survivorship. Figure 73 (p. 274)

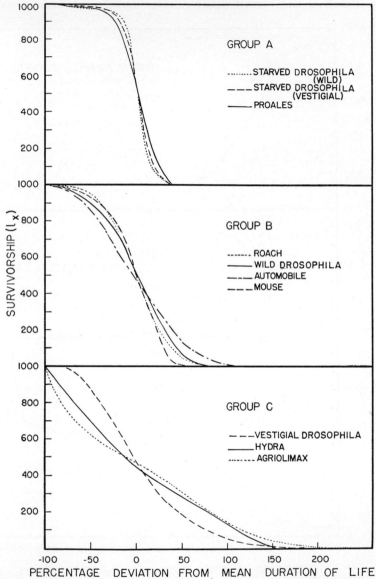

Fig. 93. Pearl's three categories of survivorship curves: Group A, "rectangular type;" Group B, "intermediate type;" and Group C, "diagonal type." (From Pearl.)

sponding ratios are 179:100 and 169:100." In addition to this general similarity the *Tribolium* curves have at the beginning of life in the imago stage a component corresponding in time and quantitative relations of its incidence to the infant mortality component of human life tables."

shows the l_x curves for *Drosophila* reared under laboratory conditions. If we re-examine this graph from our present point of view and pay particular attention to curve "3," wild type flies and curve "4," vestigial type flies, we can add a bit of information to this discussion of the life table.

This figure shows clearly that the mutation "vestigial" affects the form of the life curve exhibited by the population just as it affects the wing size of an individual fly. Whereas the wild type flies approach more closely the physiological or right-angled curve, the mortality of vestigial flies results in a curve form that is lower through early middle life and then stretches out into a long tail during old age. It should be remembered, of course, that the abscissa of this graph is a relative and not an absolute scale. Actually, the wild type *Drosophila* have a longer life duration than do the mutants.

Categories of Survivorship Curves

Pearl (1940) makes the interesting point that the form taken by population mortality varies with the species, as would be expected, but that, as might not be expected, these "forms" fall into three general groups. This can be seen in Figure 93, in which l is plotted against age expressed on a relative scale. There is considerable confluence between individual curves within each of the three categories. Pearl designates Group A as the *rectangular;* Group B, the *intermediate;* and Group C, the *diagonal* type.

The rectangular pattern, which incidentally is the closest approach to the physiological curve, describes a situation in which all the individuals of a cohort are born at the same time, live with a minimum of mortality for a considerable period of their life, and then die off rapidly. For the three examples presented (the rotifer *Proales,* starved wild *Drosophila,* starved vestigial *Drosophila*), the upper limit of the life span stands to the mean duration of life roughly as 140:100 in terms of relative age.

The intermediate pattern is typified by the roach *Blatta orientalis,* the mouse, and wild type *Drosophila melanogaster.* Here the dying off begins slowly at first, then attains its maximum rate, and finally slows down; the curve stretches out because of the ability of a few individuals to outlive considerably their companions. The upper limit of the life span stands to the mean as 185:100.

The diagonal pattern is illustrated by the mortality of vestigial *Drosophila, Hydra,* and the slug, *Deroceras agreste* = (*Agriolimax agrestis*). In this form the death rates are approximately constant until extreme old age is attained. There is also a large ratio of total life span to mean life duration. This, for the three species, is about 300: 100.

There is, as Pearl recognizes, a fourth logical possibility as regards the l_x curve. This is another rectangular curve inverse in form to the one discussed. It is sometimes called the "positive skew" rectangular type in contradistinction to the "negative skew." For this curve there would exist an explosive mortality in early life followed by a lingering of the few survivors for a considerable period. No actual illustration of this curve can be provided at this time, although it seems likely that certain species must have this form of mortality, as, for example, May fly imagoes. Probably the closest known approach (actually not very close) is derived from the life table for the human population of India. There, a great infant mortality eliminates a sizable component during the first year of life. The mean duration of life is also low.*

It has seemed of some importance to describe these types of survivorship curves. In the first place, the fact that organisms can be differentiated into groups according to the form of their mortality suggests an ecological principle of some significance. Secondly, as life tables accumulate for various species it will be technically useful to know into which group the particular organism falls.

The Logistic Curve

One of the most active, and in some ways polemic, areas of population biology has centered for the past twenty years around the development and application of the logistic curve to the growth of populations (see section on History p. 61). In this chapter it is our purpose to discuss briefly certain of the basic assumptions underlying this curve, assumptions which the ecologist should understand and then evaluate for himself. The next chapter on Population Growth-Form contains a number of illustrations of the curve applied to

---

* On the basis of old statistics (1901 to 1910) for India assembled by Glover (1921), it can be shown that of an initial population of 100,000 males, about 45,000 die during the first five years of life; 50,000 by the tenth year; and 85,000 by the fifty-fifth year! Comparable figures for, say, Swedish males are (approximately) 13,000; 15,000; and 38,000.

actual data. The following discussion leans heavily on the book by Gause (1934) and to some extent a paper by Thomas Park (1939).

Taking it for granted that the logistic curve is a reliable picture of group increase, what biological facts and suggestions can be inferred from the study of the curve itself? Inherent in the curve are the following properties of significance in an analysis of population growth (Pearl and Reed, 1920; Pearl, 1924):

1. The area (and/or volume) upon which the population grows is a finite area with definite limits, however large.

2. The number of individuals (population density) that can be supported in a specified area is limited; in other words, the asymptote of the curve approaches a finite number.

3. The lower asymptote of the curve is zero; negative populations are unimaginable.

4. Population growth may be cyclical in character with new logistic cycles additive. Adaptive changes between the population and its environment may initiate a new cycle of growth superimposed on the other one. For example, the agricultural stage of human culture supported higher population densities than did the pastoral stage.

5. The general shape of the curve shows, first, that populations have a slow rate of growth; second, the rate increases until it reaches a maximum (the inflection point of the curve); and third, the rate becomes progressively less until the curve stretches out nearly horizontally in close approach to the upper asymptote.

The differential equation from which the logistic curve is derived is:

$$\frac{dN}{dt} = bN \frac{(K - N)}{K},$$

where b is the maximum potential rate of reproduction for each organism in the population; N is the total population size at any moment of growth; t is time or age; and K is the maximum population possible under the obtaining ecological conditions. Gause (1934) stated this equation in word form as follows:

The underlying rationale of the logistic curve becomes clearer when an application is made to an actual case. Gause has done this for the growth of small laboratory populations of *Paramecium caudatum*. In his work five individual infusorians were placed in 0.5 cc. of nutritive medium. The experiment was repeated, and counts of organisms were taken at twenty-four hour intervals for six days. When fitted to a logistic curve, the actual observations correspond closely with the curve itself. This is seen in Figure 94, in which age of the culture in days is plotted on the abscissa and total population size on the ordinate. This graph describes a population *trend* (see next chapter). The feature of Gause's study and logistic application is that something can be constructed about the population growth factors by assuming that the population actually grows in this fashion and then calculating certain values from the curve equation. As Gause puts it, we are interested in the question: "What is the potential rate of increase of *Paramecium* under our conditions, and how does it become reduced in the process of growth as the environmental resistance increases?"

From an inspection of Figure 94 it can be seen that the maximal population possible under the respective conditions is 375 paramecia per 0.5 cc. of medium. This value is called K. In fitting the curve, b, or the rate of reproduction, is 2.309. This means that in a twenty-four hour period every individual protozoan has the capacity to produce 2.309 others. Knowing these two values, Gause computes certain other expressions that have generalized population importance. These are summarized in Table 23. The first line shows the change in number of organisms during the initial four days of growth. The population increases from 20.4 individuals to 137.2, to 319.0, to 369.0. If the ecological conditions are not altered, N remains around 369. The second line of the table expresses the potential increase of the population per day, or the number of offspring that a given population can potentially produce within twenty-four hours. This is a geometric increase and is not actually realized by the population (p. 272). The unutilized op-

$$\left\{ \begin{array}{l} \text{The rate of popu-} \\ \text{lation growth} \end{array} \right\} = \left\{ \begin{array}{l} \text{The potential increase} \\ \text{of the population per} \\ \text{unit of time} \end{array} \right\} \times \left\{ \begin{array}{l} \text{The degree of realiza-} \\ \text{tion of the potential} \\ \text{increase} \end{array} \right\}$$

portunity for growth is indicated by the ratio $\frac{K - N}{K}$, which approaches one on the first day and is reduced to 0.016 on the fourth day, when few additional paramecia

(Gause's $1 - \frac{K - N}{K}$). The last entry of the table indicates the rate of population growth. This is actually the arithmetical solution of the logistic equation. The figures

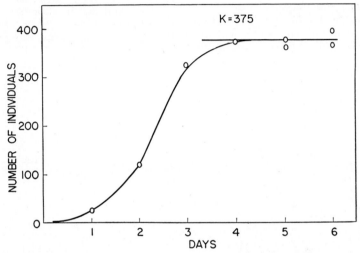

Fig. 94. The growth of a laboratory population of *Paramecium caudatum* fitted to the logistic equation. Circles are observed counts; line is the fitted curve. (From Gause.)

are added to the total. The reason the potential increase becomes successively lower as the population grows is related to the fact that the utilized opportunity for growth

show that the population grows rapidly between the first and second day, after which the rate of increase slackens. For example, 44.5 individuals are added to the culture

Table 23. The Growth of a Population of Paramecium caudatum

	Time in Days			
	1	2	3	4
N (number of individuals; derived from the logistic equation)	20.4	137.2	319.0	369.0
bN (potential increase of the population per 24 hour period)	47.1	316.8	736.6	852.0
$\frac{K - N}{K}$ (unutilized opportunity for population growth)	0.945	0.633	0.149	0.016
$\frac{N}{K}$ (utilized opportunity for population growth)	0.055	0.367	0.851	0.984
$\frac{dN}{dt} = bN \frac{K - N}{K}$ (rate of population growth)	44.5	200.0	109.7	13.6

(designated by Gause as "environmental resistance") approaches 1.0 with time, and as the population nears its asymptote the potential increase remains almost entirely unrealized. We express this as the ratio $\frac{N}{K}$

during the first twenty-four hours; 200.0 during the second twenty-four hours; 109.7 during the third, and only 13.6 during the fourth.

Gause designates these relationships as "characteristics of competition" and has illustrated them graphically. Figure 95, adapted from his book, depicts on a relative scale and in pictorial fashion the interoperation of these factors for the *Paramecium caudatum* illustration. The drawing adds nothing to what has already been said, but affords a succinct summary.

It would not be a fair appraisal to leave the logistic curve without mentioning that it has been subject to criticism. Possibly the

the empirical representation of growth phenomena. It does not appear that either curve has any substantial advantage over the other in the range of phenomena which it will fit. Each curve has three arbitrary constants, which correspond essentially to the upper asymptote, the time origin, and the time unit or 'rate constant.' In each curve, the degree of skewness, as measured by the relation of the ordinate at the point of inflection to the distance between the asymptote, is fixed. It

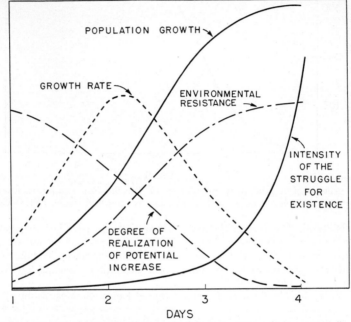

Fig. 95. Schematic representation of Gause's "characteristics of competition" exhibited by a population of paramecia growing logistically. In the text Gause's "degree of realization of the potential increase" is referred to as "unutilized opportunity for growth," and his "environmental resistance" as "utilized opportunity for growth." (From Gause.)

most general criticism is a simple one: populations characteristically grow in a sigmoid or S-shaped fashion; the logistic curve is a sigmoid curve which describes their growth; therefore, there is nothing unique about the fact that the logistic equation "works." In short (the criticism holds), it is fallacious to designate the logistic as a "law" of population growth. Other curves can be applied to population increase. For example, Wright (1926) discusses the "Gompertz" curve, named after Benjamin Gompertz, who discovered it in 1825. Winsor (1932, p. 7) compared this function with the logistic and came to the following conclusion:

"The Gompertz curve and the logistic possess similar properties which make them useful for

has been found in practice that the logistic gives good fits on material showing an inflection about midway between the asymptotes. No such extended experience with the Gompertz curve is as yet available, but it seems reasonable to expect that it will give fits on material showing an inflection when about 37 per cent of the total growth has been completed. Generalizations of both curves are possible, but here again there appears to be no reason to expect any marked difference in the additional freedom provided."

The reader may find for himself critical comments about the logistic curve in the papers by Hogben (1931) and by Wilson and Puffer (1933). The latter workers warn particularly against using extrapolations of the logistic curve in predicting the size of a population at some future specified date —a warning that we view sympathetically. They say: "If by the statement that the logistic . . . is the law of population growth, one means only that the formula is well suited to fitting the census enumerations for the period of a century or so when such enumerations have actually been made, we can take no exception to it. . . . But if the statement is to be considered as signifying that the formula affords a rational law to such an extent as to permit the extrapolation of the curve for forecasting purposes and the interpretation of the constants as constants of nature, we are forced to take serious exception to it" (p. 342).

We return to the logistic curve in the next chapter, on Growth Form, in which we show its breadth of application, and again in Chapter 22. Our present interest has been to show (1) that it does provide in many cases a convenient *description* of population growth; (2) that it is well established in population literature; (3) that it directs attention to certain compound, general factors that play a causative role in population trends and permits these factors to be arithmetically evaluated; and (4) that, while the logistic curve does not identify such factors biologically, it does stress their existence and recommends their further study. Despite the criticisms that can be leveled against it, the logistic curve, when not overinterpreted and when used intelligently purely as an empirical record of population growth, is a valuable demographic tool.

21. THE GROWTH FORM OF POPULATIONS

The major trend in size of a population through time, or, as we prefer to call it, its "growth form," is basic to the development of the population problem. The coordinates of growth form are some expression or index of numbers (ordinate) against time (abscissa). Growth form is roughly analogous to knowledge of, say, the anthropometry of a man, which provides a sort of general statement about his total structural development, or to such physiological indices as basal metabolic rate, respiration rate, heart rate, body temperature, and so forth, which evaluate in a way his total metabolic relationships.

This chapter is devoted to a description of the various population growth forms. The major trends as they might exist in a hypothetical population are discussed first. This defines the possibilities. Then, actual illustrations drawn rather extensively from the literature dealing with laboratory, natural, and human populations are presented. Data covering the course of a particular population over an extended period are unfortunately rare. Thus, we are forced to use one example to make one point and another example to make another. Chapter 22 deals with the relations of growth form to natality, mortality, and dispersion and, further, its relation to population integration.

DEFINITIONS: THE PATTERNS OF GROWTH FORM

It is convenient to define the following stages of population growth form:

I. The period of positive, sigmoid growth (the population increasing):
   A. The establishment of the population i.e., its initiation or "taking hold" in its environment
   B. The period of rapid growth rate (sometimes called the "logarithmic phase," especially by microbiologists)
   C. The period of decreased growth rate as the asymptote is approached
II. The equilibrium position. Equilibrium is defined as mean numerical stability
III. Oscillations and fluctuations. These are departures (in both phase and amplitude) from equilibrium:
   A. Oscillations: relatively symmetrical departures
   B. Fluctuations: relatively asymmetrical departures
IV. The period of negative growth (population decline or contraction). Consistent and progressive reduction of the population below equilibrium or below the lower range of usual fluctuations and/or oscillations.

V. Extinction: the passing out of the population

VI. Special cases. Accentuated, sudden changes in growth form that depart radically from the patterns in I–V:
   A. Population "spurts"
   B. Population "crashes"

The first five relations defined are shown in Figure 96, in which growth form is stylized for purposes of clarity. Observed population growth, as we shall see, frequently falls well beyond the limits of the curves shown. In fact, the periods themselves must not be understood as actually sharply defined.* As we shall soon show,

the species—or it can be true at the level of certain species population subgroups and not for others. This is to be expected.

Despite obvious objections that can be raised to Figure 96 and the ideas it summarizes, the fact that a few growth forms describe the major trends that essentially all populations follow during their total life history has both a technical and an interpretative value.

APPLICATIONS

THE PERIOD OF POSITIVE GROWTH

The growth curve that represents this period is usually sigmoid or S-shaped in

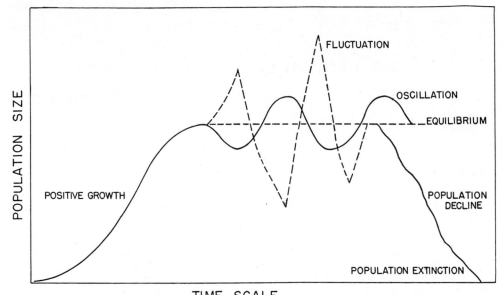

TIME SCALE
Fig. 96. Stylized representation of the various phases of population growth form.

the variability in growth of populations can be considerable. Also, some populations have their abscissal or time axis greatly exaggerated. Thus, although it is the exception rather than the rule, it is not unknown in nature for a group to reach an equilibrium that is rather closely maintained for extended periods of time. This can be true at the species level—i.e., for all members of

* In embryogeny, for example, we speak of the blastula and the gastrula as if they were temporally discrete units. This is convenient and from that point of view necessary, but obviously not rigorous, since cleavage stages merge inperceptibly into the blastula and the blastula into the gastrula.

form. This implies merely that initial growth is slow, intermediate growth more rapid, and later growth slow again. The situation is well described by the logistic curve, the applications of which to population data are many. In the last chapter the rationale of the curve was briefly presented. Now we wish to provide actual illustrations drawn from the population literature. This shows how widely the logistic has been applied. permits a judgment to be formed about the goodness of fit of the curve to actual data. and provides an adequate summary of a segment of the growth form, the period of positive growth.

Laboratory Populations

Five examples of the logistic growth curves of laboratory populations, chosen from Pearl (1930), for *Drosophila melanogaster;* from Carlson (1913) and Pearl (1930), for yeast; from Gause (1934) for *Paramecium caudatum;* from Gause (1931), for *Tribolium confusum;* and from Terao and Tanaka (1928), for the water flea, *Moina macrocopa* Strauss; are reproduced as Figures 94, and 97, 98, 99, and 100.

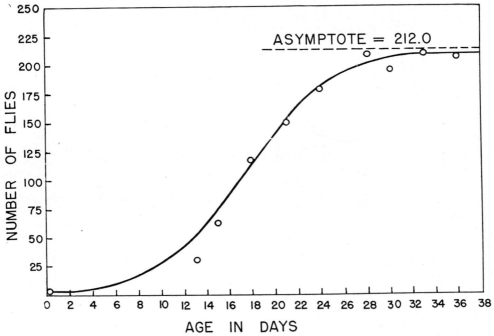

Fig. 97. The logistic growth of a laboratory population of *Drosophila melanogaster.* (From Pearl.)

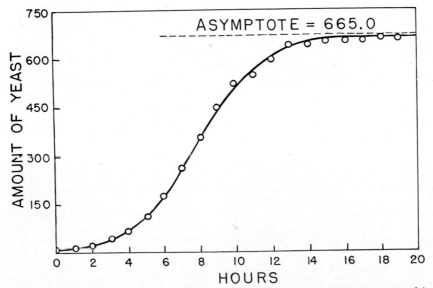

Fig. 98. The logistic growth of a laboratory population of yeast cells. (From Pearl.)

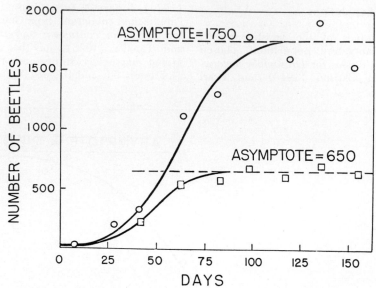

Fig. 99. The logistic growth of two laboratory populations of the flour beetle, *Tribolium confusum;* one in 64 gm. of flour (upper curve), and one in 16 gm. (lower curve). (From Gause.)

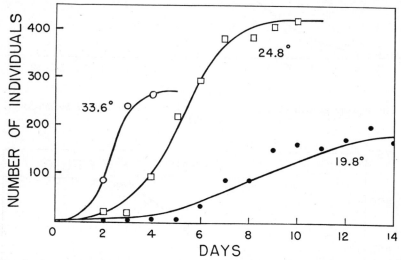

Fig. 100. The logistic growth of three laboratory populations of the water flea, *Moina macrocopa,* at three temperatures. (From Terao and Tanaka.)

Certain conclusions can be drawn from examination of these five logistic curves.

In the first place, as already noted, the general shape of a population growth figure is sigmoid and symmetrical.

Secondly, the correspondence between the theoretical curves and the actual observations, loosely, the "goodness of fit," deserves some comment. We can assume that the curves are fitted with skill, i.e., that the best possible agreement between the data and the function is represented.* While this certainly is not true in every reported instance, it seems, for reasons of discussion,

* At the risk of seeming captious, the point might be made that any published curve would, of necessity, be a moderately good fit, since an author would be loth to present one not adequate. Were this true to any extent, there would exist in the literature a bias in favor of the curve rather than the facts. We do not take this criticism too seriously.

garis. The fact that the curve fits such social groups provides a significant extension of its general applicability.

A final illustration for natural populations of insects is the study by Davidson (1944) on the growth of adult thrips (*Thrips imaginis*) living in roses. Since the curve adds nothing to what has already been said,

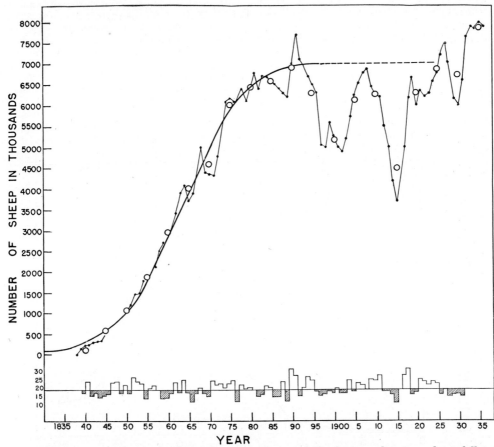

Fig. 103. The logistic growth of the sheep population of South Australia. Annual rainfall in inches appears as the lower chart. (From Davidson.)

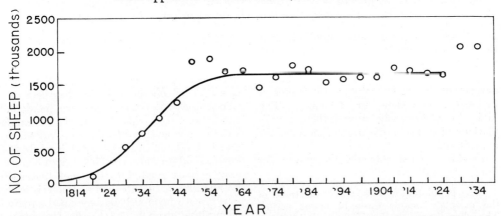

Fig. 104. The logisitic growth of the sheep population of Tasmania and the maintenance of that population in a state of semiequilibrium. The circles are averages for five-year periods. (From Davidson.)

312 POPULATIONS

it is not figured. Suffice it to say that Davidson censused the thrips at ten day intervals for approximately 100 days and fitted these data to a logistic curve. The fit is fairly close up to the point of inflection of the curve, but becomes erratic as the asymptote is approached.

Figures 103 and 104 are logistic curves fitted to the sheep population statistics of South Australia and Tasmania by Davidson (1938, 1938a). Since creditable records of number of sheep have been kept by livestock agencies and since the records extend back to 1840 for Australia and to 1819 for Tasmania, it is possible to describe the

follow the curve closely, and the dry years appear to have had little effect in reducing the population. This may be attributed to the extensive, unoccupied country available for grazing during this early period. For this reason, cattle, which attained their maximum numbers of 375,000 in 1860 and rapidly fell away again, do not appear to have entered seriously into competition with sheep for pasture. The fall in the population during 1869–72 is associated with the dry years, 1868, 1869, and the economic depression which obtained during this period. The persistent fall in the population during 1884–89 is related to the dry years of the 1880's; under the influence of good rains in 1889–90 the numbers again rose rapidly [and the asymptote was attained]."

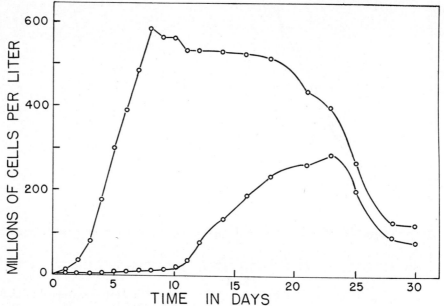

Fig. 105. Population growth of the diatom, *Nitschia closterium*. The upper curve is total population; the lower curve is number of sessile cells. (From Riley.)

growth of these populations essentially from their establishment to postasymptotic equilibrium. Looking at Figure 103 for Australia, it is immediately apparent that the agreement between points and curves is favorable. The data for Tasmania (Fig. 104) do not fit nearly so well; there are deviations of considerable magnitude near the asymptote.

Davidson comments on the curve for South Australia as follows:

"The population follows closely the trend of the calculated curve throughout this period. The sheep numbers for 1838 and 1839 are dominated by importations and fall below the calculated curve. From 1840 to 1868 they

Although it seems probable that the growth of practically all natural, aquatic populations may be represented by the sigmoid curve, it has been difficult to find cases for which the equation has been applied to actual data. There are incidental suggestions for this in R. H. Fleming (1939) for marine zooplankton organisms and in Graham (1935) for marine fishes of commercial importance. This dearth is probably in part related to the fact that such populations in nature are characteristically in a growth form already beyond the period of positive growth. As G. E. Hutchinson points out,[*] an excellent source for such

[*] Personal communication.

data would be quantitative studies of the colonization of bare rock surfaces by single species of sessile, marine organisms.

Riley (1943) has reported some interesting data on growth form for diatoms. He studied in detail one diatom, *Nitschia closterium,* as a laboratory population and then drew certain parallels between these findings and the "spring flowerings" of natural populations of phytoplankton sampled from Georges Bank off New England. The growth curve for the experimental population of *Nitschia* is shown in Figure 105, in which it is seen that growth is sigmoid in charac-

that resembled the curve for cultures of *Nitschia* shown in Figure 105.

This investigation is helpful for our purposes since it provides (1) an exception to logistic growth, because such a curve apparently can not be fitted, owing to the irregularities around the asymptote; and (2) an excellent documentation of the point that laboratory ecology has something to contribute to field ecology, and contrariwise.

Human Populations

Examples of the logistic curve applied to human populations are extremely numer-

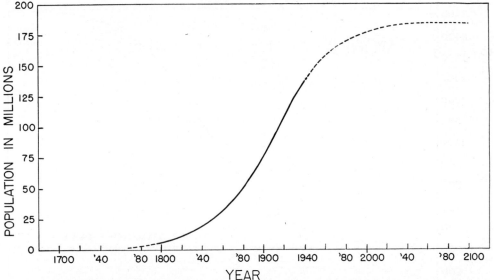

Fig. 106. The logistic function fitted to the census counts of the population of the United States from 1790 to 1940, inclusive. Broken line is extrapolation of the curve. (From Pearl, Reed, and Kish.)

ter through the point of inflection of the curve. There is an initial lag period, a period of rapid growth, followed by a period of reduced relative growth rate. After the inflection point, however, "all resemblance to the sigmoid type of population curve ended. Instead of coming slowly to an asymptote, the rate of growth remained constant for a few days and then abruptly dropped to a negative value, indicating a sharp peak in the population level, followed by a gradual decrease." Riley found that many dominant species of phytoplankton (e.g., *Nitschia closterium, Thalassionema nitschioides, Leptocylindricus danicus,* and *Asterionella japonica*) had positive growth forms *as natural populations*

ous in the literature. The curve has been applied to various sorts of demographic units: counties, cities, states, countries, and the world. A number of applications are to be found in Pearl (1930) (e.g., for Sweden, United States, France, England and Wales, Germany, and so on). We choose two cases for our purposes: the growth of the United States population (Pearl, Reed, and Kish, 1940) and the growth of the population of the world (Pearl and Gould, 1936).

Figure 106 graphs the logistic curve of growth for the United States population through the 1940 census. The curve can be extrapolated between 1700 and 1790 and between 1940 and 2100. The observed points covering these 150 years of census from 1790 through 1940 fit the smoothed curve with a high degree of fidelity. They show that the population has increased from 3,929,000 persons in 1790 to 131,410,000 persons in 1940; an increase exceeding 33.4 times. (The calculated values are, respectively, 3,730,000 and 132,756,000.)

A word is here appropriate about the use of the logistic curve in the prediction of future population size. In 1920 Pearl and Reed reported a curve that described the United States population through the 1910 census. It is of interest to compare this lo-

106) predicts for the same year an asymptotic population of about 184,000,000 persons. This difference of 13,274,000 individuals results from the inclusion of three more observed points (the 1920, 1930, and 1940 censuses) in the computations. Thus there is danger, as common sense dictates, in accepting an extrapolation too literally. On the other hand, extrapolation is undoubtedly of more value than pure guesswork.[*]

Figure 107, adapted from Pearl and Gould (1936), is a logistic curve fitted to

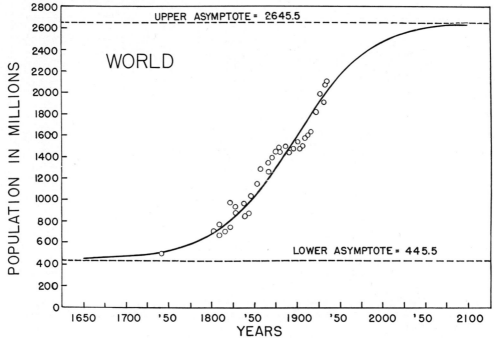

Fig. 107. The logistic curve fitted to an interval of recorded data from the population of the world. (From Pearl and Gould.)

gistic with Figure 106, which is corrected by the actual observations through 1940, and to examine the difference between the two. The first curve missed the counted population by *"16 parts in a thousand in excess in 1920; by 2.5 parts in a thousand in defect in 1930, and by 37.3 parts in a thousand in excess in 1940. The error in 1940 is of perhaps about the same order of magnitude as that probably inherent in the count itself. But it is considerably larger than that made by the curve in either 1920 or 1930."* The first curve predicted an asymptotic population of about 197,274,000 persons in 2100. The second curve (Fig.

known census data for the world from the seventeenth century to 1931–1932. The observed points cover roughly one-half the total span of the curve. The lower asymptote occurs at about year 1650, at which

[*] Should the reader wish to pursue further this question of prediction, his attention is called to the paper of Whelpton (1936), which approaches the question from a different point of view. Here the author attempts to arrive at the future course of the population, not through the use of a theoretical function such as the logistic curve, but through certain assumptions about reproduction and mortality and then calculating empirically the population increase on the basis of these assumptions.

time the population of the world was estimated to have been about 445,500,000 persons and when industrial and commercial procedures started to come to the fore with their consequent acceleration of population growth. The upper asymptote, attained in 2100, estimates the world's population at that time to be in the neighborhood of 2,645,500,000 individuals. The fit between points and curve is only moderate.

An instructive feature arising from Figure 107 is that one logistic curve is not considered adequate to describe the growth of the human population over its entire history. Pearl has repeatedly pointed out that a population follows a particular logistic curve only so long as there has been "no serious or cataclysmic alteration of the conditions (climatic, geological, biological or social) under which its earlier growth has taken place." He has also suggested that several curves can be arranged one upon the other to describe a population's growth as it meets and adjusts to major changes in its total environmental relationships (see discussion of Logistic Curve, p. 301). Thus, one might speculate, somewhat boldly to be sure, that before the middle of the seventeenth century the population had passed through a series of logistic cycles representing adjustments from hunting, to pastoral, to agricultural, modes of living. Then, with the advent of industrialism, commerce, and public health practices, a new and excessively steep cycle of growth originated.

There are, of course, other logical possibilities as to the quantitative state of the world population before 1650. These are recognized by Pearl and Gould and schematized in Figure 108. In this figure the "first hypothesis" is that just discussed. The "second hypothesis" holds that for thousands of years the population stood relatively stable between roughly four and five hundred million persons. This stability represents an asymptote of a growth cycle long before consummated. The "third hypothesis" maintains that "during some period or periods in this vast span of at least 100,000 years of man's life on the earth the world *population was much higher* than 445 million, and subsequently lessened, for reasons wholly unknown, to reach that figure when reasonably reliable population history begins."

These three possibilities are examined by Pearl and Gould. They exclude the third immediately as untenable. It is more difficult (they argue) to judge between the first and the second, although they decide that "on the balance'" there are more data supporting the first, which, consequently, is tentatively accepted as the most probable representation of world population growth.

EQUILIBRIUM

In the discussion of equilibrium, as in the following treatment of Fluctuations and Oscillations, it must be remembered that, while it is possible to define these growth forms with mathematical precision, as actual illustrations it is possible to differentiate them in relative terms only. The point can be put differently. There probably exists no "perfect case" of equilibrium or oscillation. There are many instances for which it is difficult to say "This is the one" and "This is the other," since elements of both are present. There are, of course, many other instances for which this is not the case, and then it is easy to separate one growth form from another. In final analysis the issue becomes a matter of judgment. Does the fact that it would be possible to arrange an extensive series of population data all the way from marked fluctuation, grading into oscillation, or into equilibrium detract from our definition of these three growth forms as true descriptive population characteristics? We think not. In fact, we believe that this strengthens the concept since it is just the way a series of biodemographic units, such as the population, might be expected to behave. Therefore, in speaking of equilibrium, oscillation, and fluctuation we recognize that they are relative rather than absolute concepts, but that they have great descriptive value in depicting the course of populations, irrespective of the type, through time.

Equilibrium could be defined in various ways, some more or less complex. It seems appropriate and adequate enough to define it simply as mean numerical stability, i.e., the average size *held* by a population over a considerable period of time. To illustrate this it is necessary to find examples in which the oscillation and/or fluctuation is at a minimum, examples in which the equilibrium approaches a straight, horizontal line.

Laboratory Populations

The first example, taken from Richards (1932), concerns the growth of pure strain populations of the yeast *Saccharomyces cerevisiae*. Figure 109 shows this trend for four different yeast cultures over 1200 hours of observation. The abscissa records the number of cells in 1/250 mm³. The asymptote is attained between 180 and 200 hours. Subsequently (and this is the pertinent point for present purposes) an equi-

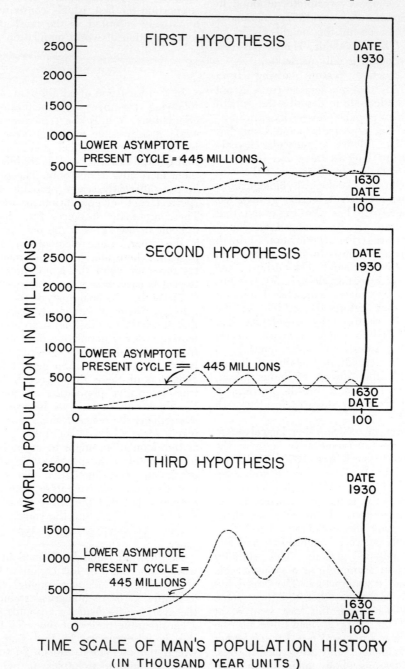

Fig. 108. Three alternative hypotheses to account for the growth of the human population of the world. (The slight backward bend displayed by each of the last three logistics in the three diagrams is inaccurate.) (From Pearl and Gould.)

librium is maintained that displays a minimum of variability. This is a good example. The points cluster near the mean line; the line is practically horizontal; none of the four populations deviate substantially from the curve; the observations cover a

gests that this drop was associated with four factors: "(a) the prevalence of sheep scab, which necessitated the passing of the 'Scab Act of 1870;' (b) the prevalence of fluke in certain pasture areas; (c) the development of the rabbit pest, which neces-

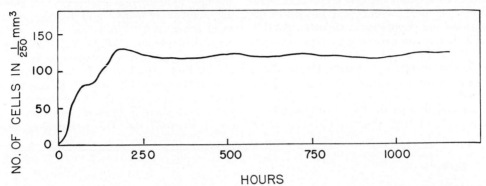

Fig. 109. The equilibrium maintained by a laboratory population of yeast for approximately 1000 hours. (From Richards.)

long enough period of time to have validity as a trend.

Populations of Domesticated Animals

Davidson (1938a) reports a long period of equilibrium for the sheep population of Tasmania, extending from 1859 to 1924. This is shown in Figure 104, earlier discussed in connection with logistic growth, in which an equilibrium line is fitted to the observed points. There is some obvious

sitated the passing in 1871 of 'An Act to Provide for Destruction of Rabbits in Tasmania;' (d) the persistent fall in the price of wool which dropped from 22d. a pound to 15d. a pound between 1862 and 1870." By 1874 the population had reconstituted itself.

Natural Populations

A semiequilibrium position in which the population maintains a low level with min-

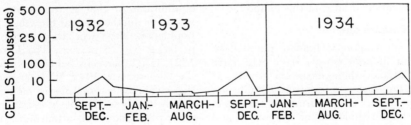

Fig. 110 Fluctuations in numbers of the diatom, *Rhizosolenia styliformis*. The ordinate scale between zero and 100 is exaggerated. (From Lucas.)

variation between points and curve, and this case also would be suitable as an illustration of moderate fluctuations. However, the equilibrium line actually remains essentially horizontal for the sixty-five year period, attesting to considerable stability by the population. The curve shows that in 1870 there was a considerable drop in population size; this is the greatest departure from the equilibrium. Davidson sug-

imum variability for a considerable period is described by Lucas (1940) for the diatom *Rhizosolenia styliformis*. This is a small fragment of a comprehensive study of oceanic plankton populations, the objectives and general plan of which have been set forth by Hardy (1939). This group of English investigators used an ingenious device called "the continuous plankton recorder," which is drawn by ships as they cross the North Sea, usually from Hull, England, to seaports on the Dutch, German, and Scandinavian coasts.

Figure 110 shows a particular series of records covering three years of observations made with the plankton recorder over 250 miles of the "Copenhagen line." It is of interest for our present purpose since the *Rhizosolenia* populations exhibit an equilibrium during the February to September intervalr of 1933 and 1934 characterized by its relative constancy, despite the small total size of the population (in some cases the populations appear to fall essentially to zero) and despite the fact that this species is capable of large fluctuations. The latter,

It is possible, however, to select arbitrarily an illustration that shows a semi-equilibrium from the admirable collection of demographic data assembled by Linder and Grove (1943). The yearly census records for the state of Delaware from 1900 through 1940 provide a fair example. When the number of males and females of all races other than white is plotted by years, a graph is obtained (Fig. 111) that shows that this population component is quite stable. From 1900 to 1917 the population is in striking equilibrium. There is a slight depression and recovery during the next ten years and then a gradual but consistent rise from 1927 on. The latter component

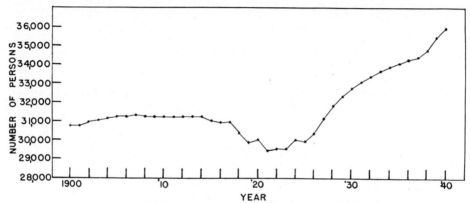

Fig. 111. Population trend of "nonwhite" inhabitants of the state of Delaware, 1900 to 1940. Note that base line of graph is 28,000 persons instead of zero.

especially those associated with the seasons, will be mentioned later in this chapter.

Human Populations

Most contemporary human populations for which modern census data exist have not yet attained their maximum growth, so that it is impossible to report an equilibrium state for them. This is true, for example, for the total population of the world and for the United States as well as for numerous other political units. Undoubtedly, there have been certain occasions in the past when human populations have reached an equilibrium and held it for a considerable period of time, but accurate data to illustrate this point are hard to find.[*]

[*] It is a likely assumption that native populations everywhere, beyond the influence of modern technology and isolated from each other, have been in equilibrium, more or less. Illustrations are afforded by New Guinea, New Zealand, or practically any South Sea Island. Consult also Pearl (1930).

is probably a true departure from the equilibrium in that it represents, for one reason or another, a real growth. The mean population size over this forty-one year period is 31,715 persons. The lowest year, 1921, is 7.1 per cent below this mean, and the highest year, 1940, 13.4 per cent above the mean. This example is included here merely to show that it is possible for human populations to attain and maintain something of an equilibrium. It will be interesting, of course, when demographers at some future date study this question after the populations of large countries and the world as a whole attain their asymptotic size.

FLUCTUATIONS

Whereas the problem of presenting examples of equilibrium and oscillation is one of trying to find adequate examples, that of presenting population fluctuation is one of exclusion. The implication here, of course, is that populations are commonly found in a state of fluctuation. The data on fluctuations of laboratory populations (especially for protista and insects) are fairly numerous and those on natural populations profuse. In this section we select certain examples that seem to provide a satisfactory view of the range and character of fluctuation.

Population fluctuations have been defined as relatively asymmetrical departures from equilibrium. This does not necessarily imply that they are characterized by their asymmetry: in many cases they are rather regular over large periods of time.

Laboratory Populations

Figure 112 shows the fluctuations of populations of the ciliate *Glaucoma piriformis* cultured under three nutrient conditions at constant temperatures (25° C). The protozoa of population IX were maintained in a solution of caseinpeptone, KH₂PO₄, and distilled water. Population X had in addi-

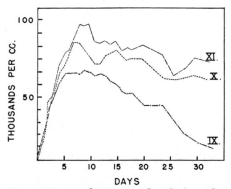

Fig. 112. Population trends of the ciliate, *Glaucoma piriformis*, in three different media. (From Hall and Shottenfeld.)

tion a relatively small amount of thiamine (vitamin B₁), while ten times the concentration of this substance was added to XI. The authors, of course, are interested in showing that "the available concentration of thiamine definitely affects the density of population during the maximal stationary phase and the secondary stationary phase and also influences the time at which the major phase of death begins." Thus our interest lies in the three curves from about day seven on. The trend is definitely downward and is somewhat exaggerated by the absence of thiamine. This is a favorable illustration of population decline with minimal fluctuation. The final phase, that of the actual extinction of the population, has not been thoroughly studied, although the

authors report that it is of long duration in some cases, even exceeding eight months.

An illustration of fluctuations in three experimental populations of granary beetles is afforded by the study of Thomas Park, Gregg, and Lutherman (1941) on *Tribolium confusum, Gnathoceros cornutus,* and *Trogoderma versicolor.* The first two are tenebrionids, the last a dermestid. The populations were maintained as single-species cultures in the same kind and quantity of medium and under controlled and identical conditions of temperature, humidity, and experimental manipulation. The trends, therefore, reflect the pattern of growth of these forms as species and can be compared on that basis. Figure 113 shows the average behavior of a number of the cultures. The following points are to be noted:

1. *Tribolium confusum* builds up the largest mean populations, followed by *Trogoderma versicolor* and *Gnathoceros cornutus,* in that order.

2. *Tribolium* exhibits the minimum of short, sharp fluctuations from one census to another, but does display a single large fluctuation (or oscillation) with a low point around day 300. This is followed by a rapid recovery to higher density.

3. *Gnathoceros* does not display a single, major fluctuation, but instead fluctuates abruptly over a small range from count to count, the tendency being for one count to be high, the next to be low, and so on.

4. *Trogoderma* grows most erratically of the three. The individual population curves for this species are quite different from each other, a fact not true for *Tribolium* and *Gnathoceros.* Thus, some *Trogoderma* cultures start high and drop low and then partially recover; others start low and build up high; and still others start in between and tend to stay there.

5. The general conclusion so far as the population fluctuations of these three forms go is that, while fluctuation is characteristic of all, the pattern of the fluctuation differs between each and represents real species differences at the group level.

We return to this example in another connection in a later chapter (p. 368) when the problem of Interspecies Competition is discussed.

Natural Populations

John Ford (1937a) reported on the population fluctuations of Collembola and mites that inhabit tussocks of the grass, *Bromus erectus,* during the winter months. This author developed a sampling method which enabled him to estimate the fauna in terms of the number of organisms per square meter. Figure 114 shows the extent of the fluctuations during November, December, January, February, and March. This figure is concerned with the collembolan, *Pseudachorutes subcrassus,* and the mites, *Asca aphidioides* and *Hypochthonius pallidulus.* It will be noted that the former is about

fauna and the drying up or wetting of different regions of the tussocks causes migrations of certain species within them" (p. 111).

Davidson (1944) notes that insect populations fluctuate in one of two general ways, depending largely upon their reproductive pattern. Certain species consist of individuals present in all stages of development and belonging to different generations—"complete overlapping generations." Other species are dominated at particular pheno-

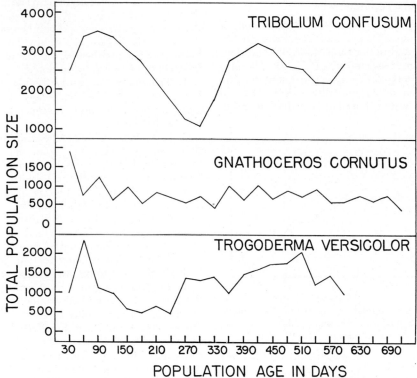

Fig. 113. Population trends of three genera of granary beetles. (From Park, Gregg, and Lutherman.)

five times more numerous than the latter. Ford draws a number of conclusions about the fluctuation pattern, several of which are as follows: "A fluctuation of the population, with increases in November and December, early February and late February, with intervening minima, was shown to characterize the Collembola and Acarina. . . . The February minimum was shown to correspond with a period of high evaporation rate, during which contrary winds destroyed the tussock structure. . . . Moisture is of great importance for the existence of this

logical intervals by individuals in essentially the same stage of development—"incomplete overlapping generations." The latter category, exemplified by the collembolan *Smynthurus viridis* in Davidson's study, exhibits a distinctive upward and downward trend in each generation. This results in a growth form that rises high during "active" seasons of the year and drops low during "inactive" seasons when only eggs represent the species in nature. This must be a relatively common type of fluctuation among insects in temperate climates since it is an adaptive response to the rigors of winter. For such cases the concept of mean density or balance in time seems to have less validity than it has for species with overlapping generations.

concludes that these data are of considerable value in that they reflect the comparative abundance of the species, in a local area at least, from year to year. He is concerned with the course of the Miramichi

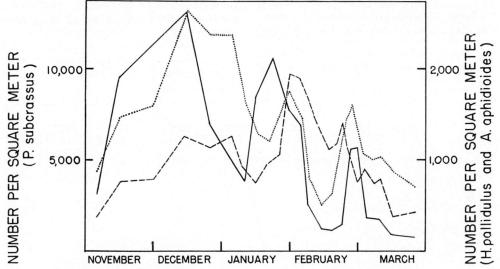

Fig. 114. Smoothed population trends of three arthropod species inhabiting tussocks. Dotted line *P. subcrassus;* solid line, *H. pallidulus;* dash line, *A. aphidioides.* (From Ford.)

Some valuable data on the fluctuations of populations of salmon over a long period of observation are reported by Huntsman (1937, 1938), who comments that the

fishery near Chatham, New Brunswick, Canada, on the Atlantic Coast.

Figure 115 plots the salmon catch and mean rainfall in inches for July to August

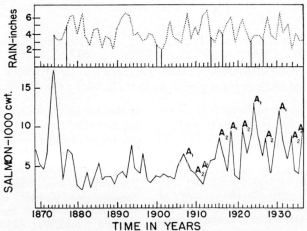

Fig. 115. Fluctuations of salmon populations in the Miramichi fishery, 1870 to 1936. Rainfall appears at the top of the graph. (From Huntsman.)

"fluctuations in fish abundance and their causes is the central fisheries problem" (1938). There are statistics on the salmon catch from about 1870 on, and Huntsman

at Chatham from 1874 to 1936. Rainfall is of interest, for Huntsman believes it is one of the most significant factors that affect the fishes when they are young and still living in the rivers. This mortality in the young salmon is reflected in later years in the size of catch of older forms. On this point Huntsman says:

"Study of the river life has revealed the chief mortality of the larger parr as due to fish-eating birds (belted kingfisher and American merganser), which nest and rear their young along the salmon streams. These birds are largely unable to secure food when the streams are swollen and murky, as in rainy weather. I have accordingly explored the possibility of dry summers being responsible for increased mortality of the large parr (of the

For our present purposes this study furnishes an example of fluctuations in a natural population and advances a partial explanation of the observed changes in abundance. It is to be noted that the curve is, in general, of the sharp peak and valley variety somewhat reminiscent of that shown for *Gnathoceros* (Fig. 113), although more exaggerated.

Another illustration of fluctuation in fish populations, reported by Russell (1942), concerns, among others, the haddock, a bottom fish caught commercially in Icelandic waters. Russell reports the total fishing yield

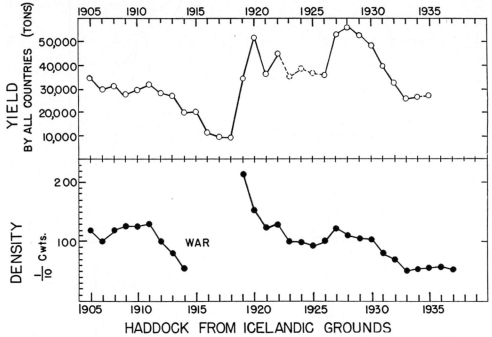

Fig. 116. Haddock density and yield from Icelandic fishing grounds. (From Russell.)

smolt year-classes related to the times of salmon scarcity) by restricting their habitat and exposing them to attack by birds. The last scarcity affected chiefly the 1926 and 1927 smolt year-classes and in correspondence with this the summers of 1923 to 1926 prove to have been dry, as shown by both rainfall and river discharge records. Pronounced scarcity of salmon is thus seen to follow with the proper interval, a succession of dry summers" (pp. 13–14).

Figure 115 shows a fair correlation between the number of salmon and the summer rainfall. Huntsman stresses that the years of particular scarcity were preceded "at the proper intervals" by periods of four successive dry summers.

of this species by fishermen of all participating countries from 1905 through 1935. The density of the population is estimated also by computing the "landing per day's absence" from port. This author makes the following points which the reader can confirm for himself from Figure 116: (1) Fishing depleted the population before the first World War. (2) The stock regenerated when fishing was interrupted by hostilities. (3) After the war the catch remained high until 1926 because the haddock had replenished themselves somewhat and because of increased fishing effort. (4) In 1926 an improvement in fishing gear facilitated efficiency of catch. (5) After

1929 the yield fell regardless of effort and techniques. (6) During the postwar period of 1919 to 1933 the general trend in density was downward. We are particularly interested in these curves because they describe population fluctuations that are the result primarily of a specific type of mortality, that owing to exploitation by man.

In the discussion of equilibrium we described the trend of populations of the diatom, *Rhizosolenia styliformis,* based on the work of Lucas (*loc. cit.*), and pointed out that this species existed in a state of relative constancy during a number of spring and summer months for several years. The graph (Fig. 110) also illustrates fluctua-

varying hare (*Lepus americanus*) in the Hudson Bay watershed area of Canada. We discussed MacLulich's methods of estimating hare abundance in Chapter 18 (p. 270) and pointed out that by using four sorts of criteria (fur returns, statements in the literature, questionnaires, and field work) he was apparently able to obtain a relatively accurate picture of the population growth form of this species over many years. Figure 117 describes, with an unreported gap from 1825 to 1844, these fluctuations from 1786 to 1903 on the basis of records released by the Hudson's Bay Company and from 1903 to 1935 on the basis of questionnaires.

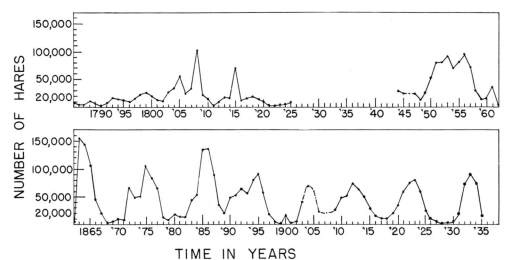

Fig. 117. Population trends of the varying hare in the Hudson's Bay watershed. (From MacLulich.)

tions since it can be seen that there is a rise in numbers of the form in the autumns of 1932, 1933, and 1934. It seems probable that these "autumnal patches" are related in some way with the seasonal changes involved.

Natural population studies of mammals afford many illustrations of fluctuations. Certain of these are well summarized in Elton's comprehensive book (1942) as well as in numerous research reports. We wish to present briefly some data on the varying hare and the lynx taken from MacLulich (1937), and the mouse and the fox from Elton.

MacLulich's investigation, summarizing and extending the literature beginning with Seton, is a detailed discussion of the cyclic nature of fluctuations in populations of the

It is worthwhile to examine Figure 117 carefully since it is an excellent illustration of a long-time fluctuation pattern. The striking point about the trend is its regularity coupled with the fact that in low years the curve always returns to a point near the baseline, and in peak years the maximal population sizes are rather similar with occasional exceptions. The elapsed time between peaks varies somewhat, but usually is of the magnitude of nine to ten years. It is clear merely from inspection that these are not random, haphazard fluctuations, but are instead regular, and even predictable, cycles. In a later chapter, when considering population cycles in general, we extend MacLulich's analysis and discuss causal factors (p. 367).

MacLulich also discusses the cyclic character of fluctuations of lynx populations in the same area in Canada (Fig. 118). He concludes that "the abundance of the lynx was shown to be definitely correlated with that of varying hares," and that these fluctuations were *not* associated with sunspot activity. The trends are clearly regular and cyclic, and the mean period of time between peaks is 9.7 years. It should

plotted against months of the year for nearly three years. The figure also records the percentage of adult females pregnant in each month. Elton has this to say about the mice:

"The diagrams are most easily understood if one looks at the three winter seasons, say November-February. During the first winter the mice were not breeding at all (actually not from October to March). The numbers showed

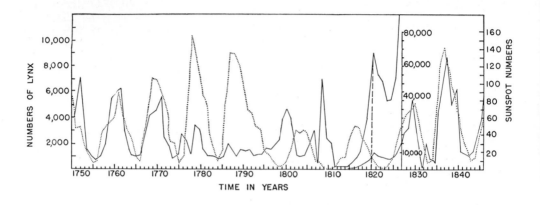

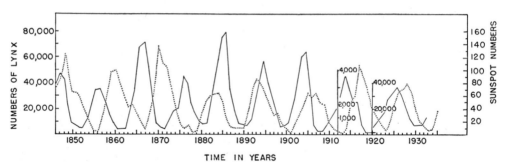

Fig. 118. Population trends of the lynx (solid line) graphed against sunspot numbers (dotted lines). (From MacLulich.)

be noted that the lynx populations do not fall so low during the periods of depression as do those of the rabbits. Apart from this fact the general correspondence between the two species is remarkably close. (See discussions of predation, page 370, and of cycles, page 366.)

Elton (1942) reports some data on fluctuations of the English field mouse, *Apodemus sylvaticus,* a form ecologically not unlike the American deer mouse, *Peromyscus.* These mice were trapped in a woods not far from Oxford University. Figure 119 shows the number of mice caught in traps,

a general falling in trend: the mice were not balancing their budget of population. But when summer breeding began the numbers in the traps went up again. In the second winter breeding practically stopped, but it went on further into the autumn and began sooner in the spring. The numbers began to drop in November, but there was an extraordinary increase in the number caught early in 1927, which we attributed to abnormal movements. The usual summer increase occurred that year. The following winter was remarkable, for breeding practically never stopped, and the population never fell to the low level it had reached in 1926" (pp. 165–166).

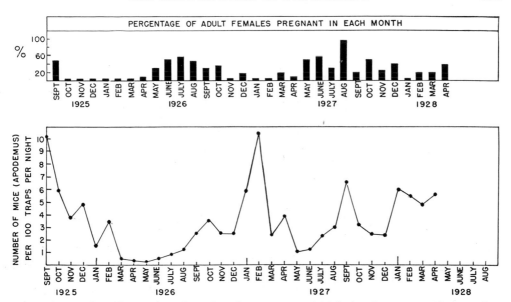

Fig. 119. Number of mice *(Apodemus)*, and percentage of adult females pregnant by months, plotted against time. (From Elton.)

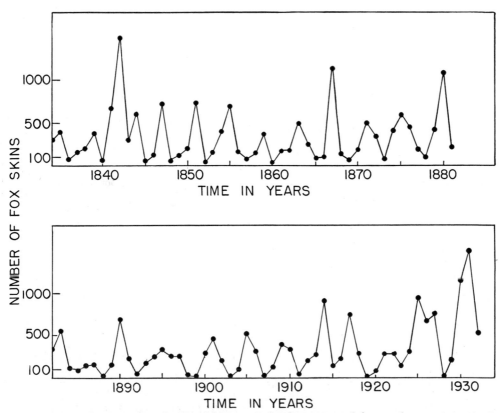

Fig. 120. Population cycles of colored foxes in Labrador computed from pelt returns reported by Moravian Missions. (From Elton.)

Our final illustration of fluctuations in natural populations of mammals concerns the "coloured fox" in Labrador. This is also discussed by Elton (1942) and is based on fur trade statistics from Moravian Missions and, later, the Hudson's Bay Company. This, a striking case of cyclic regularity, is clearly summarized in Figure 120 and covers fur returns from 1834 to 1932. The curve, as Elton phrases it, "hits the eye at once." For the ninety-two years (1834 to 1925) during which the fox trade was under the control of the Missions, the mean length of the cycle was precisely four years and the intervals in years starting in 1835 were 4, 3, 2, 3, 4, 4, 4, 4, 4, 4, 4, 5, 3, 3, 4, 5, 6, 4, 4, 5, 3, 4, 4. Elton assembles these figures in a frequency distribution as follows:

Length of cycle 2   3   4   5   6   7
Frequency 1   5 13   3   1   0
Percentage frequency 4 22 57 13   4   0

This shows that the modal frequency is 4 and that the distribution is slightly skewed to the left.

Elton quite properly stresses that these findings are based, not on a total census of the population, but on pelt records, and is properly critical for that reason. Even so he believes, one would judge, that this reflects in truth something real in terms of actual fox-fluctuations. In fact he says, "The manner in which the cycle colours even small trapping results and comes at places hundreds of miles apart gives it a bold and almost cosmic quality. There must be some very powerful forces behind it" (p. 272).

Data on fluctuations in bird populations are not so extensive as those for mammals and fishes. Some observations along this line appear in the book by Stoddard (1932) and in the monograph on the song sparrow by Nice (1937). A helpful treatment is the analysis by Kendeigh (1944) of census methods applied to bird groups, and it is from this source that we choose one case for review.

Kendeigh has this observation to record about the possible cyclic character of the bobwhite population:

"There is still a difference of opinion among students of the bob-white as to whether the species is cyclic in numbers, irruptive, or relatively constant. Perhaps there will be differences between regions (compare with Erring-ton, 1941), but for Ohio this curve strongly suggests variations of a rhythmical or cyclical nature with former peaks in 1911 or 1912, 1923 or 1924, and about 1935, with low points about 1909 (?), 1915, 1928 or 1929, and 1940. Eliminating the doubtful low year of 1909, these points in the curve come at intervals of 12 or 13 years" (p. 82).

Oscillations

We have already suggested that population oscillations are hard to illustrate by actual example because most departures from equilibrium are asymmetrical rather than symmetrical. We shall, however, present several selected cases that serve the purpose fairly well.

Gause has interested himself in the possible oscillation in numbers in interspecies populations in which one species is the prey component and the other the predator component. We return to this problem in more detail in Chapter 22 when discussing Predation. Our concern with it here is that it affords perhaps the best illustration of demonstrated oscillation. Lotka (1934) and Volterra (1926) concluded on the basis of purely theoretical considerations that a biological system comprised of two species, each dependent upon the other, will exhibit regular, periodic fluctuation in the relative and absolute abundance of each species. This is true even when random fluctuations caused by external environmental factors have been eliminated. Gause investigated this conclusion in the laboratory, using several species of microorganisms and mites as experimental material. His findings appear in a number of papers, including two monographs (1934a, 1935). To make the point, we reproduce one graph (Fig. 121).

This particular experiment, the details of which can be omitted, was conducted with mixed populations of the yeast, *Saccharomyces exiguus*, and the ciliate, *Paramecium aurelia*. The figure shows that essentially smooth oscillations of the Lotka-Volterra type actually occur under these controlled experimental conditions. The three cycles shown for each species are regular, depart but slightly from the observed census points, and are of approximately the same magnitude.

Studies somewhat similar to those of Gause have been reported by DeBach and Smith (1941) and deal with interactions between populations of an insect host (the housefly) and its pupal parasite, *Mormoniella vitripennis*. These, again, will be mentioned in Chapter 22. Suffice it to say here that DeBach and Smith also concluded that "the populations of both host and parasite followed closely the theoretical predictions" —that is, predictions of oscillations.

It is well to stress that the examples just discussed and others like them concern oscillations reported from experiments conducted under rigorous, simplified, and carefully controlled conditions; in fact, the authors were interested in trying to demonstrate to oscillations in natural populations as we have been able to find.

Decline and Extinction

Our next consideration under growth form concerns population decline and extinction. As stated on page 305, by decline is meant consistent and progressive reduction of the population below equilibrium or below the lower range of usual fluctuation and/or oscillation: by extinction is meant, obviously, the final dying-out of the group, whether of the species as a whole or of an

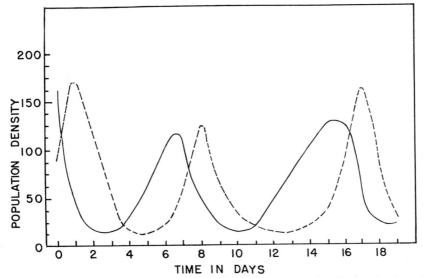

Fig. 121. Fluctuations in population density of *Paramecium aurelia* (broken line) and yeast, *Saccharomyces exiguus* (solid line). The first species censused per 15 cc. of media; the second species, per 0.1 c.mm. of media. (From Gause.)

strate their existence. It is not possible, so far as we are aware, to present cases for natural populations that approach these in symmetry of trend lines. This is to be anticipated on the ground that animal groups in nature characteristically inhabit a rather labile and changing environment when contrasted with those of the laboratory. To put it differently, oscillations, in contradistinction to fluctuations, are the exception rather than the rule when such departures from equilibrium are considered. However, the reader should glance back through the section on fluctuations and reexamine especially Figures 117, 118, 119, and 120, dealing with the varying hare, the lynx, the field mouse, and the colored fox, respectively. These are, plainly, regularized fluctuations, and are as close an approach

individual population. It seems to us that these two growth forms, though separable by definition, actually belong with each other. That is, once a population gets well under its normal limits of abundance and barring important ecological or genetic changes, it frequently, though not necessarily, becomes extinct. Therefore, for purposes of convenience, these two aspects are considered together.

There are, of course, many instances of known decline and extinction of species, and certain of these are discussed in the section on Evolution (p. 679). Notable examples mentioned in passing include the Arizona elk, the great auk, the Labrador duck, the passenger pigeon, the Carolina parrakeet, the Eskimo curlew, and the heath hen. There are also instances in which populations have reached (probably) a perilously low level: e.g., the house mouse of St. Kilda, the sea otter, the ivory-billed woodpecker, the white-winged dove, the trumpeter swan, and the California condor.* The difficulty with these examples from the point of view of the population student, however, is that they are reported *after* the event, so that quantitative data describing the decline and/or extinction are rarely available. This means that we must turn primarily to a few experimental illustrations to show how a group declines from period to period.

Before mentioning these experimental studies, however, it is appropriate to dis-

have been restricted to Martha's Vineyard alone. The course of the population from 1890 to 1926 is shown in Figure 122. There it can be seen that approximately 200 birds remained in 1890 with a slight decline extending until 1907. This decline may have been caused by the introduction of prairie chickens that probably interbred with the heath hens and by an increase in the desirability of the bird as a collectors' item.

In 1907 Massachusetts inaugurated sound conservation procedures with a resulting increase in population size, to a total number of 2000 by 1916. That year a combination of factors (a fire, a gale, a cold winter, and

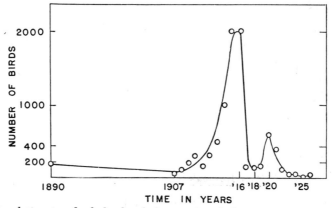

Fig. 122. Population trend of the heath hen on Martha's Vineyard (Massachusetts) from 1890 to 1926. (From Gross.)

cuss the decline and extinction of the heath hen. This case involves a natural population for which census data are available and certain of the factors understood. The matter is summarized by Gross (1928) and put in more general perspective by Allee (1938).

Populations of heath hens were originally abundant in Massachusetts and probably much of New England. Through hunting, these birds were gradually driven eastward until about 1850 the species existed only on Martha's Vineyard and contiguous islands, and among the pine barrens of New Jersey. From 1880 the heath hen seems to

an unusual predation pressure by goshawks) reduced the population to fifty breeding pairs or less. Again, the numbers rose slightly by 1920, but thereafter a steady and inexorable contraction set in so that by 1928 only one male could be found. This bird was later banded and released and was last seen alive on February 9, 1932. It is reasonable to conclude that the species is now totally extinct. Gross suggests that the decline of the heath hen was accelerated by an inadaptability of the species, excessive inbreeding, and, during the later period, an excess of males.

Gause, Nastukova, and Alpatov (1934) studied decline and extinction in populations of two species of paramecia, *P. caudatum* and *P. aurelia*, when cultured in homotypically and heterotypically conditioned media, i.e., media altered by and containing waste products liberated by the organisms living in them. Their report is useful

* An interesting, theoretically probable, erratic fluctuation concerns hibernating frogs and toads. An exceptionally severe winter, if also without adequate snow cover, may kill a large proportion of the hibernating individuals. Severe cold alone will not do it. Frogs introduced in Iceland were said to have been exterminated by this combination of factors.

for our purposes since actual counts are given in four day intervals as the cultures contract. After the two forms had attained equilibrium, they were placed as single species into a medium of the two conditioned types.

These decline and extinction curves are instructive for their description of negative growth as well as for the light they throw on conditioning. Gause, Nastukova, and Alpatov offer these comments:

"The analysis of the curves of decline shows the existence of an essential difference between *P. caudatum* and *P. aurelia*. The population of

nected with the lower absolute values of growth on the *P. aurelia* medium. It seems that here the waste products of the species itself are more toxic than those of the other species . . ." (p. 230).

Another example of decline and extinction of a laboratory population is reported by Park, Gregg, and Lutherman (1941) for mixed cultures of the granary beetles *Gnathoceros cornutus* and *Trogoderma versicolor* (Fig. 123). Here, the essential factor was not environmental conditioning, for this was eliminated by appropriate manip-

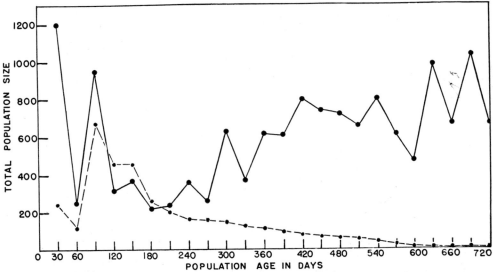

Fig. 123. Population trends in competing cultures of *Gnathoceros cornutus* (solid line) and *Trogoderma versicolor* (broken line). The graph illustrates the decline and extinction of the latter species. (From Park, Gregg, and Lutherman.)

P. caudatum dies out rapidly and disappears entirely on the eighteenth day. The rate of the decline varies . . . under different conditions, but these differences are small. Another state of affairs is found in *P. aurelia*. When about 90 per cent of the population has already perished, the remainder (the experiments were made with pure cultures!) adapt themselves to the rather unfavourable conditions and continue to live for a certain time. Later there appears a second cycle of decline sharply separated from the first. The second cycle of decline in *P. aurelia* presents an extraordinary sensitiveness to the homotypic and heterotypic conditioning of the medium: (1) *P. aurelia* in pure culture on a 'homotypic' medium possess a relatively lower level of the second cycle than on a "heterotypic" one (6 per cent as compared to 19 per cent . . .), and it is of shorter duration (8 days instead of 14). The level is here taken in a relative form and is apparently not con-

ulation, but, rather, interspecies competition (p. 368).

Special Cases

In the introductory section of this chapter we recognized a category of growth form designated as "special cases." These are accentuated, sudden changes that depart radically from the normal pattern of equilibrium and refer particularly to population spurts and crashes. This aspect has received considerable attention, particularly from workers studying the control of economically undesirable insects and mammals as well as, of course, epidemics. These aspects are not discussed in detail at this time since the background is already laid through our treatment of fluctuations and since we shall have more to say about certain of the points in Chapter 22. It seems fair to conclude that many accentuated changes in numbers represent primarily selected extremes of the population curve, although undoubtedly there are some such events that occur so infrequently, or are such a severe departure from the usual, that they must be looked upon as special cases.

Carpenter (1940) reviews in interesting fashion insect outbreaks in Europe. He defines an outbreak as "the time during the fluctuation cycle of an insect (or other animal) when it is abundant or injurious enough (or both) over an appreciable area to warrant a record being made by observers." We interpret this definition in our terms as an excessive, maximal, fluctuation peak. He goes on to study the reported outbreaks of injurious insects for most of Europe, including a considerable part of European Russia. On the basis of this gross, historical synthesis Carpenter concludes that outbreaks tend to occur in the same groups of years, or are closer together than would be expected on the basis of chance alone. Certain of the insects studied or mentioned are somewhat periodic in their outbreaks. For example, the cockchafer (*Melolantha*), the cicadas, the May beetles, and migratory locusts fall in this category. An interesting, although admittedly sketchy, analysis of the locusts in Eurasia is presented with sporadic data going back to 300 A. D. The conclusion is reached that the locust peaks of abundance were probably attained in the following years (The question marks refer to questionable cases): 595, 695, 885, 935(?), 1095(?), 1165(?), 1205(?), 1245(?), 1335(?), 1405(?), 1475(?), 1545, 1635(?), 1695, 1715, 1745, 1785(?), 1815, 1855, and 1895.

A key to Carpenter's thinking on the matter of outbreaks is contained in the following quotations: "Since one of the hypotheses underlying this study is that the biotic community reacts as a whole to its environmental conditions, the analysis of data is made with this in mind. According to this idea we may expect a general reaction of an ecological population on any area to its environmental conditions. If, instead, each species-population reacted in its own way to its environment, one might well expect a similar number of outbreaks (i.e., peaks of fluctuation cycles) every year,

but, as we shall see, this is rarely the case" (p. 112). And again: "If the synchronization of outbreaks is a reality, it can be explained in various ways. It is suggested that the outbreak of one species may cause disturbances in the community which may generate similar outbreaks in other species" (p. 144).

Elton (1942) presents many pertinent data on excessive changes in population abundance and should be consulted for details. It is appropriate for our purposes to note that many forms at one time or another do attain unusually high densities, and the case of the lemming comes immediately to mind. Elton is particularly interested in pointing out that periods of great mammal abundance are not infrequently followed by epidemics—a point we shall discuss later. He reminds us that Charles Darwin had this thought clearly in mind when he wrote, in the *Origin of Species*, "When a species, owing to highly favourable circumstances, increases inordinately in numbers in a small tract, epidemics—at least, this seems generally to occur with our game animals—often ensue." Elton also stresses that such epidemics are reported for a number of mammals, among which can be enumerated voles, water-voles, lemmings, mice, rats, muskrats, beavers, gerbilles, squirrels, marmots, ground squirrels, rabbits, hares, capybaras, moles, hedgehogs, foxes, weasels, deer, zebras, hippopotami, kangaroos, opossums, and others.

This concludes the chapter on population growth form. We have tried to make, by means of actual illustrations, the following points:

1. A population has a certain life history roughly divisible into periods or phases.

2. These periods vary in duration (abscissal axis) and in numerical size (ordinate axis) with the particular species; with the stability or lability of the effective environment both physical and biotic; and with chance events.

3. It is meaningful to study population growth form since it provides a numerical measure of the population's past history up to the time of most recent observation; summarizes a wealth of knowledge about the group in question; and, in so doing, raises particular questions for analysis and synthesis.

22. POPULATION FACTORS AND SELECTED POPULATION PROBLEMS

A classification and illustration of the more important factors affecting populations is here presented; and the integration of population phenomena is attempted by the discussion of the interdependence and interaction of such factors in laboratory and natural populations, of both terrestrial and aquatic species.

Classification of the factors affecting populations presents certain difficulties. The problem, on the one hand, is to avoid a classification so general that it is meaningless, and, on the other hand, to avoid one so specific that it is inflexible. It is helpful to examine the classification developed by certain students interested in host-parasite populations and the control of insect pests, since this exhibits some agreement on basic principles. These students have been primarily concerned with the factors that eliminate certain members from a particular population; that is, with sources of mortality.

Howard and Fiske (1911), in their paper on the gipsy moth, discuss the natural causes of mortality in insect populations. They divide this mortality into two large categories: "catastrophic," and "facultative." Catastrophic refers to factors that destroy a constant percentage irrespective of the abundance of the form. Facultative refers to factors that destroy a percentage increasing as the density increases. This distinction was recognized by Thompson (1928), an important worker on this subject, who renamed catastrophic, "general or independent," and facultative, "individualized or dependent." The first group of factors comprises largely the physicochemical aspects of the environment and those "intrinsic defects in adaptation characteristic of the species; the second group comprises the predaceous and parasitic organisms" (Thompson, 1939, p. 331).

Thompson (1939), in further discussion of these distinctions, points out that the mortality caused by general factors was considered by Howard and Fiske as "independent of the numerical value of the population in which they act" and that this view depends on the assumption that "the distribution of individuals with respect to these factors remains unaltered, in spite

of increase or decrease in numbers." He has this comment regarding the individualized factors:

"The 'individualized or dependent' factors are . . . limited in this action by the fact that they are not all-pervading influences, but concrete beings of a certain kind, restricted to spots where the environment is not too distant from the optimum and subsisting for a limited period of time. One of the most important factors in determining the status of parasites and predators is the relative abundance of the food supply, i.e., of their hosts. The more perfectly uniform and continuous the distribution of the hosts, the more likely are the parasites to flourish. Furthermore, since the essential characteristic of the parasite or predator is that it increases *at the expense of its host,* the regions in which the host is abundant are those *in which it is likely to be most effective as a controlling factor*" (p. 331).

In 1935 H. S. Smith reconsidered this classification on theoretical grounds from the point of view of host-parasite interrelations, adopted it in essence, and again changed the terminology. He proposed the terms "density independent" and "density dependent" mortality factors. The former factors destroy a constant percentage of organisms in sparse, intermediate, or dense populations and thus are basically analogous to the "catastrophic" of Howard and Fiske and to the "general" of Thompson. The density-dependent factors destroy a percentage that increases with density and thus are basically analogous to the "facultative" and "individualized" factors of the other authors. Smith also recognized another group of factors, which destroys a percentage that *decreases* as density increases, but he made little of it. Since Smith's terms are essentially self-defining, we shall adopt them in preference to those of the earlier writers.

A further step in the growth of this classification system appeared in a paper by Allee (1941), who was interested in formalizing in a more specific way the fact that mortality can decrease, as well as increase, with density. Allee, accordingly, proposed that density-dependent factors be split into "direct" and "inverse" categories. Direct density-dependent factors are those just discussed, i.e., mortality increasing with density in Smith's sense. Inverse density-dependent factors are those "eliminating influences which take a decreasing percentage of the individuals present as the population increases."

We are left, then, with the following classification system of population factors:

Density-independent mortality factors
Density-dependent mortality factors
    Direct
    Inverse

Figure 124 schematizes a possible operation of these agents in a hypothetical population.*

"catastrophic," but for the most part independent of density—hence, "density-independent." A particular characteristic of certain biotic factors, e.g., competition, predators, parasites, and pathogens, is that they exert an effect on numbers that is dependent on density—hence, "density-dependent." Fluctuations in population growth form obviously are caused both by physical and biotic factors. However, Nicholson (1933) and Smith (1935) contend with cogency, largely on theoretical grounds, that, by their very nature, density-independent factors operating alone cannot determine and maintain an average population density over long periods of time—a view that has

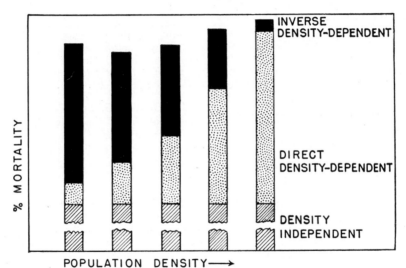

Fig. 124. Schematic representation of density-independent and density-dependent operations. (After Allee.)

This classification has developed primarily through theoretical considerations substantiated here and there from observations derived largely from experience with control of host-parasite insect populations. Fundamentally, but not exclusively, the classification distinguishes between the operation of the physical environment from the biotic environment as these determine the "balance" or "steady state" of a population in time, at least insofar as it is realistic to speak of the existence of such a mean density in nature. The effect of physical factors on abundance may be great and

much to commend it.

In this chapter we consider first the physical environment at the population level, making frequent reference to the autecological principles presented in Section II. This is followed by consideration of food and the biotic environment under which population density per se, and selected problems of population ecology, are discussed. Then a general case is presented for which both physical and biotic factors can be identified in terms of a particular population along with certain suggestions about their possible interactions. The chapter ends with a brief discussion of Population Integration intended as a general summary.

It would be desirable, of course, if each factor considered, whether physical or bio-

* A general classification of ecological factors that affect populations has been proposed by Voûte (1943), and applied to forest insects (1946).

tic, could be factually examined in terms of its density-independent and density-dependent components. Unfortunately, the present state of knowledge does not permit this, so that the best we can do is to deal systematically with factors that seem of more general significance and to suggest, or speculate about, their mode of action whenever possible. In our treatment we extend this classification beyond the insect populations for which it was originally proposed to include other terrestrial and aquatic groups. Also, our attention is not limited to mortality; natality and, in some instances, dispersion are reviewed.

THE PHYSICAL ENVIRONMENT AT THE POPULATION LEVEL

Uvarov (1931) outlined the principal climatic factors that affect insect population growth form primarily through density-independent action. This outline serves as an appropriate point of departure for our discussion and is reproduced in the next paragraph. Since we also wish to consider aquatic populations, it is necessary to list the more important factors that can affect them, irrespective of their density, and these, too, appear. It must be stressed here that the purpose of this chapter is not a systematic analysis and synthesis of the physical and biotic components of the environment at the autecological level. That was done in Section II and will be continued in the discussion of Communities. Our concern rather is to provide selected cases in which density-independent operations can be detected, or at least suggested, at the group level. Our treatment of this topic is limited to the presentation of enough illustrations to bring forth the fundamental ecological principles involved. A number of related topics have already been considered in Section II dealing with the Physical Environment, and we shall refer to certain of these where appropriate.

The following, in somewhat modified form, is Uvarov's classification of the climatic factors that affect abundance of terrestrial species:

1. Temperature as a controlling factor:
   (a) Direct injury by high and medium temperatures
   (b) Effect of high temperature on reproduction
   (c) Winter mortality and general effects of low temperatures
   (d) Favorable effects of temperature
2. Precipitation:
   (a) Excess precipitation
   (b) Deficient precipitation (drought)
   (c) Winter precipitation
   (d) Effects of rainfall in tropical climates
   (e) Rainstorms and hailstorms
3. Wind
4. Atmospheric pressure
5. Thunderstorms
6. Temperature and rainfall
7. Temperature and humidity
8. Temperature and light
9. Food quality and quantity as related to climate

The following factor-categories seem most significant for aquatic populations from the point of view of the physical environment[*]:

1. Physical properties of the water
2. Chemical properties of the water
3. Water movements, both regular and irregular
4. Light penetration
5. Substratum effects
6. Certain aspects of quality and quantity of food.

Our task now is to provide illustrations of certain of these items by choosing examples from the literature dealing with terrestrial and aquatic, natural and experimental populations. As was mentioned, we do not discuss every possible type of operation, nor do we imply, even though for reasons of analysis we treat the various factors individually or at best in combinations of twos, that a single factor is the only one effectively operating. Obviously, in many cases a number of environmental factors are affecting the population, and these may be both density-independent and density-dependent in character. Later, we attempt to show something of this in discussing integration. Our general philosophy about the wholeness of the environment has been stated on page 1.

TEMPERATURE

Experimental Populations

Terao and Tanaka (1928) showed that the water flea *Moina macrocopa*, when abundantly fed, produces different-sized

[*] These general categories receive detailed, systematic treatment in Welch (1935) and Sverdrup, Johnson, and Fleming (1942).

populations, depending upon the temperature at which they are cultured. For example, at 19.8° C. the asymptote attained is 199 of these cladocerans per unit-container; at 24.8° the asymptote is 429; and at 33.6° it is 271 (Fig. 100). They conclude that there is a relationship between the size of the population and the temperature optimal for reproduction. In another paper Terao and Tanaka (1928a) measure the number of births per female day over a range of ten constant temperatures extending from 3.2° to 37.7° C. They report the highest reproduction at 28.1°, above which the rate drops sharply and below which it declines more gradually. Gause (1931) analyzed their population growth data mathematically and showed that when temperature is plotted on the abscissa against asymptotic population size on the ordinate, the resulting curve exhibits, essentially, a normal distribution with its central high value at about 28° C.

It is not permissible to conclude that temperature is the only factor operating here and that the action is entirely density-independent, since competition must obtain in all the cultures. In fact, Terao and Tanaka (1928b) demonstrated that increasing density lowers fecundity, and Pratt (1943) clearly shows for *Daphnia magna* that the considerable effect of temperature on mean population size operates by modifying the action of population density. However, for *Moina* it seems apparent that the primary cause is density-independent and operates through the differential effect of various temperatures on female reproduction.

Natural Populations

Kendeigh (1942) studied losses in the nesting of fifty-one species of birds and showed that temperature played a role in this matter. The percentage of eggs that are addled or infertile is high at low and high temperatures, but relatively low at medial temperatures. For example, if mean monthly temperature is plotted against percentage of eggs not hatching, it can be shown for the house wren that between about 15° and 21° C. only 5.3 per cent fail to hatch. Above or below this range the percentage increases so that at 12° and 25° it is about 10 to 11 per cent. Kendeigh is not entirely sure of the nature of the

temperature effect, but believes that this factor in some way has a direct influence on the birds because "a relation between reproductive vigor and temperature is at least indicated by the facts here presented" (p. 26).

Gunter (1941) has reported on the effect of unusual cold upon the marine fish populations in the Aransas Bay area of Texas. The winter of 1939–1940 was most severe, and local weather reports showed that, in this region, January of 1940 averaged colder than any previously recorded month. On January 18 a "norther" struck, and the temperature fell in four hours from 65° to 25° F., and then reached 16° F. during the night. This drop in temperature resulted in an excessive fish mortality in the general area as detected by experimental seining and fisheries statistics. Many dead fishes were seen along the shores. For example, on January 24 Gunter personally saw 15,000 to 20,000 dead piggy perch (*Lagodon rhomboides*) in the storm basin at Aransas Pass. The air temperature was 1.5° C., and the water temperature, 4.7° C.

This severe and sudden cold had a decided effect upon the Texas commercial fisheries catch, as is brought out in the accompanying table, reporting catch in pounds.

Year	September–January	February–April	Decline (Per Cent)
1937–1938	2,171,997	1,331,302	39.6
1938–1939	1,972,864	911,133	52.7
1939–1940	1,412,090	335,431	76.2

The figures show a general decline in the over-all September to April catch from 1937 to 1940, but the important point is the sharp decline of 76.2 per cent from the September–January to the February–April period in the season of the cold spell, when compared with the two preceding years. (The February to April catch is always smaller since only three months, rather than five, are considered.) Gunter believes, quite correctly we think, that this drop is largely attributable to cold. When the reports are broken down in various ways, by areas, species, and so forth, the same point holds true. Of all the fishes, the flounder population was most affected. It declined from 74,306 pounds in the five months before the freeze to 3840 pounds after the freeze, a difference of 94.8 per cent. Gunter reported that many of the invertebrate populations were more resistant to cold than were the fishes. Some of the invertebrates appeared completely dead at the time, but soon revived.

Ward (1940) conducted an intensive survey of the seasonal fluctuations of Entomostraca dwelling in ponds in the region of Cincinnati, Ohio. She developed methods for consistently sampling the population turnover of Cladocera, Copepoda, Ostracoda, and Phyllopoda. These records of abundance were correlated with a number of physical, chemical, and biotic measurements. Ward concluded that temperature was the most important single factor controlling entomostracan populations and that much of its influence was direct upon the organisms themselves. "Undoubtedly temperature both directly and indirectly played a great part in inducing seasonal fluctuations in numbers and in controlling the appearances and disappearances of various species as the yearly cycle progressed" (p. 678). She confirms a much earlier opinion of Birge (1898a) that temperature controls reproductive rhythms in these forms and that seasonal distribution is primarily a description of the reactions of the Crustacea to this factor as it affects productivity.

A particular illustration is instructive. The cladoceran *Allonella karua,* a southern form, in all probability has recently extended its northern range to the Cincinnati area and is present in the ponds studied by Ward. "This species appeared abruptly and in considerable numbers on July 2, 1938, . . . when the temperature was 26° C., a reading first recorded for that year in the observations of the preceding week. It appeared consistently at every collection thereafter until September 24, when the temperature fell below 20° C. for the first time. With this drop to 17° C., the species disappeared completely from collections, although it was several weeks before water temperatures became much further reduced."

Certain other probable direct effects of temperature have been discussed in Section II. On pages 103 and 104 the concept of Heat Hardiness was developed; on pages 99 to 103, the concept of Cold Hardiness; and on pages 207 to 211 some general relations between heat and moisture, along with an introduction to the climograph, appear.

HUMIDITY, AND HUMIDITY AND TEMPERATURE

The direct effect of humidity on populations, and the effect of humidity when associated with temperature, have been considerably investigated.

Experimental Populations

Utida (1941) studied experimental populations of the Azuki bean weevil, *Callosobruchus chinensis,* as affected by humidity and population density, and his paper affords an illustration of both density-independent and density-dependent operations. Figure 125 summarizes certain of the findings when reproductivity, as indexed by number of progeny, is assayed in the presence of a wide series of parent weevil densities and under three conditions of relative humidity: 32 per cent, 52 per cent, and 76 per cent. The graph clearly shows that both density and humidity are potent agents in terms of their effect on reproduction. Relative to the former it is to be noted that the total number of progeny (at 76 and 52 per cent humidities) increases with density until 192 parent weevils per container is attained and then declines sharply. The reproductive rate, when expressed as number of young *per female,* was highest in the lowest density and decreased with each successive stage of parental crowding.

The effect of humidity is equally clear and easily summarized: The order of productivity in the three humidities is 76 per cent, 52 per cent, 32 per cent.

The component humidity effect that is basically independent of density can be ascertained and thus advanced as an illustration of a direct density-independent effect induced by atmospheric moisture and influencing reproduction. Utida showed that weevils maintained at essentially 100 per cent relative humidity did not reproduce effectively because a filamentous fungus got established, which checked the normal hatching of the weevils' eggs and made the beans unsuitable as food for the larvae.

Lund (1938) reports the effect of humidity, among other things, on the productivity and longevity of adult *Trichogramma evanescens.* This is a chalcid fly that, in these experimental populations, parasitized the eggs of the Angoumois grain moth, *Sitotroga cerealella.*

In his experiments Lund controlled the temperature at 25° C. and recorded the number of progeny produced, and the longevity of males and females in four conditions of humidity, namely: saturation (0 mm.), and in saturation deficiencies of

sexes is considerably reduced. "Since the products of saturation deficiencies (governing rate of evaporation) and the longevities (duration of evaporation) at 10 and 15 mm. are about equal (43.0 and 45.0 respectively for the females and 44.0 and

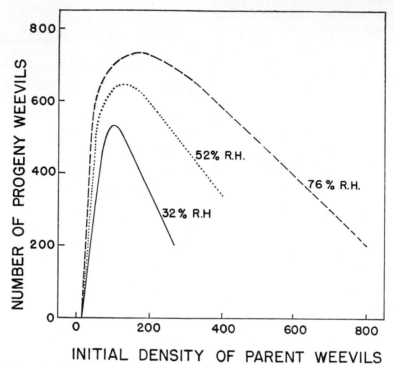

Fig. 125. Smoothed curves indicating the relation between parent weevil density, progeny, and relative humidity. (After Utida.)

5 mm., 10 mm., and 15 mm. His findings are as follows:

Humidity (Saturation Deficit)	Factor Observed	Mean ± S.E.
0 mm.	Number of progeny	64.0 ± 1.7
	Male longevity (days)	6.8 ± 0.3
	Female longevity (days)	5.2 ± 0.2
5 mm.	Number of progeny	66.1 ± 2.5
	Male longevity (days)	6.3 ± 0.3
	Female longevity (days)	5.7 ± 0.2
10 mm.	Number of progeny	58.4 ± 2.0
	Male longevity (days)	4.3 ± 0.3
	Female longevity (days)	4.4 ± 0.1
15 mm.	Number of progeny	51.9 ± 1.2
	Male longevity (days)	3.1 ± 0.2
	Female longevity (days)	2.4 ± 0.1

Certain conclusions can be drawn from the table. At saturation deficiencies of 10 mm. and 15 mm., the longevity of both

36.0 for the males) the total amounts of water evaporated from the parasites at these two conditions were about equal. This would indicate that in these cases the limiting lethal factor is probably desiccation and that the desiccation limit is around 44 mm-days" (pp. 433–434). Lund concludes that since death in the 5 mm. saturation deficiency experiments is similar to that in saturated atmospheres (0 mm.), therefore, under the former conditions, it cannot be the result of desiccation, but is attributable to some other factor. The effect of humidity on productivity is less pronounced, but the general trend is the same with a progressive decrease in the number of progeny after the 5 mm. saturation deficiency level is passed. The differences between the means 66.1 and 58.4 and between 58.4 and 51.9 are significant in relation to their standard errors.

This affords another illustration in which an environmental factor, humidity, analyzed for its effect on an organism, is found to be primarily and, in part at least, density-independent. As in most of these cases, the possibility of density-dependent action relative to humidity is not excluded. For example, it is quite conceivable that different densities of chalcid flies would react differentially to the saturation deficiencies just discussed. But it seems clear that there is

populations decreases. This is brought out in Figure 126. The graph shows survivorship definitely and consistently highest at a saturation deficiency of 4 mm. (89 per cent relative humidity), with a large decrease in percentage survivors against time as the relative humidity drops 17 per cent to 72 per cent, followed by still further decreases at 55 and 27 per cent humidities. Survivorship of the fleas when away from the rats is then inversely proportional to

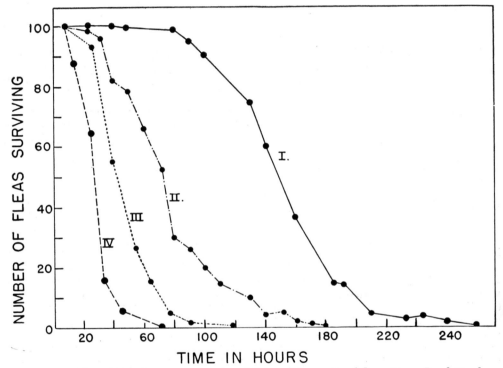

Fig. 126. The relation between saturation deficit and longevity of fleas. Curve I, relative humidity 89 per cent, and saturation deficit 4 mm.; II, 72 per cent and 10 mm.; III, 55 per cent and 16 mm.; and IV, 27 per cent and 26 mm. (After Uvarov.)

an underlying direct effect exerted on the individual members of the population.

Natural Populations

An interesting study combining research in the field and laboratory and concerned with both temperature and humidity is reviewed briefly by Uvarov (1931). This concerns the effect these factors exert on adult flea populations and the consequence of this for epidemics of bubonic plague. It can be shown experimentally that as humidity lowers, in the presence of a constant air temperature of 32° C. and constant air movement, the mean longevity of flea

the saturation deficiency. Temperature also is effective. If the saturation deficiency is constant, a 10° C. rise in temperature reduced life duration by 50 to 66 per cent.

These experimentally determined facts relate to the success or failure of epidemics of plague. Uvarov comments on this point as follows: "A variation of the saturation deficiency from 5 mm. to 35 mm., such as occurs in the plains of Northern India, would, accordingly, shorten the average duration of life of wandering rat fleas in the proportion of fifteen to one. This accounts for the fact that plague does not maintain itself in an epidemic form when the temperature rises above 26.6°, and is accompanied by a saturation deficiency of over 8 mm." (p. 149). The climatic controls of the flea populations in question may also involve other stages of the life history.

Reference should be made to the study of Holdaway (1932) dealing with *Tribolium confusum*. This affords another example of the effect of humidity on population size.

PRECIPITATION: EXCESS AND DEFICIENT

The relation of rainfall, as well as other climatic factors, to the development or suppression of locust outbreaks has been the subject of considerable attention in various parts of the world. The topic is too complex, and the literature too extensive, to review in detail, but a particular instance can be sketched to illustrate how the amount of precipitation functions as a controlling, density-independent factor. These observations are taken from a paper by Key (1942) dealing with the Australian plague locust, *Chortoicetes terminifera*.

A most severe outbreak of this species took place in Eastern Australia in 1937–1938, the second season of a cycle which had its start in the spring of 1936–1937. An area of 123,000 square miles was infested in New South Wales, 28,000 square miles in Queensland, and 1700 square miles in Victoria. In the following year (1938–1939), the incidence of the locust plague was relatively unimportant. Ecologically, the infested areas were diverse. As the swarms migrate they tend to follow a humidity gradient, and about 65 per cent of the swarms fly toward and arrive in moister regions than those they started from. The rate of spread of the infestation is highest at the start of the outbreak, at which time it may exceed 100 miles a day.

The life cycle of the locusts proceeds without essential interruption only so long as the effective rainfall and temperature remain within certain limits. These, then, are two of the critical meteorological conditions the effect of which on the population is essentially density-independent. Key illustrates this point in part as follows: "In New South Wales, hatching of the over-wintered eggs normally takes place when the temperature rises above the threshold for development, for the moisture conditions at this time are usually favourable. Interruption of the life-cycle by drought quite frequently occurs during one or more of the summer months, in which case the precise incidence of the dry period determines its effect on the population. If it occurs during the hopper stage, heavy mortality results, whereas if it commences during the egg stage, the population is little affected unless the dry period exceeds three months" (p. 85).

As is true of many ecological phenomena, a final, particular event frequently depends upon many preceding successful interactions. This is true for locust outbreaks: an outbreak does not develop unless a number of conditions have been satisfied. Thus, although rainfall is definitely important, it is only one factor in a complex system. Andrewartha (1940, p. 76) suggests this point nicely in the following quotation:

"There is considerable evidence that favourable weather for several successive years is necessary before a major outbreak can occur. Swarms are likely to develop in the outbreak area when rain is adequate during the warm months. Two or more favourable seasons in this way may be required to produce large or dense swarms. Similar conditions are necessary for swarms to develop in the intermediate breeding areas. For the outbreak to continue its development in the agricultural districts a dry autumn is required. The whole sequence is necessary for a major plague. The cycle may be broken at any point; when this occurs the incipient outbreak will be destroyed."

Errington (1939) has studied the effect of drought on muskrat populations in Iowa. The summer of 1934 was a season of severe drought, followed by dry years in 1936 and 1937. Muskrat populations during these three seasons are compared with those of other, more normal, years. Even when their habitats begin to dry out, most of the muskrats remain in their original home ranges. Some do move to new areas and, by and large, are killed off at a higher rate than those that stay behind. As the drought becomes more severe a number of events may take place. There is an increase in "intraspecific strife," which usually assumes the form of accentuated fighting between old and young of both sexes. Fighting between males is prevalent in the spring, primarily as a manifestation of sexual unrest and aggression. Fighting may be heightened after dry summers and leads to incapacitating wounds and actual death. This is brought about especially when muskrats leave their old ranges because of the drought and enter new, well-populated areas. Thus, the primary "trigger," drought, is density-independent and sets off a chain of events starting with increased emigration. The latter brings about more stringent competition for and within habitat niches—this is basically a density-dependent operation. With increased emigration goes an increased vulnerability to predation. Also, some of the muskrats actually die from direct exposure during their wanderings, particularly in winter, when the food supply is inadequate and the temperature low.

Shelford (1943) reports that rainfall and snowfall are important climatic factors affecting the growth form of populations of the collared lemming (*Dicrostonyx groenlandicus*) in the Churchill, Manitoba, area of Canada. He found that the local ecological dispersal of lemmings "varies from year to year with some correlation with the autumn rainfall. Following wet autumns they were limited to the sandy ridges and generally distributed in drier years" (p. 483). From a series of weather analyses Shelford tentatively concluded: (1) The capacity of a lemming population to increase is favored by the occurrence of average (or higher) snowfall during the first three months of winter, particularly if the snow stays on the ground so as to provide protection all winter. This holds when the snowfall is combined with temperatures near normal (or higher) during the season. (2) Temperatures of July and August that are above normal probably also favor population growth. (3) Two successively favorable years (or at least one average year followed by a favorable year) seem to be required before a maximum population of lemmings can build up. The reader will here recognize an operation functionally similar to the development of locust plagues.

In the chapter on Growth Form an effect of drought on salmon abundance was discussed (p. 321). Here, the initial factor, drought, apparently increased the hazard of predation upon young river salmon. This affords another illustration of drought acting primarily as a density-independent factor, but followed by secondary, density-dependent consequences.

Excessive rainfall, in contradistinction to average rainfall and drought, also can exert a considerable effect on certain natural populations. Uvarov (1931, p. 141) summarizes an illustration of this for bark-beetle populations as follows:

"Excessive rainfall during the flight of the adults checks their activities and reduces their progeny, while adults making burrows, as well as eggs and larvae, are liable to be drowned in the sap, which is more abundant when the moisture content of the soil is high. This statement is not based solely on theoretical considerations, since the development of bark-beetles in a tree can be checked to a considerable extent by supplying water to its roots, or by defoliating it and thus recording the loss of water through transpiration."

The reader is urged to reexamine certain pertinent cases reviewed in Section II. Of particular interest is the treatment of Bonitation (page 209).

STORMS

McClure (1943), in an extensive study of natural populations of the mourning dove, *Zenaidura macroura*, discusses among other things the question of nesting losses. By observing a group of these birds consistently for three years in the vicinity of Lewis, Iowa, he was able to catalogue and evaluate certain agents that destroy the nests and the birds and eggs in the nests. Storms figure prominently among these agents. Practically every storm regardless of kind, blew poorly placed nests to the ground. Hail storms frequently killed many adults and young when direct hits were scored. Cloudbursts were also effective both in dislodging nests and possibly by drowning the birds. Sustained, high winds, in addition to blowing down the nests, snapped off the supporting limbs and felled the trees. The doves usually behaved so as to afford some protection to the young, but were not always successful. For example, during heavy, wet snows in April the birds remained constantly on the nest until well after the snow stopped: during strong winds the brooding parents protected the nest by facing into the wind. "Both parents were often seen sitting on the nest facing the cold, strong winds. One bird was apparently on the eggs and young, and the other on the edge of the nest" (p. 394).

McClure concluded on the basis of three years' observations that he could account for 46 per cent of the total nesting losses, but that the other 54 per cent resulted from an unknown cause or causes. Of this 46 per cent, inclement weather, a density-independent factor, was by far the most important decimating agent, producing about 25 per cent of all losses. The factors comprising the remaining 21 per cent included such items as predation by fox squirrels (4.4 per cent), blue jays (2.4 per cent), and cats (1.9 per cent); sterile and deserted eggs (4.2 per cent); young falling from or dying in the nest (1.6 per cent).*

CHEMICAL FACTORS

A number of factors affect populations in a density-independent fashion roughly classifiable as "chemical factors of the environment." These are of particular significance for natural, aquatic groups, but examples also can be found among studies of laboratory and natural, terrestrial populations. In this section we select a few illustrations sampled rather widely from the literature and dealing with a diverse series of forms.

Hydrogen Ion Concentration

There was a time not many years past when ecologists considered pH to be an omnipotent environmental agent. This opinion, as mentioned in the Historical section, has been considerably revised, and it has now frequently been found difficult to prove that acidity or alkalinity within ranges commonly experienced in nature have any limiting or stimulating effect on populations whatsoever. The underlying chemical basis for pH; the pH values of a number of natural environments; the relation of this factor to the ecological distribution of animals; and certain generalizing statements are to be found in Section II (p. 172).

Edmondson (1944) studied the distribution of sessile rotifers in a number of inland lakes and attempted to correlate this distribution with chemical factors of the medium and with floral and substrate factors. He found, after appropriate statistical analysis, that many pairs of species are associated together as natural populations more frequently than would be expected on the basis of a hypothesis of independent, random distribution. There were a few cases of apparent mutual exclusion, but these were so rare in comparison with in-

* Consult also the paper of Baskett (1947) dealing with nesting losses in populations of the ring-necked pheasant (*Phasianus colchicus torquatus*).

stances of associations that the conclusion was reached that "while external factors favorable or unfavorable to species are of major importance, competition does not appreciably affect the composition of the fauna" (p. 64).

It was shown that many rotifer species are sensitive to the chemical nature of their habitat and frequently occur with higher incidence in those lakes on one side of the median of concentration of specific, dissolved materials than in lakes on the other side of the median. Both hydrogen ion and bicarbonate concentrations were extensively studied. Edmondson concluded that "some species are very likely excluded from lakes by high bicarbonate concentration, but not necessarily high pH" (p. 64). Some rotifers were tolerant as populations of media of considerable alkalinity, but not specifically of higher bicarbonate concentrations. A few forms could not tolerate high concentrations of either.

Substratum was an important factor in distribution. Edmondson reports that thirty-two species of rotifers are limited by "chemistry" or markedly associated with particular substrates. Of these thirty-two, the distribution of fifteen was correlated with both the chemical and substratal features, fifteen with substrate alone and independent of the chemistry, and two with chemical factors alone.

For our purposes the general conclusion emerging from this interesting study is that, while a few sessile rotifer populations may be specifically sensitive to hydrogen and/or hydroxyl ions, in most cases in which chemical factors are influential at all, it is the bicarbonate concentration that is significant. Thus, although pH may function as an important environmental index, it is not *per se* a factor of much general import.

The principal reason for reporting Edmondson's study at this point is to strengthen somewhat at the population level our general argument that pH when critically examined may not be so important ecologically as it may seem at first glance. This is not to deny, of course, obvious and proved cases of pH effects, certain of which have been already considered in Section II (p. 172).

Salinity

Andrews (1940) discusses the effect of changes in salinity on natural populations of the snail *Neritina virginea*. He and others observed off and on for many years a "salt pond" in the vicinity of Kingston, Jamaica, which at certain times was connected with the ocean, while at other times the pond-ocean junction was effectively blocked by accumulated sand. During the connected intervals the salinity of the pond water was lower and much like that of the sea; during the isolated periods evaporation went on regularly, there was scant rainfall and little drainage into the pond from the land, and the salinity increased. This sequence of events set up a natural experiment from which it can be concluded that after extended periods of high salinity the *Neritina* population is larger in terms of number of forms, but composed of dwarfed individuals; after extended periods of low salinity the snails are larger in size, but less numerous. Andrews attributes these differences primarily to the action of salt concentration operating essentially in a density-independent manner. It appears that this finding is not limited to gasteropods, since certain other mollusks behave somewhat similarly.

It seems reasonable to conclude that salinity does not ordinarily function as a limiting factor for animal populations. Stenohaline organisms capable of surviving only narrow changes in salt concentration are usually found in environments in which the salinity is relatively constant. Euryhaline organisms capable of tolerating wider changes in salt concentration are found when considerable variability in salinity is likely. This, of course, follows as an obvious point. It can be argued that there is a greater abundance of species and individuals of marine organisms in coastal regions because of the lower salinity existing there. This is a dangerous, and possibly specious, argument *a priori*, however, since the coastal waters may be more favorable in other ways also; e.g., greater food supply. As seems true for *p*H, it is easy to reach the *ad hoc* conclusion that salinity is an effective factor, but such a conclusion is hard to prove without recourse to experimentation.

Cowles (1930) supports this point in discussing the ecological distribution of diatoms. "It is well established from a study of geographical distribution that certain diatoms (oceanic) are characteristic of waters of high salinity, such as that of the open ocean; that others (neritic) are char-acteristic of waters of lower salinity found along the sea coast and in estuaries; and that still different ones frequent the fresh waters or rivers emptying into the ocean. But, also, it is well known that many of these diatoms are able to stand a large range of salinities and that oceanic as well as neritic diatoms are often found in estuaries where the salinity is very low" (p. 317).

Calcium

Certain aspects of calcium and magnesium ions as elements of the aquatic environment were discussed in Section II (p. 203). An extension of this subject at the species population level is afforded by the observations and experiments of Jewell (1939), which are concerned with the relation of calcium bicarbonate content of fresh waters to the distribution of sponges (Spongillidae) in northern Wisconsin. Jewell showed that some sponges are sensitive to calcium bicarbonate concentration and appear to be limited in their distribution by this factor. Other sponges have a wide range of toleration. For example, *Ephydatia mülleri* is absent from waters both high and low in calcium, but is found in the intermediate range of 5.6 to 16.3 mgm. of calcium per liter. Populations of this species, however, are largest in the middle and lower parts of this range. There is thus a spectrum of possible toleration within which lies a more restricted optimum. On the other hand, *Spongilla ingloviformis* is extremely sensitive to calcium tension and is not found when a concentration of 3.16 mgm. per liter is exceeded, despite the fact that sturdy populations are present in habitats of lower tensions. The other extreme is exemplified by *Heteromyenia repens*, which tolerates the impressive range of 2.66 to 53.4, a range beyond which fresh waters in Wisconsin rarely go. Jewell also concluded that calcium and magnesium in organic combinations are not important agents in sponge distribution.

Pollution

The pollution of rivers by sewage and trade wastes offers an interesting opportunity to study this factor as it affects population abundance, distribution, and succession. It is frequently possible to trace the source of pollution to a particular region, and observations and measurements can be made of the fauna above and below this source, thus furnishing a control area which is not contaminated and an experimental area which is. The experimental area typically exists as a gradient, characterized by excessive contamination where the wastes are discharged and followed by a progressive decrease in contamination downstream. This question has been rather well studied for the Mississippi, Illinois, and other American rivers, and, although the literature cannot be reviewed in any detail, certain points merit attention.

In a general way, pollution has both a direct and an indirect effect on the populations. Acting directly, it can drive forms from their habitats; it frequently predisposes the fauna to disease and infection; it may increase disproportionately egg and juvenile mortality; and it may actually kill adult members of the group. Acting indirectly, it reduces oxygen supply; it changes the character of the bottom; it may harm or at least alter the vegetation; and it may limit both the number of habitat niches and the food supply. It is also true, of course, that some species such as members of the Tubificidae thrive on pollution, so much so, in fact, that they are frequently called "pollution-index forms."

A brief illustration of the effect of pollution on fresh-water fish populations is afforded by the studies of Thompson and Hunt (1930) on the fishes found in the west branch of the Salt Fork River (Illinois) above and below a source of pollution. Collections in both localities were made over a quadrat 330 yards square, and the forms were segregated by species, number, and size. In the clean-water quadrat twenty species were recorded, while in the contaminated-water quadrat fifteen of these were not present at all and four of the five that were present were reduced in number from 320 to one; twenty-two to one; seventy-one to eighteen; and 126 to two. There was also a suggestion (though from meager data) that the five species taken in the polluted sample were smaller in size.

Invertebrates as well as vertebrates are subject to depletion by pollution. Galtsoff, Chipman, Hasler, and Engle (1938) have presented an excellent illustration of this for oyster populations of the York River, Virginia. During the last twenty years or so this population and the industry dependent upon it have been declining seriously, and the authors set forth comprehensive evidence that this decline is caused by liberation of a trade waste from a pulp-mill plant located on the river. The various effects of this waste on the oyster were studied, along with an ecological survey of the stream environment. The findings can be summarized somewhat as follows:

In the first place, the York River, apart from pollution, was about as favorable for the oysters as productive neighboring streams. For example, studies of the cycles of salinity, temperature, and plankton productivity showed these to be quite normal and conducive to robust populations. Also, the York River forms, when transplanted to nearby localities, flourished, thus suggesting that nothing was intrinsically wrong with the oyster stock.

This indicates that the observed population decline actually resulted from the pollution, certain effects of which on the physiology of the oyster were assayed experimentally. The pollutant brought about contraction of the adductor muscle with the consequence that the valves remained closed for an abnormal length of time. This naturally interferes with feeding and respiration. The waste also inhibits ciliary action in the gills and reduces the efficiency of the complex pumping mechanism. The last two influences cause the oysters to become dwarfed, and they fail to store a normal amount of glycogen. Unless the forms lived too long under polluted conditions these physiological inhibitions could be removed by returning the animals to clean water. In clean water normal growth rates were reestablished, glycogen was again stored in adequate amounts, and lime was deposited in the shells.

Despite these adverse effects of pollution, the oyster population did not entirely cease propagation. But the decline was steady and caused the authors to make the following justifiable recommendation: "That the presence of pulp-mill waste in the water is the cause of the failure of oysters to grow and fatten in the upper part of the river and that the elimination of pulp-mill pollution is therefore a prerequisite for the restoration of the oyster industry in the York River" (p. 42).

This is a first-rate illustration for our present purposes. A single density-independent environmental factor (pollution) was identified; the effect of this factor on population growth form was estimated; and the physiological channels through which the factor operates were assayed.

Oxygen

The minimal oxygen concentrations tolerated by natural populations of fresh-water fishes have been investigated by Moore (1942) in five Minnesota lakes under summer and winter conditions. During the summer he found that, in general, when oxygen concentrations reached 3.5 ppm or lower at temperatures of 15° to 26° C., most of the eight species* examined died within twenty-four hours. On the other hand, concentrations of 5.0 ppm or higher were completely adequate under the conditions of observation. This minimal threshold is lower during the winter. Of twelve species† tested at 0° to 4° C., the reduced oxygen supply must reach 2.0 ppm before fatalities result, and the fish can withstand this concentration for forty-eight hours. Reduction of the oxygen to 1.0 ppm is lethal for all the fishes except for an occasional *Ameiurus melas.* Concentrations above 3.0 ppm are adequate for all species during the winter season.

In both summer and winter the small forms display a greater tolerance of reduced oxygen than the larger forms. In this connection Moore reports an interesting observation made at North Farms Reservoir, Wallingford, Connecticut, where conditions of high temperature, quiet water surface, a large water-bloom in process of decay, shallow water, and probably a high organic content of bottom mud, all reacted together to bring about almost complete oxygen depletion. This resulted in a truly spectacular mortality among the fish populations. It was estimated that over 400,000 fishes died in this small lake (less than 150 acres) because of oxygen starvation. G. E. Hutchinson‡ observed, however, that many individ-

* The species studied were *Esox lucius, Huro salmoides, Pomoxis sparoides, Aplodinotus grunniens, Eupomotis gibbosus, Perca flavescens, Helioperca macrochira,* and *Ameiurus melas.*

† The species studied were the same as those above, excluding *Aplodinotus grunniens* and including five additional forms: *Ambloplites rupestris, Apomotis cyanellus, Allotis humilis, Fundulus diaphanus,* and *Notemigonus crysoleucas.*

‡ Unpublished material.

uals of two of the smaller species (*Eupomotis gibbosus* and *Notropis bifrenatus*), all of which were less than 32 mm. in length, continued to swim actively at the lake surface at the time when most of the forms were dying at such a great rate. He suggested that these individuals were able to survive because a thin film of oxygen-rich water at the surface was available and the fish escaped death by making use of this supply. Moore's study provides an illustration of the density-independent action of reduction of oxygen, which sometimes actually becomes a source of mortality for natural aquatic populations.

A number of the general ecological relations of oxygen were discussed in Section II (p. 192).

Carbon Dioxide

Davidson (1933) reports a most interesting, though somewhat controversial, illustration of excessive fish mortality probably caused by a sudden rise in carbon dioxide pressure. He was working around sunset along a salmon stream in Alaska in early August when suddenly many salmon (*Onchorhynchus gorbuscha*), trout, and freshwater bullheads turned belly up, as if suffering from suffocation, and then died "as though some immediate death dealing substance had been thrown into the stream." The total salmon population consisted of 80,000 fishes, 5000 of which succumbed.

When the fishes were dying there was no wind at all and the water was still. As the sun sank behind a mountain, the air chilled perceptibly. Davidson and some colleagues made certain environmental measurements in the stream at the death locality and downstream from it. The pH readings were instructive: at the place where the fishes were dying the pH was 5.6 at 65° F., while in the water below the spot it was 6.1 at 65° F. The fixed carbonates were the same in both areas, as was the specific gravity.

After about thirty minutes, during which time the fishes were dying, a cool wind came up, and the salmon and other species recovered, and those remaining started to mill about in characteristic fashion. Davidson believes that the lack of air movement formed a temporary air blanket over the stretch of the stream where the 80,000 salmon were swimming. Since the pH of the water was low, this blanketing effect of the quiet air probably resulted in a sharp rise in the carbon dioxide concentration of the water, a rise great enough to induce asphyxiation. It is not likely that the acidity of the water was caused by something other than the carbon dioxide, because the pH at the other station was not 5.6, but 6.1. As the fresh wind blew over the stream, the pH rose from 5.6 to 6.0, and the population recovered. The following summer, when a school of only 10,000 salmon was in this region of the stream, repeated water analyses showed the pH to be 6.3 at 61° F. for both stations, and there was no such catastrophic mortality. In short, this particular and unique series of events did not repeat itself.

Davidson cites the work of others to make the points (1) that carbon dioxide pressure increases rapidly with a lowering of pH in water with a low alkaline content, and that theoretically this pressure at the place and time of death should exceed that in other regions of the stream where the pH was 6.1 by approximately 50 per cent; and (2) that experimental studies show that an increase in carbon dioxide pressure in water causes an increase in blood acidity in the fish with consequent destruction of red blood cells.

If this admittedly speculative analysis is correct (it seems reasonable so far as the observations and evidence go), Davidson's study affords a striking, even if rare, illustration of the toxic effect of sudden accumulations of carbon dioxide on a natural population.

Miscellaneous Chemical Factors

A number of chemical factors, discussed in Section II, that have relation to our present interest cannot be considered further at the population level because of space limitations. However, reference should be made to this section, particularly to passages dealing with silicon, copper, phosphorus, nitrogen, osmotic balance, oxidation-reduction potentials, hardness of water, and trace chemicals in soils.

The reader should not infer from the foregoing discussion that the physical environment exerts an effect on populations which is exclusively independent of density. In fact, we believe that this general position has been overstressed. Smith

(1935) has written cogently about this point, and the following quotation expresses the matter in balanced perspective and serves as something of an admonition as well:

"Climate does not always act as a *density-independent* factor, but often operates quantitatively in much the same way that is characteristic of biotic factors, that is, it destroys a percentage which increases with density. So far as the writer is aware, no careful studies have been made to elucidate *just how* climate has this effect. It would require a type of study which would be extremely difficult to carry out, since it would necessitate the determination of the causes of death of a large number of insects at two or more densities, under perfectly natural conditions in the field. But climate so obviously limits geographic distribution and determines the average number of so many species that, even in the absence of proof, we must admit that under certain conditions it is capable of acting as a *density-dependent* factor.

"It seems most probable that this takes place through the existence of protective niches in the environment which are more or less limited in number. Individuals in excess of this number and which cannot therefore attain these niches are destroyed by unfavorable climate, while the others survive and prevent extermination of the species. Climate affecting the numbers of a species in this way would operate as a *density-dependent* factor, since its relative effect would increase and decrease with increasing and decreasing density. Climate can also affect the equilibrium position indirectly by modifying the efficiency of the *density-dependent* factors" (p. 894).

FOOD

The importance of food as a factor of population significance is obvious in the sense that there is some sort of relation between population growth form and food availability. But it is difficult to generalize about this factor and particularly difficult to place it neatly into a classification of density-independent or density-dependent categories or, for that matter, into other classificatory schemes. For example, suppose an essential limitation of a particular food substance for a defined population results in an insufficient amount of the substance for all. On logical grounds it could be assumed that this would have an effect on the population irrespective of its density, or that the limitation might establish a competition within the group for the substance, in which case density would certainly enter as a factor, or there might well be a combination of both. It seems that the answer as to which of these possibilities is actually true would be forthcoming only after investigation of the particular situation.

It is also obvious that the chain of events in nature may be even more complicated. A climatic condition may operate so as to affect the food supply; for example, favorable rainfall could bring about lush vegetation. This in turn could be exploited by members of a herbivorous species, even though there was much more food available than could be utilized.

This discussion leads us to the point that food furnishes such an inextricable meeting ground in ecology between the physical and biotic environments that it is difficult, and possibly not even worthwhile, to attempt a further breakdown. This is a well-recognized issue. Chapman (1931) speaks to the point as follows:

"It cannot be said that nutrition is a purely physical factor of ecology for the reason that no animal [except probably the phytoflagellates], so far as we are able to discern, is able to live upon a diet which does not contain some compounds which have been synthesized

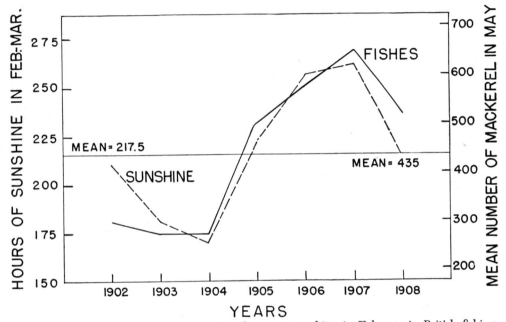

Fig. 127. Catch of mackerel in May plotted against sunshine in February in British fishing grounds. (After Allen.)

This matter requires brief elaboration here primarily to set the stage for the more detailed treatment of Food Chains that follows in the section devoted to Communities.

There is some reason for thinking of food in terms of quantity, or amount required by a population, and quality, or the kinds of food substances needed by a population, Both quantity and quality may be directly affected by soil and climate in the case of terrestrial species and by climate, substratum, and physicochemical properties of the water in the case of aquatic species. In addition, population size and/or density along with their consequent competitive pressures can influence, and be influenced by, both quantity and quality of food.

by another organism. We have therefore arrived at the point where physical autecology and biotic autecology are merged, and it is an arbitrary matter as to whether this chapter is to be included under physical autecology or biotic autecology. All animals are dependent upon at least one other organism for the preparation of their food . . . There is probably no better example in all nature of the interdependence of organisms than that of nutrition itself" (p. 155).*

* Actually this question is probably not so closed a case as Chapman's quotation implies, particularly so far as the protista are concerned. Mast and Pace (1933) present suggestive evidence for "chemoautotrophic nutrition" in *Chilomonas paramecium* (p. 358). Such forms apparently grow in a medium without photosynthesis.

With these points in mind we now present an illustration of food affecting populations in what appears to be primarily a density-independent way, and several, later in this chapter, in which such density-dependent elements as competition, predator-prey, and host-parasite relations can be detected.

Allen (1909) reported a suggestive relationship extending over a seven year period between the amount of sunlight in February and March and the abundance of mackerel caught off the West Cornish coast in May of the same year. This correlation is diagrammed in Figure 127, in which the abscissa is time by years (1902 to 1908); the left ordinate, the amount of sunlight; and the right ordinate, the mackerel catch in hundreds. The two curves show considerable confluence, more than could be reasonably expected on a chance basis. Bullen showed (1909) by stomach content analysis that the mackerel fed primarily on zooplankton and especially on copepods, and that there was a close association between mackerel landings and the size of this zooplankton population. He also showed that there existed no consistent relation of a positive sort between the phytoplankton as such and the mackerel. The causal chain linking the sunlight on the one hand with the mackerel catch on the other is somewhat speculative, but the story runs something like this. The amount of sunlight in February and March affects directly the productivity of the phytoplankton. When there are many hours of sunshine, the plankton are more abundant, and vice versa. Since it is well known that the zooplankton feed on phytoplankton, it may be assumed that years of lush phytoplankton crops will favor large zooplankton populations. The latter apparently reach their maximum around May, and the mackerel then move in from nearby to feed, as reflected by the local fishery statistics reporting size of catch.

THE BIOTIC ENVIRONMENT AT THE POPULATION LEVEL

The discussion starting here includes, first, an analysis of the nature and operational aspects of population density, and, second, a consideration of problems in which density plays a significant role. These problems have been selected because of their theoretical importance for population ecology; taken as a group, they encompass both intraspecies and interspecies phenomena.

More specifically, population density is first discussed from the viewpoint of general orientation, followed by a treatment of coactions within populations, of environmental conditioning, and of microclimate. Then certain problems are outlined, along with which an effort is made to adduce principles of general ecological merit. These problems are considered: (1) population dispersion; (2) the analysis of population cycles; (3) the "mixed species" problem: interspecies competition; (4) intraspecies and interspecies predation; (5) organized predation by man: the problem of the optimal yield; and (6) host-parasite interactions.

The intent behind our discussion of these six problems is not to set forth in systematic fashion all ramifications of population ecology, but rather to establish those broader aspects that are considered, for purposes of emphasis, reasonably discrete units by investigators in the field and that are under study to a greater or less degree at both the natural and the laboratory levels.[*]

POPULATION DENSITY

General Aspects

Certain preliminary comments about population density are in order before pro-

[*] A number of population problems other than those mentioned are dealt with elsewhere in this book, both in the present section and in the sections on Communities and Evolution (IV and V). Thomas Park (1946), in a discussion of the scope of population ecology, lists fourteen subjects or problems of then-current interest. These are: (1) studies describing the growth form of populations; (2) the effect of various physical-chemical factors on population growth form; (3) analysis of population equilibrium; (4) the problems of underpopulation, optimal population, and overpopulation; (5) the productivity of populations, and factors that influence it; (6) the problem of the optimal yield; (7) description and analysis of population cycles; (8) analysis of dispersion within and between populations; (9) analysis of range and territory phenomena exhibited by natural populations; (10) epidemiological aspects of the interactions between host and parasite populations; (11) intraspecies and interspecies competition; (12) the organization of social populations; (13) improvements and extensions of population census techniques; and (14) the integration of populations.

cccding to an illustration of selected density-dependent operations. Population density was defined in Chapter 18 (p. 266) under the heading "Space-Relative Population" as the number of organisms per unit of space they occupy. This index affords a statistical measure of their concentration and, as was pointed out earlier, can be very meaningful when intelligently applied.*

Practically all students of populations have given attention to the study of density. This is so, not simply because the effect of density on groups lends itself to analysis, but also because such analysis frequently yields data that are, in themselves, of biological interest. Density effects, resulting either directly or indirectly from the coactions between the group components, are influential in affecting population growth form. Pearl (1930, p. 145) referred to this when he said, "In general there can be no question that this whole matter of influence of density of population, in all senses, upon biological phenomena, deserves a great deal more investigation than it has had. The indications all are that it is one of the most significant elements in the biological, as distinguished from the physical, environment of organisms."

A logical analysis of population density can be developed under three arbitrary categories: first, the kinds of processes and events that have been shown to be influenced by density; second, the type of end result induced by density, irrespective of the process involved; and, third, the nature and constitution of density *per se*. These will be briefly considered merely for purposes of orientation and then developed in more detail by examination of particular cases.

In discussing the processes influenced by population density, it is only necessary to present a partially complete list to make the point that the crowding of organisms within a restricted environment elicits many diverse responses on the part of the component members. The following events (among others) have been shown to be affected by population density: natality, mortality, and dispersion, the three primary factors that control population growth form (p. 272); responses such as the post embryonic development of insects, the

growth of individual organisms, rate of oxygen consumption, protection from environmental poisons, resistance of marine forms to hypotonic sea water and other unusual physical conditions, communal activity of bacteria and protozoa, the determination of sex in certain organisms, and morphological expressions such as the development of wings by aphids and the initiation of phases in locusts. It is obvious that these and other diverse events, while always of intrinsic physiological interest, are not necessarily of especial populational significance unless they eventually affect in the statistical sense birth, death, and/or dispersion (see Chapters 19 and 20).

In terms of its effect on the growth form of populations, density usually has one of two general influences: Either population growth is inhibited, or else it is stimulated, at least temporarily until new density relations are established. Growth inhibition has been the subject of much study and is clearly related to population control and "balance"; growth stimulation has received considerable attention primarily by Allee and his students (Allee, 1931, 1934a, 1938).

It has long been recognized that the increased crowding of organisms in a population reduces the population growth rate and even brings about population decline. This view has been demonstrated for laboratory and natural groups and has been advanced for human societies. As early as 1843 Farr* proposed an equation in which he attempted to establish that human mortality is a function of crowding. Experimental and field studies have corroborated findings of this sort. On the other hand, Allee has marshalled evidence from diverse sources to substantiate the point that "undercrowding" as well as overcrowding can be a hazard. Examples illustrating both types will be presented in this chapter (see also Chap. 23).

The nature of population density, while obviously a problem of importance, is frequently one about which precise information is scanty. Density has been defined in formal terms as the number of organisms per unit of space they occupy. Although

---

* A criticism of the term "density" and some of its implications will be found in Hogben (1931) and Robertson and Sang (1944).

* Farr's equation states that if the death rate has the notation R, and population density the notation D, then,

$$R = cD^m$$

with c and m being constants.

this definition is a convenient statistical index, it leaves much to be desired from the ecologists' point of view. For example, when a density response is demonstrated, the question arises: What actually brings about this observed effect at the operational level? Information pertinent to this question gets at the core of density-dependent population operations. There is a tendency in the older literature to think of crowding in "psychological" terms, to attribute causation to something unique in the number relationships themselves. This has led at times to a certain mysticism. Undoubtedly, there are situations—as, for example, in human and other social groups—in which such an explanation may be legitimate, but it

action," or the influence of the population on the habitat. A primary cycle could take place between one organism and its habitat. However, since grouping of organisms is the rule in nature, the primary cycle for any particular population would be constituted by the summation of many actions and reactions.

There is a *secondary cycle* in addition to the primary one. This is based on those operations that come about as a result of the grouping of the population members. Clements and Shelford call these operations "*coactions*," by which they refer to interorganismic relations along with such reciprocal effects as these relations may have with their habitat.

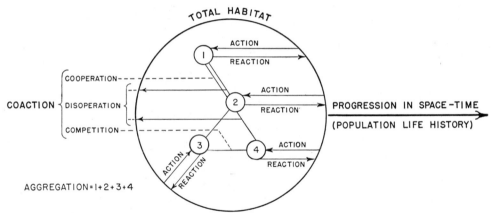

Fig. 128. Schematic representation of the Clements-Shelford action-reaction-coaction operations within ecological assemblages.

should not be invoked until other reasonable possibilities have been excluded.

There is some meaning in thinking of the basic ecology of populations in the same terms that Clements and Shelford (1939) use for communities.* Their ideas in simplified form are illustrated in Figure 128, which should be referred to in the brief discussion following. Habitat is defined as the total, effective physical-chemical environment. The concept is presented that a *primary cycle* of cause and effect results from an interplay between the habitat and the population members inhabiting it. This cycle consists of two reciprocal operations: "*action*," or the influence of the habitat on the population, and "*re-*

* Although we develop, define, and use in part this system of classification, we are not completely satisfied with its terminology, and we recognize that it has limitations.

Coactions influence the population (or community) through (1) "*cooperation*," which has survival value for at least a majority of the cooperating organisms; (2) "*disoperation*," which has deleterious effects on the coacting organisms, either through influence on the habitat, on contiguous group members, or both; and (3) "*competition*," which is an expression of the fact that certain coactions are directed towards exploiting an environment limited in its potentialities. Competition may be either favorable or unfavorable in terms of long-range results. A fourth category, "*toleration*," is added and discussed in the section on Evolution (p. 704).*

This concept, when more closely related to our present interest, suggests that while density-independent phenomena involve es-

* An "ecosystem" would be characterized by interacting primary and secondary cycles.

sentially the primary cycle, density-dependent phenomena may stem either from the secondary cycle and, therefore, involve coactions, or from those differences in intensity of the primary cycle induced by varying degrees of crowding, or from both.

Population Pressure Resulting from Coactions

One of the most thought-provoking illustrations of the coaction aspect of the population problem is found in investigations concerned with the relation of crowding to fecundity in the fruit fly, *Drosophila melanogaster*, despite the fact that the studies are somewhat "artificial" from the ecological viewpoint. This problem was formulated and developed by Pearl (1932) and has been extended by Bodenheimer (1938) and especially by Robertson and Sang (1944). We shall first review the findings of Pearl and of Bodenheimer and then discuss these briefly in the light of Robertson and Sang's more recent critical analysis (see also p. 396).

In 1922 Pearl and Parker set up experimental populations of *Drosophila* at initial imago densities ranging from one to fifty pairs per half-pint bottle. The bottles contained a culture medium the surface of which was inoculated with yeast. The number of progeny produced by the parents in these densities was counted, and the resulting data showed that as population density increased the number of offspring per bottle decreased. In short, an inverse relation between productivity and crowding is established under the conditions of this experiment.

In a later paper Pearl (1932) attempted to answer these questions: (1) What physiological process or processes that would explain these results are actually influenced by density, and (2) what factor or factors dependent upon the density relations influence this process? In considering the first point it was reasoned that the rate of reproduction must be a major factor varying between the different densities. That is to say, the flies in general would have to reproduce faster at low than at high densities if the observed result was to be realized. Such a difference in reproduction could involve an alteration of fecundity or fertility, or both. Appropriate experimentation showed that fecundity was greatly affected by the number of imago flies in the bottle; the oviposition rate, expressed as a rate per female per day, fell rapidly as the density increased. No important relations between crowding and fertility were reported (p. 289).

With this fecundity effect established, Pearl attempted an analysis of the population factors actually influencing oviposition. Experiments were performed in which the air volume in the bottles above the medium was varied while the area of agar surface was kept constant. The experiments showed that, although the extent of the air space had no marked relation to fecundity, the extent of crowding of the flies on the agar surface was highly important. Differently put, Pearl's findings suggested that the chief density coactions took place on, and perhaps below, the surface medium and not in the flying space above.

Bodenheimer (1938) reports experiments that substantiate some of Pearl's ideas. His experiments were so designed that agar volume and air volume could be varied while agar surface was maintained constant. It was found that the asymptotes attained by the fly populations growing in these various situations were the same regardless of the volume manipulations. This again indicates that the agar surface exposure is important.

To explain the decrease in fecundity with progressive crowding, Pearl advanced the following ideas based on experimentation and observation: (1) *Drosophila* females will not oviposit if they are in contact with, or disturbed by, other flies; (2) crowded flies stimulate each other so excessively that energy is dissipated that might otherwise be used in reproduction; and (3) individual imagoes do not obtain their full share of food (i.e., yeast growing on the agar surface) under these crowded conditions owing to the disturbance of their feeding behavior brought about by their neighbors. These three relations can be thought of in ecological terms as density-dependent competitive coactions. As cultures become more crowded, the flies compete with each other primarily for food and perhaps for oviposition space, and this competition results in lowered fecundity. Since the coactions compound with density, egg production drops as the flies get more crowded. Finally this reaches a point, above 100 flies per bottle, beyond which egg production is not further affected to any appreciable extent.

In a stimulating paper, Robertson and Sang (1944) reexamine Pearl's work and extend it by a series of ingenious experiments. They show that the fecundity of *Drosophila* is highly sensitive to changes both in the quantity and quality of the yeast food and advance the following conclusion pertinent to our present interest:

"Crowding of adults leads to only a slight lowering of fecundity when the flies are adequately fed. There is also little evidence of competition for oviposition space within the limits tested. So the decrease of fecundity demonstrated by Pearl (1932) can take place only when there is competition for food and is the direct result of this competition. This is the correct explanation of his results" (p. 258).

Thus Robertson and Sang also conclude that fecundity may be reduced by crowding, but only when the food supply is inadequate: "If food is scarce then the success with which it is found depends on the number of flies in the culture." This suggests that Pearl's work is a special rather than a general case. The general case can be stated in this fashion: When the food supply, both qualitatively and quantitatively, is optimal, little in the way of density-dependent coactions affecting oviposition are operating in *Drosophila* cultures, and egg production is not greatly impaired.

The experiments of MacLagan and Dunn (1936) with the grain weevil *Sitophilus oryzae* afford another illustration of population pressure resulting from coactions that lead to a reduction in fecundity with increased crowding. When ovipositing, the female weevil lays a single egg in a small cavity which she excavates in a grain of wheat. For populations that are not crowded—that is, where many grains are available for each weevil to exploit—the female oviposits only in the hairy apex of the grain and usually avoids damaged seeds. In dense cultures oviposition seems to occur indiscriminately over the entire surface of practically all the grains.

MacLagan and Dunn showed, as might be anticipated, that as imago density increased more eggs were laid per grain since there were more reproducing beetles, but the rate of egg production per individual female declined. An interesting relation between maximum fecundity and the availability of wheat grains grew out of these observations. The female weevils would not oviposit at their maximum rate unless more grains were present in the culture containers than were actually utilized. The authors comment on this point as follows: "This surprising result indicates that the female *S. oryzae* will not lay this maximum number of eggs unless the number of grains available for oviposition is at least eleven times that actually utilised. Any reduction in this number of grains is accompanied by a reduction in the number of eggs laid per female, despite the fact that she is utilising only a small proportion of the number of available grains" (p. 133). This may foreshadow an ecological principle of broader application than is commonly appreciated (see Chap. 25).

In addition to these relationships, coactions are also described between individual weevils that stand in significant relation to reproduction. For example, when considering the decreased fecundity of *Sitophilus* with increasing density, MacLagan and Dunn's explanation is markedly reminiscent of Pearl's conclusions based on *Drosophila*. They consider that the "collisions" or increased contacts between weevils in crowded cultures is a fundamental factor and remark that "it operates organically through the reduction of the times available for feeding, ovipositing, and resting; thereby causing adverse effects upon the physiological processes of reproduction" (p. 136).

It should also be mentioned that Crombie (1942), working with the grain beetles *Rhizopertha dominica*, *Oryzaephilus surinamensis*, and *Acanthoscleides obtectus* and the grain moth *Sitotroga cerealella*, reached the general conclusion for all these forms that increased imago density led to a reduction of fecundity with egg fertility not affected. When the media were not "conditioned" (p. 352) "the reduction of fecundity was, it appears, entirely a result of competition for the oviposition sites usually for two purposes, viz., oviposition and feeding. That is to say, at such densities the effect of crowding upon oviposition was of a behaviouristic [coaction] nature" (p. 339).

Another most instructive illustration of population pressure resulting from coactions is afforded by the work of Crombie (1944) on the relation of *larval* population density to subsequent larval dispersal. Crombie worked with two species of granary insects: the beetle *Rhizopertha dominica* and the moth *Sitotroga cerealella*. The larvae of these infest wheat grains. It is possible to introduce a designated number of larvae into the seeds and thus establish larval densities of either species ranging from one to eight larvae per grain. It is also possible to introduce larvae of both species into the same grain so that interspecies relations can be studied.

Crombie's findings can be summarized briefly in this way. The adult females of

"When two larvae in the first, second, third or fourth instars were put together into a small hole drilled in a wheat grain and watched under a binocular microscope, they were often seen to attack each other with their mandibles, and eventually either one or both left the hole. When a larva entered such a hole it always went to the bottom and turned round so as to face outwards. Other larvae trying to enter the hole were fiercely attacked. Sometimes such combats resulted in the body wall of one of the antagonists becoming punctured and its bleeding to death. In their tunnels in wheat grains larvae of all instars were always found curled up with the head facing towards the way they had entered. Furthermore, in all

Table 24. *Effect of Density on the Reduction in Numbers of* Rhizopertha *First Instar Larvae Competing for the Same Grain of Wheat (Crombie, 1944)*

(1) Initial Number of First Instar Larvae per Grain	(2) Number of Grains	(3) Total Number of Larvae	(4) Total Number of Larvae Killed or Emigrating	(5) Observed Mean Number of Larvae Killed or Emigrating per Grain	(6) Observed Mean Per Cent of Larvae Killed or Emigrating per Grain	(7) Per Cent of Larvae in Column 4 Which Emigrated
1	100	100	0	0		
2	106	212	17	0.16	8	89
3	42	126	16	0.38	12.7	81
4	38	152	35	0.92	23	66
5	13	65	33	1.69	34	55
8	10	80	46	4.6	57.5	31

both *Rhizopertha* and *Sitotroga* oviposit in wheat grains that contain niches suitable for the development of the larvae. These larvae, however, usually move during their first instar and thus "choose" the exact spot in which to develop. It is the cause of this change of grain and its relation to crowding that we wish to examine. Crombie concludes that the larvae disperse not because of limitations of food, oxygen supply, or conditioning within the seed, but rather as the direct result of competition for space leading to fighting. "Larvae will attack each other directly after encounters at random within wheat grains, and the supernumerary individuals are either killed or forced to migrate." Thus the probability that a certain larva will live is in inverse proportion to the initial number of larvae in the seed. Crombie's observations about what happens when *Rhizopertha* larvae meet are informative since this is the specific coaction responsible for the observed density effect.

grains dissected during the experiments to be described, whenever two larvae were found in the same tunnel at least one of them was always dead. It thus seems probable that whenever two larvae meet within a grain they will attack each other, with the result that either or both will migrate or be killed" (p. 138).

An actual illustration of the relation of crowding within grains to survival and movement in *Rhizopertha* appears in Table 24.

This table clearly shows how population pressure, as measured in terms of increased larval death and dispersion, is accentuated by larval crowding. Columns 6 and 7 are particularly informative.

An ecological principle of considerable general significance emerges from Crombie's investigation. This can be formulated somewhat as follows: When the total environment is essentially unlimited or at least unsaturated—that is, when there are many wheat grains available for larval occupation—the increased emigration induced by crowding leads to survival. The emigrating larvae find unexploited niches and develop successfully therein. However, when the total population is "asymptotic" or nearly so, a point is reached "when migration from one grain to another merely leads to death in another place." Parallels to this can be found in natural, as well as other experimental, populations. In fact, we have already discussed one case (that of muskrats, reported by Errington, page 338) which is similar in some respects.

Environmental Conditioning

The discussion thus far has dealt largely with coactions, the focus centering on the aggregate responses between individual organisms of a defined population and the relation of these to the population's growth form. We shall now consider "environmental conditioning:" This is defined as a modification of the effective environment by population-group activities. Such activities fall into the category of "reactions" as well as "coactions." A situation in which the environment is conditioned by the population through *reactions* obtains when numerous summed reactions result in the conditioning. A situation in which the environment is conditioned by the population through *coactions* obtains when numerous summed coactions result in the conditioning. Actually, in most populations both reactions and coactions play a role in conditioning.

It is helpful to clarify these ideas first by means of a hypothetical, oversimplified example and then by actual cases. Suppose ten sexually mature green sunfishes of equal size and with similar respiratory rates are living together in an aquarium. Suppose further that each sunfish as an individual member of this population liberates one x unit of carbon dioxide into the water per stated time interval. Such liberation constitutes a reaction. The physical habitat is modified by the organism living within it. The total population then liberates $10x$ units of carbon dioxide over the period. Assume further, a not unreasonable assumption, that the ten fishes so behave towards each other (coactions) that they move about more than they would if isolated, and as a consequence their production of carbon dioxide increases 0.35 units per fish

per interval.* From this it follows that the total carbon dioxide produced by the population for the period is 13.5 units, of which 10 units result from reactions and 3.5 from coactions. This illustrates, in a somewhat naïve fashion perhaps, a population conditioning system with both reaction and coaction components.

Should the sunfish population be increased from ten to 100 in the same aquarium and should the rate of carbon dioxide production per fish remain the same (an unlikely event because of crowding) the conditioning resulting from reactions would increase from 10 to 100 units. The amount resulting from coactions would also increase, either at the same rate (i.e., $0.35 \times 100 = 35$ units) or, more likely, at a higher rate since the coactions would compound with increase in density. The total carbon dioxide conditioning thus has density-dependent aspects in terms of both reaction and coaction. It should be repeated that this model is oversimplified for purposes of illustration.

On the basis of research carried out on various natural and experimental populations and on various processes, conditioning can be considered by actual cases under the following practical categories: (1) reduction of the available food supply; (2) partial distribution of available food; (3) addition of contaminants to the environment; (4) liberation of a "growth-promoting," or some other needed, substance, to the environment; (5) fixation by the population of toxic substances ("detoxification"); (6) osmotic regulation of the aquatic environment; (7) physical conditioning of the substratum; (8) compound conditioning: combinations of certain of the above as, for example, categories one, two, and three.

Selected examples will now be presented, and it will be indicated how they illustrate the above points.

Flour Conditioning by Tribolium *Populations.* Because conditioning of flour by populations of the beetle *Tribolium confusum* has been extensively studied and because it affords an illustration of conditioning probably resulting both from reduction

---

* It would be as reasonable to suppose that the coactions would quiet rather than agitate the fishes (as in a winter aggregation). In this event the group rate of carbon dioxide production would be reduced. See Shlaifer's (1938, 1939) reports on goldfishes.

of the available food supply and addition of contaminants to the environment, it merits review in some detail. Summarizing statements are to be found in the following papers: Park and Woollcott (1937); Park, Miller, and Lutherman (1939); and Park (1941).*

Obviously, as a population of *Tribolium* inhabits its flour (which it never leaves), the flour becomes progressively more altered, or "conditioned," with time as a result of the beetles' activities. The rate and extent of such conditioning are in proportion to the population density. It does not necessarily follow, however, that the conditioning will so affect the beetles individually that population growth form will be altered. This must be determined experimentally, and the particular, causative process or processes identified.

It has been shown that heavily conditioned flour, i.e., flour in which large cultures have lived, induces population decline primarily through reduction of fecundity and increase of the length and hazard of larval development. It has also been shown that less heavily conditioned flour also reduces egg production significantly. Before discussing the implication of these points, an outline summary of the major effects of conditioned flour upon *Tribolium confusum* are in order.

I. Flour taken from "run-down" *Tribolium* populations (i.e., heavily conditioned flour) has the following known relations to the beetles' physiology:
   A. It reduces their egg-cannibalism (p. 371) to about half that of control beetles living in unconditioned flour.
   B. It reduces their fecundity:
      1. *Perceptibly,* by lowering it three or more times below the fresh-flour control level;
      2. *Quickly,* since some effect is noticeable within five days after exposure to conditioned flour and since the maximum effect is attained after twenty days; and
      3. *Reversibly,* since the rate of oviposition can be returned to control levels by reintroduction of the beetles into unconditioned medium.

* An "aggregation effect" has been shown for *Tribolium confusum* populations where, in early stages of population growth, the most rapidly reproducing cultures are neither the smallest nor the largest. This general question is more appropriately discussed in Chapter 23 (p. 403).

C. It may reduce fecundity through its effect on males as well as through the females. In one group of experiments, females living in fresh flour, when mated with males from conditioned flour, had a significantly lower rate of reproduction than did females from the same source mated to males from fresh flour.
D. It increases the relative variability of the females' egg production.
E. It apparently does not alter in any consistent fashion *egg fertility*. In other words, once laid, eggs from conditioned-flour beetles have as good a probability of hatching as do eggs from fresh-flour beetles.
F. It increases the duration, variability in respect of duration, and mortality of larval development.
G. It does not significantly alter the rate of oxygen consumption of imago *Tribolium,* since there is no apparent difference in this between beetles reared in fresh flour as compared with those reared in conditioned flour. However, a definite sexual difference is demonstrable: the females have a higher rate of oxygen consumption than the males.

II. The "dilution" of heavily conditioned flour with fresh flour to form a graded series of conditioned media (5, 10, 15, 20, 25, 50, and 75 per cent conditioned) has these relations to *Tribolium* reproduction when compared with fresh flour and conditioned flour controls:
   A. The fecundity of the beetles is roughly inversely proportional to the amount of conditioned flour in the medium. As the flour becomes progressively more conditioned, egg production decreases. This statement is subject to this correction: There is no significant difference in fecundity between the beetles in the 5, 10, or 15 per cent conditioned flours, yet these three groups are far below the fresh-flour controls and significantly above the beetles in a higher conditioned series.
   B. The fecundity of beetles living in conditioned media can be restored to control levels by reintroducing them into fresh flour.
   C. Egg fertility again is not affected by such graded conditioning.

III. The relation of conditioning to *Tribolium* metamorphosis:
   A. Conditioning brought about by *larvae:*
      1. If the culture medium is renewed, larval development and pupal mortality are not affected by the degree of larval crowding.

2. If the culture medium is not renewed, larval and pupal mortality increase with increase in density. Also, under these conditions pupae and imagoes reared from the crowded larvae weigh less than do those from sparse cultures.

3. The duration of the pupal period is not significantly altered by density, sex, or conditioning.

B. Conditioning brought about by *imagoes*. When a series of *Tribolium* populations are established consisting of a constant number of larvae (10), but a geometrically increasing number of male imagoes (1, 4, 16, 32, and 64), in a constant volume of flour, the following effects are noted:

1. The duration of the larval period is extended as the density of the imagoes increases.

2. The larvae living in crowded imago cultures grow more slowly in terms of body weight than those in less crowded imago cultures.

3. The duration of the pupal period is not significantly affected by the crowding of imagoes with the larvae.

This outline summarizes the physiological responses of *Tribolium confusum* known to be affected by conditioned flour, but makes no attempt to evaluate them as they may be related to population growth form. Such an evaluation is now in order. The original impetus underlying the conditioned flour study grew out of the following facts: (1) *Tribolium* populations decline as they age if their flour is not frequently renewed; and (2) the flour in which such populations live becomes progressively more conditioned. The latter fact was recognized as early as 1896 by Chittenden, who, in discussing the general biology of granary beetles, said, "When the insects [*Tribolium*] have time to propagate, they soon convert the flour into a gray, useless mass." It follows from these two points that conditioning is an expression of population decline and population size since the number of beetles (themselves) is responsible for the rate and amount of conditioning.

Because conditioning does go hand-in-hand with population decline, another question is raised: Is such conditioning a result, a cause, or both? That it is a result is self-evident because, as already mentioned, it reflects population age and density. That it is a cause of decline is not self-evident

since knowledge of the physiological effects of conditioning upon individual beetles is not available without experimental study. Such experimentation has unearthed the material presented in the outline. Our immediate task is to sort these facts into those that contribute to population decline and into those that do not.

It is clear that conditioning does not influence decline through the agency of egg cannibalism (I-A). Even though this is definitely affected by conditioning, the effect—i.e., that the adult beetles eat fewer eggs if they are living in conditioned flour than they do if in fresh flour—favors population increase rather than contraction, since more eggs escape being eaten and thereby the likelihood of their hatching into larvae is increased.

The relation of conditioning to egg fertility (I-E; II-C) is not important in terms of growth form since it has been impossible to demonstrate that this is either increased or decreased by exposure of the ovipositing females to conditioned medium. The studies of oxygen consumption (I-G) also suggest nothing of significance in relation to population decline.

It was shown in an earlier chapter that natality is one of the three primary variables affecting population survival, the other two being mortality and dispersion. Thus, any factor influencing these must be carefully evaluated. On the basis of the information presented in the outline it appears that conditioning brings about population decline largely through its effect on fecundity (I-B-C-D; II-A-B) and, to a lesser degree, on larval metamorphosis (I-F; III). This is supported not only by the analyses of heavily conditioned flour, but also by those dealing with differential conditioning. The latter have shown, first, that the effect of conditioning on fecundity is cumulative (i.e., it becomes more extreme as the medium gets more conditioned), and second, that even a slight amount of conditioning lowers the rate of oviposition. The last point suggests that *Tribolium* populations are rarely under optimal conditions so far as fecundity is concerned, since the flour typically is conditioned to some extent. It is, of course, possible, even probable, that other factors compensate for this during the earlier stages of population growth and so keep conditioning, operating through fecundity, from being an important cause of population senescence until later.

It is now fair to conclude that this conditioning of the medium, entirely brought about by population activity, contributes significantly to the decline of *Tribolium* cultures largely through reduction of reproductive rate. It is not yet definitely known just what constitutes conditioning, but the *a priori* assumption that both nutritive depletion and an increase in the concentration of toxic waste products are involved seems reasonable. This is a matter for further experimental analysis. There is some collateral evidence supporting these two assumptions. First, it has been shown by a number of authors (for summary, see Park and Burrows, 1942) that fecundity performance of *Tribolium* is highly sensitive to quantitative and qualitative changes in nutritive levels of the medium. Second, in addition to the obvious fact that flour beetles in a dense culture release metabolic wastes into the medium in proportion to their number and exposure time, it has been shown by Roth and Howland (1941) and Roth (1943, 1944) that the imagoes, particularly when crowded, liberate a gas from specialized "odoriferous glands" that causes morphological abnormalities and probably lowers the general well-being of the beetles. This substance has been identified by Alexander and Barton (1943) as "ethylquinone."

Before a definitive statement about the conditioned flour problem for *Tribolium* can be made, chemical analyses of the flour must be forthcoming and experiments conducted that demonstrate to what extent the observed effects are caused by nutritional deficiencies and/or metabolic contamination. With these data at hand, an unusually complete analysis of a *habitat → population → habitat* nexus will exist.

Some interesting extensions of the conditioning problem have been reported by Crombie (1942, 1943). This investigator worked with the granary beetles *Tribolium confusum, Oryzaephilus surinamensis, Rhizopertha dominica,* and the moth *Sitotroga cerealella.*

Crombie's findings are in general agreement with the data that fecundity is reduced by conditioning, but that normal control levels can be restored by reintroduction of the beetles into fresh medium,

and that egg fertility is not significantly affected. He concludes further, for *Rhizopertha* at least, that "It is believed that conditioned medium operates upon fecundity through 'poisoning,' and that the effect is upon oviposition rather than, as that of starvation, upon egg-production" (1942, p. 339).

Crombie also studied "heterotypic," in contradistinction to "homotypic," conditioned medium in relation to the fecundity of these beetles. Homotypic medium (see Allee, 1931) refers to self-conditioning of the habitat. Heterotypic medium refers to conditioning of the habitat by another, or several other, species. The following heterotypic situations were explored by Crombie in comparison with homotypic controls:

Rhizopertha in *Oryzaephilus*-conditioned med.

Rhizopertha in *Sitotroga*-conditioned med.

Oryzaephilus in *Tribolium*-conditioned med.

Oryzaephilus in *Rhizopertha*-conditioned med.

Tribolium in *Oryzaephilus*-conditioned med.

From these experiments Crombie reached the general conclusion that heterotypic conditioning produced no striking change in fecundity over and above (or below) that displayed by homotypic conditioning when the media were conditioned to the same degree. A minor exception to this is noted when the fecundity of *Oryzaephilus* is assayed in *Tribolium* and *Rhizopertha* flours. In this case "fecundity in 100 per cent *Rhizopertha* medium is significantly higher than that in media conditioned to the same degree by *Oryzaephilus* or *Tribolium.*"

Conditioning of Water by Goldfishes. Another facet of the conditioning problem is well illustrated by the investigations of Allee and his collaborators dealing with the conditioning of water by populations of goldfishes and the demonstration that this is related to growth rate. The roots of this study extend back to the eighteen-fifties when Jabez Hogg (1854) showed that crowding caused snails to be stunted. From then on there has been a steady series of reports showing that growth is reduced by overcrowding.

On the other hand, a number of reports suggest that increased growth is a result of crowding.* It is to provide an illustration of this phenomenon that the work of Allee on goldfishes is reviewed (1938).

It is relatively easy to show that mixed-species populations of many animals may grow faster than do populations of single species. The common experience of aquarists that the presence of the snails in aquaria increases the rate of growth and well-being of their fishes is a case in point. Their experience has been somewhat verified by laboratory experimentation. A more crucial test involves individuals of the same species as, for example, all snails, or all goldfishes. This leads to a brief formalization of the problem: Is there some optimum size of the population at which individuals grow most rapidly?

In the analysis of this question a synthetic pond water is made up by dissolving in distilled water selected salts of high chemical purity. Into such water three-inch long goldfishes are placed so as to provide a "conditioning coefficient" of about twenty-five. This coefficient is obtained by multiplying the number of fishes by their mean length in millimeters and then dividing by the number of liters of water in the container. Living in this water, the fishes condition it by liberating organic matter and carbon dioxide. They are left in the water for twenty-one hours, while a similar amount of the same water stands under the same conditions except for the absence of fishes.

At the end of this period the clean control water is siphoned into a number of clean jars, and a small photographically measured goldfish is placed in each. At the same time the conditioned water is siphoned into clean jars, either with or without removing such particles as excrement that may be present. A group of small, measured goldfishes such as those used in the control jars is transferred into the conditioned water. These small, "assay" fishes have been feeding for about two hours before their transfer. The larger conditioning fishes are allowed to feed for a somewhat longer time before being washed to re-move food residues and replaced in another lot of water to condition that.

After some twenty to thirty days of such care, each fish is again photographed to scale, the photographs are measured, and the relative growth is determined for the forms that have daily been placed into perfectly clean, synthetic pond water, as compared with those daily put into conditioned water—water in which other goldfishes have lived for a day. Allee found that the fishes in the conditioned, i.e., slightly contaminated, water grew significantly more than did those in clean water. "Hence we have demonstrated that under the conditions of our experiments the goldfish grow better in water in which other similar goldfish have lived than they do when they are daily transferred to perfectly clean water" (1938, p. 94).

The question now arises: What are the factors involved that make conditioned water a more suitable medium for the growth of goldfishes than an unconditioned medium? Although this matter has not yet been completely analyzed, Allee has unearthed some important leads.

The conditioning fishes, it will be remembered, are fed for two or more hours daily and are then washed and placed in a fresh batch of water. Although the fishes are never fed in the water they are conditioning, within a few hours after their transfer into it from the feeding aquarium the water becomes more or less cloudy with regurgitated food particles. These bits of food are large enough so that the growth-assay fishes can strain them out of the water. When such particles are removed by filtering, the growth-promoting power of the conditioned water is greatly lessened, but not completely lost. In one group of experiments Allee showed that suspended food particles accounted for about 80 per cent of that increased growth displayed by the experimental forms. This suggests the presence of some factor, apart from food intake, which is also operating to produce the total observed effect.

Certain statements about the possible existence of a "growth-promoting" substance can be made. For example, it is known that the skin glands of goldfishes secrete slime. When a chemical extract of this substance is prepared, a growth-promoting factor can be recovered. This seems to be a protein, and it is effective as a growth stimulant

---

* These reports are not limited to growth *per se*, but concern also such related phenomena as graft transplants (Price, 1941; Rawles, 1936), regeneration (Wilson, 1910; Galtsoff, 1925; Chu and Pai, 1944), hatching enzymes (Merwin, 1945), and egg cleavage (Allee and Evans, 1937).

when diluted 1:400,000 or even 1:800,000 times. At these dilutions it is not probable that this factor is affecting growth by furnishing food material.

There exist other possibilities, some of which have been explored by Allee and his group. The increase in growth is not caused, for example, by a change in the total salt content of the water, for this does not vary in the experiments. It is not caused by differences in acidity or oxygenation, nor, so far as careful quantitative analyses have revealed, by changes in the chemical elements present. It is also a possible hypothesis that the fish population removes some harmful substance from the water. This sort of conditioning will be discussed shortly.

The most recent statement summarizing the status of this problem is that of Allee, Finkel, and Hoskins (1940, p. 436):

"Evidence available in 1936 indicated that the caloric food value of these minute particles is the major growth promoting factor in our conditioned medium and we have no reason to modify this conclusion. That this is not the only growth accelerating factor which is acting is indicated (a) by the relatively beneficial effect of water contaminated only by the presence of starved conditioning fish; (b) by the growth promoting power shown by filtered conditioned water and, most significant, (c) by the effect of protein extracts prepared from the surface of other goldfish. It seems highly significant that these latter will promote additional growth over that shown by controls when one part is dissolved in 400,000 parts of water. The caloric value of such a medium must be very small and no mechanism is known whereby fish might concentrate such a dissolved food substance until it would have significant caloric food value."

Commenting upon the ecological significance of this investigation, Allee (1938, pp. 97–98) says, "Whatever the explanation, we are certain of the facts, and we know that we have demonstrated a device such that if in nature one or a few fish in a group find plenty of food, apparently without willing to do so they regurgitate some food particles which are taken by others, a sort of automatic sharing. Again, in water that changes rapidly, such stagnant-water fishes as goldfish, if present in numbers, are able to condition their environment, perhaps by the secretion of mucus, so that it becomes a more favorable place in which to live and grow."

This analysis of habitat alteration by goldfishes contributes to our survey of the conditioned medium problem primarily by illustrating two aspects of the conditioning process: (1) partial distribution of available food, and (2) liberation of a growth-promoting, or some other needed substance, to the environment.

The "Allelocatalytic Phenomenon" in Protozoan Populations. The favorable conditioning of the habitat by its population through the elaboration of a growth promoting substance is suggested by the long series of studies dealing with "allelocatalysis" and conducted by many investigators working with a number of species of protista. Their work merits a short review.

In 1921 T. B. Robertson published a report on the population growth rate of two ciliate protozoans, *Enchelys* and *Colpoda*. He found that when either of these two forms was introduced into a small volume of fresh culture medium, the fission rate per organism was increased by a certain amount of crowding. Specifically, two infusoria in the same environment reproduced from 2.5 to ten times as fast as did isolated individuals. This difference was significant statistically. Robertson called these events and their interpretation "allelocatalysis." It is important to distinguish carefully between the *fact* of allelocatalysis just outlined and the *theory* to follow.

In explaining his observations, Robertson stated: "During nuclear division each nucleus retains the charge of autocatalyst with which it was provided, and adds to it during the course of nuclear synthesis. At each division the autocatalyst is shared between the nuclear substance and the surrounding medium in a proportion determined by its relative solubility and by its affinity for the chemical substances within the nucleus. The mutually accelerated or allelocatalytic effect of contiguous cells is due to each cell's losing less of the autocatalyst to the medium because of the presence of the other" (Allee, 1931, p. 166).

The evidence in support of the allelocatalytic theory seemed feeble. Whether for this reason or another, a number of investigators started working along similar lines, using various flagellate and ciliate species. Most of these early workers reported negative results, that is, data showing that the isolated organisms reproduced as fast as or faster than the grouped organisms. None of the investigators seemed particularly attracted to the theoretical explanation, especially since they had little confidence in the phenomenon. This attitude persisted for about five years until Yocom in 1928 reported results with *Oxytricha* that he interpreted as allelocatalysis. He found that the rate of fission of infusorians cultured singly in four-drop cultures was 10 per cent greater after twenty-four hours than that of single forms in ten-drop cultures. In other words, by reducing the volume the reproductive rate had been accelerated.

During the next year Petersen (1929) obtained results with *Paramecium* that showed that in a small volume of medium there was no difference in fission rate between single and grouped organisms. However, in a larger volume the grouped forms divided significantly faster than did the singles. The importance of this work is its demonstration that reproductive rate could be varied through the manipulation of a known experimental variable. Petersen did not subscribe to the explanation advanced by Robertson.

Johnson (1933), using *Oxytricha*, made an important contribution. After confirming Petersen's findings, Johnson proceeded to analyze further the factors involved when the volume of medium was changed. In sum, he showed that the bacterial flora of the cultures is important in controlling the fission rate. A series of cultures was set up in which the bacterial population varied from a high to a low concentration, and into each of these a single infusorian was introduced. Under these conditions the rate of fission was significantly highest in intermediate bacterial concentrations and fell off as the bacterial density either increased or decreased. This is convincing evidence for the existence of an optimal bacterial density for maximal reproductivity. Johnson showed further that if paired, as well as single, organisms were introduced into the various bacterial concentrations, the former reproduced faster in the supraoptimal bacterial densities. This is probably related to the point that the paired *Oxytricha* control and reduce, during early population growth, the bacteria more effectively than do the isolated forms.

Johnson's work fails to corroborate the theory of allelocatalysis, although it again shows that the type of results found by Robertson are experimentally possible.

As Allee (1934a, p. 18) says; "The work leaves unsolved the question of the relative importance of bacterial as opposed to some other sort of biological (i.e., populational) conditioning through the production of excretory matter or of some X-substance. It does indicate that the introduction of a second infusorian may reduce the supraoptimal numbers of bacteria towards the optimum; that the introduced protozoan may introduce more suitable bacteria, or less suitable ones; in short, his work has made it necessary that in future experimental attacks on the problem the bacterial flora shall be under control."

Two interesting affirmative reports on the subject appeared in 1938. One, a paper on the soil amoeba, *Mayorella,* by Reich, showed that when the amoebae are grown as mass cultures free of bacteria, those with small initial populations have a lower division rate than do those with larger initial populations. Although no explanation is advanced by the author, these findings clearly support the validity of the phenomenon.

The other papers are those of Mast and Pace (1938, 1946), and Pace (1944). These investigators worked with the flagellate, *Chilomonas paramecium,* which they cultured in a sterile solution containing only relatively simple chemicals in known proportions. Their experiments were set up so that density and volume relations were varied by design, and the rate of multiplication was assayed. Their general conclusion is best summarized in their own words:

"The results . . . demonstrate that the rate of reproduction in *C. paramecium* varies directly with the density of population under some conditions and inversely under others, and that these results are not dependent upon variation in the amount, the kind, or the availability of food but upon the concentration of an unknown substance (X) produced by the chilomonads. However, the fact that such substance is produced by *Chilomonas* obviously does not prove that similar substance is produced by other cells and it therefore does not prove that Robertson's conclusion is valid; but it nevertheless does lend some support to this conclusion. The results presented in the preceding section of this paper seem to prove that *Chilomonas* not only produces growth-promoting substance in accord with Robertson's views but that if this substance is concentrated, it retards and inhibits growth and kills the organisms" (1938, p. 379).

A highly stimulating paper, and one of considerable interpretative value in terms of the Robertson effect, was published by Ludwig and Boost (1939). In brief, these investigators showed that when the data of some nineteen authors, studying bacteria, yeasts, and protozoa and concerned in one form or another with the phenomenon of allelocatalysis, were analyzed in a new way, it could be shown that a stimulation of fission rate by certain degrees of crowding was the rule rather than the exception. This held true even for several cases in which an author himself claimed that his investigations ran counter to a Robertson type of effect. To put it differently, Ludwig and Boost concluded that no conclusive case against the *fact* of allelocatalysis had been recorded, while some actually positive evidence had been incorrectly interpreted as negative.

Ludwig and Boost pointed out that most of the earlier data were plotted in the same form as that used in graphing a logistic curve, i.e., numbers plotted against time (see p. 301). They restudied the problem by graphing the data on a different coordinate system based on equations of their own derivation.

If available space is unlimited and if the environment is held reasonably constant, then it can be shown that

$$\frac{1}{N}\frac{dN}{dt} = K$$

where N = population size, t = time and K = a constant. If the space is limited so that N^* = the number of individuals that can exist in it, the logistic equation holds. In the notation of Ludwig and Boost this becomes

$$\frac{dN}{Ndt} = K(N^* - N), \qquad \text{(where } K = >0).$$

This equation upon integration yields a logistic curve.

Since it is hard to distinguish "allelocatalytic" or other effects from the population growth curve because of random fluctuations and individual variability, Ludwig and Boost proposed that a more accurate and interpretative curve is afforded by plotting specific growth rate, or for these cases fission rate, $\frac{1}{N}\frac{dN}{dt}$, on the ordinate, against total population growth on the

abscissa. When this is done, the type of effect can be adduced directly by inspection of the graph. Thus a linear relationship indicates equilibrium; a convexity (i.e., where the curve is convex to the zero point or point of joining of the coordinates) indicates deceleration or inhibition of population growth; and a concavity indicates acceleration.

In the "Empirischer Teil" of their paper Ludwig and Boost apply this analysis to various published studies and, barring the initial or lag phase, reach the afore-mentioned conclusion about the usualness of stimulation of reproduction by population size.

It is suggestive that, despite their substantiation of the Robertson *effect*, Ludwig and Boost cast doubt upon his explanation and suggest a "more harmless" one. In general terms this runs somewhat as follows: Since, naturally, protozoans exist as populations of variable density, they are best adjusted to this density range or at least to part of it. Therefore, the optimum conditions of pH, oxidation-reduction potentials, and so forth that, to some extent at least, are dependent on metabolic products, would be present in cultures of such densities, and the division rate or growth rate would not depend on any such highly specific mechanism as that postulated by Robertson.[*]

For a recent and suggestive contribution to this general problem the work of Kidder (1941) on the ciliate *Tetrahymena geleii* merits attention. Kidder showed that a conditioned medium, one which has supported populations of this species for as much as sixty hours, has both accelerating and inhibiting properties for growth. If the conditioning population is removed from the medium by centrifugation, acceleration of the assay culture results. If the conditioning population is removed by filtration, using a Seitz or Berkfeld filter, inhibition results. Kidder advances the interesting suggestion that *Tetrahymena* cultures elaborate two types of substances. One is an accelerator that "acts freely during the early growth phases but which is removed either by filtration or by adsorption. The other substance produces inhibition of growth, and when the accelerator

[*] We have discussed the paper of Ludwig and Boost with Dr. Benson Ginsburg and are indebted to him for his comments.

is removed its full effect is noted" (p. 225).

Finally, should the reader wish to consult a treatment of the "allelocatalytic phenomenon" written from the point of view of a microbiologist, he is referred to Chapter 10 by Richards in Calkins and Summers (1941). In the same volume, Chapter 9 by Hall also rewards reading.

Fixation of Poisons by Goldfish Populations. In addition to its relation to such factors as reproduction and growth, conditioning may also affect mortality. This it may either increase, as when larval *Tribolium* were grown in heavily conditioned flour, or it may confer upon the total population a lowered mortality by protecting that population against some environmental vicissitude. This latter aspect, now to be briefly developed, falls under our category "fixation by the population of toxic substances" and is well illustrated by the study of Allee and Bowen (1932) on goldfishes.

Allee and Bowen observed the survival of isolated goldfishes compared with groups when both were subjected to an environmental poison, colloidal silver. Seven experimental units were set up, each consisting of ten fishes in a liter of water plus a colloidal silver suspension. The seven control units consisted of seventy isolated fishes each in one liter of water and in colloidal silver of the same strength and same suspension as that to which the grouped fishes were exposed. The life duration of both control and experimental forms was recorded. It was found that the latter lived on the mean 507 minutes, while the controls lived only 182 minutes. The grouped fishes thus had a mean life duration exceeding that of the controls by 325 minutes, a significant statistical difference.

In the experimental units the silver was precipitated, while in the control units it remained largely in suspension. When exposed to the toxic colloidal silver, the grouped fishes shared between them a dosage easily fatal for any one fish. Apparently the slime secreted by the groups changed much of the silver into a less toxic form. As this experiment was conducted, the silver suspension was somewhat too strong for any fish to survive, but probably with a weaker suspension some or all of the grouped animals would have lived. Even as carried out, the group

gained for its components a longer life, and it seems likely that in nature it might have had that many more minutes for, say, rain to have diluted the water or for some other disturbance to have cleared up the poison and thus give the population an opportunity for complete recovery.

Conditioning of Water by Procerodes *Populations.* Allee (1931) and Oesting and Allee (1935) studied the mechanism by which the marine flatworm *Procerodes wheatlandi* protects its populations through conditioning from a hypotonic environment. These worms are abundant along certain seashores where they live near the low tidemark level or a little beyond. There they frequently are found on the undersurfaces of stones, perhaps as a protection from wave action, and usually they are aggregated.

A worm removed into the laboratory and put into fresh water swells and begins to cytolize. If the *Procerodes* are thoroughly washed to remove sea water from their surfaces and then placed both as isolated individuals and as groups into fresh water, the latter survive for a definitely longer time. The first worms to die in the group do so about as soon as the first isolated worms. However, as the dead worm disintegrates, the habitat is altered, and, because of this alteration or conditioning, the remaining members of the group have an increased life expectancy beyond that of isolated individuals.

This can be extended. A sort of "worm soup" is prepared by killing a number of well-washed worms and allowing them to remain in the water in which they had died and so condition it. Freshly collected *Procerodes* live longer as individuals in such conditioned medium than do similar worms isolated into clean pond water. The difference between the two media is only that in one the worms had liberated products of disintegration, while in the other such was not the case. This survival differential persisted even when the total amount of salt in the two types of water was made identical by adding dilute sea water to the clean pond water. In such experiments the worms still lived significantly longer in the conditioned medium than did those in dilute sea water of the same salt concentration.

When the *Procerodes* are in a hypotonic environment their survival is increased if the osmotic pressure is raised by the addition of sea water. This is a straight physiological observation. Also, their survival in such dilute media is increased by population conditioning. This conditioning may be either *homotypic*, as was seen when, upon the early death of grouped worms, needed products were liberated into the water or in the "worm soup" experiments; or it may be *heterotypic*, since it has been demonstrated that living, fresh-water planarians so condition the environment for *Procerodes* that the latter survive longer. Thus, the conditioning process appears to have two principal aspects. The first is concerned with osmotic regulation in the sense that conditioning raises osmotic pressure by liberating salts. This is a more general aspect. The other is more specific and refers to the demonstration that dead and disintegrating worms, or, more slowly, living worms, release calcium into the water. This available calcium has a protective action for marine animals put into distilled water *out of all proportion* to its effect on osmotic pressure.

The *Procerodes* study illustrates population conditioning (1) through the liberation of some needed substance into the environment, and (2) osmotic regulation of the aquatic environment. Such conditioning probably at times confers survival value upon the worms in nature.

Physical Conditioning of the Substratum. Probably the most usual sort of conditioning in the sense of frequency of occurrence involves the various alterations a population impresses upon its physical substratum. Although this usually is not thought of as a conditioning process, it actually is one in that it falls within the definition presented earlier (p. 352). While the matter cannot be developed in detail, in part because of lack of space, but primarily because of lack of quantitatively studied cases, a few comments are appropriate simply to put the issue in proper perspective.

It seems self-evident that most natural groupings, whether intraspecies or interspecies populations or communities, modify in one way or another the substratum upon which or in which they live. The degree of such modification obviously varies with the size of the group under consideration.

Many examples of such substratum conditioning come to mind: the dissection and tunnelling of soil by burrowing forms such as earthworms, insect larvae, certain rodents; the modification of the sea bottom by populations of annelid worms; the creation of special microhabitats in logs through the decomposition and/or comminution activities of such forms as bacteria, fungi, and wood-boring insects (see Savely, 1939); or the modification of the substratum by forest-floor forms living in the interface between the soil and such objects resting upon it as leaves, logs, boards, and so forth. This last niche is a modification of such significance that a fairly particular fauna or assemblage, the "cryptozoa," inhabit it (see Cole, 1946).

Investigations that approach this field problem as a study in conditioning, and that analyze the relations between the size and composition of a particular population or set of populations and the amount and pattern of substratum alteration that results, are to be desired. These findings then should be appraised as they relate to the subsequent life history of the populations in question. As an extension of this topic the reader should refer to Section II, particularly the discussion of soils (p. 216), and to the pertinent botanical literature on succession as affected by successive modification of the substratum.

Microclimate Primarily Dependent on Density

The point has already been made that for many instances the primary effects of climate upon populations are essentially independent of density. There is evidence, however, that the microclimate (p. 211), i.e., the climate of the immediate environment in which organisms live, may be secondarily affected by crowding. Whether this is merely incidental for a particular species or is actually significant in respect of group survival becomes a matter for empirical analysis.

Michal (1931) worked with large larval cultures of the mealworm *Tenebrio* in which the larvae were dispersed, not at random in the medium, but grouped into aggregations or "nests." He was able to show that the temperature within this aggregation was higher than that of the air immediately above the culture surface and that the former temperature tended to approach the optimum for development more closely than did the latter. In other words, when the external temperature was unfavorably low, the nest temperature was not far from the optimum.

Michal reports observations made on a population of mealworms over ten days with surrounding air temperatures and nest temperatures recorded three times each day. We have constructed a graph, based on his data, which summarizes the findings (Fig. 129). From this graph, Michal's table, and discussion the following points can be made:

the optimal temperature (33° C.) is approached when external temperatures are low, and but slightly elevated when these temperatures are high. So far as we can discover, Michal does not discuss the source of the extra heat increment produced by the aggregation. Possibly this stems from the increased metabolic activity of the clustered larvae plus heat conservation brought about by the insulating properties of the medium. This hypothesis

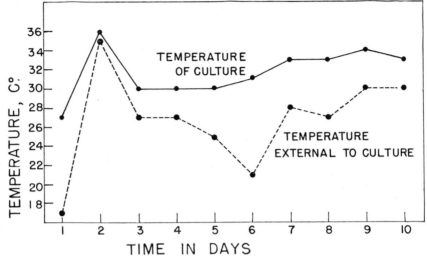

Fig. 129. Temperatures taken within an aggregation of meal worms (larvae of *Tenebrio molitor*) plotted against temperature taken at the same time above the surface of the culture.

1. The nest temperature is always above the outside air temperature.

2. The greatest divergence between nest and air temperatures occurs when the latter is low. The temperature within the larval aggregation may be as much as 10 degrees higher. For example, at an air temperature of 17° C., the nest temperature was found to be 27° C.

3. The least divergence between the two temperatures occurs when the air temperature is high, although the nest temperature is always slightly higher. For example, at air temperature readings of 35°, 30°, and 30°, respectively, nest readings of 36°, 34°, and 33° C. were recorded.

Our particular interest in Michal's work lies in its demonstration that a nonsocial insect population ameliorates its local effective temperature by a relatively simple coaction, an aggregation probably induced by thigmotaxis. The regulation of nest temperatures assumes a pattern such that

would not account for the close approximation of nest and air temperatures when the latter are high.

Several other insect examples of the modification of microclimate by population activities deserve brief mention. Hase (1926) observed that wax-moth caterpillars (*Galleria melonella*) live in dense colonies in honeycombs and that the temperature within such colonies may be 17° to 22.7° C. higher than that of the surrounding atmosphere. The case is not completely analyzed, but it is suggested that this extra heat is produced partly by fermentative processes and partly by the body temperature of the larvae themselves.

Cases of group thermal control are well known among the social insects. Wellenstein (1928) and Steiner (1929) worked on nest temperatures of the ant *Formica rufa rufopratensis*. They noted a zone within the nest at a depth of 15 to 50 centimeters in which the temperature remained quite stable over a range of 23° to 29° C. This range, which presumably coincides with the physiological optimum for reproduction and development, is about 10 degrees higher than that of the surrounding soil at the same depth. The temperature appears to be regulated, first, by insulation of the exposed, crater-like part of the nest, and, second, by certain specific behavior activities exhibited by the workers. The latter open or close the nest exits that are either exposed or away from the direct rays of the sun in such a way as to admit heat or screen it out.

Perhaps the best-known instance for all poikilotherms is the regulation of temperature within beehives, a regulation resulting from cooperative coactions on the part of population members. A brief summary, by Uvarov (1931, pp. 134–135), is here quoted.

"Réaumur (1740) discovered nearly two hundred years ago that the temperature inside a beehive is in winter much higher than that of the outer air, and observed that the bees can raise the temperature by wing movements. Since his time, the problem of the temperature conditions in beehives has been investigated thoroughly by a number of authors. It has been found that a fall in the outside temperature induces the bees to form a dense cluster. With a further fall in temperature (below about 13°), they become restless and begin to move. As a result of these movements the temperature in the cluster rises to about 25–30°, at which point these movements begin to slow down. The temperature inside the cluster then begins to sink until it reaches about 13°. The fluctuations in the external temperature are reproduced faithfully by the corresponding, but inverse, fluctuations inside the cluster, i.e., when the air temperature falls very low, that of the cluster becomes very high owing to the more energetic movements of the bees. In this way the micro-climate is kept practically independent of the climatic conditions."

The quotation stresses the behavior of bees as the outside temperature falls with consequent increase of hive temperature. The opposite of this, equally well known, deserves mention: namely, the fact that in warm weather the bees cool the hive. In summer the hive is maintained at about 34° to 35° C., and if the temperature goes beyond this range the bees cool the nest by fanning movements of the wings and possibly by the carriage of water.

It seems obvious on *a priori* grounds

alone that many natural populations of wide taxonomic types must ameliorate their surroundings to a certain extent (p. 211). This phenomenon cannot be discussed further because of space limitations. For additional discussion the reader is referred to the literature, and he should realize that the matter is not limited to insect populations or even to terrestrial groups. Allee (1931) cites examples in which aggregations of marine invertebrates modify their effective environment to an appreciable degree, and sometimes this modification confers added survival to the aggregants. At the vertebrate level Gerstell (1939) presents a convincing study of temperature conservation by bobwhite quail populations. The discussion of microclimate included in Uvarov's (1931) comprehensive review should also be consulted (see also p. 213).

POPULATION DISPERSION

The movements of organisms and their populations constitute an important segment of modern ecology and afford a significant point of distinction between the ecological relations of plants and animals. These movements are discussed from various points of view throughout this book. In Section II the relation of length of day to bird migration was reviewed (p. 121). Migration receives further treatment and definition in the section on Communities (p. 539). There are also selected considerations of animal distribution on a geographic scale (p. 580) and of the relation of zoogeography to evolution and speciation (p. 608).

It has been stressed repeatedly in this section that dispersion, along with natality and mortality, can be one of the major factors controlling population growth form and behavior. In order to round out the general treatment of dispersion we now wish to discuss briefly an aspect, not considered elsewhere, that is peculiarly populational in character. This is the distribution of organisms within an intraspecies, or relatively simple interspecies, population. The focus here is on the *pattern* of distribution as it may be expressed quantitatively over a circumscribed and defined area (or volume).

Within a particular area the population components may be distributed essentially at random, or they may be aggregated to a greater or less degree and depart from a random distribution because of this, or, as is particularly true of certain vertebrates, they may be apportioned into special areas sometimes called "territories."[*] It is obvious that the pattern of distribution can vary within the species, its abundance, and density; with the availability, distribution, and character of the habitat niches; and with other physical and biotic factors. It is equally obvious that not enough is known of the quantitative dispersion of many forms to state just what the actual pattern is. Further, it seems probable that as more knowledge is acquired numerous variations in the distribution pattern will emerge. We present here several examples of population dispersion taken from insect

Park (1933) pointed out that imago flour beetles (*Tribolium confusum*) are distributed according to a Poisson series throughout their flour. This was shown by dividing the flour into equal-sized cubes and counting the beetles in each cube. The observed findings, and their agreement with a distribution expected assuming the Poisson, are shown in Table 25. When the difference between observed and expected frequencies is tested by chi square, it is shown that the two do not differ significantly from each other (probability = 11 per cent). Thus these beetles did not aggregate to any appreciable extent within the flour volume.

Cole (1946) has examined in detail the quantitative distribution of certain forest floor invertebrates that live, among other

Table 25. Random Distribution of Flour Beetles in the Medium

Classes of Cubes with Respect to Number of Beetles Found Therein	Observed Number of Cubes with Their Beetle Distribution	Expected Number (Poisson Distribution)
0	237	246.3
1	161	147.3
2	45	44.1
3	3	8.8
4	2	1.3
5	0	0.2

studies. These illustrate both random and aggregated distribution.

The number of organisms within a unit area, or volume, of habitat varies from one unit to the next even when environmental conditions are extremely uniform. Because this number is always an integer, and, by working with values of 0, 1, 2, 3, 4, 5 . . . n organisms per unit, it follows that the distribution of the units is discontinuous. "If each unit in a given area is equally exposed to infestation, so that they differ from one another entirely at random, they will agree with the Poisson series" (Bliss, 1941). When these qualifications are satisfied and when the dispersion data can be fitted to a Poisson distribution, the conclusion can be drawn that the organisms are distributed essentially at random. It seems probable that in nature a distribution pattern so simple as this is likely to be the exception rather than the rule.

[*] It is apparent that these are general categories subject to wide intergradations extending as natural populations from quite simple to extremely complex situations.

places, under boards in the interface between the board and the ground. He was concerned with a series of organisms that Dendy (1895) had called the "cryptozoa" and had defined as "the assemblage of small terrestrial animals found dwelling in darkness beneath stones, rotten logs, the bark of trees, and in other similar situations." Dendy further concluded that the cryptozoa should be studied as a unit distinct from the true soil or subterranean fauna and from the fauna of other microhabitats, a conclusion supported by Cole's findings.

Cole placed on the forest floor many boards of similar dimensions in various selected regions of the woods. At regular intervals, for all seasons and for several years, the number of inhabitants was estimated species by species. Cole was interested in analyzing these records from various aspects. Our interest in this study is that it affords illustrations of patterns of dispersions that have been statistically analyzed and are based on large numbers, and that different groups were considered: i.e., spiders, isopods, diplopods, and insects. Cole was able to distinguish both random and "contagious" dispersion patterns.

The only group examined by Cole that showed a random distribution of individuals under the boards was the spiders (Table 26).

Scytonotus granulatus (Table 27). Here, the observed and the expected do differ significantly (by chi square) from each other, there being more instances of no forms per board than would be expected on the hypothesis of random dispersion, and also more instances of 4, 5 and more

Table 26. *Distribution of Spiders under Boards*

	Number of Spiders per Board				
	0	1	2	3	More
Observed frequencies.........	159	64	13	4	0
Expected (Poisson)..........	157.0	66.5	14.2	2	0.3

Test of observed against expected frequencies by chi square shows that these do not differ significantly from each other (P = 52.7 per cent). In other words, as great a deviation between the observed and Poisson distributions could be anticipated about 53 per cent of the time as a result of chance alone, so that there is certainly no reason for assuming a nonrandom dispersion of spiders under the boards. Cole also found that the spiders were distributed at random in all the observational areas for all seasons of the year.

individuals per board than expected. Thus, instead of finding frequencies of 3.4 with 4 diplopods per board, 0.7 with 5 diplopods per board, and 0.1 with more than 5 diplopods per board (see table), Cole actually found frequencies of 8 with 4 diplopods per board, 5 with 5, and 3 with more than five. This, of course, strongly suggests aggregation or grouping of the *Scytonotus* under the boards. The data of Table 27 are also graphed in Figure 130 with number of stations on the ordinate against number per station on the abscissa

Table 27. *Distribution of the Diplopod,* Scytonotus granulatus, *under Boards*

	Number of *Scytonotus* per Board						
	0	1	2	3	4	5	More
Observed frequencies....	128	71	34	11	8	5	3
Expected (Poisson)......	100.5	94.5	45.5	14.4	3.4	0.7	0.1

The other species of this Illinois woodland showed, not a Poisson, but a "contagious" distribution (see Pólya, 1931; Neyman, 1939; Cole, 1946a). The distinguishing feature of such distributions so far as they apply to Cole's study is that, by allowing for aggregating tendencies, they show that the boards sheltering the larger number of animals occur more frequently than would be true if the dispersion were random.

The point is well illustrated by the under-board distribution of the diplopod,

and with the observed and Poisson curves plotted within these coordinates. The contagious character of the distribution becomes immediately apparent. The two curves cross each other at about the level of the frequency class. "Three diplopods per board." Of this Cole says: "More detailed investigation might reveal that when about three *Scytonotus* are present under a board of this size, they serve to attract other diplopods to the board or influence wandering individuals to remain once they find that particular board. Thus any 'social instinct' on the part of the animals would lead to contagious distributions of the type here observed."

This aspect of dispersion has been briefly reviewed at this place primarily to indicate something about the quantitative pattern of distribution of terrestrial invertebrates within their population configuration. Obviously, the discussion could be greatly extended to include more examples

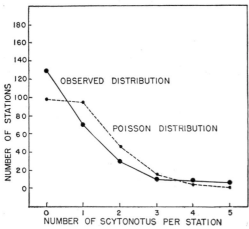

Fig. 130. Nonrandom or "contagious" distribution of the diplopod, *Scytonotus granulatus.* (After Cole.)

such as those just treated: examples of forms displaying different, and perhaps more intricate, patterns of dispersion, and examples of ecologically different species such as aquatic, aerial, infrasocial, and social forms. Limitations of space prevent further discussion of this interesting and highly important topic. The reader should be aware of the considerable literature that deals with these problems from several points of view, but always stresses the quantitative or census approach.*

* Some data concerned with marine populations are to be found in Sverdrup, Johnson, and Fleming (1942) and in Redfield (1939). From the limnological point of view something of general character appears in Welch (1935) and in papers of Edmondson (1944, 1945) on rotifers. Particularly stimulating publications about insect populations that contain both data and imaginative, statistical analyses are the following: for *Lepidoptera*, Williams, Cockbill, Gibbs, and Downes (1942), Beall (1941), and Dowdeswell, Fisher, and Ford (1940); for *Coleoptera*, Beall (1941a), and Bliss (1941); for *Diptera*, Jackson (1933, 1936, 1939, tsetse flies); Patterson (1943), and Dobzhansky and

THE ANALYSIS OF POPULATION CYCLES

The population ecologist is primarily interested in these aspects of population cycles:

1. Statistical description of the cycles of a certain species.

2. Statistical description of those cycles exhibited by a predator population that exploits a particular, and cyclic, prey population.

3. The identification of causes underlying the cycles. Do the causes lie outside the population system, as, for example, weather and sunspot activity, or do they originate within it, or both?

4. The relation of cycles to the particular community in which the cyclic species live.

The study of population cycles, of course, is merely a special instance of population fluctuation (p. 318) in which the interval between population maxima (or between minima) is relatively fixed over a considerable period of time. Such cycles have been actively studied, particularly of mammals and, to a lesser extent, of birds and insects, for a number of reasons, some of which follow:

1. The cycles may constitute, or be related to, plagues and thus be important in their own right, in terms of the public health, or in relation to certain human enterprises such as agriculture, aquiculture, and fur trapping.

2. The cycles may be related to conservation of natural resources.

3. The cyclic character of the population growth form may be, or alleged to be, related to such extra biologic, controlling periodicities as weather, sunspot activity, and the like. Explanations of this sort have seemed peculiarly satisfying intellectually to certain workers, and, in our opinion, enthusiasms have too frequently tended to outdistance evidence.

4. The cycles may be studied because of their impact on other populations or upon the community.

5. The cycles may be studied because of their spectacular nature as a result of great variation in numbers or their regularity, or both.

Wright (1943) on natural populations of the Drosophilidae; and Gilmour, Waterhouse, and McIntyre (1946) on the sheep blowfly.

Despite the ecological significance of the problem and the volume of work reported in the literature, there is some confusion about population cycles. The confusion arises largely from the attempt to identify the causes of cyclic phenomena. Some particular cases are well established and adequately interpreted, but many explanations of cyclic phenomena are not yet definitive (p. 326).

The case is excellently stated by Hutchinson (1942) in a thoughtful review of Elton's *Voles, Mice and Lemmings* (1942), a book largely devoted to population cycles. We quote from Hutchinson as follows:

" . . . [A real periodicity] . . . may presumably be due to cyclical events outside the ecosystem or to the generation of cycles by mechanisms inside the biological system, the former condition corresponding to forced vibrations in mechanics, the latter to free vibration. In the case of two isolated but climatically and geographically close populations of an animal, if the periodicity is externally determined or forced, the fluctuations in the two populations may reasonably be expected to be synchronous. In more remote regions, the oscillations might show a constant phase difference, but any irregularities in one region should correspond to irregularities in another. If the oscillation is free, there is no reason why the two populations should fluctuate in phase or with correspondence in their irregularities. The exact number of possible ways in which free fluctuations may occur is hard to ascertain *a priori,* but most cases probably reduce formally either to the symmetrical, so-called *classical oscillations* involved in the *predator-prey* relationship (Lotka-Volterra periodicity, developed in a different form by Nicholson and Bailey) or to the *relaxation oscillations* of Gause. Gause's theory involves the building up of the population to a certain critical level, after which it becomes unstable and declines suddenly, the most obvious causes of the decline being exhaustion of food, or abnormal opportunities for the spread of epidemics, when the critical density is reached. A final word of warning is needed; it is tempting to suppose a multiple causality, and this is no doubt correct, but it is clear that one must not postulate interaction of periodic causes with different periods, not multiples of each other, and then hope to obtain a highly regular set of maxima. This has been done in the past by authorities who should have known better" (p. 355).

An illustration of a population cycle is afforded by MacLulich's (1937) study of the varying hare, *Lepus americanus,* in Canada. On page 270 the census techniques used by MacLulich in the estimation of hare abundance were enumerated; on page 323 the cycle over a many-year period was figured (Fig. 117); on page 324 the relation of lynx abundance to hare abundance was mentioned and graphed in Figure 118.

With this background we need only remind the reader that the hares studied by MacLulich exhibited a cyclic growth form with a mean span between maxima of 9.7 years. After rather intensively investigating various possibilities, MacLulich concluded that the cycle was of the "relaxation oscillation" type resulting chiefly from operations within the population system; that the population "crashes," which started during the eighth year and continued on a reduced level during the ninth year, were primarily the result of nonspecific, explosive epidemics; that the lynx cycle is definitely correlated with the hare cycle (p. 324), and that the "fluctuations in numbers of neither lynx nor varying hares are correlated with sunspots."

In connection with sunspots it is of interest to note that Elton, in *Voles, Mice and Lemmings,* observes: "I do not intend to go very deeply here into this theory about the sunspots. There can be little doubt that it is wrong: the arguments against it have been reviewed by MacLulich, and they agree with my own unpublished evidence. The chief point is that the biological rhythm is slightly shorter than that of the sun-spots, and long series of fur returns shows that the two cycles pass right out of phase . . . The sun-spot theory is mentioned chiefly because I also suggested [Elton, 1924] a correlation between the early records of mouse plagues in Great Britain and the sun-spots, which can also no longer be seriously upheld" (p. 160).*

Although some authors (for example, MacLagan, 1940) apparently are still impressed by apparent correlations with the sunspot cycles, our general position is that sunspot activity has been too readily invoked as an explanation of population cycles; that in any investigation the more immediate environmental factors, whether

* For further introduction to the literature on population cycles several other citations are recommended: Hamilton (1937), Cross (1940), and Stoddard (1932).

physical, biotic, or both, should be studied comprehensively and excluded before extramundane influences can be accepted; and that, even in the event that local environmental conditions can not be shown to shape the cycles, there is no justification in assuming a control by sunspot activity until that too has been most vigorously analyzed in its own right.

THE "MIXED-SPECIES" PROBLEM:
INTERSPECIES COMPETITION

Students of laboratory populations stress an aspect of interspecies population analysis designated as the "mixed-species" problem. This problem is primarily distinguished by the way it is viewed instead of by the techniques employed or the individual principles considered. Such studies are by no means confined to the laboratory, however, as Elton (1946) and Lack (1947) have pointed out.

In the study of such interspecies phenomena as, say, predator-prey or host-parasite operations attention is characteristically focussed primarily on a single, major interaction (*viz.*, predation or parasitization) as that interaction relates to the growth form of the two interacting populations. In mixed-species studies attention is focussed on the growth form of the two-species unit, irrespective of a particular coaction (or action-reaction) selected on the basis of prior knowledge or interest, but usually involving competition for food, niche, or space. Thus the first, or major coaction, approach starts with the premeditated view that a certain function is highly important, and the analysis follows, while the second or mixed-species approach starts with the view that what *results* when two species are brought together is significant, with further analysis suggested by the findings. Actually, both approaches are productive and are not necessarily mutually exclusive. Thus Gause (1934, and in a series of individual papers) works from both points of view. On the one hand, he sets up several kinds of laboratory, mixed-species cultures and plots the resulting growth curves of the two populations. On the other hand, Gause's choice of experimental material stems from a desire to explore selected operations. By a wedding of the mixed-species approach (which to date is largely a laboratory exploration)

with the other approach, Gause studies in micro-organisms "mechanism of competition in yeast cells," "competition for common food in protozoa," and "the destruction of one species by another." The last phase, involving the predation of *Didinium* upon *Paramecium,* is reviewed on page 372.

Mixed-species studies are particularly well adapted to laboratory analysis because relatively simple populations can be established that can be controlled and manipulated according to a preconceived plan. A particularly meaningful application of this approach obtains when two species that occupy identical, or nearly identical, niches are brought together as competitors, and the influences of the two populations upon each other's growth form are assayed. Such investigations, conducted under laboratory conditions in which accurate census counts are feasible, yield dependable and interpretable, though simplified, knowledge about competition and selection. They also exhibit a minimum of artificiality because the problem is directly related to more complex (and harder to analyze) situations that exist among natural populations. Since control populations of single species constitute an integral part of such studies, it becomes possible to differentiate intraspecies from interspecies operations, and owing to the way the experiments are designed, to form some judgment also as to the role of the physical habitat.

Such analyses can be extended either by further, careful dissection of the factors responsible for a demonstrated two-species interaction, or several species that occupy more divergent niches can be brought together in the same microcosm in order to measure quantitatively the ecological generalization that competitive pressure between two locally associated species varies in direct relation with the similarity of the niches they occupy.*

* Several mixed-species population studies have already been dealt with earlier in this section from various points of view. In Chapter 21 Gause's investigation (1935) of oscillations between yeast and paramecia cultures were discussed (Fig. 121). In the same chapter the findings of Park, Gregg, and Lutherman (1941) about extinction of *Gnathoceros* and *Trogoderma* cultures were reviewed briefly (p. 329). In this chapter a number of points are made,

Following are some of the types of end results that can occur when two species compete as mixed-populations. [*]

1. One population may become extinct, owing to the pressure exerted against it by the other. This is the usual outcome of competition when the two species are ecological equivalents and, therefore, make some common demand on their shared environment. (Crombie, 1947; T. Park, 1948.)

2. The two populations may reach respective equilibrium, or semiequilibrium, particularly if they inhabit somewhat different niches. The nature of the equilibrium is specific for each species under the conditions of experiment and tends to be maintained so long as food is available and the physical habitat is not appreciably altered. Under such conditions the equilibria are probably largely functions of biotic interactions. These equilibria, of course, are not fixed indefinitely; they shift with significant alterations of the environment.

3. The populations may vary in synchronous or semisynchronous fashion so that either oscillations or fluctuations between the two species are established. This growth form pertains especially to predator-prey and parasite-host situations. As Volterra pointed out (p. 271) in his "Law of conservation of the averages," the mean numerical density of both species can be maintained over considerable periods of time.

These three statements are derived on the basis of logic and experience; they are in part a priori and in part based on empirical observation. Crombie (1945) reexamines various mathematical models such as those proposed by Lotka (1932), Win-

sor (1934), Gause (1935), and Kostitzin (1937) and concludes that these correspond to the following biological possibilities:

"(1) Each species inhibits its own potential increase more than that of the other and both continue to exist together; (2) the second species inhibits the potential increase of the first less than it inhibits its own, while the first species inhibits the potential increase of the second more than it inhibits its own, whatever the initial number of the two species: the first species drives out the second; (3) this is the opposite to (2) and the second species drives out the first; (4) each species inhibits the other more than itself: one drives out the other depending chiefly on the initial sizes of their populations (cf. Park, Gregg and Lutherman, 1941)" (p. 364).

An illustration of a mixed-species population study is seen in the work of Park, Gregg, and Lutherman (1941) that has been already mentioned in other connections elsewhere in this section. This study analyzes in quantitative terms what results when three genera of granary beetles (*Tribolium confusum*, *Gnathoceros cornutus*, and *Trogoderma versicolor*) are brought together as competitors. The approach consists in establishing *control* populations of each of the three species cultured singly and *experimental* populations cultured as planned mixed-species groups. In an investigation of such design it is possible to differentiate those effects upon growth form that are purely intraspecies in origin from those that are interspecies, i.e., those new relationships that emerge when a taxonomically distinct and competing population is added to the ecosystem.

In these experiments a food medium was developed that proved suitable for all three species and could be sifted for census taking. The total habitat was kept as optimal as possible by replacing the medium at each examination period; by using the same volume of flour in all populations; and by maintaining temperature, humidity and light at certain designated levels. At regularized intervals counts of larval, pupal, and imaginal beetles were taken. The populations were set up as follows: controls, consisting of single species cultures; experimentals, consisting of two species introduced in initially equal numbers; and experimentals, consisting of various

---

using data derived from mixed-species studies: see especially treatments of the coactions between *Drosophila* and yeast (p. 349); the relation of *Didinium* to *Paramecium* (p. 372); the interactions affecting fecundity between four genera of granary beetles grown under homotypic and heterotypic conditions of culture (p. 355); and the relation of conditioning brought about by planarian worms to survival of *Procerodes* (p. 360). The sections concerned with "predation" (pp. 370–377) and with "environmental conditioning" (pp. 352–361) also contain general discussions directly pertinent for the mixed-species problem.

[*] Elton (1946) has examined in a novel way the effects of competition between populations in relation to community organization,

species combinations with one form initially introduced at a numerical advantage over the other. The experiments were run for more than two years with examinations each thirty days. Not all the conclusions can be presented here, but these are perhaps the more significant: (1) As single species populations, *Tribolium, Gnathoceros,* and *Trogoderma* each have a characteristic growth form (see p. 320 and Fig. 113); (2) in mixed-species populations *Trogoderma* and *Gnathoceros* are usually driven out by *Tribolium,* although understandable exceptions occur; (3) in mixed-species populations *Trogoderma* and *Gnathoceros* are more evenly matched, although *Gnathoceros* is favored in most instances; in populations consisting of all three species, *Trogoderma* becomes extinct first (at about 120 days), *Gnathoceros* second (at about 510 days), while the *Tribolium* populations gradually increase in size, as the pressure from competition with the other two forms is gradually reduced, until they attain normal (i.e., control) densities. The particular factors involved in this mixed-species study have not been analyzed, but Hutchinson (1947) has dealt with this case, among others, from a mathematical viewpoint.

A recent paper by Thomas Park (1948), published too late for detailed inclusion here, discusses competition between two species of the same genus (*Tribolium confusum* and *T. castaneum*)—a competition resulting invariably in the extinction of one of the two forms. It is further shown that the presence of a sporozoan disease alters the extinction pattern markedly (p. 727).[*]

INTRASPECIES AND INTERSPECIES PREDATION

The ecologist is interested in predation from several points of view: as a natural historian studying morphological, physiolog-

[*] Other mixed-species studies that deal largely with laboratory populations of protistan and arthropod species are the following: Smaragdova (1936), Vladimerova and Smirnov (1938), and the significant and analytical paper of Crombie (1945) on population interactions between *Rhizopertha dominica* (a beetle) and *Sitotroga cerealella* (a moth) in renewed and in conditioned media and on the relation of these two species to a third competitor, *Oryzaephilus surinamensis* (a beetle). Crombie's 1944 paper dealing with larval interspecies competition has already been discussed.

ical, and behavioristic adjustments between a prey and its predator; as a student of evolution concerned both with the evolution of such adjustments and with the relation of predation to natural selection; as a student of communities in which predation is an important component of the food-chain nexus; and as a population biologist. The viewpoint of the last worker is directed towards the statistical appraisal of the effectiveness of predation as that factor influences the growth form of both predator and prey populations. Predation thus emerges as a source of prey mortality, and this can have real quantitative consequences for consumer and consumed alike. Errington, Hamerstrom, and Hamerstrom (1940) contribute to this point when they say, "One of the causes of the disputes often elicited by the mere mention of predation is confusion of the *fact* that predators prey upon certain animals with *effect* that such predation may have on numbers of the prey. The *fact* of predation may usually be ascertained with relative ease through field or laboratory studies; evaluation of *effect* of predation upon population is another matter and one just beginning to receive a small measure of the attention that is its due" (pp. 817–818).

Leopold (1933, p. 231) lists five variables that influence the annual direct mortality from predation in a given species of "game" on a given range. These are:

1. The density of the game population
2. The density of the predator population
3. The predilection of the predator, that is, its natural food "preferences"
4. The physical condition of the game and the escape facilities available to it
5. The abundance of "buffers" or alternative foods for the predators

We shall not discuss these variables one by one, but it is helpful to have them so formalized. They will be partly illustrated in the examples that follow.

An experimental demonstration of cannibalism in relation to density is afforded by studies of the flour beetle *Tribolium confusum.* Chapman (1928) pointed out that adult beetles eat their own eggs—a coaction of some importance in regulating the upper limits of population growth of the colony. It was his conception that when a *Tribolium* culture reaches certain levels of density, the excess eggs are removed by

cannibalistic pressure. Chapman spoke of this self-limitation by the population as "environmental resistance" of which he considered egg-eating to be an important component.

Thomas Park (1933) presented further observations on *Tribolium* egg cannibalism. He showed that the imago beetles move through their flour medium essentially at random and that, if the eggs are deposited at random, as is presumably the case, the rate of egg consumption thus becomes a matter of the probability of a beetle finding and eating an egg. This rate obviously will vary with the number of adults (predators) and eggs (prey), and this provides an illustration of a coaction (cannibalism) that is density-dependent (p. 405). Park also showed that *Tribolium* imago males, virgin females, and fecundated females eat eggs at statistically similar rates, although later observations by Stanley (1942) and Boyce (1946) suggest that females may be more cannibalistic than males.

Chapman and Baird (1934) recorded egg-eating rates when male imagoes were present in six different densities. They found, according to expectations, that "when a population was high in proportion to the size of the environment, the eating went on at a greater rate; and as the population became lower the chance of a beetle's eating an egg became less and less."

Crombie (1943) has recently carried out a study of cannibalism. He set up experiments in which male *Tribolium* were present in the following densities: 1.25, 2.5, 5, 10, 20, and 40 insects per gram of medium. To each of these cultures eggs were added at a rate of fifty-five each twenty-four hour period, and the percentage of eggs eaten daily was ascertained. These percentages for the six increasing imago densities are as follows: 7.7, 17, 20, 39.7, 70.2, and 98.4. The differences between these figures (by *t*-test) are all statistically significant. Evidence is again presented showing that the percentage of eggs eaten per unit of time is directly proportional to predator density.

This is an uncomplicated and straightforward illustration of predation. It occurs within a single species; basically follows a pattern that varies with prey and predator concentrations; and the coaction involved,

eating of an egg, is a relatively simple one.

Interspecies predation is a problem of greater complexity than cannibalism and also of much more general ecological significance. Such predation is certainly related to natural selection (p. 48) and constitutes in its own right an interesting aspect of population study with obvious density-dependent implications. It is the latter that we touch on briefly here.

It is clear that the predation of one species population upon another ranges from situations relatively simple to those exceedingly complex. The coaction basis for the simpler phenomenon depends upon something approaching "random searching" (see Nicholson, 1933) by the predators, with the prey, if not distributed at random, at least not highly secluded or inaccessible. When these requirements obtain, it would be expected in a general way and on *a priori* grounds that (1) when the prey and predator populations are both large, predation would be rather consistently intense; (2) when the prey population is large and the predator population small, the intensity of predation per individual predator would be high, but the total predation light; (3) when the prey population is small and the predator population large, the total predation would be intermediate; and (4) when the prey population and the predator population are both small, the total predation would be light. More complex predation situations are established when the prey population, upon meeting the pressure of predation, compensates for this in some manner.

To illustrate certain points about predation by actual examples, we discuss briefly an experimental study of predation in laboratory populations of microorganisms, predation in fish populations, and predation in higher vertebrate populations.

An illustration of predation in laboratory populations is seen in the investigations of Gause (1934). Gause set up cultures in which a bacterial population (*Bacillus pyocyaneus*) was at the base of the food chain, a population exploited by the ciliate *Paramecium caudatum*. The latter in turn was eaten by another ciliate, *Didinium nasutum*. Thus, *Didinium* constitutes the predator group and *Paramecium* the prey group. Gause's interest lay in seeing if he could reproduce the "classical oscillations" in growth form (p. 326) between predator and prey predicted by Volterra on theoretical grounds.

Gause's experiments were of three designs. In the first type a "homogeneous" or clear medium was used into which bacteria were introduced along with one seeding of *Paramecium* and one of *Didinium*. In the second type a "heterogeneous" medium was developed, consisting of a clear

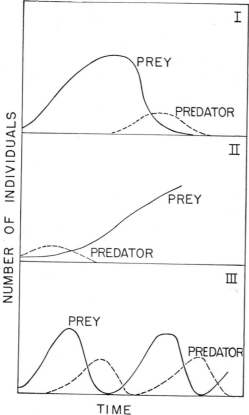

Fig. 131. Predator-prey interactions between two infusorian populations. The prey is *Paramecium caudatum;* the predator, *Didinium nasutum.* Case I, "homogeneous microcosm without immigrations"; Case II, "heterogeneous microcosm without immigrations"; and Case III, "homogeneous microcosm with immigrations." (After Gause.)

portion in which both ciliate populations could live and a cloudy portion available only to *Paramecium*. Into this heterogeneous medium bacteria, paramecia, and didinia were introduced, again as a single seeding. The third set of experiments were carried out in the homogeneous medium, but, in addition to the initial seeding of

prey and predators (the bacteria being abundant, of course), *Paramecium* and *Didinium* were added to the culture at regular intervals. This situation is designated by Gause as a "homogeneous microcosm with immigrations."

The population interactions are different in the three experiments. The results are well summarized in Figure 131, from which the following conclusions can be drawn: In the homogeneous microcosm the prey multiplies rapidly, thus providing a dense culture for exploitation by the predators. The latter are efficient, find all the prey, and bring about their extinction.* Then, with the food supply exhausted, *Didinium* perishes. By making the microcosm heterogeneous so that a refuge is provided for the prey, an entirely different end result is attained. The predator exploits the prey available in the clear portion of the medium and for a time multiplies slightly. Some paramecia, however, remain or escape into the cloudy portion and there cannot be eaten. The predator population devours the prey it can get at and then dies. The prey population, released from the pressure of predation, now multiplies vigorously and establishes itself as a successful culture of *Paramecium*, exploiting, of course, the bacteria.

The bottom chart of Figure 131 depicts events when both species are introduced into a clear medium with subsequent reintroductions or "immigrations." Here, the following things happen:

"(1) At the first immigration into the microcosm containing but few Paramecia the predator did not find any prey and perished. An intense growth of the prey began. (2) At the time of the second immigration the concentration of the prey is already rather high, and a growth of the population of the predator begins. (3) The third immigration took place at the moment of an intense destruction of the prey by the predators, and it did not cause any essential changes. (4) Towards the time of the fourth immigration the predator had already devoured all the prey, had become reduced in size and degenerated. The prey introduced into the microcosm originates a new cycle of growth of the prey population. Such periodic

* This sort of result is probably largely limited to experimental populations. It would seem likely that in most natural populations enough of the prey would escape by one means or another so that complete extinction would be avoided.

changes repeat themselves further on" (Gause, 1934, pp. 125–126).*

We have already cited two illustrations of predation in natural populations of fishes. These are Russell's report on the haddock (p. 322) and Huntsman's report on the Atlantic salmon (p. 321). The former was concerned with a special, but effective, form of predation—the commercial fishing activity of man. It was shown that the haddock population (as indexed by the commercial yield) dropped regularly for several years before World War I, a period when predation was intensive, increased markedly during war years while fishing was either suspended or reduced, and again declined sharply during postwar years with the renewal of fishing effort. This is an interesting case, for, better than most, it suggests how destructive predation pressure can be in the absence of checks working against the predators. It will also be recalled that Huntsman in his studies on salmon pointed out that when rainfall was low, the salmon parr were more vulnerable to predation by local birds; this predation resulted presumably in a noticeable contraction of subsequent salmon populations in the next few years.

Foerster and Ricker (1941) report a most interesting study dealing with the predation pressure exerted by several species of fishes against a prey population of young sockeye salmon. This study was conducted at Cultus Lake in British Columbia, Canada, an area where adequate ecological and taxonomic records were obtainable and field manipulations were feasible.

Cultus Lake has a fish population of at least ten species. Of these, four are important predators on the sockeye: squawfish, trout, char, and coho salmon. The investigators consistently removed these predators from the lake, along with other incidental forms, by gill nets, seines, bait lines, and cage traps, and then evaluated the effect of this on the prey popu-

* Winsor (1934) has certain pertinent reservations about Gause's methods. He says: "In a large part of his published work the number of points on the growth curve is small; and in many cases the scatter is so great as to make any curve fitting highly arbitrary. In his work with protozoa he seems . . . to have used populations which are probably too small to expect even a qualitative agreement with theory."

lations. Gill-netting, the most efficient method, was utilized from 1932 through 1938, and over this seven year period 10,602 squawfish, 2310 trout, 935 char, and 730 coho salmon were caught. This netting reduced those squawfish over 200 mm. in length and the char to about one-tenth of their original abundance. The trout populations were probably reduced somewhat, though not so much as the other two species. The effect on the coho salmon was obscure.

Along with this reduction of the predator populations, there went a corresponding increase in survival of immature sockeye salmon, as indexed by the number of migrant smolts counted each spring. This survival rate of the "eyed-egg stages" increased "to 8.98 per cent from a previous average of 3.61 per cent; the survival rate of free-swimming fry planted in the lake increased to 13.04 per cent from a previous average of 4.16 per cent. The survival rate of eggs in female sockeye spawning naturally increased to 7.81 per cent from a previous average of 1.78 per cent" (p. 335).

Foerster and Ricker attribute these increases in prey populations directly to the planned reduction of the predators. They point out that two other types of ecological factors could logically account for the observed increase: namely, changes in Cultus Lake other than those involved in predation and/or an increase in food available to the sockeye; but after careful consideration of the evidence these alternatives are rejected.

Up to this point predation has been treated as a relatively uncomplicated situation. In discussing predatory phenomena in bird and mammal populations, examples can be presented that are also relatively uncomplicated. It is necessary, however, to point out that predation patterns are frequently more complicated in these groups, owing largely to the fact that many of these prey populations are themselves highly organized and, when meeting the pressure of predation, compensate in some manner. Some illustrations of both types follow.

An instructive aspect of the predation problem centers around the point that predators are frequently euryphagous (p. 236) and prey upon what is available. Such stenophagous or monophagous forms as ant and termite eaters are the exception rather than the rule. N. Tinbergen (1933) reported on the food consumption of a population of long-eared owls (*Asio otus*) during the successive winters of 1930–1931 and 1931–1932. During the first winter, when the vole (*Microtus*) was abundant, this species constituted 86 per cent of the owl's total food. The wood mouse (*Apodemus*) furnished 7 per cent; other mammals, 2 per cent; house sparrows, 2 per cent; and other birds, 3 per cent. During the second winter the voles were scarce, and the owls turned to other prey. Voles constituted 30 per cent rather than 86 per cent; wood mice, 15 per cent; other mammals, 7 per cent; house sparrows, 30 per cent; and other birds, 18 per cent. Shifts in predation pressure of this sort have obvious implications for zoogeography and community studies as well as for the strictly populational aspects.

These comments focus on a predator population. This has a corollary in terms of the prey population. The general ecological principle can be stated in this way: A predator may exploit several prey species, while, conversely, a prey species may be exploited by several predators. The latter point finds illustration in Stoddard (1932). He showed that the percentages of bobwhite nests destroyed—that is, through eating of the eggs—by natural enemies over four years' observation were as follows: 1924, 46 per cent; 1925, 41 per cent; 1926, 38 per cent; and 1927, 34 per cent. Skunks, cur dogs, house cats, cotton rats, opossums, blue jays, crows, turkeys, snakes, the thief ant *Solenopsis molesta* (which enters the egg to feed as soon as it is punctured by the emerging chick), man, and "unknown agencies," among them foxes, weasels, and other animals, were incriminated.

Another significant point emerging from Stoddard's tabulation, a principle of general ecological moment, is that predation is frequently directed against the immature stages of the prey and as such may constitute an effective limiting factor.

There is considerable evidence in the literature suggesting that the abundance of a predator is associated with the abundance of its prey. This is particularly true when the prey constitute the major food item in the predators' diet. To the field naturalist this is, of course, an old story. He frequently notes a large increase in predators during years when the prey populations (especially rodents) are large. This increase may result from increased predator immigration into the region, from heightened and more effective reproduction, or from both. The phenomenon is well illustrated by Elton (1942).

A more analytical example of this, developed by MacLulich (1937), concerns the relation between the varying hare and the lynx in North America. In 1905 MacFarlane said: "The yearly catch of lynxes rapidly diminishes in volume as soon as the rabbits become scarce and when the latter are comparatively rare a large proportion of the great but now dwindling crowd of lynxes suffer privation, and some actually starve to death." Seton (1925) pointed out that in the winter of 1906–1907 in the MacKenzie River valley, when, presumably, the rabbits were sparse, an examination of the stomach of twelve lynxes showed no food present at all. These animals were dying of starvation—"mere walking skeletons."

MacLulich examines this predator-prey cycle in Canada (Fig. 118). He finds that the varying hare has a cycle with a mean duration from peak to peak (or dip to dip) of 9.6 years, the lynx of 9.7 years, and that the two are essentially confluent. A correlation coefficient was calculated between rabbit and lynx records arbitrarily designated "scarce," "intermediate," and "abundant" for records extending from 1847 to 1934, inclusive. This coefficient, with the value + 0.55 ± 0.05, indicates appreciable correlation between population sizes of the two species. "Therefore there is good ground for believing the decreases in numbers of lynxes are caused by starvation when the hares disappear, or at least by inability to withstand adverse circumstances and winter conditions on short rations" (p. 102).

One of the most noteworthy studies of predation that has yet appeared is that of L. Tinbergen (1946; see also the review in English by Hartley, 1947). This is primarily concerned with the effect that the European sparrow hawk (*Accipiter nisus*) exerts against populations of the house sparrow (*Passer domesticus*), the chaffinch (*Fringilla coelebs*), the great tit (*Parus major*), and the coal tit (*Parus ater*). The four prey species are censused or estimated in an adept way, making use of several methods appropriate for each case. For example, the sparrow population was estimated by sampling the number of males per house during the spring, after which this mean figure was multiplied by the number of houses and then converted to total population through knowledge of the winter sex ratio derived from field studies.

An approach based on male singing frequency was used for the chaffinches and titmice. The mean monthly mortality factor, s, for the latter (*Parus*) was calculated as follows:

$$(1 + j)(1 - s)^{12} = 1$$

in which j is the number of young reared per adult and the exponent 12 represents months of the year.

For the sparrows and chaffinches, s was obtained by the notation

$$(1 + e)(1 - s)^{12} = 1$$

in which e is the ratio; number of first year birds ÷ number of adults.

One specific illustration of sparrow hawk predation can be given as it affects the two titmice species in a particular location for two intervals of the year. Tinbergen's method allows him to compute the total expected mortality against which the number of birds actually killed by the hawks can be contrasted. This illustration is as follows:

	May	June 16–Sept. 15
Coal Tit		
Expected (total mortality)..	357	5,569
Sparrow hawk mortality	132	138
Great Tit		
Expected (total mortality)..	210	2,906
Sparrow hawk mortality	93	529

Similar data representative of the entire study led Tinbergen to the generalizations that sparrow hawk predation caused approximately 50 per cent of the summer mortality for the house sparrow, 25 per cent for both the chaffinches and great tits, and only a negligible percentage for the coal tits.

For our present purposes the major ecological principle emerging from this investigation is that, within certain limits, the intensity of predation is proportional to the abundance of the prey, or, in other words, predation is demonstrated to have density-dependent aspects. Hartley (1947) says: "The upper limit of predation intensity is reached when the prey species is increasing so much more rapidly than the predator species that the most intense predation contributes a smaller and smaller part of the total mortality."

Errington (1937a) discussed certain of the more complicated aspects of predation as it affects a prey population. His general theme is stated thus: "Life to wild animals unquestionably is often harsh, but the demands of predators in temperate regions are not apt to be so drastic as to make existence a neck and neck race between the great appetite of predation and the breeding rates of the prey animals" (p. 243). Errington goes on to quote McAtee (1936), who concluded that animal populations only rarely approach the limits of food supply. Errington is of the opinion that predators, at least those that are higher vertebrates, are no exception to this rule. "Predators may occasionally starve, and predator pressure may at times be about all that a prey species can stand, or conceivably more than it can stand; but, for all that, predation still seems to be essentially a byproduct of population rather than a broadly dominant influence on population" (pp. 243–245).

Errington elaborates this concept in reporting observations on the effect of predation by the great horned owl (*Bubo virginianus*) upon populations of the bobwhite quail (*Colinus virginianus*). Wintering bobwhites were studied for six years at Prairie du Sac, Wisconsin, where Errington determined the quails' density and the intensity of owl predation.

These findings are partially reported in Table 28. It should be noted that this study area had a "carrying capacity" that remained constant so long as hunting, starvation, or unusual weather conditions did not obtain. The major point brought out in the table is that when the quail populations did not exceed this carrying capacity, the predation was low; conversely, when the area was supersaturated, the predation was high. For this case it thus appears that Errington views predation as an incidental rather than a controlling factor affecting population growth form. The owls remove the excess quail, and, as the latter return

Table 28. Horned Owl Pressure upon Wintering Bobwhite Populations (From Errington, 1936)

Winters	Horned Owl Pellets Containing Bobwhite Remains from Area	Bobwhite Winter Population Density (per mi²)	Bobwhite Winter Carrying Capacity (per mi²)	Percentage to Which Carrying Capacity of Area Was Filled by Wintering Bobwhite Population
1929–1930..........	2 = 5.6% of 36	24	66	36
1930–1931..........	4 = 6.3% of 64	51	66	77
1931–1932.........	13 = 16.0% of 81	80	66	121 (insecure)
1932–1933.........	5 = 6.8% of 74	81	66	123 (insecure)
1933–1934..........	3 = 14.3% of 21	87	58	150 (insecure)
1934–1935..........	8 = 19.0% of 42	82	58+	141 (insecure)

to densities that the local environment can support, the predation drops off.

During periods of overpopulation when the carrying capacity is exceeded, certain individual quail appear to be weakened from hunger, injuries, and disease, and exhibit an increased vulnerability to predation. Under such conditions of overcrowding some coveys are forced into niches that are decidedly unfavorable, while still others wander from one occupied or uninhabitable covert to another. "Badly situated coveys, whether they keep moving or attempt to station themselves in inferior environment, bear the brunt of pressure from enemies" (p. 249).*

Errington's report on owl and quail populations also furnishes an illustration of predation patterns that are somewhat more complex. This complexity arises primarily because of the organization of the prey population as a territory-inhabiting species. Such organization reduces predation to a point where, in terms of the prospective history of the prey, it is incidental rather than controlling. The quail possess a series of territories which support for any length of time a limited number of individuals—some sixty to sixty-five per square mile for those discussed here. This upper limit is

* It is to be noted in Table 28 that during the winter 1932–1933 the quail population was "insecure," but owl predation as shown in the right-hand column was also low. This is not an inconsistency (says Errington), but rather reflects the fact that a predator (or predators), in addition to the owls, is feeding on the quail. "One thing that seems characteristic of insecure populations is their common vulnerability to a number of different predators, even predators differing greatly in prowess and hunting tactics" (p. 249).

set by agencies other than predation. When it is exceeded, the predators, regardless of kind, seem to remove the excess. It appears reasonable to assume that these supernumerary quail would be removed by one means or another in the absence of all predators. For this case, then, predation is proportional to *over*population rather than to population, as is frequently the case in "simpler" population systems. Studies on this subject and tending to this conclusion form a major contribution of ecology to practical "game management."

Perhaps the final point to be made about predation is that it can have obvious survival value in terms of the prey population. Cartwright (1944) definitely suggests this for the sharp-tailed grouse and Hungarian partridge in Canada. His conception is stated in his own words as follows:

"This brings us to the rôle of the predator. It is obvious that a species with a 3-year life span which produced all its young uniformly in June would become extinct if three successive adverse seasons destroyed the hatch. Hence, predation, by destroying a substantial proportion of the first and second nestings, *staggers the nesting attempts and thus becomes a major factor in the survival of the species.* To be effective, the predation must be substantial. Recorded observations show that approximately 60 per cent of the first nestings are destroyed by various predators and other causes. Let's just apply this to a theoretical 100 females.

$$100 - 60 = 40 \times 6 = 240$$
$$60 - 36 = 24 \times 6 = 144$$
$$\overline{384}$$

Thus 100 females suffering 60 per cent predation on two successive nestings produce 384 young. Add 100 males and you have 200 adults producing 384 young. Under such conditions a population is thriving."[*]

ORGANIZED PREDATION BY MAN

The Problem of the "Optimal Yield"

The problem of optimal yield[†] can be stated in this way: To what extent can a particular population under specified conditions be exploited (preyed upon), maintain itself within a certain size range, and at the same time yield a reasonably high catch to the exploiting agency? This, in population terms, is one of the central problems of conservation, for when an answer is found, it is possible to predict the most favorable ratio between the reconstitution of a group in relation to exploitation exerted against it.

Russell (1942) is concerned with many aspects of this matter from the point of view of the fisheries biologist. "Put in a nutshell [the problem] is this, that up to a point you can increase yield by increasing fishing, but after this maximum is reached the more you fish the less weight of fish you catch" (p. 75). The evidence supporting this statement has already been presented for haddock populations in the chapter on growth form (p. 322; Fig. 116).

The question of yield versus exploitation was formulated in theoretical terms by Russell (1931), who concerns himself with the factors that determine the level of a stock subjected to commercial fishing. In a self-contained stock of fish of one particular species which is systematically fished the fishing gear catches only those fishes that have attained a certain length. The fish population (S) thus can be divided into those forms (S₁) that are catchable

and those that are not. In the course of a year's fishing the catchable stock changes through death, through catching, of course, and because some of the younger fishes grow enough to enter the S₁ category. The various factors pertaining to the *weight* of the stock at the end of this hypothetical year (S₂) are as follows:

> S = the total stock (weight)
> S₁ = the starting catchable stock
> S₂ = the catchable stock at the end of the year
> A = the recruitment, i.e., the influx of smaller fishes that attain catchable size during the year
> G = the total growth increment of the surviving individuals
> M = the natural mortality
> C = the year's total catch

Those factors that increase the weight of the stock are $A + G$; those that decrease the stock are $C + M$. The following simple equation then can be written for the weight of the stock at the end of the year:

$$S_2 = S_1 + (A + G) - (C + M)$$

S_2 therefore will be $>$, $=$, or $<$ S_1 according as $(A + G)$ is $>$, $=$, or $< (C + M)$. Differently put, this means that (1) if fishing takes more out of the catchable population in a year, i.e., $(C + M)$, than is replaced by natural processes, i.e., $(A + G)$, the total weight of the catchable or available population is reduced; (2) if loss and gain balance each other, there will be no change in the population; and (3) if the natural replenishment exceeds loss owing to fishing effort and other mortality, the catchable stock at year's end will have increased.

A complication arises in that the population may stabilize at different levels of density. The level will depend primarily upon the rate of capture, because this factor, operating through fishing mortality, determines to a considerable extent the age distribution of the stock.

"We may expect rate of growth and rate of recruitment to be affected to some extent by the rate of capture. Thus if the rate of capture is low, we may get an overcrowded stock, with a slow rate of growth, and, probably, a slow rate of recruitment, since there will be little room for incoming stock. If the rate of capture is increased, leaving more room for the stock to grow and recruit itself, we may expect the rate of growth and rate of recruitment to be greater. If rate of capture is very high indeed and greatly reduces the number of spawners it is conceivable that the rate of recruitment may be adversely affected. But the number of eggs produced by each spawner is so great, and the proportion that can find room to grow is so small, that we need not for the time being consider this possibility too seriously. So far as we know at present, there is no obvious correlation between the number of eggs spawned and the number surviving to reach the catchable stock, in any of the important species" (p. 83).

This argument is admittedly oversimplified since it rests upon the large assumption "that environmental conditions remain constant, that there is, for instance, the same average annual production of fish food."

The crucial question as to the optimal yield now arises: What level of population stabilization safely permits the greatest weight of catch, or, as Russell cogently puts it, how may a stock be subjected to "rational exploitation?" A general, first approximation is deducible from Russell's formulation. If M is not great in proportion to C, the maximum value of C obtains when $A + G$, which is equal to $C + M$, is maximal. Assuming that the average value of A is not considerably influenced by moderate changes in the intensity of fishing activity, and assuming further that the stock is subjected to active commercial fishing, $A + G$ will vary roughly in proportion with G. Since G is the yearly upgrowth of the population with the exclusion of the fishes that are captured or otherwise eliminated, it is when G is maximal that the greatest steady yield obtains.

Suppose, says Russell, that two populations are fished at different rates: one at 30 per cent reduction year by year in terms of number of catchable stock, the other at 60 per cent reduction. At the 30 per cent rate the mean age and weight of the fishes both in the catch and in the population will be greater than at the 60 per cent rate. Therefore, these differential exploitations result in a changed age distribution because of differential rates of mortality. Under the 30 per cent procedure there will be proportionately more and heavier and older fishes. As the intensity of fishing increases there eventually comes a time when the total weight of the catch decreases. "It follows also that a very intense fishery may actually yield no more than a very moderate fishery, both being well under the possible maximum" (p. 85).

A hypothetical, yet reasonably realistic, illustration of the relation of fishing intensity to yield has been published by Graham (1938). This is presented pictorially in Figure 132, which contrasts events in a population exploited at a rate of 90 per cent capture per year with one at 30 per cent capture per year. The natural mortality is assumed to be 5 per cent per year for each population. Yield, in terms of weight of catch, is shown, and the effect of the differential exploitation on both stock and catch is made clear. It is evident that under the 90 per cent rate the catch consists primarily of small, light-weight fishes. With one-third this amount of fishing the catch consists of few small fishes and more large fishes in their third and fourth years of age. The total weight of the catch is exactly the same in both cases, but under the 30 per cent procedure a large stock, some six times as great, of fourth-year forms remains. "So that in a case like this you can catch as much in weight by fishing at a moderate rate as you can by fishing three times harder" (Russell, p. 86). The general ecological and conservation principle that emerges is this: With intense exploitation the catch consists of a preponderance of small forms of low weight, while with more moderate exploitation fewer forms are caught, but these are of larger size. Thus, what is gained as numbers through intensive effort may be offset by a reduction in actual weight.

Perhaps this is the chief point that can be made about the optimal yield problem: For many populations (at least for populations such as those that concern the marine fisheries biologist) there exists an exploitation rate, neither too high nor too low, that, when in operation, results in the maximum steady yield. When this yield is realized, the product of the number of fishes multiplied by their average weight is maximal.

It is obvious that our treatment of the optimal yield problem, which is an adumbration of Russell's treatment, is presented in an oversimplified way. The role of certain factors such as natural mortality, growth rate, density effects, food supply, and so forth, has not been adequately evaluated. In part this oversimplification is a deliberate attempt to present clearly the essentials of the problem without confusing complications. But, largely, the various other factors are omitted because not enough is known of their operation in natural populations subjected to such organized human predation. This is well recognized by Russell, of course, who, in discussing the relation of growth rate to the entire problem states:

This problem of the optimal yield obviously could be developed in much more detail for fish populations and for other groups as well. Our responsibility has been to indicate the nature of the problem, to suggest its considerable theoretical significance and pragmatic importance, and to stress that much in the way of further research remains to be done.

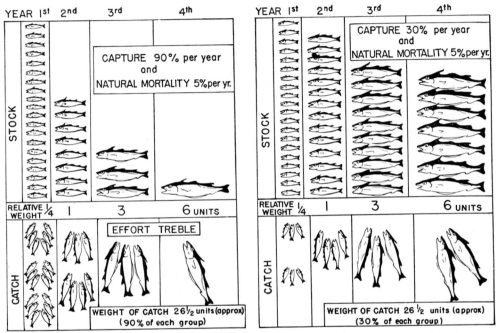

Fig. 132. Comparison of the effects of high and low intensity of fishing on the exploited populations. (After Graham.)

"We see then that the reduction in yield due to increased intensity of fishing may be counterbalanced in varying degree by an increase in growth-rate, and this may serve to remind us again of the complexity of the factors involved in the overfishing problem. Increase in growth-rate is not an unmixed blessing, for it means that the fish are exposed to capture at an earlier stage in their life. To quote Raitt [1939] again: 'Reduction in numbers means less competition for food, which means greater growth-rate, which means earlier fishing out, all of which indicates reduction of potential fertility, which in turn would mean still further reduction in numbers and so on. On the other hand, once decrease in rate of depletion were established, greater survival would mean more competition for food, less growth rate, later entry into the trawl, greater survival to spawning age, larger broods and so on.' There are therefore many biological factors involved, and their interrelations are complex" (pp. 95–96).

We have suggested that the optimal yield problem is an aspect of the larger problem of predation. In the examples discussed here the predator, man, has exploited marine fish populations that are relatively simple in the sense that they are not so highly organized as are certain bird and mammal groups. We wish to direct the reader's attention again to the general discussion of predation immediately preceding in which it was shown that frequently these more highly organized populations so compensate for predation pressure that predation becomes somewhat incidental rather than causative in terms of its effect upon growth form.

HOST-PARASITE INTERACTIONS

"Workers with an appreciation of modern developments in biology are finding that infectious disease can be thought of with profit along ecological lines as a struggle for existence between man and microorganisms of the same general quality as many other types of competition between species in nature" (Burnet, 1940). "All living things have an ecology, and those producing disease are no exceptions. Some of the viruses may not be alive, yet their ecology, if one is permitted to use the word in this connection, is so similar to that of living things that they may for the purpose of this discussion be considered collectively with other infectious agents. . . . The behavior of infectious diseases in a population is nothing more than an expression of conflicts between various forms of life in an effort to arrive at a satisfactory equilibrium. . . . At least, my approach to epidemic diseases at the present time will be along biological and ecological lines" (Rivers, 1947).

These two quotations serve two functions as an introduction to our brief treatment of host-parasite interactions. First, they indicate that the modern medical epidemiologist views this problem in the same fundamental way as does the ecologist. The principal difference, apart from technical considerations, between the two groups of workers is that the epidemiologist of necessity works chiefly with one species of host population (man) and limits himself to parasites that are pathogenic upon that host and that, to a considerable extent, induce morbidity instead of mortality. The emergent principles are essentially similar in both cases. Owing to the nature of his methods the clinical epidemiologist must deal largely with blocks of data that accumulate after an epidemic has run its course ("descriptive epidemiology"). That is to say, he rarely has anything to say in advance about the controlled planning of the investigation. His method therefore is almost exclusively statistical.*

* W. H. Frost (1927) published an excellent essay that defines comprehensively and philosophically the science of epidemiology while at the same time critically discussing, then defending, the "circumstantial" character of epidemiological data. About the latter point Frost says: "Given sufficient scope and accuracy of observations, a conclusion as to the nature and spread of a disease may often be established quite firmly by circumstantial evidence well in advance of experimental confirmation."

The population ecologist, as exemplified particularly by certain economic entomologists, utilizes the statistical approach as well, but frequently employs experimentation as an additional analytical tool. Of recent years investigators motivated by clinical considerations have also turned to experimentation with notable reward. An excellent illustration is the work of Greenwood, who established epidemics of various diseases in colonies of laboratory rodents, studied the course of such epidemics under controlled conditions, and, observed host mortality (see especially Greenwood, Hill, Topley, and Wilson, 1936, and Wilson, 1945). The second point made by Burnet's and Rivers' quotations is the obvious implication that both the ecologist and the epidemiologist have much to learn from each other.

In addition to the two general approaches to host-parasite population interactions, there is also a theoretical, and largely mathematical, aspect. This is dealt with as a special instance of the interspecies competition problem by such authors as Lotka and Volterra (see pp. 271, 326, and 367). It has also received extended and more numerical treatment by Nicholson (1933) and Nicholson and Bailey (1935) and by Thompson (1939), who present somewhat divergent viewpoints.

Nicholson and Bailey attempted to formulate a comprehensive theory dealing with the competition that develops within animal populations, both within the same species and between distinct species, as they search for various necessities of life along with the relation of such competitions to population growth form. Thompson examines these ideas and is critical of certain of them, both on methodological and theoretical grounds. An extended discussion of their disagreement cannot be attempted here. There is, however, one basic assumption underlying the theory of Nicholson and Bailey, and attacked by Thompson, that, because of its general ecological interest, merits our attention. This is the hypothesis of "random searching." After making the obvious point that all organisms must obtain food, mates, and suitable niches in which to live, Nicholson and Bailey conclude that these are found *by populations* through a process of random, or completely unorganized, search. They conclude further that since organized search by populations is unknown among animals with the possible exception of certain territorial species, the concept of random search can be considered "a true fact of nature" and that the competitive pressures resulting from such search can be depicted by a curve of general application. Nicholson and Bailey differentiate carefully between the search by individuals and that by populations. They assert that even though the former may be systematic, the latter is random and follows a so-called "competition curve." This theoretical curve, as applied to population groups, is reproduced as Figure 133 and graphs "area

the theory of random searching is inconsistent with events as they occur in nature.

It will be remembered that Nicholson and Bailey concluded that even if individual population members searched systematically, the total searching effort exhibited by the population would still be random and would lead to the expectations shown in their competition curve (Fig. 133). In discussing this point Thompson says:

"This argument may apply to the searching *of areas* in the sense that though one animal may take care never to retrace his steps, or cross his own track, he may cross the track of

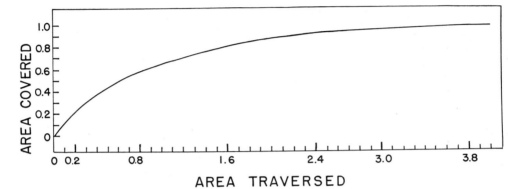

Fig. 133. The Nicholson-Bailey "competition curve." (After Nicholson.)

covered" on the ordinate against "area traversed" on the abscissa. By a further extension of this argument Nicholson and Bailey reach the reasonable opinion that as the intensity of competition increases, the success of an individual finding the things it seeks decreases. In other words, the amount of new area discovered as time goes on diminishes progressively according to the law for random distributions.

On the basis of an extended review of a literature largely concerned with the finding and exploitation of hosts by parasites, and on the basis of a lengthy theoretical argument, Thompson observes that animals "do not in general search the environment at random for things they require." This, he asserts, follows in part because nature is organized according to a system of "sign-posts" which correspond to the perceptive powers of the animal in question, and in part because these perceptive powers establish a definite connection between the animal and whatever it seeks that is, at least to some extent, independent of distance. In sum, Thompson feels that

others of the same species. It may apply also to the searching of *suitable environments,* because the visit of one animal to an environment may not prevent the visit of another animal to it at a later date. It does not, however, apply to the searching *for* environments. It is evident that if individuals do not search *for* suitable environments at random, then populations do not search *for* them at random either. The general property of non-random action belongs to the population, just as it belongs to the individual" (pp. 358 and 359).

This issue has been clarified and given more precise definition by Varley (1941).

Returning now more specifically to the topic of host-parasite interactions, we may develop this cursorily by presenting certain formal considerations that are utilized by the epidemiologists and then by reviewing several experimental studies that deal with host-parasite relations among insect populations.

Jordan and Burrows (1945) discuss host-parasite interactions from a population viewpoint. They say: "The infectious diseases of man constitute a series of special cases of the host-parasite relationship, differing from one another with respect to mode of transmission, incubation period, period of infectivity, immunity, case fatality, etc. The studies on infectious disease have taken two forms: one, the theoretical analysis of epidemic spread; and the other, the experimental investigation of controlled epidemics among populations of laboratory animals . . . " It is the analysis of epidemic spread that is reported here.

Considerable insight can be gained into the development of a single epidemic wave by a general, theoretical treatment of the dissemination of an infectious disease, provided certain simplifying assumptions are made. This can be approached, as did Frost (see Zinsser and Wilson, 1932), by an arithmetical method involving finite differences, or by methods based on the calculus, as did Soper (1929). We review here Frost's method as presented by Jordan and Burrows.

If $C =$ the number of cases reported for a particular disease, $S =$ the number of susceptible hosts, and $N =$ the contacts per twenty-four hour period, then the contact rate per day, r, is given by the formula

$$N = rCS \quad \text{or} \quad r = \frac{N}{CS}$$

The following assumptions are made: (1) that each case is infectious; (2) that one exposure contact produces the disease in an individual who is susceptible, and (3) that the twenty-four hour unit of time is short enough so that S and C do not change markedly during this interval. Granting these not unreasonable assumptions, the number of contacts per unit of time, t, is

$$Nt = rCSt$$

From this it follows that the probability of contact, p, is

$$p = \frac{Nt}{S} = rCt$$

and the probability of avoiding contact, q, is

$$q = 1 - p = 1 -$$

There are $1/t$ units of time for the entire period, and therefore the chance of avoiding contact over this period, Q, is

$$Q = (1 - rCt)^{\frac{1}{t}} = e^{-rC}$$

and the number of new cases infected during the twenty-four hour period, PS, is

$$PS = (1 - e^{-rC})S$$

Jordan and Burrows construct a hypothetical epidemic wave by substituting certain values in the last equation. First, they assume that the incubation period of the disease is twenty-four hours, or, in other words, "the contact of one day is the case of the next." They start with an illustrative population of 10,000 susceptibles, one case, and a contact rate, r, of 0.0002. For the first day the formula takes this form:

$$(1 - e^{-.0002}) \, 10,000 = 2 \, (\text{new cases})$$

For the second day: $(1 - e^{-.0006}) 9998 = 6$. For the third day: $(1 - e^{-.0018}) 9992 = 18$, and so on for the course of the complete epidemic wave. It is possible to introduce various modifications into this treatment e.g., the introduction of case fatality and the development of immunity, the extension of the incubation period, and so forth.

The significant point is that such a hypothetical epidemic shows "a remarkable similarity to observed epidemics of disease, and, although the factors entering into the determination of the value r are highly complex, it is evident that the probability of chance contact is a factor of primary importance in the evolution of the epidemic wave" (Jordan and Burrows). McKendrick (1940) has shown that if the host population consists largely or entirely of susceptibles, this probability of chance contact is high and the disease spreads rapidly. As the number of susceptibles is reduced through conversion to actual cases, fatalities, and immunes, the probability diminishes and the epidemic subsides.

A schematized representation of the course of an epidemic wave adopted from Jordan and Burrows is presented as Figure 134, in which the ordinate depicts numbers; the abscissa, time; the upper curve, numbers of susceptibles; and the lower curve, number of cases. The points made by this diagram are self-evident. They afford both an extension of our arithmetical example as well as a summary of this short discussion.

We now present several illustrations of host-parasite interactions among insect populations.

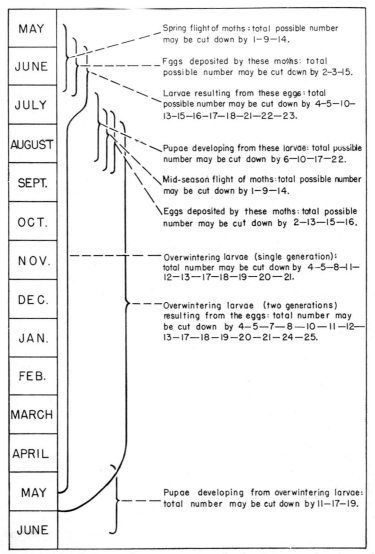

MAY — Spring flight of moths : total possible number may be cut down by 1—9—14.

JUNE — Eggs deposited by these moths: total possible number may be cut down by 2-3-15.

JULY — Larvae resulting from these eggs: total possible number may be cut down by 4—5—10—13—15—16—17—18—21—22—23.

AUGUST — Pupae developing from these larvae: total possible number may be cut down by 6—10—17—22.

SEPT. — Mid-season flight of moths: total possible number may be cut down by 1—9—14.

OCT. — Eggs deposited by these moths: total possible number may be cut down by 2—13—15—16.

NOV. — Overwintering larvae (single generation): total number may be cut down by 4—5—8—11—12—13—17—18—19—20—21.

DEC. — Overwintering larvae (two generations) resulting from the eggs: total number may be cut down by 4—5—7—8—10—11—12—13—17—18—19—20—21—24—25.

JAN.

FEB.

MARCH

APRIL

MAY — Pupae developing from overwintering larvae: total number may be cut down by 11—17—19.

JUNE

Fig. 137. The life cycle of the cornborer in New England. The numerals refer to factors tabulated in the text that affect the population's abundance. (After Barber.)

already made and as an illustration of the fact that more than one environmental factor typically acts on a particular population process.

Barber stresses, as was documented in the last chapter, that many insect populations vary markedly in abundance from year to year and that much is to be gained when the reasons for this variability are understood. He concludes that such information is of assistance in planning effective measures of control for insect pests. His work on the corn borer centered in the New England states, where the population growth form during the early nineteen-twenties is well known. During 1923 a sharp decline in the general population occurred which carried over into 1924, and it is with the factors responsible for this decline that Barber is particularly concerned.

Barber's study will be developed, first, by outlining the life cycle of the corn borer; second, by listing the known environmental factors that influence the populations; and, third, by showing the method by which, and time at which, these factors operate in producing their effects.

The life cycle of the corn borer is best understood by reference to Figure 137.

The moths have a spring flight in the mid-May to early July interval. They then oviposit from late May to mid-July. These eggs hatch into larvae, the earliest of which appear about the first of June. These larvae result from the early moth flights with their subsequent oviposition. The larvae continue to hatch through July, and pupae are present from early July until early September. The larvae that hatch late in the season do not pupate, but overwinter in the larval stage to become pupae during late April through mid-June of the following year. The first batch of pupae, however, pass through their development rapidly and provide the new generation of moths during the mid-July to mid-September interval (year I). These also have a flight and lay second generation eggs, which complete hatching by mid-September. All the second generation larvae overwinter, which means that there are no second generation pupae formed during the first year. Pupation of the second generation larvae, along with the late, first generation residue, occurs in the late April to mid-June period of the following spring. The eclosion of these pupae produces the adult moths that start the new year's reproductive cycle.

Barber classifies the factors that limit the seasonal abundance of New England corn borer populations into these major groups: weather, enemies, agricultural practice and control, overpopulation, and change in "preferred" host plant availability. Of these, the first group is primarily density-independent; the second and fourth are primarily density-dependent; and the third and fifth have elements of both. The list follows:

WEATHER:
1. Heavy winds and rains destroying moths
2. Heavy winds and rains preventing moths from depositing a normal number of eggs
3. Unfavorable temperature causing moths to deposit a smaller number of eggs
4. Heavy drought resulting in lowered egg fertility
5. Heavy rains resulting in the destruction of newly hatched larvae before they have had time to bore in
6. The seasonal proportion of individuals that have only a single generation
7. The abundance of larvae that fail to become full grown before feeding is discontinued because of cold weather
8. Winter mortality of overwintering larvae

ENEMIES:
Birds:
9. Feeding on moths
10. Removing the insect from burrows in the growing plant
11. Feeding on the overwintering larvae
Mammals:
12. Mice feeding on the overwintering larvae
Insect Predators:
13. Heteroptera and other predaceous insects feeding on larvae
14. Asilidae (robber flies) and other predators feeding on adult moths
15. Miscellaneous egg predators
Insect Parasites:
16. *Trichogramma minutum* (chalcid fly) parasitic on eggs
17. Miscellaneous native parasites feeding on larvae and pupae
18. Disease of the larvae

AGRICULTURAL PRACTICE AND CONTROL MEASURES:
19. Burning of crop refuse containing larvae
20. Plowing under infested corn stubble in the fall
21. Feeding infested corn stalks to cattle
22. Early planting of trap crops
23. Delayed planting of corn
24. OVERPOPULATION
25. CHANGE IN "PREFERRED" OR OPTIMAL HOST PLANT AVAILABILITY

The meaning of the majority of these twenty-five items is self-evident, but a few comments are appropriate. Item 3 refers to the fact that if night temperatures get much below the optimum range ($66°$ to $68°$ F.) during the period of flight, as happened to the midsummer brood of 1923 when the mean temperature was $57.6°$ F., fecundity is lowered. Item 5 refers to instances in which first instar larvae drown or are washed away by rainfall before they can tunnel into the corn stalks and there gain protection. Item 6 refers to the fact that in certain years there is a greater proportion of single than of double generations for one reason or another, and this contributes to decline.

Item 22 describes a corn borer control practice in which strips of corn are purposely planted early in the year. These particular plants function as oviposition sites for moths during their first flight period, and thus they become a reservoir for a considerable portion of the eggs of the local population. After this oviposition the corn is destroyed. If the time of planting the main corn crop is delayed (Item 23) so that the plants appear above the surface after many of the moths have flown, a population reduction ensues because the moths are forced to seek less favorable food plants in which to lay their eggs. This measure is most effective when combined with the planting of trap crops.

During years of excessive corn borer abundance, such as that of 1922, a larval overpopulation (Item 24) results, frequently attaining a density of one to two million individuals per acre of corn. This is so severe that the corn is reduced to mere shells by larval feeding, and many of the borers die of starvation. Overpopulation thus functions as a self-check when abundance outstrips resources. Item 25 refers to the practice of rotating weed crops on fields, which crops are progressively less favorable for the borers than the corn plant itself and thus gradually reduce the pests' numbers by this means.

Barber worked out a pattern showing how these twenty-five items affect the various stages of the corn borer life cycle and thereby bring about population decline. He was not able, on the other hand, to evaluate the relative, quantitative weight in terms of number or percentage of individuals lost that a certain factor actually exerted in a particular year. The latter demonstration would be instructive, indeed, but, in its absence, much is to be gained by examining the pattern. This is summarized in Figure 137, in which the numbers appearing after the various life cycle stages pertain to the specific items.

A tabulation of the items reported in Figure 137 indicates that there are sixteen instances in which "weather" operates to reduce the size of the corn borer population; twenty-eight instances in which "enemies" are effective; eleven instances of "agricultural practice and control;" one, of "overpopulation," and one, of "change in host plant availability." This tabulation, of course, tells nothing about whether item 8, say, is more, or less, destructive than item 11; it only indicates that both are functioning. In fact, Barber reached the conclusion that the decrease of the population noted in 1923 and 1924 was caused "by an association of factors, some of major importance, others contributory but increased in value through the effect of the major limiting factors."

Abundant corn borer infestations would be explained on the basis either that there is a generally low level of effect contributed by all the listed items, or else that a particularly severe effect contributed by one or several of the items only would need to be offset by an unusually slight contribution on the part of the others. Sparse corn borer infestations would be explained by an especially stringent combination of several items—as, for example, two, eight, seventeen, and eighteen—or a generally effective combination of most of them, or by an aggressive program of control.

It is interesting, and possibly suggestive, that apart from these man-instituted control measures, Barber was able to identify density-independent and density-dependent items in about equal numbers. It is not possible to suggest whether or not this generalization is true for most natural populations. Additional, comprehensive research is needed to clarify the point, research concerned especially with the population as a whole interpreted in so far as possible in its complete, spatial, and temporal, effective environment. From our point of view Barber's study has both raised and answered questions, but it has proved most useful as an illustration of such a "total ecosystem" approach.

It is relevant to quote briefly from Stirrett (1938), who also investigated corn borer populations in some detail twelve years later than did Barber. Stirrett says (p. 681):

"The factors causing population fluctuations are complex, and in many cases, interdependent. The important factors, however, causing fluctuations in borer population have been found to be initial moth population, larval survival, egg production, egg mortality, pupal mortality and corn refuse clean-up. Temperature, especially temperature of certain definite characteristics, has been shown to have a great influence upon most of these factors, but especially upon the rate of larval establishment, pupal mortality, egg mortality, and the number of eggs produced."

For a more recent study devoted to an analysis something like that of Barber's, but with a greater theoretical content, the reader is referred to Varley (1947).

POPULATION INTEGRATION

Before closing this chapter, it is desirable to draw some of the points together. If there is any validity to the concept that a population is an objective biological entity, and, granting that considerable knowledge exists about populations, it should be possible to assemble this knowledge in some form from which will emerge a picture of population integrative mech-

based on information gained from many sources. It should be stressed also that the diagram is merely a highly generalized, illustrative tool and obviously not a com-

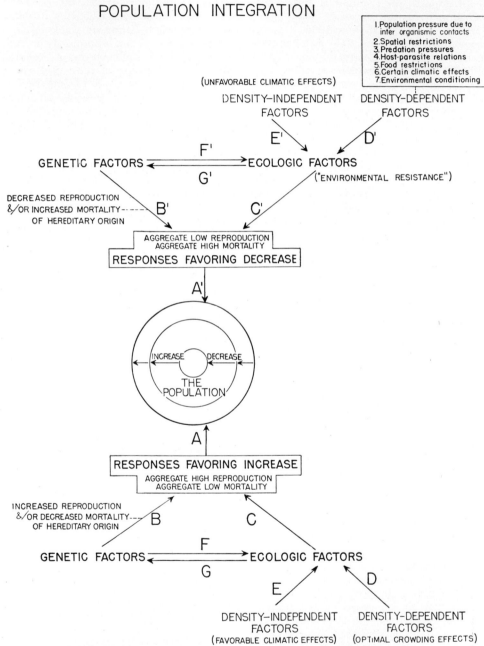

Fig. 138. A schematic representation of the interplay of factors that affect populations.

anisms. Figure 138 is an elementary attempt at such synthesis, and the discussion following centers on this diagram. Nothing unique is claimed for the figure, which is

plete, detailed representation of population factors and their interplay.

It is to be noted that the figure has a fundamental symmetry. The operations are so depicted that one family of factors contributing to population decline is balanced by another family of basically similar origin, either ecologic or genetic, contributing to population increase. Thus, the letters without prime superscripts (e.g., A, C, D, E) are associated in one way or another with growth, while those with superscripts (e.g., A', C', D', E') are associated with decline. The arrows may be thought of as "population pressures" that are cumulative. For example, A' has a B' and C' component; C', a D' and E' component, and so on.

The figure is drawn to focus attention on population size, which, as discussed earlier (p. 305), is a meaningful end index of population activity. The population is represented as a circle of particular area at any particular moment, whose circumference enlarges or contracts with changes in the natality-mortality relations symbolized by arrows A and A'. The population may fluctuate between a lowest attainable size below which it would become extinct and a highest attainable size above which its excess members could not be supported by the exploitable potentialities of its environment. The size of the circle is fixed for any stated time because of an existing balance between all the factors that operate in its expansion and those that operate in its contraction.

In the final analysis, if dispersal is excluded, all changes in population size result from the interaction of reproductive performance with mortality (see p. 272). Other things being equal, high birth rate and low death rate favor increase. Since these factors are population or group attributes, they must be viewed in aggregate terms, as suggested in the diagram.

The diagram further suggests that ecological factors capable of affecting population size through their influence on reproductivity and mortality fall into the category of density-independent and density-dependent factors. These, having been discussed in detail, need no further treatment here beyond pointing out that both sets of factors may be potent, yet different in mode of action. In a broad sense, density-independent factors appear to set the limits of possible abundance for a population in its physical habitat, besides inducing particular changes in density; while density-dependent factors, operating primarily through competition, appear to regulate population density through time, thereby achieving whatever condition of equilibrium or "balance" actually obtains.

There are at least two ways in which genetic factors can influence population size. They may directly affect natality and reproduction, as has been demonstrated for certain species. Also, the genetic composition of a population may influence the mode of response of that population to its particular environment.

Although Figure 138 stresses the relations of natality and mortality to population growth form, it does not imply that high reproductivity is necessarily associated with low mortality, or the converse. There are, of course, many possible intergradations, both in theory and in fact, between these factors. However, it is clear that for population growth to obtain, A must exceed A'.

Other formulations from the diagram of change in size can be set forth symbolically as follows:

Equilibrium: A essentially equal to A'

Fluctuation: $A > A' > A > A'$, and so on in time

Decline: A' consistently greater than A

The figure shows further that population size is not explained when one merely discusses natality and mortality. These responses, as end products, are intimately under the control of the genetic and ecological factors that emerge from the reciprocal interaction between the population and its environment. In the diagram the arrows represent pressures or lines of force that stem from specific operations. Their character, symmetry, and interrelations form the basis of population integration.

In its treatment and focus on reproduction the pattern proposed in Figure 138 is somewhat modified from that usually presented. The point can be made as follows. In the writings of Chapman (1928), Gause (1934), Smith (1935), as well as in the rationalization underlying the logistic curve, reproduction has been dealt with as a sort of species or group "constant"* that

* The "b" constant of the logistic equation; "reproductive potential" of Chapman; "potential reproductive capacity" of Smith. A novel method of empirically determining "biotic potential" has been proposed by Birch (1945).

has a certain potential, maximal value. When a mortality component is subtracted from this highest possible rate of reproduction, the difference represents the actual size of the population at that moment. Such a mortality component is under the control of "environmental resistance" (Chapman, 1928), which induces the mortality and can be factored into density-independent and density-dependent influences.

This situation can be restated somewhat as follows:

Population growth = potential reproduction — environmental resistance.

This is a highly useful representation, particularly for the mathematician, since it helps him keep a situation already highly complex as simple as possible. H. S. Smith states the case well when, in discussing the reproductive potential concept, he says:[*] "It seems to me that this is a useful concept even though largely theoretical. If we wish to measure the effect of the environment on populations, is it not easier to work with the interaction of one constant and one variable, than with two variables? I do not see that the concept of a maximum reproductive capacity does any great violence to sound biological reasoning even though it is difficult to measure."

To return to Figure 138. Here it can be seen that reproduction is not viewed as a constant of maximal value, and mortality is not treated as a factor that is always *increased* by environmental influence. Rather, it is suggested that both natality and mortality can fluctuate from a high to a low value and that certain environmental and genetic influences affect these rates in either a positive or a negative direction. Population shifts still are explained as a function of birth rate minus death rate. But the focus is placed as much on the variability in reproductive performance as on mortality. While we have no quarrel with the more simplified point of view as a pragmatic device, we do believe that the interplay schematized in the diagram is more in accordance with the evidence and therefore more descriptive of actual population workings.

Earlier in this chapter examples were presented that deal with the following aspects stylized in the diagram. These are:

[*] Personal communication.

1. Density-independent factors favoring population decrease; the contribution of E' to C'
2. Density-independent factors favoring population increase; the contribution of E to C
3. Density-dependent factors favoring population decrease; the contribution of D' to C'
4. Density-dependent factors favoring population increase; the contribution of D to C

These require no further discussion here.

What, then, *is* integration at this infrasocial level? Obviously it is the interaction of pressures caused by categories of factors of the type represented in the figure without indicating whether they are additive or multiplicative. These pressures are statistical in the sense that they arise from group phenomena. A particular pressure grows out of a particular operation. It merges with another that is closely related. These in turn join with others and finally emerge as a pressure such as A or A' that is the product of many factors and performs some major function in the population. These pressures are integrated in the sense that, as in an organism, change in one affects another and always results in some compensatory regulation in the system. There is nothing inherently mystical in this statement. If more complete data were available about a certain population, it should be possible to express the integration in arithmetical terms. To a great extent we have been able to treat here a problem that is basically quantitative in qualitative terms only. Our inadequacies probably are related largely to incomplete information rather than to any lack of validity of the population as a biological unit. Perhaps when more data exist we can apply to them a statistical method that takes account of the correlations between factors and evaluates the contribution one factor makes toward a particular response. This is a multiple regression problem and possibly can be analyzed by Wright's (1921) path coefficient solution. Even now we might assign arbitrary values to our diagram and obtain a stylized, numerical illustration of integration.

Despite the fact that the population has been discussed in statistical terms, it does not follow that populations are statistical rather than biological units. The fact is that they are both. It is not our purpose to suggest that, while integration in the organism is biological, integration in the population is statistical, and that therefore the two are not in any sense comparable. This would be fallacious. The operations of populations are equally biological, but typically need to be expressed in statistical terms. Evolution is recognized as one of the truly great concepts of biology, yet the theory of evolution is populational in character and is best treated statistically. The population has attributes of its constituent organisms—reproduction, death, metabolism, irritability, growth and differentiation, a genetic make-up, environmental adaptation and adjustment—but in its existence as an integrated group these attributes appear as the aggregate (or some modification of this) of individual responses. From this there emerges an integrated unit that attains a new biological status, which can be studied and analyzed. This new level has properties uniquely its own in addition to those of its parts.

Many of these properties take statistical form (see Chap. 18); for example, a birth rate or a death rate, or a gene-frequency heredity, are population attributes depending on the fact that organisms reproduce, die, and have a genetic constitution; but meaningless when applied to an organism.

If the population attains a certain level, it may become by definition "social," even emerging with a division of labor among its members (p. 435). This reaches its height of development among the social insects, in which castes are actual morphological expressions of populational division of labor with a whole series of physiological, anatomical, and behavioristic adjustments superimposed upon the general population features that in turn are superimposed upon organismic features (for a discussion of social populations, see Emerson, 1939a). This question receives special attention in the two chapters that follow.

23. ANIMAL AGGREGATIONS

Contagious distributions are the rule in nature (cf. p. 365). Sessile as well as motile animals settle or collect in favorable localities, especially when the optimal niches are limited in extent. Often the aggregations do not occupy all the space that appears equally favorable. The observations of naturalists demonstrated long ago that the collecting together of animals is a common occurrence, and aggregations often reported include the following among many others:

1. Hibernating or aestivating groups
2. Overnight aggregations
3. Collections about food
4. Aggregations on suitable but limited substrate
5. Concentrations in shelter niches
6. Breeding aggregations
7. Partial or complete family groups

A fairly complete list of animal aggregations is given by Allee (1931, Chap. II). The more dramatic assemblages have attracted especial notice, and naturalists' records abound in both casual mention and more careful description of unusually large or dense animal aggregations at all phylogenetic levels.

Oligotrophic lakes and rivers are notoriously less dense in populations than are bays and sounds along marine coasts, but such paucity does not extend to all inland waters. Near San Francisco, during the breeding season, ponds may be paved with pebble-like clusters of salamander eggs. In mid-Great Salt Lake, where the water is over 22 per cent salt, one finds surface-covering masses of aggregated *Ephydra*, and, in season, some 370,000,000 of these flies are to be found along each mile of Salt Lake beach. In nearby mountain ponds of low salt content, ostracods of the size of pin heads aggregate in groups as large as a walnut, one aggregation to each of the cow tracks that stipple the pond bottoms. Similar collections of annelid worms may occur in Indiana ponds. The concentrations of hydra, in favorable places and seasons, along Lake Michigan almost resemble the abundance of small marine hydroids in similar habitats along the shores of Cape Cod; and in some portions of spring-fed water cress swamps, the supply of planarian worms seems inexhaustible.

Some of us have gathered adult may

flies by the double handfuls from near electric lights along Lake Erie, and hibernating aggregations of ladybird beetles are even larger and more widely distributed. A flight of a chrysomelid beetle is on record that formed a belt 15 feet thick and 100 yards wide that continued for two days. Similar concentrations of various butterflies and of migratory locusts are well known. Massed populations of bats, of various birds and mammals, including the emigrating hordes of lemmings, help round out a hurried survey that will not be even approximately complete without mentioning the dense shoals of marine fishes or the water-coloring masses of smaller aquatic organisms, including various protozoans, copepods, and the euphausid crustaceans of the southern ocean. Dampier wrote of these lobster-krills in 1700: "We saw great sholes of small lobsters which colored the sea red in spots for a mile in compass" (vide Matthews, 1932).

With this rich background of naturalistic lore, it is rather surprising to find that ecologists were slow in bringing forward statistical proof of the common existence of contagious distributions of animals. One of the more complete of these, although by no means the first, that by Cole (1946), was reviewed in the foregoing chapter (p. 364). Aggregations of animals are a special phase of population density, and the preceding discussion of principles and problems related to density form a needed background for the present treatment.

FORMATION OF AGGREGATIONS

The least social animal aggregations are represented by more or less accidental collections. For example, animal-drift lines occur along the margins of many bodies of water. These accumulations are particularly noticeable on the sandy beaches of the Great Lakes, where they may extend for miles. In the animal drift near the margin of Lake Michigan one may find sizable collections of aquatic snails, small bivalves, crayfish, or even fishes thrown up by the waves. Similar concentrations of insects are also deposited with many of the individuals still alive. These may have been carried out over the lake by an offshore breeze, then caught in the water and tossed back on the land by currents and waves. So far as the different individuals are concerned, their aggregation is entirely accidental.

They may remain aggregated through inability to move or as a result of inertia. In themselves, these aggregations are near the zero mark for sociality; even the quality of inertia shown under such conditions has only slight social significance, if any.

The animal collections along the drift line are a source of food for diverse animals, making what has been called, in the nontechnical language of nature study, the "lunch counter" of the beach. The life histories of some insects fit the rough periodicity of recurrent storms that replenish the animal drift (Herms, 1907). Predaceous and scavenger insects, and some birds and mammals, including skunks, feed on the animal drift (Shelford, 1913).

Animals congregate under diverse conditions as a result of their own movements. Perhaps the simplest of a long, intricate series of types of aggregating behavior results from so-called kineses, that is, from the unoriented reflex action of the whole animal. Thus animals that are stimulated by high light intensity slow down when they enter shaded areas. If many are moving about in a given locality, such photokinesis will cause them to aggregate in the shade somewhat as automobiles, moving freely along a through highway, aggregate automatically when slowed by entering a village or by encountering other agencies that locally reduce their rate of movement.

Aggregations result from oriented reactions to light intensities, or to various gradients of environmental forces, when an oriented reaction brings numbers of individuals into a restricted region. A positive response to odors, leading animals to a restricted source of food, affords a common example. The collected forms must have a certain amount of toleration for the presence of, often for contact with, other individuals if the aggregations are to occur and particularly if they are to continue.

In contrast with the more or less automatic aggregation in response to odors, light or shade, moisture, favorable niches, and other environmental factors, there are the much more definitely social situations (p. 419) in which animals collect as a result of positive reaction to the presence of others like themselves. The aggregation of male midges "dancing" in the quiet atmosphere, or the formation of schools of fishes or flocks of birds illustrates this widespread phenomenon.

GROUP SURVIVAL VALUES

GENERAL CONCEPTS

We can now introduce an important set of ideas. Helpful interactions between organisms are evidence of the existence of *cooperation** (Allee, 1931), or at least of proto-cooperation, even in the simplest ecosystems; cooperation is accepted in this sense by Clements and Shelford (1939). Opposing, harmful tendencies may be termed *disoperation*. The two sets of processes are in fundamental opposition. With all lower forms of animal life, and often with higher ones, including man, such cooperation or disoperation is wholly nonconscious. The nonconscious character of the effects and of their underlying causation is especially evident in poorly integrated assemblages in which man is not represented. This consideration does not affect the fundamental nature of the resulting disoperation or cooperation. It is essential to remember that, possible neutral effects aside, the survival values in biotic ecosystems illustrate in simplest terms the basic social antithesis between beneficial (cooperative) and harmful (disoperative) relationships.

Competition furnishes a special phase both of cooperation and of disoperation. In general, competition occurs when there is a common demand on a limited supply. Among other situations, this criterion applies to the competition of two males for the same mate, of animals with similar food habits for a limited food supply, of organisms in general for limited ecological niches.

Competition frequently results in disoperation, although the two are not synonymous. Two protozoans in a drop culture are often in competition for a limited amount of food. The competition may result in the stunting or death of both, or in one surviving at the expense of the other.

Cooperative competition also is known. An example is furnished by the mass physiology of the spermatozoa of sea urchins. In nature, these spermatozoa, like those of

* Many aspects of proto-cooperation may be called physiological facilitation, and the entire spread between proto-cooperation and conscious cooperative social life at the human level is bridged by the addition of the concepts of biosocial and psycho-social facilitation (p. 410; Schneirla, 1946; Allee, 1949).

many other marine organisms, are shed into sea water where they may fertilize the eggs that have been similarly shed. In making sperm suspensions for experimental use, the male sea urchin is placed upside down in a clean, dry watch glass. If sexually "ripe," the spermatozoa flow out through the aboral genital pores in a viscous mass. Sperm so collected is called "dry" sperm, since it is undiluted with sea water. The massed spermatozoa of many animals, sea urchins among them, live longer and retain their fertilizing power longer than do those in diluted sperm suspensions. When the spermatozoa are shed in a mass into sea water, those near the center are activated last, and such sperm retain fertilizing power longer than if all were activated at once on escaping from the body.

The physiological processes involved are complex, but at least a part of the greater longevity of the crowded sperm mass comes from the fact that the individual spermatozoa do not move when closely packed together, as in "dry" sea urchin sperm. Also, they are relaxed under these crowded conditions, in contrast with being highly active when diluted with sea water. The relaxation is indicated by the fact that the rate of respiration of the same number of spermatozoa is much greater when the sperm are less crowded.

It seems reasonable to assume that inactivity of densely packed spermatozoa results from the lack of free space. Over a considerable range of dilution the specific activity of a spermatozoon is directly related to the cube root of the volume of sea water in which a given number of spermatozoa are suspended. Under such conditions the total initial activity is proportional to the number of sperms present and to the average amount of free space for each. If the available space is much restricted, the competition for it results in inhibition of movement, a lowering of the rate of oxygen consumption, and a conservation of essential diffusible materials; and all this is accompanied by a decided increase in longevity. Competition here has distinctly beneficial results for all the competitors; it is cooperative, as contrasted with being disoperative. This is an important consideration for general ecology, the more so since all the individuals in the sperm mass benefit from the competition.

Under more usual conditions of competition, not all individuals benefit, and yet the end result may be favorable for the species under consideration; that is to say, the final outcome even of such competition is not necessarily disoperative.

Certain aspects of survival values, and other physiological effects associated with aggregations of animals, are summarized by the curves of Fig. 139. Curve A shows results of biological processes in which the

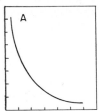 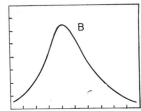

Fig. 139. In some phases of population physiology the optimum population is the smallest possible (A); in others it is intermediate in size (B). (Modified from Allee.)

highest recorded value is given by the smallest possible population. A pig born as a litter of one normally grows faster than do members of larger litters, and this is a common relation for many animals. Other illustrations of curve A have been provided in preceding chapters (cf. p. 347).

In contrast, grouped animals often show increased efficiency that is sometimes reflected in longer survival, or better growth, if neither too few or too many animals are present; they have an optimal population density at some intermediate point of the possible range of numbers. This situation is summarized by Figure 139, B. In both A and B the rate of action of the measured process is indicated on the vertical axis, and population density on the horizontal axis, with the least crowded conditions shown to the left. Under conditions summarized by curve B, life processes move faster or more favorably as the population increases until an optimum density is reached. Beyond the optimum a further increase in density produces a reversal of the observed trend. The left-hand limb of the curve represents unconscious cooperation, but after the peak is past, disoperation becomes steadily more and more the dominant effect.

Consideration of the two curves and of the phenomena on which they are based indicates correctly that under most conditions overcrowding produces harmful results. This fact has long been known and can be verified easily. The existence of harmful results associated with undercrowding is a more recent and less well-known discovery.

OVERCROWDING

Disoperations from intense overcrowding are nearly or quite universal. Pending direct experimentation, it is usually impossible to determine the population density at which such disoperations will be initiated. Some of the types of harmful effects include reduced fecundity (Pearl and Parker, 1922; Robertson and Sang, 1944); retarded cleavage of eggs (Allee and Evans, 1937; Merwin, 1945); slowed asexual reproduction of protozoans (Woodruff, 1911; Mast and Pace, 1946); decreased growth rate of individuals (Winsor and Winsor, 1935; Foerster, 1944). Animals from an overcrowded population are often stunted, and an inverse relation usually exists, at higher population densities, between numbers present and size attained (Davidson and Vaughn, 1941).

The more readily observed ecological factors promoting these disoperations include the reduction of available food, the accumulation of excreta and of their decomposition products, and the physical or chemical alteration of the medium or substrate. Diseases spread more rapidly through a dense population than through a sparse but otherwise comparable one (Greenwood, 1932), and parasites pass more freely from host to host under crowded conditions (Hegner, Root, Augustine, and Huff, 1938).

Deleterious effects associated with dense populations may result from direct contact between individuals, from indirect contact through the mutual environment, from some other sort of environmental conditioning, or from all acting together. Certain of these matters have been discussed at some length in previous pages (346–349) and need no elaboration here. In their long experience with experimental studies on the effect of population density —studies directed primarily toward exploring phenomena associated with undercrowding—Allee and his associates have always been able readily to demonstrate ill effects resulting from overdense populations. There can be no doubt that overcrowding is normally harmful, both under natural and experimental conditions.

Modern interest centers as well on the importance of the phenomena associated with undercrowding. It is this set of phenomena that Allee has steadily interpreted as providing evidence for the broad principles of nonconscious proto-cooperation (1945 and citations, 1947). These matters will be summarized at some length in the following pages.

NATURAL COOPERATION

Much of the physiological determination of unconscious disoperation, as contrasted with proto-cooperation, depends on surface-mass relations roughly similar to those that underly the operation of Bergmann's rule concerning body size of warm-blooded animals in relation to environmental temperature (p. 119). The surface of a globular object increases as the square, while the mass increases as the cube of its diameter. These surface-mass ratios hold for animal aggregations as well as for individual organisms. The disoperations of overcrowding take place when the mass is overlarge for its surface, even when suitable divisions of labor have evolved. Contrariwise, cooperation develops with increasing bulk as long as the resulting decrease in surface-to-mass ratio is beneficial. Many primitive cooperations of animal groups result from the operation of this relatively simple principle.

EVIDENCE FROM PHYLOGENY
AND EMBRYOLOGY

Protozoans usually separate when they divide asexually. The asexually produced descendents of a single cell (energid) may be regarded as being comparable with the whole body of a many-celled animal, except that among most Protozoa, each cell is free from all others. With some protozoans, like *Volvox*, the cells do not separate, and colonies result. Among other changed relations that accompany such a relatively simple collection of attached cells, the ratio of surface to bulk of the colonies differs decidedly from that of separate cells. Each cell in a temporary or permanent aggregation or in a multicellular organism presents less surface to the outside world than does one that leads an independent existence. As a result, the danger of harmful exposure to environmental effects is decreased, and, on the other hand, the difficulty of respiration, of individual food getting, and of receiving external stimuli is increased. Enlarged bulk, beyond some threshold, requires the functional differentiation of parts to become more varied and effective.

The evidence for automatic cooperation from evolution and normal embryology tends to be circumstantial. Direct evidence is readily derived from studies in experimental embryology and regeneration. One common embryological experiment is to transplant a small piece cut from a young chick blastoderm onto a blood-rich membrane of an older embryo. The egg is sealed and incubation is continued. Before hatching time, the egg is again opened, and the transplant is recovered and studied. If the grafted piece is too large, it does not receive sufficient blood supply and degenerates. Up to an optimal size, the larger the transplanted part, the higher the percentage of successful grafts and the better they grow. There is much similar evidence from comparable experiments on diverse species from varied phyla.

Many of the simpler animals have remarkable powers of regeneration of lost parts. Usually a fairly large number of cells must be left together in order for the operated animals to survive. Some sponges and other relatively uncomplicated forms can reconstitute multicellular organisms after the complete mechanical separation of their constituent cells (Wilson, 1907), provided the isolated elements can wander together and form clumps of sufficient size. Under one set of experimental conditions, complete reconstitution of a sponge occurred in aggregates of about 2000 cells. Those with only forty to 500 cells did not regenerate (Galtsoff, 1925).

The failure of the smaller aggregates to develop appears to result from their lack of enough food reserve to tide over the period of reorganization when feeding is impossible. The smaller ratio of surface to total bulk in these larger, successful aggregates is also a factor, since it is associated with reduced exposure of any given cell to bacterial and protozoan attack. Aggregates of good size frequently withstand conditions that destroy the smaller ones, yet still larger masses fail because of poor internal respiration.

The successful evolution of colonial protozoans from their single-celled progenitors was probably similarly affected both by better distribution of food stored in some of the cells and by the reduced surface-bulk ratio of the colonial forms. Such evolution occurred many times within the phylum Protozoa. Similar forces probably acted in the evolution of the many-celled primitive metazoan stock from their one-celled ancestors. Partially organized aggregations of protozoan cells supplied the basis from which all higher animals have evolved. Natural selection was a screening agency throughout this evolution, and an important basis for selection—in addition to more highly involved sexual reproduction and other advances in specialized physiology and anatomy—was the added safety in the presence of optimal numbers of cells with the concomitant values furnished by a favorable ratio of surface to mass.

MODIFICATION OF THE ENVIRONMENT

A biologically conditioned medium such as water in which fish have lived may produce beneficial results on later inhabitants, even of the same species (p. 355; Allee, 1938). Contrariwise, media surrounding populations, especially around dense populations, may become deleterious (p. 352). Sometimes the results produced are specific and not necessarily simple in interpretation so far as survival values are concerned. Thus the release into culture medium of an antibiotic "killer" substance by certain stocks of *Paramecium aurelia* has positive survival value for the "killers" and negative value for associated sensitive stocks (Sonneborn, 1947; Austin, 1948 and citations).

Many animal aggregations retard the rate of temperature changes in their midst; other aggregations generate, as well as conserve, heat, even though they are composed of partially or wholly poikilothermal forms. The well-known winter cluster of honeybees is a case in point. Protection against cold for aggregations of warm-blooded animals is diagrammatically illustrated by the better survival of closely massed coveys of the bobwhite quail (*Colinus virginianus*). At night, in cold weather, or when not feeding in daytime, the birds form a compact circle facing out-ward with their tails toward the center; they sit wing to wing (Gerstell, 1939).

The quail huddle is tighter in colder weather; with large coveys, some perch on the backs of others, forming a two-story circle. Laboratory tests under artificially produced weather conditions show that isolated birds and those in small coveys are killed by low temperatures, and that members of larger groups withstand severe temperatures in fair to good condition. In addition to the possible survival values of the supposed confusion effect when a bobwhite covey suddenly takes wing—explodes in all directions, so to speak—huddling behavior is warmth saving and, in severe winter weather, has definite life-saving values. In heat conservation, huddling of bobwhites gives another illustration of the bulk-surface rule, applied this time to an aggregation of birds.

Light-sensitive animals survive exposure to lethal illumination longer, other things being equal, if present in sufficient numbers so that now one, now another, is shaded. The situation is not simple, since fresh-water planarian worms withstand ultraviolet radiation better if several are exposed together even though no shading occurs (Allee and Wilder, 1939).

The protective value of relatively reduced surface in relation to increased mass has been demonstrated repeatedly for aggregated animals exposed to toxic materials (p. 360). Similar relations hold with increased numbers—up to optimal populations—even when the exposed animals do not collect in a compact, surface-reducing mass.

OTHER SURFACE-MASS RELATIONS

Much more complicated examples of the importance of surface-mass relations are found in the reaction of certain ungulates when attacked by potential predators. An illustration will make the point. When a group of the American pronghorn is attacked by wolves, if twelve to fifteen or more pronghorns are present, the animals form a defensive band that presents a minimum group surface, and the bucks are enabled to fight off the attackers. When the local population falls below this critical level, the animals fail to collect when attacked, but rather stampede, presenting much exposed surface to their enemies, and the weaker prongbuck are readily killed by wolves or by coyotes (Leopold, 1933).

One final illustration will introduce a still more complicated aspect of surface-mass relations, this time at a psycho-social level. Among human populations, interesting examples of the working of this principle are furnished by various kinds of cultural "islands" surrounded by people of different beliefs or social patterns. Mennonite communities in rural North America provide one such test. In earlier decades, when travel was difficult and communication with other colonies was limited, rural Mennonite colonies needed a minimum of about fifty families to maintain a socially secure community with a reasonably certain future. A Mennonite population of this size permits the basic community services —those furnished by shoeshop, barbershop, general store, as well as the common church and school—all to be in Mennonite hands. Under favorable pioneer conditions, forty families could keep such a community going, but the smaller group was usually more vulnerable. Below about forty families, inbreeding on the one hand, and more numerous "outside" contacts, including marriages, with non-Mennonites on the other, became more and more disruptive with decreasing numbers. In a way this is a sociological application of the group-surface to group-mass relationship that we have seen previously in simpler patterns. An upper safe population size also exists in Mennonite colonies above which their system of congregational organization and lay ministry does not function well; also intracolony rivalries are more likely to produce disruption when the groups are larger. Even under present day conditions of travel and communication, oversmall Mennonite colonies are vulnerable, although congregations of twenty to twenty-five families can survive, provided they maintain close contacts with their coreligionists in other communities.*

In brief general summary: Many of the protective values furnished by animal aggregations depend on the reduced amount of surface in relation to total mass that characterizes aggregated animals as contrasted with a similar number of scattered, isolated individuals. The mass protection

* Personal communication from Mr. P. C. Hiebert and Mr. J. W. Fretz of the Mennonite Central Committee.

ranges from relatively simple physico-chemical relations, protection from bacteria, or from predators, to human situations in which the aggregated colony has fewer contacts with outsiders who represent a different and a dominant culture. Presocial and social homoeostasis (p. 672) grows in part from fairly simple relations between the surface and the mass of the units under consideration. Even so, aspects other than surface-mass relationships are frequently involved.

MINIMAL AND OPTIMAL POPULATIONS

As with Mennonite colonies, populations of nonhuman organisms show phenomena associated with population size and density more or less closely comparable to those already reported for macerated sponges. Although supporting instances are known for widely diverse species, ranging from bacteria to elephants (cf. Allee, 1938), critical data as to the exact level to which a local population can fall without danger of extinction are hard to find. Conditions vary within the species in the same habitat, from habitat to habitat, and from species to species.

All too often there is no authenic record of population densities in the years preceding extinction. The decline in numbers of the heath hen of New England, a relative of the prairie chicken, is an exception (p. 328). The books by Allen (1942) and Harper (1945), surveying the recently extinct and threatened species of mammals of the world, should be consulted in this general connection. Among the species treated, the history and present status of the wisent, or Lithuanian bison (*Bison bonasus bonasus*), as reviewed by Harper, present aspects of interest. These large mammals, closely related to the American bison, stand 6 feet high at the shoulders. They were once abundant throughout Europe. Caesar records them as being plentiful in the forests of Germany and Belgium; they were apparently common throughout central Europe in the sixteenth century. The date of extinction in different localities is generally unknown, but the last bison was killed in East Prussia by a poacher in 1755. Remnants of two herds representing the Lithuanian and Caucasian subspecies, respectively, were still alive up to the outbreak of World War II in 1939.

The herd in the Bialowies Forest in Lithuania contained almost 1900 animals in 1857; by 1892 the number had been reduced to 375, with 101 more living in a neighboring forest. The main herd was the property of the imperial family of Russia and was adequately protected from poaching except during wars. Harper (p. 533) cites statements showing that the depredations of formerly formidable enemies such as bears, wolves, and lynxes were brought under approximate control. The herd suffered from diseases, from liver flukes, and from "continuous in-and-in breeding, the slowness of breeding or infertility of the cows, and the [relatively] large percentage of bulls."

In 1913, shortly before the First World War, there were some 750 wisents in the Bialowies herd, but these were killed off by poachers and disbanded soldiers. After the war, the new Polish state purchased five wisents elsewhere and installed them within the forest in a corral with an area of 240 acres. There was some slight increase up to nine pure-blooded stock and five more wisent-bison hybrids. A herd in Polish Upper Silesia contained nine animals that were wholly wisent and quite wild.

"In March, 1935, an exchange of wisent was arranged between Poland and Sweden. . . . Poland gave two Caucasus stock heifers . . . to the wisent herd near Stockholm and received in exchange a 22-year-old cow and a 5-year-old bull. These two, together with two cows that had been living in Bialowies [for 5 and 6 years, respectively] are the only ones of pure Bialowies breed remaining . . . " (Harper, p. 534).

Elsewhere, the interbreeding with introduced American bison was so conducted that bison cows were mated with wisent bulls; resulting bull calves were excluded from breeding and the hybrid heifers were bred back generation after generation to wisent bulls. "At the end of 10 generations the descendents can scarcely be distinguished from pure stock wisents. . . . "

In 1930, although Caucasian bisons were not known to be alive, Harper says (p. 537), "there was a trustworthy report of a few survivors in one of the least accessible parts of the Kuban district" and that the Russian government had established a reserve of over three-quarters of a million acres in a locality formerly occupied by the European bison, of which, however, the keepers had not found any recent trace by 1931.

It is hard to ascertain the effect of World War II on the reduced, scattered stock of wisent even though no feral animals are now known. In June, 1947, the Duke of Bedford's herd at Woburn Abbey in England contained twenty-one European bison.* The herd contained three calves of the year, of which one was a female. In addition to four bulls and mature cows, there are also four other females three years or less in age. The wisent on the European continent numbered ninety as nearly as could be discovered under the difficult conditions obtaining in December, 1946.† Their distribution was reported as follows:

Poland and Russia	42
Sweden	14
Holland	4
Switzerland	1
Germany (Springe)	14
(Munich)	15
Total	90

These ninety wisents, presumably purebred, are to be compared with the seventy three estimated by Mohr (1933) as forming the European total of such animals for 1932. Harper's concluding statement in 1945 (p. 536) summarizes the situation with an accurate understatement: "Efforts to obtain the best breeding results from this small and scattered stock appear to have been hampered somewhat by international rivalries."

A considerable amount of information is available about minimum populations in insects. Often the last individuals in a local population need not be destroyed to eradicate an insect pest from a given locality. After the pest population is sufficiently reduced in numbers, the remainder die off from natural causes, and the species does

* Personal communication from the Duke of Bedford.
† Personal communication from Miss Edyth H. Franz, Assistant Secretary, American Committee on International Wild Life Protection, based in part on a similar report by Miss Erna Mohr, Recorder of the studbook on wisent populations for the Society for the Preservation of the Wisent.

not reappear in that locality without a new immigration. In practical insect control measures the accepted practice is to reduce the given population until it is highly vulnerable, but usually not to continue until every individual has been killed (H. S. Smith et al., 1933; Soper and Wilson, 1942).

In some instances the minimal possible population can establish itself and reproduce. One pair of Norway rats is said to have successfully colonized small Deget Island in the Kattegat (Hinton, 1931), and a single pair of beavers, introduced into a suitable locality, has established a continuing beaver colony (Cook, 1943). With bacteria, despite the usual necessity for a larger inoculum among bacteria in general, a solitary anthrax bacillus inoculated into a guinea pig can become established, multiply, and eventually produce the death of the host animal (Theobald Smith, 1934). Usually with bacteria, as with many other organisms, certain viruses included, the effect of the invasion of a host depends, among other things, on the number of invaders: the smaller the inoculum, the more chance that the host will kill them all (McCoy, 1932). Such results are summarized by the left limb of curve B in Figure 139 and have definite implications concerning proto-social cooperation and disoperation.

Reindeer herds that spend the summer along the southern expanse of the Eurasian tundra have a minimum number determined by the herd's relation to the characteristic swarms of blood-sucking insects. The minimum number that can be maintained with safety in such pasturing herds is placed at 300 to 400 animals by Sdobníkóv (1935).* A smaller herd is difficult to tend and keep together. It cannot readily be put on "tandara," as the reindeer tenders call their device of stopping a herd on the morning of a hot day and making the animals remain near one place until the flight of the attacking warble flies ceases. At the opposite extreme, an overlarge herd also has disadvantages in the summer. It tramps down the pasture and worsens feeding; also a large herd collects more insects around it.

The colonies of Mennonites (p. 399)

* The English translation was kindly furnished by Mr. Charles Elton from the files of the Bureau of Animal Population, Oxford University, England.

offer another type of example of minimum populations, this time at the human level. It may be recalled that Mennonite leaders regard twenty to fifty families, depending on local conditions, as approximating the minimum population that can be expected to maintain a continuing Mennonite community. It is helpful to bring a human aggregation into the discussion for several reasons. We are encouraged to test some of the simpler human social problems against those presented by groups of other animals. We are also reminded of the complexity of the relations with which we are dealing. It is obvious that in groups of people, such factors as internal and external leadership, single-mindedness, and many other human traits tend to modify and obscure basic biological relationships, yet similarities with nonhuman populations do exist. Safety factors concerned merely with the size of a Mennonite colony illustrate some of the human variations of the problem of population minimum, just as the other instances provide bacterial, sponge, insect, heathhen, elephant, and prongbuck variations of the same problem. Recognition of the known but unmentioned human complications should make us more cautious about oversimplification of group relations among other species, in which many of the complicating factors are entirely unknown.

The existence of minimal populations implies that the optimal population size will be somewhat larger. Certain welltested instances may illustrate the extent of the phenomena and the type of situation in which optimal populations exist. Eggs of *Arbacia*, the common sea urchin of southern New England, are shed into the sea water, where they are fertilized if freely swimming spermatozoa are present. These matters can readily be manipulated in the laboratory. The number of eggs present and the closeness with which they are packed together can also be experimentally controlled. Some fifty minutes after fertilization, at usual temperatures, the eggs divide into two cells. The second cleavage takes place about thirty or forty minutes later. One set of experimental results is illustrated diagrammatically in Figure 140.

The amount of acceleration at midsecond cleavage among crowded eggs, as compared with accompanying sparse ones, may average as much as three minutes, and the difference in one long series of tests

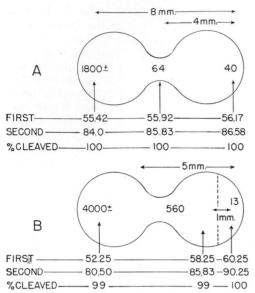

FIRST——————55.42————— 55.92————————56.17
SECOND——— 84.0————— 85.83————————86.58
%CLEAVED———100————— 100 ————————100

FIRST ——————— 52.25 ————————————— 58.25–60.25
SECOND——————— 80.50 ————————————— 85.83–90.25
%CLEAVED——————99 ——————————————— 99 —— 100

Fig. 140. The effect of crowding on the rate of cleavage of the eggs of the sea urchin. *Arbacia.* Figures below the diagrams, unless otherwise indicated, give time in minutes. (Modified from Allee and Evans.)

had high statistical probability of being real. Essentially similar results have been reported for four other genera of sea urchins. An optimal population size for rapidity of early cleavage of sea urchin eggs is clearly demonstrated; the exact number of eggs in such a population depends on many variables. Similar relations hold in populations of frogs' eggs (Merwin, 1945), and in a related field, optimal populations, somewhat larger than the possible minimum, are well established for asexual reproduction in Protozoa (p. 357) (Robertson, 1927; Petersen, 1929; Gause, 1934; Kidder, 1941; Johnson, 1941; and Mast and Pace, 1946).

The rate of reproduction is relatively low in oversmall colonies of several species of birds. Small collections of terns are less successful than larger ones, perhaps because a tern colony must reach a considerable size before the birds can form a mob large and active enough to frighten marauding gulls away from their nests. Darling (1938) has focussed attention on the possible functional significance of the numbers present in breeding groups of birds by his observations on herring gulls (*Larus a. argentatus*) and lesser black-backed gulls (*L. fuscus affinis*). Darling recognizes

three effects of colony size upon the breeding activities of these birds. The larger colonies show an earlier onset of laying, a greater synchronization of breeding, and a higher reproductive success. He and others have found that oversmall groups of certain colonial nesting birds do not breed at all.

Small numbers in a breeding colony of gannets (*Sula bassana*) result in abnormally inefficient breeding (Fisher and Vevers, 1944). There is an average of over four years' time after a new breeding locality of fulmars (*Fulmarus g. glacialis*) has been first populated before egg laying occurs (Fisher and Waterson, 1941). The possibility that a minimum threshold of numbers is necessary for producing offspring is suggested by these data. Larger colonies of yellow-headed blackbirds (*Xanthocephalus xanthocephalus*) have a higher percentage of reproductive success than smaller ones in the same region (Fautin, 1941).

Not all birds show these tendencies. Penguin colonies (*Pygoscelis papua* and *Eudyptes cristatus*), ranging in size from thirty to about 800,000 pairs, gave no conclusive evidence of earlier egg-laying or of a shorter egg-laying span in the larger when compared with smaller colonies (Roberts, 1940). An intensive study of the eastern red-wing (*Agelaius p. phoeniceus*) yielded only limited indications of group relations in their breeding colonies comparable to those reported by Darling for terns and gulls (H. M. Smith, 1943).

The population density at which adverse effects of undercrowding occur varies greatly in different animals and in different habitats for the same species. It is low with bobwhite quail, since these birds have high ability to announce their presence to others of their kind. The situation is different for the muskrat (*Ondatra zibethicus*). One creek that Errington (1940, 1943) observed in Iowa has a carrying capacity of three to four pairs of muskrats per mile. Overcrowding becomes apparent above this population density. In this instance the maximal rate of increase was attained by two to three pairs per mile. In regions in which muskrats are new invaders, there is often a lag of some years before the full reproductive rate is reached, even though no observable changes occur other than those brought about by muskrat occupancy.

The primary effect produced by these animals on their habitat seems to be the production of muskrat burrows. Old burrows are reconditioned year after year and hence aid in the development of a good muskrat population. Young muskrats driven from the home den by their mother, also use unoccupied burrows.

Minimum and optimum populations are known, too, for marsh-dwelling muskrats. In many Iowa marshes, seven pairs per ninety to 100 acres of good marsh is a minimum breeding population. In such marshes two or three pairs per acre make an optimum population when the muskrats are in a favorable phase of what sometimes appears to be a long-time breeding cycle. Although muskrats do not pair off in a fixed breeding pattern, the breeding pair is still a useful descriptive device. The failure of oversmall populations to reproduce comes from the absence of enough males to mate with the females during their short period of sexual receptivity. When too few males are present, they simply may not be around at the proper time.

It is worth continued emphasis that definite figures concerning minimum or optimum population densities often must be advanced with caution, whether the animals are relatively simple with self-contained food as in sea urchin eggs (Allee, 1938), or more complex forms as muskrats (Errington, 1945) or man. It is difficult to describe exactly these functional population levels under controlled conditions, and helpful statements regarding what constitutes an optimal population density in the field require skill, caution, knowledge, and wisdom on the part of the observer. The optimal population density also varies with the function being measured and upon whether an immediate or a long-time view is being considered.

One of the more common examples of optimal density is furnished by studies on longevity. In addition to the lengthened survival of aggregated animals in the presence of many toxic agents and other adverse environmental conditions (p. 360), increased density—up to some optimum— often increases longevity when conditions seem to be generally favorable.

The life span of *Drosophila*, under certain experimental conditions, is longest at the population density of thirty-five to fifty-five flies per 1 ounce culture bottle (Pearl, Miner, and Parker, 1927). Suboptimal numbers of flies may be unable to gain an adequate control of "wild" organisms or prevent overgrowth of yeasts on which *Drosophila* feeds. The increased death rate with higher densities is probably related, as is frequently true, to local food shortage or to an excess of excretory products or to both combined.

The situation is complex. Analogies exist between many aspects of the physiology of aggregations and of individual animals. For example, Shcherbakov (1935) reported that Rubner's rule (p. 113) holds with groups of *Drosophila melanogaster*. The rate of oxygen consumption is higher with 200 of these flies in 30 cc. of space than when only two are present. Here, as in many other instances, the effect of crowding depends on the criteria being used; metabolism, in this instance, proceeds faster in the crowded condition, and, as might be expected, longevity decreases.

Another well-tested instance of optimal population density is furnished by numbers in the litters of inbred guinea pigs (Wright, 1922; Wright and Eaton; see Allee, 1945). Those born in litters of two or even three show better survival records at weaning time at the age of thirty-three days than do those born in smaller or larger litters. The factors underlying this optimal litter size are complex. Apparently, in a vigorous strain of guinea pigs a litter of one is in itself an indication of lowered vitality. Then, too, the larger size at birth of single guinea pigs may result in birth injuries and so produce an immediate or a deferred rise in death rate (cf. p. 656). Here again the cooperation, such as it is, between two or three litter mates as contrasted with those born singly, or in larger litters, is inseparable from the general life processes of the growing organisms.

Tribolium Populations

It is hard enough to ascertain the population density that is optimal under generalized experimental conditions. The analysis of the major causal relations is more difficult. We give now one well-tested example—that of the flour beetle, *T. confusum*—in which the optimal population density for rapid initial increase is clearly above the minimal density at which reproduction occurs. The methods of culturing *Tribolium* and of assaying population growth have been given in preceding chapters together with other ecological implications of such studies, and the present discussion was appropriately foreshadowed (p. 353).

Data obtained by Chapman (1928) and analyzed by Allee (1931) revealed a more rapid early increase in population density with an initial seeding of 0.125 beetles per gram of flour than at lower (0.062 per gram) or higher densities. The results are summarized in Figure 141. As the graphs

peated the experiment, using the converse plan of holding the initial inocula constant at one pair of beetles per bottle and increasing the size of the effective environment in a regular series. Despite a reduction in the observed rate of reproduction, the optimal density for early increase fell at the same point, namely, at an initial density of 1.125 beetles per gram of flour (Fig. 142).

Another report of the same phenomenon, based on still another strain of *T. confusum*

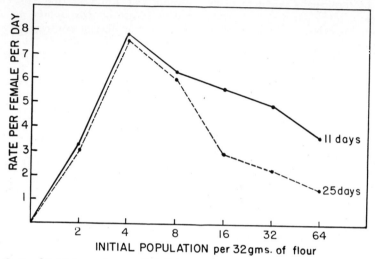

Fig. 141. Optimal initial population of *Tribolium* with volume of medium held constant. (From Chapman and Thomas Park.)

show, Chapman's populations started with one pair of adult beetles in 32 gm. of flour (0.062 per gram), and grew at a slower rate per female per day during the initial period of eleven days than did any other density tested by him at that time.

Thomas Park (1932) confirmed this part of Chapman's experiment, using a different strain of beetles of the same species and a different type of wheat flour. The agreement, even in rate of effective reproduction, is as close as could be expected from independent workers using different genetic stocks at different locations and with a few years intervening. Animals are not physical automata and do not always give identical responses even under approximately similar conditions.

These two sets of tests were made by introducing beetles in an ascending geometric series into 32 gm. of flour in each experimental microcosm. Park (1933) re-

and a different set of initial relations, was published by MacLagen (1932), who introduced 8,8,8,4,8, and 16 pairs of beetles, respectively, into 16,8,4,1,1, and 1 gm. of flour. He maintained his cultures at a slightly higher temperature and at a much higher relative humidity than did Park. Also, his stock cultures had been subjected to intense crowding for six months and had possibly been selected for ability to withstand crowding. As shown in Figure 143, MacLagen, too, obtained a definite optimum, but now at a density of two beetles per gram of flour.

So much for the demonstration of the reality of an optimal population density above the possible minimal one. Now for the known factors. Park (1933), in initiating this analysis, drew the inference from certain experiments that the decrease in rate of effective reproduction in oversparse populations results from infrequent meeting of the sexes in their random movement (p. 364) through the floury medium. Under such conditions the rate of copulation and recopulation is below that at which maximum fecundity occurs. Crombie (1943) gives supporting evidence on this *bolium* eggs by the older larval and imaginal members of the population (see p. 370; also Chapman and Baird, 1934). This removal of potential beetles increases in direct proportion to population density (Park, 1933). Also. in overcrowded popu-

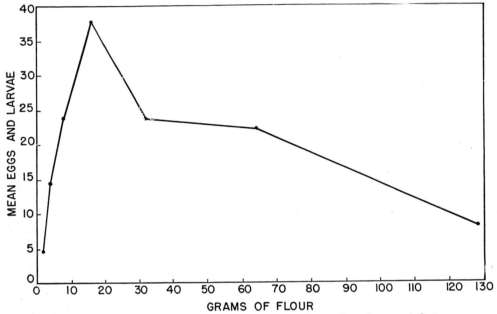

Fig. 142. Optimal initial populations of *Tribolium* with volume of medium varied. Assays were made after 11 days. (Data from Thomas Park.)

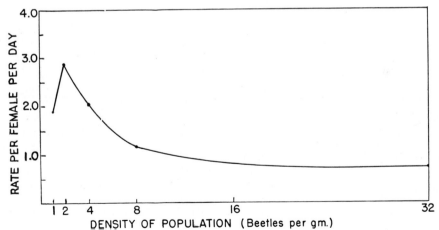

Fig. 143. Another test of optimal initial population density in *Tribolium*. (Data by MacLagen.)

point. Crombie seeded his cultures with well-copulated females specifically selected for high fecundity and, under these conditions, found no evidence of undercrowding.

The decline in rate of increase in overcrowding is a result of the eating of *Tri-* lations the females actually produce fewer eggs. Apparently the ovipositing females in crowded cultures have a reduced fecundity as a result of "jostling" or other interference by their associates (MacLagan and Dunn, 1936). Crombie (1943, p. 83) summarizes the matter thus in terms of the densities with which he worked:

"In *Tribolium*, therefore, two agents . . . cause the reduction in the number of eggs found in the cultures as density increases, viz., an actual fall in the rate of oviposition occurring between 1.25 and 5 beetles per gram and the eating of eggs which occurs at all densities from 1.25 beetles per gram upwards and increases in rate with increasing density."

A further cause of the reduction in rate of population increase in crowded cultures is probably to be found in the disoperations associated with self-conditioned flour —disoperations that have been adequately reviewed in a preceding chapter (p. 352).

This particular instance of optimal population density is of value, not only for the thoroughness with which the phenomenon has been established and the progress toward an analysis of causal factors, but also because the whole gamut of effects of undercrowding, optimal density, and overcrowding result from interactions within a homotypic population and from the relations of the beetles with a relatively simple environment. As Thomas Park has pointed out (1941), we have here a simplified analogue of the interactions on which much of outdoor ecology depends (Clements and Shelford, 1939). We turn now to a brief consideration of optimal populations when two species are present.

Heterotypic Optima

Certain problems related to heterotypic populations have been discussed in a preceding chapter (p. 346). Optimal densities exist in populations of mixed species. The situation is complex and becomes rapidly more so with each additional species in the ecosystem. Certain relations can be illustrated by partially controlled laboratory populations of the ciliate *Oxytricha fallax* and of the bacterium, *Pseudomonas fluorescens,* on which it feeds (Johnson, 1933; Gause, 1934). As in the original investigation, our presentation of the results is simplified by assaying the effects of population densities of both constituent organisms upon *Oxytricha* alone and disregarding—in fact, experimentally avoiding—many of the density effects on the bacteria.

The concentration of the food organisms modified the rate of population growth of

the protozoans. Standard suspensions of the bacteria in two drops of water that supported the highest rate of division of isolated *Oxytricha* were called concentration X. In one series of tests, each isolated oxytrichan yielded an average of more than eleven ciliates in twenty-four hours (see Fig. 144). Variations from this concentra-

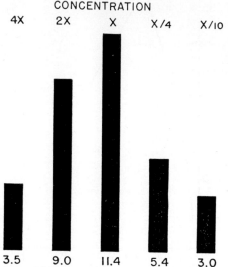

Fig. 144. Optimal population density of bacteria for maximal production of *Oxytricha*. (Data from Johnson.)

tion of bacteria produced decided reductions in the numbers of protozoans.

If too few oxytrichans are seeded into a new culture, the phenomenon of undercrowding is readily demonstrated in more dense bacterial cultures. Certain of these relations are outlined in Figure 145. Drop suspensions with X concentration of bacteria yielded 10+ *Oxytricha* per seeded individual in twenty-four hours, whether started with one or with two individuals. Consistent with this result, cultures of 2X concentration also gave a 10 to 1 rate of increase when inoculated with two individuals, but yielded 8 for 1 in twenty-four hours when seeded with only one oxytrichan. Cultures with 4X concentration of bacteria showed still further reduction in rate of increase, and some of the 5X concentrations approached, or even reached, the limit of toleration for fission of the *Oxytricha* tested. Earlier work by Chejfec (1928) gave similar indications.

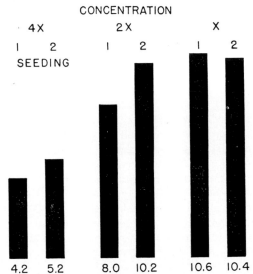

CONCENTRATION

Fig. 145. Some effects from varying the number of introduced *Oxytricha* and bacteria in drop cultures. (Data from Johnson.)

Johnson (1937, p. 13) arrived at the following interpretative summary of this situation:

"This work with *Oxytricha* confirms the existence of the phenomenon described by Robertson [see p. 357], but it does not confirm his theory of allelocatalysis. In cultures where the bacterial concentration is supra-optimal it appears that two protozoans are able to reduce the numbers to the optimal density quicker than one, and as a result exhibit a higher reproductive rate. This indicates a beneficial effect of crowding in protozoans when they are in media very dense with bacteria."

Population Size and the Rate of Evolution

We can take time to discuss only one more aspect of ecological effects arising from the existence of minimal and optimal populations. The relation between population size and density is mentioned here in part because various ecological aspects of evolution are both neglected and important, as may be seen from the treatment of that subject in a later section of this book (p. 598). Charles Darwin recognized that a relatively large population is an important factor in natural selection. In more recent years, Wright (1931, 1932, 1945) and others have presented good evidence that, at least under certain conditions, evolution proceeds most rapidly in populations of random breeding organisms that

are intermediate in size, as compared with similar populations that are overlarge or oversmall. We are especially interested in the slower rate of evolution in oversmall populations as contrasted with that of those that are somewhat larger. The rate of evolution is still more rapid when a large, widely distributed species population is broken into relatively small breeding colonies not completely isolated from each other.

Even in this last situation the more general rule still holds, and the separation of a species population into small breeding colonies with occasional interemigration is in itself one expression of optimal population density. Obviously, if the population becomes overdense and is effectively circumscribed, it cannot partially fragment, but becomes rather an overlarge population.

Wright (1945), in his review of Simpson (1945), comments:

"The reviewer wishes also to make a correction here to a statement . . . similar to ones made by other authors, in which he is credited with the conclusion that the conditions most favorable for rapid evolution are to be found in populations of a certain intermediate size. The actual statement made in several papers was to the effect that conditions are more favorable in a population of intermediate size than in a very small one or in a very large *random breeding* one (assuming a constant direction of selection). But such a statement has always been followed by the statement that conditions are enormously more favorable in a population which may be large but which is divided into many small local populations almost but not quite completely isolated from each other . . ."

Omitting all details, some of which may be found in the section on Evolution (see p. 602)* the important point for general ecology, as well as for the evolutionary processes concerned, is that one of the primary controlling factors in the rate of evolution, under many conditions, is the number of animals in the interbreeding group. This gives another illustration of the conditions summarized by graph B of Figure 139. As with many phases of individual survival, the rate of evolution is highest, other things being equal, in populations of optimal size as contrasted with those that are overlarge or oversmall. Here, the rate

* A simply expressed statement of many of the fundamental considerations is given by Allee (1938).

of evolution becomes a criterion for the existence of natural cooperation.

GROUP MODIFICATION OF STRUCTURE AND BEHAVIOR

In addition to the many instances in which animal aggregations have demonstrable survival value, only a few of which have been reviewed in the last several pages, aggregations of plants or animals, or of both, often affect the behavior, the physiology, and even the structure of the constituent organisms. Special survival values associated with such modifications are not always readily apparent and may be nonexistent. A few examples will indicate the range of this general category of group effects.

As with trees and other plants, the growth form of many sessile animals depends on the degree of crowding; barnacles and ascidians furnish diagrammatic examples. The size and details of structure of *Drosophila* are affected by population density (Eigenbrodt, 1925; Plunkett, 1926). The polarity of the zygote of the alga *Fucus* may be determined wholly or in part by the relation of a given egg to its fellows (Rosenvinge, 1889; Hurd, 1920; Whitaker, 1931). With certain aphids wing production is influenced by the degree of crowding (p. 347).

The whole modern phase theory of locusts maintains that certain species of orthopterans are polymorphic and that structural proportions, coloration, and behavior are determined by population density (Uvarov, 1928; Faure, 1932).

Space does not permit an adequate review of the many instances in which the activities of animals are modified by the presence or absence of other animals. It may be sufficient to mention the behavior related to courtship and mating. We do not know of an adequate summary of this important aspect of ecology. Such a treatment could begin with the mating behavior and the mating types of Protozoa (Jennings, 1945; Sonneborn, 1947) and, if thoroughgoing, would draw illustrations from almost all animal phyla. The article on "Courtship of Animals" by Julian Huxley in current printings of the Encyclopaedia Britannica gives an elementary introduction to this field.

ANIMAL AGGREGATIONS AND SEX

The whole gamut of the sex-related life of adults makes significant contributions to several aspects of animal ecology and general sociology. Sex-based behavior is seen to be the more important when the rich variety of parent-offspring relations are considered. Sex itself may have originated in the protista as a result of selection acting on the mutual stimulation to more rapid division that often accompanies the close contiguity of two asexual individuals. This hypothesis is most appropriate for those cases of so-called allelocatalysis (p. 357), in which the accelerated division rates appear to stem from the production and automatic sharing of a growth-promoting substance (Robertson, 1927; Reich, 1938; Kidder, 1941; Mast and Pace, 1938, 1946).

Even when bisexuality is fairly established, sex determination is often flexible and, in a number of instances widely separated in the animal kingdom, depends on the closeness of association with one or more other organisms of the same species.

Conditions described for the alga-like flagellate, *Chlamydomonas eugametos*, by Moewus (e.g., 1933, 1940) and associates seem to lend support to such a suggestion, which was independently worked out from Robertson's effect (allelocatalysis) in ciliates (Allee, 1931). Certain phases of the studies on *Chlamydomonas* have been subjected to strongly adverse criticism on statistical grounds (Philip and Haldane, 1939). The more strictly ecological aspects of the situation have been reviewed with care by Sonneborn (1942) and by G. M. Smith (1946). The last-mentioned worker, using *Chlamydomonas* from California, failed to confirm some of the experimental results reported for another species from Germany. The further development of this particular problem should be watched.

Mating types are known for certain Protozoa and have been much studied in some of the common species of *Paramecium* and in *Euplotes* (Sonneborn, 1937, 1947; Jennings, 1938, 1945; Kimball, 1939, 1943). At first the situation appeared to have a simple regularity and was quite dramatic. Each of several species was found to be divided into a number of mating varieties, each containing a limited number of mating types; there were two for each variety of *P. aurelia,* for example. Individuals of a given mating type would not conjugate with members of their own type or with members of a different sex variety. Given proper conditions, conjugation took place readily between representatives of different mating types of the same variety. Knowledge in this field is growing rapidly, and its complexity is becoming more apparent. Intervarietal conjugations are now known in *P. aurelia* and *P. bursaria,* but these do not take place so readily as do those between different sex types within the same variety. Even under these conditions, potent blocks to the free exchange of genes include "hybrid" non-viability and low viability (Sonneborn and Dippell, 1946). Evidence is growing that some varieties can so condition the medium in which they live that it will induce clumping and conjugation both between animals of different varieties and even between members of the same clone (Chen, 1945). This is a phase of ecology in which continuing rapid progress is to be expected; the present account is already partially out of date.

A variety of animals show consecutive sexuality, one and the same individual being first a male and then a female. With some, maleness is the more juvenile, and femaleness the more adult, condition. There may be the increased complexity that the duration of the male phase depends on whether the animal has female associates. This situation is developed almost diagrammatically with certain marine snails of the genus *Crepidula* (Coe, 1936), except that in all species of *Crepidula* so far studied critically, a few males do not change into females, in contrast with the hermaphroditic males constituting the bulk of the male population.

Bonellia, an aberrant, Mediterranean annelid worm, illustrates another variation of the same general principle. The large female harbors small parasitic males within her uterus. The fertilized eggs are shed into the surrounding sea water and develop into free-swimming larvae possessing both male and female potentialities. If these free-swimming young settle on the proboscis of a female *Bonellia,* they develop into the minute, parasitic males living in polyandric relation with this female host. Those that do not settle on a female, normally become functional females themselves, able to produce maleness in any *Bonellia* larvae that come their way. The sexually indifferent larvae receive some substance from the female proboscis that retards their growth and induces maleness. The external, social relations—or lack of them—determine which of the alternative paths of sexual development will be followed (Baltzer, 1925).

In other well-studied cases, population density determines the sex ratio of individuals with labile sexual potentialities, Monstrillid copepods (Malaquin, 1901) and certain nematode parasites of grasshoppers (Christie, 1929) and of chironomid larvae (Caullery and Comas, 1928), among others, illustrate this effect. In this variation of sex determination by population pressure, isolated parasites or those in small populations per host tend toward equality in sex ratios or have a preponderance of females. In denser populations the sex ratio is unbalanced toward maleness, and in some instances (Caullery and Comas, 1928) intermediate densities yield intersexes.

We can give quantitative data. Christie (1929) fed known numbers of eggs of a nematode *Mermis* to common New England grasshoppers. Four grasshoppers fed twenty to thirty eggs each—100 in all—produced eighty-six mermid parasites, all males. In contrast, twenty-one grasshoppers —all but three of the same species that had been tested with heavy infestations—fed four or five eggs each, 102 in all, yielded seventy-three parasites, of which 92 per cent were females. We are dealing here with labile sexual potentiality rather than with differential mortality.

Another variant of the modification of sex by crowding—the last we shall mention —comes from the close study of sexuality in cladoceran crustaceans. *Moina,* like many other Cladocera, lives in ponds and pools of fresh water. The populations usually consist of parthenogenetic females. Outbreaks of bisexuality occur from time to time, often at the onset of a drought or in autumn. The resulting fertilized eggs are more resistant than are the parthenogenetic ones and carry the stock over periods of environmental adversity. With the coming of better conditions, these so-called winter eggs hatch into partheno-

genetic females. Crowding females of
Moina is an effective method of inducing
bisexuality. Crowding acts both by decreasing the amount of available food (Stuart
and Cooper, 1932) and, less certainly, by
the concentration of wastes or of their decomposition products (Banta and Brown,
1939), or, perhaps, by both these mechanisms combined with other factors as yet
unanalyzed. Whatever the explanation, in
Moina macrocopa the close crowding of
many parthenogenetic females results in
the production of eggs with a different
prospective potency from that found in
other eggs produced by these same females
when uncrowded.

The survival values of adaptations that
tend toward the production of males, sexual females, and the resulting resistant
eggs, under adverse conditions, are rather
obvious. All individuals of the uncrowded
parthenogenetic stock are offspring-produc-
ing members of the population when environmental conditions favor rapid expansion. By using the type of reasoning commonly employed in dealing with problems
of adaptive evolution (p. 630), each of
the other instances cited can also be shown
to have certain probable survival values.
Thus, as a result of the specialized method
of sex determination described for the
worm *Bonellia,* the potential reproductive
waste of isolated males is largely avoided.
If a young, wandering, sexless individual
reaches a suitable environment, it develops
into a female and is then able to direct the
transformation of the next comer into a
functional male. The survival values of the
sexual situation in *Crepidula* are somewhat
similar; those connected with the population control of sex ratios of nematode parasites are more complicated and are related
perhaps, to the need for avoiding over-
parasitization of the hosts if the parasites
are to flourish.

SOCIAL FACILITATION

The nearby presence of another organism
frequently modifies the rate of performance
or even the character of a physiological
process or a behavior pattern. Certain of
these interrelations were recognized by
Tarde (1903) as phases of interphysiology
or interpsychology, ideas that can be readily expanded to include intermores physiology or intermores psychology. All such

concepts enter into social facilitation. The
distinction between physiology and psychology is made on the simplified, but perhaps truthful, assumption that psychology
is an aspect of the physiology of the central nervous system, especially of the higher
centers of the cerebral ganglion or brain.

In general, social facilitation refers to
any increment or decrement in an individual's behavior resulting from the presence
of another organism. It is one of the fundamentals of group physiology. Social facilitation usually implies an increase in frequency, intensity, or skill; it may also refer
to an increased tendency to remain quiet.
Proto-cooperation may be helpfully regarded as incidental or fundamental physiological facilitation. Schneirla (1946)
treats this in close connection with the "bio-
social facilitation" found in social insects
and the "psycho-social facilitation" illustrated by man; he thinks that both may be
considered as extensions of trophallaxis as
outlined by Wheeler (1923). These three
phases are not sharply separated; all are
shown by the high primates, for example,
and probably represent aspects of social
evolution (cf. p. 687).

The more extreme results of social facilitation range from antagonisms to synergisms; and in the twilight intermediate
zone, reactions may be subtly expressed by
variation in rate of response. Synergisms
are well known among bacteria (Burrows,
1942), among other plants, and throughout the animal kingdom. Social facilitations are especially striking among many
insects and vertebrates. The effect may be
produced as a response to an altered physical environment or as a direct reaction to
the presence of other organisms.

Let us restrict our attention to the last
two categories, and to behavior. Many
diverse animals show retarded rates of
learning when another similar form is
nearby. Thus the common cockroach learns
to run a simple maze more expertly if alone
than if another is present (Gates and Allee,
1933); the shell parrakeet behaves similarly (Allee and Masure, 1936) and does not
learn to talk human words if other budge-
rigars are present (Feyerabend, 1943).

The rate of respiration and the amount
of movement may be automatically reduced
in certain fishes when another similar fish
is nearby (Shlaifer, 1939). Attention has

already been called to the decreased activity and lengthened life of crowded spermatozoa (p. 395); many other similar examples could be cited.

Positive social facilitation is also common, even when one uses social in a more restricted sense. Carefully proved instances include the faster improvement in maze learning, in grouped than in isolated goldfishes (Welty, 1934), and in green sunfishes, *Lepomis cyanellus* (Greenberg, 1947); an increased food consumption in grouped guppies. A *Camponotus* ant digs more rapidly in the presence of others (Chen, 1937); and many animals, including monkeys, chimpanzees, and men, are stimulated to eat more and even to consume marginal foods in the company of others. Much of human education is facilitated in groups.

Some social facilitations in nonhuman animals approach what is called imitation in human behavior and may be spoken of objectively as being "contagious." Song sparrows reared in the semifreedom of an ornithologist's study showed a variety of contagious activities. When one sparrow ate, bathed, or preened, the others often did likewise; when one flew to the desk, for example, another usually followed (Nice, 1943). Grouped chimpanzees that have considerable freedom of movement show waves of specialized activities apparently passed along by contagion (Köhler, 1925).

The food-procuring behavior of many different kinds of animals changes, depending on the number present. The group fishing of the double-crested cormorants near San Francisco gives an example of elaborate and flexible group cooperation. These cormorants may fish singly, in small coordinated flocks of from ten to twelve, or in larger flocks that may contain as many as 2000 birds. Fishing usually begins before the larger flocks are fully formed. The basic pattern in small flocks consists of a circle with all birds facing the same direction. This pattern changes with the large flocks; then, a long, narrow, well-packed line moves forward, fishing as it goes. Some cormorants swim at the surface, others dive and swim at the same rate; those left behind by the rapid advance take to the air and fly forward again to become members of the line of fishers.

The large flocks swim decidedly faster than do small fishing groups—an example of another kind of social facilitation; they also pursue a given school of fish until the hunger of the cormorants is satiated, or until the school escapes (Bartholomew, 1942, 1943). Thus the persistence of a large flock is greater than that of a small one.

ORGANIZATION OF ANIMAL GROUPS

The simplest animal aggregations show little, if any, discernible social organization. Primitive, partial integrations arise, in some instances from the constant pushing toward the center of those on the periphery, as in schools of very young bullheads (*Ameiurus*). Highly integrated insect groups—colonies of bees or ants, for example—have types of organization that we can only partially perceive and which we do not yet fully understand. Our present knowledge of integrating and regulating mechanisms in social insects will be summarized later (p. 426); for present purposes we can state that in many insect colonies the individual seems to be strongly group-dominated.

The contemporary organization of vertebrate groups, often more or less crudely approaching some aspects of human organization, is based on the application of three general principles: the holding of territory; domination-subordination; and leadership-followership. These different types may occur in fairly pure form, or they may grade into each other, even in schools of fishes, to give complicated organizational patterns.

Each of these principles—territoriality, social hierarchy, and leadership—operates to some extent among invertebrates. Certain crabs, spiders and insects defend small territories (Pearse, 1939). The small hermit crab (*Eupagurus longicarpus*) displays dominance based on individual contacts (Allee and Douglis, 1945); an order of social ascendancy exists among associated fertile females of the wasp *Polistes gallicus* (Pardi, 1948: and p. 430); and some ants show leadership relations (Schneirla, 1933; Chen, 1937a). The greater part of our information concerning these principles of group organization deals with vertebrates, especially among the bony fishes, lizards, birds, and mammals.

Unlike proto-cooperative phases of animal aggregations, organizational aspects may involve definite conflict—often severe fighting—between members of a contact pair. This is particularly true for the holding of territories and the maintenance of status in a social hierarchy. In both these relationships, group organization grows out of a series of pair conflicts even within the limits of a more or less closely knit group, rather than from mass encounters. Leadership sometimes devolves on the most potent fighter in the group.

Intraspecies organizational struggles appear later in the evolutionary series than does primitive, automatic proto-cooperation. It is made possible, in part, by the presence of natural mutualism within the species, and by group-oriented behavior which, together with environmental gradients, lead to the formation of aggregations. Only animals that are somewhat aggregated can become organized.

TERRITORY*

Territoriality includes homing or the defense of a given area, or both. Homing reactions are concerned with an animal's becoming so adjusted to a specific area that returns are made, perhaps to the precise spot, when activities or environmental accidents cause removal. The distance covered in the return may be only a few millimeters or centimeters in certain mollusks. Homing pigeons may return for miles, and displaced men often travel notable distances. Insects give essentially similar reactions under a variety of conditions.

Homing territories in man are based on preferences that result from learned behavior. They may be similarly established, to a greater or less degree, by other animals. "Preference" territories are not necessarily defended, although they may be. Defense of boundaries occurs to such an extent among territorial birds that ornithologists define bird territory as a defended

* We have read much of the extensive literature on territoriality in animals and present the following account as a generalized summary without careful documentation for each statement. Initiated students will recognize, as do we, our indebtedness to the competent scholarship of Margaret M. Nice (1933, 1937, 1939, 1941, 1943).

area. Defense against territorial invasion is well developed by many fishes, lizards, and mammals as well as by man. It is also known for the fiddler crab *Uca* (Crane, 1941). Territoriality is based both on a positive reaction to a given space and, within that, often, on a negative reaction to invaders of the same species, except for a mate or mates.

We know more about the territorial organizations of birds than that of most non-human groups. Birds show the following types of territories:

1. Mating and nesting combined with space in which to collect food during the breeding season
2. Mating and nesting with food collected elsewhere
3. Mating station only
4. Nesting region only:
   a. Solitary individuals
   b. Colonial birds
5. Nonbreeding territories including:
   a. Roosting territories
   b. Feeding territories

Varied types of territorial defense are known among birds when "any defended area" is regarded as being a "territory." Although the variations are great, especially when different species are considered, certain general rules can be recognized: Males are more active than females in maintaining territories, and they are most active during or near the breeding season. Not all species of birds maintain territories, and of those that do, unmated males may or may not defend permanent holdings. Some birds remain territorial during the winter, although many do not. Often the female does not defend the boundaries kept by her mate, though she may do so; in general, female territorial behavior is much more varied than is that shown by males. Some flocks hold and defend definite areas, others do not; when held, a flock territory may be subdivided or remain a group-defended unit.

Territories tend to be larger when population pressure is low and to be compressed when more nesting birds are present in the area. The amount of space defended also depends, in part, on the fighting ability and the aggressiveness of the male; its location is related both to date of establishment and to general prowess. Although there is much active fighting, the combats may be formalized, and in many species, singing and other kinds of more passive defense are common. As an example among mammals, hordes of howling monkeys maintain territories that they defend from invasion by neighboring hordes by howling encounters, not by active fighting (Carpenter, 1934). Development of substitutes for actual combats conserves much energy and prevents fatigue and inattention to the approach of predators.

The territorial habit has a number of hypothetical and, to a certain extent, even probable values, among which may be listed: (1) the more or less automatic organization of a local population into a sort of well-spaced aggregation; (2) the promotion of monogamy, which is often important in rearing helpless young; (3) limitation of the breeding population and hence partial control of an increase in numbers beyond the carrying capacity of the habitat; (4) the provision of a reserve of unmated males and females, making possible the prompt replacement of a lost mate in a breeding territory; (5) with larger territories, the insurance of an adequate supply of easily accessible food; (6) a reduction in the rate of spread of parasites or disease; (7) close acquaintance with the locality, giving an advantage to the territory holder in hiding from predators; and finally, (8) for psychological reasons that are not wholly known, there is an increased vigor of defense by the occupant and decreased aggressiveness by the invader that make for social stability. Sometimes, at least, these psychological factors may be effective outside a delimited territory, but bear a recognizable relation to the relative distance of the birds from their territorial centers (Odum, 1941, 1942).

Territoriality also has evolutionary connotations (pp. 376 and 691).

SOCIAL HIERARCHIES

Territorial organization has close interrelations with the dominance-subordinance hierarchies that develop in many small groups of fishes, lizards, birds, and mammals. A few green sunfish (*Lepomis cyanellus*), for example, housed in a small aquarium, soon organize themselves into a dominance hierarchy as a result of a series of pair contacts. With larger space available, the males often take up territories, especially as the breeding season approaches, and territorial establishment is the easier if the habitat is already partially subdivided into niches. When a hierarchy passes over into a territorial organization, the most subordinate fish is the last to obtain a territory that it is able to defend and, under many conditions, may not be able to gain a place it can defend against all comers (Greenberg, 1947).

Development of knowledge of social hierarchies illustrates some of the possibilities of the interplay between laboratory and field studies in ecology. The modern development of this subject is based on the work of Schjelderup-Ebbe (1922), using the common domestic fowl, and has been much elaborated by, among others, Allee and his associates with various laboratory animals (Allee, 1938, 1945; Collias, 1944). Eventually the laboratory findings were tested in the field with frequent substantiation and extension (e.g., Odum, 1941, 1942; Emlen and Lorenz, 1942; Carpenter, 1940, 1942; Jenkins, 1944).

Many workers have summarized the qualities that make for high social status in groups of vertebrates. There is fairly general agreement on the following list:

1. The stronger individual usually wins its pair contracts, but there are frequent exceptions because experience may be more important than strength. On first meeting, robust animals usually defeat those that are ill.

2. Mature animals usually dominate those less mature; thus hens dominate younger chickens, and dominance based on age may continue long after the younger animals are physically superior to their elders. This rule has many exceptions, such as are furnished by the fact that newly matured canaries may dominate their fully mature associates, and half-grown kittens can keep old cats away from food.

3. In many animal groups, such as fishes, turtles, lizards, and chimpanzees, the larger animals usually have higher social rank than their smaller associates. When the difference in size is not great (and sometimes when it is), larger size does not insure dominance. In White Leghorn hens the "degree of determination of success" by weight in a series of staged pair contacts

between strangers was approximately 2 per cent in contrast with freedom from moult, amount of male hormone present, and social rank in the home flock, each of which respectively "determined" 26, 22, and 6 per cent of success (Collias, 1943); White Leghorn hens also dominate hens of other breeds that are decidedly heavier individuals (Potter, 1947).

4. The location of the first meeting is often important since many animals fight best in or near their home territory.

5. In strange territory, an animal accompanied by others from the home flock or horde often wins from a stranger more easily than if alone. The association of acquaintances may be more important than being within the home range (Douglis, 1948).

6. Animals with young, especially females with young, tend to fight more fiercely than at other times.

7. Males usually dominate females, particularly in those species in which the male is the larger and showier sex (Schjelderup-Ebbe, 1935). Often there are two rank-orders in a bisexual group, one for the males and another for females, and these scarcely overlap (Carpenter, 1942).

8. The amount of male hormone present, within an indefinite physiological range, often increases social dominance of either sex. The sexual component of the drive for dominance in sword-tail fishes (*Xiphophorus*) may be distinguished from the social drive by gradual cooling; the sexual appetite was lost at 10° C., and the drive for social status continued until the water reached 6° (Noble, 1939).

9. The female consort of a dominant male tends to be accorded his social status so long as she remains near him (Carpenter, 1942). This can be expanded to the more general rule that in closely associated pairs of animals, the social status of both tends to be that won by the more dominant individual.

10. An ordinarily successful animal may be temporarily tired or ill and so may lose a combat that it might well be expected to win. This is a common cause of triangles of dominance in which $a > b > c > a$; even the omega individual has been known to dominate the otherwise alpha hen of a flock.

11. Individuals standing high in their own social groups are more likely to dominate a stranger than are those with low social status. Winning, if repeated, tends to produce continued victories in pair contests; continued losing predisposes towards further defeats (Ginsburg and Allee, 1942).

12. The paired reactions of animals to each other tend to become fixed with repetition, and an old or even an ill individual may continue to dominate vigorous associates long after it has lost the power to defeat them in actual combat.

13. It is hard enough to judge critically concerning psychological factors in human affairs; the difficulty is much greater with other animals, but there is much evidence of the importance of such effects in winning social status. One animal acts as though intimidated by the appearance of a stranger and gives way without fighting. In other cases, both act as if frightened; the one that recovers first usually wins (Schjelderup-Ebbe, 1935). Another psychological aspect is the appearance in non-human animals of reactions toward flock mates that in man would be regarded as expressing individual antipathy or favoritism. Thus high-ranking cocks of the common domestic fowl, when in bisexual flocks, may suppress the mating behavior of some subordinate cocks and allow others even to push them away from the copulating position (Guhl, Collias, and Allee, 1945).

14. Hereditary differences are important, as well as factors related to recent experience; for example, inbred strains of mice may differ both in aggressiveness and in fighting ability (Scott, 1942; Ginsburg and Allee, 1942; Beeman, 1947).

15. Seniority of membership in flocks of similarly aged hens shows a high correlation with high social rank (Guhl and Allee, 1944).

The most certain sign of social dominance is the winning of an encounter with another individual, either by fighting or by some milder substitute. Often a series of such contacts is needed before the pair relations are definitely established; in some instances, especially between males, the defeated individual repeatedly attacks.

Defeat is often accompanied by easily observed changes in attitude. A defeated fish may drop its challenging posture of tense body and erect fins; the fish seems to hang limply in the water; it backs slowly away and then turns and flees. Many animals, among them hens, mice, and boys, not infrequently emit characteristic cries when beaten. The head furnishings of defeated hens sometimes blanch, while those of the victor remain flushed. Defeated mice rear up in characteristic postures.

Other signs of low social rank include the avoidance of encounters with superiors; defeated hens move about quietly, often with head held low, or hide in out-of-the-way places or in protected niches. Animals of low rank sometimes accept or even offer to assume, the female position in a copulation; monkeys and cats have this tendency.

LEADERSHIP

In the best sense, leadership consists in giving guidance by going before and drawing others along the same course or pattern of behavior. A leader is often able to attract others to follow, but sometimes compulsion is relied upon to control and even to secure followers. The leader of a group of animals may be young, mature, or old, and of either sex; often the followers vary similarly. The leader may be one individual, or there may be a group of leaders. The position of real leadership is held by the animal that initiates, stabilizes, or integrates behavior patterns, whether these call for activity or for quietude, and he (or she) may occupy the apex position when the group changes location or otherwise shifts to a new line of activity. Often, however, the animal moving in advance is not the real originator of the movement. Other pertinent qualities or tendencies include such items as freedom of action, responsibility for others, and guidance of them. In social and subsocial aspects of ecology we are primarily concerned with the situation in which the leader and the led all belong to the same homotypic group, but important heterotypic leadership also occurs.

Leadership may or may not be associated with social dominance. In flocks of hens, leadership often rests in the midsocial ranks rather than with the *alpha* hen, but even these birds are quite dependent on being followed (cf. Fischel, 1927). Leadership exists among ants, where individual-to-individual dominance is unknown (Chen, 1937a), and the leader is often dependent on her followers. The raiding columns of the American army ants (*Eciton*) have a shifting type of leadership; the ant or a small "pushing party" of ants at the apex of the advancing column moves forward less than an inch and turns back to the advancing larger mass (Schneirla, 1933).

Leadership in flocks of birds presents many unsolved problems mainly related to the difficulty of identifying individuals in the field. In one heterotypic flock (Nichols, 1931) the real leadership of a flying flock, as with hens, rested in the body of the flock rather than with the single, conspicuous golden plover that flew out in front after the slower flying black-bellied plovers determined the direction; and these, in turn, would deviate from a straight course when the yet more slowly flying dowitchers fell behind.

Among groups of mammals the socially dominant animal is often also the leader. An exception is shown by the herds of red deer of Scotland that have been carefully studied by Darling (1937). During most of the year the males remain away from the herds of hinds and younger animals. The leader of the hinds is an alert old female with fawn at foot. There is little evidence of social dominance in such herds. The stags enter the scene at the onset of the rutting season, and each male rounds up and dominates as many hinds as he can. Still he is not the real leader, for in case of danger the stag runs away, and leadership is seen to remain with the experienced female that usually leads the herd.

These female herds often have subsidiary leaders that help maintain strict watch, reminding one of the accounts of Sclater (1900) concerning leadership in hordes of African baboons. The baboons associate in groups that may number a hundred individuals. When moving, the old males are usually on the outskirts and form a rearguard. When resting, a sentinel or two are always on the lookout for approaching danger.

The comment of John Phillips (see Allee, 1931, p. 349) is worth quoting:

" . . . The sentinel is exceedingly sharp and detects the least noise, scent, or appearance of man or leopard. In East Africa I have seen other species of baboon behaving in the same manner. The sentinels are often the largest, strongest males, that is with the exception of the real leader of the group; they will remain faithfully at their post 'waughing' (the typical note of danger is 'waugh,' 'waugh,' very guttural and somewhat alarming) despite the proximity of danger. Upon these notes of warning reaching the ear of the leader, he will immediately assemble the leaders of the group, marshaling the males at the rear and along the sides, the females and the young at the forefront, or within the cordon of the males; he himself will alternately lead or bring up the rear, according to the plan of flight or the degree of danger. When things get too hot for the sentinels, they scamper off a short distance, mount some high position, and give a further warning to the leader. In times of slaughter, the young are protected by the parents, often with great danger to the latter."

If one may extrapolate from observations of captive baboons (Zuckerman, 1932) to those in the field—and biological extrapolation always involves some uncertainty—the leader among the baboons is also the socially dominant individual. Certainly dominance and leadership go together in the hordes of introduced rhesus monkeys that Carpenter (1942) has observed on Santiago Island off the coast of Puerto Rico. If the leader is strongly dominant and aggressive, his group ranges unmolested over a wider territory than do those led by less able individuals. Here we have a clear interplay of the three types of social systems based, respectively, on territory, hierarchy, and leadership.

The observations on the size and success of male-led baboon groups and rhesus monkey hordes warn against too complete acceptance of the suggestion of Darling (1937, p. 93) that among mammals "matriarchy makes for gregariousness and family cohesion. The patriarchal group can never be large, for however attentively the male may care for his group he is never selfless. Sexual jealousy is always ready to impinge on social relations leading to gregariousness."

Although there is much support for Darling's suggestion, especially in the contrast he gives between the size of the female-led herds of red deer and the small families of male-dominated roe deer, such generalizations cannot be applied too strictly. In addition to the success of hordes of rhesus monkeys led by aggressive males, another reason for caution is supplied by the situation existing within the companies of howling monkeys on Barro Colorado Island in the Canal Zone. Carpenter (1934) found that leadership in these territorial hordes resided in a group of males, and a sexually receptive female member of the local horde is possessed first by one male and then by another with no sign of social tension.

Another type of group organization, leadership, and territoriality of a kind, has been described by Sdobnikov (1935) for the reindeer herds of northern Eurasia. These herds are not simple mechanical associations of a number of animals. Rather, each herd is divided into two main groups that may be roughly recognized as "fringe" and "middle" reindeer. These groups are not accidental and variable, except as disease or some other debilitating factor may cause an animal to shift from the middle to the fringe. The young often remain with the group to which the mother belongs. Age and sex make no difference. The fringe reindeer are also divided similarly into subgroups: (a) "vanguard," (b) "side," and (c) "rear" or "tail" groups. The side reindeer belong either on the right or left side, but apparently not now to one side and later to the other.

The animals from the different sections of the herd show behavior differences. *Vanguard* reindeer are generally the most restless and nervous. They are timid and relatively wild. They are the first to finish eating, first to lie down and chew the cud, and first to get up again. They include the individual leaders of the herd if such are to be found. These leaders are not always present; they occur more frequently in older herds that have been formed for a long time. In the spring season, leadership is apparently more often assumed by females.

Side reindeer do not differ much in behavior from those of the vanguard. They are also timid and restless, and they frequently leave the herd and thus become chiefly responsible for fragmentation.

Rear or *tail* reindeer tend to be quiet and submissive; the latter do not run fast; they stay near the herd and spend most of their time feeding. They are frequently the best fed of all the animals, despite their eating what others have trampled and left behind. This is a handicap during winter, especially in large herds; in fact, in winter herds of 4000 or 5000, rear reindeer are always weak and badly nourished.

Middle reindeer are more quiet, peaceful animals, and they suffer less from predators than do those from the fringes of the main herd.

Within these different groups, more closely knit bands often occur that may have as many as thirty animals, but are generally smaller. They are formed by kinship or apparent friendship relations, and each such subgroup has an old female as a leader. They account for only a minority of the herd; most reindeer keep on their own within their general subdivision of the herd.

The territoriality shown by such aggregations is based on position with regard to associated animals, rather than to topographic or other features of the environment. The full extent to which such territoriality occurs elsewhere in the animal kingdom is a matter for investigation.

Leadership allows greater flexibility of behavior than is usual in territorial or hierarchal organizations. Territory and leadership both have fairly obvious survival values. The biological values associated with the system of social hierarchies are more obscure. It is easy to demonstrate individual selection accompanying high status in the social order, but the group survival values growing from this type of social organization, as such, have not yet been adequately analyzed.

At the individual level, highest ranking individuals in a social hierarchy lead the freest lives; they have more ready access to food and mates and to habitat niches. High ranking hens lay more eggs (Sanctuary, 1932), and cocks with high social status mate more frequently (Guhl, Collias, and Allee, 1945) and sire more chicks (Guhl and Warren, 1946). Similar relations hold in many penned mammals (cf. Cooper, 1942, for lions) and probably also in nature (cf. Carpenter, 1942, for rhesus monkeys). Conversely, low position in the social gradient carries restrictions that may be severe or even fatal in extreme cases.

We have no data as yet on the short-run or long-run success of relatively unorganized groups of animals in comparison with other groups of the same species arranged in a dominance hierarchy. Some critical work indicates that accepted social status, whatever the ranks involved, confers values not found in a group undergoing organization or reorganization. As an illustration, the sage grouse of Wyoming and other western states presents a modification of the habit of mating in restricted localities. The males assemble at each mating place in early spring and organize themselves with a "master cock" that does most of the copulating; "subcocks" are less successful socially; "guard-cocks" are still less active in mating; and the remaining cocks, constituting the majority of the entire male population, do little breeding (J. W. Scott, 1942).*

In one instance the cocks of a certain mating place shifted ground as a result of snow. This brought them near another set of mating males, and fighting continued through the usual mating hours. Females coming to the mating places with the first dawn, collected in numbers about the area where much fighting was in progress. Later in the morning, as the fighting between the males continued, the hens tended to move off to a mating place that was well organized and quiet† (see Guhl and Allee, 1944).

Groups of common domestic hens also show survival values related to quiet, organized hierarchies. Members of such flocks accept their usual social status, and there is much less tension than exists in flocks undergoing reorganization with continued strife. The hens in the organized flocks pecked each other less, consumed more food, maintained weight, and laid more eggs. These are qualities that might well have survival value in nature. Apparently the social organization in such groups is of importance, less as an end in itself than as a means of reducing fighting and other extremes of social tension.

There is justification for thinking that these laboratory findings are indicative of certain conditions in nature. If so, individual-against-individual competition, such as results in the peck-order type of social organization, may help to build a social unit

---

* These are the relations Scott has reported more than once, yet in the absence of banded birds, he is not completely sure how long a given individual remains in a given social rank.

† Personal communication.

better fitted to compete or cooperate with other flocks at the group level than are socially disorganized aggregations. Similar conclusions are suggested by naturalistic evidence.

There are many strong indications that cooperation at the individual level may also result in groups with increased compe:ence in competition or in cooperation at the group level. Any smoothly working group organization, however achieved, is helpful under many conditions. Probably the relations between individuals forming simple groups are repeated when such groups as social units become compounded into a more complex social order. Even when society becomes still more involved, unit-to-unit cooperation—or competition, if not too severe—may lead to group organization that increases the effectiveness of the larger unit in its competitions and cooperations (cf. Collias, 1944; Allee, 1945).

SUMMARY FOR NATURAL COOPERATION

Having brought the discussion of group organization to the point at which survival values have been considered, it is now fitting that we draw together many of the threads of thought running through this chapter by considering the evidence of natural cooperation in summary form. This summary may also serve as a partial substitute for a mass of data that cannot be presented here in detail. The evidence, however, clinches, with Darwin-like thoroughness, the preexperimental insight of Espinas (1877), Wheeler (1923) and others (History, p. 30) and the conclusions of Allee (e.g., 1947) based on experimental as well as naturalistic evidence, that natural, unconscious mutualism is one of the basic principles of biology.

1. At all levels in the animal kingdom, and under a variety of conditions, there is added safety in numbers up to a given point. There is danger also in overcrowding, but it is the ill effects from undercrowding that give the most generalized evidence for natural cooperation or at least for proto-cooperation among living organisms. Macerated cells of a sponge will not develop if too few are present, and the smallest embryonic transplants often fail to grow when somewhat larger ones succeed.

If a population in nature becomes reduced to a few individuals, it is in danger of dying out, even though apparently able to persist.

2. Many plants and animals are able to modify an unfavorable environment to such an extent that, though some or all of the pioneers may be killed, others following and some associated with them can survive and even thrive when they could not do so in a raw environment.

3. Certain vital processes are adaptively retarded by increased numbers up to a given population density. For example, scattered spermatozoa of many marine animals lose fertilizing power more rapidly than they do when massed together.

4. Other biological processes are beneficially accelerated in the presence of populations of optimal size and density. Such processes are retarded both with oversparse and with overcrowded populations. The cleavage rates in sea urchin eggs and certain other aquatic eggs follow this rule.

5. Various kinds of Protozoa show an acceleration in rate of asexual reproduction with a medium rather than a sparse population density. Similar phenomena may have been a forerunner of the evolution of sex that, according to this attractive hypothesis, grew out of certain proto-cooperations of asexual organisms. Once evolved, sexual relations have played a large part in the further development of the social life of animals, including man.

6. Colonial Protozoa could hardly have arisen from solitary forms unless the colony of cells that remained attached to each other after divisions had shown survival values over and above those exhibited when the cells were scattered singly.

7. The evolution of the many-celled animals, the Metazoa, from the Protozoa was probably based on similar relationships.

8. Each advance in complexity of metazoan individuals came from the natural selection of an increased ability in natural cooperation on the part of the evolving stock.

9. Charles Darwin recognized that a relatively large population is a highly important factor in evolution by natural selection. There is more recent evidence that evolution proceeds more rapidly and certainly in populations of interbreeding animals that are not too small.

10. The interdependence of organisms is shown by the repeated observation that all living things, from the simplest to the most complex, live in communities. This is easily seen in such microcosms as those of a protozoan culture dish, or a small lake, or in biocoenoses, like those of an oyster bed.

11. The evolution of truly social animals, such as termites, bees, and ants on the one hand and man on the other, has occurred independently in widely separated divisions of the animal kingdom. These could hardly have arisen so many times and from such diverse sources if a strong substratum of generalized natural proto-co-operation—call it physiological facilitation, if you prefer—were not widespread among animals in nature. Such tendencies precede and condition the formation of animal concentrations, the existence of which is prerequisite for the development of group organization.

12. No animal is solitary throughout its whole life history.

13. As in the individual organism, each advance in complexity of the social life of any group of animals is based on the development of some means of closer cooperation between the individual units of the evolving group.

24. THE ORGANIZATION OF INSECT SOCIETIES

The social insects illustrate the culmination of the action of various factors upon invertebrate population groups (p. 393, Chap. 22). They have the general properties of populations that have already been discussed at the beginning of this section (Chapters 18–23): natality, mortality, dispersion, growth form, and density (p. 272). The social insect colony, like other populations, resembles an organism in that it has structure, ontogeny, heredity, and integration, and forms a unit in an environment (p. 683).

Statistical and experimental analyses of population factors have been applied more rigorously to infrasocial populations, particularly to laboratory populations. The social insects lend themselves to certain types of quantitative analysis (p. 310; also see Emerson, 1939a), as may be seen in the studies by Talbot (1943, 1945), Bodenheimer (1937), and Pickles (1935, 1936, 1937, 1938, 1940).

The growth curve of a social insect colony has been shown to be sigmoid or logistic (Bodenheimer, 1937; see also Fig. 102). This results from factors influencing the reproductive capacity of a few individuals, or even of a single queen, together with dispersion and mortality factors operating upon various stages in the life cycle, upon sterile castes making up the bulk of the adult population, and upon reproductive adults. In some respects the colony population is comparable to populations of infrasocial species (Fig. 101). In other respects, populations of colonies are comparable to populations of reproductive individuals of infrasocial species.

Analysis of social populations may sometimes necessitate a further refinement of methods usually adequate for infrasocial groups. For example, Pickles (1938) divides density of ant species into three categories. *Lowest density* is the total population divided by the area covered by the census; *economic density* is the total population divided by the territory actually occupied; *greatest density* is the population of the nest at night. Proportional relations of such densities to weight of the ants per unit area vary with species and conditions and facilitate a more refined comparison and interpretation (Emerson, 1939a). These terms may also be applied to certain infrasocial populations.

Many gradations of integration may be found in various subsocial populations (family systems and aggregations of adults) that connect the social insects with the various types of infrasocial groupings. In some instances the subsocial species may be considered a phylogenetic stage in the evolution of the social insects (pp. 686 and 687).

In other instances the subsocial population is not ancestral to the strictly social forms; nevertheless, it illustrates principles of integration and division of labor that logically connect the infrasocial and strictly social. The beetles, in particular, offer many examples of subsocial population systems that have not evolved societies in the strict sense (p. 687; Wheeler, 1921; 1928b, p. 17).

The organization within intraspecies populations reaches its most diagrammatic expression in the strictly social insects (p. 687), i.e., those that exhibit adult division of labor in their societies (Isoptera and certain Hymenoptera). We here examine some of the factors that facilitate the grouping of the individuals into such a society. More extensive discussion, together with details of social activities, will be found in the works of Wheeler (1907, 1926, 1928a, 1928b), Hegh (1922), and

greater efficiency associated with specialization of function—and thus illustrate the principle of division of labor characteristic of all levels of biological integration (p. 683).

A well-defined division of labor is characteristic of the strictly social animals. Separated functions of the parts make coordination necessary. Division of labor and integration advance as reciprocal manifestations in both ontogeny and phylogeny of the social population, paralleling similar manifestations in the organism. This parallelism between the organism and the society is included in the concept of the

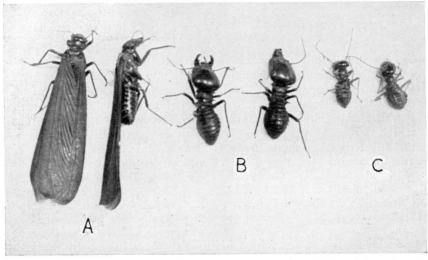

Fig. 146. The three primary castes of the termite, *Syntermes snyderi*, from British Guiana; *A*, winged reproductives; *B*, mandibulate soldiers; *C*, workers.

Emerson (1938, 1939, 1939a, 1942, 1943, 1947). An examination of the division of labor between individuals composing the group and the integrative mechanisms that give unity to the group should afford a perspective both for an understanding of aggregations in general and for the analogous human society of which we are a part.

DIVISION OF LABOR AMONG SOCIAL INSECTS

A self-sustaining biological unit must acquire the energy for life from the environment, protect this energy from exploitation by other organisms, maintain ecological position, and reproduce its kind. The fundamental adaptations for these biological necessities are somewhat separated in the organism—probably because of the

supra-organism (pp. 427, 435, 693, 698).

The reproductive castes function for the maintenance of the species and for the founding of new colonies. In becoming specialized for reproduction, enlargement of the gonads in the queens is accompanied by specialized sexual behavior and regression of feeding and protective adaptations. The reproductive castes may thus be analogized with the gametes of the organism, which have also become specialized for maintenance of the species and do not develop the functions of the somatic cells.

In the more primitive social Hymenoptera (wasps, bees, and ponerine ants), the worker caste is the only sterile caste and is always female. In the termites, the worker (Fig. 146) is found only among the more specialized families and may be either a sterile male or female. Among the primitive termites, nymphs of the other castes perform the functions of the workers, which are primarily nutritive and collect food from the habitat (trophoporic field). In a few instances the worker termites and ants cultivate gardens of fungi (pp. 713, 714) or, among certain ants, tend animals such as aphids or coccids (p. 719) that may be guarded and enclosed within shelters. Food may be stored by the workers, either in portions of the nest or in their own bodies ("repletes" of honey ants). The workers feed the other castes and young, either with the gathered food or with digested foods or secretions. Shelters ranging from simple burrows to elaborate constructions are built by the workers.

largest form of a polymorphic series) remain in the ground nests unless disturbed; they then emerge in great numbers for the defense of the colony. Their function seems to be wholly protective. In some ants with a sharp morphological difference between the soldier and worker (i.e., *Pheidole*), experimental colonies composed of reproductives, larvae, and soldiers, without workers, are maintained in a healthy state by the soldiers (Gregg, 1942).

REPRODUCTION IN SOCIAL INSECTS

The reproductive castes of social insects are least modified in comparison with their solitary ancestors. A wasp queen is known to have laid ten eggs in twenty-four hours, and mature queens of primitive bees, ants,

Fig. 147. Side view of army ants (*Eciton hamatum*) transporting their larvae slung under their bodies during a change of the bivouac site. A large white-headed "soldier" stands guard beside the trail in the upper left. (Photograph by Ralph Buchsbaum.)

Soldiers are primarily the protective caste. The soldier is the primitive sterile caste among the termites (Fig. 146), may be either a male or female, and in the final ontogenetic stage functions wholly for the protection of the colony against predaceous enemies. Soldiers are absent from the bee and wasp societies, in which the worker defends the colony in addition to its other functions. Among the ants, the soldier is always a sterile female, and shows many intergradations of structure and behavior with the worker caste. The army ant (*Eciton*) "soldier" is the largest form of a polymorphic series of workers (Fig. 147). It captures and transports the prey, as well as defends the colony with its sting and large mandibles. The smaller army ant workers also defend the colony with their stings and smaller mandibles. In the leafcutting ants (*Atta*), the soldiers (also the

and termites often do not have greater fecundity. The female in the more highly social forms has increased her egg-laying capacity and often shows an enlarged abdomen commensurate with her enlarged ovaries. Army ant queens periodically produce as many as 20,000 eggs in a few days. A honeybee queen is known to have laid 3021 eggs in a day. A queen of a large termite colony (Fig. 148) may lay 6000 to 7000 eggs within twenty-four hours, and she keeps up this rate without diel or seasonal periodicities for many years (estimated as long as fifty years). Having relinquished feeding and protective behavior, as well as the care of her eggs and offspring, she is in effect a specialized egg-laying machine. She has exudate glands that are partially responsible for the feeding and grooming bestowed upon her by the workers. Great fecundity of queens is correlated with high social organization and large colonies.

The males of the social insects are only slightly modified, compared with the males of their solitary ancestors. In the Hymenoptera they function for the fecundation of the new queens and seem to have no other social value. They do not accompany the fertile queen when she founds a new colony. In the queen honeybee, the sperma-

In addition to the production of gametes and insuring their fertilization, the reproductives of social insects also reproduce the colony unit. Thus colonizing behavior has been added to the antecedent sexual behavior and oviposition. In this connection it should be noted that the ecological ages (p. 285) in the life history of individuals are in part characteristic of the whole social insect colony (p. 310). Although the

Fig. 148. Model of a royal cell of the termite, *Constrictotermes cavifrons*, from British Guiana. The queen with an enlarged abdomen occupies the center of the chamber with her head toward the right. The king is at the lower left. Most of the individuals are workers. A few nasute soldiers with "squirt gun" heads and reduced mandibles are at the left. A termitophilous staphylinid beetle, *Corotoca guyanae*, with a physogastric abdomen is below the head of the queen. (Courtesy of Buffalo Society of Natural Sciences.)

tozoa stored in the spermatheca at the time of the single copulation remain capable of fertilizing eggs laid during the six to eight years of life of the queen. In the ants, queens may lay fertile eggs for as long as fifteen years. In the termites, spermatozoa are not stored for long periods of time, and copulation occurs at short intervals throughout the life of the queen. The male termite accompanies the female and assists in founding the new colony. He has exudate glands that attract workers who feed and groom him.

queen in a growing colony may be producing workers, colonizing reproductives may be produced only in a mature colony. Before the colonizing flight, many winged reproductives are present in the colony. Holdaway, Gay, and Greaves (1935) reported 2.4 per cent alates (44,000 in a total population of 1,806,500) in a colony of *Nasutitermes exitiosus* in Australia.

Colony senescence and death occur especially in temperate regions, but it is an open question whether the colony as a unit has a physiological age comparable

nest-building activities for their captors. *Polyergus* workers starve, even in the presence of abundant and suitable food, if deprived of their slaves. In observation nests, one slave can keep ten slave-makers well fed. The original colony of slave-makers probably is founded by a queen that invades a *Formica* nest of an appropriate species, kills the queen, and takes her place. When the *Formica* population is depleted, the slave raids replenish the population of slaves.

SHELTER AMONG SOCIAL INSECTS

The nests of the social insects stabilize the physical environment and thus control various ecologic factors at more optimal values (pp. 428, 439, 672). Nests of primitive social insects, are often merely burrows in the soil or in dead wood. Elaborate structures may be built of earth particles glued with organic excretions and secretions (termites, ants), or plant materials such as wood particles or chewed bark (termites, ants, wasps), of excrement (termites), or secretions from special glands (wax of bees). Certain nests may stabilize temperature (Figs. 150, 151), humidity, or gaseous exchange (Figs. 231–233). Some termite nests have rain-shedding covers or ridges (Figs. 154, 235). The nests of some social insects may serve for the storage of food or the cultivation of fungi. Most nests probably protect their builders from predators. The social homeostasis attained through nest construction often enables these insects to inhabit otherwise unfavorable habitats. For example, the mound nests of ants and termites in periodically flooded grasslands or swampy regions enable the insects to maintain ecological position (p. 671) in relation to water. Nest construction and shelter tubes enable termites to become abundant insects in desert regions in spite of their susceptibility to death from evaporation in dry air.

The structures built by social insects are usually formed of dead or nonliving material external to the insect. Some nests, however, are composed partly or wholly of secretions. Rarely, as in the bivouacs of army ants or the clusters of bees, the bodies of the insects themselves may be used for homeostatic control (p. 431; Fig. 152). In each of these cases, subtle and often highly complex social behavior and cooperative effort are manifest.

DEFENSE FROM PREDATORS

In the more primitive social Hymenoptera, the worker caste defends the colony from external attack. In the more highly integrated insect societies of ants and termites, the defensive function is performed primarily by the soldier caste. Primitive termites (i.e., Kalotermitidae) lack adult workers, and only soldiers constitute the adult sterile caste. More specialized termites (i.e., Termitidae) have 3 to 16 per cent soldiers in the adult sterile-caste population. The percentage of soldiers gathering at points of attack or disturbance may be as high as 100 per cent (Fig. 149).

Defensive adaptations of the soldier ant, like that of the antecedent solitary hunting wasp, is often linked with predatory adjustments. In some instances, however, it is possible to separate the adaptations for offense from those for defense. The soldiers of the ant genera *Colobopsis* and *Cryptocerus* have phragmotic heads that have convergently evolved as plugs for the entrance holes of the nests (p. 233, Fig. 63). Each colony of *Cryptocerus* occupying an enlarged hollow twig contains only one or two soldiers, whose only function seems to be that of being "doorman" for the colony, preventing the entrance of predators and trespassers, and allowing the workers easy entrance and exit. The soldiers of certain genera of termites (*Cryptotermes, Glyptotermes,* and their relatives) have evolved phragmotic heads (also convergently) that plug the internal burrows and thus protect the colony from invasion. The mandibles of these soldiers are somewhat reduced, compared with those of their relatives whose soldiers have no phragmotic adaptation.

The minor soldier of the termite, *Rhinotermes,* has reduced mandibles; the labrum is prolonged into a slender grooved structure with a forked pubescent tip. A fluid from the opening of the frontal gland in the head is exuded, rolls down the groove of the labrum and rests at the tip until it evaporates, in this manner producing a repellent and somewhat toxic gas. The major soldier in the same colony has large biting mandibles, and the frontal gland is much smaller than in the minor soldier.

The nasute soldier (Figs. 148, 149), characteristic of a number of genera in the sub-family Nasutitermitinae, has reduced mandibles and a prolonged frontal portion of the head with the glandular opening at its tip. The frontal gland in the head secretes a viscid and chemically irritating that are attached by silken threads spun from the mouths of the larvae. Some workers hold the leaves together while other workers bring the larvae to the edges of the leaves, where they are moved back and forth as they spin the silk that attaches the leaves firmly together. By the recipro-

Fig. 149. Nasute soldiers of the termite, *Nasutitermes ephratae,* standing guard at a break in the surface of their nest. Heads of workers repairing the break can be seen at the edge of the hole at the middle right and upper right. (Photograph by Ralph Buchsbaum.)

fluid that is forcibly shot out of the "squirt-gun" for a distance of half an inch. The nasute soldier effectively defends the colony against such enemies as ants.

DIVISION OF LABOR AND ONTOGENY

Rösch (1930) reports a temporal division of labor in the life of an individual honeybee worker. This sequence of activities, roughly outlined in Table 29, is indicative of an order often to be found, but should not be construed rigidly. Rösch says that the division of labor is flexible without any hard and fast time schedule. Young field bees may return to nursing functions if there is a need.

An example of a social function at different stages in the life cycle is found in the Old World genus of ants, *Œcophylla.* The nests of these ants are constructed of leaves

cal action of the workers and larvae, an arboreal nest is constructed.

MECHANISMS OF SOCIAL INTEGRATION

Division of labor and integration are associated principles. Integration has no function unless there are differentiated parts that must act in relation to the whole. Specialization of function cannot occur unless the specialized parts are coordinated. Efficient homeostasis follows an increase in the special functions of integrated parts. These principles apply to every organismic level (p. 683) from the cell to the ecosystem, but are particularly well exhibited by the population of a colony of social insects.

These facts afford proof of the unity of the population (p. 389). Of course, at this stage of our knowledge we are far from

Table 29. *Temporal Division of Labor Often Found in the Life of an Individual Adult Worker Honeybee (From Rösch, 1927, 1930; Morland, 1930)*

Stage	Duration in Days	Age in Days
1st period: Nurse bees		
Incubating brood, preparing brood cells...........................	2–3	1–3
Feeding older larvae with honey and pollen........................	3	3–6
Feeding young larvae with brood food............................	4–9	6–15
2d period: House bees		
First trial flight		
Storekeeper (receiving, ripening, and storing nectar)		
House cleaner ⎫	10	10–25
Wax secretion ⎬		
Guard at hive entrance ⎭		
3d period: Field bees		
Forager for water, pollen, nectar, and propolis......................	20–30	20–55

having complete information concerning all the details. For that matter we are in an early stage of comprehension of functions and integration that make any organism an organism. But we know enough to see that the social insect colony has a pattern significantly similar to that of a lowly multicellular organism such as a sponge. The correlations may be synthesized under the concept of a social supra-organism (p. 435). We shall review here a few of the mechanisms of social integration among the insects.

GENETIC INTEGRATION

The primary link between individuals of an intraspecies population is hereditary continuity. Autocatalytic gene patterns are passed along from generation to generation. They initiate ontogenetic patterns of development and function. Wright (1934) concisely summarizes the relation of genetic and physiological systems in the development of the organism.

It is true that "the different offspring of a single queen cannot be genetically identical, for the factors in which their mother is heterozygous must segregate. . . . Such genetic variability, however, . . . seems not to be utilized in producing polymorphism" (Fisher, 1930, p. 181). With the exception of sex differentiation, the different castes of most social insects seem to develop from genetically similar eggs.

Physiological agents acting at certain thresholds of development determine the direction the individual will take. This situation parallels the genetic capacity of the fertilized egg cell under appropriate physiological conditions to produce any type of differentiated cell characteristic of the particular organism. Thus the analogy of somatic tissues with the sterile castes of social insects is founded upon fundamental biological similarities, and the sterile castes may be properly referred to as somatic individuals in the social supra-organism.

Sex determination among the social insects follows the same systems as are found in their solitary ancestors. A discussion of some of the evolutionary implications of the haploid male and diploid female in the Hymenoptera will be found later (pages 687 and 688; also see Flanders, 1939, 1946). It is well to point out here, however, that convergent social systems have evolved with many astonishing parallelisms in the ants and termites (p. 435), one with haplodiploidy, the other probably with sex chromosomes. The fact that sexually and therefore genetically different individuals can be incorporated into a social supra-organism is proof that the population represents a different level of integration compared with a multicellular individual, and that the similarities between these systems are strictly analogous and not homologous, even though some of the mechanisms of differentiation and integration may be remarkably similar.

PHYSIOLOGICAL INTEGRATION

Like the hormones and induction agents of the organism, chemical agents seem to integrate the social supra-organism.

Particularly through the experiments upon termites conducted by Light (1942–43, 1944) and his associates, it is well established that the presence of mature males, females, or soldiers, respectively, inhibits the development of the same caste from undifferentiated nymphs. Gregg (1942) has also experimentally demonstrated that soldier ants inhibit the development of more soldiers (see also Flanders, 1945, 1946). The most adequate theory to account for the facts is that each of these castes gives off an exudate or "exohormone" that passes to the developing individuals, or possibly to the unlaid eggs in the Hymenoptera, by licking or feeding or nutritive physiology, thus inhibiting the development of either reproductives or soldiers unless the population increases beyond the minimum threshold effects of a certain amount of the inhibiting agent. Theoretically, the worker does not inhibit the development of other workers, but inhibition by reproductives and soldiers results in the development of workers. This theoretical physiological mechanism accounts for the periodic production of mature reproductive individuals in the colony. We may thus see a possible analogue to the hormonal mechanism that periodically controls the production of mature gametes in the vertebrate organism.

It might be expected, if these physiological mechanisms determine caste production in termites, that the proportion of the castes would be automatically controlled. Some evidence has been reported by Miller (1942) that the numbers of soldiers of Prorhinotermes simplex in experimental colonies reach an average proportion (one soldier to 3.5 "workers," with a standard deviation of 2.3 and a standard error of 0.55) regardless of the number of soldiers at the beginning of the experiment.

In the honeybee, the worker and drone larvae are fed brood food (royal jelly—a nitrogenous secretion from pharyngeal glands opening into the mouth) for the first two or three days, and are fed bee bread (a mixture of nectar and pollen) for another three days, after which the cells are capped. Queen larvae are fed entirely with royal jelly—normally for five and one-half days. The trophogenic substances may carry activating or inhibiting agents that direct caste development.

BEHAVIOR INTEGRATION

As might be expected in a population system without protoplasmic contact between the individuals of the group, integration is established through behavior mechanisms. The behavior is initiated through sensory stimuli, particularly through senses responsive to temperature, humidity, and auditory, chemical, visual, and tactile stimuli.

The sensory apparatus involved in reactions to temperature and humidity in insects are unknown, but there is no doubt of the response. Bumblebee and honeybee workers station themselves at the entrance to their nests on hot days and circulate air by vibrating their wings (see pages 215 and 363).

Ant mounds of a few north temperature species (i.e., Formica ulkei, F. rufa, and F. truncocorum) may be constructed with a long gradual slope toward the south and a steeper slope toward the north, thus offering more surface for the absorption of the sun radiation. Dreyer (1942) reports a 40 per cent greater area of the sunny slope compared with that of the shady slope of a mound of Formica ulkei in northern Illinois (see p. 362).

The meridian mound nests of a tropical termite (Amitermes meridionalis) in northern Australia are oriented with a long axis of about 10 feet running north and south, and a short axis of about 2 feet running east and west, and a sharp edge on top (Figs. 150, 151). It is presumed that the shape of the nest, with its broad faces toward the rising and setting sun and its narrow edge toward the vertical rays, gives a relatively stabile internal nest temperature during the daytime.

Without experimentation, it is difficult to separate the reactions to temperature from those to humidity. Worker termites that construct definitive mound nests (i.e., those of the termitid, Amitermes foreli, in Panama) always move to the moist end of a humidity gradient. One may conclude that the nest-building behavior of termites produces a homeostatic humidity close to 100 per cent within the nest environment

(Fyfe and Gay, 1938), that the control of temperature is secondary to the control of humidity, and that light unassociated with temperature or humidity is not a factor

Fig. 150. East face of the meridian nest of the termite, *Amitermes meridionalis*, in northern Australia. (Courtesy of G. F. Hill.)

Fig. 151. South edges of several nests of the meridian termite, *Amitermes meridionalis*, in northern Australia. (Courtesy of G. F. Hill.)

determining the behavior of blind termites.

Sound signals are used by some of the social insects and doubtless are responsible for some coordinated activity. Some ants,

notably *Termitopone* (*Syntermitopone*) *commutata*, stridulate sonorously during their raids upon their termite prey. Soldier termites belonging to widely separated taxonomic groups hammer their heads on the substrate when disturbed, often producing a rapid tapping audible to the human ear. Waves of tapping may be heard moving through a colony.

Probably the most important of the senses used in colony integration is the chemical sense. On occasion olfactory organs may be separated from organs of taste, but these chemical senses in insects are often difficult to distinguish (Wheeler, 1928b, p. 231).

Reactions to colony odor have been demonstrated in every group of social insects. Strange odors initiate antagonistic responses in most groups. The odor of an individual may be easily modified experimentally. Not only is it possible to initiate antagonism to another individual in the same colony of ants, termites, or bees by changing the odor of the individual, but it is also possible to introduce strange individuals into a colony by giving them the colony odor. Individuals from different colonies may be given similar odors by keeping them in the same nest for a few hours, but protected from each other, by anesthetizing all present with the same gas, or by cooling them in a refrigerator, and allowing them to recover together. Dropkin (1941) was thus able to condition different species and even different families of termites to live together amicably. It may be assumed that a neutral substance on the surface of the insect absorbs the odor of the environment and that individuals react antagonistically to any insect that does not have the colony odor, whether the insect is of the same or a different species. Termitophilous beetles are accepted or rejected by a termite colony on the basis of their odor in much the same manner that an individual termite may be accepted or rejected. In addition to the modifiable odor, there are probably inherited odors that separate species.

Subtle chemical differences may determine cannibalistic action common among ants and termites. Cannibalism is often initiated by injury. One may even see that the injured part attracts attacking individuals. The parallel to phagocytosis within the organism is fairly obvious. Cannibalism is increased among termites at periods when nitrogenous material is deficient (Cook and Scott, 1933). Cannibalism at times probably regulates the colony population much as phagocytosis regulates some aspects of the cell population within an organism, and may consequently be considered adaptive behavior.

The adaptive drone-elimination behavior of honeybee workers (p. 690) is probably initiated by odor stimuli, although the details of the mechanism are unknown. Drone elimination is the most remarkable case of population control known among the social insects.

Pardi (1948) gives an interesting account of social dominance and a social hierarchy among the several overwintering females of the wasp, *Polistes gallicus*. In Italy these are associated with the founding of a colony in the spring. Farther north, the colony is usually founded by a single female.

In the "polygynic" Italian colonies, one of the females remains on the nest, lays eggs, is less active in construction work, and dominates her associates. The dominated females are more active in bringing in food and building the nest, but lay fewer eggs. The ovaries of these "auxiliary females" gradually decrease in size and function. After the workers appear, the auxiliary females are eliminated by the sting of the dominant female (queen) or by exclusion from the colony. The dominance-subordination relations establish an order for the division of labor and thus benefit the group if not too severe.

In the contacts among the females and also between females and workers, and among the workers, the dominant individual repeatedly strikes the head of the other with her antennae, and the subordinate individual takes a characteristic position (*akynesis*) with head lowered. During the first contact, the dominant individual gives liquid to the subordinate. Later the subordinate regurgitates liquid that may be sucked by the dominant. The subordinate gives more liquid to the dominant than it receives.

The dominant generally maintains its position with the same individual in later contacts until dominance is lost with age. Fighting often occurs during the establishment of the order. Sometimes individuals are equal and are intolerant of each other.

A linear hierarchy is often established not unlike the hierarchy of hens (see p. 413). Triangles occur in some cases. Males are dominated by both females and workers. If the queen is eliminated, the next lower female takes her place, and her ovaries increase in size and function. Workers can take the place of the queen and can rapidly develop egg-laying capacity. There is a close correlation between dominance and size of ovary.

Although hierarchical relations may influence the social system of primitive social insects, there is little to indicate much importance of such relations in the more advanced insect societies. Possibly the more cooperative types of integration replace the social hierarchy based upon individual competition as the societal system advances during development and evolution. In this connection it should be pointed out that a social hierarchy resulting from individual combat depends upon a capacity to learn, and the establishment of social order of such a type would be expected to be much more characteristic of vertebrate animals than of insects.

Wheeler (1918) proposed the concept of *trophallaxis* (exchange of nourishment) as a mechanism of integration among the social insects. Olfactory as well as gustatory exchanges are included in the concept (Wheeler, 1928b, p. 231), and the theory may also be expanded to include tactile stimuli (Schneirla, 1946). Many larvae as well as adults have glandular secretions that induce social activity. These glands may be generally distributed over the surface of the body or may be localized in the so-called exudatoria. Direct feeding by glandular secretions, like the royal jelly secreted from the pharyngeal glands by the worker honeybee, may occur. In most instances the secretions have special, attractive qualities that induce licking and grooming. Such secretions may carry physiologic agents that influence growth as well as induce behavior reactions (p. 428). The fact that other participants in the trophallactic circle, such as the termitophiles and myrmecophiles, convergently develop specialized glandular secretions that seem to enable them to adjust to the social systems of their hosts is proof of the importance of these chemical substances for social integration (see pp. 719–721).

The queen termite not only attracts considerable special attention from the workers who feed her, groom her, and remove her eggs to adjoining nursery chambers, but seems also to be the center of a behavior gradient that results in the spherical symmetry of nest-building activity. Particularly in the round arboreal nests of the genus *Nasutitermes,* the walls of the queen cell and neighboring cells are much thicker than those of the peripheral cells of the nest. Not

(1938, 1944, 1945, 1947). The army ants have temporary bivouacs in sheltered niches. The bodies of the living ants compose the structure of the bivouac (Fig. 152) in which live the brood and the photonegative queen. Large numbers of predatory workers issue forth on raiding parties, subject to certain periodic stimuli. The queen of *Eciton hamatum* becomes physogastric and produces large numbers of eggs (more than 20,000 within a few days) at intervals of thirty-five

Fig. 152. Bivouac of army ants (*Eciton hamatum*) on the underside of a fallen log in Panama. The larger white-headed individuals are large workers or "soldiers." (Photograph by Ralph Buchsbaum.)

only is there an activity gradient of nest-building behavior centering about the queen, but the walls are chemically different, with gradations in the amount of organic material used in their construction (Holdaway, 1933). The queen is thus a social analogue to a center of physiological dominance within the organism and probably induces activity gradients in behavior through chemical stimuli that are responsible for the spherical symmetry of these termite nests.

The intricate social-stimulative effects of trophallactic agents are illustrated by the organization and periodicity of army ant behavior. These have been carefully studied in the field and laboratory by Schneirla

or thirty-six days. The activity of the moving larvae excites the workers, and this excitement increases progressively throughout the colony by means of interindividual stimulation. Any stimulation that increases general excitement augments raiding, and three or more extensively developed raiding systems during each day of this period inevitably lead to a bivouac change in the afternoon (Fig. 153). This nomadic period lasts about seventeen days. When the brood has become enclosed in cocoons, the colony becomes statary (minimal raiding and absence of bivouac change) and remains in this condition for about nineteen days, during which time only a single raiding system is developed each day and the bivouac remains in one place. The moving pupae within the cocoons stimulate the workers to open the cocoons, and the restless movements of the callows excite the workers tactually and perhaps chemically. When the level of raiding activity is raised, the nomadic change of the bivouac site is resumed. The day-night rhythm is based upon excitation by light. Approximately seven days after a given statary period, a new

tion between infant and mother during breast feeding. He points out that the "social outcome of insect trophallaxis is largely set by hereditary factors; the social outcome of human trophallaxis is highly variable and plastic, in dependence upon a given cultural setting."

We accept the significance of Schneirla's discussion of the analogous trophallaxis in the social integration of ants and man, but

Fig. 153. Army ants (*Eciton hamatum*) transporting their larvae slung under their bodies during a change of the bivouac site. Note the different sizes of the workers. (Photograph by Ralph Buchsbaum.)

batch of eggs is produced by the queen, who develops a physogastric condition only during the short egg-producing period.

Schneirla has thus shown that intra-societal factors, such as the reproductive cycle of the queen and the brood cycle, are basic in determining the pattern of army ant behavior, and that factors external to the colony impart diel rhythms and other special characteristics.

Schneirla (1946) not only accepts trophallaxis (including exchange of nourishment, chemicals, and tactile stimuli) as an important mechanism for the stimulation of social response among the insects, but he applies the theory to human social processes and cites as an example the mutual stimula-

in the same paper he concludes that the analogy between organism and supra-organism, and also the comparison of dominance hierarchies found in various vertebrates, are inadequate for the study of comparative social behavior. Instead of dismissing the concepts of the supra-organism and social hierarchy as insignificant, we think that they are significant in both the analysis and synthesis of convergently evolved social systems. Circular effects are doubtless involved in explaining the interactions within an organism or within a social insect colony. The survival of the whole is the mechanism that brings about the evolution of the parts adapted to each other, and the parts in turn determine the activities of the whole.

The experiments of von Frisch (1942, 1943, 1946) illustrate many aspects of behavior integration of honeybees, and also demonstrate the role of conditioned or learned behavior in association with various chemical, tactual, and visual responses. By placing sugar-water in dishes on various colors and shades of cards, von Frisch trained worker bees to come to certain colors. He was thus able to determine their visual response and sensitivity. The workers are color-blind for scarlet red, reacting to this color (above 650 μμ) as they do to black. The bees react to ultraviolet light (down to 300 μμ). By switching colored cards during the approach of the bee to the food, while the bee is feeding, and while the bee is leaving, it was determined that the bee returns to the color associated with the food at the time of approach, and not to the colors placed under the food at the time of feeding or leaving. A "scout" bee that locates a food supply returns to the nest and performs a dance on the honeycomb in the presence of other workers. The dance consists of motion in small circles with short steps. It may last a minute or longer and may be repeated in different places on the comb. Other bees, pushed by the dancer, are excited and may be seen touching the abdomen of the dancing bee with their antennae. Soon a group of bees is stimulated to follow the dancer to the food source and its associated color. When the group returns to the hive with filled crops, each bee in turn may perform a dance and stimulate other bees to follow it back to the food source.

Bees may also be trained to respond to certain odors. The scout bees impart the odor associated with the food to other bees in the hive. This is probably the explanation of the tendency of bees to visit one kind of flower for a definite period. Were it not for this temporary specialized behavior, bees would not be the efficient pollinizing agents that they are and flowers would probably not have evolved the remarkable adaptations for pollination by such insects (pp. 248 and 250). During the food dance, von Frisch transferred pollen from *Campanula* to *Rosa* and found that the bees trained on *Campanula* returned to the *Rosa*, thus showing that the scent of the pollen took precedence over the scent of the flower.

The scout bee is able to communicate the direction and distance of food to other workers by means of its food dance on the comb. If the food is 50 meters or less from the hive, the scout performs a turning dance. If the distance is between 50 and 100 meters, the dance includes a short straight run between the turns. The abdomen is wagged during this straight run. At distances greater than 100 meters, the number of straight runs decreases per unit of time, while the wagging motions increase. If the food is toward the sun, the straight run is vertically upward on the comb. A downward run indicates direction away from the sun. A deviation of 10 degrees to the right of the vertical indicates food 10 degrees to the right of the sun. Any angle to the right or left of the vertical corresponds to the angle to the right or left of the sun. If the comb is on its side, the straight run of the dance is in the direction of the food. Direction and distance are thus communicated to other workers by the scout bees (Schmieder, 1947).

Bees with partially filled crops or pollen baskets do not perform dances, so that the number of bees visiting any source of food is in proportion to the abundance of the food. Flying bees are also attracted to rich sources of food by the emission of scent by the bees that have found the food. The dorsal scent gland is in a fold between the fifth and sixth abdominal segments, which are stretched out in the presence of abundant food.

It is often difficult to separate the chemical and tactile sense involved in a particular behavior pattern among the social insects. Possibly both types of sensory reponse are associated in the commonly observed mutual antennal tapping among ants. As already pointed out (p. 430), both chemical and tactile senses are included under the concept of trophallaxis.

The sexual attraction between male and female termites (*Reticulitermes*) after the colonizing flight surely involves both olfactory and tactile response, but the two responses are separable (Emerson, 1933). The male is attracted to the female by an odor emitted from her raised abdomen. Once the male has touched the female, she lowers her abdomen and moves off with the male following in tandem. The tandem behavior results from the symmetrical tactile stimulation of the eighth, ninth, or tenth antennal articles of the male. Abnormal behavior always occurs in experiments in which less than eight articles are left in one antenna, and sometimes occurs with the removal of the eighth, ninth, or tenth article. Experimental removal of a portion of the left antenna behind the eighth article results in the male moving forward to the head of the female on her right side. This behavior of the male may also occur with experimental removal of the eighth, ninth, or tenth article. He moves forward on her left side if the right antenna is removed behind the eighth article, and this action sometimes happens if the eighth, ninth, or tenth article is removed. Removal of the peripheral portion of either or both antennae beyond the tenth of the seventeen or eighteen articles in the complete antenna does not modify tandem behavior. Removal of both antennae behind the eighth article always destroys the tandem response.

The sensory stimulus that seems to determine whether the queen bee will lay a fertilized egg that develops into a worker, or an unfertilized egg that develops into a drone, is the slightly different thickness of the side walls of the drone and worker brood cells constructed by the workers. The walls are 0.076 to 0.092 mm. thick in worker cells, and 0.127 to 0.152 mm. thick in drone cells. One may guess that this difference in thickness stimulates the closing or opening of the spermathecal duct through which the spermatozoa pass to the vagina, where the egg may be penetrated by a sperm cell (Flanders, 1939).

The action of army ants in using their own bodies in the construction of smooth and level roadways and of their bivouac (Fig. 152) is also probably a reaction to tactile and kinesthetic sensations.

The geometrical precision and obvious sensitivity to subtle spatial factors and subtle stresses and strains in the walls of the abodes of the social insects are extraordinary and indicate complex group behavior, the mechanisms of which are almost wholly unknown. Species specificity of the nest patterns (Figs. 231–233) and the construction by sterile workers that have no way of learning from previous generations of workers, indicate that nest construction by the social

insects is genetically determined in almost all cases, and thus illustrates remarkable instinctive group and social behavior.

The architecture of the social insects shows many spatial and geometrical relations that would seem to be explicable only through tactile and kinesthetic senses (Emerson, 1938). Such aspects as the size

Fig. 154. Nest of the termite, *Procubitermes niapuensis*, with chevron-shaped rain-shedding ridges on the trunk of a tree in the rain forest of the Belgian Congo. (Photograph by Herbert Lang.)

of the nest cells or chambers, the horizontal shape of the chambers, the layering of the tiers of cells, the supporting pillars of the chambers, the replication of ventilation pores (p. 633), the radial symmetry of the "mushroom-shaped" nests of *Cubitermes* having a rain-shedding cap, the bilateral chevron-shaped rain-deflecting ridges on the tree trunks above the nests of *Constrictotermes cavifrons* (page 645 and Figure 235) and *Procubitermes niapuensis*

lake are two examples in an almost infinite series of communities that owe their existence to an almost infinite variation in the earth's total environment. The species populations that compose the community are never isolated units, unrelated to each other. Their existence is possible only by the continued existence of other species populations of the community, since the life of each organic member of a species depends upon the fulfillment of two broadly interpreted necessities, nourishment and protection.

The inevitable chain of consequences may be summarized thus: Anabolic cellular demands require almost continuous satisfaction. In most plants these vital requirements are inorganic salts in the substratum or surrounding medium, carbon dioxide, water, and a portion of the radiant energy of the sun. The photosynthetic input is in turn utilized directly by herbivorous animals, and hence indirectly by carnivorous animals or less commonly (Darwin, 1875; Wray and Brimley, 1943) by carnivorous plants, and still more indirectly by saprophytic and saprophagous organisms. Thus the demand for nourishment must be fulfilled by the environment, and food is a prime ecological influence. The late William Bayliss (1924, p. 548) sums up this general idea by stating that "the whole existence of living organisms on the earth depends on the receipt of radiant energy from the sun . . ."

It follows that continuous activity would eventuate in excessive demands followed by exhaustion and death. Periodic recuperation is usually accompanied by relative inactivity, and in this condition the animal seldom responds as rapidly or completely to external stimuli, and hence is exposed to natural enemies during periods of physiological recuperation. Rest and sleep, or their physiological equivalents, are consequently generally consummated within a more or less sheltered place. This is the habitat niche or home. Physiological recuperation, therefore, is consumated within the environment, and sheltering is an ecological influence.

These two general requirements of food and shelter are selfish in that their satisfaction prolongs the life of the individual. A third basic drive, reproduction, is more concerned with the future of the species, although its immediate fulfillment in bisexual species, where more or less area must be quartered by an individual of one sex in search of one of the opposite sex, requires environmental adjustment.

These three organismal drives, with their various ecological adjustments, are salient features of the organism, and were included by Wheeler (1911) in his formal definition. Having gone this far in defining an organism, we should realize that if this definition is even approximately sound, then organisms would tend to form natural groups of foods and feeders—in other words, would form communities. Since each kind of organism inherits a more or less specific arrangement of genes, the resulting protoplasmic demands are similarly more or less restrictive. It follows that communities are composed, not of a random assortment of species, but of ecologically compatible species populations whose collective ecological requirements of food, shelter, and reproduction are satisfied, in the last analysis, by a certain range of environments. Therefore, communities with broadly similar requirements have a broadly similar range of environments, and their collective adjustments produce a broadly similar community pattern. Upon this basis, a community may be said to have a characteristic anatomy, an equally characteristic physiology, and a characteristic heredity.

The formation of the community may be considered as a resultant of ecological selection, in which the building blocks, or organisms, unable to exist alone, fall into place to produce a self-sustaining whole of remarkable complexity. Organization of such an accumulation is obligatory and the universality of the community is the proof of this general proposition.

The functional integrity of the community is a logical extension of the facts examined, since it becomes apparent that the community must be the natural unit of organization in ecology, and hence is the smallest such unit that is or can be self-sustaining, or is continuously sustained by inflow of food materials. It is composed of a variable number of species populations, which occupy continuous or discontinuous portions of the physico-biological environment, the habitat niches. Thus a bracket fungus contains certain kinds of mycetocolous animals (Weiss, 1920, 1920a, 1920b; Park, 1931a). These saprophytes

serve as a link between their insect inhabitants and the forest. Within certain limits
the association is fairly close, certain kinds
of insects, inhabiting certain kinds of fungi,
breeding on or near the latter, passing their
life cycles within the fungus tissues, and
feeding thereon. In the cyclic development
of this habitat a point is reached at which
the fungus is no longer a suitable environment for its animal inhabitants. Its density
of population is rising while the potential
food supply is falling, and this is accompanied by relative dehydration through
perforation and loss of woody tissues, with
resulting lowering of the relative humidity
of the interior. The occupants leave the
fungus to feed and oviposit on another
similar fungus substratum. The fungus is
the home or habitat niche of these myceto-
coles, providing them with food and shelter. At the same time, the fungi grow upon
dead or dying trees, and are unable to exist
without such a food supply; the tree, therefore, is the habitat niche of the fungi.

At either end of this example, other adjustments are made. The mycetophagous
insects are themselves fed upon by carnivorous animals that are facultative or obligatory inhabitants of the surrounding forest.
The trees are primary constituents, since
they indirectly support this chain of activities, as well as numerous other sequences
of food and feeder. Nevertheless the trees
are restricted to a given area, the restriction being a function of bacteriological,
edaphic, and climatic influences. They produce a forest by more or less successful
competition for light, soil moisture, and
soil salts and by inter-specific and intraspecific cooperation; for example, their increasing bulk serves as a windbreak and
insures increasing annual increments of
leaves remaining on the forest floor each
autumn for future incorporation into the
growing mold. Such a forest community is
self-sustaining.

From this viewpoint, the forest is a
major community as previously defined,
whereas the fungus alone is not. Unfortunately, the problem of community boundaries is not so simple as it would appear
from the foregoing. In a limited sense, each
habitat is a microcosm containing a biocoenose. Not only are the associated organisms limited by their immediate environment, but they change the environment
through their own multifold activities, or
indirectly through the products of their
metabolism. Again, as many cells of the
organism are continually being replaced by
other cells, so the elements of the forest
community are continually in the process
of replacement. This replacement is at
different rates and different levels of importance. Thus the community arises,
matures, eventually becomes senescent,
and its location is occupied by another type
of community. Destructive influences may
be of such violence, as in prolonged flooding due to a change in water table, or soil
impairment and stand injury by fire or human influence, that community wound
repair is not possible and the forest ceases
to have an effect upon the eventual oc-
cupiers of the area. Obviously, between
progressive evolution and eradication there
are diverse intermediate conditions that
do not result in loss of forest personality
since their impact can be absorbed.

The initial example of the bracket fungus
and its inhabitants, in relation to the whole
forest, presents no novelties. The chain of
events could have been illustrated by other
habitats within the same community, such
as the nest of the forest deer mouse (*Peromyscus leucopus noveboracensis*) and its
associated organisms. Pertinent illustrations
could be taken from any other community
—for example, the burrows of prairie rodents, such as *Citellus* and *Cynomys*
(Bailey, 1905; Gregory, 1936; Howell,
1938); the burrows of the gopher tortoises
(*Gopherus*) in dry sandy soils (Hubbard,
1893); the burrows of the crayfish (*Cambarus diogenes*) on the floor of temporary
ponds (Creaser, 1931); the gastropod
shells appropriated by hermit crabs (Eupa-
guridae) of the marine littoral; the bromeliad epiphytes of the neotropical rain forest
(Picado, 1911, 1913); the ant-plant
(*Tachigalia*) of the British Guiana rain
forest (Wheeler, 1923). The list could be
greatly expanded. These instances of subordinate habitats, drawn from a wide range
of communities, involve the dependence of
organisms upon the habitat for food and
shelter, or both, and of the relation of the
habitat to the more permanent, self-sustaining community. The habitat may be
created by the original occupant, as in the
case of *Citellus*, partially created as in the
perforation of the petioles of *Tachigalia* by
silvanid beetles, or simply occupied (Eupa-
gurids). The habitat may be part of the

physical environment (burrows of *Citellus,
Cynomys, Gopherus, Cambarus*) or of the
biological environment (bracket fungi,
Tachigalia, epiphytes), or may be a product
of the biological environment (hermit crabs
occupying snail shells). In all these examples the original or primary occupant is
joined by other, secondary occupants.
These fill spaces not otherwise in use, and
by their multifold secondary adjustments
pyramid the complexity of the habitat.* Occupants of these habitats modify their
homes; consequently the community at
large, by aerating the substratum, altering
its temperature and the rate and amount
of gas exchange of the medium; by their
catabolic wastes and feces, their deciduous
integumentary products, and eventually
their decomposing protoplasms, share in
this equilibration. Organisms die and are
replaced by their descendants or ecologically equivalent organisms; habitats are destroyed or modified while other habitats
are created. During this continual activity
the community remains relatively stable,
and its characteristic aspect and taxonomic
composition are substantially unchanged.

This is a relative stability, since communities tend to evolve, under normal conditions, to a highly stable end point, the
climax community.

In many cases the functional boundaries
of a community are not clearly discernible.
A given area may be subjected to more or
less periodic flooding, and if such a condition occurs in regions supporting deciduous
forest communities, the flooded depression
forms a temporary pond during the spring
while the same area supports a woodland
glade by summer; or temporary ponds replace marshy meadow in prairie areas; or
such ponds replace semidesert in arid regions. In all such cases these temporary
ponds form more or less rapidly and have
a characteristic biota whose ephemeral
active phase places a premium upon repro-

duction, and whose prolonged dormancy
places a premium upon capacity for aestivation, hibernation, encystment, and dispersal. Such a vernal pond usually supports an abundant and varied fauna
and flora, including amphibious animals
such as ducks and frogs, burrowing
crayfish whose subterranean burrows supply
dormancy niches for the rich plankton
(Creaser, 1931), sunfishes from ephemeral
stream connections, colonial flagellates
(*Volvox*), Cladocera, Copepoda, Ostracoda
and notably phyllopod crustaceans (*Eu-
branchipus, Eulimnadia, Apus*). These
ephemeral communities hold many ecological equivalents, to be discussed later, and
as they gradually disappear, there is a
space of time in which pond-glade, pond-
meadow, or pond-desert is not clearly defined. Their relation to the community as a
whole may be seen in the gathering of
predators to their borders as they dry up.

Another example of this lack of definitive boundary is seen in the food supply
of caves. The cave community is clearly
defined and is composed of a distinctive
fauna (Bailey, 1933; Banta, 1907; Eigenmann, 1909; Hyman, 1937; Jeannel, 1926;
Maheu, 1926; Packard, 1888; Valentine,
1932). The absence of chlorophyll-bearing plants is accompanied by the nearly
complete absence of herbivores, so that
cave animals tend to be saprophagous
or carnivorous. This gives no normal base
to the community food supply; such assemblages, although typically communities
in other respects, often rely on periodic
floods for the base of the food chain
(Hawes, 1939; Park, Roberts, and Harris,
1941), or upon bat dung in special cases.

Finally, societies of man, ants, and termites, although they have an increased
control over the environment, still normally
form a part of a general ecological community.* This control over otherwise periodic influences is much less developed in
nonsocial communities, and forms a distin-

* An unhackneyed example showing plasticity
of adjustment is furnished by the observations
of Mr. Henry Dybas, of the Chicago Natural
History Museum. Early in the 1940's, hermit
crabs were found on the island of Saipan
(Marianas) in numbers as much as three miles
inland from the nearest salt water, and up to
about 1200 feet altitude. These crustaceans
were inhabiting shells of an African land snail
(*Achatina fulica*) that was introduced by the
Japanese in the early 1920's. (Personal communication.)

* The large city is a peculiar case in that it
has evolved a notable degree of dependence
on adjacent communities, since, unlike the
societies of ants, termites, and smaller human
settlements, its food supply is transported by
various types of carriers at various times of
the twenty-four hour period; the waste products
of its metabolism are incinerated or processed
in sewage disposal plants instead of being returned directly to the community (O. Park,
1941a).

Table 30. Comparison of the Cell Doctrine and Organismal Doctrine with the Community Doctrine

Cell	Multicellular Organism	Community
Composed of definitive proto-plasms	Composed of definitive cells and tissues	Composed of definitive organisms and species
Has anatomy (cytological)	Has anatomy (tissues and organs)	Has anatomy (pyramid of numbers)
Has symmetry and gradients	Has symmetry and gradients	Has aspects of symmetry and gradients (stratification)
Has ontogeny (cell development)	Has ontogeny (embryology)	Has ontogeny (succession)
Has limitations of protoplasmic amounts (size, surface- volume ratio)	Has limitations of cell numbers (size, surface-volume ratio)	Has limitation of population numbers
Regeneration of parts	Regeneration of parts	Regeneration of parts
Division of labor between proto-plasms	Division of labor between cells	Division of labor between organisms and species
Cycles of protoplasmic behavior	Cycles of cellular behavior	Cycles of organismic and species behavior
Self-sustaining organization (dynamic equilibrium)	Self-sustaining organization (dynamic equilibrium)	Self-sustaining organization (dynamic equilibrium)
Successful integration of whole determines survival of parts and repetition of parts	Successful integration of whole determines survival of parts and repetition of parts	Successful integration of whole determines survival of parts and repetition of parts
Homology of cytological parts	Homology of tissues and organs	Homology of phylogenetically related species in different communities
Senescence and rejuvenescence of cell	Senescence and rejuvenescence of organism	Senescence and rejuvenescence of community
Phylogeny of gene pattern	Phylogeny of cellular pattern	Phylogeny of species pattern
Selection of whole cell unit determines survival of gene pattern	Selection of whole organismic units determines survival of cell pattern	Selection of whole community determines species and organism pattern
Controls internal protoplasmic environment and establishes optima	Controls intercellular environment and establishes optima	Controls environment within community and establishes optima
Selects or rejects protoplasmic building materials	Selects or rejects tissue-building materials	Selects or rejects organisms (species) that harmonize or do not harmonize with community
Retrogressive evolution of cyto-logical structure (chloro lasts)	Retrogressive evolution of tissue structure and of organs (eyes of cave fish)	Retrogressive evolution through species elimination

guishing criterion for these highly organized assemblages (Emerson, 1938, 1939). Certain phases of their special activity pattern are to be discussed later. At this point we are concerned in observing the difficulty that may arise in establishing the functional boundary of certain communities.

The majority of major communities are clearly defined and, in a sense, self-sustaining assemblages. It has been suggested also that there are exceptions to the definiteness of functional boundary, and to the self-sustaining aspect of the food supply. Such exceptions do not impair the major community concept; they are to be expected in such a universal, slowly evolving system. Thus the cell doctrine is not impaired by the lack of structural boundaries in a syncytium, and the concept of the organism is not harmed by the problem of organismal limits in colonial protozoans (Volvocidae, Vorticellidae), colonial rotifers, bryozoans, sponges, and colonial tunicates.

Thus cells, organisms, populations, societies, and communities are progressively complex biological systems. All five are protoplasmic, interdependent integrations in the struggle for nourishment and other interrelations. Their protoplasmic nature is obvious, but the complete interdependence of organisms and their arrangement into organized communities for survival is only now becoming realized. This realization suggests an extracellular extension of the Cell Doctrine (Table 30).

Exceptions are known to all three doctrines noted in this table; these few exceptions may be real, or are consequences of incomplete information or of incomplete synthesis. In these doctrines the organism is the essential connecting link; it is the hinge on which both cells and communities depend for continued existence. In the same way, organismal survival is dependent on cells for assimilation, and communities for food supply.

Study of the organism, therefore, belongs to all biologists. Study of its parts embraces anatomy and physiology, its inherited features occupy the geneticists, its environmental adjustment is the realm of autecology, its classification with relation to other organisms is a concern of taxonomy, and its association with other organisms becomes the study of synecology. This last phase has been slower to receive biological support, since, because of its innate complexity and its dependence on synthesis of many aspects of biology as well as analysis, it has appeared as a point of view more often than as an organized field of study. An example of a critical attitude toward

synecology is that of Uvarov (Riley, 1944). Such criticism is to be expected until this complexity can be thoroughly analyzed and the biological necessity of the community— i.e., the counterdependence of the organism on its community—is more generally appreciated. Both the organism and the community change through time; this is implied in the doctrines just stated. In organismal evolution there are some documentary data to show that the evolved product is the function of genetic changes of the germ plasm, operating through the soma, and selected by the environment. Modern ecology has a definite contribution to make in the study of organismal evolution, which will form the basis for a later section. The evolution of communities, or succession, is an especial phase of synecology and is considered in the present section.

The general structure, functions, and evolution of major communities form three points of departure from which synecological principles may be examined. To some extent this procedure limits the field of inquiry. Community classification (Warming, 1909; Shelford, 1913; Pearse, 1939) and the detailed examination of a single community (Carpenter, 1940a) or detailed examination of certain phases of synecology (Clements and Shelford, 1939) recently have been emphasized, and these several bodies of information and theory will be drawn upon extensively.

26. COMMUNITY ORGANIZATION: STRATIFICATION

The community usually has a characteristic appearance. This general aspect is difficult to describe briefly, but is easily apprehended after sufficient field experience. Recognition in the field depends upon the rapid integration of numerous criteria, the summation of which presents the observer with a mental image of a particular community type. Such a typical aspect or habitus implies a general ecological demand by the community that is the net result of the numerous demands of the contained constituents. It is safe to conclude that as familiarity with species taxonomy and ecology increases, there is a gain in finer perception of community habitus. As the total taxonomic composition of any two

communities, or related series of communities, approaches similarity, the total ecological requirements of such assemblages become more similar. Conversely, as the total taxonomic dissimilarity increases, the ecological requirements become progressively dissimilar.

Despite great differences in habitus, all self-sustaining communities have certain features of organization in common. Such features are of prime importance, since their nearly universal occurrence suggests fundamental consequences innate in the interdependence of taxonomically disparate populations. Study of these common structural features forms the basis of community morphology. This common structural plan is to be anticipated when it is realized that a community is, in large part, the obligatory gathering of many organisms for survival. In this sense the community is a supraorganism. Just as the common structural plan of mollusks pervades many thousands of species, belonging to hundreds of genera and dozens of families, general community structure is discernible through a wide variety of types. Similarly, as each family of mollusks presents a particular taxonomic habitus, so each community type (the forest community, for example) shows a particular modification of general organization.

One of the outstanding general principles of community organization is that of stratification. For present purposes, stratification is applied in the broadest meaning of the term and embraces all objectively delimitable vertical or horizontal layers of organisms, their by-products, or the results of their activities upon the environment. Consequently, when this principle is applied to communities, and the total volume occupied is examined for evidence of stratification, nearly all communities share a well-defined lamination into either (1) a column of strata upon a vertical organismal gradient ("layers" of many botanists, strata in the limited meaning of some authors; Lippmaa, 1939); or (2) a series of strata on a horizontal organismal gradient (zones of many hydrobiologists; belts or girdles); or (3) more commonly the community is at least partially separable into both vertical and horizontal series of strata.

Complete stratification is uncommon, although most communities show this pattern in parts of their organization. In other instances one gradient will be obvious, while another will be much less apparent, as in the marine littoral on sand or mud where the horizontal stratification is well developed and obvious to the eye, while the vertical gradient is not so apparent until samples from different depths are analyzed.

The reasons for stratifications are fairly obvious. The process is effected (1) by initial colonization of a stratified environment by what may be thought of as primary residents. These invading plants and animals belong to species, the populations of which adjust to the stratified environment and hence are directly stratified as a result of their specific tolerations and adaptations. (2) As soon as this initial stratification of organisms is consummated, there is a tendency for the process to be reenforced as a consequence of the very bulk of the organisms, their excretions and by-products, and lastly through the chemical reactions taking place between these by-products and the physical stratification. (3) Finally other organisms take up temporary or permanent residence as a direct response to the presence of initial residents, rather than to the initial environmental stratification. These may be considered as secondary residents in general, although they may be divisible into secondary, tertiary, and so on, depending upon their orientation with respect to the first comers.

The primary and secondary species may or may not be irreplaceable in the community. At the primary level the role of numerous species may be essential, but transferable within an ecologically equivalent group, so that we have the principle of community stratification affected by the principle of ecological replaceability. There are undoubtedly fewer species of primary residential value than there are of secondary residential value, which brings to mind the further suggestion that, within the principle of ecological replaceability, the number of species tends to increase as their relative importance in determining the basic organization of the community decreases.

When what has been said is applied to the human community, at a level of integration found in a large city, the immediate application is both interesting and obvious. First, considering the human species from the point of view of numerous functional groups, each with its own occupation, it will be seen that the roles of some of these "occupational species" are of primary importance. That is, the essential framework of the human community is a product of their activities. On the other hand, these relatively few groups of primary residential value serve as a direct stimulus to more numerous "occupational species;" these latter are of secondary residential importance and by their manifold activities serve to fill out this complex frame. In addition to man, many other species respond to the composite human stimulus generated and may be considered as tertiary residents whose physiological requirements are satisfied in this community. These are themselves of diverse ranks and may be of temporary or permanent residence. Such tertiary inhabitants would include athlete's foot fungus, dog and cat fleas and lice, human lice, numerous pathogenic bacteria and viruses, dysentery amebae, as well as numerous pets brought into the community by the human component.

Such established organismal gradients are both quantitative and qualitative, and the integration can be detected and measured by direct examination of the environmental gradients with inferential data concerning the organismal stratification; or the latter can be studied and environmental relations deduced, or, preferably, both environmental influences and the biological indicators may be utilized at the same time. It is perhaps unfortunate that data obtained from this last plan of study cannot be presented here in their natural unity. Such a combined treatment would require repetition in this section of details of physical stratification that have been given appropriately at some length in preceding sections.

VERTICAL STRATIFICATION IN AQUATIC COMMUNITIES

Vertical stratification is well developed in many aquatic habitats. These show readily detectable vertical gradients in temperature (p. 93), light intensity (p. 449), wavelength absorption (p. 124), other physical conditions, including distance from surface and substrate (p. 158), dissolved chemicals (p. 198), pH (p. 172), redox potential (p. 195), and dissolved gases (p. 193). Thermal stratification in summer and winter stagnation under ice, together with the intervening periods of ventilation produced by vernal and autumnal overturns, occur throughout the world in temperate lakes of the second order (p. 95).

With these points concerning the gradiented environmental background of freshwater communities in mind, a little-understood, but essential, group of gradiented influences deserves attention. Up to this point organic materials have been brought in obliquely, as in the decomposition of organisms falling from epilimnial to hypolimnial strata. We have been more directly concerned with discussion of gradients of such physical influences as temperature and light, or hydrogen ion concentration and redox potential, or inorganic salts of iron, calcium, phosphorus, and nitrogen, or gaseous oxygen, carbon dioxide and the carbonates and bicarbonates, and hydrogen sulfide.

Organic materials have two sources commonly recognized in lakes, but not easily separated as to their effects. In the first place, there are the allochthonous organic materials, derived from the external terrain by seepage, or carried into the lake by drainage. Second, there are the autochthonous materials, produced within the lake; that is, they are of internal origin and are derived from the decomposition of the bodies of the organisms living in it. These latter materials deserve special notice since they are more direct products of the community and in great part determine its self-sustaining capacities. Autochthones are derived primarily from the epilimnion, since the bottom organisms, although they add their own bodies to the total organic potential, are more or less dependent upon the regular increment from above. Such organic materials, regardless of their external or internal origin, and regardless of their original stratal position, tend to accumulate in the deeper levels of the hypolimnion and build up the bottom materials. These organic particles diminish in size, with progressive decomposition, and gradually, through complex stages involving oxidation-reduction systems and biological action of bacteria, produce inorganic components, or unite with external radicals. One of the significant end products is the building up and seasonal dispersal of raw materials that may be used in future protein synthesis, such as nitrates and phosphates. The reactions taking place are chiefly the cause for oxygen deficiency and other typical hypolimnial features, so that it should be kept in mind that the lake organisms in death are as important to the future of the community as are the living organisms.

As lakes mature with age, there is usually an increase in total vegetation, resulting in concomitant increase in organic materials, from phytoplankton and phanerogamic plants, and from the associated herbivores, carnivores, and saprovores. Increase in organic supply plays its part in filling up the hypolimnion, together with inorganic sediment, so that study of organic materials is desirable for both a present view of community mechanics and for a clearer understanding of community development.

As organic materials settle in the hypolimnion they become the focal point of complex dynamic influences, among which bacteria are notable agents. These materials, by selective settling out and preservation, form a part of the lake bottom. Such bottom deposits include silica (from diatom shells), calcium carbonate, and organic materials (Wilson and Opdyke, 1941).

Organic materials comprise both dissolved and particulate portions. The dissolved organic materials (Birge and Juday, 1934) of Wisconsin lakes were shown to comprise about 75 per cent carbohydrates and 25 per cent proteins, with a trace of fats. Birge and Juday found that the total organic material, in lakes which were largely autochthonous, ran about 4 mg. per liter, of which 16 per cent was planktonic. The average of all lakes they studied in Wisconsin (autochthonous and allochthonous) ran 16 mg. per liter of organic materials, with plankton forming 8 per cent. This indicates that total organic materials increase in allochthonous lakes, while plankton-organic materials decrease, and suggests a higher degree of productivity in autochthonous lakes. This indicates that such lakes support more closely balanced and self-sustaining communities.

If we assume with Rawson (1939) that the amount of dissolved organic material is about seven times as large as the amount of plankton, then two questions arise: How is this dissolved organic component made available for protoplasmic synthesis, and to what extent is this material utilized? The general view is that lake bacteria break the dissolved materials into phosphates, nitrates, and ammonia, from which inorganic dissolved compounds, phanerogams, and phytoplankton build their protein. Our ignorance here concerning many bacterial and biochemical problems is large.

Another view, less generally accepted, is that planktonic plants and animals can utilize dissolved organic materials directly in their protein synthesis, without recourse to the bacterial-inorganic portion of the cycle. This is a broadened Pütter hypothe-

sis, discussed previously (see Index). The hypothesis is of interest here since it bears upon the basic relationships of the food chain within the aquatic communities (pp. 497, 500). Pütter (1909) postulated that most small zooplankters derived much of their nutrition from the dissolved organic materials in water. This controversial hypothesis is still stimulating research. Hasler (1935) found that *Daphnia magna* were able to digest protein and carbohydrate, presumably as particulate food, through the agency of an intestinal proteolytic enzyme similar to trypsin. Gellis and Clarke (1935) found that this cladoceran could derive nourishment from colloidal organic matter. An intermediate position was taken by Klugh (1927), who found some entomostracans could utilize fine detritus, but that their chief food was phytoplanktonic green algae. Krogh (1930) did not find dissolved organic substances of importance in nutrition of aquatic animals, and (1931) concluded that, although some utilization might occur, it was on too small a scale to become important. Stuart, McPherson, and Cooper (1931) raised bacteriologically sterile *Moina* and found them unable to subsist on dissolved organic material, and Bond (1933) found a similar negative correlation. Clarke and Gellis (1935), turning their attention to marine copepods, found that their chief foods were bacteria and other nannoplankton.

From this summary we emerge with the belief that we need a more comprehensive knowledge of the role of bacteria in the breakdown of organic materials dissolved in water and the use of bacteria as food by small aquatic animals, better methods of assay, a rigorous application of techniques to insure that experimental media are free of bacteria, and a wider sampling of the plankton. Until these precautions have been widely applied, we may not completely discard Pütter's early assumption. At present, the preponderant balance of evidence is in favor of some utilization of dissolved inorganic substances in nutrition of animal plankton; although, as suggested by Varga (1934), direct utilization of dissolved organic substances cannot be excluded. When more information has become available, we may find that Pütter's hypothesis is too limited in application to be treated as a general factor in planktonic nourishment, but rather is to be considered a specific physiological adaptation for a few species.

Dissolved and particulate organic and inorganic substances affect the rate of penetration, amount, and composition of light in natural waters. This is the factor of turbidity in the broad sense of the term, although the suspended particulate state is more commonly recognized. The reduction in total light by turbid water is a fairly obvious phenomenon, but it must be remembered that suspended and dissolved substances have a selective action on light, and may profoundly modify its character. The resulting direct effects upon light, their indirect effects through photochemical reactions, and indirect effects upon the oxidation-reduction cycle afford opportunities for research.

Light is often of limiting importance, and, since utilization of light is low, turbidity becomes significant. The ways in which turbidity affects the community include its action upon: (1) the composition, size, duration, and occurrence time of phytoplankton pulses directly and, hence, zooplankton indirectly; (2) rate of photosynthesis by phytoplankton, at various depths; (3) vertical stratification of the microcrustacea in particular; and (4) size of catches of commercially important fishes— for example, the sauger (*Stizostedion canadense*) (Chandler, 1942).

In summary, the fresh-water environmental background is characteristically stratified. This organization not only exhibits gradients with respect to such obvious influences as water pressure, temperature, and light, but also for many additional factors, including dissolved gases, dissolved and particulate organic and inorganic materials, hydrogen ion concentration, and oxidation-reduction potential.

The salt water environment similarly exhibits gradients. In addition to a rather uniform difference in chemical composition and physical characteristics, fresh-water and salt-water environments differ quantitatively. Such differences, as those of pressure, currents, and tides exist principally by virtue of the great differential in volume.

The organisms composing fresh-water and salt-water communities adjust to this stratified environment, both vertically and horizontally.

Available information on vertical distribution of bacteria in inland water has been summarized by Henrici (1939), and, although the data are conflicting in certain cases, a few generalizations are worthy of notice here with respect to inland lakes of Minnesota and Wisconsin. In lakes with a rich epilimnial plankton "bloom," bacteria are numerous at the surface. There is no marked difference between the plate counts of bacteria in the epilimnion and hypolimnion, except in strongly stratified lakes; in these latter such differences as do exist in the bacterial count are thought to be a consequence of thermal stratification, and hence fit our general concept of community organization. Microstratification may be associated with sharp local differences in vertical distribution. The most abundant bacterial flora is that of the lake bottom. Bacteria are always numerous there, especially at the mud-water interphase, and they decrease regularly above and below this level. This is to be expected in view of the accumulation of organic materials on the bottom.

The vertical distribution of bacteria in the sea is generally similar to that in fresh water, and has been discussed succinctly by ZoBell (1946). In general, where bacterial counts have been made, bacteria are distributed vertically. Such distributions are generally expressed in quantitative terms of numbers of bacteria per milliliter (ml.), and depth in meters or fathoms. Species composition of the sample is less often available. Few seasonal studies of vertical distribution have been made, but these suggest great seasonal variation (ZoBell and McEwen, 1935). Only the most general of statements are admissible. A search of the literature shows that there is seasonal variability, but details differ as between different areas of the same sea at the same depths, as well as between different seas.

In general, the curve of bacterial populations follows that of the phytoplankton for the first 100 meters, relatively few bacteria being found at the sea surface (1 to 200/ml.), gradually becoming more numerous and reaching a maximum between 25 and 50 meters (500/ml.), then gradually decreasing in abundance to the bot-

tom. On the bottom the bacterial population undergoes a dramatic increase. Drew
(1912) reported up to 160,000,000/ml. of
bottom mud off Andros Island, West
Indies; ZoBell (1946) found few bacteria
at 200 meters, but the number suddenly
increased to 9×10^8 per gm. of mud on the
bottom off the coast of Southern California.

The vertical distribution of nonbacterial
plankton is marked in both fresh-water and
salt-water communities. In the discussion
of community stratification to this point, we
have attempted to present the reader with
a single principle at a time. Of course,
stratification is notably influenced by seasonal, lunar, and day-night periodicities,
and these rhythms will be examined in the
chapter on periodism. Such forces markedly
affect vertical plankton gradients.

Since the plankton consists of small organisms unable to move against waves or
currents, they drift through the water at
various levels. Sharp thermoclinal stratification aside, vertical distribution of plankton in fresh water is not so clearly defined
as in the sea, chiefly as a consequence of the
great depth of the latter. The early work
of Birge and Juday (1911) is still one of
the best sources of information on vertical
gradients, and has been recast successfully
with respect to quantitative and qualitative
plankton gradients by Welch (1935, Fig.
31). The subject is so complex that few
generalizations can be suggested. The composition varies not only with season, but
with time of day, local weather, and type
of lake (Welch, 1935; Prescott, 1939;
Chandler, 1942a).

As to fresh-water phytoplankton, it may
be said that lakes large enough to be thermally stratified tend to have a vertical
gradient in amounts, if not in kinds of,
phytoplankton during summer stagnation.
During the vernal and autumnal overturns
the organisms become thoroughly mixed by
the circulation of the water, and at these
limited periods this vertical gradient disappears. The distribution gradient is the result of the need by chlorophyll-bearing organisms for effective light intensity and
quality, which consequently predetermines
the level at which they can exist. Even in
relatively large second order lakes, the vertical gradient is not complete in shallow
areas. For example, the vertical distribution
in quality and quantity of phytoplankton is
highly irregular in western Lake Erie
(Chandler, 1942a), since in shallow waters
(10 meters or less) wind action causes an
almost continual circulation from top to
bottom. Such shallow areas of second order
lakes duplicate the pattern in third order
lakes as a whole, save for periods of protracted calm, when regular stratification
may occur. Lakes with a deep hypolimnion,
as would be expected, have no green phytoplankton at deep levels.

Usually each species of phytoplankter
has its own level of maximum population
density, its quantity diminishing both
above and below this zone. A few generalizations can be made (Welch, 1935): (1)
Maximum populations of total chlorophyll-
bearing plankters are usually at a level
below the surface stratum; (2) the blue-
green algae and green algae usually have
their maximal concentration at a higher
level than the diatoms, which may be a
consequence of the greater specific gravity
of the diatoms. Much information regarding
such distribution in different lakes can be
obtained from Birge and Juday (1911, pp.
113–138 and Figs. 116–142).

Zooplankton is also distributed vertically
in fresh-water communities, although identical patterns for any two lake communities
are to be expected no more frequently
than, say, identical patterns for two forest
communities. Indeed, when we attempt to
appreciate the numerous small differences
between broadly similar environments, the
degree of general convergence in vertical
distribution is notable. Welch (1935, p.
221) has suggested some tendencies in
vertical distribution of zooplankton: (1)
The Sarcodina are in greater abundance toward the bottom of the vertical gradient;
(2) Dinoflagellata are in greater abundance in the upper levels; (3) Ciliata, as
a class, are generally scattered over the
gradient; and (4) there is a differential
distribution between the nauplii and imaginal stages in Crustacea.

Factors influencing the vertical distribution of zooplankton are separable into two
groups (Rylov, 1935): (1) physical factors, such as the mechanical effect of specific gravity and of current, temperature,
and light; (2) biological factors, such as
level of food and dissolved organic materials. Langford (1938) believed that light
was the most important influence in Lake

Nipissing, although this factor was qualified by many others, such as food, temperature, chemical constituents, wind, gravity, and age and sex of zooplankter. As noted by Tressler (1939), gravity affects all plankters heavier than water, and most of these must actively exert themselves to maintain their position in the gradient. Food is undoubtedly important. Naturally it should be pointed out that seasonal and twenty-four hour migrations, discussed later, influence the vertical position of these organisms.

The specific nature of such vertical gradients must be realized. Tressler (1939, p. 82) states that in each lake "or perhaps

bulk of the concentration zones within the hypolimnion."

From an extensive study of thirty-six New York lakes by Tressler, Bere, Wagner, and others, still in progress, some valuable generalizations have appeared (Tressler, 1939): The average depth of these thirty-six lakes was 22.6 meters, and the range in depth from 5 to 50 meters. The average maximum abundance of the chief zooplankters is shown in Table 31.

The variation of maximal population density with depth is caused by (a) differences in species composition of a given plankton group, (b) time of day, and (c) season. Differentiation within the several zones is

Table 31. Vertical Distribution of Chief Groups of Fresh-Water Zooplankton in New York Lakes (Modified from Tressler, 1939)

Zooplankton	Maximal Population Density at:	Range of Depths for Maximal p.d. for Thirty-six Lakes
Protozoa	5.3 meters	0 to 15 meters
Cladocera	6.5 meters	0 to 25 meters
Copepoda	7.1 meters	0 to 30 meters
Rotifera	7.5 meters	5 to 40 meters
Nauplii	9.9 meters	0 to 35 meters

in each type of lake, every organism has its own preferred level." In Wisconsin lakes with thermal stratification it has been demonstrated (Woltereck, 1932) that each stratum has its own peculiar group of *Daphnia* and allied genera. This population-domination of the gradient gives individuality to each community. We will return to this subprinciple later in the discussion of the vertical organismal gradient in terrestrial communities.

Whenever a particular taxonomic group is investigated for vertical stratification, its more uniform physiological requirements permit attention to be focussed upon the lower taxonomic units, and the distributional gradient becomes more apparent, as in the studies of Woltereck just cited. This is clearly evident in the careful analysis of Campbell (1941) of the plankton Rotifera of Douglas Lake, Michigan. Concerning distribution of rotifers, he says (p. 15): "Certain characteristics of the distribution patterns of rotifers are in part due to the distinct distributional patterns of the more abundant species. That is, certain species are, in the main, responsible for the surface or near-surface concentration zones, and certain deep-water species form the

brought about either directly by differences in the physical environment, or indirectly through the effects organisms produce on the environment, or also indirectly by the reaction of residents to each other.

The vertical distribution of marine plankton exhibits distinctive features (Russell, 1927; Pavillard, 1935). The marine plankton gradient varies with season, with the twenty-four hour cycle, with latitude, and with turbidity and local weather. Its chief characteristics are determined primarily by the physical environmental gradients, as in the fresh-water communities. The plankton distribution is apparently correlated with both the intensity and composition of the penetrating sunlight. Seasonal and day-night migrations are discussed later, and attention is focussed here on the stratification of the community.

From accumulated oceanographic research it is clear that, notwithstanding the relative uniformity in the proportion of the more abundant mineral salts in solution (Coker, 1938), and despite the reality of stratification, there is little taxonomic uniformity in horizontal distribution of plankton in the ocean from locality to locality. The areas are too vast, subject to too much variation in latitude, to have a uniform environmental background, even in open ocean. Thus the great variety in habitats, with their concomitant variety in environmental stratification, is paralleled by an equally great diversity in the details of plankton composition (Bigelow, 1925; Allen, 1934).

The uppermost stratum of the sea is termed the photic zone (p. 124). In the photic zone the upper 500 meters of water absorb all the red component of light, while the shorter wavelengths, such as the blue and violet, extend to greater depths (p. 125). Below the photic zone the water

diatoms, dinoflagellates, coccolithophores, and a few species of green algae. The abundant and characteristically diversified zooplankton is also primarily resident in the upper portion of the photic zone. Marine plankton in these first few hundred meters has been examined intensively, and the productivity and variation within this stratum can be studied by consulting the literature (Murray and Hjort, 1912; Johnstone, Scott, and Chadwick, 1924; Bigelow, 1925; Allen, 1934; Pavillard, 1935; Sverdrup, Johnson, and Fleming, 1942; Coker, 1947; with their several bibliographies).

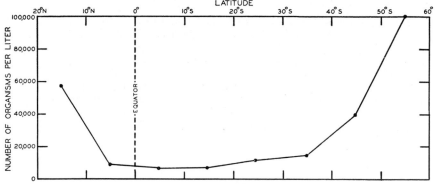

Fig. 155. Amounts of total plankton in the upper 50 meters of the South Atlantic. (After Sverdrup, Johnson, and Fleming.)

rapidly becomes less illuminated, until at 5578 feet sensitized plates are unaffected after an exposure of two hours. The aphotic zone below about 1500 meters is essentially dark, although it may be faintly illuminated by luminescent fishes or other nekton which can exist under great pressures (Beebe, 1934). The aphotic zone is indifferently known when contrasted with our information on the photic zone and may be of vast depth, as in some areas of the Pacific Ocean where it embraces a vertical layer of 9500 meters.

The aphotic zone continues to the sea floor, where both active and sessile benthos and nekton exist under great pressures. This stratum is discussed later under Horizontal Stratification.

Returning to the upper levels of the gradient, it is clear that the photic zone is not uniformly populated (Fig. 155). Conservative writers place the lower photosynthetic limit at 200 meters. This limits the phytoplankton, consisting largely of

Study of vertical distribution in the sea is best accomplished by examination of a limited taxonomic group. Marine dinoflagellates are excellent material since they are widespread, numerous in species, and characteristic of the photic zone. In this group the genus *Ceratium* is familiar. Karsten (1907) first suggested that certain marine plankters inhabit the lower strata of the photic zone, and these species he described as a "shade flora." Nielsen (1934), reporting on collections made by the *Dana*, found that about one-third of the species of *Ceratium* in the southern Pacific inhabit the lower levels of the photic zone and should be called "shade species," while two-thirds inhabit the upper relatively well-illuminated levels. Nielsen found that general plankton density affects the vertical distribution of the shade species. In areas where the plankton is rich the shade species live at higher levels, presumably because the abundant plankton absorbs so much light that the shade forms tend to occupy higher strata where there is sufficient light for photosynthesis.

If this is the correct explanation, it affords a striking illustration of the biological effect, by the whole plankton, on the vertical arrangements of its constituents, with the chlorophyll-bearers reacting primarily to the light gradient and secondarily to population pressure.

These shade species of *Ceratium* have their cells thin-walled and crowded with chromatophores, in contrast with the sun species. Nielsen compared these shade species with the shade plants of the tropical rain forest which inhabit lower strata of the forest community and which have the leaf surface increased, the leaf thin, and have an increase in the number of assimilating cells.

Graham (1941), using the extensive *Ceratium* collections of the *Carnegie* from the North Atlantic, North Pacific, and South Pacific, presents an analysis of this genus in relation to the environmental influences. His data check and amplify the general conclusions of Nielsen as to vertical distribution. Thus, Graham studied fifty-eight species of *Ceratium,* and of these twenty were shade species and showed an increase in frequency from sea surface to the 100 meter line.

Within the range of a group there is usually a specific distribution pattern, as shown by the various species of *Ceratium* in the upper portion of the photic zone. For example, within the prawns, *Acanthephyra purpurea* is fairly abundant from 1000 to 2000 meters, reaching maximal daytime density between 1200 and 1400 meters; *Systellaspis debilis* has the same range, but reaches a daytime maximal density at 100 meters; *Hymenodora gracilis* becomes increasingly abundant downwards, reaching a maximal daytime density at 2000 meters.

The pelagic strata of the North Atlantic discussed here have been treated as biomes by Clements and Shelford (1939, pp. 317–320). This is not tenable if by such treatment these authors suggest that each of these strata is equivalent to the grassland or the deciduous forest biome. Pelagic subdivisions depend upon the phytoplankton of the upper few hundred meters for their food. This means that they form interdependent portions of a vast marine

major community at the self-sustaining level in which the upper stratum would be ecologically comparable to the deciduous forest canopy and the sea floor comparable to the floor of such a forest.

Klugh and Martin (1927) checked the growth rate of marine algae against depth of submergence. The algae were found to have a specific stratum at which they grew more rapidly; this increase in growth rate was attributed to adjustments to different amounts of light. Summarizing their data: *Scytosiphon lomentarius* grew more rapidly at 1 meter, *Ectocarpus confervoides* and *Enteromorpha linza* at 2 meters, while *Fucus vesiculosus* grew more rapidly when just submerged beneath the surface.

Lastly, this distribution of algae with respect to light can be shown by direct field methods. Working in the comparatively shallow waters of Puget Sound, Shel-

Table 32. Vertical Distribution of Light Intensity in Puget Sound (After Shelford and Gail, 1922)

Depth in Meters	Light Intensity in Foot-Candles
Above surface	8650
At Surface	6550
1	5400
2	3960
3	3140
4	2590
5	1990
6	1620
7	1397
8	1190
9	990
10	830
25	335
35	206
50	129
75	74
100	38*
120	14

* Many plankters, the "shade species," in the open ocean reach their general limit at the 100 meter line. Its light intensity, about 38 foot-candles, in the littoral zone is about the average intensity for the floor stratum of north temperate mature deciduous or evergreen forests at noon in midsummer, as well as the floor of tropical rain forests at midday. It is amusing to note that civic twilight is placed at 33 foot-candles (Smithsonian Tables for 1918), so that the concept of "shade" or "twilight" would appear to be fairly unanimous for *Ceratium, Homo,* and a motley array of silvicoles.

ford and Gail (1922) measured light intensity with a Kunz photo-electric cell and found that the depths at which brown and red algae were most abundant per square meter of bottom to be at 10 to 15 meters' depth. The gradient in light is given in Table 32.

This difference of 5 meters represents a considerable reduction in light intensity and is in general agreement with the experimental data of Klugh and Martin (1927) and with the examination of the *Carnegie* data by Graham (1941).

This uppermost stratum is in many respects broadly analogous to the epilimnion of second order lakes. Both are relatively well illuminated, relatively high in dissolved oxygen, and relatively low in carbon dioxide; both contain the bulk of the plankton with its numerous sidechains of nektonic herbivores and carnivores; both require large amounts of nitrates and phosphates for plant protein synthesis; in both, these nutrients have a seasonal variation (discussed in the following chapter). The analogy is best applied in open ocean, where in summer a discontinuity layer develops at between 10 and 20 meters. Some parts of tropical seas are continuously thermally stratified.

For pelagic stratification, the best known area, the North Atlantic, has been relatively well studied. In this oceanic area definite vertical stratification of animals has been established to 5000 meters. In the cold waters of the North Atlantic, between 60 and 80 degrees north (from the Wyville Thompson Ridge to Franz Joseph Land), the upper 200 meter zone has a characteristic fauna associated with a rich phytoplankton. The stratum includes whales, herring, mackerel, scyphozoans, arrow worms, and copepods, especially *Calanus finmarchicus* (Bigelow, 1925; Murray and Hjort, 1912; Sverdrup, Johnson, and Fleming, 1942).

South of the Wyville Thompson Ridge, at least from 60 to 10 degrees north, there appear to be three defined strata. From the surface to 150 meters (Murray and Hjort, 1912, pp. 669–670; Gran, 1912; Clements and Shelford, 1939, p. 319), there is a rich zooplankton of Foraminifera, Radiolaria, Copepoda, pteropod mollusks, scyphozoans, tunicates, and Portuguese man-of-war. The nekton is especially character-

ized by scopelid fishes, there being at least seven species of *Myctophum* and seven genera of cephalopod mollusks.

From 150 to 500 meters (Murray and Hjort, 1912; Beebe, 1929, 1932, 1932a; Clements and Shelford, 1939, pp. 318–319), the zooplankton is composed chiefly of copepods, amphipods, ostracods, arrow worms, pteropods, and small medusae. The nekton is made up largely of small fishes that are typically laterally compressed, with a silvery skin, large eyes, and usually with numerous luminescent organs. Of these fishes, the telescope-eyed fish (*Argyropelecus*) is representative of the stratum.

From 500 to 5000 meters (Murray and Hjort, 1912; Chace, 1940) is a deep stratum, probably substratified. This includes the lower portion of the photic zone as well as a large section of the aphotic zone. Within its range is a relatively sparse fauna characterized by bathypelagic fishes, such as the slender, dark-colored *Cyclothone*, and bathypelagic crustaceans, such as the typical *Acanthephyra*.

Chace has thoroughly investigated these crustaceans off Bermuda, between 800 and 2000 meters. The caridean decapods studied belonged to species recorded from the bathypelagic stratum of many other areas. Wide distributions in this zone demonstrate that the marine faunistic regions are not developed in it, and Table 33 illustrates

Table 33. *Number of Species of Bermudan Caridea Reported from Other Areas (From Chace, 1940)*

Mediterranean Sea	2
South Atlantic	2
South Pacific	4
Sargasso Sea	4
Off coasts of Ireland	5
Hawaiian Islands	5
Eastern Pacific (California to Peru)	6
Off Cape of Good Hope	6
North Atlantic (north and west of the Gulf Stream)	6
Bahamas and the West Indies	9
Malay Archipelago and Philippines to Japan	9
Equatorial Atlantic	11
Eastern North Atlantic (Bay of Biscay to Cape Verde Islands)	11
Indian Ocean	15

the cosmopolitan geographic range of these bathypelagic prawns.

Even allowing for insufficient knowledge and for unequal effort in these fourteen areas, the presence of so many species of prawns common in Bermudian waters is a striking illustration of their cosmopolitan residence in the bathypelagic stratum. The crustaceans of this fauna are characteristically of some shade of red in life and are typically bioluminescent (Beebe, 1934a; Chace, 1940).

HORIZONTAL STRATIFICATION IN AQUATIC COMMUNITIES

We have demonstrated a similarity in organization of aquatic communities with respect to vertical gradients. We turn our attention now to the second of two fundamental patterns in such communities, namely, the horizontal gradients. The subject can be more economically surveyed, since a large part of the inanimate background already outlined applies directly to both vertical and horizontal distributions of organisms.

In both inland water and marine communities there is a general tendency for the higher plants to be stratified in more or less parallel zones on the margins of lakes and seas. This horizontal zonation may vary from an irregular pattern, where special expression of climatic or edaphic factors retards or inhibits rooted vegetation, to an almost ideal progression of concentric strata.

Inland Waters

The lake floor is generally divisible into three major horizontal strata or zones (Eggleton, 1931, 1939). The first of these, the littoral (paralimnion), embraces the area lying between the water's edge or shore line and the lakeward extension of rooted vegetation. The second or sublittoral embraces the lake bottom from the lakeward limit of rooted vegetation to the average upper limit of the hypolimnion. The third or profundal covers the bottom from the upper hypolimnial line to the deepest parts of the lake floor. A fourth zone, the abyssal, for the deepest lakes, embracing lake bottom below 600 meters, is theoretically possible, but is not used often among limnologists since few lakes of this depth exist, and, of those few, all have not been critically examined for profundal-abyssal differentiation.

A typical lake littoral transect in the north temperate latitudes (Welch, 1935) is summarized as follows: 1. Emergent hydrophytes include bulrushes (*Scirpus*), cat-tails (*Typha*), wild rice (*Zizania*), arrow-head (*Sagittaria*), sedges (*Carex*). These plants occupy the shoreward stratum, from water edge to about the 2 meter depth line. Within this zone there may be secondary cleavages, but all such plants have the chief photosynthetic surface raised above the water.

2. Floating hydrophytes include water lilies (*Nymphaea,* and the like), some smartweed (*Polygonum*), some pondweed (*Potamogeton natans*). These plants usually occupy the second lakeward belt, often interdigitated with emergent vegetation, from 10 centimeters' to 3 meters' depth. They are rooted in the lake bottom, and their foliage, connected by long petioles, floats on the water surface or extends a little above it.

3. Submerged hydrophytes include most pondweeds (*Potamogeton*), water milfoil (*Myriophyllum*), water weed (*Elodea*), *Vallisneria,* and other genera. These plants usually occupy the third lakeward belt, often interdigitated with the floating vegetation, from 2 to 6 meters in depth. They are rooted into the bottom, and their photosynthetic surface is submerged, so that their carbohydrate production is dependent upon light penetrating the water above them. This third horizontal stratum is only slightly visible from above, but may, and usually does, form a large crop.

Such horizontal distribution of rooted plants affects the shoreward distribution of lake bacteria (Henrici, 1939). Periphytic and profundal bacteria are quantitatively proportional to the amount of vegetation, being notably more abundant with increase of more complex plants.

The primary horizontal phyto-gradient of fresh-water littoral areas is of great importance in determining similar gradients of animals. Its plants are usually perennials and present a more stable structure than the open water phytoplankton. Among them there is a general tendency to develop aerenchyma, or spongy tissue, which is of special physiological importance to their aquatic life and also to the invertebrates associated with them (Wilson, 1939).

The zonation of vegetation affects the shelter and food of the several life-history stages of lake animals. These effects are diverse, both direct and indirect, and often operate jointly. The more important influences are listed by Welch (1935) as including: (1) alteration of bottom, through both mechanical stabilization by roots, and retention of accumulating bottom deposits; (2) mechanical support for hydras, sponges, bryozoans, egg masses of insects, rotifers and snails, insect larval cases, and many algae; (3) breeding habitats, eggs being laid both upon and in their tissues by many insects; (4) reduction of light; (5) temporary shelter from predators; (6) reduction of wave action; (7) dispersal of animals, by the breaking off of leaves and stems; (8) marl formation; (9) production of dissolved oxygen, in excess of their respiratory needs; and (10) consumption of carbon dioxide.

Where zonation of higher vegetation is absent, as on the bare sand bottom of some lakes, the apparently deserted strand above the water line holds a diversified and abundant fauna. The microscopic animals composing this littoral zone (psammolittoral habitat) are subject to drastic fluctuations of the physical environment. These include two opposing movements of water: the upward stream of capillary water, between sand grains, rising from the lake and being evaporated, and an intermittent, relatively vigorous downward stream, from waves and from rains. Within this limited horizontal stratum there is microstratification. The mean water content for certain Wisconsin lakes (Pennak, 1939) is 80 per cent saturation in the top centimeter of sand at 100 centimeters from the water edge, 40 per cent saturation at 200 centimeters, and 20 per cent at 300 centimeters. The width of this strip is greatly influenced by slope. For example, a sand beach with an 8 degree slope has an aquatic populated zone 150 centimeters wide, while one with a slope of 3 degrees may have this stratum 300 centimeters wide.

Such a habitat supports an astonishingly large biota (Fig. 156). An average 10 cc. sample of sand (Pennak), taken 150 centimeters from the water's edge, will contain between 2 and 3 centimeters of water, and its fauna and flora consist approximately of: 4,000,000 bacteria; 8000 protozoans; 400 rotifers; 40 copepods, and 20 tardigrades.

Of interest is the fact that even this sandy beach, with its horizontal microstratification, is vertically microstratified by aqueous and evaporation gradients, and further, that the animals are vertically stratified within the top 8 or 10 centimeters of sand. This vertical gradient is especially well shown by the copepods and rotifers, which usually occur with decreasing frequency from the top centimeter downwards.

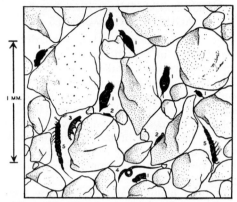

Fig. 156. Diagram of abundance of minute organisms in the psammolittoral habitat. *1*, Rotifers; *2*, gastrotrichs; *3*, tardigrade; *4*, nematodes; *5*, harpacticoid copepods. (After Pennak.)

The sublittoral zone is generally transitional in character, of variable extent, and typically lacks rooted vegetation, but has much vegetable debris. Within this area there is often a "shell zone," a belt characterized by empty shells, and formed from the thriving molluscan life of the littoral stratum. This shell zone is well developed in the sublittoral of Lake Michigan and has been found in numerous lakes of northern Germany (Lundbeck, 1926) as well as inland lakes of Wisconsin, Indiana, and Japan (cf. Eggleton, 1939).

The true profundal zone is formed in lakes that become thermally stratified. Lakes of the second order, especially in temperate regions, have this lowest stratum developed. Conversely, lakes of the third order are so shallow that no thermal stratification occurs, and rooted vegetation may transform the whole bottom into a littoral zone. The profundal region is no more self-supporting than the epilimnion above, the several vertical and horizontal compartments being interdependent.

From this point of view the vertical and horizontal strata are not self-supporting, whereas the pond or lake which they collectively comprise is a relatively independent unit. This is simply a more modern way of saying that the lake is a microcosm (Forbes, 1887); it is a major community. This generally accepted viewpoint is summarized by Eggleton (1939, p. 123): "If any one characteristic of lacustrine ecology is more often apparent to the limnologist than any other, it is this interdependency of the physical, chemical, and biological phenomena whose constant interplay weaves a complex design in the fabric of the life of inland waters." Still more recently Lindeman (1942, p. 399), in an important paper dealing with the trophic-dynamic aspects of lakes, reaffirms this microcosmic view and states: "A lake is considered as a primary ecological unit in its own right, since all the lesser 'communities' mentioned above are dependent upon other components of the lacustrine food cycle for their very existence."

The lower portion of the sublittoral usually merges into the upper portion of the profundal. Where the littoral areas are sandy, the bottom may grade insensibly from sand, muddy sand, sandy mud, to the mud of the profundal region. Many lake animals reach a population maximum, during the summer, in a band termed the "concentration zone," which typically occupies a belt in the lower sublittoral-upper profundal. This concentration zone is formed (Deevey, 1941) as the result of two influences: (1) the upward migration of characteristic profundal species, such as those of *Chaoborus* (= *Corethra*) among Culicidae, and (2) the increase in numbers of chironomid larvae.

As in the psammolittoral habitat, there is evidence of vertical microstratification of the microscopic fauna of profundal mud (Lenz, 1931), and this zone is also the place of origin for the imperfectly understood diurnal migrations of corethroid larvae (Juday, 1921).

The profundal region, when typically developed, is in strong contrast with the littoral zone horizontally and with the epilimnion vertically. Here water temperature, light, and dissolved oxygen are minimal, while water pressure and carbon dioxide are maximal; many gases of decomposition, such as hydrogen sulfide, and usually an acid pH, typify the profundal mud and the water just above. One would anticipate under such conditions that Liebig's "Law of the Minimum" would operate with respect to dissolved oxygen, since this necessary element is typically low or absent in many profundal areas during stagnation periods. To this end, the hemoglobin of the chironomid "blood-worms" may be supposed to allow these characteristic profundal larvae to exist under almost anaerobic conditions; i.e., this suggests one of the adjustments to low oxygen tension.

In relation to generally adverse conditions, the profundal zone may have a rather large population, chiefly of arthropods and mollusks, composed of small to moderate-sized individuals of a relatively few species. Lake Michigan's (Eggleton, 1937) profundal floor produces organic matter equivalent to at least 20 kilograms of dry organic material per hectare; Lake Mendota (Juday, 1922) produces at least 33,000 individuals per square meter; and Third Sister Lake (Eggleton, 1931) produces at least 71,000 individuals per square meter.

One of the characteristic features of the profundal habitat is its great variation in seasonal population density. Making allowances for type of bottom, this variation is best explained by the rhythmical emergence of the predominant insects. These include Diptera (*Chironomus, Chaoborus*), hydroptilid Trichoptera, zygopterous Odonata, Ephemeroptera, and Heteroptera. Many of these emigrate vertically and emerge from the epilimnial surface to lead an aerial existence as imagines; others emigrate horizontally into the shallower waters of the sublittoral and littoral before emergence, giving a disproportionate emergence index for these latter areas (Scott and Opdyke, 1941).

Marine Major Community

With respect to area, the horizontal zones of seas bear the same relation to those of lakes as do the vertical gradients of fresh-water and salt-water communities to each other. A schematized diagram of the sea floor (Fig. 157) begins with a relatively narrow tidal zone. This zone supports the littoral strata, and gradually, with deepening water, passes into an extensive sublittoral zone of the continental shelf. This shelf terminates relatively abruptly, usually in the vicinity of the 200 meter line, where the ocean floor becomes gradually more steeply declivous. This declivity is termed the "continental slope." Below about the 2000 meter line the ocean floor descends into the abyssal zone of from 4000 to 10,000 meters.

Eulittoral Zone

The intertidal area, delimited by the high and low water marks of spring tides, supports a rich and varied biota. These organisms inhabit the littoral region. The area occupied depends primarily upon the degree of slope of a particular portion of the

gradiented; both stratifications are especially well shown by belts of algae on rocky shores. In general, this sea-weed zonation is characterized by three bands of vegetation, depending primarily on the physical gradient imposed by tidal action (Russell and Yonge, 1928): green seaweed (*Enteromorpha*) growing in pools near or slightly above high-water mark; brown seaweed (*Fucus*), especially characteristic of the intertidal limits; and red seaweeds in shallow water offshore, or at the bottoms of deep rock pools.

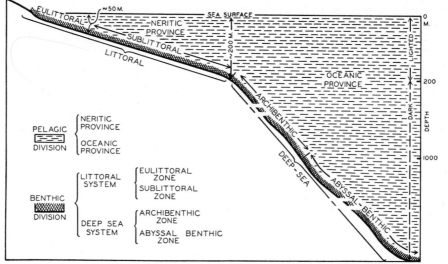

Fig. 157. Diagram of horizontal stratification in the major marine community. (After Sverdrup, Johnson, and Fleming.)

continental shelf, and it may be relatively wide or narrow. In general, there are three types of littoral habitat: (1) rocky shores, (2) sandy shores, formed by the deposition of wave-eroded material, (3) muddy shores, formed by deposition of silt from waterborne runoff from the land.

These three littoral types, and the many intergradations between them, are subject to drastic environmental changes. Tides periodically cover and uncover their surfaces twice every day-night period, and corresponding alterations in temperature, evaporation, light, and friction are features of this stratum. Burrows are periodically covered and uncovered; inhabitants of rock pools at low tide may be subjected to high temperatures in summer; and evaporation increases the local salinity.

As in the fresh-water littoral, the marine littoral is also vertically and horizontally

Chapman, (1941) discussed these marine algae, in general terms, for British coasts, and the basic zonation on rocky shores is stated to be as follows: (1) upper *Enteromorpha-Urospora-Codiolum* belt; (2) *Pelvetia canaliculata* belt, extending from high-water mark shoreward through the spray zone; (3) *Fucus spiralis-F. platycarpus* belt, just seaward of the second stratum; (4) *Ascophyllum nodosum*; (5) *Fucus vesiculosus*; (6) lower fucoid belt, characterized by numbers of *Fucus serratus* (this sixth belt may be dominated by the red algae in other areas, or followed by *Porphyra, Laurencia,* or *Gigartina*; still another variation is the development of epiphytic algae (*Cladophora, Lomentaria*) on *Laurencia* in summer); (7) the belt of *Himanthalia*. The essential characteristics of this algal stratification are repeated in the horizontal gradient of plants on rocky shores the world over, although the taxonomic composition may change with locality.

A recent study of vertical distribution of macroscopic marine algae is that of Doty (1946) along the coast of northern California and Oregon. Here, as elsewhere, such algae are distributed in a series of intertidal zones. The vertical widths of these strata are directly correlated with the tide range, and the stratal limits with certain critical tide levels.

Doty found peculiarities in the variations of the tide, and termed them tide factors. He found that the operation of such factors generally provided sudden twofold or threefold increases in exposure of the algae to other environmental influences (Fig. 158).

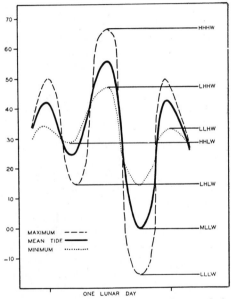

Fig. 158. Tide levels in feet above or below mean lower low water (*MLLW*) at San Francisco. *LLLW* = lowest lower low water; *LHLW* = lowest higher low water; *HHLW* = highest higher low water; *LLHW* = lowest lower high water; *LHHW* = lowest higher high water; *HHHW* = highest higher high water. (After Doty.)

Changes of such magnitude are considered sufficient to account for the abrupt restrictions in the observed vertical zonation. So far, the nature of the restriction is not understood, that is, whether the restriction results from light, temperature, gas tensions, or other direct factors, or is brought about by other influences directly affected by tide

factors, or by desiccation and consequent osmotic changes.

Furthermore, the variation in vertical seaweed belts appears to be correlated with diel, lunar, and annual variation in the levels at which tidal phenomena occur, as well as with variation in the reproductive periods of the algae, and with local topography.

The global influence of tidal activity has induced an apparent vertical distribution of intertidal organisms in the marine littoral. In general, the intertidal zonation of animals and plants is both directly and indirectly induced, after account is taken of the obviously less marked zonation of the motile animals.

The resident animals react to the flora in part, and to the environmental gradient in part. They may be roughly divided into four categories on the basis of their most abundant habitat. In the first place, there are those that live exposed on the rocks or upon the algae. These include sessile acorn-barnacles (*Balanus*), often forming a "Balanus zone" especially near high-water mark and thus associated with the green seaweeds; abundant marine mollusks that browse upon the rock-attached green seaweeds, such as the common limpet (*Patella*), periwinkles (*Littorina*), and top-shells (*Gibbula* and *Calliostoma*). The distribution pattern in this zone is highly varied. For example, there may be a tertiary stratification within the *Littorina* population: on British coasts *Littorina rudis* lives high on the rocky shore, often untouched by sea water for several weeks at a time; *L. littorea* is lower on the shore, but always on the rocks; and *L. obtusata* is zoned with *littorea*, but always on the brown fronds of *Fucus* (cf. Verrill, 1873, and also Allee, 1923, for *Littorina* zones on the Massachusetts coast). These seaweeds support a large population of hydroids and other organisms, while over the upper half of the shore the limpets and top-shells are preyed upon by a tertiary resident, the dog-whelk (*Purpurea*), and nearer low-water mark the rocks become covered with sponges (*Halichondria, Crantia*), tunicates (*Botryllus*), bryozoans, mussels (*Mytilus*), and scallops (*Pecten*).

A second rocky littoral habitat develops in the sheltered niche beneath loose stones. Beneath these stones, near high-water mark, live Collembola among insects, and a variety of crustaceans (*Ligia, Orchestia, Gammarus*). Beneath such stones, lower on the shore where the tides always flood them, are nemertean worms (*Lineus*) and annelids (*Eulalia, Cirratulus*). Still nearer to low-water mark are numbers of certain species of *Nereis*, shore crabs (*Carcinus*), hermit crabs, starfishes (*Asterias*), sea urchins (*Echinus*), and a variety of shore fishes.

Holes and cracks in the rocks are occupied by various annelid worms, crustaceans, small sea cucumbers (*Cucumaria*) and rock-boring bivalves (*Pholas*).

The fourth rocky shore habitat, the rock pools, is distinctive. Here the enclosed organisms escape direct wave action and are exposed to high water temperatures and increased salinity in summer. The walls of such pools are covered by seaweeds, sponges, hydroid coelenterates, bryozoans, tunicates, and sea anemones and shelter a variety of active benthic animals, such as sea slugs (*Aeolis, Doris*) and prawns (*Hippolyte*).

The reefs built by corals flourish only in relatively shallow waters of tropical seas, apparently usually originating on rock coast, and the resulting reef habitat is more comparable to the rocky littoral than to the other types of seashore. Such coral reefs are developed in water seldom deeper than 60 meters, and their building activities progress where surface sea temperatures do not fall much below 20.5° C. This restricts their distribution to a broad band between 30 degrees north and 30 degrees south latitudes (Darwin, 1842). Within this region barrier reefs, fringing reefs, and atolls form through the accumulation of the calcareous thecae of the cooperating polyps, are buffeted by waves and tidal action, and support one of the most distinctive littoral assemblages of organisms.

The chief structural difference lies in the substrate, which in the coral habitat is constructed by the dominant species of plants and animals, especially the calcareous algae and the corals, while the true rocky littoral erodes away instead of growing upward against the surf.

Given a sufficiently high water temperature, corals and other lime-secreting organisms manufacture limestone at variable rates, depending upon such influences as the depth of their submergence, the amount of water motion, the presence or absence of sediment, and lack of dilution of the sea water. Coral reef habitats also tend to be both physically and biologically stratified vertically and horizontally. Lastly, such a habitat contains organisms that live on the exposed reef, under loosened coralline boulders, in holes or cracks in the reef, and in coral reef pools.

The coral reef and the rocky littoral offer many striking parallels. Whether acting upon organismally or geologically produced substrata, the primary environmental gradient sets up biological stratification. On rocky shores seaweeds attach to rocks and in turn form attachment surfaces for numerous animals; on coral reefs, especially in the Indian Ocean, calcareous seaweeds or nullipores attach to the coral rock. Paradoxically, on rocky shores seaweeds have relatively little effect other than being attached to the rocks and forming attachment surfaces for animals, while on coral reefs calcareous algae aid in the consolidation of the reef-building process.

The coral reef habitat has been studied both above and below the sea surface, and descriptions of its exotic fauna can be examined in Davis (1928), Beebe (1928), Hesse, Allee, and Schmidt (1937, pp. 207–221), and in the reports of the British Museum's Great Barrier Reef Expedition (1930), and Yonge (1930).

The coral polyps are suspension feeders, drawing in microplankters by their corona of tentacles, and many species have their gastrovascular cavities nearly obliterated by symbiotic organisms (zoochlorellae and zooxanthellae), which carry on photosynthesis eventually to the mutual benefit of both polyps and algae. These symbiont-bearing polyps are sufficiently near the sea surface to permit light utilization by their symbionts, so that in a very real sense the physical and biological gradients overlap and are interdependent.

There is an almost world-wide littoral intergrade of rocks and sand, the biota of which includes constituents of both the rocky and the sandy littoral habitat. On the northern French beaches of Brittany and Normandy live multitudes of the platyhelminth worm (*Convoluta roscoffensis*). The worms, although solitary, carnivorous, and nocturnal in their youth, become gregarious, indirectly herbivorous, and diurnal when mature. This profound change in the ecology of the adult population is attributable (Keeble, 1910) to their incorporation with symbiotic organisms (zoochlorellae). These turbellarian worms are sand inhabitants and migrate landward and seaward with spring and neap tides, as well as vertically over the day-night period. Horizontally, *roscoffensis* occupies a narrow zone limited towards the sea by maximal light intensity commensurate with sufficient water to partially cover the worms, and limited towards the land by the high-water mark of neap tides.

Further seaward, in shallow water not usually withdrawn, even at low tide, a second species, *Convoluta paradoxa,* lives among the rock-attached seaweeds.

Another special littoral habitat is afforded by wharf piles. From a broad view the vertical, relatively dense, piling surface is in the category of the rocky littoral, and is produced by man and set in place somewhat as coral rock is biologically produced by polyps, in distinction to the natural rock shore. Wharf piles bear a well-known invertebrate fauna. Among the more recent treatment, that of McDougall (1943) summarizes the vertical zonation on piles off the North Carolina coast.

McDougall thinks that the vertical stratification is determined by three general processes: (1) Larvae settle abundantly at a particular pile level and grow to maturity (the cirripedians *Balanus amphitrite* and *Chthamalus fragilis,* and the mussel *Modiolus demissus*); or (2) larvae settle at all pile levels, but adverse conditions destroy them above and below certain limits (hydroids and the bryozoan *Bugula neritina*); while others (3) are motile adult forms and tend to move into and remain at particular pile levels (such as the echinoderm *Arbacia* and the oyster-drill *Urosalpinx*). Light intensity and gravity responses appear to control the level at which larvae tend to settle, while the stratified food-animals influence other organisms, such as the oyster-drill.

It is unnecessary to discuss further the numerous parallels existing between the rock littoral, the coral reef, and the wharf pile habitat. The essential point would seem to be that the initial environment is physically stratified, and this condition imposes a parallel stratification on the inhabiting organisms.

The second littoral type, the sandy shore, when characteristically developed, is inhabited by a wholly different assemblage of organisms. The more labile substrate offers little attachment surface; hence seaweeds are typically sparse or absent. This reduces the species populations of encrusting animals, such as sponges, hydroids, and bryozoans. The sandy littoral, lacking a resident photosynthetic industry, has no normal base in its food web, and its residents are primarily scavengers and carnivores, with the exception of species capable of feeding upon the littoral phytoplankton.

Sand-dwelling marine animals are in great part burrowers. The sandy littoral has been studied by Pearse, Humm, and Wharton (1942) at Beaufort, North Carolina. They report in detail on this portion of the Atlantic littoral, and their description applies in general to similar shores elsewhere; their bibliography may be consulted for this literature.

At this point it should be remembered that there are all degrees of mixing of sand with mud, producing a modified littoral habitat. This sandy-mud substrate is an extensive habitat and forms an intergrade between that of the sand shore and the mud shore. Probably the most typical among many inhabitants are the bivalves, such as the cockles (*Cardium*), the clams (*Venus, Tellina,* and *Donax*), and the razor clams (*Solen*). Another group, the worms, are nearly, if not quite, as typical of the sand floor, including the suspension-feeders (terebellids in general, *Amphitrite*), carnivores, such as sand-worms (*Nereis*), and sand-swallowers (*Arenicola*). Here, too, are found the elongated holothurian, *Synapta,* burrowing sea urchins (*Echinocardium*), shrimps (*Crangon*), and flatfishes of many kinds, all adjusted to an existence on or beneath the sand or sandy-mud.

Species populations inhabiting this substrate must adjust to both sand and mud particles. This is evident in respiratory adaptations, but is also discernible in locomotor and food-obtaining behavior.

The fauna of the sandy-mud is more extensive than that of either the pure sand littoral or the mud littoral. This suggests the principle that there are more species, and at times more individuals, in a habitat with a mixed substrate than there are in any of the component materials where these latter exist in a relatively pure state.

The third littoral type, the mud shores of estuaries and depositing banks, is ecologically much more closely related to the sand littoral than to the rock littoral. Mud shores offer the same shifting substrate as sandy shores, and there are many intergradations between the two types. Burrowing mussels (*Mya, Scrobicularia*) and worms (*Sabella, Myxicola*) are characteristic. Mud snails (*Nassa*), boring whelks (*Murex*), starfish (*Asterias*), and some anemones (*Sagartia bellis*) are common. This mud littoral is both horizontally and vertically stratified.

Sublittoral Zone

Seaward of the littoral zone is the second large-scale horizontal stratum. This is the sublittoral zone, generally extending from low-water tide-mark down to the 200 meter line. This relatively shallow water region is secondarily horizontally stratified (Russell and Yonge, 1928), in the North Atlantic at least, into several substrata. Near low-water mark, just seaward of the *Himanthalia* belt of the rocky littoral, a thick girdle of the seaweed *Laminaria* is fully developed; for example, *L. digitata* at low-water mark and *L. Cloustoni* in slightly deeper waters of the English sublittoral. Where the bottom is more or less sandy these species are supplanted by *L. saccharina* (Chapman, 1941).

The sublittoral bottom is of soft consistency and composed largely of sand, mud, and clay in which stones and numerous molluscan shells are deposited. The marine and fresh-water sublittorals have a parallel development of a "shell zone." To a depth of 100 to 120 meters there are calcareous seaweeds or nullipores (*Lithothamnion*); beyond this depth plant life, except for bacteria, becomes rare. The bottom fauna holds multitudes of Foraminifera; masses of sponges (*Clione*) with their secondary inhabitants, e.g., crustaceans and worms; echinoderms, including crinoids, brittlestars, starfishes (*Solaster, Porania*), sea urchins and sea cucumbers in variety; colonial coelenterates in thick growths, such as sea fans and sea pens; worms, including

leathery sipunculids, nemertines, polychaetes (*Chaetopterus*); crustaceans, as, for example, the Norway lobster (*Nephrops*), rock lobster (*Palinurus*), hermit crabs, spider crabs (*Maia*), stone crabs (*Lithodes*); mollusks, including many whelks (*Buccinum*), boat-shells (including the carnivorous *Scaphander*), scaphopods (*Dentalium*), bivalves, such as *Cyprina islandica* of the North Sea, *Spisula*, which occurs on the Dogger Bank in patches 20 by 50 miles with a population density of 1000 to 8000 per square meter, and scallops (*Pecten*). There are several genera of octopi (*Eledone, Octopus*) and numerous species of fishes. This extensive fauna, including both active and sessile benthos, as well as nekton, is primarily engaged in bottom-straining, scavenging, and in carnivorous activities.

Turning our attention to the European side of the Atlantic Ocean in general, we find that during the present century the sublittoral areas of the North Atlantic have been intensively studied, especially by such Scandinavian investigators as Petersen (1913, ff.). The Atlantic Ocean adjacent to the British Isles, English Channel, North Sea, Baltic Sea, Kattegat, Danish half of the Skagerrak, and a narrow strip along the western fimbriated coast of Norway are not deeper than 200 meters (Philip, 1934). This extensive sublittoral is intruded upon by the deep sea zone off the Norwegian coast where deeper water lies near shore and follows narrowly into the Norwegian half of the Skagerrak.

In Danish water there are eight distinct minor communities that have been recognized by Petersen (1914, 1915, 1915a, and 1918). One of these minor communities is, properly speaking, a littoral biocoenose, and is exposed at low tide (the *Macoma* community in the Ringkoebing Fjord).

Intrazonal stratification of the sublittoral corresponds to similar intrazonal stratification elsewhere in the major marine community, and attests to the general nature of the process. It is found in the narrow sublittoral of northern Norway (Soot-Ryen, 1924), eastern waters of Greenland (Spärck, 1933), off Iceland (Spärck, 1929, 1937), off Massachusetts (Verrill and Smith, 1874; Allee, 1923a, 1923b), and in the northeastern Pacific in the waters ad-

each lengthening of the physical gradient, corresponding changes occur in the fauna.

Once this process is begun, its intensity is progressive and usually not reversible, so that stratification leads to further microstratification until the maximal condition is approached in the mature community. It follows that as vegetational strata develop, there is an increase in potential food and shelter niches for animals. In a well-appropriated stratum the resident animals tend to be adapted structurally to the exigencies of the habitat. The numerous, well-described adjustments of many species—for example, the arboreal or fossorial adjustments of many forest-dwelling animals (Hesse, Allee, and Schmidt, 1937, pp. 421–441)—are visible evidences of such stratal selection.

One of the most apparent differences between aquatic and terrestrial stratification lies in the gravitational difference. Since organisms are heavier than air or water, position must be maintained against gravity in any stratum through which they would otherwise fall. In aquatic communities all strata above the floor are composed of water, and there is a sustained effort, variously ameliorated by structural adjustments and changes in behavior to bring about flotation to maintain position. In terrestrial communities the strata above the floor are based fundamentally on vegetation, and this series of "false bottoms," as it were, places less survival value on such mechanisms for resident animals with respect to maintenance of position, although this does not necessarily imply a lack of survival value for maintenance of foothold. Rather, selection is towards maintaining a foothold on the vegetational stratum—e.g., prehensile appendages—and movement is thus freed for reaction to local stimuli connected with food, shelter, and reproduction.

Just as the shorter food chains of the tundra are more easily understood than the longer food chains of the equatorial rain forest, so is the study of stratification facilitated by examination of a relatively barren area rather than a rich woods. Such short food chains or pioneer surfaces are not necessarily as easily appreciated; in fact, the wealth of detail in more luxuriant regions makes initial recognition much simpler, but also complicates any serious study.

Among such barren surfaces none could be more stark than the exposed surfaces of flat rocks. On such surfaces the air-rock interphase is sharply defined. On unweathered rock the initial inhabitants have no soil, rock particles or humus; hence the community of which they form a part has no subterranean stratum. Total lack of a subterranean stratum is rare, and its absence at once simplifies the dynamics of the community. The initial stages in the colonization of such surfaces are similar, so that it would appear that the specific chemical influence of the rock substrate is of less weight than the toleration of pioneer organisms to the exposure (Cowles, 1901).

Granite flat-rocks of the southeastern United States, studied by McVaugh (1943), present a typical picture of early capture of such a barren surface by organisms. It is apparent that upon such exposed rocks physical conditions for existence are extremely adverse. Organisms are directly exposed to the full strength of sunlight, and through insolation, indirectly to extensive reradiation, to the daily and seasonal range of temperature, to precipitation and subsequent water erosion through flooding and runoff, and to wind and strong evaporation.

Despite these, often violent, variations in weather, such rocks are colonized successfully. The first inhabitants are crustose lichens and mosses, the former of little effect on soil formation, the latter relatively good humus accumulators. Corrosive action of the lichens on the granitic surface, which would tend to soften the rock, is nullified by the transportation of such loosened rock particles through wind and water action; hence a new surface is often exposed (Whitehouse, 1933). Clinging to the rock, these mosses and lichens form the only vertical as well as the only horizontal stratum of the community.

Associated with these pioneer plants, especially with the mosses, is a characteristic fauna of hardy species, often cosmopolitan in mosses over the world, and especially signalized by their ability to withstand otherwise limital temperature and evaporation, through sundry adjustments, such as the formation of cysts. Enumeration of these animals, their adjustment to adverse local weather, and pertinent literature have been previously summarized (Hesse, Allee, and Schmidt, 1937, pp. 355–357). This fauna includes free-living protozoans, acarinid mites, tardigrades, and certain herbivorous beetles. They are preyed upon by other mites and stray carnivorous beetles.

The short food chain and the single vertical and horizontal stratum indicate that this rock assemblage is primitive. There is almost no community control over the physical environment, and the assemblage may be small in area and volume. Nevertheless, given air, sunlight and water, this is a self-sustaining and self-reproducing complex. This aspect of community organization gives a criterion for community validity at the level of survival through cooperation and clearly shows why the shelf-fungus on a forest tree is not a self-sustaining community, although the fungus is microstratified from cortex to medulla, and although both shelf-fungus and granitic rock community may be similar in area or volume.

The granitic rock community is one of the few instances in which there is but a single stratum. At this point in its development this unstratified condition may be merely a lack of human appreciation, since for bacteria, protozoans, and nematodes the crustose lichens and mosses might be physically microstratified. Such an apparent lack of stratification soon vanishes. With the accumulation of moss, humus, and rock particles above the rate at which they can be carried off by wind and water, foliose lichens and vascular plants invade the mat, and stratification becomes evident.

This process of invasion follows a generally reliable pattern that results in concentric horizontal stratification. This has been well summarized by Oosting and Anderson (1939):

"These invaders advance centrifugally over the mat at about the same rate that the pioneers spread upon the rock, and they may themselves be superseded by other species [of plants] which again invade the central area. This results in a series of more or less concentric zones or girdles, each representing a stage in mat development. The pioneer stage is invariably at the periphery, the most mature at the center."

It is interesting to observe that even such a restricted community soon passes from the unstratified to a stratified condition, increasing the amount and kind of food and shelter for the concurrently invading animals, and increasing the biological impact upon the primary physical gradients. It is also of interest to note the parallel between the zonation of such a granitic community and the major features of the suppositional dispersal pattern of the world biota (Matthew, 1915). In both, the primitive types are peripheral, and the more highly evolved or adjusted ones are at or near the center. This is evidently no more than an analogy. In the rock community the pioneer plants are unable to compete centrally where their humus has made possible the existence of more highly evolved plants. Such pioneer species do not move to the periphery; rather, their place is taken wherever they have sufficiently ameliorated their habitat.

The extensive and numerous communities of desert, semidesert, grassland, and forest, together with their intergrades, have not been fully studied as regards vertical and horizontal organization. When attention has been directed to a single community—for example, semidesert—the inherent peculiarities of such a community often obscure the fundamental organization which it shares with all other communities. When this is the case, the fundamental stratification, well shown in the forest or sea, is not stressed, since its particular development in the community under examination may be either reduced or obscured by diurnal and nocturnal population shifts.

All terrestrial communities, at the level of self-sustenance, are stratified in the broad meaning of the term. In general, the vertical gradients are relatively much better developed than the horizontal gradients; the latter may or may not be broken into more or less discrete zones. Such communities have a subterranean stratum, frequently further stratified, above which is a floor stratum, followed by at least one stratum of vegetation. While the subterranean stratum of soil and the floor stratum of organic debris may be diversely constituted, and qualitatively and quantitatively variable within a given community, they are structurally continuous. On the other hand, the elements of the succeeding vegetational stratum, or strata, are discontinuous since each plant arises from the floor as a unit. In forests, where there are several vegetational strata, this structural discontinuity is partially alleviated by the overlapping of foliage and the binding action of vines.

Soil plants and animals have been classified in a variety of ways. According to their size, they may be divided into (a) *microbiota*, including bacteria, algae, fungi, protozoans, rotifers, larvae, small species of nematodes, and minute mites; (b) *mesobiota*, consisting of small forms just visible with a hand lens up to animals several centimeters long, and holding such groups as Enchytraeidae, many nematodes, and the majority of soil-inhabiting mites, crustaceans, centipedes, millipedes, spiders, insects, and other arthropods, as well as snails; and (c) *macrobiota*, consisting of plant roots, earthworms, and vertebrates, such as toads, certain lizards, snakes, rodents, moles, and other relatively large animals (cf. Fenton, 1947).

As to community organization, the subterranean and floor strata hold a variety of organisms that may be classified according to their food habits and their effects on the soil. Such a system has been discussed and revised by Fenton (1947), and this may be further extended: (1) *chemical agents*, such as bacteria and fungi, that are directly and indirectly involved in the chemical conversion of humus; (2) *ectophagous agents* (Jacot, 1939) that consume leaves from without and in entirety. Such agents include (Fenton, 1947) (a) species concerned only with mechanical breakdown and partial chemical conversion of the floor litter, such as green leaf eaters (snails, caterpillars, many chrysomelid beetles, rodents, birds, deer), and animals feeding upon the autumnal or seasonal fall of leaves from higher strata and the floor detritus (snails, mites, Collembola, and certain larvae of flies); (b) species concerned not only with subdivision of the litter, but also with its incorporation into the soil. Here belong the important lumbricid worms, ants, millipedes, certain termites in subtropical and tropical floors, and rodents, particularly of grassland communities (Grinnell, 1923). (3) *Entophagous agents* (endophagous animals of Jacot,

1939, and Fenton, 1947) that feed inside of litter units, and are divisible into (a) leaf miners of fallen leaves (hoplodermatid mites and the larvae of some sciarid flies); (b) tunnelers of dead rootlets, providing a system of minute channels down which may be swept finely divided products of decomposition (such as many tyroglyphid and oribatid mites, and certain collembolans and fly larvae). (4) *Predators*, embracing (a) mesofauna which, by reason of their relatively small size, make little direct contribution to the mixing of mineral and organic materials (centipedes, spiders, carabid, staphylinid, and pselaphid beetles); (b) macrofauna which, by reason of their relatively large size and active fossorial habits, make a larger contribution to the mixing of mineral and organic materials (moles, certain rodents and shrews). (5) *Shelterers* that use the floor and subterranean strata for hibernation, aestivation, or as a protected niche in which to pass a resting or developmental stage, or for protection against attack by enemies. This is a large and complex group, including animals that make regular seasonal and diel vertical movements into these lower strata, as well as horizontal movements from other communities. Furthermore, these five categories of soil organisms are modified by another classification that places emphasis upon the amount of time soil organisms spend in the subterranean stratum and in the floor stratum.

Burrowing and tubicolous marine polychaetes are paralleled by burrowing terrestrial oligochaetes, not only in habitat niche, but in having the orifices of their burrows opening on the surface of the succeeding stratum. Among these annelids the sand-swallowing and mud-swallowing marine species occupy an analogous feeding niche with the soil-swallowing and debris-swallowing earthworms. In a similar analogous position are such burrowing forms as sea cucumbers, while the numerous burrowing crustaceans occupy a feeding niche analogous to that of the burrowing soil insects.

The subterranean stratum is well provided with fossorial vertebrates that live all or a part of their lives within its boundaries, together with numerous species that excavate into this stratum from the floor above. These include amphibians (caecilians and many burrowing frogs), reptiles (certain limbless lizards and many snakes), birds (the burrowing owls and bank swallows), and a wide variety of mammals. Such mammals are especially well adjusted for life in this stratum (Shimer, 1903; Lull, 1920; Hesse, Allee, and Schmidt, 1937, p. 423). Others feed upon the herbaceous stratum, travel on the floor stratum, and excavate burrows into the subterranean stratum for the brooding of their young, or as a habitat niche for daily physiological recuperation, or as a protection against both adverse weather and natural enemies. Others—for example, the American badger—dig into the subterranean stratum or pursue burrowing prey. Finally, such animals as swine travel on the floor stratum and dig for a part of their food in the subterranean stratum. Although many species are more or less fossorial, only a few mammals are, strictly speaking, inhabitants of the subterranean stratum; most of the larger vertebrates utilize several strata in the vertical gradient, as do certain bottom-feeding fishes already mentioned, and hence may be thought of as binding species in the community.

STRATIFICATION IN GRASSLAND COMMUNITIES

Grassland in general is limited to terrestrial areas with an annual precipitation of between 20 and 40 inches, little of which is deposited in the hot season, and by the edaphic characteristics of the soil and the population of grazing animals. Grassland, limited by climatic, edaphic, and biotic factors, includes diverse communities at the level of self-sustenance. Despite differences in the area that such communities occupy, and their degree of relative maturity, they all agree in having a stratified structure.

Grassland communities have three vertical strata: namely, subterranean, floor, and herbaceous (Vestal, 1913; Cameron, 1917). The subterranean stratum has been investigated for substratification of the root systems of grassland plants (Weaver, 1920; Pavlychenko, 1937); such studies show a well-developed system of layering. These subterranean extensions of the herbaceous cover, chiefly grass roots, directly affect other subterranean plants (fungi and bacteria) and herbivorous animals in making food available. Indirectly they affect aera-

tion and drainage, and provide a more profitable hunting area for carnivores.

Snails are fewer in number in the grasslands as compared with forests, and earthworms are not so common (Pearse, 1939). Insects are among the most abundant macroscopic animals of grasslands (Vestal, 1913; Wolcott, 1937). Grasshoppers and their allies are notably abundant and characteristic (Uvarov, 1928; Isely, 1938, 1938a, 1941), and since many oviposit in the upper portion of the subterranean stratum, the soil is directly utilized for a portion of their life cycles. Burrowing spiders and grassland ants excavate in this stratum. Here also are the burrows of numerous grassland mammals (Haviland, 1926; Petry and Visher, 1926; Clements and Shelford, 1939, Chap. 8; Hamilton, 1939), including a rich fauna of rodents (Table 35). Some rodents (pocket gophers and Asiatic mole-rats) not only have their burrows in the subterranean stratum, but feed in it as well, sometimes tunneling several feet below the surface of the soil, and feeding on bulbs and roots. Such animals are characteristically adjusted to their specialized habitat with vestigial eyes, stout barrel-shaped bodies, short and powerful limbs with fossorial forepaws, and vestigial tails.

Other grassland constituents, typical of higher strata, utilize the subterranean portion of the community. Bank swallows in the pampas dig their holes in the walls of the extensive entrances of the viscacha burrows and are dependent upon the latter for nesting sites. Many birds (sand martin, rollers, bee-eaters of the Asiatic grassland; cf. Haviland, 1926) and mammals (jack rabbit) breed in holes often deep enough to be subterranean and further bridge the gap between the floor and subterranean habitats. Subterranean burrows of fossorial rodents are used by other animals. For example, the viscacha's burrow and ancillary trenches are used as nesting sites by the pampas sand martin (*Atticora*), burrowing owl, six species of sand wasps, a species of reduviid bug, and a species of nocturnal cicindelid beetle, none of which is commonly found elsewhere. In North America the prairie rattler (*Crotalus viridis*) is typical of the floor stratum, but since the snake is essentially nocturnal and one of its chief foods is

each lengthening of the physical gradient, corresponding changes occur in the fauna.

Once this process is begun, its intensity is progressive and usually not reversible, so that stratification leads to further micro-stratification until the maximal condition is approached in the mature community. It follows that as vegetational strata develop, there is an increase in potential food and shelter niches for animals. In a well-appropriated stratum the resident animals tend to be adapted structurally to the exigencies of the habitat. The numerous, well-described adjustments of many species—for example, the arboreal or fossorial adjustments of many forest-dwelling animals (Hesse, Allee, and Schmidt, 1937, pp. 421–441)—are visible evidences of such stratal selection.

One of the most apparent differences between aquatic and terrestrial stratification lies in the gravitational difference. Since organisms are heavier than air or water, position must be maintained against gravity in any stratum through which they would otherwise fall. In aquatic communities all strata above the floor are composed of water, and there is a sustained effort, variously ameliorated by structural adjustments and changes in behavior to bring about flotation to maintain position. In terrestrial communities the strata above the floor are based fundamentally on vegetation, and this series of "false bottoms," as it were, places less survival value on such mechanisms for resident animals with respect to maintenance of position, although this does not necessarily imply a lack of survival value for maintenance of foothold. Rather, selection is towards maintaining a foothold on the vegetational stratum—e.g., prehensile appendages—and movement is thus freed for reaction to local stimuli connected with food, shelter, and reproduction.

Just as the shorter food chains of the tundra are more easily understood than the longer food chains of the equatorial rain forest, so is the study of stratification facilitated by examination of a relatively barren area rather than a rich woods. Such short food chains or pioneer surfaces are not necessarily as easily appreciated; in fact, the wealth of detail in more luxuriant regions makes initial recognition much simpler, but also complicates any serious study.

Among such barren surfaces none could be more stark than the exposed surfaces of flat rocks. On such surfaces the air-rock interphase is sharply defined. On unweathered rock the initial inhabitants have no soil, rock particles or humus; hence the community of which they form a part has no subterranean stratum. Total lack of a subterranean stratum is rare, and its absence at once simplifies the dynamics of the community. The initial stages in the colonization of such surfaces are similar, so that it would appear that the specific chemical influence of the rock substrate is of less weight than the toleration of pioneer organisms to the exposure (Cowles, 1901).

Granite flat-rocks of the southeastern United States, studied by McVaugh (1943), present a typical picture of early capture of such a barren surface by organisms. It is apparent that upon such exposed rocks physical conditions for existence are extremely adverse. Organisms are directly exposed to the full strength of sunlight, and through insolation, indirectly to extensive reradiation, to the daily and seasonal range of temperature, to precipitation and subsequent water erosion through flooding and runoff, and to wind and strong evaporation.

Despite these, often violent, variations in weather, such rocks are colonized successfully. The first inhabitants are crustose lichens and mosses, the former of little effect on soil formation, the latter relatively good humus accumulators. Corrosive action of the lichens on the granitic surface, which would tend to soften the rock, is nullified by the transportation of such loosened rock particles through wind and water action; hence a new surface is often exposed (Whitehouse, 1933). Clinging to the rock, these mosses and lichens form the only vertical as well as the only horizontal stratum of the community.

Associated with these pioneer plants, especially with the mosses, is a characteristic fauna of hardy species, often cosmopolitan in mosses over the world, and especially signalized by their ability to withstand otherwise limital temperature and evaporation, through sundry adjustments, such as the formation of cysts. Enumeration of these animals, their adjustment to adverse local weather, and pertinent literature have been previously summarized (Hesse, Allee, and Schmidt, 1937, pp. 355–357). This fauna includes free-living protozoans, acarinid mites, tardigrades, and certain herbivorous beetles. They are preyed upon by other mites and stray carnivorous beetles.

The short food chain and the single vertical and horizontal stratum indicate that this rock assemblage is primitive. There is almost no community control over the physical environment, and the assemblage may be small in area and volume. Nevertheless, given air, sunlight and water, this is a self-sustaining and self-reproducing complex. This aspect of community organization gives a criterion for community validity at the level of survival through cooperation and clearly shows why the shelf-fungus on a forest tree is not a self-sustaining community, although the fungus is microstratified from cortex to medulla, and although both shelf-fungus and granitic rock community may be similar in area or volume.

The granitic rock community is one of the few instances in which there is but a single stratum. At this point in its development this unstratified condition may be merely a lack of human appreciation, since for bacteria, protozoans, and nematodes the crustose lichens and mosses might be physically microstratified. Such an apparent lack of stratification soon vanishes. With the accumulation of moss, humus, and rock particles above the rate at which they can be carried off by wind and water, foliose lichens and vascular plants invade the mat, and stratification becomes evident.

This process of invasion follows a generally reliable pattern that results in concentric horizontal stratification. This has been well summarized by Oosting and Anderson (1939):

"These invaders advance centrifugally over the mat at about the same rate that the pioneers spread upon the rock, and they may themselves be superseded by other species [of plants] which again invade the central area. This results in a series of more or less concentric zones or girdles, each representing a stage in mat development. The pioneer stage is invariably at the periphery, the most mature at the center."

It is interesting to observe that even such a restricted community soon passes from the unstratified to a stratified condition, increasing the amount and kind of food and shelter for the concurrently invading animals, and increasing the biological impact upon the primary physical gradients. It is also of interest to note the parallel between the zonation of such a granitic community and the major features of the suppositional dispersal pattern of the world biota (Matthew, 1915). In both, the primitive types are peripheral, and the more highly evolved or adjusted ones are at or near the center. This is evidently no more than an analogy. In the rock community the pioneer plants are unable to compete centrally where their humus has made possible the existence of more highly evolved plants. Such pioneer species do not move to the periphery; rather, their place is taken wherever they have sufficiently ameliorated their habitat.

The extensive and numerous communities of desert, semidesert, grassland, and forest, together with their intergrades, have not been fully studied as regards vertical and horizontal organization. When attention has been directed to a single community—for example, semidesert—the inherent peculiarities of such a community often obscure the fundamental organization which it shares with all other communities. When this is the case, the fundamental stratification, well shown in the forest or sea, is not stressed, since its particular development in the community under examination may be either reduced or obscured by diurnal and nocturnal population shifts.

All terrestrial communities, at the level of self-sustenance, are stratified in the broad meaning of the term. In general, the vertical gradients are relatively much better developed than the horizontal gradients; the latter may or may not be broken into more or less discrete zones. Such communities have a subterranean stratum, frequently further stratified, above which is a floor stratum, followed by at least one stratum of vegetation. While the subterranean stratum of soil and the floor stratum of organic debris may be diversely constituted, and qualitatively and quantitatively variable within a given community, they are structurally continuous. On the other hand, the elements of the succeeding vegetational stratum, or strata, are discontinuous since each plant arises from the floor as a unit. In forests, where there are several vegetational strata, this structural discontinuity is partially alleviated by the overlapping of foliage and the binding action of vines.

Soil plants and animals have been classified in a variety of ways. According to their size, they may be divided into (a) *microbiota,* including bacteria, algae, fungi, protozoans, rotifers, larvae, small species of nematodes, and minute mites; (b) *mesobiota,* consisting of small forms just visible with a hand lens up to animals several centimeters long, and holding such groups as Enchytraeidae, many nematodes, and the majority of soil-inhabiting mites, crustaceans, centipedes, millipedes, spiders, insects, and other arthropods, as well as snails; and (c) *macrobiota,* consisting of plant roots, earthworms, and vertebrates, such as toads, certain lizards, snakes, rodents, moles, and other relatively large animals (cf. Fenton, 1947).

As to community organization, the subterranean and floor strata hold a variety of organisms that may be classified according to their food habits and their effects on the soil. Such a system has been discussed and revised by Fenton (1947), and this may be further extended: (1) *chemical agents,* such as bacteria and fungi, that are directly and indirectly involved in the chemical conversion of humus; (2) *ectophagous agents* (Jacot, 1939) that consume leaves from without and in entirety. Such agents include (Fenton, 1947) (a) species concerned only with mechanical breakdown and partial chemical conversion of the floor litter, such as green leaf eaters (snails, caterpillars, many chrysomelid beetles, rodents, birds, deer), and animals feeding upon the autumnal or seasonal fall of leaves from higher strata and the floor detritus (snails, mites, Collembola, and certain larvae of flies); (b) species concerned not only with subdivision of the litter, but also with its incorporation into the soil. Here belong the important lumbricid worms, ants, millipedes, certain termites in subtropical and tropical floors, and rodents, particularly of grassland communities (Grinnell, 1923). (3) *Entophagous agents* (endophagous animals of Jacot,

1939, and Fenton, 1947) that feed inside of litter units, and are divisible into (a) leaf miners of fallen leaves (hoplodermatid mites and the larvae of some sciarid flies); (b) tunnelers of dead rootlets, providing a system of minute channels down which may be swept finely divided products of decomposition (such as many tyroglyphid and oribatid mites, and certain collembolans and fly larvae). (4) *Predators,* embracing (a) mesofauna which, by reason of their relatively small size, make little direct contribution to the mixing of mineral and organic materials (centipedes, spiders, carabid, staphylinid, and pselaphid beetles); (b) macrofauna which, by reason of their relatively large size and active fossorial habits, make a larger contribution to the mixing of mineral and organic materials (moles, certain rodents and shrews). (5) *Shelterers* that use the floor and subterranean strata for hibernation, aestivation, or as a protected niche in which to pass a resting or developmental stage, or for protection against attack by enemies. This is a large and complex group, including animals that make regular seasonal and diel vertical movements into these lower strata, as well as horizontal movements from other communities. Furthermore, these five categories of soil organisms are modified by another classification that places emphasis upon the amount of time soil organisms spend in the subterranean stratum and in the floor stratum.

Burrowing and tubicolous marine polychaetes are paralleled by burrowing terrestrial oligochaetes, not only in habitat niche, but in having the orifices of their burrows opening on the surface of the succeeding stratum. Among these annelids the sand-swallowing and mud-swallowing marine species occupy an analogous feeding niche with the soil-swallowing and debris-swallowing earthworms. In a similar analogous position are such burrowing forms as sea cucumbers, while the numerous burrowing crustaceans occupy a feeding niche analogous to that of the burrowing soil insects.

The subterranean stratum is well provided with fossorial vertebrates that live all or a part of their lives within its boundaries, together with numerous species that excavate into this stratum from the floor above. These include amphibians (caecilians and many burrowing frogs), reptiles (certain limbless lizards and many snakes), birds (the burrowing owls and bank swallows), and a wide variety of mammals. Such mammals are especially well adjusted for life in this stratum (Shimer, 1903; Lull, 1920; Hesse, Allee, and Schmidt, 1937, p. 423). Others feed upon the herbaceous stratum, travel on the floor stratum, and excavate burrows into the subterranean stratum for the brooding of their young, or as a habitat niche for daily physiological recuperation, or as a protection against both adverse weather and natural enemies. Others—for example, the American badger—dig into the subterranean stratum or pursue burrowing prey. Finally, such animals as swine travel on the floor stratum and dig for a part of their food in the subterranean stratum. Although many species are more or less fossorial, only a few mammals are, strictly speaking, inhabitants of the subterranean stratum; most of the larger vertebrates utilize several strata in the vertical gradient, as do certain bottom-feeding fishes already mentioned, and hence may be thought of as binding species in the community.

STRATIFICATION IN GRASSLAND COMMUNITIES

Grassland in general is limited to terrestrial areas with an annual precipitation of between 20 and 40 inches, little of which is deposited in the hot season, and by the edaphic characteristics of the soil and the population of grazing animals. Grassland, limited by climatic, edaphic, and biotic factors, includes diverse communities at the level of self-sustenance. Despite differences in the area that such communities occupy, and their degree of relative maturity, they all agree in having a stratified structure.

Grassland communities have three vertical strata: namely, subterranean, floor, and herbaceous (Vestal, 1913; Cameron, 1917). The subterranean stratum has been investigated for substratification of the root systems of grassland plants (Weaver, 1920; Pavlychenko, 1937); such studies show a well-developed system of layering. These subterranean extensions of the herbaceous cover, chiefly grass roots, directly affect other subterranean plants (fungi and bacteria) and herbivorous animals in making food available. Indirectly they affect aera-

tion and drainage, and provide a more profitable hunting area for carnivores.

Snails are fewer in number in the grasslands as compared with forests, and earthworms are not so common (Pearse, 1939). Insects are among the most abundant macroscopic animals of grasslands (Vestal, 1913; Wolcott, 1937). Grasshoppers and their allies are notably abundant and characteristic (Uvarov, 1928; Isely, 1938, 1938a, 1941), and since many oviposit in the upper portion of the subterranean stratum, the soil is directly utilized for a portion of their life cycles. Burrowing spiders and grassland ants excavate in this stratum. Here also are the burrows of numerous grassland mammals (Haviland, 1926; Petry and Visher, 1926; Clements and Shelford, 1939, Chap. 8; Hamilton, 1939), including a rich fauna of rodents (Table 35). Some rodents (pocket gophers and Asiatic mole-rats) not only have their burrows in the subterranean stratum, but feed in it as well, sometimes tunneling several feet below the surface of the soil, and feeding on bulbs and roots. Such animals are characteristically adjusted to their specialized habitat with vestigial eyes, stout barrel-shaped bodies, short and powerful limbs with fossorial forepaws, and vestigial tails.

Other grassland constituents, typical of higher strata, utilize the subterranean portion of the community. Bank swallows in the pampas dig their holes in the walls of the extensive entrances of the viscacha burrows and are dependent upon the latter for nesting sites. Many birds (sand martin, rollers, bee-eaters of the Asiatic grassland; cf. Haviland, 1926) and mammals (jack rabbit) breed in holes often deep enough to be subterranean and further bridge the gap between the floor and subterranean habitats. Subterranean burrows of fossorial rodents are used by other animals. For example, the viscacha's burrow and ancillary trenches are used as nesting sites by the pampas sand martin (*Atticora*), burrowing owl, six species of sand wasps, a species of reduviid bug, and a species of nocturnal cicindelid beetle, none of which is commonly found elsewhere. In North America the prairie rattler (*Crotalus viridis*) is typical of the floor stratum, but since the snake is essentially nocturnal and one of its chief foods is the diurnal prairie dog, this rattler pursues its prey into the burrows. The situation is rendered more complex by the presence of burrowing owls, which may feed upon the young rodents or may live in abandoned prairie dog tunnels. This is far from the supposedly friendly association of prairie dog, rattlesnake, and burrowing owl. There is obviously no mutualism involved (Brehm, 1914; Seton, 1909). These examples suffice to demonstrate how animals of different grassland strata move interstratally and utilize different periods of the twenty-four-hour cycle.

The subterranean stratum of the grassland community is of considerable importance. This is partially a consequence of the relative and seasonal aridity of grassland, and the relatively slight protection afforded by the herbaceous stratum to high summer day temperatures and high light intensities as contrasted with the analogous protection of the canopy of forests. The importance of the fossorial habit in this connection has been discussed by Shelford (1915). This author used data compiled by Seton (1909) to compare Manitoba forest and steppe mammals on the basis of stratification, as summarized in the following table measuring nearly three and one-half million inches ($\pm$ 60 miles); where wild oats are grown in competition with weeds in six-inch rows with eighteen to twenty plants per foot, the average for single wild oat plants is 38,452 inches (less than one mile). Thus wild oat plants produce from eighty-three to ninety-nine times smaller root systems in competition than as single plants. It appears that the occupation of the soil by native grassland plants in free root competition, and their development of a dense root mat, seldom penetrates more than 7 feet below the surface.

Herbivores seldom go beneath this potential food reservoir. Most grassland insects do not penetrate below 3 inches (Cameron, 1917), and pocket gophers seldom below 2 feet, usually between 4 to 12 inches beneath the soil surface. At least two groups of prairie animals go beneath the grass root substratum. Colonies of prairie ants may penetrate the soil for 9 feet (Hungerford and Williams, 1912), and the gregarious prairie dogs may extend their burrows to a depth of 14 feet. Carnivores preying upon these residents may descend to this lowest substratum in search of their food. The prairie rattler doubtless

Table 34. Comparison of Number of Species of Forest and Steppe Mammals in Vertical Stratum Occupied (Based on Shelford, 1915, after Seton, 1909)

Stratum	Forest Mammals	Steppe Mammals
1. Subterranean	6%	47%
2. Floor	68%	53%
3. Vegetational (Arboreal, etc.)	26%	0%

table. From these percentages it will be seen that approximately one-half of the steppe mammals inhabit the subterranean stratum for all or a part of their lives.

The primary constituents of the vertical gradient—namely, the grassland plants—extend their root systems for a vertical distance into the soil for from 60 inches in wild oats to 30 inches for Marquis wheat, wild mustard, and Hannchen barley. These figures of vertical penetration by no means allow us to appreciate the amount of root surface made available for consumption by herbivores. One wild oat crown-root will have a combined length of all its root branches of 4.5 miles. Pavlychenko (1937) showed that where a single wild oat plant grows in an area 10 feet square, free from all root competition, it produces a root sys-

descends to the bottom of prairie dog burrows. The bull snake (*Pituophis sayi*) enters the more superficial tunnels of the pocket gopher in search of food. In fact, it has been shown that the bull snake may actually remove earth from a lateral tunnel of a pocket gopher's burrow in order to reach the animal (Hisaw and Gloyd, 1026).

The floor, or second stratum, is both intermediate and transitional between the subterranean and herbaceous strata in amplitude of such operating physical influences as light intensity, temperature, and precipitation. Its matrix is subject to erosion by wind and water and consists of a complex of soil particles mixed with waste products and organic debris from decomposing portions of animals and plants, from both floor and vegetation, in all stages of humus formation.

In comparison with forest floors, grassland floors have less bulky leaf mold litter, but may have as high or higher humus content in the soil. This is partially a result of the continental climate of grasslands over the world, especially the typically deficient rainfall in the latter part of the hot season. This climatic limitation not only influences the distribution of grassland (Thornthwaite, 1931; Carpenter, 1940a), but indirectly reduces stratification, with the correlated reduction in bulk of vegetation and consequent lowering of the amount of litter. Low litter deposit on the grassland floor, in comparison with forest floors, is also partially a consequence of increased erosion potential. Erosion has an important effect upon the immediate prosperity, as well as the long-term stability, of the entire steppe community. If the vegetation is considered in the role of a windbreak, the natural wind erosion potential of grassland is greater than that of forests. Wind-blown humus and soil (Sears, 1935a), taken from one area and carried as dust to another area, denude the floor in the former instance and may bury the original floor in the latter case. Such dust storms, whether due to drought or to intensive cultivation of the soil by man, or by both these agencies, seriously affect the grassland plants and animals, including man. Water and waterborne soil and humus are inevitably integrated in the erosion complex, both through direct and indirect effects. The water-holding capacity of the soil (chresard) of the subterranean stratum below, and the windbreak action of the herbaceous stratum above, are affected by, and affect, the floor stratum. To the chresard must be added the mat of roots previously alluded to, as well as the activities of burrowing animals, as factors affecting the amount of erosion in the grassland community.

The animal population of the floor stratum comprises (1) those tunneling in the subterranean stratum, but obtaining all or a part of their food from the floor; (2) primary floor inhabitants; (3) animals that pass their inactive periods on the floor, but feed upon the vegetation, either ascending the latter (grasshoppers) or by grazing

(antelope); and (4) animals that have a seasonal change in their inactivity niche.

In the tall grass prairie of parts of North Dakota (Bailey, 1925; Hanson and Whitman, 1938) and Manitoba (Bird, 1930) in recent years, the herbivore consuming most grass is neither the large grazers (prongbuck, bison) nor the summer-active burrowing rodents and invertebrates, but is a small rodent, Drummond's vole (*Microtus drummondii*). It measures between 110 and 145 mm. in total length, but occurs in such numbers that several runways are encountered over almost every square foot of the prairie. It feeds wholly upon the seeds and tender shoots of the steppe herbaceous stratum, such as wheat grass (*Agropyron Richardsonii*), *Koeleria*, *Agrostis*, and *Stipa*. Of these, wheat grass keeps its flower heads throughout the winter, giving a characteristic aspect to this particular steppe community, and Drummond's vole is active throughout the year, feeding upon the rich herbaceous stratum, but constructing summer nests in the subterranean stratum and winter nests of woven grass on the floor stratum.

These investigations also emphasize the point that composition of a stratum is more easily determined than are the exact ecological relationships of the several stratal constituents. For example, the familiar cow feeding in the pasture is in competition with numerous herbivorous grassland insects and such mammals as meadow mice. We have just seen that the latter consumed more grass than the large grazers. Wolcott (1937) found that under certain conditions cows ate less economic grasses and clovers than did the grasshoppers in New York pastures:

"Expressing the data obtained in terms of the weight of the insects themselves made possible direct comparison with what the cows were obtaining from the pastures. Surprisingly enough, it was found that where there were few cows in the pasture, they scarcely equalled in weight the total of the wild life present there, and the insects ate more of the grasses and clovers than the cows did. Indeed, the cows obtained a larger share of the pasturage only where they kept the vegetation so short that it afforded scanty protection for the crickets, grasshoppers and leafhoppers, and was more attractive to the robins, who foraged there in greater numbers, and still further reduced the number of insects" (Wolcott, 1937, p. 89).

Herbivorous, cursorial, hoofed animals are well-known examples of the prairie grazing group. They form a noteworthy list of ecologically replaceable or equivalent species in both temperate and tropical grasslands. Some of these stratal equivalents are listed in Table 35, in which stratal equivalence or replaceability is emphasized. It should be pointed out that this tabular comparison does not differentiate between tropical savannahs and temperate prairies. These grassland community types are touched upon later in this chapter and discussed in more detail in the chapter on the biome. In the second place, this table does not differentiate between diurnal and nocturnal species. Such periodism and its far-reaching influence comprise the subject matter of a separate chapter. Attention is directed, however, to the close stratal congruence within the grassland communities of the world, which in turn reemphasizes the essential similarity in structure of such communities.

The majority of the cursorial, herbivorous hoofed mammals mentioned in the table occur in large aggregations. Through their grazing activities they compete directly with agricultural man and other prairie animals, for example, the meadow mice (*Microtus*), which may populate grasslands in excess of fifty mice per acre (Hamilton, 1940). The combined action of all these herbivorous groups is a large-scale intracommunity cooperative influence restricting the vegetational stratum within certain growth limits. On the other hand, these herbivorous grassland groups are limited in their dispersal and increase through the amount and distribution of naturally developed prairie vegetation, and that introduced and cultivated by man (wheat, barley, rye, oats, corn). The dominance of agricultural man in prairie communities varies with the geographic location of a particular grassland community, his sociological emergence, and the period of history examined.

The responses of herbivorous mammals to the primary vegetational zone of the grassland, the herbaceous stratum, is responsible for at least three widespread biotic effects.

The first is the presence of predators in sufficient numbers to maintain a biotic balance with their food supply (p. 370).

They consequently regulate the herbivorous population in part, and in part have their own numbers regulated by the abundance of their food, in the same general way in which the herbage and herbivorous population exert a reciprocal effect (p. 706). These predators include reptiles, birds, and mammals feeding chiefly upon insects, rodents, and ungulates. Probably the most widely known of these carnivores are the predaceous cats and dogs (Table 35). These are typically adjusted for stalking or running down their particular foods (p. 242), either as solitary hunters or in hunting packs, and either in the active or inactive period of their prey, depending upon the activity cycle of both the predator and prey (p. 544). The general relation between the number of herbivores and the number of predators within a given grassland community is shown in Table 35. For example, in the mammals, the rich grassland herbivore population of Africa is paralleled by an equally rich predator population. In contrast, Australian plains have fewer native predators and fewer large native herbivores. This latter instance, in which the marsupial population has radiated and flourished in the absence of effective competition, is an illustration of how isolation may affect the stratal composition of a community (p. 666).

Herbivorous hoofed animals of grassland, in the second place, contribute to the invertebrate life of the floor and subterranean strata by their dung. This affords sustenance directly to coprophagous insects, and indirectly to the parasitic and predaceous insects that feed in turn upon them. The relative importance of these dung-inhabiting animals is not apt to be appreciated if the methods of assay do not take animal droppings into account. The number of species and individuals inhabiting ungulate dung is high in unwooded pastures—for example, in central Illinois (Mohr, 1943) and New Jersey (Wilson, 1932), where dung is provided by sheep or cattle droppings.

The scavengers feeding upon the dung include scarabaeid beetles of the subfamilies Geotrupinae, Aphodiinae, and Coprinae, and numerous flies (*Cryptolucilia, Haematobia, Sarcophaga,* and *Sepsis*). These flies and beetles oviposit on the

Table 35. Stratal Equivalents in Grassland Communities

Stratal Categories	Asia	Africa	North America	South America	Australia
1. Saltatorial herbivores with habitat niche on floor and feeding niche in herbaceous stratum: a. Acridid grasshoppers	*Locusta migratoria*	North Africa *Locusta migratorioides* *Stauronotus maroccanus* South Africa *Schistocerca peregrina*	*Melanoplus spretus, differentialis, maculipennis, ponderosa*	*Schistocerca paranensis*	
b. Mammals	Asiatic gerboa (*Glactaga*)	Springhaas (*Pedetes caffer*)	Prairie hare or jack rabbit (*Lepus campestris*)		Red kangaroo (*Macropus rufus*)
2. Fossorial, herbivorous mammals: a. Habitat niche in subterranean and floor strata; feeding niche in herbaceous stratum	Suslick (*Citellus*) Hamster (*Cricetus*)	African ground squirrels (*Xerus*)	Ground squirrel (*Citellus*) Prairie dog (*Cynomys*)	Viscacha (*Vizcacia*) Pampas cavy (*Cavia*)	European rabbit (*Oryctolagus cuniculus*) (introduced by man)
b. Habitat and feeding niches in subterranean stratum	Mole-rat (*Spalax*)	Golden moles (Chrysochloridae)	Prairie moles (*Scalopus aquaticus*) Pocket-gopher (*Geomys; Thomomys*)	Tucotucos (*Ctenomys*)	Marsupial mole (*Notoryctes*)
3. Cursorial birds with habitat niche on floor and feeding niche in floor and herbaceous strata.	Ostrich, recently extinct	Ostrich		Common rhea Darwin's rhea	Emu

4. Cursorial, herbivorous, gregarious mammals (habitat niche on floor; feeding niche in herbaceous stratum)	Saiga antelope Goitered antelope Gazelle Maral stag Wild ass Tarpan or wild horse (recently extinct)	Zebra Eland Springbok Gazelles (several sp.) Black wildebeest (*Connochaetes gnou*) Blue wildebeest (*Gorgon taurinus*) Bubal (*Bubalis buselaphus*) Bontebok (*Damaliscus pygargus*) (30 odd genera of antelopes in this category)	Pronghorn antelope Bison	Pampas deer (*Odocoileus bezoarticus*) Guanaco (*Lama huanacus*) Marsh deer	Pig-footed bandicoot (*Choeropus castanotis*)
5. Cursorial predators (habitat and feeding niches on floor stratum):					
a. Snakes	Common cobra (*Naja naja*) Asiatic moccasin (*Agkistrodon halys*) Chinese elaphe (*Elaphe dione*)	Puff adder (*Bitis arietans*) Black-necked cobra (*Naja nigricollis*) Rock python (*Python sebae*)	Blue racer (*Coluber c. flaviventris*) Bull snakes (*Pituophis*) Prairie rattler (*Crotalus viridis*)	*Cyclagras gigas* *Rhadinea merremii*	Death adder (*Acanthophis*) Tiger snake (*Notechis*)
b. Carnivora	Manul cat (*Felis manul*) Corsac fox (*Canis corsac*) Cheetah (*Acinonyx*) Wolf (*Canis lupus*)*	Lion (*Panthera leo*) Serval (*Leptailurus serval*) Caracal (*Caracal*) Cheetah (*Acinonyx*) Cape hunting-dog (*Lycaon*)	Coyote (*Canis latrans*) Wolf (*Canis lupus*)* Puma* (*Felis concolor*)	Pampas cat (*Felis pajeros*) Red wolf (*Chrysocyon*)	Equivalent marsupial: Tasmanian wolf (*Thylacinus cynocephalus*) (originally inhabiting the Australian mainland, now confined to Tasmania)

* Indicates "entrant" primarily from another community.

dung, and their larvae feed upon this rich source of energy. In other instances the coprine scavengers (*Canthon, Copris, Onthophagus,* and *Scarabaeus*) usually first cut out portions of the dung and roll these balls either into a protected niche in the floor, or bury them deeply in the subterranean stratum before oviposition. In either case these coprophagous insects are eaten in their immature stages by a variety of predators, including histerid and staphylinid beetles.

In addition, the mature and immature scavenger flies and beetles are sources of transportation or food for the essential coprocolous bacteria, myriads of larval, nymphal, and mature mites (Parasitidae), and parasitoid Hymenoptera (Figitidae).

During the period when ungulate droppings retain their individuality, passing from a moist irridescence to a hard, dry chip (p. 568), they represent insular areas with coprocole populations, concentrically stratified, on the grassland floor. Later the matrix of these islands becomes incorporated into the subterranean stratum by leaching and absorption through weathering and erosion.

Droppings of the larger animals, while supporting large populations, are directly affected by chemical conditions (host diet and physiological state) and physical conditions (light intensity, air temperature, precipitation, and evaporation). Both physical and chemical conditions on the floor about the droppings, and within its matrix, affect the bacteriological industry carried on within the dung. These three influences are important in regulating the activity and substratification of the coprocolous biocoenose of the grassland community.

Fly and beetle scavengers that once thrived upon bison and prongbuck dung of the North American plains now feed upon the excrement of our domestic cattle (Hayes, 1929). Some idea of the importance of dung to the grassland community may be had by a brief examination of the herbivore population. Seton (1909) estimated that at one time the North American prairie was inhabited by one bison per 20 acres. Henry and Morrison (1923) found that beef cattle produce 52 pounds of dung per 1000 pounds of live weight per day. If we estimate the average hoofed mammal of the steppe at 500 pounds, and the average daily dung component at 25 pounds, then the hypothetical minimum dung component from large ungulates alone works out at a little more than 1 pound of dung for each acre of grassland per day. If we assume an equal amount for all other grassland animals, we would have, at a conservative estimate, 2 pounds per day per acre. Assuming that half of this amount is blown or washed away, eaten by coprophages, or otherwise made unavailable for direct fertilization of the subterranean stratum, the amount remaining would be not less than 100 pounds of dung per acre for the growing season of grasslands.

In the third place, the grassland floor herbivores, through their droppings, further influence the community. When one considers grassland from a general point of view, the amount of manure available for fertilizer affects the growth and vigor of the herbaceous stratum more than is usually appreciated. Consequently, in addition to extracommunity fixation of atmospheric nitrogen (p. 190), we have intracommunity regulation of plant growth directly, and animal growth directly and indirectly through humus formation, and directly by increasing the fertility of the soil.

The herbaceous stratum of the grassland communities varies from a relatively close carpet of green, soft, broad-leaved grasses and other perennial herbs to coarse, hard, narrow-leaved stands, and similarly varies in height from 6 to 120 inches. Dominant stratal species belong to such genera as *Andropogon, Bouteloua, Koeleria, Agropyron, Stipa, Calamovilfa, Panicum, Carex, Artemesia* (Warming, 1909; Carpenter, 1940a; Hanson and Whitman, 1938), which penetrate deeply into the subterranean stratum and are adjusted to desiccation. In addition, steppes have vernal plants with bulbs or tubers (Liliaceae) and short-lived annuals.

When man disturbs the natural structure of grassland beyond the limit of community repair, as in excessive and unscientific cultivation or overgrazing, wind and water erosion may remove the floor stratum completely and partially destroy the subterranean stratum. In such cases it is of immediate interest to note that one of the most effective measures to combat erosion is the planting of a new herbaceous stratum, often with introduced species. Such introductions should be stratal equivalents of the original species. Table 36 lists the U. S. Department of Agriculture's deliberate imports for the control of soil erosion according to the region of their nativity.

tatomidae, Coreidae, Lygaeidae, Cicadellidae, Psyllidae, Aphididae), many species of which feed on this stratum of plants.

Grasslands support large populations of these macroscopic invertebrates, the majority of which are directly or indirectly dependent upon the herbaceous stratum for food. For example, Morris (1920) found 3,586,088 insects per acre of permanent pasture in Cheshire, England. A comparison of several investigations is given in Table 37, in which it is of interest to note

Table 36. Herbaceous Equivalents Used in Soil Erosion Control (Reorganized from U. S. Department of Agriculture Yearbook, 1938)

China	U. S. S. R.	South Africa	North America	Australia
Ephedra sinica	Agropyron elongatum Agropyron sibericum Elymus dahuricus Elymus juncus Elymus sibericus Hordeum bulbosum	Calamagrostis pseudophragmites Chloris berroi Chloris gayana Eragrostis curvula Eragrostis lehmanniana Pennesetum clandestinum	Agropyron dasytachyum Agropyron inerme Agropyron smithii Andropogon furcatus Andropogon scoparius Bouteloua gracilis Bouteloua curtipendula Buchloë dactyloides Elymus canadensis Ephedra viridis Hilaria jamesii Hordeum nodosum Poa ampla Poa nevadensis	Atriplex semibaccata

This vegetation, varying in height and density of stand, scorching in the hot, dry summer or billowing in the wind, gives a characteristic aspect to the community. Its ecological equivalents or their cultivated

that there is a small suggestion that tropical pastures have a higher population density than temperate pastures, but there are insufficient data available to test the statistical significance of this point.

Where land is put into cultivation by man, its herbaceous stratum is shielded from natural competition and becomes dom-

Table 37. Pasture Populations of Macroscopic Invertebrates

Locality	Animals per Square Foot	Animals per Square Meter (Recalculated) (Estimate)	Author of Study Cited
Cheshire, England	82	869	Morris, 1920
Barneveld, New York	68	720	Wolcott, 1937
Pt. Cangrejos, Puerto Rico	110	1166	Wolcott, 1924

replacements support numerous floor herbivores (grasshoppers and rodents). In addition, the population of this grassy stratum *per se* is large and varied, consisting chiefly of herbivorous bugs, beetles, and lepidopterous larvae (Hayes, 1927). The bugs considered alone include a noteworthy number of important families (Pen-

inated by a single plant species as a rule. Under such conditions there is a correlative increase in the number of insects adjusted to this abundant, relatively uniform, concentrated food supply. Many of our agricultural pests, such as grasshoppers, the squash bug (*Anasa tristis*), and the chinch bug (*Blissus leucopterus*), derive their abundance from such unintentional human cooperation. Man then attacks such herbivores by spraying this stratum with insecticides or otherwise applying economic checks and controls to maintain a condition of biotic instability adjusted in his favor. In this he is aided by the natural stratal predators. Included in this latter category are numerous insects (phymatid and reduviid bugs, many carabid beetles, parasitoid wasps, and a large number of grassland spiders).

Insectivorous lizards (for example, *Takydromus* of Eastern Asia and *Chamaesaura* of Africa) with elongated tails and/or bodies, are structurally adjusted for moving rapidly through the grassland canopy or over the surface of the herbaceous stratum. In these grassland reptiles we have a stratal convergence analogous to the position occupied by the gyrinid whirligig beetles and gerrid bugs, which skate over the surface of fresh-water habitats. The small gyrinid beetles also dive below the surface somewhat as the lizards weave back and forth between the grass stems. In both limnological and grassland communities these organisms occupy equivalent stratal and feeding niches.

In this predation all strata are more or less involved. Subterranean floor, and herbaceous levels effect occasional or continuous control on plant and animal increase. The usually vegetarian meadow mouse will eat stray insects; our most typical prairie birds (horned lark, meadow lark, prairie chicken, and their stratal equivalents) are generally floor feeders. Such birds typically have a seasonal shift in diet (Chap. 28). For example, the prairie chicken feeds upon insects (especially grasshoppers) from April to October and chiefly on vegetation or its products between November and March; the horned lark takes up to 20 per cent animal (chiefly insects) and 80 per cent plant food, while the meadow lark takes 73 per cent animal (chiefly grasshoppers, beetles, and floor caterpillars), and

27 per cent plant food. This complex interstratal predation forms but a part of the complex food web of a community (Chap. 27).

With stratification as a principle of organization, it follows that there is a high degree of stratal equivalence or replaceability among the constituents of any stratum within the limits of their position in the gradient. The principle of stratal equivalence directs attention to the fulfillment of similar ecological requirements and, consequently, to the segregation of community constituents upon an ecological rather than a taxonomic basis. Similarly, consideration of stratal equivalence focusses attention upon the principle of community habitus. The presence of strata, with all that this implies, gives a characteristic aspect to a given community type.

Examination of the whole system of grassland communities indicates that three influences exert a profound effect upon present day community maintenance and on current shifts in community boundaries. Two of these influences (precipitation and temperature) exert their initial effect as extracommunity forces, operating singly or in unison, in extremes of local weather. The third influence is biotic. Here should be included the activities of man, involving both economic and noneconomic aspects of his civilization and having to do with all manner of commercial and agricultural enterprises—for example, the effects of certain kinds of pollution upon the herbaceous cover of the grasslands, or their intense cultivation for food or forage. In addition to man's influence, there is the influence of the vast populations of wild herbivores (Table 35), which certainly act as an important biotic control within the grassland communities of which they are a natural part.

Since the distribution and seasonal growth of grasses are influenced by temperature, local abnormalities of this factor may alter the extent of a grassland community from year to year. Any disturbance of the biotic balance is reflected in all parts of the community. The subject has been given increased attention, especially the relative influence of air versus soil temperature. In general it may be stated that soil temperature has a much more important role. In controlled experiments with three common pasture grasses (Kentucky bluegrass, Bermuda grass, and orchard grass), Brown (1943) found that a high soil temperature (100° F.) was much more harmful than a high air temperature. Similarly, when grasses were exposed to eight weeks of continuous air temperature of 100° F. and 70° F. soil temperature, the plants remained normal in appearance, and grew.

More obvious results are observed in an unusually dry period. The North American prairie has three well-defined types of grassland communities: tall grass, mixed grass, and short grass (Clements and Shelford, 1939; Carpenter, 1940a). The tall grass type has a relatively continuous stand of dominant grasses, such as *Andropogon,* forming the herbaceous stratum matrix, with an understory of a few discontinuous, low-growing grasses. The mixed grass type has a more marked substratification in which the herbaceous stratum has a dominant tall grass and a dominant short grass stratum.

Weaver (1943) studied the tall grass prairie of eastern Nebraska and central Kansas during an unusually dry climatic cycle extending over seven years (1934 to 1941). In 1941 the tall grass prairie had been replaced by mixed grass prairie, with changes in the taxonomic character of the herbaceous stratum as well as a shift from one to two layers of dominant grass species in this stratum. Such a profound change in the structure of the top stratum was brought about by drought over an area 100 to 150 miles wide. This appears to be an outstanding example of the influence of drought on grassland, and with the changes not attributable to man's direct effect upon the vegetation or his indirect effect through grazing cattle.

Temperature and precipitation also act together to change grassland communities. There appears to be a good correlation with weather and the abundance of such important insects as chinch bugs. Shelford and Flint (1943) found these insects to be sufficiently abundant to cause crop damage in grassland maintained by man in the upper Mississippi valley in periods when temperature was above and rainfall below normal.

Human influences upon the grassland community are obvious and important. It is especially well shown through their effects upon the structure of the several strata. In addition to obliteration of the community by human dwellings, man's influence runs the gamut from chance pasture in vacant lots to the complete rebuilding of grassland, with cultivated plants forming the equivalent of native tall grass, and beef or dairy cattle the equivalents of prongbuck and bison.

Such rebuilding of grassland by man amounts to maintaining substituted equivalents that can be consumed or profitably manipulated, on areas that would otherwise support a competitive grassland community.

Another type of grassland develops in an area that would otherwise support different communities—for example, forests. The cutting-off of the forests in the corridor of states from New York to Indiana has produced an artificial steppe, now being actively invaded by some of the steppe fauna. Another example is afforded by some 126 million acres of western United States that are in range service. Within forests (Campbell, 1940), the problems of cattle grazing versus timber growing, virtually side by side, have not yet been fully harmonized. Forest grazing is a definite part of Louisiana's cattle-raising industry. In a survey of 118 farms where cattle were grazed in forests, more than half of the herds grazed in small open glades or meadows between trees for the entire year (Campbell and Rhodes, 1944). During this period the cattle obtained 69 per cent of their food from these grassland inclusions.

Overgrazing is an uneconomic and biologically inept human influence upon grassland. One immediate result is the deterioration of the basic food supply for the grazing population. When either overcultivation or overgrazing, or both, are practiced, the floor of the community is eroded away. This is followed by erosion of the surface layers of the subterranean stratum until the entire grassland community is destroyed and its regrowth prevented until the soil cover can again be formed.

A by-product is the destructive dust storm (Clements and Chaney, 1936).

Often the results of overgrazing are indirect, and are sometimes beneficial to native grassland species. In eastern Texas the jackrabbit (*Lepus californicus merri-*

ami) is found on open blackland prairie. Taylor and Lay (1944) observed that cattle grazing eliminates the vegetative cover, and with the decrease in the herbaceous stratum there is a corresponding increase in breadth of the horizon, which benefits the rabbits. This is an example of unconscious cooperation between two species of floor animals, although if the grazing became too severe, the food supply for both would be impaired. Hence the degree of cooperation depends upon the activity level examined in relation to the welfare of the whole community.

Overgrazed grassland may owe its recovery to intelligent husbandry, but its recovery may also result from much less satisfactory events—for example, the rise in parasite populations. This is demonstrated in the Uganda Protectorate of Africa. In the northern part of this district badly overgrazed grasslands are making steady recovery since the invasion of the tsetse fly (Thomas, 1943). In these areas, badly overgrazed and secondarily gullied by erosion following loss of herbaceous stratum, destruction of cattle by fly-borne trypanosomes resulted in grass regrowth in three years to a stratum 3 feet high. In the valley of the Kidepo River, near the Uganda-Sudan boundary, the tsetse flies invaded many years ago, and here the herbaceous stratum is now 6 feet high.

CONCEPT OF THE ECOTONE

Structure of grassland at its boundaries is affected by impingement of other communities. This tension zone is not exclusive to grassland, but is always formed where two or more communities are in contact. Such a transition is known as an *ecotone*. Ecotones occur so generally that we may discuss their formation and peculiarities in the broad terms of an ecotone principle.

First, it would appear that the principle of the ecotone is biologically new at the level of the community. Within the limits of our technological equipment and methods, we have sharp boundaries with no overlap between nucleus and cell, between cell and cell, between organ and organ, and, colonial organisms excepted, between organism and organism. In bacteria, if the assumption is made that nuclear material is present, the absence of well-defined particulate nuclei would appear to constitute an exception. However, modern work in which certain bacteria are examined through ultraviolet light at high magnifications appears to demonstrate submicroscopic nucleoids with sharp boundaries. Size of nuclear particles is not involved; it is the boundary which is important for this discussion. For example, the multinucleate *Opalina* has its nuclear bodies as sharply set off from the surrounding cytoplasm as obtains in a uninucleated *Amoeba*. It would appear, therefore, that the ecotone is a peculiarity of communities, or that at the least the ecotone is so well developed between communities that its presence is a definitive characteristic. We are not speaking here of any particular blade of grass, rodent, or sapling, since these are organisms and have their own sharp boundaries. Rather, we are speaking of the total marginal zone as a highly integrated reality.

As used here, the term "ecotone" refers to this marginal area between communities. It does not refer to extensive areas of biome intergradation. For example, in Africa, as one proceeds from the Congo rain forest northward to the Sahara, there are all gradations between rain forest, tropical savanna, steppe, semidesert, and desert (Hesse, Allee, and Schmidt, 1937). This vast stretch of territory may be considered a zone of intergradation involving thousands of communities, but this stretch of territory could not be considered an ecotone in the sense used here. Rather, each of the thousands of communities involved has its particular ecotone with those other communities with which it is in contact. Again Carpenter (1940a, p. 672) states that the mixed-grass prairie is "in a sense, a relatively broad ecotone or transition between the two other associations of the biome, but nevertheless possesses certain characteristics peculiar to itself." By the two other associations in the quotation are meant the tall grass prairie and the short grass prairie. In this case the mixed-grass prairie is an intergradation in the Hesse, Allee, and Schmidt sense, but is not an ecotone in the sense used in the present discussion. Consequently we could conceive, throughout the range of the mixed-grass prairie, of many separate mixed-grass communities with stream-grassland ecotones, grassland-forest ecotones, tall grass-mixed grass ecotones, short grass-mixed grass ecotones, and many more.

By using ecotone as a term covering a more or less sharply defined competitive zone between two self-supporting communities, the concept becomes reasonably concise. As a synonym of biome intergradation, it loses its usefulness, since it could be argued that we have a single area of intergradation from pole to equator.

When a community is destroyed, its ecotones are destroyed unless the ecotone remains behind, adjusted to the modified area once occupied by the whole community and developing a mixed growth that persists as a self-supporting but more pioneer community with much the same boundaries as the one destroyed of which it once formed the periphery. From this it will be seen that the ecotone varies in width, degree of sharpness, and stability. It will be remembered that Weaver (1943) observed the destruction of the tall grass prairie and the occupation of the area by mixed-grass prairie, involving many communities and their boundaries, as a case in point. Ecotones are naturally intermediate between the communities concerned in their physical environment and biota. Since this is essentially a zone of competition between communities, its instability is furthermore a function of the biotic potentials of the communities concerned; consequently the stratification of ecotones is intermediate.

The ecological reality of the ecotone is attested by the fact that, in addition to organisms penetrating this boundary area from both communities involved and living therein for all or a regular part of their lives, there are other organisms that find the biotic and physical environment of the ecotone more stimulating than the conditions prevailing in either community. Such organisms may be properly called ecotone constituents.

In a neglected paper, Cameron (1917), discussing the ecological relations of insects in English pastures near Cheshire, discusses interpenetration very well:

"Often the line of demarcation between one association and another can be strictly delimited, so that species which may be introduced into an association which is alien to their habits react negatively to the prevailing physical factors of their new abode and tend to turn back. On the other hand, where two distinct associations are in juxtaposition and gradually merge into one another, as in the case of woodland and grassland, many species from both will intermingle, especially so at the places of transition."

In the parkland of central North America the Great Plains merge with the deciduous forest on the east and with deciduous forest (poplars) and coniferous forest on the north. In this area of merging, a narrow belt of country, in which both forest and prairie intermingle, forms a characteristic zone of intergradation. This intergrading region was characterized by Bird (1930) as having the forests stretching far into grassland along rivers, and by groves of trees with interspersed prairie. Within this grassland-deciduous forest and grassland-coniferous forest border are many self-supporting forest and grassland communities and, consequently, numerous grassland-deciduous forest and grassland-coniferous forest ecotones. Griggs (1934) studied forest edge in Alaska. Hanson (1938), Pool, Weaver, and Jean (1918), and Weaver and Himmel (1931) have given a detailed picture of plant composition in prairie inclusions within the deciduous forest and the prairie forest margin.

The subterranean stratum of the forest edge in the shelterbelt zone has also been examined. As with grassroots in the subterranean stratum of the grassland community, the trees in the grassland-forest ecotone have their root systems vertically stratified. There are the deep-rooted trees such as bur oak, western yellow pine, and hackberry with roots 10 to 20 feet deep; an intermediate layer of root systems of green ash, American elm, and red cedar at 5 to 10 feet below the surface, and finally a shallow-rooted layer, including Jack pine, Scotch pine, willow, and cottonwood with root systems extending from 1 to 5 feet in depth. The subterranean stratum of the forest-grassland edge is deeper and more secondarily laminated than that of grassland; it is less so than in the forest proper.

Both the physical environment and the biota of ecotones need much study. Not only is there an intermediate but developed vertical stratification, but horizontal zonation is especially clear. There is an easily demonstrated horizontal gradient from ecotone into grassland and ecotone into forest, of such important influences as light intensity, air temperature, soil temperature, relative humidity, wind velocity, and rate of evaporation. There are less easily measured gradients in erosion and humus composition. The windbreak effect of the forest-grassland ecotone, operating with the wind velocity factor, establishes an easily demonstrable horizontal gradient in numbers of wind-dispersed plants. There is also a horizontal gradient in wind-blown drift. This gradient in wind-dispersed plants is naturally different from the horizontal gradient in bird-dispersed plants.

Studies on forest edge birds have been reported by Beecher (1942), Carpenter (1935), and Van Deventer (1936), among others. The last-named carried out observations on winter birds in New York where an extensive ecotone existed between upland forest and swampy woodland. In this study particular attention was paid to the tree sparrow, black-capped chickadee, downy woodpecker, and white-breasted nuthatch. All four species selected primarily the swamp-forest edge during the period of study between December, 1934, and February, 1935. Van Deventer estimated the probability of chance association of any two of the four species at approximately 5 per cent, calculated by ascertaining the percentage of the total bird population of the area constituted by each species, then averaging all possible combinations of these percentages. Two or more of these four species were associated on 31 per cent of all observations. This gave an actual percentage of association approximately six times as great as association resulting from pure chance. This is statistical confirmation of the general belief that ecotones, while not existing apart from the parent communities, still have a characteristic biota.

The importance of the ecotone has been realized by Kendeigh (1944) in a discussion of bird populations. He calls attention to the necessity of separating forest-edge birds from forest-interior birds in computing population densities.

The earlier seasonal development of the ecotone, its abundance of habitat niches, and the distinctive variety of foods available, as well as the relative security from immediate pursuit, combine with the twenty-four hour and seasonal intermediate character of its physical environment to maintain a distinctive biota.

The ecotone biota in general has received little study. One of the few papers is that of Carpenter (1935), studying areas of community competition in central Illinois, where the ecotone biota had a structure intermediate between meadow and forest, strongly affected by seasonal factors, owing to its exposed surface, and with a sufficient number of ecotone species to give such margins a characteristic habitus. It should be remembered that there is a general tendency for ecotone animals and plants to persist along roadsides and fence rows for a certain length of time after the original communities have been destroyed.

The prairie-forest ecotone owes its composition to (1) statistically significant fractions of species populations found in grassland or forest, or both communities; (2) stray or incidental species present for temporary protection; and (3) ecotone species present by preferential selection.

STRATIFICATION IN FOREST COMMUNITIES

At a distance, the mature forest appears as a distinctly bulky, unorganized mass of vegetation. At first one is apt to be impressed by this mass rather than by the organization of the community. Such first impressions are succeeded by a realization that the forest consists of many living units, the most obvious of which are trees.

Further consideration suggests at least three important generalizations. First, sheer bulk of the forest changes the physical environment so that those physical influences acting upon the forest are themselves modified, and the forest consequently tends to have a characteristic climate.

Next, the arrangement of the forest organisms is not haphazard, but tends to be orderly throughout. This is more obvious in plants (Gleason, 1936), but not necessarily less true of animals, although, as a consequence of their activity, they are less obviously integrated. As has already been shown, a patent feature of this orderly arrangement of organisms within the community is its stratification. Since each stratum (lamiation of Carpenter, 1938) occupies a definite horizontal or vertical portion of the community, the general forest climate is subject to stratal modification.

and each stratum may be said to have its own microclimate. This being so, each stratum has its own stratal population of resident organisms, in addition to organisms that may regularly or irregularly visit the stratum for food, temporary stratal residents—that is, those species having their principal habitat niche or home within a given stratum, which utilize the stratum for periodic physiological recuperation—are often highly adjusted to the structural peculiarities of the stratum, its particular microclimate, or the available food (Chap. 27). The more perfect their structural and functional adjustment, the less able are they to live in other strata. Such organisms are stratal indices.

Finally, as a consequence of this stratification, the forest community has a large intracommunity surface in proportion to its volume, and the active inhabitants of the forest (the animals, as distinct from the more passive inhabitants or plants) have a greatly increased variety of food and a more moderated climate than are to be found in adjacent communities. Let us examine these three general ideas of forest climate, forest stratification, and forest animal life in relation to the whole community and to the several communities which take part in the formation of forest ecotones.

The chief reason for the more moderated forest community climate is the blanketing effect of its dominant species, the trees. The degree of moderation depends upon many factors. In north temperate deciduous forests, with well-marked seasonal cycles of vernal foliation and autumnal afoliation, such as an oak-hickory or a beech-sugar maple community, there is less moderation in winter, when vegetation is largely bare of leaves, than in late spring and summer, when the trees are in leaf.

Evergreen forests are an exception, since their leaves are shed more or less continually and insure more or less moderation all the time. One such type is the tropical rain forest, which exhibits some instability in quality, if not in the volume of vegetation, depending upon the periodic flowering, fruiting, and leafing out of dominant trees in relation to numerous influences, often including regional wet and dry periods.

Another type of evergreen community is that of the coniferous forest, where the annual temperature cycle is marked, in sharp contrast to the evergreen rain forest. In coniferous forests the snowfall is heavy in winter, and snow tends to bank upon vegetation, moderating the forest climate (Park, 1931).

Another factor affecting forest climate is the degree of maturity of the community. This may be a relative maturity in relation to its exact position in the seral sequence (cf. Chap. 29), or it may be an actual maturity in terms of its particular life history. Both concepts are affected by the state of community health. Within recent times such forest hazards as fire (either through physical agency such as lightning, or as a result of man's activity), unnatural flooding (often as a result of modification of the watershed by man), diseases of epidemic proportions (caused chiefly by bacteria, viruses, and fungi), overgrazing, exposure through clearing for crop planting, and lumbering, retard, change the seral position, or destroy the community. The total result depends upon the toleration of the primary constituents of the community, the trees, and the extent to which floor litter has been removed, with exposure of top soil to leaching and erosion.

Burning over an experimental pine stand was found to be less detrimental to the animals of the subterranean and floor strata than the complete removal of litter (Pearse, 1943), since the latter changed the soil habitat so completely that dependent animals died or decreased significantly.

Two or more forest hazards may operate jointly or consecutively. The once extensive Southern Appalachian spruce forest communities have been depleted chiefly as a result of fire following destructive logging. The forest community was usually wholly destroyed (Korstian, 1937), since the trees not cut down were burned out, and the surface soil was ignited beyond recovery except by long-time processes.

In addition to obvious destruction of vegetation after a severe forest fire, there are numerous more subtle reactions. Destruction of floor litter not only removes the floor stratum, but exposes the subterranean stratum to ignition and erosion, or in a small conflagration serves to decrease the stability of the soil microclimate. Those earthworms (*Eisenia, Diplocardia, Bimastus*) found abundantly in forest soil become notably fewer after burning over (Pearse, 1943).

The recuperative power of a particular forest community in relation to the destructive power of the inimical agencies at a given time determines its chances for survival to maturity. Since there is a reciprocal relation of the whole forest to its strata, just as there is a reciprocal relation between the organism and its organs, any injury to the one will injure the other, and furthermore community injury and its possible recovery directly affect the stratal occupants initially concerned, and indirectly the entire stratification, both with respect to immediate state and relative maturity. Injury and recuperation affect the total biota.

The blanketing effect of vegetation is complex and moderates the several interacting physical influences that compose the forest climate. The light intensity is always lower in forests than in the more open adjacent communities (Allee, 1926; Park, Barden, and Williams, 1940). In the Chicago area at noon on a clear summer day, the light intensity will be of the order of 10,000 foot-candles in the open as compared with 50 foot-candles on the shaded forest floor, or roughly $\frac{1}{200}$ of the available light (Park 1931; Park and Strohecker 1936). As this light passes down through the forest canopy, each succeeding stratum is potentially less illuminated (Allee, 1926), so that the plants are affected directly by the amount of light available for photosynthesis (Coulter, Barnes, and Cowles, 1911), and the animals are affected directly as their photic responses are modified and indirectly with respect to the plant food supply. There is also a differential change in the quality of the light (Strohecker, 1938). These changes in the spectrum also affect plant and animal reactions, both directly and indirectly.

Forest temperatures are generally lower in summer and higher in winter than temperatures of adjacent areas (Williams, 1936). This is a general consequence of the vegetation, and especially a consequence of the thick layer of vegetable mold on the forest floor. Similarly, forests are cooler during the heat of the day and warmer during the night than areas external to them (Park and Strohecker, 1936).

Relative humidity is characteristically higher and evaporation rate lower within the forest than in adjacent, less dense terrestrial communities (Fuller, 1911, 1914; Ullrich, 1915; Williams, 1936). Similarly, relative humidity is higher and evaporation rate lower within forests during the night than in daytime (Park, Lockett, and Myers, 1931; Park and Strohecker, 1936).

Relative humidity, absolute humidity, rate of evaporation, and saturation deficit (Baker, 1936) affect each other in various combinations (Hammond and Goslin, 1933; Thornthwaite, 1940) and are affected by wind velocity (Shelford, 1914) and air temperature.

The weight of snails (Strandine, 1941), behavior of forest floor arthropods (Lunn, 1939), behavior of salamanders and wood frogs (Shelford, 1913a), behavior of forest deer mice (Chenoweth, 1917), activity of dendrophagous passalid beetles (Park, 1937), and aggregation of terrestrial isopods (Allee, 1926b), for example, are in turn modified or determined by one of these influences, or by several factors operating together.

These and other diverse effects of the forest climate upon the contained constituents determine eventual selection of habitat niche and, consequently, are important in forest stratification, both vertical and horizontal.

Wind velocities are greatly reduced within the forest when compared to those operating simultaneously external to the forest periphery. During the afoliated period, deciduous forests offer tree trunk and branch interference to air movement. This interference is cumulative and is in direct proportion to the horizontal distance (separation from the ecotone), or the vertical distance (separation from the canopy) through which the wind must act. As the season of foliation develops, there is corresponding increase in the interference, which reaches a plateau of maximum blanketing in early summer.

Thus there is from 13 to 20 per cent more air in motion on the forest floor in winter than in summer (Williams, 1936), and the ratio of reduction of wind velocity to distance from the forest ecotone is similar in afoliated and in foliated forests

(Figure 159), although actual reduction is greater in the foliated period.

Botanists have said much about the mechanical effects of wind on tree form and structure and upon the role of wind in transpiration. The influence of wind upon dispersal of tree species is an important ecological factor, and the particular effect

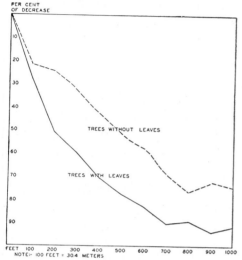

Fig. 159. Horizontal gradient in wind velocity from peripheral ecotone toward the center of a forest community, in both the period of afoliation and the period of foliation. (After Williams.)

of air in motion upon local distribution and establishment of trees has received less attention. Forests tend to fade out where high mountains begin to form isolated peaks; above this point tree growth is found only where there is local protection from wind (Belyea, 1925).

The points enumerated are relevant to the consideration of stratification in the community. Given the initial establishment of the primary constituents, in this case the dominant species of trees, a windbreak is formed at the periphery. Such a primary response forces the deposition of externally wind-dispersed seeds at or near the periphery. This deposition produces an ecotone rich in such plants, whereas bird-dispersed seeds tend to be deposited throughout the community. Further, any original forest plants that are inherently wind-dispersed are insured against excessive dissemination and loss, since their seeds

tend to drop to the floor in the relatively still forest interior.

The periphery, once stabilized, presents a relatively brightly illuminated surface. In the ensuing photosynthetic competition, the ecotonal zone and forest canopy may become densely covered with lianas, and the former tends to support numerous herbs and shrubs.

The interaction of these and other physical and ecological influences produces (1) a typically rich ecotone; (2) in part an initiation of horizontal and vertical stratifications; (3) a reenforcement of horizontal and vertical stratification; (4) increase in the kinds and amounts of foods available for animals; (5) increase in the kinds and amounts of shelter niches available for animals; and (6) a more stable, moderated community climate.

To sum up, the forest community in general tends to have a relatively dark, cool, moist climate with the internal strata protected from the full force of wind. Since protoplasm has a high water content and since water is vital to its continued existence, the loss of water by evaporation from the surface of terrestrial animals is physiologically uneconomical and biologically to be avoided.

The forest community, by its very nature, solves the problem of water conservation for a host of animals and plants, making unnecessary for them the specific adaptations to economy of water that may be essential in other terrestrial environments. For these and other reasons the forest community as a cooperative whole is a highly evolved and successful unit.

Turning our attention from the over-all interplay between climate and community to the application of principles of stratification to forest community organization, we find that these communities typically have six basic vertical laminations: (1) subterranean, (2) floor, (3) herbaceous, (4) shrub, (5) tree, and (6) a layer of air above the canopy. All six are present in most forests. All are interdependent; each has a particular microclimate and a particular biota, and is subject to, and responds characteristically to, extraforest and intraforest physical and biological forces.

The biota of the sixth stratum may differ considerably from air strata in general, but little is known of this layer. As early as

1926 it was thought that this level "remains a fertile field for investigation from a properly equipped aeroplane" (Allee, 1926a, p. 446). In fact, our knowledge of forest stratification may be said to be directly proportional to the distance of any given layer from the ground, with the subterranean and floor strata best known and the canopy the least understood.

Any of the first five strata may be substratified. This is increasingly true as one proceeds from pioneer to climax communities. For example, the forest of Barro Colorado Island in the Panama Canal Zone has been shown to have eight strata: (1) the air above the forest, (2) tree tops above the main forest roof, 125 or more feet high, (3) upper forest canopy, 75 to 100 feet high, (4) lower tree tops (second story trees or midforest), 40 to 60 feet high, (5) small trees, 20 to 30 feet high, (6) higher shrubs, 10 feet high, (7) forest floor, and (8) subterranean, according to Allee (1926a). The herbaceous stratum in such forests is poorly developed. On the other hand, the herbaceous layer is often well developed in north temperate deciduous forests. The "Big Woods" of Minnesota (Daubenmire, 1936), dominated by sugar maple and basswood, have, in addition to the subterranean and floor strata, six defined layers of vegetation, three of which are herbaceous: (1) dominant tree, (2) small tree, (3) tall shrub, (4) tall herb-low shrub, (5) low herb, and (6) moss.

The equatorial rain forest may have several strata of trees with several developed canopies, "forest piled upon forest" (Fig. 225). For example, the detailed physiognomic study of British Guiana rain forest by Davis and Richards (1934) shows four tree strata: (1) a layer of occasional, scattered trees with crowns up to 90 to 120 feet that forms the canopy, but is not a closed stratum; (2) a layer 75 feet high; (3) a layer at 45 feet; and (4) a lower layer at 20 feet. This organization is generally true of the American rain forest communities, although the uppermost stratum of trees may be absent (cf. Benoist, 1924, for French Guiana rain forest). The true rain forest having at least three tree strata, is not so widespread as generally supposed, and there are many other types of tropical evergreen forest that may be labeled "rain forest" in popular parlance (Beard, 1944).

In the western hemisphere such typical rain forest is fully developed in the Guianas, from the Orinoco to the Amazon, in a strip some 150 to 200 miles wide paralleling the coast; in the Amazon basin; parts of lowland Central America, Colombia, and Ecuador; and in restricted areas of some of the Lesser Antilles (Trinidad). Such a forest is shown in diagram form in Figure 160. This same general stratification is not

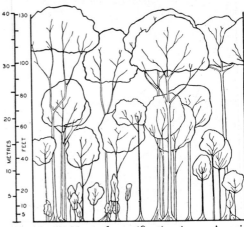

Fig. 160. Vertical stratification in an American rain forest community on Trinidad. (After Beard.)

restricted to a particular hemisphere, but may be found in African forests, for example, that are separated from the Amazonian forest by thousands of miles in longitude (Fig. 161). Furthermore, the same general principle is applicable to nontropical forests—for example, the Canadian coniferous forest, separated from tropical forest by thousands of miles in latitude (Fig. 162), attesting to the universality of community organization.

Epiphytes, especially in tropical forests, may swell the mass of available habitat space. Tree trunks with their ancillary branches and vines form more or less vertical highways between the several strata of the forest and are extensively so used by forest animals. Similarly, the floor, with its vertical discontinuations such as tree holes and "second floors" (p. 485), adds to the complexity.

Certain general principles may be noted. The vegetation forms the primary biotic gradient in terrestrial communities. Stratification serves to increase the organic vol-

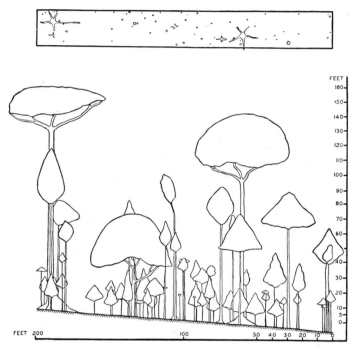

Fig. 161. Vertical stratification in an African rain forest community on the Gold Coast. (After Foggie.)

Fig. 162. Vertical stratification in a coniferous forest in Canada. (After Kendeigh.)

ume of the community and hence increases kind and amount of shelter and foods, directly for herbivores and indirectly for carnivores and carrion-feeders and dung-feeders. It follows that the taxonomic complexity of the community increases with its increase in stratification. The process of stratification is intensified as the ontogenetic age of the forest increases. Stratification usually increases in direct proportion to the seral age of the forest. Finally, it follows that stratification becomes a criterion of both actual and relative maturity.

The subterranean stratum has been defined in general terms. This layer has been contrasted with the corresponding layer in aquatic communities, and this stratum has been compared in grassland and forest. A dynamic view of soil is essential for a better understanding of soil problems. Rommell (1930, p. 843; 1935) emphasized this concept: "It is more and more generally recognized that a natural soil, like a living organism, must be studied as a whole to get a correct idea of its responses." The subterranean portions of plants of the higher strata, the resident subterranean plants and animals, and the soil jointly compose this lowermost level in the vertical forest gradient.

In general, forest soils have a rich, black, porous humus component that may reach a depth of 9 feet in some equatorial forests (Warming, 1909). Usually forest soil is inhabited by animals for at least 1 foot. This animate substratum varies with the development of the natural vegetation, i.e., the development of root systems. As the community matures ontogenetically, the heavier vegetation of the higher strata is matched by a corresponding increase in the volume and complexity of the root mat. Since rootlets are always dying in some parts of the mat, even in forest perennials, fungi of the soil feed on these dead portions, reducing them to a soft matrix. Saprophytic soil animals, especially oribatid mites, eat away this soft core, leaving a tubule, varying from 1 to 20 mm. in diameter, with relatively indigestible bark walls. In old forest soils such a system of tubules aids in aeration and drainage, as well as in the formation of potential microhabitats. The saprophytic arthropods leave their feces within the tubules, adding to the soil fertility.

A logical classification of soil animals is that of Jacot (1936), whose system is extended here. First, there are the *geobionts*, true soil organisms that normally spend all their lives in the soil. This is a large and important category. Here would be included a notable population of bacteria (Dubos, 1928; Ramann, Schellhorn, and Krause, 1899; Skinner and Mellem, 1944; Waksman, 1932); soil algae (Transeau, Sampson, and Tiffany, 1940, Chap. 47); fungi (Ramann, Schellhorn, and Krause, 1899; Waksman, 1932); and soil protozoans (Sandon, 1927; Woodruff, 1938). These are all basic inhabitants, responsible for certain phases of soil formation and structure, and in the formation of much raw produce vital to the life of the whole forest community. The point is worth reemphasizing that, although there must be a necessary preliminary physical formation of soil from rock, such soil would be incapable of supporting life as we know it. The transition from mineral soil to rich humus takes place through the action of organic agencies; through the slow working over and adding to the preliminary rock particles (Nikiforoff, 1942).

Besides these minute organisms, many other *geobionts* are important in soil formation or structure. For example, certain species of the following groups are important: nematode worms (Cobb, 1915), enchytraeid and lumbricid worms (Darwin, 1881; Olson, 1928), micromyriapods [Pauropoda (Starling, 1944) and scutigerellids], tardigrades, oribatid mites, Collembola, Protura, Thysanura, many tropical termites, mole crickets (Gryllotalpidae), many ants in the genera *Ponera, Myrmecina, Brachymyrmex, Solenopsis* (Jacot, 1936), and the leaf-cutting, fungus-gardening, and other ants (Weber, 1941; Wheeler, 1926), moles, and possibly shrews, (Hamilton, 1939; Hamilton and Cook, 1940; Taylor, 1935). Others, chiefly insects, although neither feeding on decayed plant parts nor excavating, are continually using the minute subterranean channels and hence aid in their maintenance. Such insects include thrips and many predaceous beetles of the families Staphylinidae and Pselaphidae (Jacot, 1936; Pearse, 1943, 1946).

In the second category are the soil transients (*geocoles*, = *geophiles* of Jacot). They spend a regular or irregular portion of their lives in the soil and include certain reptiles, birds, mammals, and a host of insects (Bryson, 1931, 1933; McColloch and Hayes, 1922). Such organisms aid in soil formation, soil transfer, aeration, and drainage. They use the stratum for oviposition, pupation, hibernation (Weese, 1924), aestivation, or as a sheltering niche during their diurnal or nocturnal periods of relative inactivity.

Finally, there are the *geoxenes*. These are stray or accidental animals in the soil that have little permanent effect upon the stratum.

Forest geobionts generally are adjusted to the moist, cool, dark, relatively stable microclimate and relatively dense matrix of the subterranean stratum. In contrast to the relatively progressive instability of higher strata, and their contained epigean residents, the forest geobionts are in less danger from extreme temperature changes, excessive radiation, and desiccation. Correlated with these influences is a low toleration for high temperatures and light intensities. Many are white or bleached in color, have no eyes or have rudimentary or vestigial vision, and are structurally adjusted for digging. In a very real sense, soil animals are important in the construction of their stratum.

In quantitative work it is difficult to separate the fauna of the H-layer of the floor (usually 2 to 3 mm. deep) from the A_1-layer of the soil (Fig. 54).

The floor is a complex stratum. It is intermediate between subterranean and epigean levels in microclimate, matrix continuity, foods, habitats, and taxonomic composition. It is the recipient of diverse organic increments from higher strata (flower parts, fruits, seeds, twigs, leaves, feces, dead animals). These organic materials are deposited regularly in part and irregularly, seasonally, and continuously, depending upon the latitude, altitude, and total composition of a given forest. Such a rain of debris parallels the building up of the profundal or abyssal strata of aquatic communities.

The floor is diverse in aspect. Mushrooms, the bodies of dead and decomposing animals, fallen logs, and broken stumps are apparently isolated, yet in reality are integral parts of the stratum, each with its own closely knit food chain (Chap. 27),

activity pattern (Chap. 28), and successional pattern (Chap. 29). These microcosms or biocoenoses are surrounded and progressively covered by leaf mold and litter.

Ignition by fire or transportation by storm winds and floods may remove parts of the floor. Barring destruction by civilized man, all these diverse parts are eventually reduced and transported in large measure to the subterranean stratum of the community involved.

In addition to these obvious, apparently detached, floor parts, there are other portions less readily discerned. For example, the standing dead tree is a vertical, columnar extension of floor log mold. It comes to be inhabited by typical log mold animals and in addition is used as a shelter or nesting site by woodpeckers and squirrels. Where falling trees and limbs are prevented from reaching the ground level as a consequence of the density of higher strata, decomposition of their tissues and mechanical interception of dead and decomposing organic fragments from the canopy produce, for a time, a "second floor." Such accumulations of litter are not uncommon in rain forest, may be of small to moderate size, and during the time they exist apart from the floor proper, support a large population of floor animals (Onychophora, oribatid mites, ants, and numerous spiders).

There are also the tree holes. These are small to moderate-sized, more or less hemispherical cavities in tree trunks, usually where limbs or branches have been removed. If such holes are not repaired by the tree, fungus decay sets in, and rain water is trapped in summer and snow in winter. As the holes age, they enlarge by decay of their walls and may pass from an above-ground aquatic community to a filled-in, moist log mold habitat above the floor. Such a process is parallel with the filling up of ponds and lakes. Some animals are tree-hole specific. For example, the tree-hole mosquito (*Anopheles barberi*) breeds exclusively in the water of tree holes, and the adults seldom get far from their breeding grounds (Headlee, 1921a). The tree hole reservoirs of water sufficiently permanent to maintain a distinctive biocoenosis in the tropical forest are familiar to biologists who have visited the Barro Colorado Laboratory in Panama. Tadpoles conspicuous in this association in Panama are those of the brilliantly colored tree frog *Agalychnis dacnicolor,* which suspends its egg masses above the water on the trunk of the tree; and the tadpoles of the equally vivid terrestrial dendrobatid, *Dendrobates auratus,* which are transported into the water holes by the adult male (Dunn, 1931).

The tree hole, as a discontinuous extension of the floor, has a population of log mold animals as its walls soften and the cavity begins to fill with litter. Such animals include oribatid and parasitid mites, predaceous carabid, staphylinid, and pselaphid beetles, and numerous ants, to mention only a few forms.

Considering the whole floor, animals of this layer may be divided into *patobionts,*° those living all their normal life in this stratum; floor transients (*patocoles*), those spending a regular portion of their life outside of the floor; and *patoxenes,* or accidental visitors.

The patobionts are numerous in species and in individuals. One of the best word pictures given this layer is that of Jacot (1935, p. 425), which merits quotation:

"Deer, jumping mice and the oven-bird are denizens of the forest floor by virtue of using it as their substratum, but there is also a host of curious animals which use the forest floor, especially the litter of dead leaves, twigs, branches and fruit parts, as their walls, ceiling and sub-basements. Looked at from the eye level of the cockroach, this litter becomes a several-story edifice of enormous extent. The various floors are separated by twigs, midribs, petioles, fruit husks, samaras, skulls, elytra and feces. The lower one descends, the more compact is the structure. The leaves become more fragmentary, the feces of worms, which have come up from the soil, of caterpillars which live in the trees and of the inhabitants themselves, as well as grains of sand brought up by the worms and a heterogeneous assortment of beetle skulls and wing covers, become more abundant. This complex is rendered more intricate by the growth of minute fungus moulds which feed upon the dead leaves and other organic refuse, weaving it all into a compact mat by their myriad white hyphae. Thus is the woof woven into the warp of the woodland rug."

The floor residents are either primarily engaged in a ceaseless reduction of floor leaf and log mold to soil humus or secondarily engaged in feeding upon these

° From the Greek *patoma,* floor.

mold eaters. Under favorable conditions, complete reduction of a leaf fall is consummated in two years in the moist virgin forests of warm temperate zones. In northern softwood forests the litter reduction is accomplished much more slowly (Jacot, 1936a). Whether the criterion of reduction be the total amount of feces, or oxygen consumption as a measure of total activity, or food consumption (Bornebusch, 1930, 1930a; Thamdrup, 1932; Ulrich, 1933), this process is a basic industry of the floor stratum and vital to the whole community.

Mold transformation is a large-scale, cooperative process. Cellulose-splitting bacteria and fungi (Waksman, 1932); oribatid and hoplodermatid mites (Jacot, 1936a, 1940; Williams, 1941); millipeds of such typical genera as *Diploiulus* (Lyford, 1943), *Fontaria* (Rommell, 1935) and *Spirobolus;* snails, such as *Punctum pygmaeum, Striatura milium* (Jacot, 1935a) and *Anguispira;* myriads of Collembola; numerous termites in tropical log mold (Allee, 1926a); many ants; larvae and adults of many elaterid, passalid, and tenebrionid beetles; these are a few representative groups united in this general activity.

In this reduction complex the response of a resident to the mold may be general or specific. A common forest milliped (*Diploiulus caeruleocinctus*) was shown to have a differential feeding response between leaves from the same tree, between leaves of neighboring trees of the same species, and more strongly between leaves of different tree species. These feeding reactions, covering a two year experimental period (Lyford, 1943), were found correlated with the percentage of calcium in the leaf. Basswood, elm, and hickory leaves were eaten more freely than those of beech and oak.

As for coniferous leaves, available information suggests that firm, undecomposed needles are not attacked by floor arthropods. Such leaves must first be acted upon by fungi, which reduce the cell contents and much of the mesophyll, leaving the needle a shaft of soft punk. In this state such needles as those of spruce, for example, are attacked by phthiracarid mites (Jacot, 1936a, 1939). This may be a partial answer to the relative slowness of litter reduction of coniferous floors previously noted. These needle-fungus-mite reaction chains are specific in spruce forests, and

Diptera; at least four families in Lepidoptera; and many Tenthredinidae in Hymenoptera.

All four orders have larvae that converge in form and general behavior (Fig. 164). They are conspicuously flattened and have reduced legs. Some mine leaves of a single

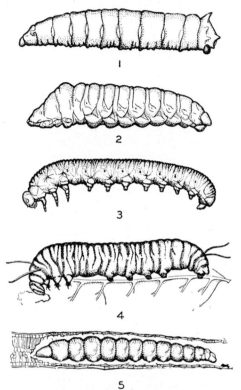

Fig. 164. Convergence in form of three types of leaf-mining larvae: (1) *Hylemyia* (Diptera); (2) *Metallus rubi* (Hymenoptera); (3) external feeding sawfly (Hymenoptera); (4) external feeding caterpillar; and (5) leaf-mining caterpillar (Lepidoptera), illustrating reduction of the thoracic legs and abdominal prolegs and horizontal position of head in contrast to 4. (After Frost; in part original.)

plant species. Others tunnel leaves of species of plants in the same genus, and still others feed upon groups of related plant genera within a family. Some feed upon many plants of unrelated genera. Obviously, the majority of leaf miner larvae are stratified in the forest.

Leaf miners can be found for each epipatomic layer. Thus in Agromyzidae, *Agromyza borealis* mines the leaves of the jewelweed (*Impatiens*) of the herbaceous

stratum, *Agromyza melampyga* in various lilacs, *Agromyza aristata* in elm. A volume has been written on the leaf miners alone (Frost, 1923; Needham, Frost, and Tothill, 1928). Then there are the leaf-rolling insects (seventeen families of Lepidoptera); gall-forming insects, mites, and nematodes. Felt (1917, 1940) listed 1440 North American species of gall makers: 162 Eriophyidae (mites), twelve Coleoptera, seventeen Lepidoptera, sixty Homoptera, 701 Diptera, and 488 Hymenoptera.

Gall insects attack mainly epipatomic strata; they attack all parts of plants (buds, leaves, petioles, flowers, twigs, branches, trunk bark, even roots in the subterranean stratum); over half of the plant families are attacked. Wasps of the family Cynipidae attack species of *Quercus* almost entirely (Kinsey, 1929). Felt found 500,000 cynipid wasps attacking a single oak tree.

Then there are the boring insects. These have a convergent larval form, usually cylindrical (in some groups where the larvae bore close to the exterior, the form is flattened), legless, reduced antennae, head capsule telescoped into the thorax, strong wood-cutting mandibles. Borers are conveniently separated into two groups (Frost, 1942): those species with larvae feeding on living tissue, and those feeding on decaying or dead tissue. The latter group overlaps with the floor stratum, including many species boring in prostrate logs and dead standing trees. The former group includes species that bore in buds, excavate the cambium, or fruit, or stem, and even the roots in the subterranean stratum.

Wood-borers are well developed in Coleoptera. Here are numerous species of Buprestidae, Cerambycidae, Elateridae, Brentidae, Curculionidae, and the bark beetles or Scolytidae, to mention a few of the many families with wood-boring larvae or adults.

Nor must we omit mention of the myriads of insects which suck the leaf sap or are bark feeders (Aphidoidea, Coccidoidea), or those which eat the leaves by cutting out portions (many Scarabaeidae, such as adult *Serica, Phyllophaga*).

Forest communities, with their well-developed epipatomic vegetational strata, have numerous herbivores that are species-specific, in a part of their life cycle at least, and are stratal indices. Lengthy tables

Table 40. Stratal Equivalents in Forest Communities

Stratal Categories	Eurasia	Africa and/or Madagascar	North America	South and/or Central America	Australia and/or Pacific Islands
1. Predators:					
a. Snakes of shrub and tree strata	Golden tree snake (*Chrysopelea*) Asiatic boigas (*Boiga* spp.) Prehensile tailed pit vipers (*Trimeresurus* spp.)	Black tree snake (*Thrasops jacksoni*) African forest boiga (*Boiga* spp.) Prehensile tailed viper (*Atheris* spp.)	Black chicken snake (*Elaphe obsoleta*) Rough green snake (*Opheodrys aestivus*)	Green tree boa (*Boa canina*) Prehensile tailed pit viper (*Trimeresurus schlegelii*) Common boa (*Constrictor constrictor*)	Green tree python (*Chondropython viridis*) New Guinean boiga (*Boiga irregularis*)
b. Snakes of floor stratum	King cobra (*Ophiophagus hannah*) Banded krait (*Bungarus multicinctus*)	Gaboon viper (*Bitis gabonica*)	Black snake (*Coluber c. constrictor*) Pine snake (*Pituophis melanoleuca*)	Fer-de-lance (*Trimeresurus atrox*)	Diamond python (*Python spilotes*) Rough ground boa (*Enygrus asper*)
c. Snakes of subterranean stratum	*Calamaria* spp. *Typhlops* spp. Shield-tailed snakes (*Uropeltidae*)	*Miodon* spp. *Typhlops* spp. *Calabaria reinhardti*	Worm snake (*Carpophis amoena*) Mud snake (*Farancia abacura*)	*Typhlops* spp. *Atractus* spp.	*Typhlops* spp.
d. Owls, nocturnal, nesting in tree stratum, feeding in all strata above subterranean	Tawny owl (Britain to Ural Mts., Syria to Turkestan) Ural owl (North Europe to Siberia) Dusky owl (Mongolia, China) Mottled wood owl (India) Long-eared owl (Europe, China, Northwest India) Screech owl (Europe to Turkestan)	Tawny owl (North Africa) Long-eared owl (North Africa) Screech owl (North Africa)	Barred owl American long-eared owl (to lower Mexico) North American screech owls	Stygian owl (Brazil) Crested screech owl (Amazon basin)	Dusky owl (Japan) Long-eared owl (Japan) Australian hawk-owl Screech owls (Malaysia and associated islands)

e. **Felidae**, arboreal and floor strata	Wild cat (*Felis silvestris*) (British Isles to Caspian Sea) Leopard (*Panthera pardus*) (Persia, India) Clouded leopard (*Neofelis nebulosa*) (Southeast Asia) Marbled cat (*Felis marmorata*) (Southeast Asia) Leopard cat (*Felis bengalensis*) (Southeast Asia) *Lynx lynx* (Europe, West Asia)	Golden-haired cat (*Felis rutila*) Sierra Leone, Gambia Leopard	Jaguar (*Panthera onca*) South Texas and Mexico Ocelot (*Leopardus pardalis*) Southwest U. S. Canada Lynx (*Lynx canadensis*) Bobcat (*Lynx rufus*)	Jaguar (to Patagonia) Ocelot (to Paraguay) Jaguarondi (*Felis jaguarondi*) (Brazil to Mexico)	Clouded leopard (Dutch East Indies, Formosa) Leopard cat (Philippines, Borneo, Sumatra) Marsupial equivalents: Tasmanian wolf (*Thylacinus cynocephalus*) Spotted-tailed dasyure (*Dasyurus maculatus*) (Tasmania, Australia)
2. Herbivores: a. **Psittacidae**, canopy: diurnal, chiefly frugivorous		Grey parrot (Equatorial Africa) Brown-headed parrot (Zanzibar) Great vasa parrot (Madagascar)	Carolina paroquet (recently extinct) Louisiana paroquet (recently extinct) Thick-billed parrot (central Mexico)	Blue and yellow macaw Green parrot Green-necked Amazon parrot Hyacinthine macaw (Brazil)	Sulphur-crested cockatoo (Australia and Celebes) New Guinea black parrot Great white-crested cockatoo (Moluccas) Ducorps cockatoo (Solomons)
b. **Cervidae**, cursorial on floor, feeding from herbaceous, shrub and lower tree strata	Red deer (*Cervus elaphus*) Irish deer (*Cervus giganteus*) (recently extinct) Moose (*Alces alces*) Fallow deer (*Dama dama*) Kashmir stag (*Cervus hanglu*)	Fallow deer (*Dama dama*) (North Africa)	Wapiti (*Cervus canadensis*) Moose Virginia deer (*Odocoileus virginianus*) (Canada to Mexico)	Virginia deer (Mexico to Peru) Brocket deer (several spp. *Blastocerus*) (from Guatemala to Brazil)	*Sika nippon* (Japan) *Sika taevanus* (Formosa) *Sika philippinensis* (Philippines and Ladrones)

could be prepared to show such stratification in mirid bugs (Knight, 1941), aphids (Patch, 1938), scale insects (Britton, 1923), sawflies (MacGillivray, 1916) or borers (Felt, 1905, 1906).

In all these instances the genetic background is reenforced by the proximity of the food plant, often in abundance, from which an ovipositing female has fed during her earlier life (cf. Hopkins' Host Principle, in Index).

Feeding upon these countless herbivores, including many larger animals (cf. Table 40), are predators and parasites. For example, Mantidae in Orthoptera, Reduviidae in Hemiptera, the aphid-eating ladybird beetles (Coccinellidae), Syrphidae and

selection of stratum, substratum, or habitat-niche by warblers in their breeding season.

It must not be supposed that food is the only limiting influence restricting a species to a group of communities, to a single community type, a particular stratum of a community, or to an especial habitat-niche within a stratum.

Over-all stratification is the result of many influences, of which food is an important component. Elsewhere in this book numerous other influences have been discussed that have to do with the spatial organization of species populations and individuals, with respect to the stratified structure of the community, and the selec-

Table 41. *Warbler Stratification in a Forest Community*
(Reorganized from Kendeigh, 1945)

Habitat-Niche	Warbler
Top level of evergreen trees	Blackburnian
Middle level of evergreen trees usually	Black-throated Green
Low level of evergreen trees	Magnolia
Secondary deciduous trees	Redstart
Tree trunks	Black and White
Shaded shrubs	Black-throated Blue
Sunlit shrubs	Chestnut-sided
Wet shaded floor	Canada
Wet sunlit floor	Yellow-throat
Dry shaded floor	Oven-bird
Dry sunlit floor	Nashville

Asilidae in Diptera, spiders as a group, ants, numerous parasitoids in the Hymenoptera, many forest mammals and birds (cf. Balduf, 1935; Clausen, 1940; Hamilton, 1943). These predators and parasites are less definitely stratified than are the herbivores on which they feed. Even so, numerous parasites prey upon a given herbivore and hence may be limited to a particular stratum.

Even such highly motile animals as birds are often characteristic residents of a particular forest stratum, or even of a particular level within a given stratum, although food may or may not play a leading role in such organization. For example, Kendeigh (1945) found breeding warblers generally stratified, and substratified, in a sugar maple-beech-hemlock forest of New York. He finds that such (p. 433) "diversification in niche requirements reduces interspecific competition and permits a greater and more varied population to inhabit an era." Table 41 demonstrates this

tion of the community by a species or the selection by the community of a species.

This problem has been studied by ornithologists. They find, in general, that community selection, stratum selection, and habitat selection by birds are complex. For example, on a broad zoogeographic basis, species of birds are limited by physical barriers and climatic conditions they can not tolerate (Kendeigh, 1934). When such limits of tolerance coincide with a range of communities, selection of a given community type may be the consequence of a variety of influences.

In such case the selection may be the result of some obligatory relation of the bird species to a particular type of community (Beecher, 1942; Pitelka, 1941). Within this community type, local segregation of species into different communities, strata, and habitats may be obvious, but the causes may or may not be obscure. Lack and Venables (1939) discuss the limitation of British woodland birds to a variety of forest habitats, and the selective action of these habitats on the bird populations of the several forest communities. Many influences are discussed by these authors. Thus food may be the predominant factor (crossbill, p. 586), or the feeding habit (flycatchers), or the song post (blackcap), or nesting site (hole-nesters), or nest-building material (nightingale), or roosting place (pheasant).

Microclimate may be important in local segregation, but is a difficult factor to evaluate (Kendeigh, 1945; Moreau, 1934).

Kendeigh (1945) analysed the restriction of birds, especially warblers, during the breeding season, near Albany, New York. In this study four types of communities were involved: grassy fields, mixed shrubs and small trees, hemlock-beech forests, and beech-sugar maple-hemlock forests. He concluded that the selection of shrubby fields or forests rather than grassland was correlated with more elevated positions for (1) feeding areas, (2) nest

sites, and (3) song posts; that the selection of forests rather than shrubby fields was correlated with (1) avoidance of high light intensity, and (2) greater restriction of free movement; and that selection of either evergreen or deciduous forest is correlated with the size and shape of leaves and their arrangement on the twig, rather than with persistence of foliage, microclimate, or food supply. Finally, this author believes that patterns of behavior through succeeding bird generations stabilize the local segregation of species into different community types, and into their several habitat and stratal positions in these types.

In the preceding pages the forest community has been discussed, where feasible, in terms of each stratum. As in the grassland community (Tables 35 and 36), the principle of geographic stratal equivalence is readily demonstrated. In Table 40 a few stratal categories are listed to emphasize further the importance of this viewpoint.

27. COMMUNITY ORGANIZATION: METABOLISM

One of the fundamental causes of the adaptive utilization of the space-time community lattice is the drive for nourishment. An organism must eat to live, and the food it consumes maintains the balance between physiological input and output of energy. Since food must be obtained from the environment and since there is a limit to the productivity of any given area, there is not enough food to maintain an unlimited number of organisms, even though in actual life food may not set the primary limits to population density. The food supply of a community, and the relative availability of various food elements for the several species populations cooperating in community maintenance become limiting influences governing community size and complexity and the density of the populations whose intertwining makes up the major community.

Since species have specific protoplasms and inherit specific physiological requirements, their ecological needs are necessarily more or less specific. These environmental adjustments must be made through the agency of both general and particular modifications of structure and function. In-

evitably, the survival of the species depends upon its association with foods sufficient to meet these requirements. In the overwhelming majority of organisms this is accomplished by each species becoming a member of a food-feeder nexus. These natural, cooperative groups are relatively self-sufficient, and the component species populations are spatially integrated and stratified.

These subcommunities appear to be a series of interwoven elements, and their collective effect may be likened to the total effect of the physiological processes of an individual organism. The sum total of the organismal nutritional and assimilative responses of the community may be considered to be the metabolism of the community, just as the sum total of the physicochemical processes in the organism is thought of as the metabolism of the individual. In both instances these metabolic wholes are composed of spatially integrated and stratified responses.

We are only at the threshold of comprehension of the community. No complete analysis of even a simple food chain, or food web, is possible until intraspecies population pressure is known for every participating species, and until all the interspecies population characteristics are evaluated for each link in the food chain and the varied energy relations are assayed.

Furthermore, it must be remembered that over-all metabolism of a community is the result of an always varying biologi-

There are no known exceptions concerning bacterial activity, but the photosynthetic input of certain cave communities is indirect. As aspects of the concept of community metabolism, both these key industries are anabolic processes. The bacterial industry is essential if soils and waters are to support life. The heterotrophic

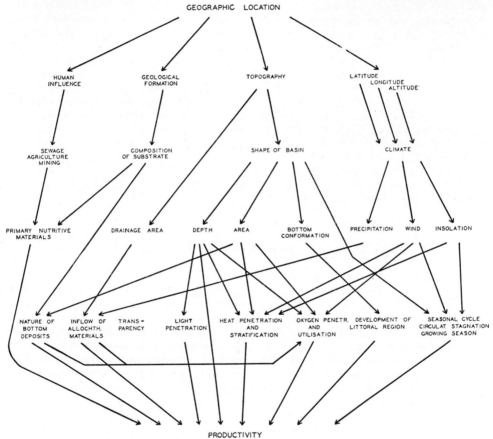

Fig. 165. Diagram of certain inanimate and animate influences involved in the metabolism of a lake community. (After Rawson.)

cal system of great complexity. This system is affected by, and affects, the inanimate portion of the community environment. Some of the influences involved are suggested in Figures 165 and 177.

Before discussing general aspects of community metabolism, the nature of food interrelations of aquatic and terrestrial communities must be examined. Nearly all communities have two interlocking key industries, the reorganization of inorganic and organic compounds by bacteria, and the photosynthetic activity of green plants.

bacteria live by the oxidation or fermentation of substances of organic origin, whereas the autotrophic bacteria derive their energy from inorganic materials.

The autotrophs are commonly divided into two groups: the chemosynthetic species, which live by oxidation of such inorganic materials as ammonia, carbon monoxide, hydrogen, iron, and sulphur; and the photosynthetic species, which apparently contain complex pigments capable of utilizing sunlight. The chemoautotrophs are characteristic of soils and have been treated extensively by Waksman (1932). The photo-autotrophs, such as the red and the green sulfur bacteria, utilize sunlight to synthesize carbon dioxide and hydrogen sulfide into organic materials. Photosynthetic bacteria are chiefly aquatic; Van Niel (1931, 1935, 1936) has studied them.

In their multiple relations with media, heterotrophs are consumers and autotrophs are producers; both are transformers of raw materials in the food web of the community. The bacteria may be said to have three chief roles in community metabolism.

First, they function in decomposing the organic substances continually added to the community as its constituents die. This function is taken over by the heterotrophs. They consume and break down the lifeless bodies of plants and animals. By this activity protoplasms are disintegrated, and much of the organic matter becomes inorganic, i.e., is freed for resynthesis.

Secondly, these inorganic materials may be further oxidized or transformed by chemo-autotrophs or may be used directly by higher plants. In any event, these inorganic compounds are made available for organic synthesis by photosynthetic plants of a given community, whether aquatic or terrestrial.

Thirdly, both heterotrophs and autotrophs are available as food for animals; for example, the soil protozoans and zooplankton (Baier, 1935).

The first of these three basic functions is to be considered the most fundamental. There is some question concerning the rank of bacteria as producers. In this latter function they compete with higher plants. This is especially true of the photo-autotrophs, about which relatively little is known. Our paucity of information on these photosynthetic species is in marked contrast with the rapidly growing store of fact and theory about the much-cultured heterotrophs familiar to medical research. Birge and Juday (1922), concluded that bacteria as producers are of relatively small importance in the metabolism of the lake community as compared with the algal phytoplankton.

A true picture of bacterial importance in the metabolism of communities may not be gained from an outline of separate functions unless these general functions are exemplified by summarizing certain of the chief processes at work.

The role of soil bacteria is better understood than that of the bacteria of aquatic communities. The bacterial floras of soils are engaged in many fundamental reorganizations that are vital to the metabolism of terrestrial communities with respect to nitrogen, phosphorus, sulfur, and iron. A brief statement of each will serve our general purpose.

The importance of the nitrogen cycle is well known and has received a great deal of attention (Waksman, 1932; Wilson, 1940; Rahn, 1945; Frobisher, 1945).

Upon the death of a plant or an animal, its protoplasm is disintegrated through the agency of heterotrophic bacteria. More exactly (Frobisher, 1945, p. 414): "As soon as protoplasm ceases to live, and as soon as any organic matter returns to the soil, it begins to undergo spontaneous oxidative changes and also the biological decomposition process of *decay*, which is aerobic decomposition, or *putrefaction* and *fermentation*, which are anaerobic decomposition of proteins and carbohydrates, respectively. Through these processes the nitrogen and other elements become available to plants. Decomposition results from the action of hordes of bacteria and other creatures found in all soil and in natural waters."

A part of the residual material of protoplasmic disintegration is protein. Certain bacteria digest the protein to relatively simple amino acids, and by combination of water with NH_2^- ions form ammonia. This first series of reactions is known as *ammonification*. It is fundamental to the well-being of the community.

Nitrogen in the form of ammonia is combined into ammonium salts in part, and in part is oxidized by such bacteria as *Nitrosomonas* to form nitrites (*nitrosification*). If this did not happen, the fixed nitrogen would be lost partially into the atmosphere, just as it is lost from compost heaps, and might be greatly delayed in returning to the soil system.

These nitrites are in large part useless to plants in the community until other bacteria, such as *Nitrobacter*, oxidize them to nitrates (*nitrification* in the strict sense). The two processes of nitrosification and nitrification are at times combined loosely under the term "nitrification," but are sufficiently distinct to warrant separation.

At this stage in the nitrogen cycle the soil nitrates can be utilized by green plants to form plant proteins.

At the same time, still other bacteria reduce the nitrites and nitrates to gaseous nitrogen in a fourth reaction chain known as *denitrification*. Still other bacteria transform the free, gaseous nitrogen of the atmosphere pervading the forest or grassland community back into amino acids. These amino acids are stored in these nitrogen-fixing bacteria in a fifth chain of reactions, termed *nitrogen fixation*. Such bacteria belong to two groups, both of which are residents of the subterranean stratum of terrestrial communities. They either are free-living in the soil, or live symbiotically upon the root systems of legumes. In either case, as these bacteria die, the stored amino acids are available for ammonification.

These five sets of reactions are concerned with the production of raw materials of plant proteins. Such bacterial activities in the community metabolism are analogous to enzyme chains in organismal metabolism.

In this connection it must be remembered that about 1000 pounds of atmospheric nitrogen are fixed annually by lightning for each square mile of the earth's surface (p. 190). This annual increment of nitrogen undoubtedly affects bacterial activity in communities. Just how important this annual nitrogen addition is in the metabolism of communities is not known. Nevertheless, in view of the problem of the availability of dissolved organic substances in the sea, any fixed inorganic nitrogen falling into the ocean, where it may be utilized by phytoplankton, even in considerably less amounts than cited, may be of great importance in the nitrogen cycle. Furthermore, nitrates, nitrites, and ammonia are carried into the sea in substantial amounts by rivers. For example, the Mississippi river carries some 361,000 metric tons of nitrate nitrogen annually into the Gulf of Mexico (calculated from Clarke, 1924).

Phosphorus is also an essential element in the residue of decomposing protoplasms. It is finally resolved into phosphoric acid by soil bacteria in a series of reactions that may be called *phosphatization* and is stored in the soil in the form of phosphates of aluminum, calcium, iron, and magnesium. Again such phosphates are protein-building blocks in the metabolism of the community.

Soil bacteria are also engaged in less well-defined systems of oxidation-reduction. One is the transformation of iron compounds, in some cases the oxidation of ferrous to ferric iron. In this instance the bacteria obtain energy that enables them to synthesize their sugars; hence they are autotrophic. At other times deficiency of soil iron in alkaline areas may result directly from bacterial action or indirectly by the production of water-insoluble compounds.

Sulfur is also an important part of some protein molecules. It is obtained by green plants in the form of soil sulfates. When a plant or an animal dies, the released sulfur is attacked by sulfur heterotrophs to produce hydrogen sulfide, which is then oxidized into sulfur dioxide by other sulfur bacteria. Still other bacteria oxidize the sulfur dioxide into sulfuric acid. This acid reacts molecule by molecule with a variety of soil bases to form highly important compounds. One of these bases is calcium, which unites with sulfuric acid to form calcium sulfate, which can be utilized directly by green plants. This complex chain of reactions to produce sulfates is known as *sulfofication*. In apposition to this process is a converse series of reactions known as *desulfofication*, in which bacteria reduce the soil sulfates to hydrogen sulfide. This latter process results, temporarily at least, in a depletion of available soil nutrients.

The foregoing summary of four important, separate series of bacterial activities is but a small part of the total biochemical reactions that take place continuously in the subterranean strata of grassland and forest communities. A more detailed account of bacterial activity may be obtained from such treatises as that of Waksman (1932) and Frobisher (1945), but the essential matter for consideration here is the point of view.

These really vital bacterial activities are outlined in most modern texts on general biology and general botany, often in harmony with the subject matter (Transeau, Sampson, and Tiffany, 1940). They are much less widely recognized in texts on general ecology or in lectures upon this subject. This is lamentable, since bacteria are fundamental to the formation and maintenance of any terrestrial or aquatic community. The formation of calcium nitrate, sulfate or phosphate by soil bacteria is as important in the community as, say, the production of hormones in the individual organism.

Bacteria are fundamentally important in the metabolism of aquatic communities. The activities of these organisms in such communities are not so well understood as the bacterial processes in soils. The general outline of activities of aquatic bacteria follows the usual pattern. Lifeless plankton, nekton, and benthos are decomposed by heterotrophs, to help set up the gradient in organic materials previously discussed (p. 443), and their proteins are broken down to ammonia; the ammonia eventually is oxidized to nitrates by aquatic autotrophs. The nitrates are available to the phytoplankton in their synthesis of organic compounds.

There is an interesting difference between aquatic and terrestrial communities. In both groups the heterotrophic bacteria break down protoplasms to ammonia, and autotrophs build up ammonia and other materials into salts capable of being used by the primary green plants. In terrestrial communities the resulting salts are formed by bacteria and used by the root systems of green plants in the same stratum, viz., the subterranean; whereas in aquatic communities, especially those with any considerable depth, the phytoplankton that must use these salts live chiefly in the uppermost strata, which, as a consequence of their photosynthetic function, form the analogue of the canopy stratum of forests. In this case, then, the depletion of salts in the epilimnion and their accumulation in the hypolimnion make necessary the replenishment of the epilimnion by upward diffusion of salts from the lower zones through partial solution pressures and by convection currents. In both types of communities the results are the same, and the basic processes are similar; the density of the interstitial medium and the size of the individual photosynthetic units are dissimilar.

The roles of marine bacteria are generally similar to those of fresh-water and terrestrial bacteria, but certain complexities render the marine problem much less understood.

For example, there is nothing now known concerning pressure or temperature that would inhibit the growth and reproduction of abyssal bacteria (ZoBell, 1934, 1946), and yet too little is known to justify wholesale transference of facts from soil bacteriology to marine bacteriology.

One difficulty is in the great distances through which decomposing organisms must fall. Whereas in a forest or a lake community, a disintegrating organism may fall from several to a hundred meters, and decomposition takes place largely in the lowermost strata, the decomposing organism in the open sea might sink through distances up to 10,000 meters. It has been pointed out (Coker, 1938, 1947, p. 85) that, since the predominant marine organisms are minute, their sinking rate is slow. Protozoans, diatoms, and coccolithophores sink gradually, while even a large copepod, falling at the rate of 2 feet per minute, would cover only a mile in two days. Since the available food supply for animals of the intermediate strata, between the photic zone and the abyssal zone, must be derived in large part from this falling and decomposing food, not much disintegrating material would reach the bottom strata directly. The smaller dead creatures, certainly, would be wholly decomposed. Coker concludes that, barring deposition of skeletons, there is no great accumulation of solid organic waste on the sea floor. If this is so, then the heterotrophic bacterial industry, so essential to community metabolism, would be relatively smaller in the marine floor stratum and relatively greater in the intermediate strata than in fresh-water communities. In fresh-water lake communities the difference from the marine zonation in this respect becomes progressively less in proportion to the depth of the lakes.

There is a great accumulation of dissolved organic material in the upper and intermediate levels of the sea. Krogh (1934) estimated that such dissolved organic materials are equivalent to 300 times the quantity of living organisms in these areas at any given time. He further postulated that this vast amount of organic substances has largely gone out of circulation; that it is no longer available for the metabolism of the community.

This store of dissolved organic materials, according to Pütter's hypothesis, should be available to zooplankton if other conditions of temperature and pressure are favorable. In the ocean depths where these dissolved materials are maximal in amount, Krogh (1931) reported a zoological desert. If Pütter's original hypothesis is extended to include the utilization of colloidal solutions (Gellis and Clarke, 1935), this problem of recombination of organic materials in the sea water is still further obscured by a dearth of exact information. At present (Bond, 1933; Krogh, 1934, 1934a; Sverdrup, Johnson, and Fleming, 1942) the evidence for such utilization is restricted to bacteria.*

On the basis of an earlier view that there is a steady increase of dissolved organic material becoming unavailable to the organic cycle in oceanic depths, the eventual prospect is indeed gloomy. This view may be a consequence of lack of information concerning the place of bacteria in the metabolism of the marine community. Investigations by Waksman (1934), Waksman and Carey (1935, 1935a), Waksman and Renn (1936) and others reported by Sverdrup, Johnson, and Fleming (1942), and ZoBell (1946), suggest that the activity of bacteria in the sea is on a large scale and involves the decomposition of organic material by heterotrophs.

A second body of information tends to clarify the results of bacterial activity in the oceanic abyssal strata. These data are applied inferentially, since they appertain to the profundal strata of lake communities. In the sediments on the bottoms of lakes, under anaerobic conditions, organic materials are reorganized by heterotrophs into marsh gas, or methane, and hydrogen (Henrici, 1939). As these gases diffuse upward into the aerated water, they are oxidized by autotrophs. Another example in lake metabolism applicable to marine problems is the reduction of sulfates to sulfides by heterotrophs under anaerobic conditions. As these salts diffuse or are carried upward

by convection, they are oxidized to sulfates again by autotrophs. It is reasonable to assume, therefore, that there are broadly similar bacterial activities on the sea floor and in the abyssal region. The permanent accumulations of hydrogen sulfide in the depths of the Black Sea and in certain Norwegian fjords appear to represent exceptional situations; the situation may be more general (ZoBell, 1946, p. 109).

Information gleaned from studies of marine littoral strata present a well-rounded picture of characteristic bacterial activities in the marine community. Large amounts of organic material are washed into shallow waters. These materials have been studied on the Beaufort beaches of the North Carolina littoral by Humm (Pearse, Humm, and Wharton, 1942). It was shown that such organic matter is decomposed, mineralized by bacterial action, and returned to the sea. Bacterial activity apparently goes on at the greatest rate in the intertidal zone when tides are out. The conclusion was reached that ammonification, nitrification, denitrification, and nitrogen-fixation are carried out in littoral waters along sand beaches at or near the sand-water interface.

Humm found an average of 200,000 bacteria per gram of seashore sand. This stratal population figure was an average of 256 plate counts of sand samples taken in the intertidal zone. The numbers of bacteria ranged from 5000 to 1,250,000 per gram of intertidal sand, and the average population figure was considered from 70 to 90 per cent of the total number of aerobic bacteria that would form macroscopic colonies on the plate medium used.

In these intertidal sand samples examined, several pure cultures were obtained of *Sarcina subflava*, *Micrococcus halophilus*, and *Micrococcus varians*. In addition, occasional plates were poured of ordinary fresh-water nutrient agar to discover what bacteria from marine sand would develop in fresh-water media. On such fresh-water plates an average of 2000 bacteria per gram were grown from intertidal sand habitats. This shows that some bacteria, or bacterial strains, may be identical for fresh-water and marine communities, while many are certainly ecologically equivalent. Findings of Humm, and of Stanier (1941) suggest that there are specific

---

* If the original Pütter hypothesis is extended to include the utilization of dissolved mineral nutrients, an entirely new approach is available. Such an extension is a logical suggestion, and is an application of Bayliss (1924) that food is any substance taken into any organism and used for any purpose.

marine bacteria, and this view may be maintained until the same species or strains are found growing naturally in non-marine habitats. Numerous fresh-water bacteria have been found that can develop in salt concentrations higher than those of sea water, although the death rate of many fresh-water bacteria is thought to be high in salt water (Burke, 1934).

Our general conclusion is that bacterial activity is of fundamental importance in the metabolism of all major communities; that these activities are essentially similar in all major communities; and that these processes are carried out by many ecologically equivalent species of bacteria.

Ecologists as a group have been more aware of the place of the second key industry, photosynthesis, in the metabolism of communities than they have been of the role played by bacteria. The photosynthetic process in which chlorophyll synthesizes carbohydrate in the presence of water, carbon dioxide, and radiant energy from the sun, has been investigated by many plant physiologists and biochemists; its importance has been noted in previous pages. We are concerned now with the more specific community aspects of this fundamental industry.

Photosynthetic carbohydrate production is an anabolic process from the point of view of the metabolism of the whole community. The photosynthetic output is limited chiefly by intensity and wavelengths of light, cloudy weather, atmospheric dust, turbidity, amount of available carbon dioxide, and temperature of the atmosphere. All these conditions act as a whole to regulate green plant production, growth, and well-being. Where plants compete for light or animals reduce the chlorophyll by direct or indirect actions, this productivity, growth, or health is correspondingly accelerated or retarded or otherwise affected.

For example, in communities where the plants are relatively fixed, as in forests, the shape of the leaf, thickness of the leaf blade, amount of mesophyll, amount of stem elongation and crown volume are modified by the physical and the biological environment. Intensity and composition of light and direction of the light beams are especially important influences of the operational physical environment (Warming,

1909; Coulter, Barnes, and Cowles, 1911). Thus a plant species may be, first tolerant or intolerant of sun or shade in various degrees; second, the total plant population may adjust to the light gradient by positional stratification; and third, the individual plants may adjust to seasonal and daily permutations of forest illumination.

On the other hand, in communities where the chlorophyll-bearing organisms, the major "producers" of Thienemann (1926), are not fixed, as in the marine photic zone, the response to reduced light, as a consequence of increase in population density above them or for other reasons, is a general movement upward by those capable of swimming. Thus the shade species of *Ceratium* (Graham, 1941) move vertically in response to changes in light intensity, and this response is ecologically equivalent to the several positional adjustments of the leaves of forest plants. This extends the postulate of Nielsen previously noted (p. 448).

In aquatic communities the original carbohydrate "producers" are chiefly floating algae or weakly swimming chlorophyll-bearing flagellates, rooted vegetation, and, to a lesser degree, photosynthetic autotrophic bacteria.

The general process will be discussed with respect to the photic zone of the marine community, first, by a brief description of the chief groups of nonbacterial "producers," and second, by an analysis of the diatom cycle of the open North Atlantic waters. The marine photic zone holds prodigious numbers of a few groups of these primary producers composed of a small number of basic types. Five such groups deserve a brief discussion.

1. The only large seaweed that is free-floating on high seas belongs to species of the brown seaweeds or *Sargassum* (Phaeophyceae). These algae are broken from their littoral rock habitats and reproduce vegetatively as they are carried by ocean currents. Before the death and disintegration of this alga, it forms the food and shelter of many zooplankters, some of which apparently may not live elsewhere (Coker, 1938, 1947).

2. Green algae (Chlorophyceae), abundant in surface layers of fresh-water, are represented in the sea by a few species that may become locally abundant. An example

is the "punti verdi" (*Halosphaera viridis*) of the Mediterranean fishermen.

3. Coccospheres or coccolithophores (Coccolithoporidae) are poorly known since they are so minute in size that they must be collected by centrifuge. Although they pass through the finest nets, they are considered as constituting a large proportion of marine phytoplankton. Their bodies contain calcareous plates or processes typical of the abyssal Globigerina ooze. They are widely distributed, are sparse to absent from polar seas, and are especially characteristic of tropical and subtropical seas. (The interested reader will find Calkins, 1926; Coker, 1947; Kudo, 1931; and Russell and Yonge, 1928, of service in their further study.)

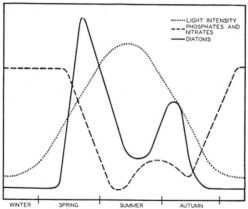

Fig. 166. Interrelation of the seasonal cycle in abundance of diatoms, light intensity, phosphates, and nitrates in the open North Atlantic. (From Park, Allee, and Shelford, after Russell and Yonge.)

4. Peridinians (Dinophyceae, Dinoflagellata) are abundant in the photic zone, important in photosynthesis and contain such well-known genera as *Ceratium*, discussed previously (p. 448). Their important place in the marine food web has been much studied by Böhm (1931), Graham (1941), Gran (1912), Jörgensen (1920), Kofoid and Swezy (1921), Nielsen (1934) and Peters (1934).

5. Diatoms (Bacillarophyceae) probably are the most important taxonomic group in the marine photic zone from the point of view of carbohydrate anabolism in the vast marine community. They have been chosen for especial mention. The area to

be discussed is the open North Atlantic, where the characteristics of the annual population cycle have been shown to be expressions of a sensitive response to the operating factor complex of the photic zone (Russell and Yonge, 1928). For convenience of presentation, this diatom cycle will be discussed with reference to the four seasons, as indicated in Figure 166.

Winter

The surface water is as cold as or colder than the aphotic layers; there is no region of temperature transition; light intensity is minimal (1000 to 2000 foot-candles or less.) Under these conditions the inorganic nitrates and phosphates, which have been produced through the bacterial industry in the intermediate layers, now diffuse upward, under partial pressures, until the distribution of these salts is relatively uniform. This accumulation of raw protein precursors is possible since there is insufficient light for large-scale diatom photosynthesis; consequently the diatom population is minimal.

Spring

By March or April the upper layer of the photic zone warms up. This warming process is progressive, and by May or June a transitional temperature zone (partial discontinuity layer) forms at between 10 and 20 meters (p. 94). Light intensity increases rapidly. This rise in illumination after the renewal of needed mineral nutrients in the surface waters makes possible the dramatic reproduction of diatoms known as the "spring pulse." This vernal increase is chiefly responsible for the annual yield of diatoms, and is indirectly responsible for the great productivity of the sea. For example, in the English Channel off Plymouth, the annual diatom crop is 5.5 tons (wet weight) per acre of sea surface. This is a minimal weight figure. The vernal pulse accounts for one-third to one-half of this total and is of high significance in the food web of the marine community. The salts accumulated through the winter months are sufficient for the diatom metabolism. The light intensity is high enough (6000 to 7000 foot-candles) at the surface of the water for several hours in the middle of the day to allow diatom photosynthesis.

The diatom response to these two critical factors is rapid and spectacular.

Summer

By middle May to early June the diatom population has reached a maximum and begins a rapid decline. This decrease continues through the summer into early autumn. This is paradoxical, since the intensity of daylight is maximal in the summer (7000 to 10,000 foot-candles at the surface); consequently this season has the highest potential photosynthesis. The rapid decline in diatom abundance is a consequence of the delicate balance of influences operating in the photic strata of the community.

There is a great loss of diatoms through their consumption by herbivores. Second, the weak marine thermocline, now at its strongest, separates the relatively warm photic layer from the cold aphotic layer. This strong temperature differential, with its associated electrical properties, prevents rapid up-welling of nitrates and phosphates by diffusion and reduces mixing by convection currents. From the viewpoint of community metabolism, the thermocline acts like a semipermeable membrane separating the upper and lower strata of the community. Were it not for this temperature and density barrier, the diatoms might have sufficient salts for protein synthesis and, with the favorable light intensity, would continue to increase in numbers. The summer diatom population is several times larger than the winter population, but only one-fifth to one-sixth as large as the spring pulse.

Autumn

The surface layer of the photic zone begins to cool in correlation with the decreasing air temperature. This surface cooling causes a reduction of the discontinuity layer, which gradually disappears as the upper and lower layers approach each other in temperature. With loss of the thermocline, there is an upward diffusion of nutrient salts. This upwelling is aided by the churning forces of autumnal gales. With sufficient amounts of critical salts for protein synthesis, there is an increase of the diatoms; this increase is not spectacular, since the light intensity is now decreasing, and photosynthesis is reduced.

This combination of influences causes the autumnal pulse of diatoms. It is about twice the summer density of population but about one-half that of the spring pulse. With onset of winter weather, the diatom population density returns to the minimal condition.

This general account of diatom productivity again demonstrates the delicate balance between physical and biological factors in a community. It should be remembered that this basic photosynthetic key industry is related to, and dependent upon, the bacterial key industry. The abundance of diatoms is a result of this balance. In turn, these minute phytoplankters, with their allies, and the bacteria are at the base of the food web of the marine community.

Obviously, photosynthesis in the sea is largely the work of the phytoplankton. Attached algae and the higher plants of littoral areas play a relatively small part in the over-all industry, though perhaps important in the immediate zones occupied by them.

In fresh-water communities, the role of the macroflora is relatively greater in carbohydrate anabolism than it is in the marine littoral. The higher plants become progressively more important as ponds and lakes fill up, and the growth of pond weeds and their ecological equivalents restricts the open water where phytoplankton may carry on photosynthesis.

The green "producers" of fresh-water include, among other forms, the blue-green algae (Myxophyceae), green algae (Chlorophyceae), diatoms (Bacillarophyceae), the peridinians (Dinoflagellata), the euglenas (Euglenoidina), and the Volvocales. This producer plankton is similar ecologically to its marine counterpart. The bibliographies of Fritsch (1935), Smith (1938), and Tiffany (1938) will open the subject for more intensive study. Rapid vernal multiplication results in "pulses" or "water bloom;" they are dominated by algae or the algae-like flagellates. Both sets of producers depend upon light for photosynthesis, and on dissolved inorganic salts for protein synthesis; both are fundamental in community metabolism.

Fresh-water algae, as a group, comprise six seasonal categories: spring annuals, winter annuals, perennials, summer annuals, autumn annuals, and ephemerals. In large temperate lakes, at least, these six groups give an over-all picture of population density similar to that of the marine community, that is, a relatively high peak in April-May-early-June and a second, smaller peak, in August-September-early-October. Small lakes (Pennak, 1946) may or may not follow this pattern.

This seasonal parallel is clear when a single group is used—for example, the diatoms. Year-around, quantitative studies on Lake Erie (Chandler, 1942a; Gottschall and Jennings, 1933) and on Lake Michigan (Daily, 1938; Damann, 1940) demonstrate a clearly defined vernal and an autumnal

obtained since they must take into account the reproductive potential of each species under annual environmental conditions, average life span of each species, and average weight of each species (Welch, 1935). One of the few reliable estimates of annual production is the early figure of Birge and Juday (1922) for Lake Mendota, Wisconsin. These authors estimated 12,000 kg. of dry total plankton per hectare of lake surface. This works out at about 10,700 pounds of plankton per acre per year, which roughly equals the annual crop of diatoms only, in the English Channel (p. 502). In other words, the diatom annual

Table 42. Total Crop of Rooted Hydrophytes in Wisconsin Lakes

Southern Wisconsin (After Rickett 1922, 1924)	Total Crop in Kilograms (Dry Weight)	Average Crop in Grams per Square Meter
Lake Mendota	2,100,000	202.00
Green Lake	1,527,900	178.00
Northern Wisconsin (After Wilson 1935, 1937, 1939)		
Little John Lake	111	000.52
Muskellunge Lake	882	000.45
Silver Lake	17	000.08

pulse, dominated by six genera of diatoms (Asterionella, Cyclotella, Fragilaria, Melosira, Synedra, and Tabellaria).

Chandler's data for Lake Erie may be summarized for the general picture in large temperate lake communities. The vernal pulse of nonbacterial phytoplankton reached a maximum of 374,000 organisms per liter between March 14 and May 28; of this pulse, the diatoms composed 98 per cent. The observed autumnal pulse occurred in two parts and never exceeded a maximum of 34,000 organisms per liter between September 13 and November 29; of this pulse, the diatoms composed 60 per cent.

These data refer to the standing crop, viz., the total amount of phytoplankton in the water at a given time. They do not represent the annual crop, viz., the total quantity of phytoplankton produced in a given year. Annual crop data are not easily

production of the marine community about equals the total phytoplankton, plus total zooplankton annual production of the fresh-water community, per unit of water surface, in about the same range of latitude.

The rooted aquatic vegetation of the fresh-water community makes up the balance of the photosynthetic industry, exclusive of the work of autotrophic photosynthetic bacteria about which relatively little is known. In the United States five Wisconsin lakes have been studied with reference to total crop. These data are summarized in Table 42.

Using data in the right hand column, it will be seen that there is a great range in dry bulk of rooted plants in lakes relatively close to each other. Wilson (1939) correlates this disparity in anabolic potential with several factors, the most obvious of which is type of bottom. Thus the lakes studied in southern Wisconsin had bottoms with a much greater ratio of silt and clay, whereas those of northern Wisconsin had bottoms with sand predominating. Consequently, type of bottom partially controls the amount of rooted hydrophytes and indirectly the anabolism of plant carbohydrate of the community. Also involved in this general problem are numerous other influences; for example, the "hardness" and "softness" of water. It follows that the physical environment is an important limiting factor in total community metabolism, just as it is in the metabolism of the component organisms.

Lake community productivity has been correlated with type of lake by Prescott (1939). Oligotrophic lakes, with sufficient dissolved oxygen at all depths during summer and winter stagnation, have the amount of phytoplankton, and attached hydrophytes of shore and bottom, relatively reduced; autotrophic lakes, with little or no dissolved oxygen in the hypolimnion during summer stagnation, have a relatively high yield of phytoplankton and attached hydrophytes. In such autotrophic communities the yield of the rooted vegetation is as much as 882 kg. per square meter for 52 per cent of the floor stratum. Consequently oxygen supply, as well as floor materials, influences the productivity in aquatic, as well as in terrestrial, communities.

The stream community differs physically and biologically from the lake community. Its phytoplankton, investigated by Tiffany (1938), and other major aspects deserve summarizing here. The great variation in rate of flow over the course of a stream system, from imperceptible movement in ponded portions to turbulent rapids, accompanied by radical changes in character of bottom, turbidity, and dissolved gases, creates many habitat types in a relatively short distance. Stream algae frequently are adjusted to current. Many have holdfast adjustments. These are found in *Lemanea,* growing in waterfalls, and *Cladophora,* growing on submerged stones.

Diatoms are plentiful and multiply as they are carried downstream. Generally the slower the current, the more numerous are these free-floating individuals. Sluggish streams may develop a "water bloom" of diatoms, euglenoids, and blue-green algae. Streams differ taxonomically from lakes

in their photosynthetic species, and such fluviatile communities generally have a smaller standing crop of phytoplankters per unit of surface.

Since streams lack a thermocline, there is no summer stagnation, and when turbidity does not interfere with photosynthesis, stream algae multiply rapidly. This is possible as rivers usually contain abundant nitrates, so that the biotic potential is high.

Diatoms in rivers appear to be greatly influenced by floods. High vernal peaks in the stream diatom population usually follow spring floods when the water is rich in organic materials, nitrates, and silicates. This correlates well with the vernal pulse of temperate lakes and seas.

More annual studies of lake and stream total plankton and rooted vegetation are greatly needed to evaluate energy input and productivity. Few direct answers are available. An indirect answer is found in discussions of the biological efficiencies of the several trophic levels of the community (p. 509), and a partial answer is available in the result of such biochemical activity, that is the weight of plant protoplasm produced per unit area, or plant biomass (p. 525).

Photosynthetic efficiency is not great in natural communities. It ranges from 0.1 to 0.4 per cent in lakes, and in artificially maintained plantings of field corn it is as high as 1.6 per cent (Table 43). This differential, incidentally, is an interesting datum with respect to man's effect upon other organisms and communities.

Manning and Juday (1941) have arrived at an approximate photosynthetic productivity for seven lakes in northeastern Wisconsin. Their results are in terms of the production of glucose, using a clear day in August as a basis of calculation. The highest production was 44 kg. of glucose per hectare per day (Scaffold Lake); the lowest production was 14 kg. per hectare per day (Helmet Lake).

Much needs to be done on tropical lakes and streams in general, and in regard to bacterial and photosynthetic industries in particular.

Chlorophyll physiology for terrestrial plants has been studied intensively. It is known that photosynthesis takes place most efficiently at either end of the visible spectrum. The intermediate green band is largely reflected, causing the leaf to be green to our eyes.

The chief adaptation of terrestrial plants for carrying on photosynthesis is the leaf, and leaves work most efficiently when at right angles to the light beam. This positional arrangement is well shown in forests, where, from canopy down to herbaceous stratum, the response to light exercises a profound effect upon stratification in the large and in the individual response of each leaf. Several pertinent examples are discussed by Thimann (1941), such as the maple sapling, which has each leaf at right angles to the incident light. In the com-

photosynthesizing protoplasm engaged in the common ecological response of organisms and communities to the physical environment, in the synthesis of carbohydrates.

This large-scale industry is absent from few places, though possibly from certain areas of waterless deserts and from isolated mountain peaks. This brings up the question, raised previously for phytoplankton, of the efficiency of this photosynthesis. This logical extension of the argument requires much research by physiologists. Its answer is relevant to community metabolism as well.

Fortunately, Transeau (1926) has given us one estimate, based upon a sun-tolerant

Table 43. *Photosynthetic Efficiency of Field Corn (After Transeau, 1926)*

Total dry weight of an acre of corn (10,000 plants)	6000 kg.
Less ash (inorganic matter)	300 kg.
Total organic matter	5700 kg.
Equivalent of this in glucose	6700 kg.
Plus organic substances lost by transpiration for the season, expressed as glucose	2000 kg.
Total glucose formed by an acre of corn............................	8700 kg.
Energy required to synthesize 1 kilogram of glucose	3800 KCal.
Energy required to synthesize 8700 kilograms about........	33,000,000 KCal.
Total solar energy available for one acre	2,040,000,000 KCal.

$$\text{Therefore: \% available energy used} = \frac{33 \text{ million}}{2040 \text{ million}} \times 100 = 1.6\%$$

pass plant of the Illinois prairie, this leaf adjustment is supplemented by rotation and curvature of the leaf stalk. Other factors, especially sufficient moisture, will allow "a very large fraction of the land surface to be covered with green leaves" (Thimann, 1941, p. 30).

Ability to bring leaves perpendicular to incident light and to curve lightwards through hormone regulation, results in an ecologically advantageous position for each plant. Thus each fixed forest plant makes the most of its total leaf surface. From a synecological aspect, this results in maximal photosynthesis for the whole community and is equivalent to vertical movement of plankton populations as previously noted.

It means much more than this. If we combine the generalizations of Nielsen (1934) and Thimann, there emerges a much larger, global one, namely that a large part of the planet's surface is covered with a relatively thin, taxonomically complex, structurally discontinuous layer of

species, field corn. His calculations appear in Table 43.

Plankton sampling, board feet of lumber, or tons of hay, per unit of area-time, are often at hand or can be obtained or estimated. The essential energy relationships are usually not available and are difficult to collect.

An oversimplified view of energy relationships can be obtained by a consideration of photosynthetic productivity in terms of amount of glucose produced per unit of area and time for several "average" community types. Such a comparison is presented in Table 44, and will prove interesting in a discussion of total community metabolism, if the hypothetical nature of some of the conclusions is remembered.

As we have seen (p. 502), the planktonic photosynthetic industry of aquatic communities is characterized by seasonal rhythmicities of its component populations. The major seasonal rhythm in deep lakes includes a high vernal, and a much lower autumnal, pulse. If the maximum August daily production of glucose is used as an average for the growing season (Manning and Juday, 1941), lake plankton could produce 39 pounds of glucose per day per acre. A third of this yield has been added for the glucose of rooted aquatic plants, and the growing season placed at 240 days (March to October). This is tentative for north temperate lakes, since phytoplankton often metabolize for a much longer period, possibly 300 days in parts of the area or in some years. Production for higher or lower latitudes would differ from this tentative average.

With respect to grassland, Transeau (1926) gave 200 pounds of glucose as the yield of an acre of field corn (p. 506), and the growing season for this annual herb as 100 days. Later, Transeau, Sampson, and Tiffany (1940, Chap. 20) discussed the subject of energy transformation and pointed out that this glucose yield was high, and might average as much as one-third of the maximum. This would reduce the yield to something like 70 to 80 pounds per day per acre of field corn. On the other hand, natural tall grass prairie might do better than average field corn if allowance is made for stratification. The growing season would certainly be longer, and we have substituted 150 days (April to August) for the growing season, and have increased the daily yield by 30 per cent over the average corn figure.

With respect to deciduous forest, Heinicke and Childers (1937) have given us glucose production figures for an acre of apple trees in New York. They find the growing season to be 188 days, and the photosynthetic productivity to be 93 pounds of glucose per day per acre of 400 trees. If we use this figure for the tree stratum of woody perennials, and add one-third to allow for the shrub and herbaceous strata, the conservative estimate of 125 pounds of glucose per day is obtained. This would apply to average canopy development, and not to a community of tall, old deciduous trees. An estimated season of 180 days (April to September) has been used.

These glucose productivities are estimates. They represent a portion of the potential energy stored later in plant protein synthesis. In turn, such compounds are available for plant growth and as a margin for animal consumption in the balanced, self-maintaining community.

Table 44. Estimated Photosynthetic Productivity in Terms of Pounds of Glucose, per Day, and Growing Season, per Acre for Typical North Temperate Communities

Type of Community	Daily Yield	Growing Season Yield
Lake................	54	13,000
Tall grass prairie.....	100	15,000
Deciduous forest.....	125	22,500

It must be remembered that these glucose yields are suggestive, rather than actual; that they are based on different lengths for the growing season; and that they deal with the green plants of the community only.

The postulate has just been made that the grassland community has a lower total photosynthetic productivity than the forest community. This extends the argument previously advanced that the higher development of stratification in forests is probably partially the cause of this higher productivity. This argument suggests that stratification of structure and photosynthetic productivity are expressions of the developing complexity of the community, making more space available, and increasing the amounts of carbohydrates and proteins. This increase in the utilization of the space lattice is accompanied by increasing utilization of time from the point of view of overlapping periodicities.

We have been concerned with two key industries in the metabolism of the community. These are anabolic. They have to do with the transformation of energy, and with the formation of plant protein and carbohydrates. The catabolic processes in connection with bacterial activity have been touched upon. We turn next to the study of the catabolic processes of the community, that is, the transfer and resynthesis of these plant materials into animal protoplasms, and their eventual conversion to raw products once more, in the circulation of substances in the community.

In general terms, a community at the level of self-maintenance is a self-regulating assemblage in which the populations of plants and animals hold each other in a state of biological equilibrium. This is an extension of the principle of biotic balance to embrace the whole community.

This is not to say that communities are always in static equilibrium. Rather, they are in a condition of flux in all their strata, and within each stratum the species populations are in almost continual readjustment to each other and to the varying physical portion of their environments. We may postulate safely that in any community, at any time, analysis would demonstrate some of its components in imbalance with respect to other components. This is no less true of organismal metabolism than it is of community metabolism. The unbalance may be of varying degree and duration. If serious, such maladjustment in organisms leads to impairment of function and eventually to organismal death, and in communities to community death. Usually, the unbalance is relatively small and ephemeral and occurs frequently at many widely separated parts of the organism and community. Rectification of these temporary points of unbalance is essential to optimal health and vigor. The result is biotic balance and is achieved in communities by complex regulation of these oscillations.

We have examined this important aspect of ecology previously, in terms of predator-prey regulation (p. 370). The principle of balance has a still broader application. It is one of the major influences maintaining the character and independence of the whole community. It may be an underlying cause of community development and succession (Chap. 29) in which a pioneer community finally reaches a condition of unbalance which it may not rectify, and the invading or succeeding organisms gradually, through time, develop a new community.

In the particular sense in which the concept of the major community is used in this book (p. 436), the several species populations hold each other in a system of checks and balances to the end that their intraspecies and interspecies mutualisms (p. 245) and competitions (p. 368) produce a self-sustaining assemblage of organisms. This is essential for a full appreciation of the Darwinian web of life concept. It is implied in the community concept, from the early views of Möbius (1880) and Forbes (1887) to the present moment.

The biotic potential of Chapman (1928) and the trophodynamic limnology of Eggleton (1939), Lindeman (1942), and Hutchinson (1944) reflect this general point of approach. Modern symposia, monographs, and textbooks are, or should be, leavened by its timelessness. For an opposing point of view, see Bodenheimer (1938).

The pattern of survival may be found in the complex interrelations between the several species populations of a community. For example, in the first part of the present chapter it was shown that the basic trophic relations were between plants and the physical portion of the environment (pp. 495–507). The catabolism of a community is largely a consequence of the activities of herbivores and carnivores. The chief groups of herbivores and carnivores were enumerated in the discussion of stratification (pp. 441–494). There remains the integration of these several bodies of data into the catabolism of the whole community.

In the present state of our ignorance this can be only partially and imperfectly achieved by a discussion of (1) food chains, (2) food webs, (3) pyramids of numbers, and (4) biomasses.

The food chain is both an artificial and a convenient concept. In the true sense of the term, a food chain almost never exists in nature as a complete entity. It presupposes a linear series of species in which A is fed upon by B, B by C, and so on to N, with N having few, or no enemies, A-B-C-N. One end of such a chain is composed of predators, the other end of photosynthetic and chemosynthetic plants, and the intermediate species populations or links in the chain are herbivores or carnivores, depending on the complexity of the food chain.

If these taxonomic links of food chains are grouped into energetic categories, we have, following the terminology of Thienemann (1926, 1926a), *producers* (organisms that synthesize protoplasms from inorganic compounds by energy derived from photosynthesis) and *consumers* (organisms that feed upon producers and resynthesize a portion of the latter into different protoplasms).

Lindeman (1942) used this terminology to further factor the feeding interrelationships into a series of more or less discrete trophic levels: Λ_1, Λ_2, Λ_3 . . . Λ_n corresponding to (p. 415) "producers, primary consumers, secondary consumers, etc., each successively dependent upon the preceding level as a source of energy with the producers (Λ_1), directly dependent upon the rate of incident solar radiation as a source of energy."

This is a logical extension of the realization of the vital importance of radiant

trophic level series, the less probable will be its sole dependence upon the preceding trophic level as a source of energy.

Second, there is a progressive increase in the percentage loss of energy, as a consequence of respiration, from lower to higher trophic levels. For example, Lindeman found that respiration energy loss with respect to growth was about 33 per cent for producers, 62 per cent for primary

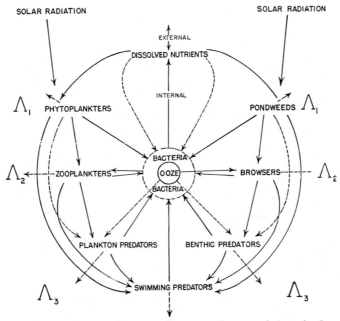

Fig. 167. Consumers are progressively more efficient in the use of their food supply in higher trophic levels. (Modified after Lindeman.)

energy summed up by Bayliss (1924, p. 548): "The whole existence of living organisms on the earth depends on the receipt of radiant energy from the sun . . . " This general conclusion has been applied to many aspects of the community (Park, 1931) and was discussed previously with respect to the photosynthetic key industry.

Lindeman's development of trophic levels is applicable to communities in general, but was derived from his intensive study of Cedar Bog Lake, Minnesota (1941, 1941a), and by his reworking of other limnological studies by several authors (1942). Three of his conclusions bear upon the immediate subject.

First, the further removed an organism is from the initial source of energy in the

consumers, and close to 100 per cent for secondary consumers.

Third, consumers appear to be progressively more efficient in the use of their food supply as higher trophic levels are examined. This at first appears to be at variance with the preceding generalization, until it is remembered that an increased activity of predators may increase their chance of finding prey, as suggested by Figure 167.

We may consider a community as having four or five trophic levels, each level containing a variable number of species, and each species containing a variable number of individuals. In the formulation of the concept that follows, the symbol Λ represents a trophic level, S is a species population, I is an individual, and t is a time component:

$$\begin{bmatrix} (I_1 \dots \dots I_n) \\ S_1 \dots \dots S_n \\ \Lambda_1 \end{bmatrix}_{t,} \begin{bmatrix} etc._1 \\ \Lambda_2 \end{bmatrix}_{t,} \begin{bmatrix} etc. \\ \Lambda_3 \end{bmatrix}_{t,} \begin{bmatrix} etc. \\ \Lambda_4 \end{bmatrix}_{t,} \begin{bmatrix} etc. \\ \Lambda_5 \end{bmatrix}_{t,} \to \Lambda_1$$

Photosynthetic Herbivores Carnivores Heterotrophic Chemo-autotrophic
plants   bacteria,   bacteria
                     fungi, etc.

In this revised trophic level system, Λ_1 includes the photosynthetic plants (either or both the higher plants and the photo-autotrophic bacteria), that is, the *producers;* Λ_2 includes the herbivores, that is, the *primary consumers;* Λ_3 includes the carnivores, that is, the *secondary consumers;* Λ_4 includes the saprophagous organisms (heterotrophic bacteria and fungi), that is, the *tertiary consumers;* and Λ_5 includes the chemo-autotrophic bacteria, that is, the *quaternary consumers.* [*]

Several variations are to be noted in this system of energetic categories. First, omnivores encompass both Λ_2 and Λ_3. Second, Λ_3 must be factored to allow for several predator grades (P) within the level, that is, the S_1 population feeds on Λ_2, but S_2 usually feeds on S_1, S_3 on S_2, and so on:

$$\begin{bmatrix} (I_1 \dots \dots I_n) \\ (S_1 \dots \dots S_n) \\ P_1 \dots \dots P_n \\ \Lambda_3 \end{bmatrix}_{t,}$$

Finally, the trophic level may or may not be synonymous with the food niche (p. 516), depending upon the particular community under examination.

[*] The growing emphasis upon feeding relationships within the community has been accompanied by the usual confusion of terms. For example: Λ_2 includes the "primary consumers" of Jacot (1940) for terrestrial communities, "browsers" of Lindeman (1942) for aquatic communities, and "primary consumers" in general (Lindeman, 1942); Λ_3 includes "secondary, tertiary, quaternary predators" of terrestrial, and "benthic and swimming predators" of aquatic communities, and "secondary consumers" of Lindeman (1942); Λ_4 includes "reducers" of Thienemann (1926a), "transformers" in part (Waksman, 1941), and "decomposers" (Lindeman, 1942).

Naturally, all organisms, whether Λ_1, or Λ_5, consume, transform, produce, and otherwise rearrange and reorganize their protoplasms and environments. The terminology, more or less apt, explains nothing.

As we have noted with respect to stratification of communities, the seas, except possibly certain shallow coastal areas, have the photosynthetic level dominated almost exclusively by phytoplankton; almost all fresh-water communities have both a phytoplankton and a rooted vegetation, while terrestrial communities have this trophic level occupied essentially by rooted, higher plants. In terms of photosynthesis, the fresh-water communities are intermediate in the series. Lindeman (1942) has rephrased this matter in other words. For example, the marine community is "mono-cyclic" with microphytic producers; the fresh-water community is "bi-cyclic" with both microphytic and macrophytic producers; the terrestrial community is "mono-cyclic" with macrophytic producers.

From this point of view, terrestrial communities have no structural equivalent to the plankton of aquatic communities. We have seen previously that the phytoplankton of aquatic communities and the canopy of terrestrial communities are physiologically parallel and occupy the same relative stratum in the vertical gradient.

Francé (1913, 1914) approached this problem from yet another aspect. He considered the microbiota of the soil (subterranean stratum + floor, in part) to include bacteria, fungi, algae, protozoans, rotiferans, tardigrades, and oligochaetid worms (and should have included mites and micro-insects). These groups of organisms Francé termed collectively the *edaphon,* and developed the concept that the terrestrial edaphon was the equivalent of the aquatic plankton. Lindeman (1942) took issue with this concept, pointing out that the analogy was misleading, since the edaphon has almost no producers in the trophic sequence and that Francé's edaphon is much more comparable to the lacustrine microbenthos.

As with many similar disagreements, this is a matter of the viewpoint from which the problem is examined. From the point of

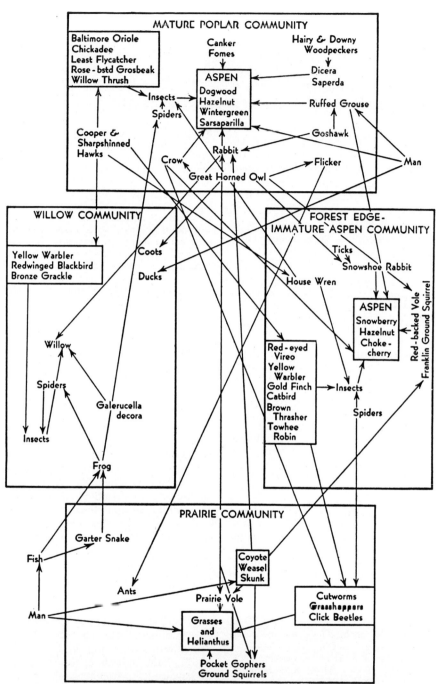

Fig. 170. Food web interrelations between communities and ecotones in the aspen parkland of Canada. (From Hesse, Allee, and Schmidt, after Bird.)

nation or aestivation, and over much greater distances in migration (Chap. 28). Aside from such periodic seasonal events, frequent visits into another food web occur, and are well shown in Figure 170, showing feeding interrelations in the aspen parkland of Canada studied by R. H. Bird (1930).

Two classic food chains are those of Darwin (1859) of an English meadow,

and of Forbes (1887), noted previously.*
The first of these showed a food chain
of at least four links: house cats—field
mice—bumblebees—red clover. It will be
remembered that the cats preyed upon
the mice, the mice destroyed the bee combs,
and the bees gathered nectar from the
clover flowers and cross pollinated them in
a mutualistic relationship. Darwin sums up
this part of the food web by stating (p.
69): "Hence it is quite credible that the
presence of a feline animal in large numbers
in a district (as a consequence, in this instance, of the house cat's commensalism in
man's society) might determine, through
the intervention first of mice and then of
bees, the frequency of certain flowers in
that district!"†

* We are concerned here with general
tendencies, principles, and concepts discoverable in food chains and food webs. The interested student will find food chain or food
web diagrams and data in the following
references: Ant nests (O. Park, 1929, 1932,
1935a); caves (Park, Allee, and Shelford,
1939, pp. 117–126); forests (Adams, 1915;
Allee, 1926a; Blake, 1926; Park, 1931a; Park
and Strohecker, 1936; Seton, 1909; Shelford,
1913; Weese, 1924); fungi (Park, 1931a); hot
springs (Brues, 1927); lakes (Bond, 1933;
Klugh, 1927; Shelford, 1913; Welch, 1935);
prairie (Adams, 1915; Carpenter, 1940a;
Clements and Shelford, 1939; Elton, 1927;
Graham, 1939; Haviland, 1926; Hayes, 1927;
Isely, 1938a; Seton, 1909; Shackleford, 1929;
Shelford, 1913); rotting logs (Graham, 1925;
Savely, 1939; Shelford, 1913); sand desert
(Buxton, 1923; Kashkarov and Kurbitov,
1930); seas (Bond, 1933; Chace, 1940; Coker,
1938, 1947; Hardy, 1924; Sverdrup, Johnson,
and Fleming, 1942; Russell and Yonge, 1928,
Chap. 9); tortoise burrows (Hubbard, 1893);
tundra (Haviland, 1926; Summerhayes and
Elton, 1923).
    Data and numerous references on bio-
coenoses, communities, and isolated food-link
relationships will be found in Chapter 26 of
this section of the book. The following references give a vast amount of food chain material: general (Brehm, 1911; Lydekker, 1901;
Williams, 1928; Hesse, Allee, and Schmidt,
1937); birds (McAtee, 1932); insects (Brues,
1946; Comstock, 1933; Essig, 1942; Folsom
and Wardle, 1934; Imms, 1924; Metcalf and
Flint, 1939); mammals (Hamilton, 1939; Seton,
1909); vectors and parasites (Belding, 1942;
Herms, 1939; Riley and Johannsen, 1938).
    † McAtee (1947) emphasizes the fact (un-
known to Darwin) that honeybees are important to the pollination of red clover, and

The concept of interdependence of feed-
ing categories has long since lost its novelty.
Darwin, in "The Origin of Species" (1859,
Chap. 3) stated, nearly a century ago:*

"Every one has heard that when an American forest is cut down, a very different vegetation springs up; but it has been observed that
ancient Indian ruins in the Southern United
States, which must formerly have been cleared
of trees, now display the same beautiful diversity and proportions of kinds as in the surrounding virgin forests. What a struggle must
have gone on during long centuries between
the several kinds of trees, each annually scattering its seeds by the thousand; what war between insect and insect—between insects, snails
and other animals with birds and beasts of
prey—all striving to increase, all feeding on
each other, or on the trees, their seeds and
seedlings, or on the other plants which first
clothed the ground and thus checked the
growth of the trees. Throw up a handful of
feathers and all fall to the ground according
to definite laws; but how simple is the problem
where each shall fall compared to that of the
action and reaction of the innumerable plants
and animals which have determined, in the
course of centuries, the proportional numbers
and kinds of trees now growing on the old
Indian ruins!"

This passage by an early ecologist, published a decade before the term was proposed by Haeckel, is prophetically modern
in content. While it lacks the recent co-
emphasis of cooperative agencies operating
with competitive agencies in bringing about
community organization, and the concept of
community self-maintenance, there are several present day viewpoints either implied
or stated. For example, we find in this
quotation (1) retrogressive succession of a
part of a community, with eventual rectification in frequency and density of species;
(2) competition for food; (3) food web;
(4) two of the three basic concepts used
to describe the interplay of species within
a community; and (5) the treatment of
communities as being in a state of flux,
tending, through time, toward a condition
of balance.
    From what has been said of unbalance in
the community, it is obvious that impair-

attacks this Darwinian food chain consequently,
without impairing the general principle exemplified.
    * A. L. Burt reprint from the 6th London
edition, p. 69.

ment of the food web, among other influences, results in loss of equilibrium in the metabolism of the whole community. Unbalance so created first affects a particular food chain, or several closely associated chains, and affects last those parts of the web ecologically farthest from the initial state of unbalance. This may bring to mind the familiar analogy of tossing a pebble into a pond and watching the concentric, ever-widening circles of disturbance on the surface of the water.

This useful analogy is not so applicable as it sounds. In the first place, the disturbance in the pond travels at decreasing force through distance, whereas disturbance in the food web may or may not do so, depending upon numerous influences. For example, if a key organism or key industry is affected, the unbalance will progress at the same, or increasing, force to the limits of the food web. If the community involved is unable to adjust or otherwise ameliorate this initial disturbance, such initial unbalance will destroy the community. Consequently, unlike the pebble-pond analogy, not only the initial force of the disturbances and the initial location of the unbalance in the food web are to be considered, but the ecological importance of the food niche must be appreciated.

This is just as true of large metropolitan communities as it is of a pond or forest. For example, a work stoppage in the manufacture of a luxury food or a relatively minor manufactured article such as hairpins may cause inconvenience. The force of the disturbance (as measured by the number of hairpins available in proportion to the demand for the article) may be dissipated or quickly buffered by adjustment (employment of substitutes) and such an initial economic disturbance may not call forth a vigorous response. On the other hand, if a work stoppage in the production or transportation of a vital fuel or food product occurs, the force is quickly felt by the entire community, and the response is rapid, vigorous, and diverse.

It will also be recalled that impairment or destruction of a link in a food chain affects both adjacent links (p. 372). Consequently the initial disturbance sets in motion two complex stimuli. This is a still further removal from the pebble-pond analogy.

In many recent instances man has created unbalance. One interesting example, in which man served in a dual role of first a link in a primitive food chain and later as an economic link, is described by Haviland (1926) and Elton (1927). In Siberia, in the region of the Yenisei drainage basin and estuary, one of the chains in the food web consists of (1) reindeer moss (a lichen)—(2) reindeer—(3) man. The lichen pastures form the chief food of the reindeer, and these plants influence both the range and abundance of this animal. Siberian man at first was almost wholly dependent upon the reindeer. It afforded him food, hide-clothing, thread from sinews, and needles from sharpened bone splinters. In this chain, man is a simple ecologic link. With the increasing demand for furs, Siberian man increased his occasional killing of arctic foxes to a professional status and, thereby, became a new link in another food chain of the Siberian food web, namely, (1) natural grasses—(2) arctic hare and/or lemming —(3) arctic fox—(4) man. He also served to connect both these chains with the involved economic chain which included the fur markets of such cities as Paris, London and New York. Here Siberian man is more than a food niche. He has become an economic entity, and desires more than reindeer steak. This "more" can be obtained by barter for fox pelts, and certain products of civilization become necessities in his eyes. But the fox population fluctuates with the lemming population as a rule, causing fluctuation in pelt-taking and in the amount of manufactured articles he can buy, and influencing the price of finished fox fur.

Man not only is directly involved in natural food chains, as we have just seen, but he also exerts a profound indirect influence upon natural community food webs in which he does not occupy a feeding niche (Gustafson et al., 1947; DeTurk, 1948; Osborn, 1948; Vogt, 1948). His activities create unbalance in river communities by pollution from sewage (Forbes and Richardson, 1919; Buswell and Boruff, 1931; Thompson, 1931) and from manufacturing wastes. Indiscriminate lumbering upsets the food web of forest communities, and, at the same time, makes available increased space for those grassland plants and animals which can invade such overcut, artificially maintained areas. Farming radically alters the grassland food web by artificially maintaining a dense population of certain cereal grains. With respect to this last point, Howard (1925) has made a classic comment:

"As we bring more and more wild land into cultivation we reduce the numbers and kinds of plants growing on it. We cover each field with the thousands of plants belonging to one species, such as corn, wheat, potatoes or apples. Each hill of corn or potatoes is planted where dozens of wild plants grew before. Insects which formerly had dozens of plants to browse upon now congregate on the few tender ones which have been substituted and often damage or destroy them. The kinds of insects which find the new plants distasteful disappear eventually, while the kinds which can thrive on them continue to multiply as fast as their food supply multiplies until some check is put upon them."

Intensive cultivation of the soil by farming also increases the possibility of dust storms (p. 468) and creates unbalance in both the natural grassland food web and the food web of which the farmer is a part. Such agricultural practices also increase the danger of erosion, which, with fire and destruction of the watershed, must be regarded as an unusually grave danger to community trophic relationships. The general effects of erosion on community relationships have been emphasized recently by Thornthwaite (1940a) in a symposium on the ecology of man.

Another aspect of food webs is that a given species, in the course of its life cycle, occupies a regular sequence of feeding niches or links, and these links may be in the same, or different, food chains in the food web. An example is afforded by the life history of the herring (Hardy, 1924). Very young herring (7 to 12 mm. long) feed upon larval mollusks, ciliate protozoans (*Tintinnopsis*), flagellate protozoans (*Peridinium*), copepods (*Pseudocalanus* and Harpacticidae), and other minute organisms. When the young herring are 12 to 42 mm. long, they feed upon *Pseudocalanus* almost exclusively. As these fish grow larger (42 to 130 mm.) they feed upon *Pseudocalanus*, larvae of barnacles (*Balanus*), larvae of decapods, mysid crustaceans, sagittid worms, and other animals. Finally, the adult herring feeds upon pteropod snails (*Limacina*), a genus of euphausid crustaceans (*Nyctiphanes*), hyperiid amphipods, and numerous copepods (*Temora, Calanus,* and the like).

Consequently we find the herring an important predator on the North Sea plankton, but its ecological position changes with its physiological requirements. On the other hand, its role is that of a plankton feeder throughout. This demonstrates that Elton's concept of the feeding niche, or the ecological feeding category is not necessarily the same thing as a link in a food chain.

For purposes of clarity, the following definitions will be used in the further discussion of the community:

A *food web* (food-cycle of Elton, 1927, p. 56) is the total complex pattern of feeding relations of an independent, self-maintaining major community in the sense of the concept used in this book. This term embodies the Darwinian web of life or "web of complex relations" (Darwin, 1859, p. 68) and has been called a "food-chain" by some authors.

A *food chain* is a linear series of feeders and foods, as discussed previously (p. 508). Such a condition seldom exists, as this would reduce the food web of a community to only a single thread of feeding relationships. The food chain, as used here, refers to a single strand of the whole web.

A *food link* is a taxonomic entity in a food chain; for example, a species or subspecies at a particular stage of its life history. It becomes a food mesh when it is considered in its total relation to the community.

A *food mesh* is a taxonomic entity in a food web; for example a species or subspecies at a particular stage of its life history.

A *food niche* is the feeding role of an organism in a community, and has no fixed taxonomic status. For example, a plankton feeder can be one of a number of species, and this category can be contrasted ecologically through a series of different aquatic communities, or the several plankton feeders of a single community can be directly compared. This is Elton's concept of the "niche" (1927, p. 64); e.g., "the niche of an animal means its place in the biotic environment, its relations to food and enemies." We have broadened this useful term to include plants as well as animals, and have renamed it "food niche" to differentiate it from the "niche" of other authors where the term was used as the home or a part of the physical environment. In this latter sense, the term "habitat niche" has been defined previously (Chap. 26).

A puzzling problem in the study of food webs is the qualitative relationship of several adjacent meshes. One can observe an animal feeding, or examine its stomach contents, or its feces, and may be able to state that this animal was eating, or had eaten, certain foods. The question arises as to the ecologic interpretation of these data, in terms of the food web. This basic question has fathered a long controversy, which is still with us, as to the relative importance, frequency, or significance of general and specific food habits.

A clearly drawn difference of opinion on this question developed in the late 1920's. Elton (1927, p. 47) stated that "it is one of the commonest things in nature to find a herbivorous animal which is attached solely to one plant for food, or for breeding purposes, or for both." Shelford (1929, p. 131) stated that few phytophagous animals "are restricted to one food plant."

Earlier, many students had reported by observation, stomach examination, and feces analysis, on the food of animals (Forbes, 1880, 1882). An analysis of the stomach contents of some 80,000 birds led McAtee (1932) to stress the availability factor as determining the general food habits of animals, especially of birds. McAtee found that his data showed birds to have indiscriminate feeding habits, eating plants and animals in proportion to their relative frequency. Dunn (1935) felt that McAtee's data could be interpreted differently, that birds were not so indiscriminate in their choice of foods as McAtee believed. Hamilton (1940a, 1940b) joined the discussion by finding that McAtee's general view on indiscriminate feeding could be applied to the summer food of the robin and to the food of larval newts (*Triturus viridescens*). In other instances both sides of the argument could be strengthened by material presented in the same investigation. Wolcott (1937), in a thorough study of meadow and pasture in northern New York, found that the robin, twice as abundant as all other birds in the grasslands studied, ate every insect of reasonable size that was available in its habitat. In the same study, Wolcott found that cows did not eat such pasture plants as moss, sorrell, buttercup, Canada thistle, everlasting, lichens, ironweed, bluets, yarrow, St. Johnswort, and moth mullein.

No categorical solution of this problem may be given, since we know only a few feeding habits with reference to the total number of described species. We are certainly a long way from this knowledge. What an animal eats in its food web is not necessarily the same food that it will accept in an unnatural situation. Any unbalance of the web may impose hunger on the occupants of a mesh, and the satisfaction of growing physiological demands will be met often by eating distasteful, even harmful, substances. For example, no one would assume that leather was the diet of mankind, but an uncritical observer might believe this were so were he to see starving snowbound men boiling their belts and moccasins in a last attempt to survive. To a less absurd extent, what animals eat, when confined in a laboratory cage, must be considered with great care before the information can be utilized intelligently. Domesticated animals eat what they are allowed to have. Another striking illustration is found in caterpillars of the corn earworm (*Heliothis armigera*). These normally phytophagous larvae turn cannibalistic when they are confined together without food (Essig, 1942, p. 427). The question, in so far as the community is concerned, is not what an animal will eat, but what does it normally eat as a mesh of the food web.

In the second place, what an individual eats under natural circumstances may or may not be its chief, or only, source of food. Observation or experimentation upon an individual or a group can seldom settle the question rapidly, since the organism or group of organisms forms only a part of a species population (p. 374). Animals of the same species may feed on different meshes at different parts of their life cycle (*vide supra*). They may feed upon different meshes in the same community as a regular feature of their daily life (many animals feed normally upon more than one species of food), upon different meshes of the same community at different seasons of the year, or upon different meshes in different communities within their geographic range (migratory birds). As a general rule, a species population tends to occupy the same food niche during the same stage of its life cycle, but there are variations to this. For example, the brown bear feeds upon salmon when these fish are migrating to their spawning grounds in the spring, and eats berries in the autumn.

In the third place, the food niche determines the meshes upon which a species feeds in a given community. The food niche, however, involves at least two antecedents, namely, heredity and environmental conditioning. The sum total of the adjustments mentioned, therefore, determines what kind of food organisms can be eaten. The nature and extent of such feeding adjustments have been examined (pp. 236–262). Their variability is as great as the diversity of foods in a community. The food niche, then, becomes an ecologic extension of the heredity of a population. Since different species have different heredities, they have different specific requirements, both within the same food niche in ecologically similar species and between different food niches in ecologically dissimilar species.

The total of these inherited adjustments automatically places a species in a particular food niche and, consequently, in a particular place in the food web. This selection by the food web renders a particular species subject to a dual role, that of a food and a feeder.

Within the inherited frame of these requirements we have the entire gamut of feeding habits, for example, from the specific food-feeder relationship of the yucca moth (*Tegeticula alba*)[*] and the yucca (*Yucca filamentosa*), to such omnivores as man, domesticated hogs, and pitcher plants.

Environmental conditioning (p. 352) is a second antecedent affecting the food niche. It has been discussed (p. 615) with reference to Hopkins' host selection principle. This factor may not influence the general character of the niche. With respect to the food web, exposure of immature animals by the parent or parents to a specific food or foods reenforces the selectivity of the food niche, as the ovipositing of species of bu-

[*] Widely known in the literature by another name, *Pronuba yuccasella* (cf. Riley, 1892; Comstock, 1933).

prestid and cerambycid beetles in a single kind of tree or in a few species of trees (Felt, 1905, 1906), and the nest-provisioning habits of many solitary wasps (Peckham and Peckham, 1898) may serve to maintain the qualitative and quantitative aspects of the food web. This, in turn, would aid in autoregulation and self-maintenance of the community at the operational level.

Finally, there is the confusing factor of availability. All the meshes of a food web, if known, would be shown on a diagram of the complete web. Some of these meshes will hold species of low frequency of occurrence (rare species for this particular community); many meshes will have species of moderate frequency; and a few meshes will be crowded with relatively large populations (common species for this particular community). Such complete information for a community never has been accumulated. Important or influential meshes may be unknown in a given sample (Allee, 1930), or the presence or absence of a mesh may be a consequence of the secretive or aggregative tendencies of its occupants. If examination of the stomach of an animal shows it to be crowded with specimens of a single species, at least two explanations occur. First, the animal in question may be able to tolerate physiologically and/or capture a single specific food; that is, it may normally feed on a single mesh. Second, the animal may have a wide range of physiological tolerance and be able to capture and feed upon a great many meshes, only one of which was available.

Frequency of the meshes in a series of related food webs or the relative frequency of individuals of a given mesh, can be analyzed by various methods. Such analysis of interspecies and intraspecies population ecology is essential for a full understanding of the community; frequency spectra (Raunkiaer, 1934) give another dimension to the food web concept.

In any community there is a relation between the life of one trophic level of the food web and that of any other level.

Each mesh of the food web has an average annual reproductive potential in the sense of Chapman (1928). The sum of these mesh potentials within a trophic level equals the reproductive potential for that level, and the sum of the several level potentials equals the reproductive potential of the whole web, that is, of the community.

Such a calculation is of theoretical interest, but is not of practical value, since we lack sufficient autecologic data for most species for calculating the reproductive potential in any but most general terms.

The data available refer to a relatively few well-known species, levels, and communities in which predation has played its role. For example, certain parasites, vectors, and commensals of man and his domesticated allies, and his chief plant and animal foods or sheltering materials offer the best sources of information.

The annual "yield" or "crop" of bushels of corn, or board feet of lumber, or pounds

succeeding level of the web. Hence λ_n is the true productivity, or rate of yield of the trophic level Λ_n.

Following the slow accumulation of information by Birge and Juday concerning Wisconsin lakes, Welch (1935), Juday (1940), Hutchinson (1941), Riley (1941), Clarke (1946), and Clarke et al. (1946), to cite a few references, have discussed this complex problem in terms of yields, annual energy budgets and productivities.

As noted by Lindemann (1942), this annual yield of a trophic level, that is, the total of organic material formed per year (Λ_n), is in reality a value usually uncorrected for dissipation of energy by (1) respiration, (2) predation, and (3) postmortem decomposition (see Table 45). To these

Table 45. Productivity Values for Cedar Bog Lake, Minnesota, in Gram-calories per Square Centimeter per Year (After Lindeman, 1942)

Trophic Level	Uncorrected Productivity +	Respira- tion +	Preda- tion +	Decom- position =	Corrected Produc- tivity
Photosynthetic plants (Λ_1)......	70.4 ± 10.14	23.4	14.8	2.8	111.3
Herbivores (Λ_2)..............	7.0 ± 1.07	4.4	3.1	0.3	14.8
Carnivores (Λ_3)............	1.3 ± 0.43	1.8	0.0	0.0	3.1

Recalculation suggests that respiration of photosynthetic plants should be 29.6, predation 16.4, and corrected productivity 119.2; that respiration of herbivores should be 6.0, and their corrected productivity 16.4. (Courtesy of Dr. L. C. Birch, University of Sidney.)

of beef or of fish per unit area or volume represents a given amount of protoplasm or of protoplasmic products. The annual rate of production of this protoplasm is known as "productivity."

Hutchinson (cf. Lindeman, 1942) considers productivity in terms of the transfer of energy. Using the trophic level symbols $\Lambda_1, \Lambda_2, \ldots \Lambda_n$ discussed previously, he considers any trophic level as receiving energy and disbursing energy. Consequently, the rate of change of energy content in a given level may be considered as having a positive and a negative component:

$$\frac{d\Lambda_n}{dt} = \lambda_n + \lambda_{n'}$$

where λ_n is the positive component and represents the rate of contribution of energy from Λ_{n-1}, the preceding trophic level; $\lambda_{n'}$ is the negative component and represents the sum of the rate of energy lost from Λ_n, or the rate of energy given to Λ_{n+1} or the

we must add energy lost by (4) incomplete assimilation (feces), (5) catabolic wastes other than respiration—e.g., nitrogenous excretory wastes—and (6) heat regulation for homoiothermal animals.

Consideration of energy transfer between trophic levels leads naturally to the question of the biological efficiency of any trophic level, or of the whole community. The efficiency of trophic levels has been studied by Hutchinson (cf. Lindeman, 1942). This author considers the efficiency of productivity of a level (Λ_n) relative to the productivity of any previous level (Λ_m) as:

$$\frac{\lambda_n}{\lambda_m} 100$$

We have here another concept: namely, the efficiency of a part of a community with reference to some other part. It will be noted that productivity is a rate of production, whereas efficiency is a ratio. Lindeman (1942), using Hutchinson's efficiency formula, considers λ_m as referring to the immediately preceding level, so that:

$$\frac{\lambda_n}{\lambda_{n-1}} 100$$

represents a progressive relative efficiency at a given level in terms of relative productivities. This manipulation gives a suggestion of the degree of utilization of the potential source of energy (food supply) for each level of the community (Table 46).

satisfactory comparison of productivity would be rate of production in energetic terms. As in glucose formation, there are too many types of inland waters, too many parts of the sea, and too many kinds of terrestrial communities yet uninvestigated in this respect to make such a comparison extensive or critical.

A useful approach is the admirable summary by Clarke (1946) on production on Georges Bank, in the North Atlantic off

Table 46. Productivities (in g-cal./cm²/year) and Biological Efficiencies (in per cent) for Two American Lakes (Modified from Lindeman, 1942)

Trophic Level	Cedar Bog Lake, Minnesota (after Lindeman 1941, 1942)		Lake Mendota, Wisconsin (Based on Juday, 1940)	
	Corrected Productivity	Biological Efficiency	Corrected Productivity	Biological Efficiency
Solar radiation (λ_0).................	118,872		118,872	
Photosynthetic plants (Λ_1).............	111.3	0.10%	480*	0.40%
Herbivores (Λ_2).....................	14.8	13.3%	41.6	8.7%
Carnivores ($\Lambda_3^{(P_1)}$).................	3.1	22.3%	2.3†	5.5%
Carnivores ($\Lambda_3^{(P_2)}$).................	(not present)		0.3	13.0%

* Lindeman (1942) considers this value too high, and Hutchinson (cf. Lindeman) thinks it may be as low as 250.

† Lindeman (1942) considers this value too low. Possibly this may be a consequence of the presence of large predators.

From a comparison of Tables 45 and 46, an interesting generalization may be made that, within a given community, the biological efficiencies increase as the rates of production, or productivities, decrease. This is seen in Lindeman's study of Cedar Bog Lake, where no large predators (game fishes) are present. It is seen in the much-studied Lake Mendota, where at least two grades of predators are in the level of secondary consumers. There is no reason to suppose that this productivity/efficiency ratio (p/e) is not universal for major communities in approximate biotic balance. We propose that this relationship be termed the Lindeman ratio, inasmuch as it was derived from his careful work. So far, confirmation is lacking for marine and terrestrial communities.

Previously, several types of communities were contrasted in terms of glucose production per unit area (Table 44). A more

the coast of Massachusetts. Three million gram-calories of energy fall on each square meter of sea surface per day on Georges Bank. The diatoms of the phytoplankton utilize a portion of this energy in photosynthesis, and their maximum efficiency calculated from the rate of diatom production is 0.3 per cent. In turn, the zooplankton feed upon the diatoms, obtaining their solar energy at second hand, and their maximum efficiency calculated from the rate of zooplankton production is about 0.015 per cent. Finally, fishes feed upon zooplankton directly in part, and indirectly in fish-eating species. The weight of whole fishes landed annually from the ten million acres of Georges Bank, between 1923 and 1945, ranged from a minimum of sixty-three million pounds (1934) to a maximum of 289 million pounds (1929). In terms of yield, this represents a production of 7 to 33 pounds per acre per year. In terms of energy, assuming an energy content of 740 gram-calories/gram of fresh raw fish, this production is equivalent to 1.0 to 7.7 gram-calories per square meter per day. In terms of utilization of solar radiation, this represents an efficiency of 0.00005 per cent to 0.00025 per cent.

In summary, Clarke's data present the following efficiencies on Georges Bank:

per cent. These general relations are shown in Figure 171.

Several general principles may be suggested, if the assumption is made that these efficiencies are relatively similar for communities in general: (1) Efficiency of producers (A_1), whether diatoms or maple trees, is low with respect to their utilization of the total radiant energy available; (2)

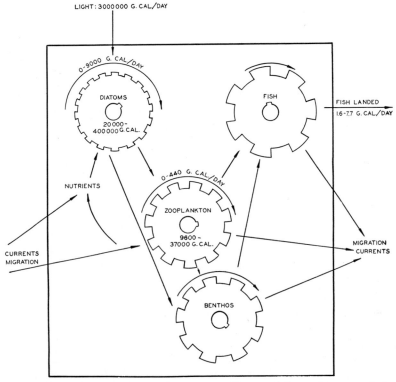

Fig. 171. Productivities within a community as illustrated by a diagram of the relations on Georges Bank. The values given are for the whole bank per square meter of sea surface. Maximum and minimum values within the cogwheels are for the standing crop, those over the wheels are for net production rate. (After Clarke.)

average, incident light, 100 per cent; diatoms, 0.3 per cent; zooplankton, 0.015 per cent; fishes, 0.00025 per cent.

These data accord with those of other investigators. For example, Juday (1940) calculated that fish production in Lake Mendota was at the rate of 19 pounds per acre per year, which is similar to the production on Georges Bank of from 7 to 33 pounds per acre per year. Again, Riley (1941) estimated the mean efficiency of net plant production in Long Island Sound at 0.31 per cent, which is similar to the diatom efficiency on Georges Bank of 0.3

rates of production decrease rapidly from lower to higher trophic levels; (3) efficiency of energy utilization decreases rapidly from lower to higher trophic levels; and (4) the extrapolation of the Lindeman ratio.

The subject of production is a basic one in the metabolism of the community, and deserves a great deal of future attention, particularly with respect to species populations. Seldom do we have production rate calculated in energetic terms for a single species, as has been done for field corn (Table 43). Instead our information is re-

stricted usually to trophic levels (Tables
44, 45, 46) in terms of glucose produced
or energy values for many different species,
each with its specific potentiality. Such
wholly understandable lumping of meshes
in the food web may hide important academic or practical principles.

Mathematical treatment of energy budgets (Juday, 1940) and efficiencies at various community levels (Krogh, 1934;
Riley, 1941, 1941a, 1944) are signs of
progress in the field of ecological theory.

respect to either individuals or species, this
fundamental relationship between size and
numbers exists for the overwhelming majority of plants and animals.

Many organisms are prolific. There are
many more seeds, spores, and eggs produced than germinate or hatch (pp. 236–
243). Furthermore, to attain sexual maturity, the hazards of the inanimate and
animate portions of the community environment must be evaded. This tends to augment greatly the numbers of organisms of

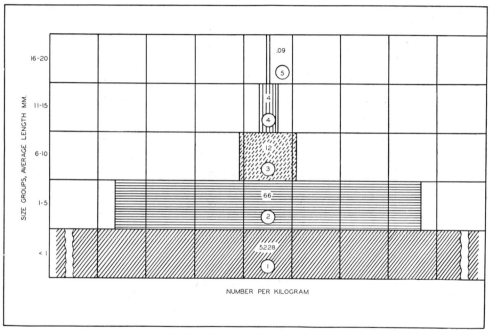

Fig. 172. Pyramid of numbers of the metazoan fauna of the forest floor stratum of Carlé
Woods, Cook County, Illinois. (From Park, Allee, and Shelford.)

Clarke, Edmondson, and Ricker (1946)
have provided a mathematical formulation
of biological productivity that may be developed for particular species populations.

When adult organisms of a community
are counted and measured, or even when
a representative sample of the community
is so studied, it is found that, in general,
the numbers of individuals present are inversely proportional to their body sizes.
Since each species population tends to
fluctuate about a mean body size, this
quantitative survey also demonstrates that
there is a progressive increase in body size
with a progressive decrease in population
size of the species present. Consequently,
whether the community is examined with

small size and to decrease the numbers of
the relatively larger organisms.

The differential in maturing of developmental life history stages, as well as seasonal and day-night intercommunity and
interstratal movements, tends to complicate
this simple picture with respect to the animals present. Periodic movements are discussed in the next chapter.

Such tendencies provide the background
for one of the more striking concepts in
community ecology, namely, the pyramid
of numbers. This is not a new concept. It
can be inferred from the 1887 essay of
Forbes and was given definite form by Elton (1927, p. 69).

When put in a graph, with size groups

on the vertical coördinate, and numbers of organisms on the horizontal coördinate, a triangular figure, now commonly known as the pyramid of numbers, is the result. In Figures 172 and 173 typical pyramids of the macroscopic invertebrates of the forest floor litter, in two widely separated communities, are examples of this concept.

The Eltonian pyramid serves to clarify and coördinate a number of aspects of community food relationships. It represents the

able, and (2) that the predator had the necessary feeding adjustments to collect and eat the food while staying within the margin of expendable energy. For example, from a biochemical point of view, a muskellunge might be able to thrive on ameba protoplasm; from a physiological point of view, the expenditure of energy required to obtain this protoplasm would be fantastic contrasted to the energy yield of the food; from the ecological viewpoint, this fish has

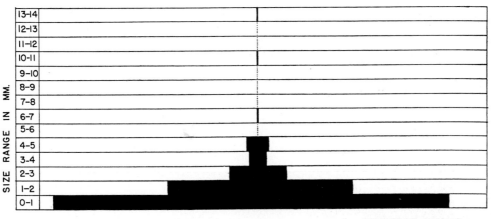

Fig. 173. Pyramid of numbers of the metazoan fauna of the forest floor stratum of the tropical forest on Barro Colorado Island, Panama Canal Zone. Based on quadrats 25 cm. square. (From Williams.)

food web in a quantitative sense, and its geometric configuration serves to accentuate the size groups in the community. These size groups may or may not be similar to the food niches and to the trophic levels present, depending upon the type of investigation undertaken, but such groupings do give another aspect to frequency.

Such pyramids are the natural result of two tendencies, (1) that smaller animals have a higher reproductive potential than larger animals as a rule, and (2) that smaller animals usually are the prey of larger animals.

The pyramid of numbers is especially applicable to predators.

Organisms expend energy to obtain nourishment. As between animals, any predator could probably be nourished by a variety of species-protoplasms if the latter could be obtained in sufficient amounts. This would imply (1) that food was avail-

no special adjustment to enable it to feed upon ameba protoplasm in sufficient amounts, and this large, fresh-water predator must obtain its food in larger pieces to conserve energy and grow. The muskellunge must feed upon the next size group or so in the food web, and so obtain its protozoan protoplasm at third or fourth hand or more.

Where a predator has special adjustments for obtaining certain foods, much more specific feeding relationships are possible, and several size groups in the pyramid may be eliminated. For instance, the aye-aye (*Chiromys madagascariensis*) hunts for beetle grubs that it finds beneath the bark of trees in the forests of Madagascar. After gnawing away the bark, it obtains the larvae by inserting its attenuated middle finger into their burrows (Fig. 174). Here the size differential between predator and prey is less exceptional than that of the anteaters. These mammals open

Fig. 174. Drawing of the hand of an aye-aye. Note the attenuated middle finger.

stout ant and termite nests with their fore-paws and can concentrate their insect food on their long, cylindrical tongue.

The availability of food is also related to the size of the animal. Other things being equal, larger animals not only eat larger pieces of food, but also quarter more ter-

portionately large area in relation to their body size.

In a small sample of forest floor leaf mold, say 2 kg. wet weight, there may be 10,000 herbivorous oribatid mites, 2000 herbivorous collembolans, and one preda-ceous pselaphid beetle. Most of these arth-ropods are minute (0.5 to 1.5 mm.) at maturity, but cover different amounts of territory at different speeds. Whereas the mites must crawl, most of the collembolans can leap, and the beetle can crawl or fly.

Reproduction also influences range and is indirectly a factor in the size and shape of the pyramid of numbers. Every nonpar-thenogenetic female must be near enough to a male to ensure fertilization within his and her life span, if they are to be instru-ments in perpetuation of the species. Par-thenogenetic species are not so restricted, but even these usually require fertilization of their ova at the approach of adverse physical conditions. This is common in roti-

Fig. 175. The paddlefish (*Polyodon spathula*) feeding on daphnids. (Courtesy of the John G. Shedd Aquarium.)

ritory to find it. Thus a grizzly bear may range over 40 square miles, a red squirrel over 5 acres, a vole over 1000 square feet, and a leaf mold mite over a few square inches.

Range, then, indirectly affects the pyra-mid of numbers, and territory is partially affected by method of locomotion. Volant animals, such as birds, may cover a dispro-

fers and aphids (p. 275) and has been carefully analysed for cladocerans by Banta (1939).

There are numerous exceptions to the size/numbers ratio of the food web. Most are apparent rather than real.

For example, the whale-bone whales and the paddlefish (*Polyodon spathula*) are dis-proportionately large in relation to the size of their food. These species are exceptions in so far as normal size relations between predator and prey are concerned. The exceptional relations arc made possible since both are specialized plankton-feeders (Fig. 175) with structural adaptations for concentrating their food.

Large ungulate grazers (bison, cattle) and browsers (giraffe), and omnivores such as man,* have bodies that are disproportionately large compared with the size of much of their food. As noted previously, the pyramid of numbers is especially applicable to predators (secondary consumers) and to the myriads of minute plants and animals at the base of the pyramid (many primary consumers and all tertiary and quaternary consumers).

Consequently size of food, amount of food, availability of food, structural and functional feeding adjustments (pp. 239–262), territory, methods of locomotion, breeding requirements, and shifts in populations (Chap. 28) between strata and between different communities are involved in the pyramid of numbers, either directly with respect to size-number ratio or indirectly.

Large numbers of organisms, especially in the lower levels of the pyramid, may not contribute directly to the pyramid succession. Many die without having been consumed, and serve as food for organisms in still lower levels.

The broad outlines of the pyramid of numbers are fairly obvious, but many aspects require critical future investigation.

Within the normal range of foods at a given level of the pyramid, the size of the

---

* Among omnivores, man is a conspicuous example, and his feeding habits may be conditioned by a variety of operating influences. For example, the Solomon Islanders of Malaita, an island on which the natives of the interior are still entirely free from government control, were formerly and arc otill to some extent sharply divided into the yam-growing tribes of the interior and the sea-going and fishing tribes of the coast. Their separation was so much accentuated by head-hunting raids that the coastal people lived on fortified offshore islets. This isolating custom was broken by a regular periodic truce of a day, when the two groups met on the coast to exchange their respective special food-stuffs. These data rest on the report to the Crane Pacific Expedition from the resident government officials in 1929. (See Shurcliff, 1930, *Jungle Islands,* p. 177.)

specific foods, as well as their population density, affects the consumer. Loosanoff and Engle, 1947, have shown that in experimental feeding of the oyster (*Ostrea virginica*) there are rather definite concentrations of food above which the density of the micro-organisms begins to interfere with the oyster's feeding. These authors found that the critical concentrations that allowed relatively undisturbed feeding corresponded to 2,000,000 *Chlorella* sp., 70,000 *Nitzschia closterium,* and 3000 *Euglena viridis* per cubic centimeter of water. Hence size of food is associated with density of food in this and similar cases. That is, many more minute organisms, such as *Chlorella,* were needed to produce the same effect as that caused by *Euglena.*

The basic energy relations of the pyramid of numbers have been described by Lindeman (1942) in terms of productivity:

$$\lambda_0 > \lambda_1 > \lambda_2 \cdots \lambda_n$$

There is much to be desired from an over-all study of the pyramid of numbers of a community. So far no community has been analyzed completely with reference to the body sizes and numbers of individuals for each mesh composing the food web. In view of taxonomic difficulties, the labor involved in counting populations, and the lack of information on parasites and the minute organisms which live in each stratum, no complete pyramid is likely to become available in the near future.

An average community population is generally in a state of flux, involving seasonal, twenty-four hours, and other population cycles (p. 366; Chap. 28), shifts across its boundaries in intercommunity migrations, emigrations, and accidental straying. Such a population is affected by, and affects, the inanimate physical and animate biological portions of its area.

Another quantitative approach to an understanding of the food web is the concept of biomass, or weight of a species population per unit area. Walter Pickles (1937) effectively used this term in a study of the ant *Acanthomyops flavus,* in which it was found that this species had a weight of 0.008 gm./square meter of territory, and of 7.037 gm./nest, over a census area of 880.51 square meters.

The following year, Bodenheimer (1938) noted that the total weight of plant production (producers) was greater than that of the herbivores (primary consumers) of an area, and the total weight of the latter must be greater than that of the total predators (secondary consumers).

Biomass data for domesticated animals and agriculturally important plant species are available, as are data on a variety of organisms computed on less than an annual crop basis.* Table 47 is an example of a standing crop analysis in terms of weight of animals per unit area.

pounds per acre of lake; allowing for the few small specimens which escaped through the meshes of the seine, Juday (1938) estimated the total fish biomass at about 365 pounds per acre for the period of investigation.

Community analyses involving biomasses are destined to become more important. Hutchinson (1943b), in a philosophical discussion of food, time, and culture in the anthropological sense, is concerned with the comparison of communities in general with man's societies. He observes that it is usually possible to study any system S from

Table 47. Fish Biomass of Lake Wingra, Wisconsin, on November 15 and 18, 1936 (After Juday, 1938)

Kinds of Fishes	Numbers Caught	Total Weight in Pounds	Pounds per Acre (Biomass)
Carp	6000	41,850	209.0
Buffalo fish	652	1300	6.5
Gar fish	2500	3500	17.5
Black bass	1100	1600	8.0
Wall-eyed pike	1000	1500	7.5
Sunfish	20,000	6600	33.0
Crappies	40,000	13,300	66.0
White bass	1500	1900	9.5
Totals	72,752	71,550	357.0

This table is of interest. Lake Wingra is shallow, with a maximum depth of 14 feet and only a small part of its 200 acre area over 10 feet deep. A small-meshed seine was used, long enough to stretch entirely across the lake and deep enough to cover the entire depth of water. The study involved the almost complete removal of fishes from the lake, that is, the removal of almost the entire population of secondary consumers of higher grades (large predators), and many primary consumers (herbivores). The total fish crop was 357

* There is a substantial amount of information on partial biomasses and data for computing the food necessary to maintain an individual animal. The interested reader will find such values for many domesticated animals and cultivated plants in the U. S. Department of Agriculture Yearbook for 1939, for limnological studies in Chapman (1931), for forest snails in Foster (1937) and Strandine (1941), for arthropods of the forest floor litter in Lunn (1939) and Williams (1941), and for grassland invertebrates in Wolcott (1937).

two general viewpoints: (1) the holological, in which energy and matter changes across the system's boundaries are observed, and (2) the merological, in which the behavior of individual systems of lower order than S are examined. Here the biomass is thought of as a total community weight per unit of area, consisting of many different intracommunity biomasses.

The original concept of biomass was the weight of a species population per unit of area. This will be called species biomass (b); the total biomass of a community will be called community biomass (B). Community biomass is composed of the sum of many species biomasses that compose the meshes of the food web, and whose populations make up the pyramid of numbers. Such species biomasses may be treated as separate populations. They may be computed for separate infracommunity levels—for example, stratum biomass, habitat-niche biomass, trophic level biomass, and the like.

Community biomass is important. It is closely associated with the productivity of the community, with its biological efficiency as compared with other communities of the same type, and as compared with communities of different types.

We have no complete biomass data for a given community, and will not have until the food web is known and the pyramid worked out. We are especially in need of organic matter in four Wisconsin lakes (Fig. 176). In this investigation it was found that the plants in two hard-water lakes weighed from three to five times as much as the plants of two soft-water lakes, and that the soft-water lakes had about one-fourth as many species of large aquatic plants as the hard-water communities.

This is an interesting conclusion. It shows again that the inanimate, physical part

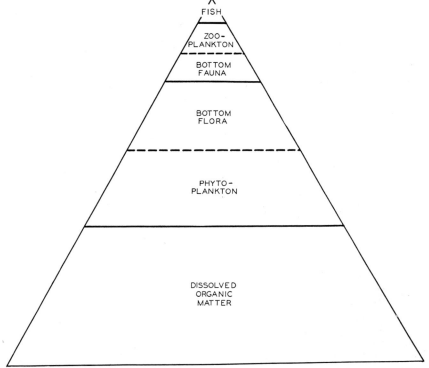

Fig. 176. Diagram of biomass and dissolved organic material in Weber Lake, Wisconsin. The weight of each constituent is proportional to the total area of the triangle. The original diagram was on a scale of 1 kilogram/hectare = 4.9 sq. mm. of graph paper. (From Juday.)

a single, complete biomass. Not only (1) is there a great deal of taxonomy involved before the equation: $b_1 + b_2 + b_3 \cdots + b_n = B$ is solved, but we are in need of information concerning (2) the several biomasses of the several life history stages of each species, and (3) the biomasses of parasites in relation to those of their hosts. A sufficient body of such data can then be used to great theoretical advantage.

At present one of the best approaches to community biomass is that of Juday (1942), in which the weight of the summer standing crop of plants and animals was estimated and related to the dissolved of the community is a material influence in regulating the biological part of the community. This has been stressed in the chapter on stratification. In the study by Juday we see the striking effect of the chemical composition of the medium upon the biomass at the first trophic level.

Excluding the fishes, the animal population of the hard-water lakes weighed two to three times that of the animal populations of the soft-water lakes. This is to be expected, since the primary consumers would be directly affected by the biomass of the producers, and the secondary consumers accordingly affected by the biomass of the primary consumers.

Juday reported that, excluding the fishes, the ratio of the plant biomass to the animal biomass was 7.3 to 7.5 for the soft-water lakes, and 12.1 to 22.2 for the hard-water lakes. In other words (p. 133) "the soft water lakes were approximately two to three times as efficient in converting their plant material into animals as the hard water lakes." This conclusion should have future value in biomass studies, since it brings out the corollary that, as between communities, higher biomass does not necessarily imply higher biotic efficiency.

In preceding pages the major community has been defined (Chap. 25), and its structure (Chap. 26) and metabolism (Chap. 27) have been examined. The following chapter carries the analysis a step further. That is, we shall be concerned with the periodic disposition of matter and energy within and across the boundaries of communities.

28. COMMUNITY ORGANIZATION: PERIODISM

In general terms, the major phenomena of the earth are cyclic. There are geological rhythms in erosion and in deposition (Wanless, 1938). Study of the annual growth rings of trees discloses evidence of cycles of climate over the last few thousand years (Huntington, 1914; Douglass, 1928); the evidence from varves is even better for late Pleistocene and early post-Pleistocene (Antevs, 1925). There is a rather confusing body of evidence relating to the positive or negative correlation of sun spot cycles (pp. 85–87) to a variety of earthly events, such as annual precipitation, bird migration (Clements and Shelford, 1939), and various other activities (Pearse, 1939). There are well-defined cycles in climate, environmental factors (p. 87), and in population phenomena (p. 366). Communities have extensive and complex seasonal rhythms, lunar and tidal rhythms, and many periodicities associated with the cycle of day and night. Within communities, there are almost countless periodicities of the constituent plants and animals, at the organismal level, that are results of both environmental and physiological rhythms.

In the present chapter we are concerned with periodic community responses. Such concern is both intracommunity and intercommunity in scope.

We are now in a better position to examine certain activities of the interdependent species populations at the level of the relatively independent major community. Such temporal activities may be discussed conveniently in terms of (1) seasonal, (2) lunar, and (3) diel or daily phenomena.

SEASONAL ASPECTS OF THE COMMUNITY

The majority of communities have a rhythmic, seasonal sequence of changes in at least some parts of their structure. This sequence is generally coördinated with, and in large part induced by, the rhythmic seasonal sequence of change in the duration, or intensity, or quality of certain basic physical influences, such as light, temperature, and precipitation operating differentially over latitude and altitude (see pp. 89, 93, 207).

Changes of seasonal character in the animate portion of the community reflect the operation of one or more of the following phenomena (Fig. 177): (1) direct action by one or more of the basic physical influences upon organisms (b); (2) direct action of the secondary physical influences —for example, density or rate of evaporation, induced by action of the basic physical factors, upon organisms (d); (3) direct action of the basic physical influences upon the inanimate medium of the community (a); (4) direct action of the secondary physical influences upon the inanimate medium of the community (e). Such direct and indirect induction of community activity upon a seasonal framework may be augmented or reenforced by (5) the endogenous rhythms of seasonal activity in certain of the component species populations of certain communities.

Our information of this fifth category of activity is less precise since such endogenous patterns are more or less in step with the seasonal march of the operating influences. Such coördination must exist in communities having a seasonal rhythm in the physical portion of environment, if the component species populations are to survive, and flourish. Consequently selection operates at the community level, as well as at the populational and organismal levels, for, although the relatively self-sustaining com-

fluences are suggested by arrows, the width of which indicates their relative community value. Nevertheless, it must be remembered that each operating influence is subject to seasonal variation in the communities being discussed at this time.

Such seasonal variations enormously complicate the community concept. Aside

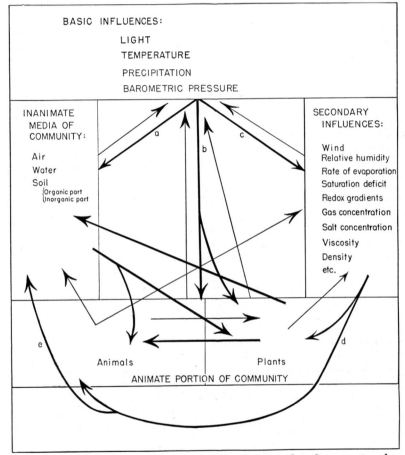

BASIC INFLUENCES:

LIGHT

TEMPERATURE

PRECIPITATION

BAROMETRIC PRESSURE

INANIMATE
MEDIA OF
COMMUNITY:

Air
Water
Soil
   [Organic part
   [Inorganic part

SECONDARY
INFLUENCES:

Wind
Relative humidity
Rate of evaporation
Saturation deficit
Redox gradients
Gas concentration
Salt concentration
Viscosity
Density
etc.

Animals   Plants
ANIMATE PORTION OF COMMUNITY

Fig. 177. Seasonal variable in most communities: direct and indirect action by primary, secondary, and tertiary influences on the animate and inanimate environment.

munity is independent of adjacent communities for survival in a periodic environment, its totality of adjustment is an integrated response of its components. This is one of the points of contact between the almost continuous selection of behavior, function, and structure which takes place in nature.

At present, we must not lose sight of the complex interactions between parts of the community. This interplay is shown partially in Figure 177. Here, important in-

from the obvious and fundamental rhythmic seasonal changes in temperate latitudes in the magnitude of both basic and secondary physical factors, the apparent, over-all seasonal changes affect different types of communities differently. Thus the inanimate medium of fresh-water communities is reactive to lowering of air temperature, followed in certain latitudes by freezing of the upper strata, wholly or in part; the most obvious change in terrestrial communities is the effect upon the animate portion of the community, as evidenced by the onset of defoliation in temperate deciduous forests; whereas the marine community is less apparently changed, since the open sea freezes only at high latitudes, and the organisms are not more obvious than the liquid medium, save for highly local concentrations of plants and animals.

Furthermore, even within a limited area the seasonal changes affect the resident communities differently. Different types of communities have an inherently differential response to the physical influences operating equally upon all of them. This differential response is a consequence of the totality of the adjustments of the interdependent species populations of each community to the occupied habitat niches.

Certain interesting points emerge. As we have seen, there are three basic drives in the life cycle of an animal, namely, reproduction, sheltering, and hunger. In a seasonal environment, such as we are discussing at this point, the broad outlines of each of these drives are on a seasonal basis; such aspects are generally qualitative. On the other hand, the day to day satisfaction of these drives is usually more specific and quantitative.

For example, most species have one or more definite periods of copulation. Such mating periods are correlated with seasons of the year, but the copulation is usually limited to the day or the night, depending upon the species population involved.

As to sheltering, the seasonal aspects are broad adjustments to adverse weather (migration, hibernation, aestivation), whereas the day to day aspect is concerned with regular periods of physiological recuperation in relatively sheltered habitat niches. Again, this daily rest is usually either nocturnal or diurnal.

The seasonal shift in dict is correlated directly with the growth, leafing-out, flowering, and fruiting of food plants in the herbivores, and indirectly so correlated in the carnivorous animals. Figure 178 illustrates seasonal shift in diet of the omnivorous raccoon, as different foods become available.

At the community level the satisfaction of these three basic drives by the numerous constituents forms a highly complex, overlapping mosaic of seasonal activities. Each type of community responds in a

characteristic manner to the changing rhythm of its physical and biological environment.

Another important point is that the majority of species that comprise any given community are full-time annual residents, or nearly so. Since this is the case in communities located in seasonal, as well as aseasonal environments, the general re-

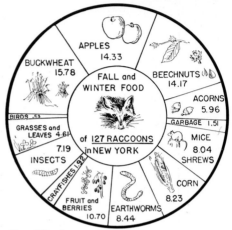

Fig. 178. Seasonal shift of available foods in the diet of the omnivorous raccoon. (After Hamilton.)

sponse to regular periods of cold or drought is that of adjustment to the adverse conditions, rather than emigration or migration.

When attention is focussed upon the seasonal abundance of organisms, or upon the seasonal abundance of particular aspects of their life history, within a particular community (Allee, 1911; Petersen, 1926), the term *"seasonal succession"* is frequently used to describe the concept. Such studies may refer to events in a particular habitat niche or to a series of equivalent niches, or to a stratum or to the whole community.

The concept of seasonal succession is not to be confused with the concept of community succession.

Clements (1905) used the term *"aspect"* to signify the seasonal impress on a community; for example, the spring aspect or the winter aspect. Later, Clements (1916, p. 130) and Tansley and Chipp (1926, p. 16) broadened this usage of aspect to include the seasonal changes within a community, especially botanical features such as the vegetative development and flowering of species of plants at certain times of the year. Nichols (1923, p. 14) changed the term to *aspection*. Aspection is equivalent to seasonal succession, if both botanical and zoological events are used. Such a general view was later espoused by Beklemischev (1931) under the term *"annual cycles,"* and as *aspection* by Carpenter (1938, p. 27), and Clements and Shelford (1939), and as either *aspection or seasonal succession* by Park, Allee, and Shelford (1939, p. 18).

Another term closely associated with seasonal succession is *phenology*. Phenology, a word already well established, was used by Shelford (1929, p. 4) to embrace the study of correlation between periodic phenomena—for example, the flowering of certain plants and the arrival of migratory birds and mammals. Later the Ecological Society of America (Committee on Nomenclature, 1935) defined phenology as that science that deals with the time of appearance of characteristic periodic events in the life cycles of organisms under natural conditions, especially those events influenced by temperature, latitude, and altitude, among other influences in the physical environment.

One of the comprehensive phenological analyses is that of Leopold and Jones (1947) for Sauk and Dane counties, Wisconsin. They analyzed 328 seasonal events, including blooming of forest, grassland, and sand area herbaceous strata, weeds, and marsh plants, fruiting of shrub and tree strata, and the dates of emergence from hibernation of local mammals and the migration data of a variety of birds. The period analyzed was the decade 1935 to 1945, for two localities some thirty miles apart. It was found that the year-to-year variability of phenological events, as compared with their own averages, tends to be greatest in early spring, and decreases progressively through May.

Certain plants showed little variability in date of first blooming, and appeared to be governed more by length of daylight than by current weather. Thus white clover, with a standard deviation of 2.4 days, was the least variable of the plants studied.

Similarly, certain birds showed little variability in arrival date of the vernal migration. For example, the rose-breasted grosbeak had a standard deviation of 3.1 days, and the upland plover of 3.2 days.

Leopold and Jones noted that bird migration responded more quickly to temperature changes than did the blooming of plants.

Correlation of stages in the life history of organisms with regular changes in the basic and secondary physical influences of the environment is usually direct with most plant constituents of a community, and either direct or indirect for animal constituents. An example of this sensitive relationship is found in the marine littoral portion of the north temperate Atlantic Ocean. Here (Russell and Yonge, 1928, p. 51) occurs a series of species of periwinkles that apparently have a critical stage of their life history directly correlated with the nature of their immediate habitat. The species of periwinkle that live nearest to the low-water tide mark hatch out in an early larval stage as swimmers; the species nearest the center of the intertidal zone appears in a later swimming stage; the species living near the high-water mark has young that are essentially like the adult in behavior, and can crawl over exposed rocks at once. In this example, tidal rhythm is used in the analysis.

The annual cycle of events within a community may be divided into a series of seasonal periods, each period characterized by certain more or less specific seasonal (phenological) phenomena. The periods of the year defined, in whole or in part, by Smith (1928), Shackleford (1929), Bird (1930), Davidson (1932), Carpenter (1938), Davis (1945), Rice (1946), Jones (1946), and others, are: prevernal, vernal, aestival (estival), serotinal, autumnal, and hibernal (hiemal). The first two periods correspond roughly to the spring, the next two to the summer, and the last two to the autumn and winter, respectively.

It must be remembered that latitude and altitude are obviously of primary importance in the seasonal periodicity of any community. In the county of Teresopolis, Rio de Janeiro, Brazil, the annual cycles of periodicity in flowering and fruiting of trees and life history events of certain mosquitoes, birds, and mammals (Davis, 1945) suggest the following division of the year: prevernal (August and September), vernal (October and November), aestival (December and January), serotinal (February and March), autumnal (April and May), and hibernal (June, July, and early August). In this area there are two peaks of flowering: a prevernal peak in August, and an aestival-serotinal peak from December to March.

types of communities. Only then can the data be surveyed as a whole and a global view of seasonal periodicity be placed on a sound statistical basis.

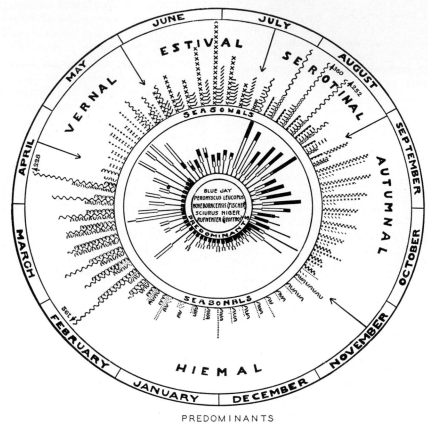

PREDOMINANTS

BLUE JAY (CYANOCITTA CRISTATA)
PEROMYSCUS LEUCOPUS NOVEBORACENSIS (FISCHER)
SCIURUS NIGER RUFIVENTER (GEOFFROY)

|| CARYCHIUM EXIGUUM (SAY)
▮ DICYPHUS GRACILENTUS PARSH.
| ERYTHRONEURA OBLIQUA SAY

SEASONALS

VERNAL SOCIETY	ESTIVAL SOCIETY	SEROTINAL SOCIETY
EPITRIX FUSCULA CROT.	= MANGORA GIBBEROSA HTZ.	BRACHYPTERUS URTICAE (FAB.)
GLYPTINA SPURIA LEC.	× PSEUDOGRIPHONEURA CREVECOEURI COQ.	DIAPHEROMERA FEMORATA (SAY)
GONGYLIDIELLUM PALLIDUM EM.	SAPROMYZOSOMA PHILADELPHICA MACQ.	= MANGORA GIBBEROSA HTZ.
PARASITUS SP.		PARASITUS SP.
PHRUROLITHUS PALUSTRIS BKS.		

AUTUMNAL SOCIETY	HIEMAL SOCIETY
PHYLLOTRETA SINUATA STEPH.	EPITRIX FUSCULA CROT.
PHYTONOMUS NIGRIROSTRIS FAB.	JUNCO (JUNCO HYEMALIS)
XYSTICUS SP.	TREE SPARROW (SPIZELLA MONTICOLA)
	TELEPHANUS VELOX HALD.

Fig. 179. Seasonal periodicity in numbers of animals in a red oak-elm-sugar maple forest community in central Illinois. (After Smith.)

Roughly six months after each flowering period there is a fruiting period.

Such a seasonal picture is related to many complex, interacting climatic and local influences. We are greatly in need of many seasonal studies in all parts of the world, at various altitudes, and in many different

Turning to an example in the north temperate region, the contrasts are notable. Smith (1928) studied the seasonal succession in several types of communities in central Illinois, and found that seasonal rhythms could be detected by the annual recurrence of groups of species in each community. This investigation included a study of seasonal succession in an elm-sugar maple forest during 1925–1926. Later, Jones (1946) added to data gathered on this forest between 1933 and 1938. Table 48 contrasts the seasonal

of habitat niches which age relatively rapidly—for example, cattle dropping in the prairie communities (Mohr, 1943), and many soft fungi (Park, 1931a) in forest communities. Figure 180 illustrates such a rapid seasonal succession in the populations

Table 48. Seasonal Succession in an Elm-Sugar Maple Forest Community in Central Illinois

Seasonal Period	Duration for Year 1925–1926 (after Smith, 1928)	General Duration for Years 1933–1938 (after Jones, 1946)	Seasonal Events (after Jones, 1946)
Autumnal....	IX.6 to XI.1	IX.1 to X.31	Migration into forest floor and subterranean strata
Hibernal.....	XI.1 to IV.26	XI.1 to II.28	Hibernation of most invertebrate populations
Prevernal.....		III.1 to IV.14	Activity of lycosid and thomisid spiders
Vernal........	IV.26 to V.29	IV.15 to V.31	Vertical and horizontal migration of many invertebrates into the herbaceous and shrub strata
Aestival......	V.29 to VII.19	VI.1 to VII.14	Appearance of many flies; vertical movement of many flies and ants into upper strata
Serotinal.....	VII.19 to IX.6	VII.15 to VIII.31	Appearance of many young spiders and mirid bugs

pictures of the same community obtained by these two reports.

Seasonal periodicity is illustrated by a seasonal diagram of a red oak-sugar maple-elm forest (Fig. 179). This diagram of the seasonal fluctuation of species populations is typical of the majority of communities, in so far as the general concept is concerned. Naturally there are exceptional circumstances or variations to be expected. In most communities certain species are dominant as to abundance in one year, and the following year occupy a less important statistical position. Again, unusual severity of weather will retard the seasonal succession. Injury to the community may impair or wholly alter the successional sequence. Furthermore, many small forms, such as diatoms, regularly have two or more maxima of reproduction within a single growing period; such species usually have brief life cycles.

Within a given community each well-defined type of habitat may undergo seasonal succession. At times this sequence is difficult to analyze, as the seasonal sequence may be progressively modified by the seral or ecological succession taking place simultaneously. This is especially true

of a soft fungus (*Hydnum septentrionale*). In this graph, on two successive years, the

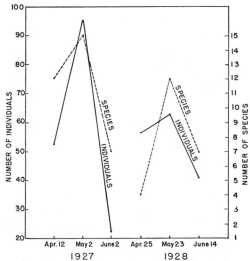

Fig. 180. Seasonal periodicity of the beetle populations in a fungus (*Hydnum septentrionale*) with respect to individuals and species. (After O. Park.)

species and individuals were recorded for two separate specimens of fungi. In each case, both number of mycetocolous species and the peak of population density were reached in the same forests during May, regardless of age of the particular fungus involved.

For many plant constituents phenological correlation is the result of a direct influence by physical factors, since their photosynthesis (Chap. 27) is partially dependent upon intensity of light. Animals show direct behavioral response to such influences as light, temperature, and precipitation, as well as indirect responses. These latter are less easily studied. Many indirect correlations occur with food plants, and many contacts are made between community response and the rhythmic phenomena of photoperiodicity (p. 121), in which adjustments of plants and animals are made to the relative lengths of day and night (Garner and Allard, 1920; Kellerman, 1926; Rowan, 1926; Schick, 1932). Any annual response by plants to physical factors is indirectly related to herbivores, and still more indirectly related to parasites and predators.

This relationship was put nicely by Chapman (1920, p. 179): "Herbivorous beetles . . . dependent upon growing plant tissue for their food may be said to have the factors of food and climatic conditions more or less merged into one. Conditions which favor the growth of plants favor the food supply, and thus the growth and development of the beetles." Applied to the concept under examination, this suggests that there is a definite, although indirect, correlation between light and the herbivores of a given community, or series of communities at a given latitude and altitude. Such indirect relationships have been demonstrated between the flowering of plants and their insect visitors (Robertson, 1889, 1928, 1929). Numerous indirect correlations are found in such diverse phenomena as the seasonal appearance of species of beetles in the vicinities of Prague (Fritsch, 1851, 1851a), and Chicago (Park, 1930), in the production of zoöplankton off the coast of Massachusetts (Clarke and Zinn, 1937), in the seasonal fluctuations of algae, rotifers, and cladocerans in Colorado lakes (Pennak, 1946), of rotifer productivity (Edmondson, 1946), of cyclomorphosis in *Daphnia* (Brooks, 1946), in the seasonal distribution of mosquitoes in Colombian rain forest

(Bates, 1945), and in the accumulated drift along the shores of large lakes.

Under normal conditions, beach drift that accumulates upon the sandy depositing areas of Lake Michigan is concentrated in particular reaches from central Wisconsin, northeastern Illinois, northwestern Indiana, to southern Michigan. This drift has a seasonal periodicity that can be used as a biological calendar. Parts of the faunas of the inland communities are blown into the lake, and eventually are deposited upon the lower beaches in a dead or debilitated condition. These animals are chiefly insects, and since their appearance in their native communities is seasonal, their subsequent appearance on the beach, often a few days after they have been observed in their normal habitat niches, can be analyzed in quantitative terms.

The biocoenose of the beach drift in general is a complex and ever-shifting seasonal phenomenon. It has been studied often in the past (Wheeler, 1887; Needham, 1900, 1904, 1917; Snow, 1902; Herms, 1907; Shelford, 1913, pp. 218–221; Park, 1930). Its matrix includes the carrion, just referred to, as well as dead fishes and water birds washed ashore from the lake community.

Feeding upon this seasonal carrion are numerous scavengers. These are chiefly bacteria, flies (Sarcophagidae), and beetles (Silphidae, Trogidae, Scarabaeidae, Nitidulidae). These both feed and oviposit on the drift.

In turn the scavengers are preyed upon by still other beetles (Histeridae, Silphidae, Staphylinidae) that feed upon eggs, larvae, pupae, or imagines of the eaters of dead flesh.

Most insects present, including these predators, may be eaten by still other predators, such as beetles (Carabidae, Staphylinidae, Cicindelidae), spiders (Lycosidae), and the toad (*Bufo woodhousii fowleri*).

This food chain shows a marked seasonal periodicity, as illustrated in Figures 181 and 182. The first of these shows the correlation of the seasonal succession of beetles in deciduous forest communities bordering on Lake Michigan with the seasonal march in air temperature, relative humidity, and radiant energy in gram-calories. The second figure shows the correlation of the seasonal succession of forest beetles, referred to in the preceding figure, with the seasonal succession of carabid beetles in the beach drift. The correlation between these two figures suggests a direct relationship be-

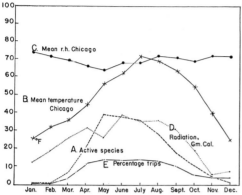

Fig. 181. Seasonal periodicity of beetles in the forest communities bordering the southern end of Lake Michigan, and the seasonal march in air temperature, relative humidity, and radiant energy. (Graph shows percentage of species active, based on data from April, 1922, to December, 1928; mean monthly air temperature in degrees F; mean monthly relative humidity in percentage; radiant energy in gram-calories/sq. cm./sec.) (After O. Park.)

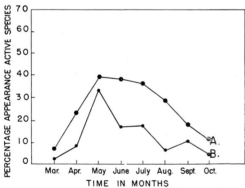

Fig. 182. Correlation of (A) seasonal periodicity of active species of beetles for the forest communities bordering the southern end of Lake Michigan with (B) seasonal periodicity of active species of Carabidae in the beach drift of Lake Michigan. (After O. Park.)

tween the phenology of inland forest and meadow communities, and the seasonal periodicity of the Lake Michigan beach drift.

In dramatic contrast with periods of relative activity and abundance is the winter or hibernal season. This is a time of relative inactivity and scarcity, in so far as the whole community is concerned. The light is at its lowest average intensity, but in deciduous forests the lower strata of the communities are relatively brighter as a consequence of the defoliation of the canopy (O. Park, 1931), whereas the banking of snow upon the evergreen canopy of coniferous communities reinforces the relative dimness below (Fig. 183). The temperature is correspondingly low, the bare branches of deciduous trees offer much less protection from winds, the forest and prairie floors are often blanketed by snow, and the smaller lakes, ponds, and streams may have the upper strata or the entire vertical system of strata frozen.

In such temperate communities the total activity is at its lowest ebb. The most obvious activities are those concerned with the search for food by the relatively few species of resident, homoiothermal animals that remain active. These usually are the winter bird population (Chapman, 1918; Sanborn, 1922; Eifert, 1941*), and certain mammals (Hamilton 1939, 1943). This state of relative inactivity deserves thoughtful attention. The activities of winter residents serve to accentuate the contrast, in the same community, between the warmth, noise, and verdure of summer, and the cold, stillness, and frozen whiteness of winter.

At the level of integration under examination, namely, the major community at the level of survival, the rhythmic winter inactivity of the majority of the interdependent species populations alternated with their summer activity, corresponds to the diel periodicity of the majority of individuals. Thus we are concerned with the life of populations, rather than with the life of individual organisms. This long-term view of the community in seasonal balance is related philosophically to the view of the community in diel balance, to be discussed presently.

* Regional lists of wintering bird populations throughout the United States may be found annually in *Audubon Field Notes*, published by the National Audubon Society (formerly published as the *Season*, a supplement in the *Audubon Magazine*). Additional information on bird populations, relating to fall and spring migration and the breeding season, is also included.

The winter diapause of temperate communities requires a great deal of ecological preparation, just as the organismal diapause requires physiological preparation. Long before the arrival of the hibernal period, the contained animals and plants are preparing for the extremes of winter (Morgan, 1939). Such preparations are diverse, may begin in the late serotinal period, and usually are completed in the autumnal period. At the latitude of northern Illinois, for example, deciduous forest

A large literature and a special terminology have developed upon the subject of dormancy. Numerous physiological changes are associated with extended periods of inactivity. In general, when the dormant period occurs in winter, the adjustments are referred to collectively as *hibernation*. Hibernation, then, is associated with relatively low temperature and physiologically inaccessible water (snow and ice). When the dormant period occurs in summer, in temperate latitudes and altitudes, or

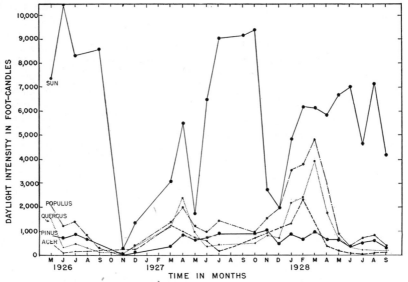

Fig. 183. Seasonal distribution of light intensity, in foot-candles, in the Chicago area, for open sun, and canopy shade of the cottonwood, conifer, oak, and beech-maple communities of the Indiana Dunes. (After O. Park.)

communities gradually complete the defoliation of their canopy, shrub, and herbaceous strata, and deposit the bulk of this potential food upon the forest floor; grassland communities have their now yellowed herbaceous stratum matted down under early snows; the upper stratum of larger aquatic communities gradually chills, with the resulting disappearance of the thermocline, and the smaller aquatic communities chill, and eventually their aqueous medium freezes.

The general response to this gradual cooling of the inanimate media is a movement away from exposed strata into more protected habitat niches, or into the lowest stratum; i.e., into the subaqueous and subterranean strata. Such movements are precursors of dormancy.

in dry seasons of the tropics, the general adjustment is known as *aestivation* (*estivation*). Aestivation is usually associated with relatively high temperature and physically inaccessible water (drought). Both hibernation and aestivation are associated with, physiologically, a lowered organismal metabolism, and, ecologically, with a lowered community metabolism.

Animals react differently to these periodic environmental extremes. Even between closely related genera the pattern of dormancy, or its presence or absence, may depend upon the species involved, or may vary among the several individuals of a given species population. In the most general terms, dormancy is to be regarded as a broad adjustment for shelter during a periodic, seasonal response of the relatively stable major community to adverse physical influences.

The habitat niche in which overwintering is consummated is designated as the *hibernaculum*. Animals begin their movement into these winter residences, and begin their physiological preparation for overwintering, at differing times and in diverse ways.

At the latitude of southern Lake Michigan, used here as a fairly well-known example, bryozoans have maturing statoblasts by middle August in certain species; freshwater sponges (*Ephydatia* and *Spongilla*) are depositing a crust of gemmules on submerged logs in middle October. By the last week of October, garter snakes are entering hibernation in loose mold and burrows (cf. also Pope, 1937, pp. 113–119). At this same time there is a large-scale movement of many species of beetles, bugs, spiders, and other arthropods into relatively protected hibernacula.

The primary impetus to such large movements would appear to be the onset of adverse weather, especially falling temperature. The distribution of arthropods in winter appears to be determined primarily by the kind and amount of shelter, and by moisture (Holmquist, 1926). In late autumn this movement may be separated into two converging streams of individuals into more protected floors of dense forest communities (Shelford, 1913; Weese, 1924; Blake, 1926; Holmquist, 1926; Park, 1930; Cole, 1946).

One of these migrations is from the less protected grassland communities and such allied and secondary habitats as pastures, weed lots and forest-enclosed clearings. The other migration is from the higher strata of forests into lower strata. Thus the horizontal and vertical migrations converge in the floor, and upper portions of the subterranean stratum of forest communities. Such an influx swells the already heavily populated lower strata.

In general, the populations of soil-inhabiting invertebrates move deeper into the subterranean stratum during the autumnal and hibernal periods (Fig. 184) and perform the opposite movement, to the upper layer of soil, or into the floor stratum, the following vernal season.

Of interest here is the close correlation of this seasonal vertical migration with the seasonal expression of the operating physical influences in a given community. Dowdy (1944) finds that both the downward hibernal movement and the upward vernal movement of invertebrates of subterranean and floor strata are close to the temperature overturns, and in most cases are coincident with them.

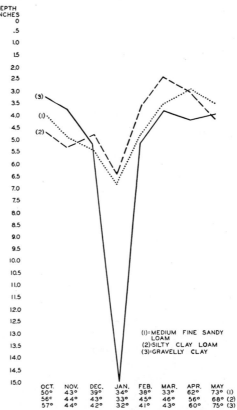

Fig. 184. Vertical migration of soil-inhabiting invertebrates into the subterranean stratum during the autumnal and hibernal periods. (After Dowdy.)

In tropical areas vertical seasonal movements occur as regularly as in temperate regions, but the general response of the soil fauna is to moisture rather than temperature. For example, Strickland (1947) found that in Trinidad the downward movement of soil arthropods was associated with decreasing humidity as the dry season advanced.

The distribution of arthropods in the lower strata may be scattered, or certain species may be gregarious in winter and form sheltering aggregations (Allee, 1927a, 1931), in which case late arrivals continue to pack suitable niches. The ladybird beetles are notable in this regard.* Such aggregations may consist of many different species of ladybird beetles, other beetles, bugs, spiders, earthworms, and other organisms, or they may consist of one species. Such heterotypic and homotypic aggregations may hold as many as 10,000 macroscopic individuals per square meter of forest floor.

Forest leaf mold and forest margins are notable, but not unique, sites for hibernacula. In western United States the rapacious tiger beetles, *Cicindela oregona,* abandon their solitary, predaceous life at the approach of winter, and burrow under flat rocks to form a gregarious overwintering aggregation (Blaisdell, 1912), and hundreds of histerid beetles, of several species of *Saprinus,* form extensive gatherings in bare sandy patches at the approach of winter in western Ukraine (Spett, 1925). In the Chicago area queens of the white-faced hornet (*Vespula maculata*) overwinter in log mold. Certain mound-building ants (*Formica ulkei* and *F. exsectoides*) form hibernating masses of individuals in the deep nest galleries above the water table, between November 1 and April 11 (Holmquist, 1926, 1928, 1928a; Dreyer, 1932, 1938).

Many terrestrial snails adjust by sealing the aperture with a thin epiphragm of secreted mucus. Many crayfish burrow into the subaqueous floor of ponds (Creaser, 1931), and there is a long list of organisms that overwinter in frozen aquatic communities by encystment (various protozoans, rotifers, nematodes, annelids and entomostracans).

Encystment would appear to be a general adjustment to adverse conditions, of which those obtaining in winter are simply one of a number of groups of stimuli. This seems clear from the evidence of investigators who find that encystment in protozoans and entomostracans can be brought about by low or high temperatures, lack of food, presence of an unfavorable concentration of waste products, or lack of oxygen

* For overwintering aggregations in general, see p. 393; for aggregations of coccinellid beetles, see Hamilton, 1885; Schwarz, 1891; Cook, 1898; Calvert, 1899; Carnes, 1912; Van Dyke, 1919; Hawkes, 1920; Park, 1930; Allee, 1931.

(Mast, 1912, 1917; Birge and Juday, 1911).

In many of these cases of adjustment, whether by encystment or moving into protected floors, loss of organismal water appears to parallel, if not precede, the loss of physiologically accessible water in the

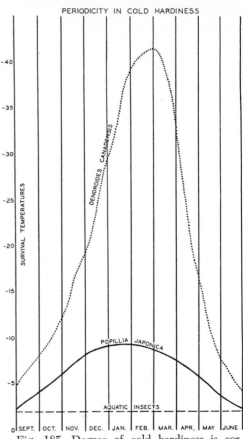

Fig. 185. Degree of cold hardiness is correlated with (1) seasonal periodicity of temperature, and (2) normal seasonal fluctuation in temperature in the community or habitat in which a given species is resident. (After Payne.)

community approaching winter. Encystment in protozoans, among others, involves desiccation. Again, many insects that move into forest floor hibernacula have previously undergone some dehydration (Payne, 1926, 1927, 1927a, 1928, 1929).

Payne's work on the development of cold hardiness in insects is of interest here, since her experimental data have broad community implications. It was demonstrated (Fig. 185) (1) that degree of cold hardiness was correlated with seasonal periodicity of temperature, and (2) that degree of cold hardiness in a series of species, from a variety of habitats in terrestrial and aquatic communities, was correlated with the normal seasonal fluctuation of temperature in that community or habitat in which a particular species was normally resident (p. 99).

These and similar data on toleration (T. Park, 1945a; Park, Gregg, and Lutherman, 1940) and mores (Allee, 1912, 1926b; Shelford, 1914, 1914a) suggest that each type of community has an inherent spectrum of toleration to normal extremes of adverse physical conditions to which it is subjected, and that this toleration is a quantitative function that operates upon a periodic seasonal rhythm.

Much that has been said about the general phenomenon of hibernation applies equally well to the phenomenon of aestivation. The latter, too, has both organismal and community aspects and involves horizontal and vertical movements into the floors of communities, desiccation of the aestivating organism, the secretion of epiphragms by mollusks, and the employment of cysts against drought. A lengthy discussion* may be obviated by noting that hibernation and aestivation are in reality two similar facets of seasonal succession, and that the essential differences lie in the different communities involved. Aestivation is typical of two great groups of communities: the desert and semidesert type of community, where the annual or pluriannual variation in precipitation is a dominant influence; and tropical communities with more or less sharply defined wet and dry seasons (Hesse, Allee, and Schmidt, 1937; Bates, 1945).

In our examination of the seasonal periodicity of the community we have limited the analysis to the resident organisms where feasible, to avoid complexity of treatment. There remains another seasonal response, having broad community implications, that involves species populations, or portions thereof, that are temporary residents of certain communities. It was pointed out

that an organism has but three choices available when exposed to adversity: it may die, adjust, or migrate. Hibernation and aestivation are broad adjustments to adverse weather or climate. Migration or emigration are still different ways of avoiding unfavorable conditions.

As in dormancy, the subject of migration, in the strict sense, has an extensive literature and a particular terminology. We are concerned with the subject as it affects the community concept, but for the student interested in the several ramifications of migration the following references are cited: Chapman (1934); Coward (1912); Hamilton (1939); Lincoln (1935); Williams (1930, 1938); Wolfson (1945).

In the general view, migration is thought of as organismal movement from one place of residence to another. With accumulation of information, this concept has become divided into at least three categories: *migration,* a more or less continuous and direct movement, under control of the animal, coördinated with or controlled by periodic environmental influences, from one locality to another, in which there is a periodic return to the original locality; *emigration* or its converse, *immigration,* a movement of a portion of a species population, often over great distances, to another locality, without a return to the original area; and *remigration,* a movement of a portion of a species population from one locality to another, with a return movement to the original locality by different individuals of the species (see also Dispersion, p. 363).

Animals exhibiting migration in the strict sense of the word include the monarch butterfly, herring, salmon, eels, certain whales, fur seals, mule deer, and a great many kinds of birds. True migration is such a distinctive feature of bird behavior that birds are classified frequently by their migratory status. Such a classification (Pough, 1946) includes the following categories: *permanent residents,* species that remain in one locality throughout their lives. It should be remembered that even in a resident species a few individuals may exhibit migratory behavior. Few species of birds are wholly resident. Examples of this first group are bobwhite, screech owls, and English sparrows. *Summer residents* are those birds that come northward to the

---

* For a further study of aestivation, consult Buxton (1923); Creaser (1931); Hesse, Allee, and Schmidt (1937); Pearse (1939); Strandine (1941a); Van Cleave (1931); Van Dyke (1902).

spring breeding grounds, rear their young in the summer, and return to the wintering grounds in the autumn. Here belong such birds as the numerous warblers, vireos, and thrushes. *Winter residents* are those birds that move from their breeding grounds in the north to spend the winter in a more southern locality where food is more abundant. In the northern United States, the junco is a common winter resident. *Transient visitants* are those birds that pass through a locality, generally twice each year, first in the spring, en route to the northerly breeding area, and again in the autumn, en route to the winter habitat. Obviously, this last group is interpreted upon a geographic point of reference, since many summer residents of one locality would be transients in other areas. *Partial migrants* are those species which include members that are migratory in the northern portion of their range, and are more or less permanent residents further south. In this last category it is difficult to state whether such a species is undergoing a southward shift of the entire population, or whether two population fragments are represented within the species, a migratory northern group and a sedentary southern group. There are also *erratic wanderers,* that move about erratically except during the breeding season. Certain herons belong in this group. These categories, well known to students of North American birds, are generally applicable.

From the community point of view, all these truly migratory animals are temporary residents, integrating into a series of disparate community food webs upon a seasonal basis. Since their period of integration for any given community varies with the local weather, amount and kind of foods available, and the endogenous stimuli that control such phenomena as breeding, oviposition, and rearing of young, the effect upon the food web is variable. In any event, the effect of summer residents on communities that lie along the route of the migration, and at the ends of such definite paths of migration, is important and tangible.

Birds, especially, follow rather circumscribed paths of migration or *flyways,* in correlation with the seasonal advance of certain isotherms (Fig. 186). The majority of birds migrate at night. Such birds travel from 200 to 400 miles per night, and recuperate and feed during the day. It is during this daytime interval that the vernal waves of warblers and other passerines impinge upon the food webs of communities along their line of migration. At these relatively briefs intervals they prey upon the then increasing populations of insects, and are in turn preyed upon by resident predators.

As a general tendency, the effect of northward migrating birds upon the communities along the flyway is inversely proportional to the distance from their southern wintering grounds. This strange relationship is a consequence of many factors. The rate of progress of an individual may be much greater than the progress of the species as a whole, and the advance of a migrating population appears to be correlated with the climatic conditions along the flyway. Thus, although a particular bird may cover several hundred miles in one night, the average daily advance from New Orleans to southern Minnesota, up the much-used Mississippi flyway, is about 25 miles a day for all species populations. As the species continue to move northward, the average rate of travel increases with the rapidly advancing vernal season. The daily average between southern Minnesota and southern Manitoba is 40 miles; from southern Manitoba to Lake Athabasca, 72 miles; and from here to Great Slave Lake, 116 miles. Five species continue on to Alaska, on an average of 150 miles daily rate of migration. As the species move northward, their rate of travel increases, and their consequent effect upon the communities along the migration path becomes less and less, until the breeding grounds for any particular species is reached, where, as noted, the impact is prolonged and important.

On the other hand, some birds migrate during the daylight hours; for example, robins, kingbirds, and swallows. Such birds feed as they travel, and traverse considerable territory in search of food.

The migration route may be long; consequently migrants come in contact with a proportionally great many communities. The barn swallow, for example, winters as far south as Argentina, and breeds as far north as the Alaskan Yukon, a distance of some 7000 miles.

In this brief survey of migration as it

affects the community, we are not concerned with an encyclopedic catalogue of the several migrating species and their particular problems; nor with the evaluation of exogenous influences such as the intensity of light, length of daylight periods, and available food; nor with endogenous factors, such as the deposition of fat, habit, and hormone production (Rowan, 1926,

latter point is illustrated by the migration of mule deer (*Odocoileus hemionus*) in the mountainous regions of the western United States (Russell, 1932). These deer in the Yellowstone and Yosemite regions occupy distinct summer and winter ranges. The migration routes vary from 10 to 60 miles in length. In the spring the deer move into the higher altitudes, and in the autumn

Fig. 186. Seasonal march of isotherm fronts and the vernal migration of the black and white warbler. (Modified from Lincoln.)

1929, 1932; Wolfson, 1945). The resulting balance between these and other external and internal stimuli causes the individual organism to move into and out of the several communities with which it is associated.

The stimuli effective for one species may not be effective, either in kind or degree, for another species; and the stimuli effective for one part of an annual movement may not be effective for another part of the same movement in a given species. This

they reverse this movement. Although mating behavior and birth of young deer are correlated with this seasonal movement, no causative relationship has been demonstrated between these organismal activities and the phenomena associated with migration. The deer become restless on their summer range with the onset of early snow storms and a drop in temperature. Fall migration to the lower winter range appears to be initiated by heavy snowfall. The spring migration, on the other hand, apparently coincides with the resumption of plant growth. This food factor is dependent upon the disappearance of snow, which, in turn, is dependent upon a rise in temperature, but the deer appear to react to the growth of fodder, rather than to melting snow and increasing temperature. If suitable fodder is available throughout the year, some or all of the deer in a particular area may not migrate. The exact migration routes taken appear to depend upon habit.

Similarly, groups of diverse stimuli, more or less complex in their origin and effects, play their parts in the migratory phenomena of the numerous kinds of animals cited. We are a long way from complete comprehension of any migratory problem, whether we are dealing with anadromous and catadromous fishes (p. 170), whales, mountain sheep, certain bats and butterflies, or with the relatively better-known migratory habits of birds.

As more and more migratory species are drawn into a discussion of migration as it affects the community, it becomes increasingly clear that the essential differences between broad, truly migratory patterns and broad shifts in community populations are less than at first appear. Length of migration route is no criterion of difference. Among migratory birds, distance traveled varies from thousands of miles in many species, to a few miles in the case of partial migrants, and similar variation occurs in other groups of migratory animals. Environmental and internal stimuli are involved in both geographic migration and in smaller intracommunity patterns. Many seasonal movements, either between different strata of the same community or between communities of the same type, or between different types of communities, are difficult to classify as migratory in the strict sense of the word, or partially migratory, or not migratory. As we learn more about population movements within and between communities, the dissimilarities become no more remarkable than the agreements.

To illustrate this difficulty, let us consider an example of seasonal movements in a terrestrial, in a fresh-water, and in a marine community. A population of the ladybird beetle, *Ceratomegilla fuscilabris,* moves from the meadow grasses and forest leaves into the forest floor during the autumn, stays in the deeper portions of the floor mold during the winter, and moves into the meadow and upper forest strata the following spring, where it breeds and feeds upon aphids and other organisms (O. Park, 1930). Seven species of pulmonate snails move into the deeper water of Douglas Lake, Michigan, at the approach of cold weather, remain in the deep water through the winter, and return to shallow water of the lake in the spring (Cheatum, 1934). Certain species of the snail, *Littorina,* move into relatively deep, salty water for the winter season, and move back into brackish water during the summer (Batchelder, 1915, 1926). Numerous species of crabs, prawns, lobsters, and squids move into deeper ocean water for the winter, and move back to the marine littoral water in the spring (Pearse, 1939).

How shall we classify these movements? They are all seasonal. They are apparent adjustments to apparently changing conditions. They are periodic journeys, of different distances and of different rates of travel. Since they are regular population shifts between two or more communities, with a return to the original area, they cannot be called emigrations. Are they, then, migrations or remigrations? Who can say for all of them? The complete answer includes a knowledge of the life span of the several species. Second, if they live long enough, do the same individuals make the return journey (which is another way of saying that an individual makes the trip twice instead of once)? But if twice, is the species truly migratory or partially migratory; that is, does the whole population regularly make the round trip, or is a part of the species sedentary? What is the relative importance of exogenous and endogenous factors? The questions cannot be answered at this time. The best that can be done now is to note that these seasonal movements are integrated aspects of the periodism of the communities involved.

Before leaving the strictly seasonal periodic aspects of communities, it should be remembered that few show seasonal rhythms in all portions of their structure. The abyssal stratum of the marine community may be regarded as strictly aseasonal, and that condition is approached in the profundal strata of certain deep lakes, while their topmost strata exhibit marked seasonal rhythms. Cave communities exhibit more or less aseasonal structure depending upon (1) the portion of the community examined, and (2) the degree to which the cave foodweb is dependent upon an epigean seasonal replenishment of foods.

On the other hand, the majority of communities show some seasonal phenomena at some parts of their organization. Two principles emerge from the survey of seasonal aspects of communities. The kind and degree of seasonality of a given community is correlated directly with the kind and degree of periodicity of the operating physical influences. The kind and degree of seasonality of any given part of a community is correlated directly with the kind and degree of periodicity of the operating physical influences at that part of the structure considered.

There remain several community phenomena that are often confused with the strictly seasonal aspects of activity: the aseasonal remigrations, and emigrations, as defined previously.

Remigrating animals (migratory grasshoppers) and emigrating animals (lemming, gray squirrel, snowshoe hare, beaver, bushy-tailed wood rat, Norway rat, among others) have been the subject of much study (Elton, 1942; Hamilton, 1939; Seton, 1909; Uvarov, 1928), and the relatively sudden appearance of the moving swarms or hordes are spectacular phenomena. The economic damage that often results, when the animals feed upon the agricultural products of man, may be large and create temporary shortages.

From the point of view of the major community, as a relatively stable and independent unit, such movements are not of great or lasting value. The chief effects are (1) the immediate and abnormal effect upon the food webs of communities along the line of travel. This is a two-way integration, in that the incoming animals feed upon a lower trophic level, usually as herbivores, and at the same time are available as food to a higher trophic level. A time lag is required for the community to readjust the food web, after the remigrants or emigrants have moved on. In the case of remigration, this effect is repeated later, when the return is made by the next gen-

eration, or by a succeeding generation, of the species involved. This is not necessarily always true, since the remigrants may return by a different route.

Such effects may be important at the time of occurrence, but no case is known where such movements have impaired or destroyed a community beyond redemption. Eventually the imbalance is corrected. This corrective process is especially interesting when the community is seen as a long-time unit with seasonal periodicity. The relatively abrupt drop in community activity during dry or cold seasons, the ensuing period of dormancy, and the resumption of plant growth in the following season, are a sequence of events most likely to correct exceptional ravages on the food supplies of the whole community. The community, then, would appear to have a seasonal protective factor against the effects of remigrations and emigrations.

Finally, there are the aseasonal, but periodic, increases in such forms as certain of the cicadas (Beamer, 1928; Davis, 1925; Marlatt, 1907; Mills, 1929; Osborn, 1902, Strandine, 1940). These insects, after passing a relatively long period of development in the subterranean strata of terrestrial communities, chiefly forest communities in which oaks are prominent, emerge to make a dramatic and noisy debut in the upper strata. The numerous species have widely differing periods of development, and are to be considered as permanent residents of certain types of communities, although their adult span is seen for a relatively brief period. The species of cicada that has attracted the most attention in the United States is the periodical cicada or seventeen-year "locust" (*Magicicada septendecim*). Some twenty broods of this species have been traced out, and one or more broods appear each year, at some part of the range.

The appearance of the adults in the higher strata of the occupied communities sets up the same two-way integration referred to previously for remigrants and emigrants. The act of oviposition kills a conspicuous amount of foliage in oak canopies, and the insects are an abundant and readily available source of food for the bird populations. The amount of food thus available is large. Brood XIII, resident in the Chicago area, appeared in 1922 and more recently in 1939. During this latter outbreak the population density was thirteen nymphal cases per square meter (51,397 per acre) for sugar maple forests, thirty-two per square meter (127,885 per acre) for black oak forests, and fifty per square meter (202,876 per acre) for red oak-white oak-maple forest communities. The adult cicadas weighed, on an average, 0.15 gm. when dehydrated in alcohol and then dried, so that the equivalent of 31,243 gm. of dried cicada per acre were available to predators per acre of red oak forest (Strandine, 1940).

LUNAR ASPECTS OF THE COMMUNITY

Moonlight is a poorly understood influence in the nocturnal period. Periodicity induced or controlled by the moon, in its orbit about the earth, is of relatively little consequence to the terrestrial communities, so far as our present knowledge is concerned.

Such effects apparently are of only slightly more consequence in the freshwater communities, but have received little attention (Shelford, 1918, pp. 42–43). The best-known lunar influence in these is the correlation between the amount of river plankton and the phases of the moon (Thomson, 1911).

The marine community, however, does show a variety of rhythmic responses to tides, which latter are chiefly direct lunar effects (p. 84).

Associated with and, in certain cases, induced by these tidal rhythms are the so-called lunar rhythms of marine animals. Such activity rhythms are usually restricted to the marine littoral strata. In the littoral zone, it must be remembered that not only is the height of tides affected, but also such marine influences as salinity, water temperature, currents, sediment, and foods are indirectly influenced by lunar rhythms.

It is not surprising, therefore, that the marine littoral zone has a number of lunar periodicities in the activities of its inhabitants. The best-known of these are the lunar periodicities in the reproductive behavior of various polychaete annelids (Grave, 1922; Lillie and Just, 1913; Mayer, 1908; Scott, 1909; Treadwell, 1915; see also p. 84).

A second general type of lunar periodicity is illustrated by a fish, the grunion (*Leuresthes tenuis*). Along the California littoral, these fishes appear exactly at high tide, on the second, third, and fourth nights following the spring tides (Thompson and Thompson, 1919). At these times the female grunion deposit their egg pods in the sand, just above the water line, and the male grunion fertilize the eggs at this time. The eggs are ready to hatch in two weeks, but will not do so until the egg pods are washed from the sand by the tides at the next dark moon. This adjustment against various adversities is summed up by Pearse (1939, p. 176):

"If spawning occurred just before the highest tides, when the high beach was being eroded, instead of just after, when the beach was being built up, the eggs would be washed out of the sand before they had developed for a fortnight. If spawning occurred at the very highest tides (dark of the moon), the eggs might not be exposed for a month or even two months. If grunions laid their eggs during the day, they would be exposed to the attacks of gulls and other predaceous animals."

In summary, then, in addition to the generally important influence of the rhythmic ebb and flow of tides (Keeble, 1910), lunar rhythms, especially as they affect the reproductive cycles, are of importance to the littoral portions of the marine community (Korringa, 1947).

DIEL ASPECTS OF THE COMMUNITY

Within the elastic frame of seasonal rhythmicity the most important periodicity is that associated with day and night. To avoid confusion, in the discussion that follows, *diel* will be used for the twenty-four hour period of a day and a night, following Carpenter (1934), and day and night will refer to the illuminated and darkened portions of the period, respectively.

Diel periodicities of the physical influences affect the community in two major ways. First, there is the variation that is a consequence of latitude, and its vertical equivalent, altitude, in which there is a regular change in the number of hours of daylight from equator to poles, or from sea level to the highest peaks, at a given time of the year. Thus, equatorial regions have day and night relatively constant throughout the year, twelve hours of light and twelve hours of darkness; polar regions have a long period of continuous darkness, and an equally long period of illumination, so that there are months when every diel is equally dark or light, as the case may be. Between these two extremes are the subtropical, temperate, and subpolar regions, which are gradually and regularly intermediate in this regard.

Second, there is the variation of the relative lengths of day and night through the year, at a given latitude or, to a lesser degree, with altitude. This regular change is closely associated with, and regularly affected by, the first mentioned variation, and is of equal importance to the community (Barden, 1942). It is with this latter rhythm that the associated photoperiodism

of herbivores. Such a response would be a general one, of unconscious coöperation at the community level.

In addition to, and associated with, the length of day and night, are numerous primary and secondary influences of the physical part of the environment. Such influences usually follow a rhythmic diel pattern (pp. 229, 232) in daylight intensity, daylight quality, temperature, relative humidity, rate of evaporation, and so forth. The result is that the day is relatively bright, warm, dry, with a high power of evaporation; whereas the night is relatively dark, cool, moist, with a low power of evaporation (Fig. 187).

The regular march of these influences

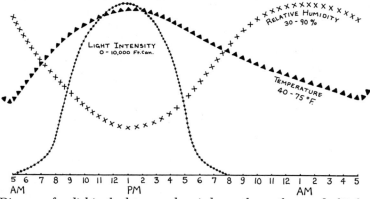

Fig. 187. Diagram of a diel in the late vernal period near the southern end of Lake Michigan.

(p. 121) is concerned, which affects the community in many ways (Garner and Allard, 1920; Kellerman, 1926). The best demonstrated effect is the series of photoperiodic correlations between relative day length and cycles in the leafing, fruiting, and flowering of certain terrestrial plants (Oosting, 1948). Such rhythms affect plants directly; for example, in the photosynthetic key industry (p. 501). Herbivores are affected indirectly, and carnivores still more indirectly, until each trophic level is drawn into the association. The photoperiodism of a plant species may be viewed as a particular correlation, of those individuals of the population involved, of endogenous and exogenous factors, within the limits of inherited toleration. When the photoperiodisms of plant species populations of a community are viewed collectively, the overlapping mosaic that results affects the general aspect of, for example, the canopy, and may tend to equalize the food supply

over the diel periods, throughout the seasonally periodic year, imposes a periodic physical environment upon the majority of communities. Exceptions are generally those communities that, because of their locations, escape a seasonal environment or have developed a complex social life, to be discussed presently.

What is not so generally recognized is that the community is more restricted in its reaction to adverse conditions than is the organism or population. Organisms and species have three choices: death, dispersion, or adjustment. A contemporary community, in the integrated sense used here, has only two choices: death or adjustment. A community may expand, contract, or shift its area through time (Potzger and Wilson, 1941), but it cannot migrate. Certain of its several component populations may migrate, emigrate, or remigrate, and they may articulate with another community and attain survival. The independent community must remain, and either survive through adjustment, or perish through lack of it. The community is more complex, stable, independent, and less mobile than its parts. This inability to migrate is a major difference between the major community and its interdependent populations.

Consequently, just as the community adjusts to the seasonal rhythm, it also adjusts to the diel rhythm (O. Park, 1940); and where certain portions of its structure are exposed to the diel rhythm, it tends to adjust locally to those portions so exposed.

These adjustments cover a wide range of activities, and are as diverse as possible within the heritable limitations and tolerations of the reacting populations. All such responses take the form of periodic diel adjustments to food, shelter, and reproduction. Such responses are also characterized by alternating periods of relative activity and relative inactivity, the amplitude and frequency of such rhythms depending upon the interplay of external, or exogenous, influences, and of organismal, internal, or endogenous influences (O. Park, 1940, 1941).

These responses are classified with reference to the period of activity, rather than the period of inactivity, into three major categories (Park, Lockett, and Myers, 1931). Activity occurring during the day is termed *diurnal;* at night, it is said to be *nocturnal.* Activity occurring both during the day and the night, under normal conditions, is said to be *arrhythmic* with respect to the diel cycle. In this respect we may speak of diurnal, nocturnal, or arrhythmic activities, organisms, or populations. An organism may carry out certain activities that are diurnal, and some that are nocturnal. The majority have a well-defined diel period of relative activity and of relative inactivity.

The periods of overlap, between day and night, when the diurnal animals are becoming quiescent, and the nocturnal animals are becoming active, or *vice versa,* represent a fundamental shift in the general community activity. These periods of dusk and dawn may have their own faunas, or peculiar activities. Carpenter (1935) divided the diel period into four periods of activity: those occurring in the dawn (*auroral* period), those in the day (*diurnal* period in a limited sense), those in the evening (*vesperal* period), and those at night (*nocturnal* in a limited sense). Carpenter (1938) used *crepuscular* to embrace both dawn and dusk activities, but the more familiar usage, of restricting crepuscular response to the evening, will be adhered to here, and crepuscular and vesperal will be used interchangeably. Similarly, for purposes of convenience, unless otherwise stated, nocturnal activities will embrace the crepuscular, and diurnal activities will include the auroral, responses.

Since the majority of animals have a diel periodicity in general behavior, the communities of which they form a part have similarly well-defined diurnal and nocturnal faunas. Although there is much autecological information on this subject, few communities have been studied from this point of view. In fact, most of the general principles attributed to synecology were based upon diurnal activities or populations, and the analogous study of nocturnal activities and populations has lagged far behind (Park, Lockett, and Myers, 1931). Many years ago Verrill (1897) remarked on the importance of nocturnal studies, and later Allee (1927) emphasized that nocturnal ecology was a practically untouched field of investigation.

At the organismal level there are numerous data on nocturnal individuals, species, and higher taxonomic categories. These are too numerous to consider here and have been discussed (O. Park, 1940). Our concern is with their integration in the several communities of which they form an important part.

The adjustments of nocturnal animals are even less well understood. In the most general terms, nocturnal adjustments are best known in two categories, the photogenic organs of photurid beetles as mating adaptations (Buck, 1937, 1937a), and the visual adaptations of invertebrates (Bennitt, 1932; Horstmann, 1935; Rau, 1935; Welsh, 1935, 1938) and of vertebrates (Walls, 1942). Of especial value is the study of parallel adjustments to day and to night in diurnal and nocturnal species in fairly close taxonomic relationship. This has not been done often. An example is the work of Walls (1931) on the lenses of squirrels. Thus flying squirrels (*Glaucomys*) are nocturnal, and have colorless lenses, whereas the tree squirrels (*Sciurus*), where investigated, have yellowish lenses and are diurnal. Both types of squirrels inhabit the same forest community in many localities, and their different periods of activity are correlated with the light-filtering ability of their eyes and the light intensities normal for those portions of the diel cycle in which they are active.

At the level of the major community much less has been accomplished. Because of the absence of daylight, investigation of the nocturnal portion of a community is usually much more difficult than the parallel study of the diurnal portion. The few methods employed involve (1) trap-

frequency of the calls or sounds produced by nocturnal animals (Crawford, 1933; O. Park, 1938); (6) the use of objective recording apparatus in the field to record the movements of an individual (Park, Barden, and Williams, 1940). (7) The Norway rat has been viewed by infra-red light (Southern, Watson, and Chitty, 1946); consequently this method may be applicable to the large-scale study of nocturnal animals in the field. (8) The use of a flash light held so that the eye-shine of animals is seen (jack lighting); finally (9) there is the record on a light, fresh snowfall.

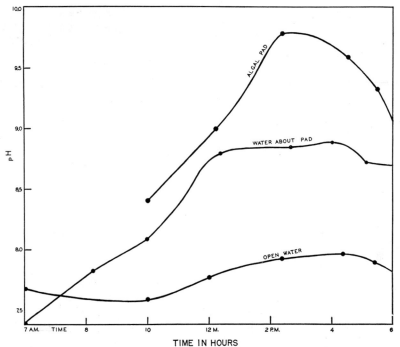

Fig. 188. Diel periodicity in pH in Crystal Lake, Minnesota. See text for relation to the metabolism of the lake community. (After Philip.)

ping, preferably live-trapping, or tagging, animals (Hamilton, 1937, 1940), (2) stomach analyses, in which the known periods of activity of the food-animals may suggest in certain cases the coincidental activity of the predator (this method is useful as a corroborative measure, but implies a great deal of foreknowledge of the food-gathering habits of the carnivore in question); (3) marking animals with various kinds of paint (Park and Sejba, 1935); (4) observation of animals by artificial lights (Park and Sejba, 1935; Park and Strohecker, 1936); (5) tabulation of the

All the methods have limitations. When several different methods are used, over a sufficient period of time, the body of evidence is mutually supportive, and leads us to the conclusion that there is a large nocturnally active segment complementing the large diurnally active segment of a given community, and that many of the principles generally advanced for the diurnal portion hold equally well for the nocturnal portion.

This complementary nature of the diurnal and nocturnal aspects of the community is basic to a full appreciation of the community concept. It will be remembered that the photosynthetic process, one of the two key industries, takes place during the diurnal hours. The result of plant photosynthesis in the community is the formation of sugars. These carbohydrates pass freely as solutes from cell to cell, and during the the working cells (Coulter, Barnes, and Cowles, 1911, p. 528; Transeau, Sampson, and Tiffany, 1940). In terrestrial communities at least, the upper strata of a community are involved generally in diurnal carbohydrate manufacture, and nocturnal

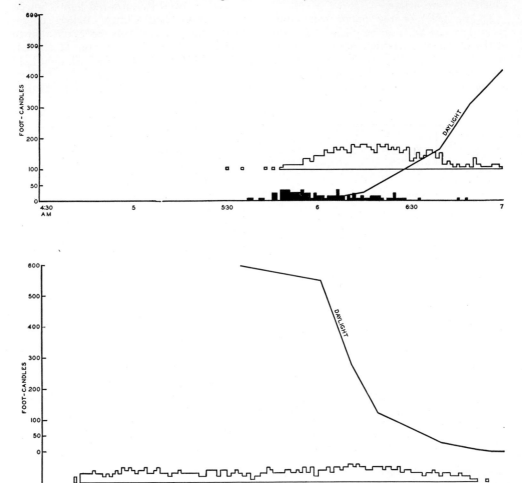

Fig. 189. Diel periodicity in sonification at dawn and dusk of forest animals (cicadas, orthopterans, frogs, birds, and monkeys) on Barro Colorado Island, Panama Canal Zone. White squares represent sounds made by mainly diurnal animals, and black squares represent those made by mainly nocturnal animals. One square represents sonification for one species for one minute. Light intensity is in foot-candles. (After O. Park, Barden, and Williams.)

day such compounds are manufactured more rapidly than they can be transported, and the excess sugar is converted into starches. The starch accumulates in the chloroplasts of the plant, and during the night many of these stored products are reconverted into sugars, and removed from transport of the excess products of this activity.

There are many similar diel rhythms in the community, and the rate and character of these periodic activities affect the several trophic levels directly and indirectly, usually in proportion to the ecological distance from the activity under examination.

A striking example is found in the work of Philip (1927) in the Crystal Lake community in Minnesota. Philip found a marked diel rhythm in hydrogen ion concentration. The amplitude increased regularly from open water, to the water surrounding algal mats, and culminated within the mats *per se* (Fig. 188). These three rhythms show a rising alkalinity of the water to a midday peak, and a falling alkalinity into the crepuscular period. The rhythmic shift in *p*H is a result of both

the mat, so that we have still another example of both inanimate and animate portions of the community affecting each other in the diel cycle. The photosynthesis of the algae will later directly affect (1) the population of the algae, (2) the algal herbivores, and (3) indirectly affect the predators, through the highest trophic level. This is in addition to any stimulus that the *p*H cycle may have upon the behavior of individual animals.

Coördinated studies of the animals of a given community, or of a portion thereof.

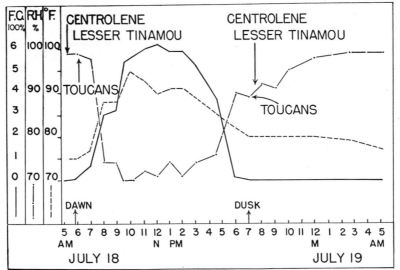

Fig. 190. Diel cycle in vocalization in a clearing in the upland forest on Barro Colorado Island, Panama Canal Zone. Dawn and dusk (2 foot-candles) are accompanied by change in activity of typical animals: diurnal toucans begin calling shortly after dawn, continue through day, and give their last call shortly after dusk; nocturnal tree frogs (*Centrolene*) and lesser tinamou stop vocalization just before dawn, and begin shortly after dusk. (After O. Park.)

physical and biological community factors. With the gradual rise in water temperature of the surface stratum, some carbon dioxide is driven off, with a peak loss in midafternoon; with the gradual fall in water temperature, there is an increased solubility of atmospheric carbon dioxide, and corresponding loss of alkalinity as evening sets in. This basic temperature and carbon dioxide rhythm underlies each of the curves in the figure. As the light intensity increases through the morning, there is a corresponding increase in algal photosynthesis and a further rise in the *p*H as the carbon dioxide in the water is utilized. This biological process affects not only the medium in the algal mat, but also the medium around

are relatively few. These include an early study of the insect fauna of a Minnesota sand dune (Chapman, Mickel, Parker, Miller, and Kelley, 1926); diel activity of a number of species of animals in a beech sugar maple forest in northeastern Ohio (Park, Lockett, and Myers, 1931) and in a similar community in northern Indiana (Park and Strohecker, 1936); rhythmic fluctuation in abundance of insects in a prairie near Norman, Oklahoma (Carpenter, 1936); and a relatively concentrated study of the Barro Colorado Island rain forest in the Panama Canal Zone (Allee, 1926, 1926a; O. Park, 1938; Park, Barden, and Williams, 1940). In all these studies there was a correlation between the physical influences operating and the relative activity of the diurnal and nocturnal animals through the diel cycle. This was true regardless of whether total vocalization was measured (Figs. 189 and 190) or whether locomotor activity was recorded (Fig. 191).

The diel activity pattern of the whole community is the sum of the diel patterns of the individuals of all species populations of the community. Therefore, whatever affects a part affects the whole; whatever affects the whole affects each part. In either

Peckham, 1898) and flower-visiting mordellid and cerambycid beetles and predaceous coccinellid beetles (Park, Lockett, and Myers, 1931), whose periods of inactivity are prolonged on overcast mornings. Parallel modification of activity occurs in the upper strata of aquatic communities, as in the movements of planktonic crustaceans in lakes (Juday, 1904).

Influence of weather on activity is especially convincing when the same individuals are observed under varying conditions. Certain silphid beetles (*Leiodes ob-*

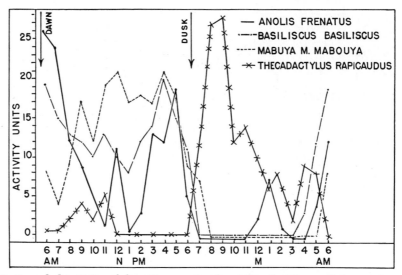

Fig. 191. Recorded activity of four Panamanian forest lizards. Three of the species are diurnal; the fourth species is a nocturnal gecko (*Thecadactylus rapicaudus*). (After O. Park.)

case the effect depends upon the strength of the influence operating, upon the part of the community concerned, and upon the time of the response, both seasonal and with respect to the diel cycle. Such changes may be immediate, or the complete reaction chain may not be apparent until much later.

It is not surprising that local weather may intervene to alter temporarily the normal diel periodicity. In general, the modification of community activity by the particular weather of a diel cycle is differential with respect to both nocturnal and diurnal animals. For example, a strictly nocturnal rodent, the springhaas (*Pedetes surdaster*) of Africa, may be active on dark days (Roosevelt, 1910), instead of going into diurnal inactivity in subterranean burrows. The reverse is true for such diurnal animals as many solitary wasps (Peckham and

soleta) were studied in the field on two nights a week apart (Park, Lockett, and Myers, 1931). The first of these nights was relatively cool and moist, and there was a relatively large number of active individuals (Fig. 192). The second night was relatively warm and dry, and there were almost no beetles active (Fig. 193). This difference in number of active beetles is in apparent correlation with such physical influences as relative humidity, temperature, and rate of evaporation.

Diel activities of the community may be considered roughly in two major categories: those concerned with reproduction, as, for example, copulation, oviposition, and pupation; and those concerned with feeding. It is interesting to note that the third primary drive in the life of animals—namely, sheltering—has to do with protection in the relative security of a habitat niche or stratal

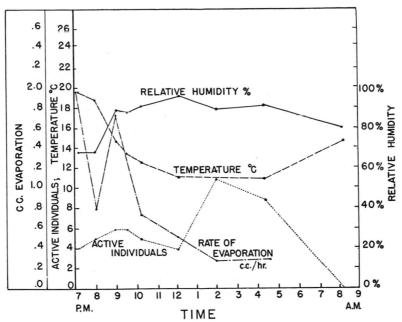

Fig. 192. Relation of weather to the nocturnal activity of a silphid beetle (*Leiodes obso-leta*) in a beech-sugar maple forest in northeastern Ohio, July 11–12, 1930; relatively cool and moist. The active beetles feed on myxomycetes (*Stemonitis* sp.) all night, and often copulate. (After O. Park, Lockett, and Myers.)

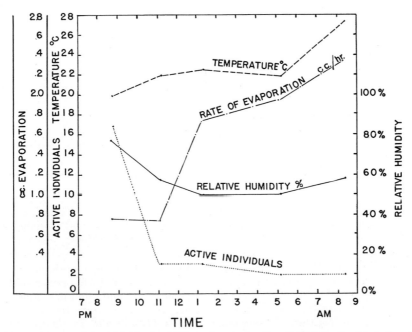

Fig. 193. Relation of weather to the nocturnal activity of a silphid beetle (*Leiodes obsoleta*) in a beech-sugar maple forest in northeastern Ohio, July 18–19, 1930; relatively warm and dry. There is little activity and no copulation. (After O. Park, Lockett, and Myers.)

location while asleep or at rest, and therefore, from the viewpoint of diel periodicity, is the complement of the period of activity.

In certain cases a species may have its chief period of activity during the day,

Altitude also may affect the activity pattern of a species population. Thus the harsh-furred mouse (*Lophuromys aquilus*) of British East Africa is usually nocturnal in the lowland brush, but the portion of the

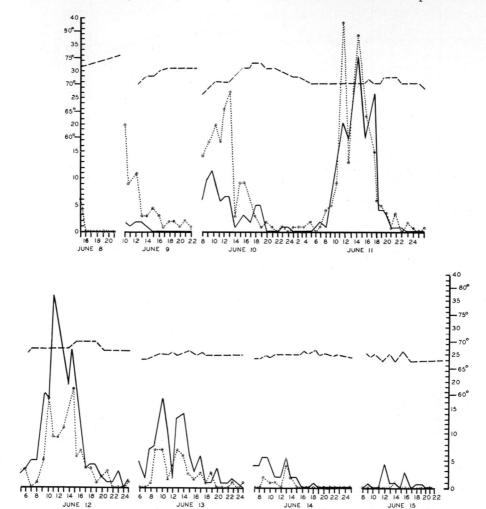

Fig. 194. Pupation rhythm in the dung fly (*Scopeuma stercoraria*). Note that the general frequency of the rhythm is maintained under conditions of relatively constant temperature (broken line) and normal daylight fluctuation. Solid line (total of males) and dotted line (total of females) show pupation peak between 0900 and 1400 hours each diel, with almost no flies emerging at night between 2000 and 0600 hours. Under constant illumination or constant darkness the rhythm continued, but with less pronounced peaks. (After Lewis and Bletchly.)

but there will be a regular seasonal intervention that alters the pattern. For example, the majority of birds are diurnal, but many birds, such as the warblers, migrate at night; the box turtle (*Terrapene carolina*) also is essentially diurnal, but during the period of oviposition the females lay their eggs at night (Allard, 1935).

population that inhabits the cold and foggy uplands is diurnal (Roosevelt, 1910).

Courtship and fighting patterns have been correlated with the nocturnality of geckos (Noble and Bradley, 1933; Evans, 1936), and there is a growing literature upon diel rhythms of pupation in moths, flies, and hymenopterans (Barnes, 1930;

Bremer, 1926; Kalmus, 1935, 1940; Lewis and Bletchly, 1943; O. Park, 1940; Scott, 1936). We are not concerned at this point with the experimental analysis of such patterns, but it should be noted that these insect pupation rhythms normally are in step with the diel cycle, although, experimentally, many such rhythms show a remarkable degree of stability under constant conditions (Fig. 194).

In any discussion of diel periodicity it is essential for a full appreciation of the whole problem to remember that a period of relative activity presupposes a period of relative inactivity. The rhythmic alternation of active and inactive states, in diurnal and nocturnal species, is complementary. Feeding and mating are consummated in active states, and physiological recuperation (rest, sleep) in a more or less protected habitat niche in inactive states.

This is generally true for the majority of metazoans under normal conditions. The literature upon sleep, or its physiological equivalent, is large, especially with respect to sleeping attitudes, times of inactivity, and the physiological investigation of the sleep of mammals.* At the community level many animals escape diurnal competition for food, or may gain protection from enemies, by a nocturnal period of activity. This may be viewed from two points of view. From the evolutionary standpoint (p. 682), many nocturnal species are thought of as more primitive than their diurnal relatives. Kennedy (1928) discussed this problem for insects and found that the primitive orders were either nocturnal in activity, or occupied cool, darkened habitat niches, or were both nocturnal and occupants of such habitats. Barbour (1934, p. 8) expressed the same general view that primitive reptiles are often nocturnal, and Clark (1914) found that such typical nocturnal animals as elephants, hippopotami, tapirs, sloths, various edentates, many lemurs, nonaquatic monotremes, geckos, onychophores, and diplopods have long palaeontological records where there is relatively little imperfection in geological history. Many such animals are found in equatorial rain forest communities, and probably the more vulnerable escape competition of a rich fauna by their nocturnalism (O. Park, 1940). Such nocturnalism should be distinguished from that of many species living in hot, dry desert communities. The latter may be viewed as the development of a nocturnal fauna, in part from the forces exerted by physical influences of the community. Both types of response, obviously, are products of long periods of selection.

This first aspect, the evolutionary aspect, of the development of nocturnality, is allied to the development of diel rhythmicity in general. Certainly the diel activities of individuals, populations, and communities are correlated with the physical environmental rhythms. That this is a real, rather than an apparent correlation, seems to be well established. Biological rhythmicity is a result of rhythmicity in the physical environment, as has been suggested often in the past (Reynolds, 1920; Bouvier, 1922; Kleitman, 1933; Welsh, 1938; Park, 1940). If the diel cycle of activity and inactivity does represent an adjustment of organisms, populations, and communities for survival, then nocturnality and diurnality become integral parts of the problem.

In addition to this long-range evolutionary aspect of the development of nocturnality, there is a second aspect, in which a population, or a part thereof, develops nocturnality as an adjustment to an immediate pressure of its biological environment. For example, Roosevelt (1910) expressed the view that in regions where game is hunted persistently, many of the persecuted animals tend to become nocturnal, whereas the same species were often diurnal in regions not systematically hunted over by man.

Diel cycles of activity of the community are best known from the data on sound production (sonification) and on vertical migrations. Almost countless animal sounds over the diel period give evidence of activity in the majority of temperate and tropical terrestrial communities. When such sounds are analyzed at the species level, the apparent diel character of this sonification, both in terms of diurnal and nocturnal species, and in the quantitative ebb and flow of the volume of sound emitted by a

* The interested student will find the following of value in pursuing the subject of sleep, in its broadest sense: Conklin (1927), Fiebrig (1912), Kleitman (1929, 1933, 1939), Pieron (1913), Polimanti (1911), and Rau and Rau (1916).

particular species, gives a partial picture of total activity at the community level. This is dramatic in the tropical rain forest, where the volume of sound at dawn and dusk, when the nocturnal and diurnal faunas are in the process of alternately exchanging roles, is both varied and relatively great (Figs. 189 and 190).

Although the crepuscular flashing of fireflies (Craig, 1917; Hess, 1920; Buck, 1935, 1937, 1937a), the chorus of howler monkeys (C. R. Carpenter, 1934), and the shrill stridulations of seventeen-year cicadas and of tree crickets (Frost, 1942) appear to be integrated responses of bioluminescence or sonification, the integration apparently is supplied by the external environment. In these examples of group activity a given sequence of flashes, or of sound production, may be initiated on the stimulus supplied by a leader, but there is no evidence that the animals coördinate to join their fellows in activity as a response, primarily to an inner, or endogenous, rhythm. The point is important in the sense that the initial stimulus, to a leaderless group, or to the group leader is, manifested in the environment, and hence represents a community coördination.

Vertical diel migrations of animals through the strata of communities are among the best-substantiated phenomena of community activity. Such migrations take place in marine, fresh-water, and terrestrial communities. As we have seen, they are subject to seasonal and local weather conditions, and, with few exceptions, the frequency and amplitude of such a vertical movement is under the control of the operating diel factor complex.

Where they have been investigated, the majority of pelagic marine animals perform periodic vertical migrations. These involve an upward movement from deeper water at the approach of evening, and a downward movement from the surface to deeper water just before, or at, sunrise. The influences regarded as chiefly responsible for these rhythmic migrations are (1) light, (2) temperature, (3) hunger, (4) salinity, (5) gravity. Light is regarded as the chief motivating factor, but there is doubt whether this influence operates through its change in intensity, or by its absolute intensity (Clarke, 1933; Johnson, 1938). There is also the possibility that light operates indirectly, by modification of the response to such factors as gravity, food, and temperature. Upward movement may be a searching reaction of animals that feed upon the phytoplankton. These latter are concentrated in the euphotic layer, and such movements have been regarded primarily as food-procuring reactions in fresh-water zoöplankton, at times of the diel cycle when light intensities are not prohibitive (Worthington, 1931). Again, gravity is a relatively invariable factor that operates constantly upon plankton, and we have noted numerous devices employed by aquatic organisms to offset or minimize this force. Swimming upward is a reaction often correlated with negative geotaxis, and it has been suggested that light intensity may be the stimulus that affects a change in sign of geotaxis (Esterly, 1917; Clarke, 1934).

Vertical movements may be regarded as complex shifts in population densities within the community, motivated internally by hunger, and controlled directly or indirectly by the periodic rhythm in light. In general terms, planktonic animals sink, or swim downward, when the intensity of light, or the change in intensity, is such that the organismal response is geopositive. At depths, with gradual weakening of the stimulus of light, a threshold is reached. Here the downward movement is arrested, and a maximum diurnal population density occurs, usually at the middle of the day. At the end of the day the reverse sequence of phenomena occurs. Lowering light intensity reverses the geotactic reaction, and the population swims upward. Feeding usually takes place at or relatively near the sea surface, and there is a maximum nocturnal population density usually near the middle of the night. This sequence of events is illustrated in Figure 195, in which diel movements are stylized for three North Atlantic plankton species, a medusa (*Cosmetira pilosella*), a copepod (*Calanus finmarchicus*), and a mysid crustacean (*Leptomysis gracilis*). Such movements in zoöplankton involve nocturnal feeding upon the phytoplankton that inhabit the surface stratum; in turn, larger nektonic animals, like the herring, feed upon zoöplankton.

In such vertical movements the upper component may encounter a sharp temperature gradient, or thermocline, that may prevent further ascent (Sverdrup, Johnson, and Fleming, 1942). Similarly, such a sharp thermocline may limit the lower component in some species populations; for example, the copepod, *Metridia lucens,* ascends to the thermocline, but not through it, in the Gulf of Maine, where the thermocline has an approximate gradient of 7° C. in 10 meters, and another copepod, *Centropages typicus,* inhabits the upper stratum of warm water (10 to 20 meters in thickness), but does not pass through the thermocline, into water of from 8° to 5° C.

logical state which causes migrations even in the absence of light (Esterly, 1917).

"Since an animal is constantly subjected to various and simultaneous stimuli, some of fluctuating intensity, the nature of the movement will depend upon the combination at any one time, and it is not always clear which is the dominating stimulus."

Pelagic copepods and chaetognaths have been studied especially in these marine vertical movements, but such movements are

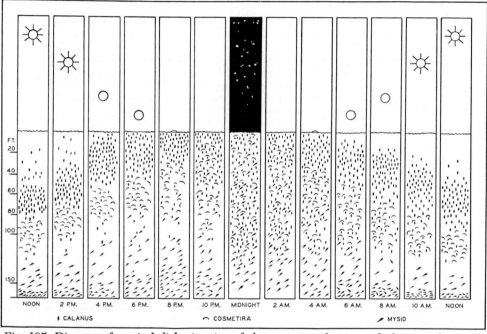

Fig. 195. Diagram of vertical diel migration of three species of marine plankters in the North Atlantic. (After Russell and Yonge.)

mocline, into water of from 8° to 5° C. (Clarke, 1933).

Consequently, the normal range in depth of the vertical movement, and the time of the movement, vary with the species response to many physical and biological factors. This complexity is summed by Sverdrup, Johnson, and Fleming (1942, p. 837):

"Not only do different species react differently, but different stages of development, and the sexes also, have their own characteristic behavior with respect to diurnal [diel] response associated with light. A further complication is encountered in that the degree of response is also seasonal, indicating changes in physiological state (Russell, 1928). Species of *Acartia* give some indication of a diurnal [diel] physio-

not restricted to species inhabiting the upper layers of water. Thus, certain sergasid prawns have a maximum population density at between the sea surface and 200 meters at night, but during the day move down to between 600 and 800 meters (Welsh, Chace, and Nunnemacher, 1937).

Diel vertical movements of plankton in fresh-water communities show the same general pattern as that discussed for the marine community, and the problem is summarized by Welch (1935, p. 232):

"Not one factor but several factors interact in the production of some, and probably all, forms of diurnal [diel] movement. The principal factors involved appear to be light, temperature, food and gravity. It is also possible that still other factors may sometimes influence the reactions."

Table 49 gives a condensed summary of certain species of zoöplankton, the extent of their vertical movements, speed of descent in the downward movement, and speed of ascent in the upward movement of these migrations. Worthington's careful work (1931) on the Lake Lucerne community, Switzerland, serves to emphasize the differential response of several species populations to the same community factor complex.

öplankton are periodic changes in the positional organization, which affect the community as a whole or in part, depending upon its size.

An indirect effect on stratification by vertical movements is described by Welch (1935) in lake communities. Winds that arise at night, when the zoöplankton is at or near the lake surface, drift the plankters into shoal water, and many of them are unable to return to the lake depths at dawn. They are trapped in the surface stratum, and may not return to deeper

Table 49. Vertical Movements of Lake Lucerne Zoöplankton (Modified from Worthington, 1931)

Species Population	Extent of Vertical Movement in Meters	Speed of Descent, One Meter per	Speed of Ascent	
			Noon to Dusk, One Meter per	Dusk Onward, One Meter per
Daphnia longispina, adults.......	10–40	5 minutes	25 minutes	6.3 minutes
D. longispina, young.............	5–60	3.1 minutes	17.5 minutes	4.3 minutes
Bosmina coregoni, adults.........	15–15	No movement		
B. coregoni, young..............	7–55	4.5 minutes	26 minutes	7.5 minutes
Diaphanosoma brachyurum......	3–10	10 minutes	No movement	12 minutes
Diaptomus gracilis, adults........	13–30	12 minutes	60 minutes	15 minutes
D. gracilis, young..............	20–37	20 minutes	60 minutes	12 minutes
D. laciniatus, adults............	25–75?	4.6 minutes	14? minutes	8 minutes
D. laciniatus, young............	22–58	4.4 minutes	28 minutes	8 minutes
Cyclops strenuus, young.........	12–46	7 minutes	60 minutes	5.5 minutes
C. leuckarti, adults.............	3–15	20 minutes	105 minutes	12 minutes

As the table shows, no generality will cover the details of the vertical migrations of all species of zoöplankton, unless it be that the majority have such movements, the details of which vary with species and age. Reaction differences between young and adult organisms of the same species preclude generalizations about the pattern for a given species population, except where such differences are known. Some organisms make vertical movements only when juvenile. Thus the larvae of a fly, Corethra punctipennis, spend the day in the profundal mud of lake communities, and rise to the surface at night (Juday, 1921), where they prey upon infusorians, entomostracans, and small larvae.

Vertical movements of animals affect the stratal organization of the community. As noted in Figure 195, the upward nocturnal, and downward diurnal, movements of zo-

strata until there is a change in the weather. Meanwhile, the stratal organization is temporarily deranged.

Again, there may be a concentration of plankton at the center of the lake surface, with a diminution of plankton in the peripheral water. This, too, may be an indirect result of vertical movements in the lake community. Welch (1935, p. 218) offers an explanation:

"Plankters which migrate vertically descend with the onset of dawn, those nearer the shore arriving at the bottom at a higher level, and, following down the slope of the basin in order to reach deeper water, tend to concentrate in the depths; on the next trip to the surface, they rise vertically from the profundal area, thus producing at the surface a greater concentration above the deep parts than above the peripheral regions."

As to terrestrial environments, diel vertical movements of animals are known for relatively few communities, although such phenomena undoubtedly form a regular feature of such stratified communities as forests, and the movement into and out of desert floors is a periodic response to the rigors of the physical portion of the environment.

In general, in the communities studied, there are definite vertical migrations in terrestrial communities. These movements apparently are under the control of, or at least are coördinated with, the rhythmic march of the operating diel factors, among which may be noted especially (1) light intensity, (2) air temperature, (3) the correlated soil temperature, (4) relative humidity, and (5) rate of evaporation. Gravity, important in aquatic communities, is relatively inoperative, since the moving animals can climb or crawl up the stable, stratified plant portions of the community in prairies and forests.

More or less satisfactory demonstrations of vertical movements are known for a sufficient variety of terrestrial communities to attest to its probable general occurrence. For example, Chapman and his colleagues (1926) were able to show a diurnal movement into the subterranean stratum, and a nocturnal movement to the sand floor, of certain insects of a Minnesota sand dune community, and Sanders and Shelford (1922) found movements between the herbaceous and shrub strata of a pine dune community near Gary, Indiana. Similar diel vertical and horizontal movements have been described for a variety of flood plain communities near Perm, Russia (Gudoshchikova, 1927); grassland, grassland-forest ecotone, and deciduous forest near Norman, Oklahoma (Davidson and Shackleford, 1929; J. R. Carpenter, 1936); and a beech-sugar maple forest near Michigan City, Indiana (Park and Strohecker, 1936).

Many small invertebrates pass their period of diurnal or nocturnal inactivity in the forest floor stratum. This is evident from certain of the studies just cited, and also from quantitative sampling of leaf mold. In the Panamanian rain forest, Williams (1941) found a relatively low population density within quadrats studied at night as compared to those studied during the day, and certain of the animals he collected in the floor by day were not discovered there at night. In one instance one of these animals, a pselaphid beetle, *Arthmius sabomba*, was collected by lights at night (O. Park, 1942).

There is evidence of two vertical diel movements in forest communities. These are (1) a diurnal movement into higher strata during the day, with a return to lower strata at night; and (2) a dusk nocturnal movement into the herbaceous, shrub, and tree strata during the night, with a return to the forest floor during the early morning hours. Such vertical movements may be accompanied by horizontal spreading over herbaceous, shrub and tree strata.

The well-defined vertical movement of the marine and fresh-water zoöplankton has its counterpart in the less studied vertical movement of nocturnal animals in forests. Herbivores and predators are involved in both movements. The vertical and horizontal movements of diurnal animals in terrestrial communities apparently have no counterpart in the zoöplankton as a whole; instead, the analogous community function may lie in vertical or horizontal movements of diurnal populations in littoral zones, or in vertical movements of larger aquatic animals.

From a more general view of terrestrial communities, there is a definite correlation between the vertical movements of smaller invertebrates and the active period of the larger and better-known vertebrates. Few data are available on either the relative proportion of nocturnal to diurnal species, or on the relative size of the populations involved, per unit of community area.

As seen from Table 50, in one case there is a striking convergence between the percentages of diurnal and nocturnal mammals from two relatively well-known areas (O. Park, 1940), the north temperate deciduous forest in the vicinity of Chicago, Illinois, and the Panama Canal Zone equatorial forest.

Contemplation of the activities of diurnal and nocturnal animals poses the question: Are such activities induced by the periodic diel rhythm in physical factors, or are they more or less endogenous, and only in apparent correlation with the cycle of day and night? The answer lies in an analysis of activity patterns under controlled laboratory conditions. Hardly more than a start

Table 50. Comparison of the Mammalian Faunas of a Temperate Deciduous Forest and a Tropical Rain Forest Region, with Respect to the Period of Activity for Species and Subspecies (Modified from O. Park, 1940)

Order	Chicago Area (Data from Gregory, 1936)			Barro Colorado Island, Panama Canal Zone (Data from Enders, 1935)		
	Total	Diurnal	Nocturnal	Total	Diurnal	Nocturnal
Marsupialia............	1	0	1	5	0	5
Insectivora............	4	2	2	0	0	0
Chiroptera............	7	0	7	10	0	10
Carnivora.............	15	4	11	9	$4\frac{1}{2}$	$4\frac{1}{2}$
Primates..............	0	0	0	4	3	1
Rodentia..............	20	12	8	16	6	10
Ungulata..............	2	$1\frac{1}{2}$	$\frac{1}{2}$	5	2	3
Edentata..............	0	0	0	5	2	3
Total subspecies.......	49	$19\frac{1}{2}$	$29\frac{1}{2}$	54	$17\frac{1}{2}$	$36\frac{1}{2}$
Total percentages......	100	39	61	100	31	69

has been made, and in such a discussion as the present one, where the community is being examined for periodism, an extensive analysis of the experimental findings on species is not feasible.[*]

From the viewpoint of the whole community, such activities have been classified as follows (O. Park, 1937, 1941):

I. *Periodic Activity*: An activity pattern in which the fundamental characteristics for a species population recur through successive diel periods
　1. *Exogenous Type:* Periodic activity in which the pattern is directly induced and controlled by the periodic environmental influences
　2. *Endogenous Type:* Periodic activity in which the pattern is resident in the organism

[*] This experimental field has been summarized (O. Park, 1940), and further information will be found in: Barden (1942), Brown and Webb, (1948), Calhoun (1944, 1945), Fulton (1941), Grison (1944), Gunn (1940), Gunn and Pielou (1940), Higginbotham (1939, 1947), Hutchison (1947), Kalmus (1940), Lewis and Bletchly (1943), Mellanby (1940), O. Park, (1941, 1941a), O. Park and Noskin (1947), O. Park, Roberts, and Harris (1941), Pielou and Gunn (1940), Smith and Cole (1941), Waloff (1941), and Warden, Jenkins, and Warner (1940).

　a. *Habitual activity:* Endogenous activity that is the result of induction or previous experiences of the individual, and, hence, indirectly induced by the environment
　b. *Inherent Activity:* Endogenous activity that is a part of the species heredity
　3. *Composite Type:* Periodic activity in which the pattern is in part exogenous, and in part endogenous
II. *Aperiodic* (Arrhythmic) *Activity:* Activity of a species population, the individuals of which do not exhibit the same average pattern with respect to the diel time sequence, but in which the individuals exhibit a varying activity and inactivity through successive diel periods.

It seems certain that (1) the periodic activity pattern of a species population is both complex and specific with respect to normal diel rhythm; (2) that the activity pattern is usually, if not always, modifiable by the environment; (3) that many forms of periodic activity are involved, such as alternation of overt active and inactive periods, rhythms in pupation and in bioluminosity; (4) that the great majority of species have composite patterns; (5) that the sum total of such patterns conforms to the normal diel rhythm, is usually in step with it, and consequently gives the community, or at least those parts exposed to diel rhythm, a distinctive diurnal and nocturnal aspect.

To turn from periodic to arrhythmic activity, the latter would hardly be noticeable in the community, unless specifically looked for, since the active individuals would always blend into the periodic activity of the diel cycle. When looked for, aperiodic species are found usually in two sorts of environments. They tend to inhabit those portions of the community structure that are not affected, or are relatively little affected, by the diel rhythm of the operating factor complex; or, second, they so control their

exposed to a normal diel fluctuation (Bently, Gunn, and Ewer, 1941); and the flour beetle (*Tribolium confusum*) was found to be arrhythmic as a population when reared under constant darkness, temperature, and humidity (O. Park and Noskin, 1947).

In the second situation noted previously are such social animals as certain ants and man. Thus McCook (1877), speaking of the eastern mound-builder, *Formica exsectoides,* observed:

"Ants at Camp Riddle, when observed during every hour of the night from sunset to sunrise, were found to be pursuing the very same labors in the same way, and in the same fields as during the day. The avenues, tree-paths, feeding stations, feeding grounds and hills were always thronged day and night."

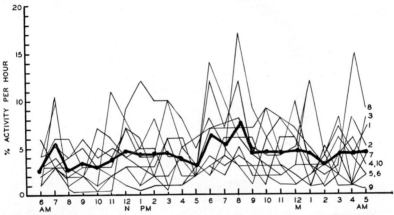

Fig. 196. Aperiodicity of the Mammoth Cave crayfish (*Cambarus pellucidus*); activity recorded under experimental conditions of constant darkness and constant temperature. Ten consecutive twenty-four hour trials are shown, with average of trials in heavy line. Note that each trial is independent of the other nine with respect to time active, and in the distribution of activity. (After O. Park, Roberts and Harris.)

immediate environment that the individuals are relatively undisturbed by the periodic diel complex.

In the first of these situations are such species as the cave crayfish (*Cambarus pellucidus*) of Mammoth Cave, Kentucky (Park, Roberts, and Harris, 1941), in which, under constant temperature and darkness, some individuals are always active (Fig. 196); or, again, essentially arrhythmic species that inhabit the relatively constant habitat of stored agricultural products. For example, the grain beetle (*Ptinus tectus*) was found to be arrhythmic as a population when reared under constant light, temperature, and humidity, but developed an habitual periodic activity when

Parallel observations are numerous (Flint, 1914; Park, Lockett, and Myers, 1931; Park and Strohecker, 1936; Talbot, 1946). Some ants are more active by day, others by night, and still others are aperiodic with respect to the diel cycle.

In man it is obvious that the species has no inherent pattern of general diel activity, and as he integrates into the complex social system he tends to become more and more aperiodic with respect to the diel cycle. The human infant is apparently arrhythmic (Szymanski, 1918); during its first year of life there is an increasing range and regularity of the twenty-four hour body temperature rhythm (Kleitman, Titelbaum, and Hoffman, 1937), and this rhythm becomes progressively less arrhythmic and more regular as the child becomes adjusted to its routine of existence in its particular habitat niche. This is an interesting parallel to the induction of periodism in the grain beetle, cited previously.

Man's adaptability is well documented (Freeman, 1935; Kleitman, 1939) in his habituation to various types of work on a periodic basis, and such periodism is paralleled physiologically by periodism in phosphate excretion, body temperature, tonicity of skeletal musculature, energy output, sleeping habits, and numerous individual skills. Thus man is highly adaptable, capa-

Diel environmental periodicity, then, is in agreement with organismal or populational periodicity, just as environmental stability is in agreement with organismal or populational arrhythmicity.

An interesting intermediate position between the two conditions conducive to aperiodicity is exhibited by the beetle, *Passalus cornutus*.* The usual habitat niche of this insect is the decaying log of the forest floor. The moist, dark log interior has a smaller range, and an appreciable lag in temperature as contrasted to external conditions (Graham, 1920, 1922, 1924, 1925,

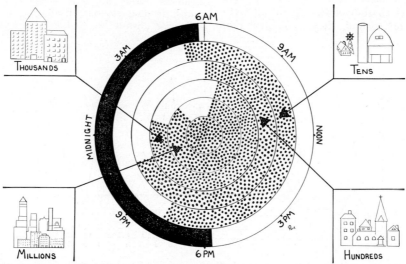

Fig. 197. Diagram of four possible levels in the degree of periodicity or aperiodicity of man with respect to the diel cycle of the inanimate environment.

ble of working and resting without reference to the diel cycle. This is an interesting parallel to the working habits of certain ants.

Methods of transportation and of communication are usually aperiodic with respect to the diel cycle in the sense that they may operate day and night, as are phases of industry, property protection, entertainment, and medical attention. The degree of social arrhythmicity varies with the degree of complexity of organization of man's society. Thus the isolated farmhouse biocoenose usually is nearly as periodic as its surroundings (Fig. 197); the country hamlet is slightly less periodic; the small city still less rhythmic; and the large metropolitan areas are never inactive as a whole (O. Park, 1941a).

1939; Savely, 1939), as noted in Figure 198.

In such relatively stable habitat niches the passalid beetles are subsocial (Wheeler, 1923; Miller, 1932; Pearse, Patterson, Rankin, and Wharton, 1936), and the adult population has been shown to be arrhythmic (O. Park, 1935, 1937).

Thus, with respect to the diel cycle, although many nonsocial, wood-dwelling animals are periodic, subsocial passalids are aperiodic; and, although certain social animals such as certain ants, termites, and

* The black, subsocial "bess-bug" so familiar in logs in advanced stages of decay, and widely known as *Passalus cornutus* Fabricius, has been reviewed in a revision of the family, Passalidae, by Hincks and Dibb (1935), and designated as *Popilius disjunctus* Illiger.

man are aperiodic, *Passalus cornutus,* with its relatively stable habitat and slightly developed sociality, is aperiodic.

two periods of seasonal change, spring and autumn, and two periods of diel change, dawn and dusk.

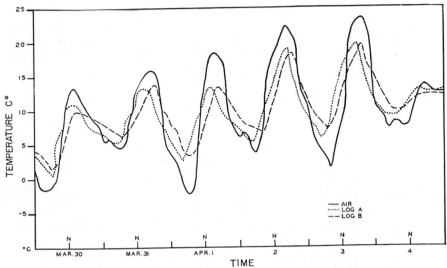

Fig. 198. The prostrate log habitat has a smaller range, and a lag in temperature as compared with air temperature about the log. (After Savely.)

The tendency toward arrhythmicity in social species is interesting. It suggests that the society, in basing its existence upon mutual coöperation, places in operation a complicated system of demands upon the individual (pp. 420, 428–435). These demands can be satisfied fully only by control of the environment. That is, a relatively arrhythmic social medium is interposed between the organisms and the periodic diel cycle. It is difficult to conceive how the highest known types of society could prosper on a strictly diel basis (O. Park, 1941a).

In closing this chapter on community periodism, it should be remembered that a majority of major communities have many of their activities and inactivities upon a seasonal and a diel basis. These two periodic patterns are in general correlation with periodic patterns of the inanimate portions of the environment; that is, seasonal periodicity is congruent with the seasonal march of operating physical influences, and diel periodicity is congruent with the march of operating physical influences through the twenty-four hour cycle.

In both instances there is a period of relative overlap between the complementary halves of the cycle. The community has

There is a basic difference in those communities at latitudes or altitudes that have sufficiently severe winters to control their pattern. The seasonal periodicity has two

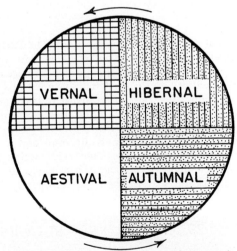

Fig. 199. Diagram of a temperate community in the form of a seasonal wheel. Hibernal and aestival periods are differentiated on the basis of the average level of activity, with the overlap of the vernal and autumnal periods suggested.

parts that differ in amount of total activity: namely, summer ("growing season"), in which there is relatively great activity, and winter ("dormant season"), in which there is relatively great inactivity. Diel periodicity, operating within this seasonal restriction, has two portions that differ in the kinds of animals active, but both day and night have a large active fauna.

This basic difference results in two dif-

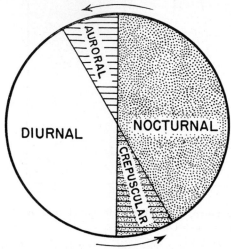

Fig. 200. Diagram of a community in the form of a diel wheel. Nocturnal and diurnal periods are differentiated on the basis of average levels of activity of populations, with the overlap of the crepuscular and auroral periods suggested.

ferent community symmetries (O. Park, 1941a). The seasonal pattern is marked by the two complementary portions of general activity and general inactivity with two interdigitating periods of overlap between activity and dormancy (Fig. 199). In this general point of view, spring is the season when the community is in transition towards the rigors associated with activity, and belongs to the summer; whereas autumn is the season when the community is

in transition towards the rigors associated with inactivity, and belongs to the winter.

The diel pattern is characterized by two complementary portions each of which contains both an active and an inactive fauna, with two interdigitated periods of overlap between the period of diurnal and nocturnal activity (Figs. 200 and 201).

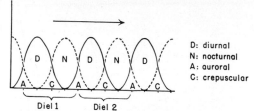

Fig. 201. Diagram to suggest the net diel arrhythmicity of a community as the result of summation of the complementary activity periods of the diurnal and nocturnal faunas.

From the general view of community activity, the dawn belongs to the day, whereas evening belongs to the night. Thus the distribution of activity periods makes possible a much more complete utilization of habitat space and time than would be possible were the community to be organized on either a nocturnal or a diurnal basis. This suggests that the diel community pattern is much more efficient than the larger seasonal pattern. There emerges a new concept of total diel activity—that of ecological symmetry. Thus by development of both a nocturnal and a diurnal fauna, both halves of the twenty-four hour cycle are utilized with respect to the space-time lattice. As the two halves of the diel pattern approach each other, the community becomes biologically more complex, more symmetrical, and more arrhythmic with respect to day and night. This general concept finds support in the literature cited in previous pages.

29. COMMUNITY SUCCESSION AND DEVELOPMENT*

In the preceding chapters the concept of the major community has been defined, and its organization examined in terms of structure, metabolism, and periodism. Our present purpose is to examine the develop-

* Community succession and development are to be distinguished from "community evolution" (p. 695).

ment and succession of the community through time.

Before doing so, it should be reemphasized that, within the concept of the relatively independent major community at the level of survival for interdependent populations, there is an almost infinite series of biocoenoses, and ecological assemblages of diverse rank, extent, and complexity.

For example, any assemblage of organisms having a relatively constant habitus and occupying a certain type of habitat or a series of habitats, irrespective of area or volume occupied, may be considered as a "community." The forest with its associated animals is a community, as is the coral reef. Both have many features in common, but they are communities of different rank. The former is relatively independent of adjacent communities, whereas the latter is dependent upon the adjacent water for its food supply. Forests in general are more closely similar to the sea than to the coral reef, and both sea and forest are major communities in the sense defined previously.

Consequently, any discussion of communities presupposes the philosophic contemplation of the content of the concept and its applicability. We recognize that nearly innumerable communities, and types of communities, may be considered and studied within the frame of the major community concept. In this book the term "community" is used both in its loose, traditional sense, and in keeping with the philosophically consistent concept of the major community, as defined on page 436.

It is obvious that lability is a characteristic of life, whether at the cellular, organismal, populational, or community level. Since communities are composed of organisms and their environments, it follows that communities change. We have examined certain of these changes in terms of organismal response (Chaps. 4–17), populations (Chaps. 18–24), community metabolism (Chap. 27), and community periodism (Chap. 28).

In addition, the community undergoes an orderly series of broader changes. It comes into being, grows, may reproduce itself by a mass budding in some direction, may shift its boundaries; it then matures, becomes senescent, and may perish. When a community dies, or more usually as it is dying, its area is occupied by another community. This process is repeated, community succeeding community, until a relatively stable community occupies the area. This is a bald statement of the process of *ecological succession*, and stands in need of examination, as there are numerous exceptions, variations, and controversial points involved.

In general, ecological succession is an orderly, progressive sequence of replacement of communities over a given point, area, or locality. Research has demonstrated that this sequence is directional, is capable of description, that the rate of change can be measured under certain conditions, and that the end product may be recognized or predicted in some cases. In succession, the entire sequence of communities, from its inception to the terminal product, is spoken of, collectively, as the *sere*. Changes taking place within the sere are spoken of as *seral* changes or phenomena. The early stages of a sere are termed *pioneer* communities, and the relatively stable end product is known as the *sere climax*.

The causes responsible for succession are numerous, complex, often interacting, and not fully understood. In the first place, such causal influences may be separated as *physical* and *biotic*.

Many physical factors are in continuous operation. For example, there are the widespread, slow geologic and geographic processes of erosion and deposition by wind, precipitation, flowing water, and wave action. Erosion and deposition affect the inanimate and animate portions of a community, both directly and indirectly, and produce *physiographic succession*. This form of succession was clearly recognized by Cowles (1899, 1901, 1901a):

"Having related the vegetation largely to topography, we must recognize that topography changes, not in a haphazard manner, but according to well-defined laws. The processes of erosion ultimately cause the wearing down of the hills and the filling up of the hollows. These two processes, denudation and deposition, working in harmony produce planation; the inequalities are brought down to a base level. The chief agent in all of these activities is water, and no fact is better established than the gradual eating back of the rivers into the land and the wearing away of coast lines; the material thus gathered fills up lakes, forms the alluvium of flood plains, or is taken to the sea. Vegetation plays a part in all these processes, the peat deposits adding greatly to the rapidity with which lakes and swamps are filled, while the plant covering of the hills, on the contrary, greatly retards the erosive processes. Thus the hollows are filled more rapidly than the hills are worn away. As a consequence of all these changes, the slopes and soils must change; so, too, the plant societies, which are replaced in turn by others that are adapted to the new conditions."

Besides these and other physical factors, biotic influences are continuously at work. These are intracommunity events, in which the resident organisms bring about changes within their community, the accumulative effect of which is a potent factor in producing, retarding, accelerating, or altering the rate and/or course of the seral changes.

These biotic changes are embodied in the special, technical sense of the term *development* in use by many ecologists. For example, Shelford (1931) employed the term "development" as the growth taking place within the community, where no succession occurs; Phillips (1934, 1935) used "development" for the growth of communities, both where no succession occurs and where it is taking place.

type of community gradually develops. Here we should remember that the change from one type of community to another usually is gradual, over a long time.

Both the development within the community and the seral sequence of communities can be followed, or modified, under the artificial conditions of the laboratory. This is best exemplified in the sequence that takes place in the culture jars of protozoans, where the successive stages are consummated in a relatively short span of time, and the changes are strictly biotic (developmental). From the standpoint of protozoology, it is both pertinent and feasible to study the interaction of excretion products and available food of protozoans with the species population, and

Table 51. *Protozoan Sequence in Hay Infusions (From Allee, 1932, after Woodruff, 1912)*

Order of First Appearance	Order of Maximum Populations	Order of Disappearance from the Surface
Monad	Monad	Monad
Colpoda	Colpoda	Colpoda
Hypotrichs	Hypotrichs	Hypotrichs
Paramecium	Paramecium	Amoeba
Vorticella	Amoeba	Paramecium
Amoeba	Vorticella	Vorticella

In the long run, it is obvious that, given sufficient biotically induced change, the occupied habitats will become so altered that the contemporary residents will languish and finally disappear. Their activities serve to change the environment on an ever-widening front, until all parts of the community are affected. The falling foliage, flower parts, fruits, seeds; excretions, feces, dead and decomposing bodies of plants and of animals; the aeration by burrowing; increase in humic acids, building up of soils, extraction of mineral substances; changes in light, temperature, evaporation rate, and relative humidity through plant growth— these are but a few of the many events that tend to alter the community.

Eventually, the constituents are unable to tolerate the changed conditions, or other species can tolerate these conditions more efficiently. Given a sufficiently long enough time, many populations die or emigrate. They either drive themselves out, or are driven out by other organisms, and a new

the effect of such items on different species populations. The stimulating work of Woodruff (1911, 1912, 1913) involved the study of changes in the protozoan fauna of hay infusions. There was a regular sequence of species populations, each population entering a period of growth, followed by a period of decline, until a relatively stable end product was reached. A typical sequence involved (1) a pioneer stage, characterized by a transparent medium, (2) the medium becoming cloudy as a consequence of the rapid multiplication of bacteria, (3) a monad flagellate stage, (4) ciliate protozoans of the genus *Colpoda*, (5) hypotrich ciliates, (6) paramecia, and (7) stalked ciliates of the genus *Vorticella*. At times (8) amebae persisted, but often these protozoans did not appear, whereas the vorticellids generally appeared, and would persist in some cultures as long as counts were taken.

Table 51 summarizes this sequence in hay infusions.

Woodruff found that *Paramecium aurelia*, when introduced into a filtered medium that had contained large numbers of individuals of this species in pure culture, was weakened in vitality; similarly, hypotrichs such as *Stylonychia pustulata* and *Pleurotricha* mecia were detrimental to paramecia, but that excretion products of hypotrichs were stimulating. Such experiments tended to emphasize the importance of these catabolic products in determining the hay infusion sequence of protozoan populations. Food

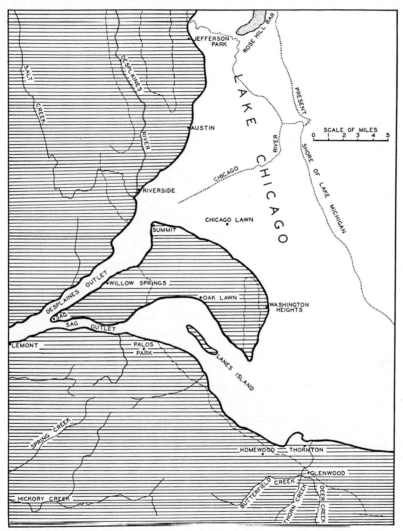

Fig. 202. Formation of the Chicago area, as the headwaters of the Illinois River system, with the drainage of postglacial Lake Chicago, exposure of the Chicago plain, and the formation of Lake Michigan after the retreat of the Wisconsin ice sheet. (After Salisbury and Alden.)

lanceolata, when placed in a filtered medium that had contained many hypotrichs, manifested a lower vitality. However, when the paramecia were introduced into the filtered hypotrich medium, the animals had an increased vitality. Woodruff concluded that excretion products of para-

exhaustion is also a factor.

On a very much larger scale, both with regard to number of species populations, and diversification of biotic activities and products, the developmental phenomena within the community, and the seral sequence of communities, are broadly similar to the regular changes that take place in a flask of hay infusion. The difference is that the natural community usually has its biotic changes augmented by the slower physiographic changes, so that its study becomes both quantitatively and qualitatively more difficult; then, too, it changes much more slowly.

In sequences of natural communities, one of the best documented is that of the forest-on-sand sere, embracing the sand dune area of northern Indiana and southwestern Michigan. This area includes a series of

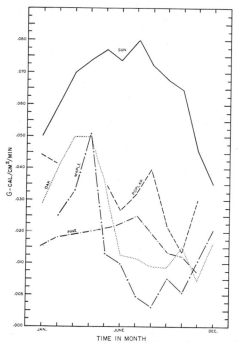

Fig. 203. Progressive decrease in amounts of ultraviolet from pioneer to climax community in the forest-on-sand sere of northern Indiana. Compare with Figure 183. (After Strohecker.)

communities that begins on the shores of Lake Michigan and continues inland several miles. Besides its documentation, the value of this example is enhanced by its geological background, knowledge of which has made possible a reconstruction of the major features of the succession of communities in terms of post-Pleistocene history.

Briefly, as the water accumulated in front of the retreating Wisconsin ice sheet, Lake Chicago was formed behind the morainic barriers. As this lake drained off through the Sag outlet, the water level gradually

fell, exposing the Chicago plain and forming the present, smaller Lake Michigan. The gradually receding water exposed a series of progressively younger beaches, so that the present sequence of communities, from the shore inland, represents horizontally what presumably occurred vertically as the lake retreated through the centuries (Fig. 202), exposing progressively lower, terrestrially uncolonized areas.

The open beach (1), including the beach drift biocoenose discussed previously (p. 534), is the initial community; it is often divided into lower, middle, and upper beach. This is followed (2) by the foredune community of sand-binding grasses and sand cherry. The first tree-bearing stage in this sere (3) is the cottonwood community, a loosely organized pioneer stage on shifting sands just back of the foredune, and exposed to the wind-swept lake front. At times the cottonwood stage is thought to precede the foredune stage. As one goes inland, the jack pine—juniper-bearberry community (4) is followed by (5) an oak forest community, or a subseries of oak stages. This latter, in turn, is succeeded by a sugar maple-beech forest (6), which has been able to stabilize its metabolism sufficiently to endure under present climatic conditions; that is, the sixth type of community listed is regarded as the climax community of this particular sere, and is analogous to the Vorticella stage in the hay infusion sequence. The particular seral sequence given here is subject to considerable variation and modification, as in the hay infusion.

Each of the intermediate forest-on-sand stages, other things remaining favorable, was in past time preceded by a more primitive or a more pioneer community or associes. Or, from another point of contemplation, each will give way to a more advanced seral stage in the series. That is, in time, if unmolested by man's activities, the present coniferous stands will give way to the oak woodlands, and these oak stands will give way to the climax of the sere. The rate of change may vary from stage to stage, or from locality to locality, and edaphic conditions may interfere, but the general accuracy of this picture is established.

For example, the physiographic and geologic background was reported by Salisbury and Alden (1899) and more recently by Fryxell (1927); the general picture of succession was developed by Cowles (1899, 1901, 1911) with particular reference to species of plants, and for plant and animal populations by Shelford (1913); the vegetation was reported upon by Fuller (1925); the annual and seasonal march of daylight intensities in the open sun, clearings, and canopy shade of several seral stages has been measured (O. Park, 1931), as has the ultraviolet component (Strohecker, 1938), as well as the soil moisture, growth-water, and rates and amounts of evaporation (Fuller, 1911, 1914). In addition, several groups of animals have been examined in terms of community distribution and tolerances, for the several community factor

In addition to polyvalent, tolerant species that range widely, possibly through an entire sere, each seral stage has its typical or characteristic organisms. Such species are biotic indicators, or *indices of succession*. They may be restricted to a particular seral stage, as a result of narrow limits of toleration or peculiar habitat requirements; or they may have a broad distribution through several seral stages, but reach a relatively high frequency of abundance in a particular type of community.

Such a sere has both physiographic and biotic (developmental) influences at work, interacting within each type of community, and shaping its normal destiny (Fig. 206).

It should be remembered that within each relatively independent major commu-

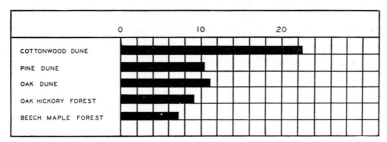

Fig. 204. Progressive decrease in rate of evaporation from pioneer to climax community in the forest-on-sand sere of northern Indiana. Measurements are mean average daily evaporation rates in centimeters from a standard atmometer during the 10 midsummer weeks for the years 1910, 1911, and 1912. (Modified from Fuller.)

complexes—for example, beetles (O. Park, 1930, 1931a), orthopterans (Strohecker, 1937), ants (Talbot, 1934), and spiders (Lowrie, 1942).

Generally speaking, this literature indicates that as one walked inland, starting at the Lake Michigan beach and ending with the maple-beech climax, the several seral stages, in the period of foliation, would show a progressive decrease in total light intensity (Fig. 183), in ultraviolet (Fig. 203), in wind velocity, and in the rate of evaporation (Fig. 204). In correlation with these decreases, there would be a progressive increase in the amount of soil moisture, in the relative humidity, and the amount of humus in the subterranean stratum, the amount of leaf and log mold on the forest floor, and in the number of micro-arthropods per kilogram of floor mold.

Each seral stage, then, has a characteristic physical environment (Fig. 205) and a characteristic biota.

nity, many minor successional processes are being carried on. These take place at different rates, and often have a highly characteristic sequence of seral stages. As a general principle applicable to major communities, these intracommunity successions in habitats or minor communities are completed before the whole community is replaced; in fact, many such minor successions are partially responsible for the developmental changes that take place within the larger whole.

Thus within the grassland communities there is a well-defined sequence of stages in the aging of the dung of animals. This sequence has been investigated by Mohr (1943) for cattle droppings in open pastures in central Illinois. The physical changes that take place are generally associated with progressive loss of water content, and are given as: (1) a pioneer stage, in which the freshly deposited dung is greenish brown with distinct tarnish and film, (2) uniformly brown and moist, (3) blackish brown with moist depressions, (4) brown with distinctly drying crust, (5) light brown with very thick crust, (6) light brown chip, and dry throughout.

Such a cattle dropping is one of the habitat niches of the grassland floor, and

weight, dry chip. In many instances, seasonal succession (p. 530) complicates the seral picture, depending upon the length of time such seral processes require. In Figure 207 the seasonal changes are in close correlation with the seral stages of cattle drop-

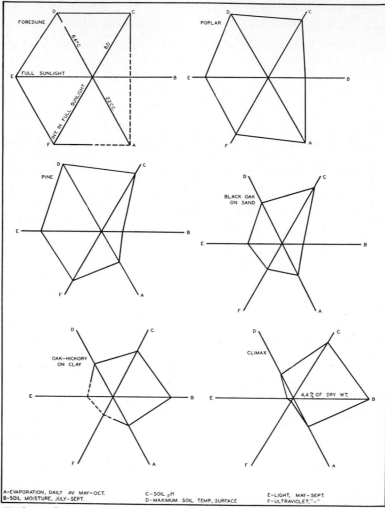

Fig. 205. Each seral stage in the forest-on-sand sere of northern Indiana has a characteristic factor complex. (After Strohecker.)

may be termed a biotope, habitat, habitat niche, a microhabitat (Mohr, 1943), biocoenose, or community without in any way doing violence to the realities of the situation. This microcosm is an integral part of the relatively independent prairie community, it obviously cannot exist without the presence of cattle (or their equivalents), and passes through a minor succession ending in the formation of a light-

pings as a consequence of the relative brevity of the seral process.

Cattle droppings (p. 472), in their last seral stage, eventually lose their identity and become a homogeneous part of the pasture community. Mohr (1943) has given the name *microsere* for such a seral sequence, and considers that the several definable stages are *microseral* stages.

This is one of many available examples

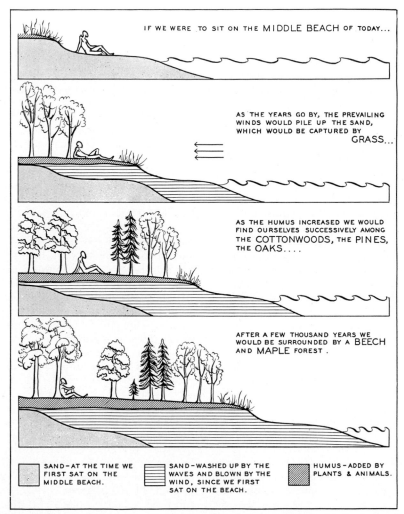

Fig. 206. Diagram of succession (physiographic influences) and development (biotic influences) operating through time in the forest-on-sand sere in the dunes of northern Indiana. (After Buchsbaum.)

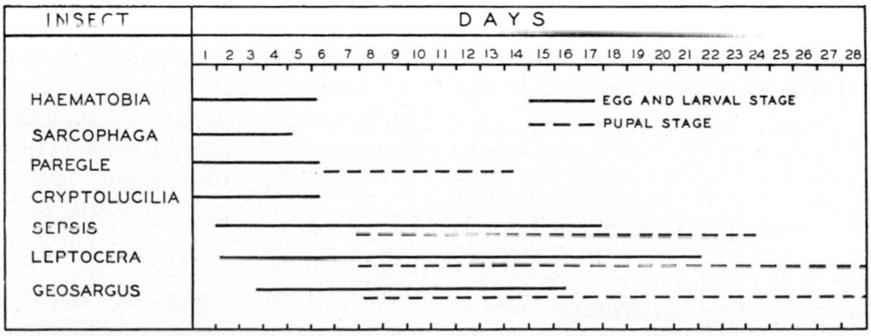

Fig. 207. Succession and development in the microsere of cattle dung. Periods during which predominant maggots were present in early stage droppings. (After Mohr.)

of microseral or minor successions that take place within larger communities.[*]

In forest communities there are many generally similar microseres. Thus the fungi that sprout from the rich leaf mold, as well as the bracket fungi growing on trees and decomposing logs, pass through a sequence of relatively short seral stages (O. Park, 1931a), and the more protracted microsere of the fallen tree is well known (Shelford, 1913; Blackman and Stage, 1924; Savely, 1939; Daggy, 1946). The decaying fungus and log, like the aging dung, eventually lose their individuality and enter a mounding period in which their substance is gradually incorporated into the community floor. In such microseres there can be no permanent end product, or climax stage; this latter is not possible where the microhabitat becomes a part of the larger whole, and such a differentiation of function becomes a criterion for separation of microsere from sere.

The microhabitat may disappear by renewed growth of its immediate environment. An example of this interesting phenomenon is provided by the observations of J. D. Brown, who watched the occupants of a tree hole for some years (Elton, 1927). At first the hollow in a beech tree was used by a nesting owl, but as the tree tissues grew, the entrance became too small for the owls and the hole was taken over by nesting starlings. Later on, the hole had a still further contracted opening, so that no birds could enter the hollow within, and wasps colonized the cavity. Finally, the growth of the tree completely closed the entrance.

Tree holes have been discussed previously (p. 485) in general terms as habitats of the forest community. Such holes have their own micro-food webs, and are involved in a tree hole microsere. Briefly, in instances where the cavity is not closed, this microsere eventually passes into the microsere of the decomposing log. If the

[*] A neglected microsere is that of carrion. Decomposing bodies of fishes washed ashore, and the remains of dead reptiles, birds, and mammals, are especially well suited for research in this connection. Associated with changes in the chemistry of the flesh are numerous problems involving bacterial activities, carrion biocoenoses, and the microseral succession of the carrion fauna.

tree closes the cavity or the orifice, the enclosed bacteria and fungi may destroy the tree, as such, in which case the tree hole microsere also merges in the decomposing log microsere. Still later, the rotten, mounded log eventually becomes incorporated in the forest floor stratum, and its substance is partially or wholly utilized in the growth of other generations of forest plants, and still later of forest animals, in the complex process of community development.

Within the major marine community there is a well-developed succession in the growth of the coral reef community or habitat. Thus corals may build upward within fixed limits. These coelenterates may not continue the reef above the sea surface, and when this point is reached, the animal-formed, calcareous substrate is invaded by other organisms. The reef form itself is related to its position in the sea. For example, many pioneer coralline species, as well as other animals that occupy exposed reefs, differ in growth form from those that live in sheltered lagoons. The exposed reef corals usually form flat incrustations, whereas the lagoon corals are more often arborescent (Darwin, 1842; Vaughan, 1919; Pearse, 1939).

There are numerous other examples of succession in aquatic communities, as, for example, the successional development of bottom organisms in the profundal stratum of water-supply reservoirs (Fig. 208) described by Gersbacher (1937), and the succession taking place in the marine littoral of Monterey Bay, California, described by Hewatt (1935, 1937). Hewatt finds that any clean area is first colonized with a film of algae (1); alga-eating animals, such as limpets (2), then appear; next, a variety of animals, including mussels, gooseneck barnacles, and rock barnacles attach themselves, during their respective spawning seasons, to the relatively pioneer surface (3); gradually these sessile animals occupy most of the surface exposed, and so render the area less available for the larger limpets, which limpets move on, into a still higher littoral zone, where mussels and barnacles are not able to flourish (4).

Up to this point we have been concerned more especially with details of succession than with the general view of the whole process. In the broadest of terms, the earth's surface is divisible ecologically into a relatively few formations of usually great extent. These climatically controlled areas are known as *biomes,* and are to be dis-

munities. Each of these communities is in its own state of flux, as discussed previously (Chap. 28), but, in the larger view, each represents a relatively fixed point in the sere of which it is a part.

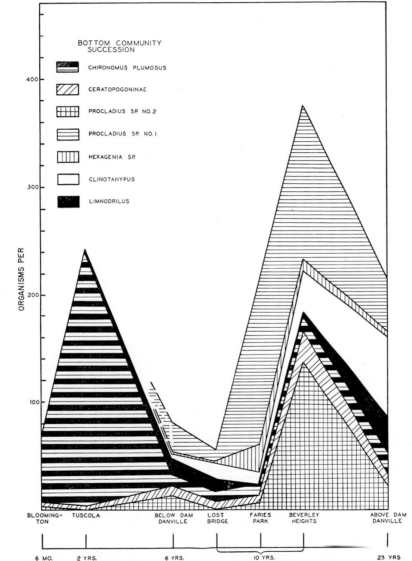

Fig. 208. Development of the profundal stratum in water-supply reservoirs. Note that the time on the horizontal axis of the figure is not plotted on a uniform scale. The vertical axis of the figure is plotted on a uniform scale of number of organisms per square meter. (After Gersbacher, from Clements and Shelford.)

cussed in the following chapter, but their scral aspects must be touched upon at this time.

Within the confines of each of the climatically controlled biomes there are almost innumerable major and minor com-

This is an essential comprehension for an over-all appreciation of the principle of succession, as well as for that of the biome. Within each community, development is taking place, including the several micro-seres operating upon the whole; each community is also, as a rule, exposed to physiographic change. In combination, these physical and biotic influences produce succession, or succession may take place as a result of physical influences alone.

Two types of succession take place in a speak broadly of two general types. (1) the *flowing water sere,* and (2) the *standing water sere.* Both may be known collectively as the *hydrosere,* and their succession spoken of as a *hydrarch* succession (see also pp. 154–157).

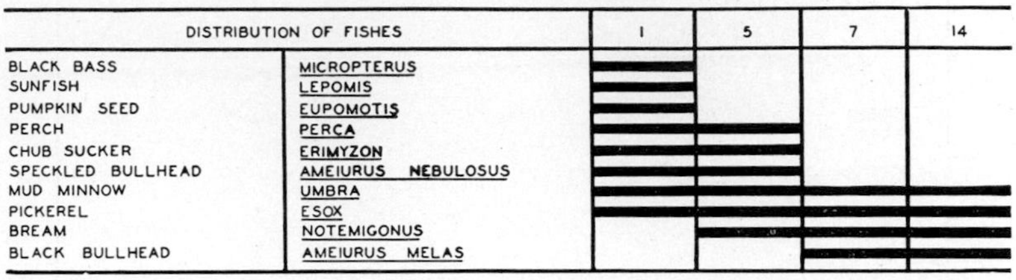

DISTRIBUTION OF FISHES		I	5	7	14
BLACK BASS	MICROPTERUS	▬			
SUNFISH	LEPOMIS	▬			
PUMPKIN SEED	EUPOMOTIS	▬			
PERCH	PERCA	▬	▬		
CHUB SUCKER	ERIMYZON	▬	▬		
SPECKLED BULLHEAD	AMEIURUS NEBULOSUS	▬	▬		
MUD MINNOW	UMBRA	▬	▬		
PICKEREL	ESOX	▬	▬		
BREAM	NOTEMIGONUS	▬	▬	▬	
BLACK BULLHEAD	AMEIURUS MELAS	▬	▬	▬	

Fig. 209. Seral succession of fishes in the pond-water lily-cattail marsh sere in northern Indiana. Numerals refer to ponds by number, in a series of about 100 ponds, differing principally in age, the youngest (pond 1) being nearest to, and the oldest farthest from, Lake Michigan. (Adapted after Shelford, from Pearse.)

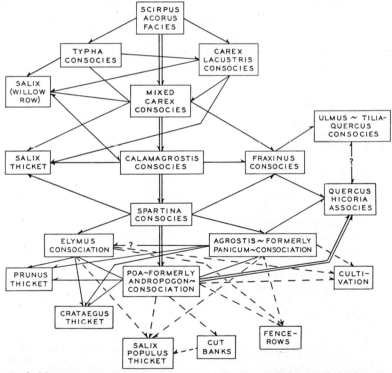

Fig. 210. Probable succession and development in the Fox Lake area of northeastern Illinois, as suggested by index species of plants. (After Beecher.)

given biome under natural conditions. Through time, many seral stages are controlled by local conditions primarily, rather than by the prevailing climatic conditions. Such sequences are termed *edaphic.* Two powerful edaphic influences are soil and water. As for aquatic sequences, we may

Thus within the deciduous forest biome there is the succession that takes place in stream communities (Shelford, 1911). As a stream increases in age, it usually increases in length, and there is a consequent increase in its drainage fan (Fig. 30); its species of pioneer fishes hold their relative ecological position by continually shifting their range so as to remain near the stream's source, or sources. Similarly, as the aging stream lowers its bed, loses velocity, and consequently lowers its capacity for carrying a load of suspended materials, the lower reaches of the stream, e. g., the oldest portions, are occupied by different fish populations (p. 155).

Still other types of edaphic successions take place in bodies of standing water; for example, in lakes, ponds, marshes, and bogs.

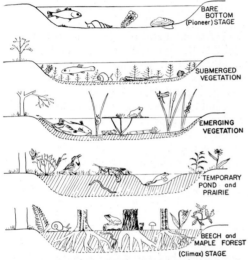

Fig. 211. Diagram of succession and development from the edaphic pond-marsh sere into either the grassland sere or the forest sere, depending upon climatic influences. The three top figures show the accumulation of bottom materials (diagonal hatching) and through time the appearance of submerged and later emerging vegetation with accompanying changes in fauna. The two bottom figures suggest climatic alternatives of grassland or forest development. (After Buchsbaum.)

A well-established classification of lakes, based upon certain aspects of productivity, involves lake succession and development. First, the *oligotrophic* lakes are poor in food materials, and usually deep, the hypolimnion is larger than the epilimnion, littoral plants are not abundant, plankton is quantitatively poor, water bloom is rare, and such lakes develop into the second type. The second type of lake in this classification is known as *eutrophic*. These are rich in food materials, often shallow, the hypolimnion is smaller than the epilim-

nion, littoral vegetation is abundant, the plankton is rich, and there is a characteristic water bloom of rapidly reproducing algae. These eutrophic lakes develop into ponds, marshes, and wet meadows.

The third type, the *dystrophic* lakes, occur in old mountain ranges, or are associated with bogs. Such lakes have little littoral vegetation or phytoplankton, water bloom is consequently rare to absent, and there is a great deal of disintegrating humus material, but a scanty benthos. Such lakes develop into peat bogs as a rule.

In general, ponds, lakes, and marshes, in addition to drainage that may or may not take place through the agency of streams, age from the bottom upward, through building up of the subaqueous stratum. Such communities tend to have an alkaline medium, and the filling of ponds is illustrative of the process.

As the level of the postglacial Lake Chicago fell, to form the present Lake Michigan (Fig. 202), a series of transverse ridges and pond-filled depressions was exposed. This pond series was studied by Shelford (1911b, 1911c, 1913) for the succession taking place, from the younger ponds, nearest the lake shore, to the oldest ponds, much farther inland on the old lake bed. Figure 209 illustrates fish succession in younger ponds of this sere. As the ponds aged, pioneer species of plants and animals disappeared and were replaced by others that could tolerate the changed conditions. For example, there was a general decrease in bare bottom, and an increase in vegetation, total food resources, and bottom deposits with age. This decreased the breeding area for pioneer fishes such as black bass and sunfishes, and the maturing ponds held an increasing population of perch, chub sucker, and speckled bullhead. Still later, with the ponds having a thick bottom deposit, and with the water becoming choked with floating and, later, emergent vegetation, black bullheads became more numerous. It should be emphasized that some species, such as the mud minnow, appeared in the early ponds and continued through most of the sere. Such species may be said to have a high seral adaptability and are of small value as seral indices, because of their range of toleration. In general, it may be postulated that the value of a species as a seral index is inversely proportional to its potential toleration within a given sere or microsere.

In general, when the edaphic pond sere passes into a cat-tail marsh (Fig. 210), other organisms appear—for example, muskrats and red-winged blackbirds (Beecher, 1942). Eventually the marsh tends to pass into either grassland or forest, depend-

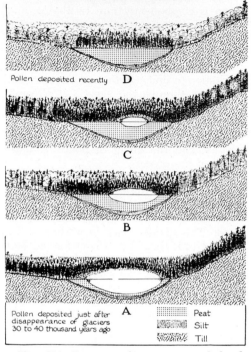

Fig. 212. Diagram of succession and development from the edaphic bog to edaphic bog-forest climax, or to the regional climatic climax forest. (After Transeau, Sampson and Tiffany.)

ing upon the biome involved. Hence there is, through time, a merging of the edaphic sere into the climatic sere of the area. Figure 211 shows the general development taking place in a pond sere, in diagrammatic form, and the eventual differentiation into grassland or forest.

Bogs often have the same end point as ponds, but reach their terminal stage by a different form of development. Here the edaphic bog sere is characterized by filling partially from the top downward, concentric zones of vegetation gradually moving centripetally, building up a supporting mass of debris and rootlets that eventually can support fairly large trees, and consequently encroaching on the open water in

the bog center. In contrast to ponds, the bog is usually acid, and the sere supports many species of plants and animals rare or absent from ponds and lakes. This edaphic bog development is illustrated in Figure 212.

From the preceding discussion several general tendencies may be stated. (1) Communities are not static, but are in a more or less continuous state of directional change. (2) These changes may arise (a) from intracommunity biotic interactions, or development, or (b) from extracommunity physical forces, as exemplified by physiographic influences involved in erosion and deposition, or (c) from a combination of developmental and physical forces. (3) The result is the gradual alteration of the community through time, and the appearance of species populations better adjusted to the changed conditions, e.g., a succession of communities over a given area, known collectively as a sere. (4) Within each community, several smaller developmental or successional sequences take place, each sequence forming a microsere. (5) The sere then, may be viewed as a series of stages, starting with a pioneer stage, or stages (associes), and ending with a climax stage, which is relatively stable under existing climatic conditions. (6) We may differentiate between microsere and sere, in that the former has no stable end product or climax, in the strict sense of the word. (7) We may differentiate between edaphic seres, controlled by such local conditions as soil or water, and climatic seres that are under the general control of the prevailing climate, and end in a climax community.*

* The terminology concerning the climax is complex, and has shifted in meaning, and in shades of meaning, at the hands of many students. This is not a subject for the unwary or for the impatient.

In this book we have used the term "climax" in the traditional sense, as a relatively stable, terminal community of a sere—for example, the climax beech-sugar maple forest, or one of its equivalents. It should be pointed out, nevertheless, that there are other usages of the term—for example, that a climax is a synonym of the plant formation, or, more broadly, of the biome.

Five terms, at least, are involved in this general area of theory. They are *postclimax, preclimax, subclimax, proclimax,* and *disclimax*. They are discussed in Carpenter (1938), Clements and Shelford (1939), and Oosting (1948).

From this general theoretical background there emerges an important principle at the level of the biome, the principle of *convergence*. In general, under natural conditions, the several seres (edaphic and climatic) tend to converge, in time, in a climax community. This is a *climatic climax* as opposed to an *edaphic climax*, and, presumably, endures as long as the pre-

max may be composed of a variety of dominant tree species (Fig. 213), in differing combinations and frequencies, including hemlock, beech, sugar maple, red oak, American elm, wild black cherry, chestnut, tulip, live oak, and magnolia, among others. For detailed analysis of this forest climax type, consult the following studies and their extensive bibliographies, that partially

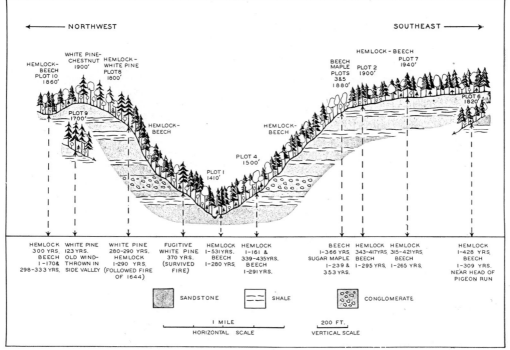

Fig. 213. Climatic climax (hemlock-beech-maple), subclimax (white pine), and second growth on the Northern Allegheny Plateau of Pennsylvania. (After Hough & Forbes.)

vailing climate endures. The structure of the climax community of a sere may vary with latitude and with altitude. For example, within the deciduous forest biome of eastern North America, the climatic climax

Postclimax may be regarded as a relict of a former climax, held under edaphic control in an area the climate of which is no longer favorable for development of the climax.

Preclimax and subclimax are terms often used to designate a seral stage that just precedes the climax.

Proclimax is a term used for those communities that suggest the extent or the permanence of a climax, but are not controlled by climate.

Disclimax is a community that originates and is maintained by some form of disturbance.

open the subject: Braun (1935, 1947), Cain (1943, 1944, 1945), Frothingham (1915), Gordon (1940), Harshberger (1911), Hough and Forbes (1943), Kendeigh (1946), Lutz (1930), Nichols (1935), Odum (1943), and Potzger (1946).

As an example of the principle of convergence, the region of northwestern Indiana, in the deciduous forest biome, is selected on historical grounds. The following organization shows convergence in this area from four separate seres: namely, sand ridge, clay bluff, pond, and flood-plain.

This classical convergence diagram may vary in its details from locality to locality, and is still receiving modification at the hands of specialists without altering its central theme. The original was prepared by Shelford from the writing of H. C. Cowles, and with his guidance (Shelford, 1913, p. 310).

convergence in Indiana, the several seres converge in the regional climatic climax; namely, the beech-sugar maple community

SAND RIDGE
Cottonwood
Gray pine
Black oak
White oak
Red oak
Hickory
BEECH AND SUGAR MAPLE
Tulip
Basswood
White elm and white ash
Swamp white oak
Buttonbush
Cattail and Bulrush
Water-lily and Water mill-foil
Chara
POND

CLAY BLUFF
Aspen
Cottonwood
Hop-hornbeam
White oak
Red oak
Hickory
Hickory
Red oak
Bur oak
Basswood
Hawthorn
Slippery elm and white elm
River maple
Black willow
FLOOD-PLAIN

Much later, Clements and Shelford (1939, p. 231) worked out a coordinated organization of convergence in north-central Indiana, adapted from the original Cowles diagram, but placed in a modern frame. That is, each seral stage of five seres is given both a plant and an animal seral index. It should be noted that in both the following and the previous arrangement of

In the regions of overlap between biomes the regional climatic climax may vary between the climax type of the biomes involved. This brings to mind the view that, just as there is an ecotone between communities (p. 476), there is, in a much larger sense, an ecotone between biomes. For example, in the forest border region of North America, between the western grass-

SAND RIDGE
1. Cottonwood
    Cicindela lepida
2. Jack pine
    C. formosa generosa
3. Black oak
    Cryptoleon nebulosum
4. White oak-Black oak-Red oak
    Hyaliodes vitripennis
5. Red oak-White oak
    Cicindela sexguttata

CLAY BANK
1. Bare ground
    Cicindela limbalis
2. Shadbush
    Polygyra monodon
3. Cottonwood
    Polygyra monodon
4. Hop-hornbeam
    Fontaria corrugatus
5. Red oak-Hickory
    Cicindela sexguttata

BEECH-SUGAR MAPLE
Plethodon cinereus

5. Hickory-Red oak
    Cicindela sexguttata
4. Elm
    Panorpa venosa
3. River maple
    Helodrilus caliginosus
2. Willow
    Succinea ovalis
1. Ragweed
    Tetragnatha laboriosa

5. Soft maple-Tulip
    Plethodon cinereus
4. White elm-White oak
    Anguispira striatella
3. Buttonbush
    Asellus communis
2. Cattail-Bulrush
    Chauliodes rastricornis
1. Water-lily
    Musculium partumeium

5. Birch-Soft maple
Plethodon cinereus
4. Tamarack
    Hyla crucifer
3. Poison sumac
    Hyla versicolor
2. Cattail-Bulrush
    Sistrurus catenatus
1. Water-lily
    Musculium partumeium

FLOOD PLAIN   SHALLOW POND   DEEP POND

land biome and the eastern deciduous forest biome, the convergence may end in either a climax prairie or in a climax forest (Figs. 211 and 214).*

With the principle of convergence in mind, several general aspects of succes-

synthetic productivity relationships, there is (1) an initial, relatively brief period of oligotrophy, followed by (2) a rapidly increasing productivity until a eutrophic equilibrium is reached. The duration of this high productivity period depends upon the

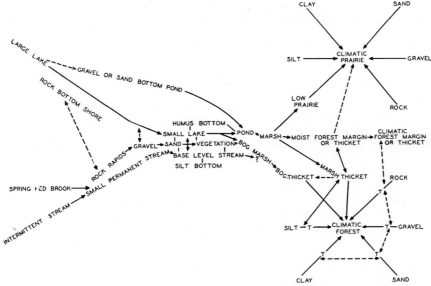

Fig. 214. Diagram of convergence of seres in central North America in the forest-border region into either prairie or forest climax. Compare with Figure 211. (After Shelford.)

sional phenomena deserve attention. In the first place, some data suggest a correlation of successional position with community productivity and efficiency. Lindeman (1942) has suggested that productivity increases in the early stages of a lake succession, or hydrosere, declines with senescence of the lake community, and rises again as the edaphic lake sere converges in the terrestrial sere, through a bog forest, and eventually into a climax forest (Fig. 215). That is, in terms of probable photo-

mean depth of the lake basin and upon the rate of sedimentation. The plateau of high productivity continues until (3) the lake

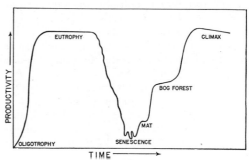

Fig. 215. Hypothetical increase in productivity in early stages of lake succession and development in cold temperate regions; decline as the lake becomes senescent, and increase again as the edaphic hydrosere passes through a bog-forest stage, and eventually into the regional climatic climax forest. See also Figure 212. (After Lindeman.)

* A discussion and evaluation of the details of development, core structure, and the associated nomenclature, lie outside the scope of this book. This subject can be pursued by the interested student in the following references: Braun-Blanquet (1932), Cain (1939), Clements (1928), Clements and Shelford (1939), Cooper (1926), Du Rietz (1930, 1930a), Egler (1942), Gleason (1926), Hansen (1921), Klugh (1923), Nichols (1917), Oosting (1948), Phillips (1934, 1935), Shelford (1931, 1932), Shelford and Olson (1935), Smith (1928), Tansley and Chipp (1926), Taylor (1927), Warming (1909), Weaver and Bruner (1945), Weaver and Clements (1929), Woodbury (1933).

community becomes too shallow for a maximum growth of phytoplankton in the upper strata, or the shallowness of the lake prevents optimal regeneration of nutrients from the bottom ooze. This decline in photosynthetic productivity continues, and is increasingly affected by climatic fluctuations, until the lake is filled with sediment. Then (4) in cold temperate regions, where lake basins are poorly drained, a mat of sedges and grasses, or sphagnum moss, develops as the initial "terrestrial" seral stage. This mat has a higher photosynthetic productivity than the senescent lake, and is succeeded by a bog forest (5) dominated by such trees as larch (*Larix laricina*), spruce (*Picea mariana*), and arbor vitae (*Thuja occidentalis*) or their equivalents. This bog forest may persist for a long time, as an edaphic climax, or is succeeded by (6) the regional, climatic climax forest.

Another aspect of the sere has developed from a study of periodic activities within the community. In the discussion on diel periodicities (p. 562) it was suggested that community efficiency increased as the nocturnal and diurnal components tended to equalize one another. This increasing utilization of the space-time lattice tended to produce a symmetrical, and hence arrhythmic, activity total with respect to the twenty-four hour diel cycle. Degree of total activity symmetry, then, becomes a measure of complexity, and we would expect the more pioneer seral stages to be more asymmetrical, in terms of total diel periodism, than the later seral stages. In other words, it has been suggested that symmetry of total community activity increases from pioneer to climax (O. Park, 1941a).

Development and succession may be altered by natural, catastrophic events such as forest fires caused by lightning, storm winds of high velocity, earthquakes (p. 130), and so-called tidal waves. Not enough attention has been given to the biological consequences of such agencies in primary communities. Recently Macdonald, Shephard, and Cox (1947) have discussed the *tsunami* in general terms.

A tsunami is a long-period gravity wave, in an ocean, that is caused by a sudden large displacement of the sea bottom or shores. A tsunami is accompanied by a severe earthquake, and both are caused by the same crustal displacement. The tsunami of April 1, 1946, was the most destructive in the history of the Hawaiian Islands. It was generated by a sudden shift of sea bottom in the Aleutian trough. Waves traveled southward to Hawaii at an average speed of 490 miles an hour, with an average wave length of 122 miles, and a height over the ocean of about 2 feet. The initial effects on Hawaii varied notably at different points along the shores. At some places waves smashed 50 feet above sea level and carried half a mile inland. Locally, flooding was accompanied by severe erosion of sand beaches, and inland soils were eroded and deposited elsewhere. Under such conditions there would be much initial damage to the marine littoral, the strand, and a variety of inland communities. The effects of such damage on succession and development have yet to be investigated, but it is obvious that these processes would be deflected, arrested, or temporarily altered.

Less spectacular natural agencies may alter succession and development. For example, Albertson and Weaver (1946) reported that a centuries old, ungrazed prairie of mixed grasses in north-central Kansas was reduced by drought and dust to a disclimax of short grasses in a relatively short period of time.

So far, this chapter has been devoted to development and succession under relatively unmolested conditions, that is, with *primary* sequences. Theoretically, this is a valuable exercise, which, in reality, seldom takes place under present, man-dominated habitats and circumstances. Much of development and succession is altered by man, and many seres are initiated, deflected, arrested, or controlled by his activities, or those of his domesticated plants and animals (Fig. 216). These are known as *secondary* sequences, in the sense of Warming (1909), Tansley and Chipp (1926), Woodbury (1933), Clements and Shelford (1939), among many students who have examined the effects of civilized man's interference with the seral course of events. These primary and secondary sequences often have been discussed as *priseres* and *subseres*, respectively, by students of the successional process.

Space limitations prevent adequate treatment of secondary seres, or subseres.*

---

* The following references will serve to open the literature on secondary seres: Bennett (1949), Campbell (1946), Ellison (1946), Johnson (1945), Gustafson *et al.* (1947), Hesse, Allee, and Schmidt (1937, Chap. 28), Korstian (1937), Larson and Whitman (1942), LeBarron and Neetzel (1942), Oosting (1948), Osborn (1948), Pearse (1939, Chap. 14), Rummell (1946), Vogt (1948).

Numerous direct and indirect human agencies alter the course of community development and succession, such as fires, quence of man's urbanization, draining of natural water reservoirs, construction of canals and roads, strip mining, overcultiva-

Fig. 216. An example of the influence of man on the development of communities: photographs of overgrazed and ungrazed grassland in Texas (above), and grazing cattle in New Mexico (below). (Courtesy of W. P. Taylor and the U. S. Soil Conservation Service.)

flooding (as a consequence of impairment of watershed), pollution, impairment or destruction of communities as a conse- tion and overgrazing (Fig. 216). Such secondary effects may be direct, as in forest fires, or indirect, as in the "dust bowl" areas, where overcultivation produced denudation of natural biotic cover (Sears, 1935a).

Where the secondary effects are not too severe, the area in question passes through a period of arrested or deflected development, and, when the secondary agency has ceased to exert a controlling influence, returns to the general pattern of the primary sequence. Under such circumstances the regional edaphic or climatic climax eventually may be reconstituted. Clements and Shelford (1939, p. 232) point out that, under certain conditions, in subseres there may be regeneration of the climax within a man's lifetime, or even less.

30. BIOME AND BIOME-TYPE IN WORLD DISTRIBUTION

Seral succession and development of communities have been discussed in the preceding chapter. When seres have existed through periods of time long enough to be referred to as geologic, the characteristic climatically controlled resulting regions, together with their communities, are referred to as biomes. Biomes may be of great area and of relatively uniform type, especially in their climax communities, but the biome must be understood as including the whole complex of seral stages and edaphic climaxes. The classification of these groups of communities involves two higher categories, the biome and the biome-type. The biome-types correspond to the principal climatic or physiographic features of the earth's surface. The biome, as just defined, may include also geographically outlying fragments of the same or similar nature that are operationally connected by continuing dispersal of their constituent plant and animal elements; it commonly includes also extensions of quite variant nature connected by gradual transition with the major area of the biome—for example, the southern extensions of the coniferous forest biome (the taiga) of North America. The distribution of the vegetation of the world, in its larger outlines, corresponds largely to the biomes of the ecologist. Reference should be made to world vegetation maps, such as those of Goode (1943) and Hesse, Allee, and Schmidt (1947).

When the biomes of the world as a whole are reviewed, it becomes evident that when operational or transitional connection between otherwise similar biomes is lost, they may be grouped as "biome-types." For example, we distinguish the biome-type tropical rain forest as including the several major tropical forest biomes, the African, the Oriental and Australasian, the Central and South American, and the Madagascan (this list is by no means complete). It is evident, by way of illustration of our differentiation of the biome-type from the biome, that the operational connections and interrelations of the outlying areas of the Congo rain forest are intimate, with only the beginnings of geographic isolation and of endemism produced by isolations, and that the "African rain forest" is properly a single biome. The operational contact between the African and the Amazonian rain forests, however, has been lost for a period of geological time so vast that profound faunal and floral differences have developed.

The phenomena subsumed in the sere, and the extensions of climax communities with gradual geographic differentiation, complicate the definition of the biome. Nevertheless, these great and somewhat heterogeneous assemblages of communities are easily recognizable as major geographic features; they have been known as life zones, biotic formations, major biotic formations, "formations" and biomes. The term "biome" is adopted for this work, with the additional "biome-type."

The relations of the biomes to the major biotic regions have usually not been clearly understood. The concept of the biome is essentially ecological, i.e., operational and contemporary; the concepts "biota," and still more strictly "fauna" and "flora,"* involve the historical factor that has produced regional endemism. Confusion between the ecological and biogeographic points of view and their conceptual tools is natural, since faunal and floral areas necessarily overlap the ecological regions (the biomes), and

* We employ the biogeographic terms *biota*, *fauna*, and *flora* with geographic (and historic) connotation to distinguish them from the more ecologically defined communities and biomes.

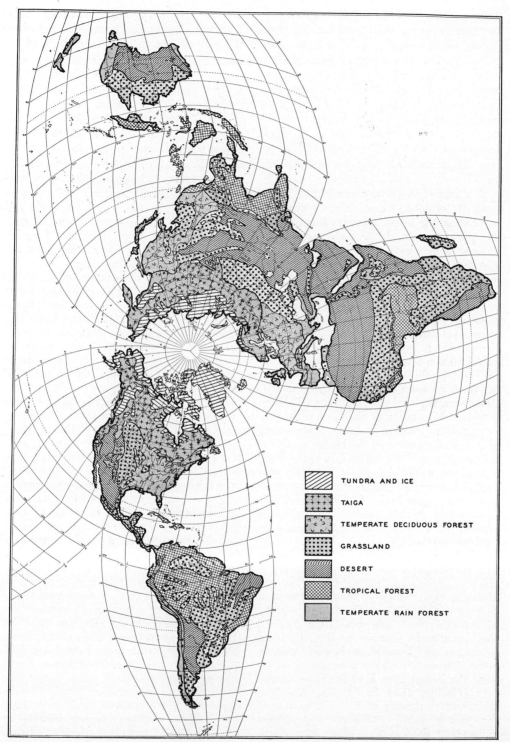

Fig. 217. World vegetation on North Polar projection. Note arrangement into latitudinal zones.
(Extremely schematic, after Goode.)

may coincide with them. We shall attempt to distinguish as ecological, rather than historic in the geological sense, the postglacial period. This in fact coincides somewhat with the ordinary distinction of historic time (in the familiar sense) from geological time. Postglacial time has been found, furthermore, on the evidence of the development of endemic species, to agree fairly well with the time required for species differentiation in vertebrates (Griscom, 1932).

It is scarcely necessary to reject the terms "animal formation" and "plant formation" in favor of the biotic concepts supported in the present work. It will nevertheless be more than ever evident in the characterization and discussion of the biomes that the animal component is in many respects secondary to the plant matrix and dependent upon it. A more extended treatment of the biomes, though under quite different terminology, is to be found in Hesse, Allee, and Schmidt (1937), and useful source books for North America are Shelford (1926) and "The Biotic Provinces of North America," by L. R. Dice (1943). Otherwise, regional geographic works often give better accounts of the biomes than do ecological or zoological studies. The study of the plant matrices of the biome, analyzed under the term "vegetation," has long been treated as a distinct department of ecological botany and has a voluminous literature; e.g., Grisebach (1872), Schimper, "Pflanzengeographie auf ökologischer Grundlage" (1898), and Engler and Drude (1896–1928).

We have attempted to answer the essential question as to the geographic inclusiveness of the term "biome" by the concept of biome-type. Much of the literature employing the term "biome," as is true equally of the ecological "life zone," has avoided this question by limiting itself to the consideration of biomes in North America alone. There is perhaps a tendency to regard the biome as a kind of supercommunity (Phillips, 1934–1935). The American treatments of the subject have the validity of recognizing the climatic vegetational climaxes as the key to a geographic classification of the complex of seral stages, together with the correlated climax, into the unified biome, as suggested in the principle of convergence (p. 575). When the biome concept is still further broadened to include the major biotic formations of the world, it is necessary to combine with it the conceptual geographic grid of historically developed biota characterized by regional endemism. For example, to regard the tropical forest of the Americas (with its associated animal life) as a component of a circumtropical or pantropical "tropical forest biome" involves so extreme a tenuity of connection in time that the biome concept at this level becomes metaphysical. The partition of the terrestrial world into satisfactorily characterized biomes must lean, therefore, upon historical biogeography whenever major physiographic separations are involved.

The ecological distribution of terrestrial communities on a world scale being essentially climatic, and affected by physiographic and certain rainfall boundaries that dominate the east-west partition of continents and climates, as the temperature and wind zones dominate their north-south zonation, the terrestrial biomes are fragmented into geographic regions in low latitudes and in the southern hemisphere, and appear to be continuous only in the circumpolar tundra and ice waste at the north.

The major marine community, in spite of its great regional biotic variation, is so lacking in effective barriers to dispersal, is so much subject to slow continuous circulation of its medium, and exhibits so much interdependence of its components from region to region and area to area, that it may be regarded as a single biome-type (cf. pp. 595–597).

The smaller fresh-water communities are for the most part transient and are so intimately related to their associated terrestrial communities through succession (p. 572), and through the edaphon (p. 510) that sharp segregation of fresh-water biomes is scarcely practical. Even large lakes, such as the North American Great Lakes, represent an edaphic climax on a large scale rather than an independent biome. The existence of a few ancient fresh-water lakes with regionally distinct faunas must be regarded as individual communities, and their geographic relations may be relegated to the province of historical biogeography (Hesse, Allee, and Schmidt, 1937, p. 345).

Fresh waters, on the other hand, invade the sea and are invaded by components of the marine community at river mouths (p. 542). They exhibit a graded transition in brackish water sounds and lagoons and marshes from fresh water to salt water, in which certain forms enter from the sea and others from the land and fresh water; while some brackish waters may represent long series of variously connected communities of a quite distinct type, perhaps best regarded as a major ecotone (Pearse, 1936; Smith, 1931).

The regular north-south series of temperature zones on the continents produces a recognizable world pattern, especially when approached from the north, with icy wastes at the poles, tundra, temperate forests, grasslands and deserts, and the more sharply interrupted series of tropical forests and tropical grasslands. Ecological equivalence (Tables 35, 36, 41) is directly correlated with the existence of geographically and climatically equivalent biomes. It has already been indicated that the significant biogeographic zonation within the larger land masses is from north to south and is ecological, whereas the world-scale east-west faunal and floral partitions tend to be historical in nature.

A grouping of individual fresh-water and terrestrial communities, whether extremely uniform or considerably diverse, into inclusive biomes involves a hierarchial classification. For example, it is legitimate to group into a biome the communities of the smaller islands of the open Pacific, many of which are almost exactly equivalent, and whose biota has the operational connection of continuing dispersion. That biome, however, must include also the larger and higher islands with their richer biota, in which endemism reflects historically continued isolation, and, further, must be related to the still larger and more diversified islands and archipelagoes that are the major sources of the original and continuing dispersion. Where to draw the boundaries for such an extremely fragmented biome offers an almost insoluble question.

The biome concept, in fact, is much like the species concept in that it is useful when used as a descriptive tool without attempting a sharp definition. The major problem of definition for the biome lies, in essence, not in the geographic fragmentation of the major types of biotic formation, but in the interdigitation, overlap, and intergradation of otherwise well recognizable terrestrial biomes, such as that between desert and grassland in North America.

Some apology is necessary for the fact that the characterization of the biomes as to animal components is so much focussed on the larger vertebrates. Critical regional lists of the major groups of terrestrial invertebrates are for the most part still unavailable. In the tropics and in many areas of Africa, Asia, South America, and Australia a vast amount of basic descriptive work is still requisite for invertebrates. Thus, the dependence of faunal definitions on the more advanced floral studies and on vertebrate distribution is again emphasized.

THE PRINCIPAL BIOME-TYPES
THE TUNDRA

The northern circumpolar tundra* is relatively the most continuous, and in some respects the most sharply definable, of all the biomes. Its vast extent from Labrador to Alaska in North America is greatly exceeded in Eurasia by the segment extending from Kamchatka to Lapland. Its dominant physiographic appearance is that of a gently rolling plain, in which the depressions are occupied by lakes, ponds, and bogs (Fig. 218). The characteristic tundra vegetation is sphagnum and various lichens such as the "reindeer moss," with a striking flora of herbaceous higher plants in sheltered places on the drier hillsides.

Certain aspects of the tundra food web have been discussed (p. 515). The characteristic larger mammals† of the tundra are the musk ox (circumpolar until postglacial times), the reindeer and caribou group, the arctic wolf, the arctic fox, and smaller forms, including the arctic hare and the

---

* Tundra is the Siberian word for the zone north of the timberline, known in boreal America as the "barren grounds." Tundra is the accepted ecological term.

† Mammals and birds, as usually the more conspicuous elements of the animal life of the terrestrial biomes, are most easily used to characterize the animal segments of the biome. We acknowledge that this use tends to conceal or perhaps to emphasize our greater ignorance of the invertebrates.

lemmings. Bird life is remarkable for its vast abundance in the brief summer, when the waterfowl of the world seem to be gathered to the treeless tundra for the nest-

permanent, as in the polar bear and snowy owl, or seasonal, as in the arctic fox and hare, and in the ptarmigan. Insect life includes a surprising number of Diptera.

Fig. 218. Tundra landscape: Muskoxen in arctic North America. The muskox was circumpolar in the tundra biome until recent time. (From habitat group in the Chicago Natural History Museum.)

Fig. 219. Polar landscape in Antarctica: emperor penguins, the largest and southernmost species of penguin. (From habitat group in Chicago Natural History Museum.)

ing season. Summer wealth is followed by extreme impoverishment in winter, when even the snowy owl may be driven into the adjacent zones. White coloration may be

There are notably large bumblebees, in which the body temperature is maintained by the by-product of heat from their vibrating wings, and conserved by their insulating covering of feathery fuzz, so that they apparently present an instance of the Bergmann Rule (p. 120).

The floating polar ice, the northernmost islands, and the icy wastes of the Greenland ice cap form an appendage to the tundra. They are by no means lifeless, but the terrestrial animals that invade the "ice desert" are either partly dependent on the tundra, like the arctic fox, which crosses great stretches in nomadic wanderings, or dependent on the sea, like the semiaquatic polar bear, whose food consists mainly of

Antarctic terrestrial life, however, is obviously an appendage to the benthic marine community. Even with the sea as an avenue of dispersal, the penguin group is strikingly fragmented from east to west. Thus the antarctic tundra is not here regarded as a distinct biome.

THE TAIGA BIOME TYPE

The coniferous forest belt is known in Siberia as the "taiga." This name we have adopted for the American as well as for the Eurasian biome characterized by the conif-

Fig. 220. Taiga landscape, Slate Islands, Ontario. The taiga biome is characteristically dotted with small lakes. (Photograph by R. C. Hosie; Courtesy of National Museum of Canada.)

seals. The life of the North Polar area proper is to be regarded as an appendage to the tundra biome.

The southern limit of the continuous principal tundra zone is the fluctuating line of permanently frozen subsoil. Even this relatively sharp and significant definition appears to break down, since there are is landlike areas of low birch forest enclosed in the tundra, and the sphagnum bog component of the tundra extends far to the south in the bog-captured lakes and in certain relict bogs in more southern areas. These latter are evidently relics of the postglacial period.

The borders of the antarctic continent and the antarctic islands bear an obscure counterpart of the arctic tundra (Fig. 219).

erous forest matrix. The taiga is of vast extent, adjacent to the tundra at the south, and continuously circumpolar, except for the interruptions of the Bering Sea and the North Atlantic. It has been discussed by Haviland (1926) and Shelford and Olson (1935), among others. The surplus of food supplied by the wood, leaves, browse, and seeds of the trees, and by the herbaceous plants that live in the deep shade of its forest floor (Fig. 220), supports a notable assemblage of animals strictly associated with the plant-defined biome. Most conspicuous of the larger animals of this biome is the moose, the range of which in Europe, Asia, and North America coincides closely with that of the taiga vegetation. Furbearers of the family Mustelidae are especially abundant and characteristic, as are a host of rodents and lagomorphs (Elton, 1942). Birds of many kinds are identical or closely representative in the two major areas of taiga. The crossbills (*Loxia*), closely confined to the taiga of both hemispheres, exhibit a remarkably effective adaptation of the bill for extracting the seeds from cones.

The fresh-water communities of the taiga are only slightly less well integrated into the biome than in the tundra. In glaciated Europe and North America, lakes of varying size and in varying successional stages (p. 577) are especially characteristic of the taiga zone, and may constitute areas of water sometimes about equal to the amount of intervening land.

The continuous Siberian and Canadian taiga biomes may each best be interpreted as a single vast major community. Their individual outliers, islands of taiga in grassland and deciduous forest, are to be interpreted as individual communities of varying extent. Such islands form one of the modes of transition to the grassland complex and to the deciduous forest biomes, discussed previously with respect to ecotones (p. 476). How intimate the latter transition may be is familiar in northeastern North America, where taiga communities may invade the adjacent biome of temperate forest in association with slight physiographic or edaphic differences. The transition from taiga to tundra is complex in that the fresh-water components of the two biomes are little differentiated, and in the graded transition of the forest through dwarfed timber to a ragged "timberline" at the limit of tree growth (p. 481).

Like the tundra, the taiga has an enormously important seasonal cycle conspicuous in the dormancy of its invertebrates and of many vertebrates, and in the spring influx and autumn departure of migratory birds (p. 539). In these northernmost biomes, indeed, bird migration forms a link with more southern biomes, a link of such far-reaching significance to community metabolism as to recall the interdependence of the ecological formations of the sea.

A curious minor physiographic inversion of those taiga communities that interdigitate with the grassland biome is to be seen in parts of the Great Plains of western North America, where in canyons and ravines forest may be entirely below the level of the grassy plains and invisible at a distance, whereas elsewhere eminences (instead of depressions) are climatically modified and conspicuously covered with coniferous forests. The problems involved in the great southward peninsular extensions of tundra and taiga in north-south mountain ranges in North America, and the quite different geographic arrangement of these formations in Eurasia, conditioned by the contrasting east-west and widely isolated mountain ranges, require separate discussion (p. 592).

THE DECIDUOUS FOREST BIOMES AND BIOME-TYPE

The temperate deciduous forest biome of eastern North America has faunally and florally allied counterparts in eastern Asia and Europe, and to a lesser extent in Western North America. These are now interpreted as the remnants of a once much more continuous series of biomes, or perhaps a single biome, of Cretaceous age.

An intelligible definition of the deciduous temperate forest biome type is more difficult than for the more nearly continuous tundra and taiga. The beech-maple climax forest (or its equivalents), the oak-hickory forests, and the more complex hardwood forests of the Appalachian region form merging groups of deciduous forest types (Braun, 1916). This biome is connected by interdigitation with the taiga, and by forest river-fringe "peninsulas," and "islands" with the grassland. A major difficulty in assortment of communities associated with this biome is the broad continuous area of pine land in the southeastern United States (Shelford, 1926), which resembles the taiga in some of its vegetation, but the surrounding deciduous forest in conspicuous elements of its fauna. The coniferous forests at its northern border (white pine, hemlock, and so forth) are no less a difficulty. Characteristic among larger mammals of this biome in North America are the Virginia deer (Fig. 221) and the black bear; among medium-sized forms are the common opossum and raccoon, and there are numerous characteristic smaller mammal components among the rodents and insectivores. Clements and Shelford (1939) employ the red-backed salamander, *Plethodon cinereus,* to characterize the "beech-maple climax" (Fig. 163). Various other widespread salamanders, such as *Ambystoma maculatum* and *Plethodon glutinosus,* range almost continuously through this biome. A notable index form among invertebrates is the purplish carabid beetle, *Dicaelus purpuratus.* In fact, southeastern North America has preserved a continuous forest through so long a period

different in biotic composition. At the south, the deciduous forest merges into evergreen broad-leaved forest. It is evident that the complexity and diversity of the biome in question are produced by the historic factor. The break-up of the relatively continuous Cretaceous forest came early in Tertiary times, and the isolation of its fragments has given time for radical changes by both evolution and extinction

Fig. 221. Deciduous forest; summer scene with the white-tailed deer, characteristic in the deciduous forest biome in North America. (From habitat group in Chicago Natural History Museum.)

of geologic time that the ecological biome is largely coincident with the faunal and floral subregion of southeastern North America.

The relative simplicity of the tundra and taiga biomes (see, however, the account of alpine and other montane zones, p. 592) is lost in the biome type composed of the deciduous forest biomes of the northern hemisphere. For example, the extensive areas of coniferous forest in the southeastern United States appear to belong with the deciduous forest, for though the floral distinction is sharp, faunal distinction, except for monophagous invertebrates, is weak. The deciduous forest of California and British Columbia is isolated from that of southeastern North America and is quite

in the fragmentary areas preserved to modern times.

The major areas of deciduous hardwood temperate forest are separated by areas in both North America and Asia where the taiga comes in contact with grassland. The biotic composition of the European oak forests is familiar, sometimes through literary sources—the red deer, the roe deer, the wild boar, the gigantic extinct aurochs, and the all but extinct European bison are the large and conspicuous animal forms. It is scarcely necessary to point to the wealth of amphibians and reptiles that characterize the European deciduous forest, many of which are types in the nomenclatural sense—*Salamandra salamandra salamandra,*

Bufo bufo bufo, and the like. It is less easy to characterize the mixed hardwood forest of eastern Asia by familiar forms, partly (and perhaps somewhat paradoxically) because this region is even more modified by man than are Europe and Eastern North America.

Excluding the Tibetan Plateau and its bordering ranges, the deciduous forest biome of China and Manchuria merges at the north with the Siberian taiga, to the northwest is bounded by steppe and desert, and to the south grades into the tropical forest of the Oriental biotic region. Characteristic large predators are the Manchurian tiger (the largest of the tiger races), various wildcats, and a true wolf. Familiar herbivores are the large representatives of the red deer (and the wapiti), and a smaller spotted deer related to the South Asiatic axis deer. The musk deer, the dwarf deer (*Elaphodus*), and the muntjac by no means exhaust the list of deer that take part in this forest biome. Peculiar types of moles and shrews, and forms of the pan-Asiatic hedgehog, are to be found. The bird life of the east Asiatic temperate forest is a rich and confused mixture of migrants and permanent residents. Among the latter the pheasants form a conspicuous group, including the familiar Reeves, golden, and silver pheasants as characteristic forms. Amphibian and reptilian life is strikingly well developed in eastern Asia, with numerous characteristic types related phyletically to parallel forms in eastern North America. These include pit vipers (*Agkistrodon*), chicken snakes (*Elaphe*), water snakes (*Natrix*), grass snakes (*Opheodrys*), pond turtles (*Clemmys*), and the Chinese alligator, the only living congener of the American alligator. Among amphibians the giant salamander (*Megalobatrachus*) represents the American hellbender (*Cryptobranchus*), and the fire-bellied toads represent the otherwise European *Bombina.*

THE GRASSLANDS BIOME-TYPE

The great number of familiar terms applied to grassland areas in various languages—steppe, prairie, plain, savanna, campo, llano, pampa (often in the plural form)—is an indication of the obviousness of this major formation, made still more familiar to man by the distinctive pastoral economy and pastoral (often nomadic) social structure developed in primitive peoples and recognizable as late as the cowboy era of the North American West and conspicuous today in many grassland regions of the world.

The boundary between the deciduous forest biome and the grassland biome, or between grassland and taiga where these formations meet, is often sharp and conspicuous, and the North American grassland in particular has had much attention as an integrated biome of great geographic extent. Intergradation between grassland and deciduous forest is mainly of the nature of forest islands or even forest peninsulas enclosed or nearly enclosed by larger areas of grassland, as in the river border forests of the western affluents of the Mississippi. Conversely, prairie peninsulas also extend into generally forested country. The transition from grassland to desert is far more complex.

The areal extent of grassland biomes, when all the continents are considered, is enormous, and the radical biotic (zoological and botanical) differences from continent to continent are extreme. Ecologically, these differences are minimized by the concept of ecological equivalence, emphasizing the role of the species in its community and biome, instead of phylogenetic relations or even general appearance, as when the gregarious kangaroos and wallabies are seen to be ecological equivalents of the savanna and plains antelopes (Table 35).

Ecologically, the grassland biome exhibits surprisingly little difference in appearance in temperate and tropical regions. Where rainfall is abundant and run-off retarded, the animal component of the grassland is extraordinarily conspicuous, with species of herbivores of large size, vast numbers, and gregarious habits, and attendant carnivores. The potential exactness of equivalence of grasslands is shown by the flourishing Tertiary horse populations on the American Great Plains, their disappearance, and their prompt reestablishment from introduced stock in historic times.

Either directly or with the intermediacy of desert transition areas, the grasslands are continuous from South Africa and Senegal to Mongolia via Central Asia, entering Europe proper in the steppe of southeastern Russia. This vast Old World series of grasslands was apparently connected, to judge from conspicuous faunal relations and well-documented emigrations and immigrations of animal types now characteristic of the plains, on repeated occasions, into and from the plains of western North America, which in modern times extend from Mexico City to central Canada east of the Rocky Mountains. These relatively related and "homologous" grasslands

Fig. 222

Fig. 223

Fig. 222. The grassland biome; characteristic animals of the African grasslands, zebra and wildebeest, Kruger National Park, Transvaal. (Photograph by Herbert Lang.)
Fig. 223. The square-lipped rhinoceros, specifically a grazing type of the African grasslands, Kruger National Park, Transvaal. (Photograph by Herbert Lang.)

may be designated as the South African, East African, Sudanese, Central Asian, and Mongolian biomes, and in North America as the Great Plains biome (Figs. 222, 223).

The grasslands of South America, the llanos of Venezuela, the campos of Brazil, and the pampas of Argentina and Uruguay, are isolated from those of the Northern Hemisphere. In late Tertiary times, there appears to have been more interchange of animal types than of plants between South and North America.

In general, the animals of the open lands are by no means incapable of entering and adjusting themselves to forest conditions, e.g., the European forest horse, the European bison (wisent), the African forest buffaloes, and the relatively few, and thereby unduly conspicuous, species of forest antelopes. The grassland biome in North America has received such conspicuous attention from Weaver and Clements (1929), Clements and Shelford (1939), and in some scores of papers in *Ecology, Ecological Monographs,* and the *Journal of Ecology,* that the student is referred to these sources, and to the treatment of the grassland communities in the present work for further documentation (p. 466). The grassland border of the Australian desert represents an extremely distinct grassland region, the Australian grassland biome.

As an example of the historic causes of interdigitation and overlap of grassland and deciduous forest, we may cite the remarkable postglacial phenomena in both Europe and eastern North America of a grassland corridor parallel to the front of the retreating glaciers by means of which various types of plants and animals characteristic of the Central Asiatic and American Great Plains regions were able to spread, respectively, westward into Europe and eastward in the United States. (Nehring, 1890; Transeau, 1935; Schmidt, 1938; Conant, Thomas, and Rausch, 1945). The European steppe era is especially well documented by fossils of conspicuous grassland or desert types from western Europe (the lion and hyena in Britain, for example) and by living relics preserved in suitable habitats in the now forested regions. Schmidt has compared the American "Prairie Peninsula" with the European "Steppe Corridor."

THE DESERT BIOME-TYPE

Ecologically, the desert communities and their association into biomes are of intense interest for the extremes of adaptation to the desert environment by both plants and animals, and for the conspicuous fact that much of such adjustment is physiological or even behavioral rather than primarily morphological. In their world distribution, deserts range as parallel bordering areas, or as chains of disconnected "islands" or even "continents" of desert alternating with grassland biomes (their area sometimes exceeds that of the associated grasslands). Thus they extend from South Africa to Egypt, from Senegal to the Red Sea, and from Arabia via the Central Asiatic deserts to Mongolia and to India. In South America there is a vast and climatically peculiar cool desert from northern Peru to central Chile west of the Andes, and small and isolated desert areas east of the Andes. In Australia, the center of the continent is occupied by the "Great Australian Desert."

Desert vegetations are conspicuously composed of thornbushes, perennial succulents (especially Cactaceae and Euphorbiaceae), sparse grasses and extremely rapidly growing herbaceous plants (Fig. 224). The animal life associated with deserts is characterized by fleetness of foot in both mammals and birds; jumping or ricocheting locomotion among mammals; great powers of hearing among mammals; burrowing in all vertebrate types and in many of the deserticolous insects and arachnids; and extreme physiologic adaptations to food scarcity and to absence of free water. Animal life in deserts has consequently been a favorite source of examples of adaptation. "Desert coloration" is remarkable for the fidelity with which bare soil and bare rock backgrounds are approximated (p. 667), though there are conspicuously notable exceptions among black animals, some of which may be nocturnal and others associated with black rock (see especially Benson, 1933, for concealing coloration in mammals; Parker, 1935, Klauber, 1939, Cole, 1943, and Cowles and Bogert, 1944, for thermal relations of lizards). Thus lizards, birds, and mammals, among quite unrelated types, exhibit desert colorations; and fringed toes for traction in loose sand are similarly widespread. Valvelike closure of nostrils, eyes, and mouth in lizards and snakes burrowing in loose sand are found equally in California and Arabia; both Old World and New World lizards and snakes may have widened bodies for burrowing by lateral and vertical movement instead of forward plowing into loose soil or sand; and the ex-

west, the grasses interspersed among sagebrush and greasewood, and even in the creosote bush desert, support some hardy cattle. Such vegetation persists even in rock desert, where the sagebrush may be no higher than the surface blocks of lava, and where narrow ribbons of excellent grass may follow dry drainage courses. In our

Fig. 224. Desert landscape in southwestern North America: Saguaro desert, Superior, Arizona. (Photograph by Howard K. Gloyd, Chicago Academy of Sciences.)

tremely remarkable helical "side-winding" of snakes is employed by the sidewinder of southwestern United States and in north Africa and Arabia by the small vipers of the genus *Cerastes.*[*]

From the standpoint of general principles, by far the most interesting aspect of the desert biomes is their extremely gradual gradation into, and transition to, grassland and to scrub forest. In Chile, for example, the blank desert, with extreme impoverishment of flora and fauna at the north, grades into the bush scrub and scrub forest of the gradually better-watered central Chile. In the North American South-

North American Southwest, grazing, since the turn of the century, sometimes on land that would support no more than one head of cattle on 20 acres, has changed what must have been grassy steppe into man-made desert. The high incidence of plants of truly desert character in these areas bespeaks an original interspersal of desert and grassland according to edaphic conditions. Mesquite may hold widely spaced mounds of sand, and be no higher than these mounds, in a mesquite desert; and may grade by insensible degrees into a mesquite forest like that of southern Texas, which is low forest rather than grassland, to which it is commonly referred.

[*] *Aspis* of nomenclaturists.

Islands of coralline limestone may have so little capacity for holding water that even in humid areas a typical rock-desert vegetation may develop, as on the small island outliers of the Greater Antilles (e.g., Mona Island, between Puerto Rico and Hispaniola).

HIGH PLATEAUS

Related in essential characteristics to both grassland and desert are the two great high plateaus of the world—the Tibetan and the Bolivian. These seem to require consideration as distinct biomes because each has a remarkable and characteristic fauna of large herbivores dependent on the grassy plains produced by melting snow. Tibet, in addition to the yak, has a variety of wild sheep and goat antelopes. Bolivia has the remarkable camelids, the wild vicuña, and the related domestic llama and alpaca. The animals of these plateaus, including man, are physiologically adjusted to oxygen deficiency and are cold-hardy and wind-hardy. Many are essentially inhabitants of rock desert bordering the watered areas, notably such rodents as the chinchilla and mountain vizcacha in Bolivia and Peru. Each of these biomes is associated, of course, with a great mountain chain, but from the evidence of endemism, each has been a center of evolution for much of the Tertiary.

THE TROPICAL FOREST BIOME-TYPE

In most respects the richest of the biomes are those composed of tropical forest. These occur on both sides of the equator in a zone of greatly varying width in three major areas, the central African, mainly in the Belgian Congo and Kamerun; southeastern Asia, from eastern India through the East Indian islands to New Guinea and northern Queensland; and the Amazonian, Orinocan, and Guianan basins east of the Andes, with a large extension into Central America.

The tropical forests are alike in being of great height, and in having a complex stratification and relatively continuous canopies (p. 482), with a striking development of associated, often purely arboreal, animals, some with extreme morphological adjustments to their environment such as prehensile tails (mammals, lizards, and snakes). The extremely rich and varied vegetation is evergreen as a whole, but with some briefly deciduous trees. The forest is characterized by a drapery of lianas that is unmatched even by the wild grape "jungle" of the southeastern United States.

The African rain forest (Fig. 225) is essentially a continuous single community from the Gulf of Guinea to the great African lakes and from the Sudanese grasslands to those of Angola. It has an essentially identical outlier in the forest strip along the coast west of the lower Niger, and equally closely related small forest islands extending to the forest strip along the Indian Ocean to the east. A relatively small area of rain forest is found in eastern Madagascar, so distinct in its animal types as to be only remotely related to the African tropical forest.

The American rain forest is scarcely less homogeneous than is the African, but differs sharply from the African in its contact with the high and continuous range of the Andes and the escarpment of the Bolivian plateau. It thus has a subtropical zone of great linear and areal extent, in contrast with the isolated subtropical forests of the widely separate African mountains.

The Oriental tropical forest biome is fragmented in the East Indies, heterogeneous in that the faunal differences from island to island and from archipelago to archipelago are much greater than are the floral, with a major historic faunal break between Celebes and New Guinea. Extensive subtropical forests are developed on the slopes of the eastern Himalaya, in the south Chinese mountains, and in New Guinea.

Details of the vertical stratification of animal life in tropical forests are beginning to be known with the focus of attention on jungle yellow fever and on the vertical cyclic movements of malarial mosquitoes. Early studies of the forest canopy by Allee (p. 231) have been extended by the Oxford University Expedition to British Guiana (Hingston, 1932) and by the Rockefeller Field Laboratory at Villavicencio (Bates, 1946).

BIOTIC ZONATION IN MOUNTAINS

All the major biotic formations exhibit striking relations to the climatic zonation of mountains. The life zone concept, especially familiar in the faunal and floral literature of North America, is useful in the description of altitude zonation in mountains (Fig. 19) in spite of a wholly erroneous theoretical base (Daubenmire, 1938; various state "biological surveys" of the Bureau of Biological Survey in North American Fauna; Shelford, 1945; see also p. 114). Where the mountains are high

American mountain goat, the ibexes of the Eurasian mountains, the chamois, and the pikas. The attendant carnivores are usually entrants from lower zones like the puma (*Felis concolor*) in the Rocky Mountains and the Andes. The snow leopard of the Himalaya appears to be the only large high-altitude carnivore endemic to montane tundra, commonly referred to as the arctic-alpine life zone in North America.

Fig. 225. The rain forest biome: border of a clearing in the Ituri Forest of Nala, Belgian Congo. (Photograph by Herbert Lang; courtesy of The American Museum of Natural History.)

enough to maintain permanent snow, the zone seasonally free from snow between the summer snow line and timber line may be closely representative of the tundra, and, as in the Rocky Mountains, may present essentially a peninsular southward extension of the animal life of the Tundra Biome in a somewhat modified plant matrix. The ptarmigan with its striking color change from summer brown to winter white, and the arctic butterflies of the genus *Parnassius*, exhibit such a relation. It is to be noted that the broken rock habitat, and the otherwise modified montane environment exclude other characteristically arctic forms and have associated with them strikingly evolved mountain herbivores like the

The taiga exhibits parallel southward extensions wherever north-south mountain ranges in the northern hemisphere form a connection with the latitudinal taiga biome. As in the montane tundra, these southward extensions tend to break up into outlying islands and to be strongly modified in biotic composition. Thus, the "Spruce-Moose" biome of Shelford, when applied to the Colorado coniferous zone, lacks the moose, and when applied to the coniferous pine forest of the Sierra Madre in western Mexico, lacks the spruce as well. In general, it seems best to base both definition and nomenclature of the biomes upon general vegetational type. Whereas the tundra and taiga zones are evidently extended southward in mountains mainly in association with temperature zones, desert and lowland forest are carried upward in association with soil type and precipitation.

The conspicuous southward extension of animal forms in the climatic zones of the

guanaco, is on the whole much different from that of the Rockies. In the northern hemisphere, the great extent of tundra and taiga, by mere mass effect, dominates the corresponding associated montane environment. In South America, the area of the

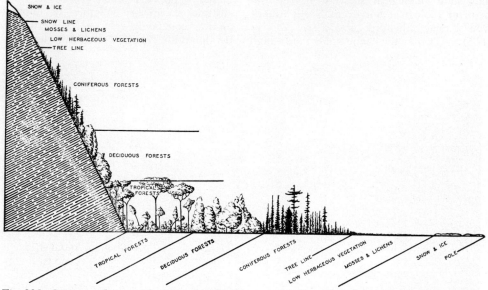

Fig 226. Correspondence of latitudinal and altitudinal life zones in North America. (Modified from Wolcott.)

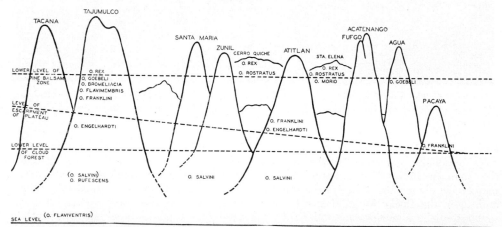

Fig. 227. Horizontal distribution of the salamanders of the genus *Oedipus* on the volcanos of the Guatemalan escarpment; the discontinuities in the ranges of the cold-limited high-altitude species are explained by the fluctuations in altitude of the life zones in glacial and postglacial times. (After Schmidt.)

Rockies is matched by certain northward extensions of lowland forms in the Andes, the guanaco of Patagonia, for example, extending to southernmost Peru.

Biotic zonation in the Andes in general, in spite of the northward range of the

temperate zones is restricted, their climate oceanic rather than continental, and the climatic effects of trade winds and ocean currents are more sharply defined. This helps to explain the fact that the Andean araucarian forest does not extend northward as narrow parallel zones. The broad-leaved evergreen forest of south Chile is strictly dependent on high rainfall, and is accordingly excluded from the temperate but xeric temperature zones on the Andes. The operation of historic factors at the level of the secular geological cycles like-

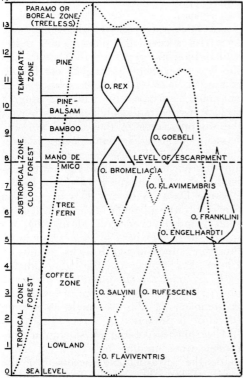

Fig. 228. Altitudinal distribution of salamanders of the genus *Oedipus* on the volcanos of the Guatemalan escarpment. Figures at left equal thousands of feet. (After Schmidt.)

wise contributes to the major differences between montane zones of the northern and the southern hemispheres.

A still greater contrast between the mainly higher latitude Rockies and the mainly lower latitude Andes lies in the development of the subtropical forest zone, in which both vegetation and animal life are derived from the adjacent tropical forest below, instead of from the latitudinal zone connected with it by isotherms (Chapman, 1917). The historic factor of dispersal along a north-south mountain range may be combined with the vertical derivation of distinctive species in the upper zones, especially in correlation with postglacial

climatic changes. This distributional arrangement (Figs. 227 and 228) may be seen in the salamanders of the genus *Oedipus* in Guatemala (Schmidt, 1936).

Merriam (1899) was right in part as to the dominance of the temperature factor in North America; but this theorem cannot be generalized for the rest of the world. In South America the precipitation factor dominates distribution, and in Eurasia the isolated east-west ranges were connected only by historical changes in climate, and historical isolation (in the sense of geological history) dominates the distributional pattern. Thus, the "Life Zone" diagram of Wolcott (Fig. 226), excellent for North America, does not apply well to tropical South America or to Mount Kilimanjaro.

MINOR TERRESTRIAL BIOMES OF VARYING SIGNIFICANCE

There remain a few conspicuously distinct biotic formations that do not fall readily into a classification of biomes. The waif biota of oceanic islands exhibits some of the difficulties of community definition of the ocean itself, for the transition, from New Guinea to Easter Island, for example, is gradual, and the ultimate dependence of island land biotas on larger land masses for their origin and upon the ocean itself for their continuity and nourishment is obvious.

The forest communities of eastern Australia, Tasmania, and New Zealand differ sharply from each other in biotic composition. They exhibit striking correlations in floristic composition with the broad-leaved forest of southern Chile as well as (in part) with the coniferous araucarian forests of Chile and southern Brazil. Their faunal relations, however, are completely *sui generis*. The distributional pattern in these cases is dominated by the historical factor (p. 682).

THE MARINE BIOME-TYPE

Distinguishing as we do between the relatively uniform and operationally integrated biomes, and the concept of biome type, by means of which the biomes may be grouped in a logical way, and by means of which the concept of the biome may be made to take into account the biotic concepts of historical biogeography, we are still faced with a major difficulty in the geographic examination of the sea.* The unified concept of the community developed in this work treats the oceans essentially as a single major community, and the whole of marine ecological associations constitutes essentially not only a single major community and a single biome, but a single biome-type.

The marine associations designated by Clements and Shelford (1939) as "biomes" are nearer the bottom of the scale of biotic ecological subdivisions, and cannot be accepted as major formations in any sense, much less in the light of the definition of the major community set forth in the present work.

Two groups of marine associations, so far as hierarchial arrangement into categories is concerned, have some similarity to the biome types of the terrestrial world. These are the benthos and the pelagial, i.e., the bottom dwellers together with the bottom-bound life ecologically directly associated with the bottom, and the free-floating and free-swimming plants and animals of the open sea, which appear to be relatively independent of the shores and bottom. The open seas of the pelagial are broadly connected, and temperature zones are somewhat less marked than in the benthos. The greatest differences of type within the benthos are those of eroding shores and depositing shores; these differences are mechanical and thus are physiographically and physically, superimposed on broad climatic zonation.

The temperature-limited and thus especially biome-like coral reef (with its various components) resembles the eroding shore type on its outer face, exposed to wave-shock, but is composed also of reef-conditioned depositing lagoons, in which the

* We are concerned in this chapter with the broad outlines of the whole marine biome-type. Special phases of this subject have been discussed previously. For example, oceanic and littoral water masses (p. 151); marine habitats and inhabitants with respect to vertical stratification (pp. 447–451) and to the horizontal zonation (pp. 453–460); marine sediments (pp. 460, 461); food web (pp. 501–503) and periodicities (pp. 542–544 and 554, 555). The interested student will find extensive correlative material in Murray and Hjort (1912), Ekman (1935), Hesse, Allee, and Schmidt (1937), Sverdrup, Johnson, and Fleming (1942), and Coker (1947).

massive corals of the reef face may be delicately arborescent and interspersed with animals adjusted to quiet water (like the sponges and soft corals) or to the coral sand bottom, like the sea cucumbers (p. 570). The separation of the major coral reef regions into an Indo-Pacific and an Atlantic subregion forms a still more striking analogue of a biome type with at least two biomes.

We must refer also to the remarkable long-term successional phenomenon represented by coral reef islands. Darwin was the first to explain the ringlike coral atolls of the Pacific as related to the subsidence of volcanoes, successively with a fringing reef, a barrier reef and lagoon, and, with the disappearance of the central volcanic remnant, an atoll. The outer Society islands, indeed, exhibit the last stages of the island and barrier reef, in which the central island is about to disappear (Darwin, 1842). Because Darwin's theory does not explain the contrary phenomenon of emergent shores, and is oversimplified in other respects, it has given rise to a voluminous literature, much of which in its critique of Darwin has "thrown out the baby with the bath" by rejecting the essentially and even obviously correct central core of his theory. A summary of this extremely interesting literature is presented by Davis (1928a).

The slowness of the physiographic succession from eroding to depositing shore marks the corresponding succession of the forms of life, through the vast evolutionary periods of time that have been available to the life of the sea; it is thus evolutionary rather than successional. Even on rock coast, however, the life of depositing shores interdigitates minutely in tide pools and sheltered crevices, however small, with that of the wave-pounded rock.

The lightless deep sea includes a most remarkable fauna, but this is dependent either primarily or secondarily upon the benthos and pelagial, and this dependence further illustrates the difficulty of recognition of true self-sustaining communities within the sea, however much their world distribution may resemble that of the terrestrial biomes. The parallels between the unified deep-sea regions and the fragmented cave-community type of the land are noteworthy.

The development of major faunal regions

with endemic faunas, some of which are so sharply defined as to cut across almost all taxonomic groups, is a phenomenon requiring isolation through great periods of geological time. The same principle applies to the development of floral regions, but with some radical differences primarily traceable to different geological ages of origin, and to quite radically different modes of dispersal. The emigrations of biotic elements and the shifts of whole biotas are known primarily from paleontological evidence. Theoretically and quite obviously, these movements imply a basis of paleoecology. Paleoecology, however, like paleogeography, is of necessity based on fragmentary evidence, sometimes even more fragmentary than are the animal and plant remains on which paleontology is based.

A large literature, unequal in merit, of animal and plant geography, differing sometimes in point of view, and with the historical and the ecological factors often not distinguished, affords direct evidence as to the outlines of the geological history of land life. An introduction to this history, and to the paleogeographic controversy as to the history of connections between the continents envisaged by many as essential to explain the patterns of the present distribution of land animals, may be obtained from "Climate and Evolution" by W. D. Matthew (1915). For the more general aspects of animal geography it is still necessary to refer to the introduction to Wallace's *The Geographical Distribution of Animals* (1876) and to his more popularly written *Island Life* (1880). Plant geog-

raphy is provided with a recent summary by Cain (1944).

The historical animal geography of the sea, because of the essential continuity of its waters, is even more inextricably interwoven with ecological factors than is that of the land fauna. Nevertheless, major isolation effects have left discernible marks on the distribution of marine life. Ekman's excellent summary (1935), for example, gives an easily accessible account of the results of the marine connection of the Pacific and Atlantic across Central America. This lasted through much of Tertiary time, and has produced a remarkable pairing of species within genera ("geminate species"), many Caribbean species having a Pacific coast counterpart. The major geographic barrier to the benthos has been the open Pacific between the South Sea Islands and the American coast, and the influence of the East Indian centers of distribution extends eastward through the Pacific Islands to this barrier, and westward via the ancient sea beaches of Tethys through the Mediterranean to the West Indies. Excellent documentation of this history is supplied by the marine fossils of the Mediterranean region.

Other major biotic provinces of the ocean appear to be quite sharply defined by temperature zones, to which whole faunas have become adjusted in geological time, and by the effect on fertility of upwelling waters on the western coasts of the continents. Minor provinces as well as major ones tend to be tied together by wide-ranging pelagic forms (Ekman, 1935).

SECTION V. ECOLOGY AND EVOLUTION

INTRODUCTION

Life shows a general progressive change in time. There is an evolution from a less balanced relationship between the internal and external environment to a more closely adjusted relationship. There is also an evolution from limited control of the environment toward much more control of the external environment. These aspects of ecological evolution parallel the evolution of internal physiological balance and control within the organism.

What place organic evolution has in cosmic processes is not clear. Life seems to maintain a dynamic equilibrium of matter and energy (metabolism), which involves chemically complex substances with large molecules such as the proteins and their derivatives. It has been thought that life may retard or temporarily reverse the general increase of entropy or degradation of energy (Breder, 1942a; Schrödinger, 1945). Needham (1943), on the other hand, thinks that living processes conform to the second law of thermodynamics (increase of entropy), that thermodynamic order and biological organization are different, and that both the physical and organic aspects of existence agree in their trend toward a more complex organization as free energy becomes less. However, complex organic systems as we know them do not arise in environments with an extremely low energy potential such as the cold surfaces of the outer planets. The evolutionary tendency toward an increase in the complexity of organization of living systems can only take place within a temperature environment neither too hot nor too cold—roughly that of water in the liquid state (p. 73).

Lotka (1944, 1945) states that the collective activities and effects of organisms indicate a direction of organic evolution toward maximal energy intake from the sun, and maximal outgo of free energy by dissipative processes in living and in decaying dead organisms. In other words, there are evolutionary tendencies toward a higher metabolic rate of the whole ecosystem. "The net effect is to maximize in this sense the energy flux through the system of organic nature." The limits of the evolutionary increase in energy flux are imposed by the earthly acquisition of the energy output of the sun and its ultimate dissipation.

Although at present the cosmic meaning of these manifestations of life eludes the scientific mind, we can study the changes accompanying evolution and the immediate antecedents of such change. Ecology offers much to the investigation of these problems, especially in the analysis of isolation and adaptation. Other biological sciences, particularly genetics, deal with various evolutionary problems. All aspects of biology have been profoundly influenced by evolutionary studies and in turn provide evidence for analysis of operational factors. A number of recent books summarize modern knowledge of the evolution of living systems (Fisher, 1930; Morgan, 1932; Robson and Richards, 1936; deBeer, 1938; Huxley, 1940, 1942; Goldschmidt, 1940; Dobzhansky, 1941; Mayr, 1942; Simpson, 1944; White, 1945).

Although ecology is an outgrowth of nineteenth century natural history with its emphasis upon evolution, modern ecologists have been somewhat reticent in developing evolutionary principles. This is surprising, considering the central position of the problem of ecological adaptation in evolutionary theory. Lamarck and Darwin, in their theories of evolution, regarded adaptation as the main theme, and Wallace came to regard every characteristic of living organisms as adaptive. Although some degree of

"the smaller and more distant an island is from the nearest mainland, . . . the fewer species will be found." New Guinea has 509 species of native land birds; the Solomon Islands, 138; the Fiji Islands, 54; Samoa, 33; the Society Islands, 17; the Marquesas Islands, 11; Henderson Island, 4; and Easter Island, none. The number of habitats as well as the degree of isolation is doubtless reflected in these data.

We may now consider a few cases in which environmentally induced mutation exhibits a response adapted to the inducing agent. In the organisms in which there is little distinction between somatic and germinal tissue or between cytoplasmic and nuclear protoplasms, direct modification of the protoplasm, if autocatalysis occurs, may result in particular hereditary changes directly adjusted to the environmental inductor (Sturtevant, 1944). If a gene produces an antigen, the antibodies induced by this antigen might react with the gene as well as with the antigen (S. Emerson, 1944). This would be a form of induced mutation with the response functionally related to the stimulus.

An example of a hereditary response to the inducing agent is found in the experiments upon pneumococci. If placed in unfavorable physical, biochemical, or nutritional conditions, reactive phases of thirty-odd known serological types of virulent pneumococci (*Diplococcus pneumoniae*) change in virulence, in their ability to form capsules, in immunological characteristics, and in colony configuration. Some of these changes are of a dissociative or degenerative nature in which the resultant degraded form loses the antigenic character of its special type (of polysaccharide haptene), but retains the antigenic action common to the various serological types of the species. The original type may be produced from the degenerate form by passing the strain through a susceptible animal, by growing the colony in a medium containing an antiserum produced by immunization with the degenerate forms, or by adding heat-killed virulent cultures of the original type to the medium growing the degenerate form. If heat-killed virulent cultures of a different type are placed with the degenerate form, it may regenerate into a hereditarily stable type corresponding to the source of the heat-killed virulent culture (White, 1938, p. 117; Morgan, 1944).

The active substance producing such transformations has been isolated and identified in an extract of Type III pneumococci (Avery, MacLeod, and McCarty, 1944). The percentages of carbon (34 to 35), hydrogen (3.7 to 3.8), nitrogen (14 to 15), and phosphorus (8.5 to 9.0) agree closely with those calculated for sodium desoxyribonucleate (tetranucleotide). The fact that this type of nucleic acid is found in nuclei and chromosomes of higher organisms lends credence to the theory that the genetic materials in the pneumococci may be affected directly (Morgan, 1944).

In most organisms the germ plasm is buffered by the soma, and the nucleus is buffered by the cytoplasm; but in the bacteria and a few other organisms, the external environment may be in closer physical or chemical contact with the germinal mechanism (Hinshelwood, 1944).

It should also be realized that selection acting upon billions of micro-organisms undergoing rapid reproduction may play a guiding role within a few days commensurate with the action of selection over a period of many centuries in slowly reproducing higher organisms. Some of the adaptations of bacteria to new media may be the result of selective elimination (Lewis, 1934; Braun, 1945; Severens and Tanner, 1945; see also pp. 628, 629), but in the pneumococci the environment seems to have a direct effect. Sonneborn (1943) points out that the transformation of the antigenic type of *Pneumococcus* by reduction to a nonspecific form, and treatment with heat-killed cells of another type, may be equivalent to removing one factor and substituting another that then activates another gene. In view of the biochemical investigations of Avery, McCleod, and McCarty (1944), it may even be possible that characteristic nuclear material itself is substituted.

It would appear that both genes and cytoplasm may be required for the expression of an inherited character over a long series of generations (Sonneborn, 1942). When certain cytoplasmic substances are initially present, the gene may stimulate their further production, but cannot produce the substance in the absence of the cytoplasmic factor (Sonneborn, 1945a, 1948).

Through experiments on the ability of certain yeasts (some undergoing cell division and some not) to acquire the enzymatic apparatus necessary to ferment galactose, Spiegelman and Lindegren (1944) conclude that such an adjustment may result from (1) the natural selection of existent variants with the desired characteristics from a heterogeneous population; (2) induction of a new enzyme by the substrate in all the members of a homogeneous population, resulting in an increase in the measured enzymatic activity of the population; (3) a combination of natural selection and the action of an induction mechanism on those selected (also see Spiegelman, Lindegren, and Lindegren, 1945; Spiegelman and Kamen, 1946).

Darlington (1944) postulates separate systems of hereditary mechanisms: (1) nuclear system (genes in chromosomes), (2) corpuscular system (plastids or plastogenes in green plants), and (3) molecular system (plasmagenes in cytoplasm with no visible bodies and chemically variable in degree of equilibrium). Darlington's nuclear system might well be divided into (a) gene and (b) chromosome mechanisms. Chromosomal aberrations and polyploidy without gene change produce hereditary modification. There may be interaction between all these systems in the cell (Sonneborn, 1945, 1945a).

Plasmagenes have striking similarity to viruses (Altenburg, 1946; Sonneborn, 1948). Both viruses and plasmagenes are proteins that require desoxyribose nucleic acid in their composition. Some induced mutations that react adaptively to the inducing agent may involve plasmagenes rather than nuclear genes (Spiegelman, Lindegren, and Lindegren, 1945).

Cytoplasmic characters, induced by either gene action or environmental agents, may persist through several generations, but gradually disappear because of a lack of persistent autocatalysis. This phenomenon has been called *Dauermodifikation* (Jollos, 1932; Taliaferro and Huff, 1940; Hoare, 1943; Caspari, 1948). Although this "cytoplasmic lag" has been interpreted as an indication of Lamarckian inheritance, especially by earlier authors, Sonneborn (1942) indicates that at least some cases

may be explained by Mendelian inheritance together with an interaction of the genes with cytoplasmic factors. Genes are always autocatalytic. Autocatalysis may be found in cytoplasmic systems, where cytoplasmic inheritance through plastogenes or plasmagenes is possible. In either case, induced modifications by the environment, even when inherited and adapted to the stimulus, are not strictly Lamarckian and had best not be used to justify Lamarckian theories of the inheritance of acquired somatic characters.

GENETIC VARIATION IN RELATION TO POPULATION NUMBERS, POPULATION RHYTHMS AND DISPERSION

"The elementary evolutionary process is . . . change of gene (or chromosome) frequency" (Wright, 1945, p. 415). A species divided into many partially isolated local populations (p. 603), each with a tendency toward fixation of a uniquely balanced gene pattern, provides an enormous potential variability through occasional crosses between populations. Selection may operate upon the group as a unit (p. 683).

When a partial discontinuity results from extrinsic causes, genetic recombinations between groups may be expected to be largely confined to a narrow zone of population overlap (Huxley, 1939a). As a large statistical generalization, a sparse population between two areas of greater density provides a hindrance to free gene flow, which will enable fixation, mutation, and selection to build up distinctive gene patterns in the two dense areas (p. 611). The extension of the ranges of these more harmonious and viable dense populations will tend to narrow the intermediate zone of intergradation (p. 623).

Species with large numbers are, in general, more variable than those with small numbers (Fisher, 1937; Mather, 1943), for with the smaller numbers inbreeding tends to increase homozygosity. There are critical points in the breeding population size above which little increase in variability occurs (Simpson, 1944, p. 67). In small populations the natural accidents of sampling result in random fixation of mutations and gene frequencies (Fig. 229). Small interbreeding populations may result from a drastic reduction in numbers following severe climatic, predatory, or epidemic mortality (p. 273); from a reduced effective interbreeding population in cyclomorphic species in which the major increase in numbers is the outcome of *cyclical parthenogenesis* (p. 686); or from the establishment of a portion of the population in a new, somewhat isolated locality by territoriality, colonization, emigration, or dispersion.

The isoagglutinogen in human red blood cells caused by the gene I^A which, in the homozygous condition, produces blood group A, is completely absent in the Indians of Peru, but has a high incidence in the Blackfoot Indians of the northwestern United States (Strandskov, 1941). It is thought that small emigrating groups, by chance, carried a widely different percentage frequency of this gene. The gene in this case would seem to be neutral so far as either positive or negative selection is concerned. If a large group emigrates, the gene frequencies in the group should, according to chance, be close to those of the original population. As an example, the blood group frequencies of American and West African Negroes are similar.

If a small population becomes isolated, random combinations of genes may become fixed with consequent nonadaptive differentiation (Wright, 1937). Wright (1941) concludes, concerning the fixation of reciprocal translocations (transfer of the chromosome ends between two chromosomes), that "such fixation can hardly occur under exclusive sexual reproduction except in a species in which there are numerous isolated populations that pass through phases of extreme reduction of numbers. The most favorable case [for fixation] would seem to be that in which there is frequent extinction of the populations of small isolated localities, with restoration from the progeny of occasional stray migrants from other localities."

Excessive inbreeding in a small population might result in the fixation of deleterious genes with consequent weakening or extinction of the isolated population. Random mutations are more likely to be degenerative than adaptive (Wright, 1942). If the selection coefficient (p. 649) (s) is 0.001, the critical size of the breeding population would be 500. If s is 0.01, the critical number would be only 50. Populations of intermediate size produce conditions of random variation that act somewhat like changes in the direction of selection. "The system of gene frequencies is kept continually on the move and this gives a trial and error process which at times may lead to adaptive combinations which would not have been reached by direct selection." Conditions for adaptive evolution are more favorable in populations of intermediate size than in small or large randomly breeding populations. If a large population is subdivided into numerous small, almost but not completely isolated groups (Fig. 229), random divergencies in gene frequencies and intergroup selection seem to provide the most favorable conditions for evolutionary advance (Wright, 1937, 1945, p. 416, 1948a; Erickson, 1945; also see p. 407). The breeding system is an adaptive character of the group as a whole and is subject to selection pressure (Mather, 1943; Wigan, 1944).

Fixation of genetic variations through cyclical parthenogenesis and asexual reproduction in such species as the aphids, malarial parasites, rusts, bryophytes, and pteridophytes, with occasional cross breeding between populations in the sexual phase, has evolutionary consequences somewhat similar to those in sexual populations partially isolated by geographic or ecologic factors (Banta, 1939a).

Elton (1930) uses the Arctic fox (*Alopex lagopus*) to illustrate aspects of the relation of numbers to gene frequency in natural populations. This species is circumpolar in distribution and has two color phases, the white and the blue, which are particularly marked in the winter season. So far as we know, these color phases are not adaptively differentiated, although the color of the species as a whole may be adaptive. (Color phases of the red fox, *Vulpes fulva*, show some indication of differential survival according to Butler, 1945.) In general, the white and the blue phases of the arctic fox are found throughout the range of the species, but on certain islands only the blue occurs, and on peninsular Kamchatka only the white is found. In the extreme north the blue occurs in the proportion of one in three hundred. Animals of both phases, when they are in the same geographic area, live together, have similar habits, and interbreed readily. Mutation pressure of the white phase toward the blue may be low.

The fox population has striking variations in numbers, with a peak every three or four years, followed by famine, epidemic disease, or emigration. In 30,000 years there would be about 8000 periods of scarcity. According to Elton, if the fox population is reduced during the depres-

Numerous cases in nature beside the white and blue foxes show the establishment of seemingly nonadaptive variants in local populations. The high incidence of black leopards in Asia and the low incidence in Africa, melanic garter snakes on the shores of Lake Erie, and black wolves, muskrats, foxes, and sheep in the central Yukon valley may be examples. Of course,

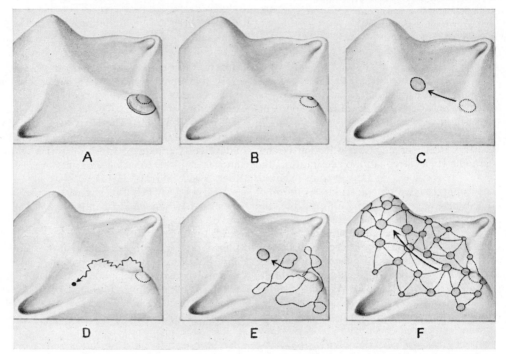

Fig. 229. The field of gene combinations occupied by a population within the general field of possible combinations under specified historical conditions indicated by the relation to the initial field (broken contour) and arrow; A, increased mutation or reduced selection (4 NU, 4 NS very large); B, increased selection or reduced mutation (4 NU, 4 NS very large); C, qualitative change of environment (4 NU, 4 NS very large); D, close inbreeding (4 NU, 4 NS, very small); E, slight inbreeding (4 NU, 4 NS medium); F, division into local races (4 nm medium). N is population number (species); U is mutation rate from gene per generation; S is selection coefficient; n is population number (race); m is population exchange with the rest of species. (From Allee, 1938, and Wright, 1932.)

sions to a small fraction of the population at the peaks, even a rare blue mutation might become established by chance in local populations, which would then expand at the periods of abundance, giving rise to a greater incidence of blues. During another depression, in a few cases the blues by chance might be the only survivors, thus establishing a local population composed entirely of blues. Elton thus suggests random extinction and random establishment as important factors in evolution.

selection might rapidly increase the incidence of certain established genes, as probably happens when adaptation is indicated—for example, black rodents on black lava in New Mexico (pp. 627, 650, 668; Fig. 245).

Although behavior resulting in regionality often has a genetic basis, yet within that framework, homing (individualized tradition) may tend to isolate populations. Study of individual birds through banding over several years reveals a strong tendency for the individuals of certain species, such as the song sparrow (Nice, 1934, 1937, 1941), to return to the vicinity of their origin, with consequent inbreeding within a small population. The evolutionary effects of such tradition would be similar to the drastic reduction in numbers of a fluctuating population, or the geographic or ecologic isolation of a small population from a larger one (Emerson, 1943; Thorpe, 1945; also see p. 619).

Monogamy, polyandry, polygamy, and the like, resulting from conditioned behavior, also affect the breeding structure of populations and doubtless produce evolutionary results. Degrees of inbreeding through various breeding structures within small neighborhood subgroups affect differentiation of populations (Wright, 1946; see also p. 608).

We conclude that the breeding structure of populations may be influenced by numbers and by mating behavior, that variations in numbers of interbreeding individuals may be produced by a variety of factors, and that such variations affect the chances of the establishment of mutations and gene or chromosome frequencies. Population genetics is thus of concern to the ecologist interested in evolution.

SUMMARY

In summary, ecologic factors influence genetic variability. Hereditary mechanisms have undergone adaptive evolution toward efficient internal balance, and the external environment has exerted selection pressure in this direction. The environment may also affect mutation pressure in certain instances. Mutation rate, although important for genetic variability, is not alone responsible for rapid evolution. Variations in the size of breeding populations exert an important influence upon reassortment of genes and chromosomes, genetic fixation, and gene frequency in populations. The unit of selection, even in the primitive organisms, often must have been the population group (pp. 602, 683, 684, 695) as well as the individual organism.

32. ECOLOGY AND ISOLATION

INTRODUCTION

Divergent evolution—the branching of the phylogenetic tree—depends upon reproductive isolation. Reproductive isolation includes any factor that prevents gene flow from one population to another such as spatial and ecological separation, as well as reproductive physiological or psychological incompatibility. Even if the characters of the two populations are the same at the time of separation, and even if the environmental conditions are the same for the separated populations, they will gradually drift apart genetically through random changes in gene frequency, genetic fixation, and mutation.

Most of the hereditary differences between human races result from differences of gene frequency rather than from presence or absence of qualitatively different genes (Strandskov, 1944). In all probability the same rule holds for the majority of animal and plant races (p. 602). We presume that mutations in reproductively isolated populations accumulate in time, thus qualitatively distinguishing separated populations, even though mutations of genes influencing the rate of growth of different structures may only produce quantitative differences between the phenotypes.

It follows that species would be expected to diverge in relation to the degree of isolation (see Vagility, p. 213), the breeding structure of the population, genetic fixation, the amount of mutation pressure, and the time lapse since isolation. Selection hastens the process and is believed to be the primary factor in divergent adaptation (pp. 655, 664). However, much nonadaptive evolution at the infraspecies and species level may take place through the action of isolating factors in the absence of selection.

Random genetic divergence in isolated populations will in time probably result in intrinsic inhibition of cross breeding through regressive evolution (pp. 672, 676). Also, if cross breeding becomes harmful to the diverging groups, selection may speed the evolution of intrinsic, i.e., genetic, isolating mechanisms. There are.

therefore, initiating factors and clinching factors that may be separated on occasion, one following the other (Patterson, 1942).

Various classifications of isolating mechanisms have recently been proposed (Dobzhansky, 1941; Mayr, 1942; Muller, 1942; Huxley, 1942; Emerson, 1943; Cain, 1944, p. 357; Mayr, 1948). Some authors emphasize permanent isolation through physiologic and genetic incompatibility, as contrasted with the possibly less permanent geographical and environmental mechanisms. On the other hand, initial isolating factors are more often the effect of geographical or ecological barriers to gene flow. Whatever the factor isolating two or more populations, the evolutionary consequences have a certain fundamental similarity.

The known isolating mechanisms may be arranged in a fairly logical order, although overlapping among categories occurs to some extent. Grouping of categories on the basis of genetics differs somewhat from grouping on the basis of ecology, but both are important.

Table 52. Isolation Factors

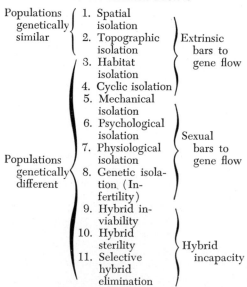

Ecologic factors are important under certain categories of isolation and unimportant under others. Population genetics and selection have isolating effects that are discussed under these headings. Linear change without divergence has sometimes been included under the term *chronological isolation*, but is possibly better considered as an aspect of selection (see Chronocline, p. 626; Orthoselection, pp. 638, 649). Reproductive isolation as exhibited by asexual species is discussed at the end of this chapter (p. 628). The isolating effects of varying population size and structure have been dealt with in the chapter on Ecology and Genetic Variation (p. 602). The genetic and physiologic bases of hybrid inviability (p. 677) and sterility are not discussed further here, since they are analyzed in embryological and genetic literature.

The other mechanisms listed (Table 52) have ecologic implications. Some, such as genetic isolation or infertility, receive more complete study in works on evolutionary genetics. Spatial and topographic isolation may be grouped under geographic isolation, but these are certainly ecologic in the broad sense. Timoféeff-Ressovsky (1940a) separates "biological isolation," including genetic, sexual, physiologic, and ecologic, from "mechanical isolation," including territorial separation. Various aspects of sexual isolation are here considered broadly ecologic, one sex belonging to the environment of the other. Habitat and cyclic isolation, as well as selective elimination of hybrids, are ecologic in the strict sense. Habitat isolation is referred to as "ecological isolation" by some authors, but our designation seems more distinctive. Habitat isolation might be considered microgeographic, but we prefer to separate the grosser geographic factors from the finer ecologic factors within a region, even though it is obvious that the two categories are not always sharply distinct.

Patently, more than one isolating mechanism may divide populations at the same time, and the data may not enable one to evaluate the relative importance of each factor. Each major category also may have innumerable subdivisions. Cases that illustrate the importance of each major isolating mechanism are discussed in the following pages, but it is seldom possible to study the action of one mechanism to the complete exclusion of all others. Hovanitz (1942, 1943) studied racial or species differences in the butterfly, *Colias*, and found indications of geographic, cyclic, habitat, and sexual isolation, together with hybrid elimination, all influencing the partial segregation of closely related populations. In practically all diverging populations, several factors contribute at the same time or in close succession to the prevention of gene flow across the population borders.

In order to detect the effect of one isolating factor, it is best to find closely related species separated by this factor and no other. It is seldom possible, however, to find such ideal examples. More often one can only eliminate some of the possible isolating mechanisms in a given case, leaving several factors that cannot be treated independently. The isolating mechanisms that cannot be separated in one instance may often be separated in other paired species, however, so that the factors appear with fair distinction after studying a large number of cases. Isolating mechanisms that partially separate subspecies deserve particular study, for the initial mechanisms of speciation are seen more clearly in such populations. The method of analyzing speciation is of necessity mainly inductive from wide evidential data rather than from clean-cut experimentation.

Varying degrees of partial isolation may be found that produce a quantitative effect upon the rate of gene flow between populations. Highly important evolutionary phenomena may be correlated with such differences in genetic interchange, even though complete reproductive isolation is not achieved (pp. 602 and 603).

In spite of overlaps and intergradations of the isolating factors, one perceives a tendency toward a temporal sequence in the operation of several isolating mechanisms. First, there is a segregation of genetically similar populations. Second, there is a genetic reorganization within each population. Third, permanent isolation is achieved through intrinsic mechanisms that prevent all gene flow between populations, whether the extrinsic barriers continue to exist or not. There are many exceptions to this chronology, such as chromosome mutation in polyploid speciation, but in general this sequence of events is a common occurrence. Under certain circumstances, some separable factors may have closely similar evolutionary consequences. For example, a gross topographic barrier without differences in habitat may result in speciation in about the same time as a microspatial habitat separation with strong selection pressures in the different environments.

SPATIAL ISOLATION

If no sharp external barriers of a topographic or ecologic nature separate portions of a large, widely distributed population, distance alone will nevertheless prevent separated individuals from interbreeding. With some mutation pressure or variation in gene frequencies, genes filter slowly from one local population to another and may commonly result in geographic variations with no sharp lines of demarcation (Geoclines, p. 626). The density of the interbreeding populations is an important factor. A sparse population inhabiting a large region might produce a local inbreeding effect similar to that in a denser local population partially isolated by various extrinsic or intrinsic mechanisms.

Thompson (1931a) showed that there is a correlation between water distance and morphological divergence within a species of fish in the rivers of Illinois. Sumner (1932) stated that he had never compared two local collections of the same species of deer mouse (Peromyscus) from points at all remote from one another without finding significant differences between them. Dobzhansky and Epling (1944) give a thorough analysis of spatially isolated races of Drosophila and define races as "populations of a species which differ in incidence of one or more variable genes or chromosome structures." Physiological differences as well as morphological distinctions between spatially separated populations are to be expected (Baily, 1939; DuShane and Hutchinson, 1944).

Absolute distance in space is not necessarily correlated with population divergence. Timoféeff-Ressovsky (1940) and Mayr (1942, p. 242) show that the range of the individual of the species is of great importance in the breeding structure of the population (see Vagility, p. 213). Widely separated populations of the teal, Anas crecca, actually interbreed. Young birds taken from the nest and banded in England were found nesting the next year from Iceland and the northern Urals to central France and central Russia. Pair formation in many migrating ducks occurs in the wintering range so that a male hatched in Maine may meet a Nebraska female in

Florida and follow her to her Nebraska breeding grounds. Such a large geographic range of individuals breaks down the isolation that might have evolutionary significance for a species with a much smaller individual range. If migrating birds such as geese (*Anser* and *Branta*) maintain a family association throughout their travels, the species is likely to break up into geographic races (Mayr, 1942, p. 242). Using nondeleterious mutations as markers, Timoféeff-Ressovsky showed that the breeding ranges of individuals of certain species of *Drosophila* are small and that even small territorial fragmentations might result in partial isolation (also see Epling and Dobzhansky, 1942). In comparable kinds of animals, individual range is usually smaller in the smaller forms. This essentially ecologic factor has been little appreciated by some students of mammalian systematics who apply the same subspecies framework to large carnivores as to small rodents.

TOPOGRAPHIC ISOLATION

Isolation of populations in separated geographic areas is one of the prime factors leading to the rise of new species. The majority of species with mutually exclusive geographic ranges (*allopatric species*) are probably isolated by topographic barriers. In order to detect the effect of topographic isolation, excluding all other isolating factors, it is necessary to find closely related species topographically separated with nearly equal population sizes and identical habitats and without cyclic, genetic, physiologic, psychologic or other barriers that interfere with their cross breeding. In such an ideal case the effect of natural selection upon genetic divergence might be eliminated, but obviously it is difficult to find an instance in which complete equivalence of natural conditions wholly eliminates selection. If the physical conditions are practically identical, there may still be some selection for internal physiological functions and balance (p. 631) and intraspecific population adjustments (p. 683). Even a small change in the associated species constituting the biotic association (pp. 695, 698) may give rise to selection pressures that play a role in survival of certain genetic patterns. In order to analyze topographic isolation, the best we can do is to cite cases in which it seems to be the most important factor in evolutionary change.

Certain organisms are limited in their distribution by their lack of adaptation for active or passive dispersal (see Vagility, p. 213; A. H. Miller, 1942). If, for example, an animal becomes adjusted to a fossorial life and loses the ability to swim or the capacity to be transported through the air, one might expect that races or species would develop on the different banks of a wide stream or canyon, provided, of course, that the stream does not change its bed, that the ranges are not connected around the headwaters or mouth, and that accidental dispersal is reduced to a minimum. The two banks of the same stream usually would not differ ecologically; selection of variations by the external environment would be of little importance.

The Grand Canyon of the Colorado river sharply separates the ground squirrel species, *Citellus leucurus*, on the Nevada side from *C. harrisii* on the Arizona side, and likewise isolates the pocket mice, *Perognathus formosus*, from *P. intermedius*, and *P. parvus* from *P. amplus* (Hall, 1946, p. 53). Subspecies of the kit fox (*Vulpes macrotis*), the chipmunk (*Eutamias dorsalis*), the pocket gopher (*Thomomys bottae*), the pocket mouse (*Perognathus penicillatus*), and the grasshopper mouse (*Onychomys torridus*) are separated by the Canyon, but intergrade around the headwaters or lower course of the river. These species are inhabitants of high ground. Aquatic and bottom land species do not show subspecific differentiation on the two sides of the Canyon.

Komarek and Spencer (1931) described a new subspecies of pocket gopher (*Geomys bursarius illinoiensis*) east of the Mississippi and south of the Kankakee River in Illinois and Indiana. Lyon (1936) pointed out that no intergradation with *G. bursarius* is known and assigned the new form to full species status (*G. illinoiensis*). The populations of *bursarius* and *illinoiensis* seem to be wholly isolated, *bursarius* west of the Mississippi and *illinoiensis* to the east, both in sandy areas. Their inability to move across this topographic barrier is further attested by their absence from the northern bank of the Kankakee River and from the Indiana dunes near Lake Michigan, where the habitat appears to be suitable. It may be assumed that topographic isolation is the initial factor in the divergence of these two populations, with little effect of selection associated with environmental differences (also see Dalquest and Scheffer, 1944).

Organisms with great vagility often fail to speciate in the same regions where sedentary types exhibit endemism. An interesting case of topographic isolation is found in the steamer ducks confined to southern South America and the Falkland Islands. These birds race over the surface of the water, using their wings as "side-wheels." One species, the flying steamer duck (*Tachyeres patachonicus*), has a range equal to the combined ranges of the other two species, which are flightless. The Magellanic flightless steamer duck (*T. pteneres*) is found only in the region of the Straits of Magellan, while the other, the Falkland flightless steamer duck (*T. brachypterus*), is found only in the Falkland Islands. The interesting fact is that the populations of flying ducks of this genus in the Magellanic and Falkland regions remained one species, probably because interbreeding occurred, while the flightless forms evolved into separate species in the two regions. The two flightless species were probably independently derived from the flying species, but what factors brought about reproductive isolation between the flying species and its flightless offshoots are unknown (Murphy, 1936). Possibly a habitat isolation was involved, because the flightless species avoid coasts having a marked tidal rise and fall on which the flying species is usually found. Although the two species often swim together, the nesting sites probably are different. The flying species nests around lakes or streams at a distance from salt water, while the flightless species nests on small islets or points near salt water. Confused field identification of these species has resulted in a lack of complete information concerning the supposed differences in nesting sites.

Doutt (1942) reports an isolated landlocked race of seals (*Phoca*) in a freshwater lake east of Hudson Bay in Canada. This form is described as a subspecies of the marine species (*P. vitulina*), but probably deserves full species rank because of complete topographic isolation. The period of isolation is estimated to be 3000 to 8000 years, with 300 to 1600 generations (Simpson, 1944, p. 19).

Worthington (1937, 1940) gives interesting instances of topographic isolation caused by falls in African rivers. The Ripon Falls separate Lake Victoria from Lake Kioga by a somewhat broken drop of about 15 feet. This would be a barrier to upward dispersion of small fishes, but not to powerful swimmers. There are a few species and subspecies differences in the fish faunas of the two lakes, but, in general, the genera and species are similar. In contrast, the Murchison Falls separate Lake Kioga and Lake Albert by a vertical drop of 130 feet that effectively separates the fish faunas above and below the falls. Many genera of fishes characteristic of the Nile do not occur in the river above the falls. Only three species in a fauna of fifty species below and 120 species above are the same.

Interconnected swamps that, because of their oxygen-deficient waters, form an ecologic barrier to most fishes, divide the Zambezi and Congo drainage systems. The two faunas have distinct species and even distinct genera, except for the air-breathing *Spirobranchus, Protopterus,* and *Clarias,* the same species of which occur on both sides of the barrier.

Worthington (1937) described another noteworthy case of partial topographic isolation among east African fishes. A small crater lake lies within Central Island in the middle of Lake Rudolph, separated from the main lake by a low ridge of water-worn boulders. The populations of the fish species, *Tilapia nilotica* (Cichlidae), in the crater lake and in the main lake are subspecifically distinguishable.

Blind cave carabid beetles (*Pseudanophthalmus*) have speciated in different caves of the eastern United States in spite of the extreme uniformity of their habitat (Valentine, 1943, 1945). After a long period of topographic isolation, species that later come to occupy the same cave remain reproductively isolated, but exhibit greater taxonomic divergence than related species from different caves.

Perhaps the most frequently cited example of the effect of topographic isolation is that of the land snails of the islands of the South Seas (Gulick, 1905; Pilsbry, 1894–1935; Crampton, 1916, 1925, 1932). These snails evidently have a high mutation rate and low vagility, with the result that distinctive populations may be recognized in valley woodlands separated by treeless ridges. Topographic and phylogenetic sequences are readily recognized without significant ecologic differences. Welch (1938, 1942) has given us a detailed study of the subspecies and races of two species of snails (*Achatinella mustelina* and *A. apexfulva*) in Hawaii. Their distributions show the effect of partial isolation, and in general confirm the conclusions of other students of speciation in these animals. Although many of the data can be explained only by the action of heritable variations and topographic isolation, Welch does show a correlation of certain color types with altitude (white colors of independently evolved subspecies of *A. apexfulva* in highlands and dark patterns in lowlands). Some selection causing convergent evolution is thus indicated, even among these animals that have provided a classical example of divergence based upon isolation.

Gall wasps (Cynipidae) show many linear series indicating topographic isolation (Kinsey, 1936). Species inhabiting different isolated "islands" of oak woods are more sharply distinct from their relatives and have a more homogeneous population than the "continental" species, which tend to form clines of gradation without sharp topographic demarcation.

Topographic isolation is, in all probability, the most important factor initiating the separation of speciating populations. It seems to be much more common on the whole than habitat or other ecologic isolation, and usually precedes physiologic, psychologic, and genetic isolation, as well as hybrid incapacitation. However, it is by no means the exclusive mechanism by which populations are divided. In our opinion, the role of geographic isolation has been somewhat overemphasized by some authors (e.g., Mayr, 1942; 1947). Without diminishing the importance of geographic separations in evolution, consideration of other isolating mechanisms in the following pages should give a broader perspective on various types of reproductive isolation.

HABITAT ISOLATION

Instances of habitat isolation, like those of topographic isolation, that do not involve other types of separation are difficult to discover. Ecologic differences emphasize the role of selection in relation to isolation even when combined with topographic or spatial isolation. Closely related species living together in the same geographic region (*sympatric species*), but occupying different habitats, should be carefully studied and analyzed. Ancient topographic or genetic isolation may be primary, and ecologic isolation secondary in many sympatric species, although this is not necessarily universal. The discussion in the following paragraphs illustrates the importance of habitat isolation without wholly excluding other factors.

Mayr (1942, p. 215) concludes that ecologic specializations help to preserve discontinuities between species, but are not responsible for their origin (also see Lack, 1944). The present isolation of two subspecies of mice, *Peromyscus maniculatus bairdii* and *P. m. gracilis*, affords an example of secondary habitat isolation, the former living on lake beaches and the latter in woods, both occurring together in Washtenaw County, Michigan (Dice, 1931). In this instance we are sure that geographic isolation preceded habitat isolation because of the circle of subspecies connected by intermediate forms that occur to the west (*gracilis, borealis, osgoodi, nebrascensis, bairdii*).

Blair (1947) reports different frequency of color genes in deer mice (*Peromyscus maniculatus blandus*) occupying different colored soils 18 miles apart in New Mexico, but no difference in the gene frequencies of mice on different colored soils only 4 miles apart. These differences in color of the more separated populations correspond to the shade of the background soils. Studies of the pelage color of the cactus mouse (*P. eremicus*) show comparable relations to the background color in somewhat separated habitats (Blair, 1947a). Blair says: "The existence of the local cactus-mouse populations distinguished by shade of pelage is attributed to selection pressure that exceeds the homogenizing effect of interbreeding between the several adjacent local populations" (see pp. 627, 650, 668).

Under special circumstances it would seem possible that initial isolation may be ecologic (Thorpe, 1945; Crombie, 1947), but critical data are difficult to find. Even habitat isolation partakes of some micro-spatial or micro-topographic separation of populations with little dispersion, so that such isolation is only different in degree from the grosser geographical types discussed under other headings. Topography may separate genetically identical populations, but ecologic factors usually separate genetically different populations that have already been guided by natural selection toward adaptive divergence, even though the populations may not be wholly isolated reproductively (i.e., with resultant ecologic subspecies or ecotypes, p. 626). If selection pressure is greater than the dispersal and cross breeding between partially isolated populations, divergence may occur (p. 616). If dispersal and cross breeding outweigh selection pressure, divergence will not occur. Other types of isolation may augment habitat isolation in any given case.

Ecologic habitats in close geographic proximity on occasion have closely related species, which have recently diverged in their adjustment to the environment. For instance, the mosquito larvae of *Anopheles melas* and *A. gambiae* from the coasts of Africa are limited by different degrees of salinity in the water medium, and such divergence could conceivably result from selection and habitat isolation (Ribbands, 1944). *A. melas* and *A. gambiae* are both adjusted to fresh water, but only *A. melas* can tolerate brackish water in which the salinity exceeds 50 per cent of that of sea water. Selection toward adaptation to a brackish water habitat with its consequent isolation from the other species may well have been responsible for ultimate speciation. *A. melas* usually occurs in brackish water under natural conditions in spite of its tolerance of fresh water under experimental conditions. When the two species occur together in fresh water, *A. gambiae* seems to compete more successfully than *A. melas*.

Another case of two widely overlapping geographic species exhibiting habitat differences occurs among the crabs of the genus *Ocypode*, found along the Pacific coasts of Central and South America (Crane, 1941a). One species, *O. gaudichaudii*, lives on protected beaches and on the shores of lagoons, feeds on minute or-

ganic matter in the sand, and is active only in the daytime. The other species, *O. occidentalis*, lives on unprotected beaches beaten by heavy surf, is a predator and scavenger, and is active in the adult stage only at night. Only occasionally are these species found on the same beach, but in each instance of ecologic overlap noted, one or the other is present only in the young stages. It is possible that some form of ecologic isolation was involved in the initial separation of these two species. Both diel and habitat isolation are now well established, together with adaptive differences in feeding.

Perhaps one of the most striking cases of habitat isolation and speciation without any considerable degree of topographic isolation at the present time is illustrated by the fishes of certain African lakes (Myers, 1936; Worthington, 1937, 1940). Since the arid period of the Pleistocene, preceding the last glaciation in Europe, adaptive radiation (pp. 664, 700) of the fresh-water fish genus *Haplochromis* seems to have occurred in Lake Victoria, which is nowhere more than 75 meters deep. This genus has a large series of endemic species ranging from some with short blunt mouths and minute hairlike teeth adjusted to feeding upon small plants and animals, to others with long protrusible mouths, large underhung jaws, and large teeth adjusted to feeding on other fishes. Some species have large flat-crowned teeth adapted for crushing mollusk shells.

Fifty-eight endemic species of the family Cichlidae are found in Lakes Victoria and Kioga—an indication of the amount of adaptive evolution during the 15,000 to 20,000 years or more since these lakes were formed. One hundred and seventy-five species of cichlid fishes belonging to twenty-three genera (twenty endemic) are reported from Lake Nyasa (Trewavas, 1935). One hundred and one of these species belong to the genus *Haplochromis*. Trewavas says, "the Nyasa species are a natural group and may, perhaps, have evolved in the lake from a single ancestral form." Five species of *Haplochromis* are found in different ecologic niches in Lake Albert (Trewavas, 1938). Mayr (1942, p. 215; 1947) makes an alternative suggestion that the large lake could conceivably be the result of fusion of once separated small lakes.

In each occupied African lake the predaceous fishes of the genus *Lates* have split into two species or subspecies. Some interbreeding occurs between these forms in some lakes. In Lakes Albert and Rudolph, one form lives in shallow waters, and the other, with somewhat larger eyes, lives in deeper waters. Two species of *Lates* in Lake Tanganyika and two large species of *Barilius* in Lake Nyasa may also exhibit such habitat isolation.

Topographic isolation is probably the main influence in speciation of fishes in different lakes without adequate interconnections, especially if the ecologic niche occupied is the same. Speciation of fishes in the same lake, with radiation into different ecologic niches, is more probably the result of habitat isolation.

Remarkable speciation producing endemic snails has also taken place in Lake Tanganyika (Yonge, 1938), which contains sixty-eight endemic species of prosobranchs out of eighty-four species of gastropods. Yonge regards these prosobranchs as arising "in the main from a common origin and gradually becoming adapted for life in the variety of habitats which are present in the wide and deep waters of Lake Tanganyika." All the species have a herbivorous diet.

In many closely related species now isolated through habitat separations, ancient topographic isolation may have initiated cessation of gene flow across the population borders with subsequent divergence and adaptation (Mayr, 1942, p. 215). Without knowing the detailed histories of the populations involved, it is impossible to be sure that habitat isolation and selection initiated the divergent evolution.

Topographic barriers are unlikely in the evolution of a blind Mexican cave fish (*Anoptichthys jordani*) that interbreeds with an eyed fish of the adjacent river (*Astyanax mexicanus*) (see p. 674; Fig. 247). One may suppose that without the habitat differences between the open stream and the underground stream, these ecologic subspecies (note that they have been assigned to different genera) would not have differentiated. Other isolating factors would seem to be secondary in this

case, although it is possible that isolation was greater at one time than it is at present. Some authors would probably classify these as allopatric species (p. 608); we call them sympatric. Such difference of opinion revolves around the definition of the categories.

Flanders (1937) described the habitat differences of three species of egg-parasitic wasps, *Trichogramma* (Chalcidoidea), in North America. Laboratory and field observations indicate that these species are not host specific. *T. embryophagum* is usually arboreal, *T. evanescens* is a field form, and *T. semblidis* is commonly found in marshes. When a species is liberated in a habitat to which it is not adapted, it soon disappears, even though suitable hosts are present. The arboreal form typically crawls in search of eggs, while the field form takes long flights. Such differences seem to be adaptive to the normal habitat of the species and may account for the lack of success in cases of transfer.

As might be expected, cases of isolation in different biotic habitats are easier to discover than cases of isolation in different physical habitats. Among the aphids there seems to have been an evolution from autecious types that complete the life cycle of the population on one species of host plant, to heterecious forms that use two host species (Mordvilko, 1928). There is some indication that the host inhabited by the fundatrices or stem-mothers is the original host. *Eriosoma rileyi*, which develops on the American elm, *Ulmus americana*, does not emigrate to another host, while its close relative, *E. lanigerum*, transfers from the elm to some Pomoideae, such as the mountain ash, *Sorbus americana*, the hawthorn, *Crataegus*, or the apple, *Malus*. In Europe, where *Ulmus americana* is absent, *E. lanigerum* has been introduced, but cannot complete its life cycle without its primary host. The parthenogenetic forms are successful on apples and other Pomoideae (Mordvilko, 1935).

There is presumably an advantage in having two hosts. A great many heterecious species have no close relatives that are autecious: the primitive autecious cycle seems to have been lost during evolution. The secondary host, when the aphid invades its roots, is not always the original host. These aphids have many parthenogenetic generations between the sexual generations (p. 703). Mutations that affect cross breeding between populations might be built up during the parthenogenetic increase (Mayr, 1942, p. 192). The two aphids, *Colopha ulmicola* and *C. graminis*, afford a possible example of such speciation. They make similar galls on their primary hosts, the elms *Ulmus americana, U. fulva,* and *U. racemosa.* The secondary hosts of *C. ulmicola* may be grasses of the genus *Erogrostis,* while the secondary hosts of *C. graminis* may be grasses of the genus *Leersia* (Patch, 1910). The ranges of the two species of aphids overlap without any indication of geographic separation, and the sexual generations seem to appear at the same time.

The primary host of the aphid, *Thecabius affinis,* is the poplar, *Populus nigra,* and the secondary hosts are species of buttercups, *Ranunculus.* During the glacial period in Europe, these plants were separated, and *T. affinis* evolved a parthenogenetic form confined to its secondary hosts. This genetically sexless form maintains itself, even when the original primary host is available (Mordvilko, 1935).

Specialized plant-feeding insects should show some speciation and further evolution with initial isolation of populations on the basis of host species rather than topographic separation (Brown, 1945), but the data are not completely clear on this point (Thorpe, 1940). Host specificity involves biochemical adjustment. In some instances the biochemical characters are found only in a single species of host, whereas in others, groups of species classified in genera or other higher categories may share biochemical characteristics and also be hosts to the same species of parasite or phytophage. It is probable that internal parasites in more direct contact with the tissues and fluids of the host are still more subject to biochemical factors than are external plant eaters or parasites.

Zimmerman (1938) cites the large number of weevils of the genus *Microcryptorhynchus* with forty-three endemic species on the small South Pacific island of Rapa. These weevils are all flightless and exhibit varying degrees of host-plant restriction. Seventeen species were found associated with a single host, but others were sometimes found on more than one host, al-though preponderantly on a single host. One species occurred on nine host plants. Topographic isolation is doubtless important in this speciation. Probably isolation on different islands separated several original stocks that were later carried to Rapa by strong winds. Further speciation on the island then probably occurred with host plants separating the evolving species. Soon after emergence the female is fertilized by a male, usually from the same host plant, and new host plants are invaded by crawling weevils.

Sears (1947) says that, within the *melanica* group of *Drosophila*, *D. melanica paramelanica* is found in the northeastern United States, *D. melanica* occupies the south and southwest, while *D. nigromelanica* overlaps both *melanica* and *melanica paramelanica* in geographic range, but is isolated from them by using fungi for food. Also, within the *quinaria* group of species, *D. quinaria, D. palustris, D. subpalustris,* and *D. transversa* are found in the same geographic region (northeastern United States). *Drosophila quinaria* lives in moist forests and eats fruit; *D. palustris* and *subpalustris* inhabit swampy areas and eat decayed plants; and *D. transversa* lives in dry deciduous forests and eats fungi.

Kinsey (1936) states that, among gall wasps (Cynipidae), "closely related species are to be expected in adjacent geographic areas on the same or on closely related hosts, or in single geographic areas on distinct but related hosts." The first portion of this quotation is a restatement of Jordan's rule, and expresses correlation with topographic isolation. The second portion would seem to indicate habitat isolation. As an example of "host isolation," Kinsey cites two species of gall wasps, *Cynips echinoides* and *C. hibrida.* He believes that the morphologic, ecologic, and geographic data indicate that an ancestral stock was present in the Rocky Mountain region where there was only a single group of deciduous white oaks. This stock emigrated into the eastern forests characterized by a variety of distinct species of white oaks; one species of gall wasp invaded *Quercus bicolor* and *Q. prinus,* while the other invaded only *Q. alba.* Each overlaps the geographic range of the other species. No one can be absolutely certain that *C. echinoides* and *C. hibrida* originated in the same geographic area concurrently. On the other hand, it cannot be presumed that divergence of these two species would have taken place without the habitat separation.

If monophagous or oligophagus groups are richer in number of species than polyphagous groups, host-plant isolation may be presumed. Petersen (1932) illustrates this relationship among certain genera of microlepidoptera.

Host isolation between closely related phytophages on taxonomically unrelated plants is illustrated by three species of beetles of the genus *Coenonycha*. All three species are nocturnal, but each feeds and mates on its host plant, *C. bowlesi* on *Artemesia tridentata*, *C. testacea* on *Eriogonum fasciculatum*, and *C. ampla* on *Juniperus californicus* (Tilden and Mansfield, 1944).

The two phases of heterecious species of rusts* are usually found on quite unrelated hosts (Arthur, 1929). Some species have a wide range of hosts for the gametophytic phase and a restricted range for the sporophytic phase, while others show the reverse relation. *Puccinia graminis* in the gametophytic phase occurs on a few species of the barberry (*Berberis*) and *Mahonia*, while its sporophytic phase is found on ninety eight species of thirty five genera of Poaceae in North America alone. *Puccinia subnitens* in the sporophytic phase is largely confined to one species of grass, *Distichlis spicata*, while its gametophytic phase occurs on ninety species of sixty-four genera and twenty-four families. Restricted hosts for both phases are found in *P. anomala*, with its gametophytic phase on *Ornithogalum* and its sporophytic phase on cultivated barley. An autecious species may occur on a single genus of plants—for example, *P. cirsii* occurs on forty-one species of *Cirsium*—or may be found on only one species of host—for example, *P. suaveolens* on *Cirsium arvense*. Many so-called physiologic races have developed within morphologic species, and these may show greater host restriction than the species as a whole. Such forms, when reproductively isolated and when genetically distinctive through their physiologic reactions to their hosts, are evidently species rather than races (p. 625). It is well known, however,

that in some instances the same race may infect a number of host species and even genera.

Varieties of wheat, barley, and oats may be detected by their reactions to certain species of rusts* and conform to the classification based on serology. Immunity of a host is more likely to occur in relation to a rust specialized for its host than to rusts with a wide variety of hosts.

Parasites can be such sensitive biologic testing agents as to differentiate groups otherwise indistinguishable. It is fairly obvious that genetic changes involving subtle physiologic relations on the part of either the host or the parasite may be subject to habitat isolation and selection, thus influencing the evolution of both the hosts and their parasites.

In rusts, the basidiospore is generally incapable of living on a host that bears the diplont (2 N chromosomes) thallus of a species infecting two host species (heterecious) (Jackson, 1931). However, the haploid basidiospores may sometimes, though rarely, have acquired the ability to infect the host normally only susceptible to infection by diploid uredospores or aecidiospores, in this manner establishing the haploid (1 N chromosomes) thallus on the normal host species for the diplont. *Melampsora amygdalinae* on the willow (*Salix*), *Gymnosporangium bermudianum* on the juniper (*Juniperus*), *Synomyces reichei* on *Stevia*, and *Puccinia komarovi* on the jewel weed (*Impatiens*), are examples. The origins of these species of rusts thus appear to be excellent examples of habitat isolation.

Ewing (1933, 1938) reports that four species of lice, closely related to *Pediculus humanus americanus* found on the American Indian, are found respectively on three species of spider monkeys (*Ateles*) and on the saki (*Pithecia monachus*) from South and Central America. The human louse differs so slightly from these four species that it is assumed that they did not evolve with the evolution of the monkey hosts, but rather that the lice transferred from man to the monkeys when the American Indian invaded South America. If this surmise is cor-

---

* The nomenclature of the complex life cycle of rusts may be found in any general textbook of botany.

* *Festuca elatior* has been distinguished from *F. pratensis* on the basis of the differential reaction of *Puccinia phlei-pratensis*, a physiologic form of *P. graminis*.

rect, this is a case of speciation correlated with initial habitat isolation.

Where the parasite has not speciated with the host—the instances are numerous —it may be presumed that the parasite is evolving more slowly than the hosts, and consequently a single parasite infects a phylogenetically related group of host species; or the parasite may be able to pass from one host to another fairly readily, as fleas do.

Among the flukes, ectoparasitic Monogenea are more likely to be strictly confined to particular hosts than are the endoparasitic Digenea (Baylis, 1938). *Nitzschia* and *Diclibothrium* are found only on sturgeons, *Discocotyle* only on fishes of the family Salmonidae, and *Dactylogyrus* only on Cyprinidae. The species are often confined to a single host species or a group of closely related host species. A number of groups of cestodes show similar specific correlation with taxonomic groups of hosts. Physiologic races or species of nematodes that are morphologically indistinguishable seem to be confined to certain hosts (*Ascaris lumbricoides* of man and pig; *Ancylostoma caninum* of dog and cat; *Hymenolepis nana* (of man and rodents).

Specificity of hosts is more marked in bird than in mammalian cestodes, among which the same genus (not the same species) may occur in several host orders (Baer, 1933). Among the nematodes, the species with a direct life cycle show a greater degree of host specificity than those with an indirect life cycle. Baylis (1938) suggests in explanation that the larvae of the forms with direct life cycles are younger and less resistant at the time of penetration and may be less tolerant of hosts to which they are imperfectly adapted. Forms with an indirect life history usually show greater specificity for the intermediate host than for their final host, possibly for the same reason (p. 702).

Host specificity is notably more highly developed in the cestodes, which have no free-living stage and are closely inbreeding, than in the trematodes (Baylis, 1938). A high degree of specificity usually denotes evolutionary specialization, and parasites inhabiting more than two hosts in a single stage are usually the more primitive. Variation of characters of a physiologic nature would allow for host selection of races. Preadaptation to invasion of new hosts may be provided by adaptation to related host species (p. 643). However, numerous parasites show no correlation between their own phylogeny and that of their hosts, and only in special cases may one assume parallel evolution of host-parasite pairs. The cestode genus *Tetrabothrius* occurs in whales, seals, and fish-eating birds of several orders, indicating transfer from one host to another through fish feeding.

Host specificity is striking among certain species of termitophilous beetles (pp. 718–721; Seevers, 1937; Emerson, 1935). The socially adapted symphiles are far more likely to be confined to the nests of one host species than are the more generalized synoeketes such as the species of the staphylinid genus *Perinthus* (Fig. 255). The specialized termitophilous fauna can be used as a means of recognizing closely related host species living in the same locality and in the same ecologic niche. Reproductive isolation of the host termites is here thought to be associated with brother-sister matings over a period long enough to allow the divergence of the species, though it is possible that some unknown ancient geographic isolation occurred. In a few instances, two related species of termitophiles may be found in the same host nest, although the original isolating mechanism is unknown (the staphylinids *Spirachtha mirabilis* and *S. schiödtei* in the nest of the termite *Constrictotermes cavifrons;* Mann, 1923; Fig. 259).

In India two races of the large hawk-cuckoo (*Hierococcyx sparverioides*) lay eggs of different color. Each hawk-cuckoo, though inhabiting the same area, is strictly parasitic on host birds with eggs the color of its own race (Baker, 1942; see p. 670). It would appear that such racial divergence is associated with habitat isolation. No knowledge is available of the reproductive isolation of these races, but the evidence points to a genetic egg coloring, and the dimorphism correlated with the associated host eggs could only be maintained by partial reproductive isolation and selection.

Host selection through conditioning has been referred to as the "Hopkins' host-selection principle." Thorpe (1940) cites the experimental transfer of the ichneumonid, *Nemeritis canescens,* to an unusual host species, and concludes that natural conditioning of this type might split a population into separate groups attached to particular animal hosts or food plants, with consequent prevention of interbreeding.

Mayr (1942, pp. 199, 215; 1947) takes the position that habitat isolation within the same region is not the initial cause of the origin of sympatric species (also see p. 659; Lack, 1944, 1946). He believes that all or nearly all sympatric species originated as geographic rather than ecologic isolates and that their ranges later came to overlap. He postulates that any ecologic distinction between species may assist in keeping them isolated, but did not originally separate them and that any ecologic differences within the same area without geographic separation would be swamped through interbreeding. Thorpe (1945) contends, however, that the conclusion that geographic isolation always precedes other kinds of isolation is premature (see also Crombie, 1947).

Wright (1945; see also p. 603) has pointed out that the intragroup competition between almost but not completely isolated populations within large species gives the best conditions for adaptive evolution of species as wholes (Fig. 229). Surely these partially isolated groups are commonly separated by ecologic as well as geographic factors. Partial habitat isolation probably often results in differences in population numbers (p. 602) with their effect upon gene frequency and gene fixation. Competition between populations in the same habitat might favor adaptive divergence (Crombie, 1947). If selection pressures guide these partially isolated groups toward ecologic adaptive divergence, the hybrids between the two successful populations would occasionally be selectively eliminated (p. 623). Selection would maintain intragroup fertility, but would not always maintain intergroup fertility, and might even favor genes producing genetic isolation if advantageous combinations were swamped through interbreeding between groups adapted to different environments. Thus habitat isolation could initiate a process of speciation (pp. 616 and 676).

Mayr (1942, 1947) emphasizes the geographic component in habitat isolation, while we are here emphasizing the ecologic component. The line of division between sympatric and allopatric distributions of closely related species is arbitrary in a great many instances. Habitat differences are also often microgeographic. However, it is well to separate these two factors in discussing isolating mechanisms, even though they overlap and usually act together, because selection in different habitats and separation in physical space may independently influence divergent speciation.

In summary, we cannot say that closely related species always replace each other ecologically, but we can say that in some instances there is a tendency for them to do so. Closely related sympatric species are usually divergent in some important adaptive characters. Habitat separation is surely an important isolating mechanism (not so important in general evolution as is topographic isolation). It plays a significant role in speciation of certain types of organisms, particularly those with narrow biotic relations such as are found among phytophages and parasites. Initial habitat isolation is difficult to illustrate, but is theoretically possible.

CYCLIC ISOLATION

Adjustments to variation in seasonal factors such as temperature or light may bring about reproductive isolation between closely related populations. Single mutational changes are not likely, however, to induce the separation of two distinct populations with nonoverlapping temperature ranges (Muller, 1942). Polygenic characters are practically always involved in such adaptational changes, and selection is likely to be a factor in balancing the genetic complex.

Banta and Wood (1928) reported a mutation in *Cladocera* that raised both the upper and lower limits of temperature toleration by 10° C. Such a dramatic change, which might conceivably separate natural populations in the same area, would probably have to be balanced with other external and internal adjustments, so that the emergence of seasonal differences would probably necessitate gradual and long evolution. Seasonal divergence may have become established with geographic isolation in many cases, but it is also possible that selection of populations at two extremes of a seasonal range, with interbreeding only between those individuals with similar seasonal adjustments, might split the species. As in habitat isolation, there might be a selective elimination of the intergrades in some instances. The genetic complexity and probable gradual divergence are illustrated by the intersterility of many species separated by seasonal isolation.

In many other cases, interfertility is not impaired between species inhabiting the same geographic region that are reproductively separated by seasonal breeding periods. Epling (Dobzhansky, 1941) has studied flowering seasons in the genus *Salvia. Salvia munzii* and *S. clevelandii* are wholly isolated because the first is past its flowering season when the second begins. Two other species of the same genus, *S. mellifera* and *S. apiana,* have overlapping flowering seasons and produce hybrids when found together in the same locality.

Two closely related species of the bee genus, *Andrena (A. peckhami* and *A. parnassiae),* visit different flowers in the same region in Wisconsin and also fly in different seasons, coincident with the flowering seasons of their hosts (Cockerell, 1931).

The moth, *Eupethecia innotata,* feeds on *Artemisia,* and a closely related species, *E. unedonata,* emerges earlier and feeds on *Arbutus* (Hogben, 1940). Pupae of the species feeding on *Arbutus* were cooled, thus delaying their emergence, and, when mated with the species feeding on *Artemisia,* fertile hybrids were produced. Of course, the seasonal isolation is associated here with habitat differences in food plants as well. It should also be pointed out that the production of fertile hybrids in the laboratory does not necessarily mean that these hybrids could survive through many generations under natural conditions. Although it is difficult to separate such a factor as seasonal isolation from all other evolutionary factors, it would appear that in some cases it may be a real hindrance to interbreeding.

Two species of grasshoppers, *Arphia sulphurea* and *A. xanthoptera,* have similar ranges from Nebraska to Texas, Florida and New England. They occupy similar habitats, except that *A. sulphurea* remains in the nymph stage in the winter, matures in the spring, and largely disappears before *A. xanthoptera,* hatching from eggs in the spring, becomes mature. In Illinois, adults of *A. sulphurea* have been taken from April to July 29, and adults of *A. xanthoptera* have been taken from July 14 to October 18 (Blatchley, 1920; Hebard, 1934).

Miller and Miller (1943) report differences in the season of the colonizing flights of two closely related species of termites, *Reticulitermes hageni* and *R. virginicus.* These two species have similar geographic distribution and inhabit the same ecologic areas. The flights of *R. virginicus* occur in south Florida from March through May, while the flights of *R. hageni* occur in the fall and winter months. In the vicinity of Washington, D. C., *Reticulitermes flavipes* flies from outdoor colonies late in April or early in May; *R. virginicus* flies in early June; and *R. hageni* flies in July and August (Snyder, 1935).

The "land-locked" sockeye salmon or kokanee of Cultus Lake, British Columbia, spawns in August and September, while the residual sockeye, from which the kokanee is probably derived, spawns in the same lake from October to December. This seasonally isolated form shows some coloration differences in the mature male and other slight differences, including a relative immunity to the parasitic copepod, *Salmincola.* It may be presumed that these seasonal differences have established either partial or total reproductive isolation and thus constitute a major factor in the divergence of these forms, which have not yet been named. The kokanee has been distinguished as a subspecies, but, as defined, it inhabits many lakes and may well be a polyphyletic group (Ricker, 1938, 1940).

After consideration of the evidence, it would seem possible for seasonal isolation, together with selection, to separate populations gradually, even within the same geographic and ecologic area, thus leading to speciation (Crombie, 1947). Seasonal isolation would thus be a sort of temporal habitat isolation. Doubtless this form of reproductive isolation is a rather minor mechanism as compared, for example, to topographic or habitat isolation.

If the life cycles of the individuals extend two years or more, such *annual isolation* within the same geographic and habitat areas may possibly have some effect upon the divergence of species. The races of the periodic cicada, *Magicicada septendecim,* may be partially isolated in this way. According to Davidson (Emerson, 1943), the races of the pink salmon (*Oncorhynchus gorbuscha*) that breed in the same streams in alternate years are somewhat differentiated. It is rare to find life cycles exhibiting periodicities that inhibit gene exchange between populations. Overlaps in the periodicities tend to swamp the differences, and in these cases there is little selection to build genetic distinctions. Annual isolation should be considered a minor mechanism of reproductive isolation and operable only in a few special instances.

Isolation through differences in breeding activity related to diel rhythms (*diel isolation*) has not been much discussed, although it is obvious that a population active at night would not be likely to interbreed with a population active only in the daytime (pp. 544–562, 611).

Closely related species of fishes, the black and white crappies (*Pomoxis nigromaculatus* and *P. annularis*), similar in food habits and general behavior, are found together in the rivers of Illinois, Indiana, and Ohio (Johnson, 1945), and a few interspecific hybrids have been found in nature. The black crappie shows nocturnal activity, and the white crappie is diurnal, thus suggesting that these species are reproductively isolated through different activity cycles. In this same family (Centrarchidae), the species that hybridize freely in regions of geographic overlap have similar or broadly overlapping activity periods (Emerson, 1943).

Diel isolation seems to be a minor isolating mechanism even among species in which it might be expected to occur. Genera of may flies and stone flies exhibit differences in diurnal and nocturnal mating behavior, but closely related species within the same genus commonly are not distinguished by divergence in such diel rhythms.

Although cyclic isolation is not of great importance in the evolution of many species, nevertheless a temporal separation in the same region and in the same habitat may result in speciation.

MECHANICAL ISOLATION

Mechanical isolation, a term used by other authors, refers to structural maladjustment of the copulatory apparatus. It may be presumed that a lack of fit between the genital organs of the males of one species and the females of another would reproductively isolate the two populations. Species of various animals, particularly of many groups of insects and spiders, are easily distinguished by the structure of the copulatory organs. Convincing evidence, however, for the importance of mechanical isolation in evolutionary divergence is surprisingly scanty.

Dobzhansky (1941, p. 267) recently summarized some data on this type of isolation. Durfour suggested the "lock-and-key" theory before the days of Darwin, and K. Jordan (1905) amplified the concept, which assumed that the genitalia in copulation fitted each other as a key fits a lock. Any substantial variation of the genitalia would, according to this theory, produce reproductive isolation (Pope, 1941).

A number of groups are known in which the males are distinct in each species, while no differentiation of the females can be detected. Interspecies copulation is known to occur (Sengün, 1944), and no mechanical barriers exist. It would thus seem that speciation associated with other types of isolation ultimately affects complex organs such as the genitalia so as to produce distinguishable taxonomic characters in some groups, but that these mechanical differences result from the process of speciation, instead of being the cause of a primary isolation (Shull, 1946). The adaptational aspects of sexual adjustment are discussed later (p. 688).

Diver (1936) cites two closely related snails, *Cepaea hortensis* and *C. nemoralis* (Helicidae), with a parallel range of variability, a wide overlap of ecologic and geographic distribution, and occurrence in mixed colonies. The genital organs differ, and the two species seem to be mechanically and psychologically isolated in nature, although they can with difficulty be made to produce viable but sterile offspring in the laboratory (Diver, 1940). Overlapping of the two species also occurs in Pleistocene deposits, indicating long-continued reproductive isolation.

Webb (1947) finds that the mating of snails of the subfamily Polygyrinae is a difficult performance, while the Triodopsinae are able to transfer semen from one individual to another with much greater ease. He thinks the greater speciation of the polygyrin species in contrast with the triodopsin species east of the Mississippi may be the result of these mechanical factors.

Mechanical isolation may play a role in the evolution of specialized insect-pollinated plants, such as orchids and the Leguminosae (Dobzhansky, 1941, p. 269; see also pp. 250 and 715).

Although some instances in which mechanical isolation proves to be the initial mechanism of speciation may be discovered ultimately, its role seems to be a minor one.

PSYCHOLOGICAL ISOLATION

Reproductive isolation through the lack of sexual attraction between two closely related species is a possibility, even though they live in the same environment and geographic region and there is no mechanical, physiological, or genetic incompatibility. This form of sexual isolation resulting from behavioristic or psychological interference with mating has been termed *ethological isolation* (Mayr, 1942). Behavior differences associated with the general habitat rather than with mating are included under Habitat Isolation (p. 610). In some examples, such as those discussed under Physiological Isolation (p. 622), the individuals avoid mating because of physiological barriers. In other instances, the barriers seem to be mainly psychological. The form of intraspecies sex attraction and interspecies sex isolation may be visual, auditory, tactile, chemical, or a combination of various stimuli (Kahn, Celestin, and Offenhauser, 1945; Mayr, 1946a). In territorial passerine birds, there tends to be an inverse relation between the development of auditory distinctiveness and visual distinctiveness[*] (Huxley, 1938).

We are here dealing with hereditary behavior. Conditioned behavior, which may also have an evolutionary effect (Sutton, 1931), has already been discussed (p. 604). The fact that physiologic and psychologic distinctions intergrade and are often difficult to separate indicates that they are closely related and that a dualistic

[*] Orioles and cardinals are exceptions.

philosophy separating psyche from body is unwarranted.

Dobzhansky and Koller (1938) have shown that in cultures containing a mixture of females of *Drosophila pseudoobscura* and *D. miranda* and males of one of these species, the males more often fertilize the females of their own species. This tendency toward homogamic matings was also observed in mixed cultures of *D. azteca* and *D. athabasca,* and to a less degree in mixed cultures of the Olympic and Whitney races of *D. miranda.* Patterson, McDanald, and Stone (1947) say that sexual preferences resulting in a lack of cross breeding are universal between species groups of *Drosophila,* and complete sexual isolation may occur between species within the same group. Mayr (1946a) has analyzed the mechanisms of sexual attraction between two closely related species of *Drosophila* (*D. pseudoobscura* and *D. persimilis*).

Thus species may be sexually isolated within the same territory. Other types of isolation, such as that afforded by topography or habitat, may precede the development of psychological isolation (p. 610). It is probably seldom possible for psychological isolation to initiate the separation of races, but it may augment other types of isolation.

Two races of salmon, the "steelhead" and "rainbow trout," belonging to the same species (*Salmo gairdneri*), spawn on the same grounds and at the same time in the upper portion of the Cowichan River and Cowichan Lake in British Columbia. The steelhead trout migrates to and from the sea, while the rainbow trout resides in fresh water, migrating only from the lake to the river and back. Scale counts indicate that there are two populations with different but overlapping hereditary characters. Data on interbreeding between these races are wanting, but there appears to be incipient speciation without geographic or habitat isolation, and one may assume at least a partial psychologic or genetic isolation associated with the difference in migratory behavior (Neave, 1944).

The population of the sockeye salmon (*Oncorhynchus nerka*) found in Cultus Lake, British Columbia, is divided into residual and migrating components. The residual population is the progeny of the migrating population, and no reproductive isolation or speciation is indicated (Ricker, 1938; see also p. 617).

Among frogs and toads, the call notes and sexual behavior reproductively isolate closely related interfertile species, even when these species occupy similar geographic and ecologic regions. The toads (*Bufo*) and the spadefoot toads (*Scaphiopus*) afford examples (Bragg, 1945, 1945a).

The common leopard frog (*Rana pipiens*) is a close relative of the pickerel frog (*R. palustris*), and the two species overlap broadly in both their geographic and ecologic ranges. They may be found breeding in the same pond at the same time, although this is unusual. *Rana palustris* secretes a mucus that has been thought to be poisonous to *R. pipiens,* and would thus prevent the male of one species from clasping the female of the other. Moore (1946), however, states that these two species will clasp each other under laboratory conditions without detectable harm to either. Moore (1941, 1946a) artificially hybridized this pair of species and raised adult frogs. They are probably psychologically isolated through their different call notes and breeding behavior. Partial ecological and seasonal isolation between them is usual. It is conceivable that these two species might have initially diverged in their defensive adaptations, inasmuch as the primary function of the more poisonous mucus of *R. palustris* seems to be to repel enemies such as snakes. The ability of the pickerel frog to exist in small populations in apparent competition with the larger populations of the leopard frog may thus be explained. This example enables us to eliminate a number of possible factors in reproductive isolation, but several others are still involved, and it is difficult to be sure of their separate evolutionary effects, if indeed the factors acted independently during speciation.

A number of species of fiddler crabs of the genus *Uca* may be found in the same locality. Crane (1941) found fifteen species, twelve actively courting, in a beach area not more than 600 feet square at La Boca, Panama Canal Zone. This number of species of the same genus occupying the same breeding area is extremely rare. A phylogenetic study of the species along the Pacific coast of Central and South America indicated some geographic and some habitat isolation, but in general there seems to be a considerable degree of speciation without clear evidence that primary isolation was caused by either geographic or gross habitat differences. Crane found the courtship behavior and coloration to be the striking differential. "Each species proved to have a definite, individual display, differing so markedly from that of every other species observed, that closely related species could be recognized at a distance merely by the form of the display." Furthermore, related species have fundamental similarities of display, and series of species, showing progressive specialization of structure, in general show similar progression in the nature of their display. Miss Crane states[*] that morphologic differentiation of closely related species is no greater in geographically or ecologically separated regions than in closely related species occupying the same habitat. It is noteworthy that the differentiation in behavior and often in coloration of the male is greater if the species are found together than if they are found in different habitats or regions.

The display pattern consists of various combinations and modifications of cheliped waving, elevation of body, position of chelae, motion of minor chelipeds, motion around the burrow, revolution (dancing), color exhibition, and other special features, including display ground. Long periods of courtship, often lasting through several days, are the rule among these fiddler crabs. Color differences in the males of different species are produced by four types of monochromatic chromatophores, each with a different pigment, together with a blue pigment not within chromatophores (Crane, 1944). The physiology of chromatophores in *Uca pugilator* is discussed by Brown and Sandeen (1948).

Courtship patterns govern species recognition in these animals and, possibly in conjunction with minor habitat and geographic separations, gradually have produced reproductive isolation between populations, followed by speciation. It would be interesting to know whether genetic isolation is also involved. The existence of hybrids between *Uca* species or the perform-

[*] Personal communication.

ance of cross breeding experiments would be crucial. No cases of either natural or experimental hybrids are known. Nor is it known how the males recognize the females of their own species.[*] The males never wave at the females of a different species, except rarely for a few seconds, even though taxonomic distinctions of females are often microscopic and difficult to detect. The speciation of *Uca* emphasizes sexual display as an isolating mechanism.

There may be selection favoring psychological isolation in sympatric species while no such selection pressure would operate on groups sharply separated by topography or habitat (p. 605). There is also a possibility that once separated forms might merge if no psychological or other isolating mechanism persisted.

Dice (1940) describes an interesting case of geographic and ecologic overlap between two species of mice (*Peromyscus leucopus* and *P. gossypinus*) with practically no hybridization in nature, though in the laboratory these two species interbreed readily and produce viable offspring. The two populations were probably separated geographically during the period in which the psychological differences arose.

George B. Saunders[†] has studied the eastern and western meadowlarks (*Sturnella magna magna* and *S. neglecta*), which broadly overlap in both geographic and ecologic distribution, although the western meadowlark is essentially a prairie form, while the eastern species is a meadow and field form. During the last glaciation these species were probably topographically isolated. In the prairie habitats west of Chicago, both species are now found nesting in the same field. In nature, hybrids occur rarely, if at all, but in the laboratory the species interbreed and produce viable offspring.

Lack (1945, 1947) suggests that speciation in the Galapagos finches (*Geospiza*) occurred through topographic isolation of small populations and that hybridization in later geographically overlapping species is prevented by psychological and sexual isolation. The shape of the bill is important in courtship and species recognition in these birds.

[*] Personal communication from Miss Crane.
[†] Personal communication.

The elaborate courtship procedures of many animals indicate that sexual recognition and stimulation are the result of adaptive evolution. Mayr (1942, p. 254) points out that sexually dimorphic species often use these characters "to facilitate the meeting and recognition of conspecific individuals and to prevent hybridization between different species." Referring particularly to the hummingbirds (Trochilidae), grouse (Tetraonidae) and manakins (Pipridae), he says (p. 261):

"It is not accidental that we find in [the] families not only the highest development of sexual dimorphism, but also the greatest difference between the males of closely related species. These differences are so striking that even the geographic races are so different in many species as to be considered to be generically distinct by earlier authors. There is necessity for highly specific recognition marks in those species in which copulation is not preceded by pair formation or lengthy engagement periods. On the other hand, sexual dimorphism tends to deteriorate on small islands on which selective species recognition is unnecessary, since no other species of the genus is present."

Fulton (1933) reported three kinds of crickets (*Nemobius fasciatus fasciatus, N. f. socius,* and *N. f. tinnulus*) that are strikingly similar in morphologic characters and are not seasonally isolated. These supposed subspecies overlap geographically, but in any one region tend to be restricted ecologically: *socius* to moist meadows and marsh borders, *tinnulus* to shaded woodlands, and *fasciatus* to intermediate habitats. In certain transitional areas such as the borders of woodlands, two forms may intermingle, but as there is no indication of hybridization in nature, these forms appear to have reached species status. The chirps of the three forms are distinct and under natural conditions probably serve to keep the populations from interbreeding. Under laboratory conditions Fulton was able to raise hybrids of *fasciatus* and *tinnulus* with intermediate songs. These hybrids were fertile, thus indicating no genetic isolation. One might assume a combination of habitat and psychological isolation in the initiation of speciation of these crickets.

Sexual dimorphism may often be favored by natural selection because of its benefit to the species as a means of bringing the sexes together and avoiding mismating. It should be noted that such benefits accrue for the species as a whole and not just for the individual, thus indicating a principle different from Darwinian sexual selection (p. 688). It is also necessary to emphasize that sexual characters may be used for threat or combat between males of the same species (p. 691), especially in the establishment of breeding or nesting territory. Here we have considered the isolating effect, but it is obvious that other factors may also play a role in the evolution of the same character in the same species.

Psychological isolation is important in maintaining species distinction in sympatric pairs or groups of species, but alone it seldom if ever initiates speciation.

PHYSIOLOGICAL ISOLATION

The separation of psychological (p. 619) and physiological isolation may be unwarranted, but it is sometimes possible to distinguish between direct biochemical interaction and psychological sexual attraction or repulsion. Physiological isolation also often merges with genetic isolation (p. 623) (see Caspari, 1948).

Patterson (1946, 1947) and Wheeler (1947) show that the mucous membrane of the vagina of many species of *Drosophila* enlarges, shortly after the introduction of semen, to three or four times its normal virginal size. The semen without the spermatozoa can bring about this reaction. In intraspecies (homogamic) crosses the vagina returns to its normal size in a few hours, but in interspecies crosses it may be enlarged for several days and undergo changes that interfere with its normal function. If a strong reaction occurs, the females may not mate again. In extreme cases eggs passing through the vagina may disintegrate. Interference with fertilization is the usual reaction. Patterson refers to this physiological change as the *insemination reaction*. In the *D. mulleri* group of *Drosophila*, the small number of hybrids seems to be the result of this insemination reaction. In interspecies copulation between the two most closely related species, *D. mojavensis* and *D. arizonensis*, the vagina in the females of *D. mojavensis* recovered sufficiently in some cases to allow the production of hybrids. The species of the subgenus *Sophophora* do not show an insem-

ination reaction even in homogamic matings. The physiological isolation described for some species of *Drosophila* would prevent the exchange of genes, and mutations affecting the protein composition of the semen could well initiate the division of a species.

Sonneborn (1941) has shown that varieties of *Paramecium aurelia* with heritable differences in their reproductive and physiological characteristics, but without morphologic differences, do not interbreed. In addition to complete sexual isolation between nonconjugating varieties, Sonneborn and Dippell (1946) find isolation between conjugating varieties caused by incomplete sexual compatibility, hybrid inviability or low viability, low viability of the F_2 or backcross generations, and an incompletely understood selective elimination of hybrids.

Paramecium bursaria is divided into three noncrossing varieties in the United States, and three additional varieties have been reported from Russia (Jennings and Opitz, 1944) and Europe (Chen, 1946). Reproductive isolation is maintained by different surface chemical reactions of the cell that prevent conjugation, or, in certain mating types of variety II from the United States and variety IV from Russia, conjugation may occur, but both members die because of physiological incompatibility (Chen, 1946a). Geographic or habitat isolation may also separate these varieties, but, even when they occur together, physiological isolation prevents the sharing of any genetic characteristics that may have arisen subsequent to their isolation. Such physiological isolation may be closely akin to physiological incompatibility between spermatozoa and eggs with resultant infertility (p. 623). Although these reproductively incompatible populations of *Paramecium* are classified as varieties of a species, they conform to the definition of a true species (p. 625), distinguished by physiologic rather than by morphologic characters.

Various classes and types of intraspecies reproductive incompatibility are summarized and discussed by Stout (1945). He classifies incompatibilities such as those found in *Paramecium* as *diplont-diplont* incompatibilities. *Haplont-haplont* types are found in the fungi in which reactions "occur in the interrelations between individuals that are haploid, bisexual and gametophytic." *Diplont-haplont* types are found among the flowering plants in which there may be an inhibiting effect of self-pollination and cross pollination occurring particularly during the "reactions between the diploid tissues of the pistils of flowers of the sporophytic generation and the haploid pollen tubes of the alternating gametophytic generation." These physiological reactions may be determined by an allelic pair of genes, an allelic series, or they may be polygenic.

Where the genetic mechanism affecting crossability is simple, one might expect occasional initial isolation between populations through physiological incompatibility (Crombie, 1947). Where the genetic mechanism is more complicated, one might assume long separation of the populations through various types of reproductive isolation.

Because of the difficulty of detection, physiological isolation may be more common than the evidence indicates at present. As in sexual isolation in general, physiological isolation would be expected to follow the effects of the various extrinsic factors of isolation. Initial separation of populations on the basis of physiological incompatibility is probably rare.

GENETIC ISOLATION

Genetic change characterizes all evolutionary progression or regression. Populations as well as individuals exhibit genetic differences. Genetic distinctions, however, may or may not prevent interbreeding between populations; in order to affect isolation directly, they must affect interfertility (p. 676). Physiologic incompatibility between the sexes of the organisms carrying the gametes is discussed under Physiological Isolation (p. 622). Lack of fertility because of chromosomal or gene balance is termed *genetic isolation* and lies largely in the field of genetics rather than in ecology (White, 1945; Castle, 1946; Patterson and Wheeler, 1947; Hughes-Schrader, 1948).

Initial infertility between individuals may rarely give rise to species divergence among animals. Hubbs and Hubbs (1946) report a species of fish (*Mollienisia formosa*) composed wholly of females that is physiologically dependent upon copulation with other species in order to stimulate oviposition and development. The offspring never inherit any characters from the males of these other species. Species divergence in this case must have occurred without any other type of isolation than infertility and parthenogenesis.

Polyploid plants and animals with many parthenogenetic generations may develop intersterility suddenly (Jackson, 1931). Recent knowledge of such isolating mechanisms is summarized by Dobzhansky (1941), Cain (1944), Crombie (1947), and Hughes-Schrader (1948).

Genetic isolation is the clinching intrinsic type of isolation that ultimately separates diverging species regardless of fluctuations in extrinsic factors. A high proportion of all taxonomic species of both plants and animals have developed genetic isolation. Together with the other intrinsic mechanisms (sexual bars to gene flow, hybrid inviability, and hybrid sterility; see Table 52, Isolation Factors, on p. 606), the development of a permanent prevention of gene flow is a criterion used by some authors in their definition of a species. We use the attainment of reproductive isolation between genetically different natural populations whether by intrinsic or extrinsic mechanisms, as the criterion of the species category (p. 625). Genetic isolation commonly results from regressive evolution of fertility (p. 676).

Genetic isolation, hybrid inviability, and hybrid sterility are analyzed in genetic and embryological literature and are considered to be internal physiological phenomena outside the field of ecology. However, inasmuch as these intrinsic factors influence the extrinsic relations of one organism or population to another, ecologists must take them into account.

SELECTIVE HYBRID ELIMINATION

Hybrids may fail to perpetuate themselves because of inviability, sterility (Dobzhansky, 1941), or through selective elimination. As ecologists, we are here concerned with the last type of incapacity. If two populations have become differentiated by adaptation to two different habitats through selection, the hybrids would probably not be so well adapted to either habitat as would the parent forms and might thus be selectively eliminated. The swamping of differentiated adaptive characters through hybridization would be so deleterious to the species that there might be selective pressure favoring any device that would prevent cross breeding. Hybridization might also interfere with sexual adaptations with resultant negative selection of the hybrid individuals.

Turrill (1936) cited an interesting example of hybrid elimination among plants. In the French Alps the campion, *Suene cucubalus,* is tall and erect and lives in hay meadows and on the edge of woodlands. *Silene alpina* has a low growth form and lives on open talus slopes, sometimes in close proximity to S. *cucubalus.* Neither species invades the territory of the other. A few hybrids are found in intermediate habitats. These species are thus known to cross in nature, and they are readily crossed in the laboratory. Nevertheless, the species remain pure under natural conditions in their respective habitats. Hybrid elimination seems to be responsible for their reproductive isolation.

Epling (1947) discusses the elimination of hybrids between two closely related heathers (*Arctostaphylos mariposa* and *A. patula*), one occupying lower and drier sites near Yosemite Park in California, the other occupying higher, shaded, and cooler sites. Many hybrids occur in overlapping areas, but both species maintain themselves. Hybrid elimination by ecologic factors is suggested.

We refer to such elimination as *ecological hybrid inviability* in contrast to intrinsic hybrid inviability, in which the mortality is caused by internal lethal effects during development.

Another interfertile pair of species that indicates ecological hybrid elimination is found in the blue-winged warbler (*Vermivora pinus*) and the golden-winged warbler (*V. chrysoptera*). In general, the blue-winged warbler breeds in northern and the golden-winged warbler in southern regions. The blue-winged warbler is found more commonly in low-lying bushy pastures and second growth woods, while the golden-winged warbler is characteristic of uplands and oak woods. The breeding areas of the two species overlap in the river valleys of portions of Connecticut, New York, New Jersey, and Wisconsin, and in these restricted habitats hybrids are occasionally

found. The most conspicuous color characters of the two species seem to be Mendelian characters (the whitish underparts of the golden-winged warbler being dominant over the yellowish underparts of the blue-winged warbler, and the plain throat of the blue-winged warbler dominant over the black throat of the golden-winged warbler in the first generation hybrid). The hybrid with the combination of these two dominant characters is known as Brewster's warbler. Back-crosses have been observed. A double recessive hybrid is occasionally produced, known as Lawrence's warbler, with yellow underparts and a black throat. Several other Mendelian characters also segregate, and there is some evidence that the throat patch may result from two segregating genes. However, the blue-winged and golden-winged warblers remain pure in their respective ranges, and there seems to be no effective transfer of genes between the two species. This is circumstantial evidence of the elimination of the hybrids over a few generations, either through the long-run psychological isolation of the species or through ecological hybrid inviability (see also Jewett, 1944; Alexander, 1945).

Thus selective hybrid elimination may reproductively isolate two species otherwise not completely separated. This mechanism may reinforce the effectiveness of habitat isolation in the origin of species (p. 616). Hall (1946) favors the theory advanced by Huxley (1939) to account for the maintenance of contiguous subspecies characters (p. 602). Subspecies of Nevada mammals seem to illustrate selective hybrid elimination.

HYBRID ORIGIN OF SPECIES

If an existing extrinsic isolating mechanism separating two populations should gradually or suddenly break down, the two populations will be brought into contact and will share their genetic characteristics, provided no intrinsic bar to crossing has developed during the period of isolation (Table 52, p. 606). If genetic differences that do not prevent interbreeding have developed between two groups, either through random fixation of genes in small populations, through mutations in one group only, or through survival of favorable combinations and the elimination of the unfit, such genetically distinctive populations may interbreed and produce intermediate forms variable in a number of characters (Hubbs and Miller, 1942). Huxley (1942) refers to the results of such fluctuations of isolating factors as *reticulate differentiation.*

If the species have been isolated for a long time, divergent evolution may have developed varying degrees of inability to cross successfully (p. 676). If there is a sharp psychological, physiological, or other intrinsic isolation, merging of the populations will not occur even though the extrinsic barriers have broken down. Instances are reported in which hybrid populations have become established, and such hybrids may possibly give rise to new species (Miller, 1938, 1939; Sweadner, 1937; Dice, 1940a; Muller, 1942; Emsweller and Stewart, 1944; White, 1945). On occasion, the branching twigs of the phylogenetic tree may fuse at their tips.

These principles of evolution have recently been applied to the production of new cultivated plants. Natural species that are reproductively isolated through chromosome unbalance, but can still produce sterile offspring, are crossed, and the drug colchicine is applied, which sometimes causes a doubling of the chromosomes (amphidiploids). These artificial autopolyploids (doubling of chromosomes in nonhybrid organisms) from initially allopolyploid plants (hybrids of two species) are thus rendered self-fertile, and a hybrid population representing a new form may be established and later artificially selected for characteristics desired by man. Polyploids (multiplication of the chromosome complement) may be artificially produced for hybridization with known polyploid plants, qualitative as well as quantitative characters may be introduced, and plants may then be selected for new or wider ecologic adaptation or other desired characteristics (Dermen, 1940; Huxley, 1942, p. 346).

Gene or chromosome combinations may produce new characters not present in either parent (Haldane, 1932, p. 96; Irwin and Cole, 1936, 1936a; McGibbon, 1944). Hybrid characters may be more favorable than those of either parents and may thus be subject to selection (Huskins, 1931; Buchholz, 1945).

The wild hempnettle, *Galeopsis tetrahit,* is a tetraploid species that probably arose in nature from the hybridization of two diploid species, *G. pubescens* and *G. speciosa,* with subsequent doubling of the chromosomes. In this instance an almost identical species has been produced artificially by following the supposed manner of origin of the wild allotetraploid (Müntzing, 1937). New species of willows with ecologic peculiarities have also arisen through hybridization in nature. Huxley (1942, p. 339) discusses these and other cases under the term *convergent species-formation.*

Under natural conditions, completely isolated species probably do not often produce hybrid species through the breakdown of important isolating factors. Because of vegetative reproduction and self-fertilization, many more examples of hybrid origin of species are to be expected among plants than among animals. However, incompletely isolated subspecies may more often reverse the process of divergence in both plants and animals (see p. 626). Probably the best illustration of such fusion of once partially separated populations is to be found among the racial intermixtures of man.[*] There is no reason to doubt that numerous instances have also occurred among other animals and in plants.

With the advent of transportation by modern boats, trains, automobiles, and airplanes, much greater mixing of the naturally isolated species of the world faunas and floras is to be expected. Species permanently isolated by intrinsic differences may be expected generally to maintain their distinctions, while species isolated by extrinsic barriers alone may often merge with closely allied species (Wiegand, 1935).

ECOLOGY AND TAXONOMIC CATEGORIES

A *species* may be defined as an evolved (and probably evolving), genetically distinctive, reproductively isolated, natural population (Emerson, 1945). Some scientists emphasize morphologic characters of species (Hoare, 1943; Sturtevant, 1944a). It would seem better to emphasize genetic characters, regardless of the type of ex-

[*] Subspecies of man may have been more sharply defined before the development of "primitive" transportation.

pression. Inherited physiologic, ecologic, or behavioristic characters are as important as morphologic in the concept of the species. Morphology, being a visual expression of physiologic development, will continue to be used by taxonomists and students of phylogeny for the practical arrangement of most species. Through the use of the term "natural population," our definition of a species and Turesson's definition of the ecospecies, to be given shortly, are in essential agreement.

A number of recent writers (Dobzhansky, 1941; Mayr, 1942; Clausen, Keck, and Hiesey, 1945) also incorporate permanent isolation, through psychological separation, inviability of hybrids, hybrid sterility, or infertility, in their definitions of a species, but extrinsic isolating agents have closely similar evolutionary consequences. Reproductive isolation, regardless of what factor keeps the genes from moving across the species boundary, is the more inclusive and more practical characteristic of the majority of recognized species. If the various potentialities of the species under domestication, as contrasted with the natural environment, need to be incorporated in the species concept, Turesson's term *cenospecies* may be used. *Cenospecies* has also been used for groups of species in nature that are separated only by extrinsic factors, but *superspecies* is a better term for such closely related species groups.

A number of terms for the subdivision of species and species types have resulted from ecologic data, particularly reproductive isolation.

Turesson (1922) defined an *ecotype* as "the product arising as a result of the genotypical response of an ecospecies to a particular habitat" (see also Gregor, 1944). The *ecospecies* was defined as "the Linnean species or genotype compounds as they are realised in nature" (see Turesson, 1931; Axelrod, 1941).

Turesson separated the genetically different populations responding to their habitat (ecotypes) from the physiologic (nongenetic) response to habitat (see Turill, 1946). He used the term "ecophene" for the latter reaction type, produced, for example, by the modificatory influences of extreme habitat factors, such as shade, tree-line, and others.

The term *geotype* may be used for genotype populations in habitats partially isolated by topographic barriers with modifications not necessarily under the influence of natural selection (equivalent to "geoecotype"; Gregor, 1932). This category includes the majority of geographic subspecies and races.

Huxley (1939) suggested the term *ecocline* for quantitative gradation through successive ecologic zones of the habitat (Fig. 230). He also used the term *geocline* for quantitative gradations based upon topographic or spatial separation, *chronocline* for temporal gradations found in paleontological sequences, and *taxocline* for gradations involving hybridization. Phenotypic characters appearing at different times in the life cycle (*ontoclines*) may be correlated with ecoclines. In African buffalos there is an ecocline ranging from pale red forest adults to black plains adults, and at the same time there is an increase of the slope of the graph of the red-black ontocline from the forest forms to the forms of the open plains.

Some clines appear to be adaptively correlated, either directly or indirectly, with environmental factors; others are caused by the localized appearance and subsequent spread of a mutation having selective advantage; and still others are correlated with emigration or dispersal (Huxley, 1939).

According to Huxley, ecoclines would include a number of ecologic gradations, some of which have been named. Bergmann's rule concerning absolute size in relation to temperature, Allen's rule concerning relative size of exposed parts of the body in relation to temperature, and Gloger's rule or rules concerning different types of pigmentation in relation to temperature and humidity, jointly embody the best-known cases in warm-blooded animals. Apparently adaptive geographical gradients are shown by many other characters as well, such as clutch size (in birds) with latitude (see p. 701), size with salinity in marine organisms, number of fin rays and vertebrae with salinity in fishes, shell thickness with aridity in landsnails, relative heart weight with temperature in warm-blooded animals, relative gut size with temperature in cold-blooded animals (but with more complex relations than in warm-blooded forms), tongue length with latitude in bees, and temperature resistance in

Drosophila. Some of this graded variation (e.g., in relative heart size) may be non-heritable modification; but the majority of these clines are wholly or mainly genetic.

Ecoclines often seem to indicate selective elimination (p. 623) and thus reflect a correlation of function with habitat. Sumner (1932) gives an interesting analysis of color variation in the subspecies of *Peromyscus polionotus* (Fig. 230; see also

is rather uniformly dark-colored, except for a gradation toward a lighter color within 20 to 40 miles of the light sandy strip. Such variation can probably be explained by selection in relation to background color, together with intermixture of coat color genes through interbreeding of contiguous populations (see p. 610). The selection in this case, since it involves animals primarily active at night, is probably the result of

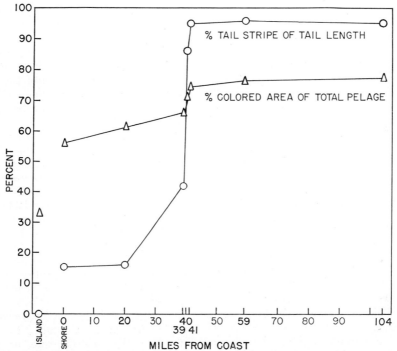

Fig. 230. The effect of selection and isolation on pigmentation of deer mice. Left hand measurements are from an island subspecies (*Peromyscus polionotus leucocephalus*) living on white sand off the Florida coast. Low values of colored area (triangles) and tail stripe (circles) indicate light pigmentation. Measurements at 0 miles are from a coastal subspecies (*P. p. albifrons*) living on white sand on the Florida gulf coast. The measurements at 59 and 104 miles are from an inland subspecies (*P. p. polionotus*) living on dark soil in Alabama. The stations at 20, 39, 40, and 41 miles are also on dark soil covered with vegetation and are probably areas of gene flow between areas of selection in relation to soil color. (Redrawn from Sumner, 1932.)

Huxley, 1939). *Peromyscus p. leucocephalus* is found on an isolated island of white sand off the Florida coast and has a uniform white coat color throughout the population. *Peromyscus p. albifrons* is found on the mainland coastal strip of light sandy soil and exhibits a marked ecocline of increased darker pigmentation as the population approaches the inland dark soil. *Peromyscus p. polionotus* is found on dark soil behind the coastal strip of light soil and

predation pressure operating against conspicuous individuals (see p. 668). Dice (1945, 1947) has experimentally demonstrated the ability of several species of owls to find *P. maniculatus* in dim light calculated as low as 0.000,000,73 foot-candle or even 0.000,000,08 foot-candle. The possibility of selection in relation to physiological effects of light is not entirely ruled out; nor should we eliminate the possibility of the kind of pigmentation as the secondary result of gene action selected on the basis of other functional adjustments of the animal. Experiments by Dice (p. 650), however, indicate predation as the probable selective factor in a similar case.

Ecotypes may differ in physiological characters rather than in visible ones. Clausen, Keck, and Hiesey (1940) experimentally studied the tolerance of different ecotypes of the plant *Potentilla glandulosa* in different habitats and found that plants produced from seeds from other and different climatic zones were unable to survive as well as plants from seeds produced locally.

Biotic conditions rather than physical factors may sometimes bring about a selective pressure that produces physiologically adapted races. Parasitic species dependent upon dispersal through vectors commonly have adjustments to the behavior as well as to the physiology of their hosts. Larval microfilariae of the nematode, *Wuchereria bancrofti,* usually exhibit nocturnal periodicity in the human blood stream in association with the night-biting mosquito that transmits them. A nonperiodic race or species of this parasite, morphologically similar to the periodic race, is carried by a day-biting mosquito, *Aëdes variegatus,* the geographic distribution of which is closely associated with the distribution of the nonperiodic filaria in the islands of the Pacific (Manson-Bahr, 1940, pp. 750, 950). If intergradations occur between such populations, ecotypes would be found based upon biotic factors of the environment.

Obviously hereditary variation in *asexual species* is based wholly upon mutations and not upon reassortment and combination, which can take place only through fertilization. Asexual species have either evolved from ancestors in which sex never developed, or they may have arisen from sexual species by means of complete parthenogenesis (White, 1945, p. 280). Reproductive isolation exists between asexual individuals after multiplication, and no mutation can pass to a new individual except through clonal descent. The continuance of a mutation must be largely through selection of the functions it affects (Lewis, 1934; Parr, 1938). A number of functional characteristics may be initiated by a single gene, so that it is possible that a mildly harmful effect may be overbalanced by a

stronger beneficial effect. Neutral characters also doubtless persist.

Certain types of adaptation are more likely to appear and persist in asexual species than in sexual species. For example, there may be speciation in a parasitic form without other types of isolation, and it may be associated with selection toward adaptation to different parts of the same host body. In a sexual species, reproductive isolation would probably not be complete enough to avoid swamping any new incipient adaptation in such a narrow ecologic niche. It is true that we do know some cases of sexual species of parasites living on different parts of the host, but it seems probable that other types of isolation than habitat isolation within microniches on the same animal or plant may have operated (Mayr, 1942, p. 204).

Wenrich (1944, 1944a) reports *Trichomonas hominis* in the intestine of man, *T. tenax* in the mouth, and *T. vaginalis* in the vagina. These species are physiologically as well as morphologically distinct and do not survive experimental transplantation from one body region to another. However, *T. hominis* has also been found in monkeys, cats, dogs, and rats, and can be experimentally transferred to the intestines of these animals. This genus of protozoans, together with other related genera, is not known to conjugate.

Protozoa of the genus *Leishmania,* pathogenic in man, produce two distinct diseases: the oriental sore or cutaneous leishmaniasis is caused by *L. tropica,* and kala-azar or visceral leishmaniasis is caused by *L. donovani.* The two species of protozoans are indistinguishable morphologically, but affect different regions of the body in both man and dogs (Hoare, 1943; Kirk, 1944).

Similar cases of such adjustment to microniches within the same host are numerous among pathogenic bacteria in which strains seem to evolve rapidly with subtle but distinctive pathological symptoms (Lewis, 1934; see also p. 601).

Asexual parasitic species could also easily become separated as they became selected for different hosts. Hoare (1940) has shown that *Trypanosoma evansi,* a widely distributed protozoan infecting domestic ungulates and other mammals, is not physiologically adjusted to the tsete fly (*Glos-*

sina). The tsetse fly is the vector for the morphologically similar *T. brucei, T. rhodesiense,* and *T. gambiense* in Africa. The natural insect vectors for *T. evansi* are horseflies (Tabanidae). The ranges of tsetse fly-borne trypanosomes and tabanid-borne trypanosomes overlap in Abyssinia and the Sudan. *Trypanosoma evansi* may have arisen from *T. brucei* or a species close to it, and through selection may have become adapted to different hosts; it is now found in southern Asia, the islands of the Pacific and Indian Oceans, Asia Minor, southeastern Europe, the Mediterranean coast of North Africa, and in some parts of West Africa. Strains identical with or closely related to *T. evansi* are also found in Central and South America. The theory of the origin of this species through natural selection is supported by experiments that show that any strain of the *brucei* group, when kept out of contact with tsetse flies for a long time through mechanical transmission, is likely to lose its ability to develop cyclically in *Glossina.*

Asexual organisms probably are more efficient in reproductive capacity, other things being equal, than are sexual types, which must face the exigencies of successful gamete attraction and fertilization. An asexual organism does not have the advantage of gene recombination that supplies a large foundation of heritable variation subject to selective pressures (White, 1945, p. 281; see also p. 641). However, mutations are more easily fixed in the asexual population, and advantageous genes are thus more likely to be selected. Neutral variations are also likely to be perpetuated over long periods of time.

Cleveland, Hall, Sanders, and Collier (1934) and Cleveland (1947) have described four species of flagellates of the genus *Barbulanympha* from the intestines of the roach, *Cryptocercus punctulatus,* all four species being found in the separated populations of the host in the Pacific and Appalachian regions. The flagellate species differ from each other in body size, number of organelles, and in numbers of chromosomes that seem to be multiples of eight (numbers 16, 32, 40, and 48 to 52 are recorded). There is no information on population numbers or possible ecologic differences, but there is no reason for assuming any exoadaptive divergence during specia-

tion. Inasmuch as these asexual Protozoa are found exclusively in the intestines of one sexually reproducing insect species, it may be assumed that speciation in the Protozoa was more rapid than speciation in the host. Other genera of flagellates also seem to have speciated in the intestine of this one host. *Trichonympha* (sexual fertilization) has seven species, *Leptospironympha* (sexual fertilization) has three species (two in the Pacific region, one in the Appalachian region), and *Saccinobaculus* (autogamous) has three species.

Although some asexual Protozoa in *Cryptocercus* seem to have evolved more rapidly than their sexually reproducing hosts, both flagellates and hosts are remarkably stable. *Cryptocercus punctulatus* shows an interesting discontinuous distribution in the Appalachian mountains and in the Pacific Northwest. Eighteen species of Protozoa are found in both populations, while four species are found in the western hosts alone and three species in the eastern hosts alone. The distribution of the roach is limited by its reliance on moist logs for protection against freezing temperatures, with relatively cool conditions in summer. The cellulose-digesting Protozoa have been shown to die if a temperature of 30° C. is maintained for twenty-four hours. The western and eastern ranges of the roach could not have been continuous later than the close of the last glacial period. Hence we have a measure of the evolutionary stability of the roach and many species of Protozoa. Protozoa from the intestines of termites often show a similar tendency toward more rapid speciation than do their hosts (Kirby, 1937, 1942a). Other termite protozoans evolve more slowly than their hosts.

Some authors (Dobzhansky, 1941, p. 378) would eliminate asexual taxonomic groups from the species category and define species as interbreeding populations. In some asexual groups, such as certain bacteria and the plant genus *Hieracium,* mutation is so frequent that species designations become impractical. In other asexual groups, such as the flagellates in the intestines of termites, species distinctions remain stable for long periods of time. The essential difference between asexual and sexual species is the complete reproductive isolation of asexual individuals in the same generation. Asexual species offer interesting material for an evolutionary comparison with sexual species, particularly when the two kinds of species have evolved together in strict ecological association.

We draw the following conclusions from our brief consideration of taxonomic categories. The concept of clines (except clines of ecophenes) emphasizes the operational aspects of evolution and, in numerous instances, may be a measure of recent or contemporary evolutionary events in contrast with ancient influences that are therefore more difficult to evaluate or analyze.

Isolating mechanisms, biotic as well as physical, are essential for evolutionary divergence leading to infraspecific and specific distinction. Various infraspecific terms may be used to emphasize the role of different isolating factors. After permanent reproductive isolation is attained, further nonadaptive divergence may take place by haphazard genetic changes, while adaptive divergence is guided by selection pressure.

Asexual species are of importance in the community relations and may serve for certain types of evolutionary analysis.

SUMMARY

The various factors that contribute to partial or complete reproductive isolation between populations have a profound effect upon evolutionary divergence. Many of these factors are environmental and therefore ecologic in the broad sense.

Some factors, such as topographic isolation, are so universal that they influence nearly all speciation to some degree. Others, such as annual isolation, are of minor importance, and only a few illustrations of their effect are known. The rare mechanisms are interesting because they offer a control over other isolating factors in some instances.

Certain types of isolation are not necessarily permanent if a junction of temporarily separated populations occurs. Other types of isolation (intrinsic) result in permanent reproductive separation, even though close contact between populations may later exist.

Some factors separate genetically identical or similar populations. Other factors, such as habitat isolation, operate on genetically different populations in most cases.

Selection pressures may be manifest after isolation, or they may assist in the isolating process. There is some evidence that isolating mechanisms may be adaptive in themselves, particularly in psychological isolation, thus indicating that there may be a survival value in preventing gene flow between differentiating populations.

In the majority of cases, more than one mechanism may contribute at the same time to the isolation of populations. Also, there may be such close sequence in the operation of isolating factors that the separate effects may be difficult to detect.

The influence of density effects may be considerable, but exact data are difficult to obtain. Critical information on all aspects of isolation is meager, and active investigations should be encouraged.

33. ADAPTATION

GENERAL CONSIDERATIONS

Adaptation is a universal biological phenomenon characteristic of all living organisms. Evolutionary adaptation in its strict sense refers to hereditary adjustment or fitness among the parts of a living system and between the whole system and its environment. (See pages 639, 640, 656, for discussion of teleological implications. Also see page 73, for a summary of the concept of the fitness of the environment.)

We are not here discussing at length the adaptability of the individual to meet changing conditions, such as the adjustment of the pupil of the eye to variations in light intensity, the greater development of leaves and branches on the sunny side of a tree at a forest margin, the acclimatization of an animal to seasonal change, or the conditioned behavior of many animals. These adjustments represent nongenetic physiologic response in contrast with genetic adaptation (Plunkett, 1944).

At the same time we should recognize that the capacity for individual adaptability may rest upon genetic factors (see p. 3). Mammals of temperate regions that commonly have breeding seasons initiated by photoperiodicities are able to reverse their reproductive cycles if transported to the south temperate region from the north (p. 124). Tropical mammals that have not evolved under the light conditions of temperate latitudes, however, maintain their breeding seasons when transported to temperate zoological parks (Bedford and Marshall, 1942). Such differences in individual adaptability probably result from different gene patterns. The germ plasm allows a plasticity of reaction that enables the individual to respond differentially to a variety of conditions. The adaptive capacity of the system rests upon a genetic basis, but the environment may stimulate or limit its expression (pp. 639 and 664).

The genetic system may also initiate the development of a capacity to control the internal environment in the face of ecologic fluctuations. Edwards and Irving (1943) report that the sand crab, *Emerita talpoida,* maintains a fairly constant metabolic rate in both winter and summer on the Massachusetts shore and continues growth and activity in the winter. This ability to stabilize internal conditions within the organism is referred to as *homeostasis* and is clearly the result of adaptive evolution (Cannon, 1941; see also p. 672).

All organisms exhibit hereditary fitness to the environment and hereditary adjustment of one part of the organism to other parts. We may roughly divide these types of evolutionary adaptation into *exoadaptation* and *endoadaptation,* but there is no sharp line separating the two categories (Sinnott, 1946). Theoretically there is no difference in the basic general causation of either type. Different organismic levels have incorporated the external environment of the lower levels of individuality into the internal environment of the higher levels (p. 683).

Ecologists are primarily interested in adaptation to the external environment, while physiologists are concerned with the balance and division of labor within the organism which are necessary for the survival of the whole unit. Because of the overlap of these types of adaptation, it is often impossible to make a sharp classification. Inasmuch as the development of an exoadaptive organ, such as the wing of a bird, involves geologic time, heredity, em-

bryologic development, physiologic mechanisms, neuromechanisms, and behavior patterns, the ecologists must lean heavily upon investigations in various subjects for a broad perspective on ecologic adjustment. Likewise, as environmental selective factors are responsible for the slow evolution of such an organ as a bird's wing, other scientists must incorporate ecologic investigations into their search for fundamental principles. Adequate study of a single adaptive organ may rest upon all the main fields of biology and many phases of physical science (Miller, 1937; Howell, 1944).

A simple example of the overlap between endoadaptation and exoadaptation is afforded by animals that roll themselves into balls, an action that protects them from predaceous enemies and also may conserve moisture in dry habitats. The best-known example is that of the armadillo, *Tolypeutes conurus,* whose hard plates on the top of the head and tail close the opening left by the rolled-up body. All parts of the body fit together in the rolled position to make a smooth, hard surface. Other examples of this adaptation are seen among the beetles of the genus *Acanthocerus* (Acanthoceridae), beetles of the genus *Agathidium* (Silphidae), isopods of the families Armadellidiidae, Tylidae, Sphaeromidae, and Cubaridae (Vandel, 1942; Van Name, 1936, p. 282), certain mites (Hoplodermatidae), and certain fossil trilobites.

These animals have convergently (p. 666) evolved structural adaptation between the front part of the body and the rear part, as well as, in special cases, between other parts, including legs or tail. During development, these portions are not mechanically connected, and yet the morphological outlines grow with exactness toward their ultimate function. Only the adult stage of the beetle, *Acanthocerus,* can form a ball, while the grub shows no such adaptation. No function other than protection is evident. Consequently, we find parts of the body adapted, even after some delay, to fit other body parts to produce a total function that is exoadaptive.

Several aspects of the organism, such as shape, size, color, and behavior, may be involved in functional adjustment. For example, Thomas (1941) studied the behavior of geometrid caterpillars that resemble twigs and found stretching and catalepsy correlated with appearance during predator activity.

Harmony of endoadaptation and exo-adaptation of a more subtle nature is commonly observed. After using certain fishes as illustrations, Sumner (1942, pp. 435, 436) says: "An animal distributes its pigment in significant patterns on the body surface and develops appendages on the skin, thus closely matching details of its usual habitat." Moreover, "the animal acquires a mechanism for color-change which is almost coextensive with the entire organism, involving as it does the eyes (see p. 126), large parts of the nervous system, highly specialized effector cells in the skin, and frequently the secretions of endocrine glands, and no function seems conceivable except that of rendering the organism inconspicuous against backgrounds of varying color and pattern."

Adaptation, either within the entire organism or between the organism and its environment, is never perfect (Cowles, 1945). When one considers the large number of operational factors, their fluctuations in the contemporaneous environment and during geologic history, and the multiplicity of organismic needs, optimal adjustment of each part of the complex organism to each factor in the complex environment would seem utterly impossible. Even the simplest organisms in the simplest and most stable environments would still present such complex relationships that functional compromises would be necessary. The ancient adjustment of the ancestors of an existing successful animal established a basic plan that limits the capacity for further adaptive modification. The evolution of the higher vertebrates from fishes imposes definite restrictions on the attainment of speed in terrestrial forms (Westoll, 1943; Howell, 1944). Adaptations toward more optimal control of the cell environment attained in multicellular plants and animals necessitated the loss of many functions in individual cells.

It may also be added that specialized nongenetic individual function within a highly complex insect or human society (pp. 420, 686, 691, 693) is made at the sacrifice of the more versatile functions of the primitive nonsocial individual (Emerson, 1942). The evolution of balanced equilibrium within an organism may be paralleled by an evolution of equilibrium within a population, both necessitating compromise (p. 426).

Though there is complete gradation from simple adaptation to complicated adaptation, it seems justifiable to separate chance modifications, which under certain circumstances may be of survival value and are likely to be produced by simple genetic factors, from adaptations that show a nicety of adjustment to complex situations and are likely to be the result of an intricate genetic pattern. On the basis of chance, a complete complex adaptation could probably not have originated *de novo* (p. 647).

If an adaptation is characteristic of a large taxonomic category, such as a phylum or a class, one may assume that such an adjustment was more important during its evolution than an adaptation characteristic of an included lower category. As an example, chelicerae adapted to predation and ultimately also to parasitism are characteristic of the superclass Chelicerata (Arthropoda), which includes the classes Palaeostraca (horseshoe crabs), Eurypterida (sea scorpions), Pycnogonida (sea spiders), and Arachnida (scorpions, harvestmen, spiders, ticks, and mites). Hence it is possible to say that adjustment to predation preceded and is more fundamental than the adjustment to terrestrial life in these animals. Predation is also characteristic of all coelenterates, although one class, the Anthozoa, is bottom-dwelling, and another class, the Scyphozoa, is pelagic in the adult stage. Classes of animals that have evolved around parasitic adaptations (i.e., Sporozoa, Trematoda [Fig. 249], and Cestoda [Fig. 250]) are found in a wide variety of ecologic habitats, but are always parasites in each association.

The evolution of exoadaptation is a primary problem for the ecologist. We are already aware that there is a chronological separation between the parts of the hereditary system, and that gradual sorting through selection (pp. 640, 648) is basic to the pattern of a functional system as we now see it in an existing organism. In the study of every organism, the environment is so much involved through selective elimination that improvement of our understanding of the organismic system depends not only upon knowledge of the present environmental relations, but also upon knowledge of the ecologic relationships of its ancestors. Such paleo-ecologic information will always be fragmentary, but in the instances in which evidence can be pieced together, it is illuminating.

An emphasis has been placed illogically upon morphological or mechanical adaptation, undoubtedly because of the greater ease of discerning functional associations between visible structures and their environment. As physiologic and embryologic techniques have developed, biophysical and biochemical functional relations have been discovered. These form a foundation for the modern attitude toward adaptation (Haldane, 1932, Chap. V), without, however, disparaging the many subtle and quantitative processes that may be illustrated by comparative morphology.

Adaptational behavior was early recognized, but the difficulties of scientific analysis of behavior causation delayed the more

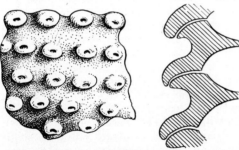

Fig. 231. A portion of the surface and a cross section of the wall of a termite nest (*Apicotermes* sp.), showing a comparatively simple system of ventilation pores. (Redrawn from Hegh.)

precise evaluation of psychologic data in relation to the evolution of adaptation. Occasionally, morphologic, physiologic, and behavior sequences are so closely correlated that there is little doubt concerning behavior evolution (Friedmann, 1929; Emerson, 1938, 1947).

The evolutionary sequence of behavior is illustrated by the nest structures of the African termite genus, *Apicotermes* (Desneux, 1948). All the nests of the species so far known are subterranean and consist of a round structure, about the size of a football, occupying a cavity under the surface of the ground. Presumably the exchange of gases between the nest and the sur-

rounding soil is necessary for the existence of these insect colonies, a requirement that is probably more imperative in moist soil. Pores with a small diameter of about $\frac{1}{2}$ mm. are molded into the wall of the nest as it

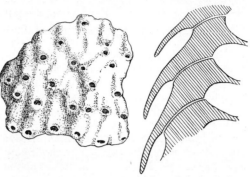

Fig. 232. A portion of the surface and a cross section of the wall of a termite nest (*Apicotermes lamani*), showing funnel-shaped openings exterior to the pores homologous to those shown in Figure 231. (Redrawn from Hegh.)

is constructed by the worker termites from their claylike excrement. A progressive sequence in complexity of these pores is apparent in three types of nests diagrammed in Figures 231, 232, and 233. This sequence

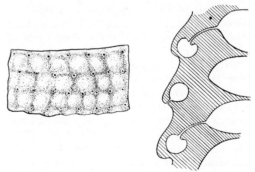

Fig. 233. A portion of the surface and a cross section of the wall of a termite nest (*Apicotermes angustatus*), showing openings into circular galleries homologous with the funnels of Figure 232 from which the ventilation pores homologous to those in Figures 231 and 232 penetrate to the interior chambers occupied by the termites. (Redrawn from Hegh.)

is in all likelihood a phylogenetic series. From an examination of the figures it may be seen that behavior evolution parallels morphological evolution in the following attributes; symmetry, replication, homology, adaptation, population integration, inheritance. To these principles may be added regeneration, regressive evolution and convergence illustrated by other termite nests (Emerson, 1938). The only conclusion possible is that the evolution of behavior results from similar forces and follows patterns similar to those characteristic of morphological evolution, and that both depend upon physiological development and genetic interactions.

At times it is well to distinguish adaptation to a general situation from specialized adaptation. The term "adaptation" is sometimes used to denote capacity to succeed, rather than functional adjustment. Generalized organisms sometimes may outlive specialized forms in geologic time. Simpson (1944, p. 31) states that "reduction of adaptability with increase in specialization" is a leading paleontologic and evolutionary empirical principle today. He also says (p. 180) that the best criterion for adaptation is the increase in numbers of the better-adapted group in comparison with the less-well adapted. Although this criterion is sometimes valid and has the advantage of being a testable and quantitative concept, in the sense of increasing fitness, numbers may be detrimental (or beneficial) to the population as a whole, particularly with an increase in population density (pp. 274, 332, 396). It is also true that a rare animal or plant may be well adapted to an environment with narrow limits, while an abundant organism may be less well adapted to an extensive environment. The slave-making ant, *Polyergus,* is a rare ant in comparison with the slaves, *Formica.* The structure and behavior of the slave-making species, however, are indicative of a high degree of adaptive specialization (see p. 424).

Fitness in terms of adjustment to special factors affords a highly important measurement of adaptation, although such fitness may be complex and difficult to compare quantitatively. For example, it may be stated that an extinct bird such as the passenger pigeon was better adapted for flight than the common chicken or grouse. It is therefore plain that adaptation is a complex phenomenon that cannot be reduced to a single type of measurement without grossly oversimplifying the concept. Numbers are highly important in a consideration of adaptation, but must be placed in

their proper perspective. Numbers should also be considered in relation to biomass (pp. 525–528). Biomass alone, however, would give an oversimplified conception of adaptation. It would be like judging the importance of a tissue in the body by measuring its relative bulk.

The combination of adaptations in a single organism to various factors in the habitat indicates an evolutionary history in the particular environment as a whole. For example, Stebbins (1944) lists several adaptations of the lizards of the genus *Uma* to their desert habitat. These include overlapping of the free edges of the eyelids, which prevents sand particles from invading the eye; a translucent area in the lower eyelid, which permits the perception of light changes when the eyelids are closed; a nictitating membrane over the eye, which expels mucus-encapsulated sand; fringe-scales on elongated toes, which assist in locomotion over the sand and in "sand-swimming" during submergence below the surface; coloration approximating the sand background with special markings that mask the eye and render the animal inconspicuous in the shadows of bushes; and behavior activities associated with life on the sand, feeding adjustments, and escape from enemies; together with adjustment to temperature variations (Cowles and Bogert, 1944; Parker, 1948, p. 308).

Adaptation is evidently not to a single factor in the environment, but to a combination of factors, and this combination is often characteristic of special habitats. When adjustments to one factor involve the impairment of adjustments to another factor, selection will guide evolution either toward adjustment to the more important factor or to a compromise between the two. No organism can survive in a habitat in which any single factor essential for its existence is lacking (Wolcott, 1942; pp. 198, 635), but organisms often—one might say always—survive with only partial fitness to each ecologic factor in the complex environment (Bacot and Martin, 1924).

In addition to its adjustment to the immediate habitat, an organism often needs to be adapted to rare and extreme conditions in order to survive—conditions that may not occur in the lifetime of an individual. Between 1886 and 1936, nine sudden cold periods or "freezes" occurred in the region of Sanibel Island, Florida (see p. 334). These low temperatures destroyed large numbers of tropical species of fishes, while the mortality of the temperate types was not great (Storey and Gudger, 1936; Storey, 1937). Obviously, the fishes well adapted to the normal warm climate may be unable to withstand occasional cold, and the range of the species may thus be limited by the unusual occurrence of extreme conditions (see p. 653). Liebig's "Law of the Minimum" (p. 198) as restated by Taylor (1934) is as follows: "The growth and functioning of an organism is dependent on the amount of the essential environmental factor presented to it in minimal quantities during the most critical season of the year, or during the most critical year or years of a climatic cycle." Similar relations hold for maximal quantities. Haldane (1932, p. 118) pointed out that ecologists may be able to determine the normal incidence of selection for a given species, but that a great disaster or an emigration may make the characteristics of a single survivor important (see p. 604).

Ancient adaptations may be retained through long periods of subsequent evolution and diversification, and consequently may be homologous within a large group of organisms. A pattern of many different characters, with presumably somewhat different genetic bases in the same organism, should indicate homology with the same set of characters found in another organism. Adaptive characters not associated with the pattern of homologies in the postulated common ancestor may be presumed to be analogous.

If we keep in mind that homology must be correlated with genetic similarities and a common phylogeny, while analogy must be correlated with functional (often environmental) similarities arising through convergence and natural selection, we can avoid many types of error common in the past (Hubbs, 1944).

Adaptation is a fundamental attribute of all living organisms and is a highly complex phenomenon. The explanation of the origin of adaptation is one of the prime problems of biology. Ecology offers much evidence for the analysis of evolutionary exoadaptation. Special aspects of adaptation will be discussed in the following parts of this chapter. The operational mecha-

nisms guiding organisms toward increased adaptation will be dealt with in the chapter on Natural Selection, and the evolutionary aspects of complex community adjustments and of ecosystems will be the subject of the final chapter.

CAENOGENESIS AND PALINGENESIS

During ontogeny the environment is often different for the successive developmental stages. Embryos and young must survive in environments that may be dissimilar to the surroundings of the adult. This necessitates adjustments that contrast strikingly with those of the adult organism. If the special adaptations of the young are not found in the adult and have evolved more recently than the adult adjustments, they are termed *caenogenetic*.

The best examples of caenogenesis are found among the insects that exhibit complete metamorphosis. For instance, the larva of a mosquito living in a pond has specialized spiracular openings near the end of the abdomen for gaseous exchange at the surface, an adaptation not needed or found in the adult. The adult, living a terrestrial and aerial life, uses wings for locomotion that develop, but are not functional, in the larva and pupa. Feeding adaptations likewise differ markedly in the larva and adult of the same individual with the same genetic constitution. The adaptations of the larva to aquatic life are chronologically more recent in evolutionary history than the wings functioning for flight in the adult.

A somewhat unusual case of caenogenesis is found in the evolution of the castes of the social termites, which develop by gradual metamorphosis. There is little doubt that both soldiers and workers are caenogenetic, exhibiting many characteristics of nymphs (Fig. 146). The soldier is the only sterile caste in the primitive termites (Kalotermitidae, Mastotermitidae) and thus originated before the worker. The soldier resembles the winged imago more closely than does the worker of the higher termites (Termitidae). The worker seems to be a caenogenetic evolution of soldier nymph characters with specialized behavior not found in either the young or adults of the other castes (Emerson, 1926; see p. 633).

Nymphal, larval, or embryonic characters may be retained in the adult, or the young stage may be sexually mature, a phenomenon referred to as *neoteny*. Examples are found among salamanders such as the aquatic *Necturus,* which has the caenogenetic gills of the ancestral larvae in the neotenous form, the typical adult stage presumably having been lost. Substitute reproductives of termites have nymphal wing buds and undeveloped eyes. The adult female glowworm (*Phengodes*) is larviform, even though it passes through a semipupa stage. The male of *Phengodes* is a normal adult beetle.

A wide variety of evolutionary modifications of developmental processes has been summarized by de Beer (1940). The environment at all stages of development has exerted a profound evolutionary effect. An adaptation fitting one stage to its particular habitat may move into either earlier or later ontogenetic stages during subsequent evolution. Man himself has apparently evolved to a marked degree by moving embryonic characters into the adult stage (Haldane, 1932, p. 149; Ariëns Kappers, 1942), a process referred to as *foetalization* or *paedomorphosis* (Gregory, 1946, p. 354), and closely similar to neoteny.

One can hardly discuss caenogenesis without mentioning the contrasting developmental principle of *palingenesis,* usually referred to as *recapitulation.* This concept is discussed more fully under Regressive Evolution (pp. 672, 673, 678). Caenogenesis may also be contrasted with *deuterogenesis*—the appearance of new adaptive characters toward the end of life (Swinnerton, 1938). Such characters as the wings of insects, which function only in the adult stage, afford a good example of deuterogenesis. Functional reproductive adaptations are also characteristic of adults only, but the advantage pertains to the new generation. In contrast with the caenogenetic evolution of the sterile castes of termites, worker and soldier ants (Formicidae) obviously are deuterogenetic. Social adaptation in ants, through division of labor (Fig. 253), is largely the result of adult modifications, each ant caste having developed by complete metamorphosis through larval and pupal stages.

The behavior of the young marsupial at the time of birth exemplifies a combination of adaptations (Matthews, 1944). The young, after birth, crawls by means of well developed forelegs into the mother's pouch, where it attaches itself to a nipple. This behavior, together with the special development of the forelimbs and their muscular and nervous connections, is surely caenogenetic, and the pouch and nipple are surely deuterogenetic. The young has a functional mesonephros at the time of birth, a palingenetic pronephros during embryological development, and later develops a metanephros that functions after the mesonephros has been reduced subsequent to emergence from the pouch.

Known evolutionary sequences are nearly always based upon morphology. It has already been pointed out (p. 634) that evolution of reflex and instinctive behavior follows the same principles as the evolution of structure (Emerson, 1938; Hooker, 1944; Figs. 231, 232, 233). One might expect homologous, convergent, caenogenetic, deuterogenetic, and palingenetic behavior. Some reservation is necessary, however, since most behavior cannot be described in terms precise enough to warrant the assumption of homology.

Humphrey (1944) describes neurons in the embryonic human central nervous system as homologous to the Rohon-Beard cells of amphibians and lower vertebrates that function as a temporary sensory apparatus in the amphibian embryos and larvae (Du Shane, 1938). These neurons seem to be nonfunctional in man and are replaced by functional intramedullary bipolar sensory cells that later develop into unipolar cells. If these primitive neurons are considered palingenetic, it is not difficult to imagine palingenetic behavior resulting from such an inherited nerve pattern. The rather futile action of dogs in scratching dirt after defecation appears to be an example of inherited behavior that has undergone regressive evolution (Emerson, 1938, p. 280).

If one grants that many characteristics of living organisms are understood only through knowledge of the functions of homologous characters in ancestral forms, and that correlations of ontogeny and phylogeny may be expected if genetic mechanisms underlie both, then many essential features of the recapitulation theory may still be accepted (pp. 677, 678). De Beer (1940) takes the opposed position that "phylogeny plays no causal part in determining ontogeny," and that it "does not explain ontogeny at all." The pattern of the genes is subject to selective sorting in terms of function during development and in the adult. Phylogeny is a history of these changes. Ontogeny depends largely on these gene systems. Can we not assume, then, that phylogeny has affected ontogeny and that ontogeny has affected phylogeny? These two aspects of life are manifestations of basic protoplasmic capacities, and these are guided during evolution by the environmental elimination of the unfit. Perspective concerning fundamental relationships resolves many controversies based upon narrow viewpoints, and both sides of the argument may often be brought into agreement (Holmes, 1944a).

We conclude that caenogenesis and palingenesis, together with their related principles of deuterogenesis, neoteny, foetalization (paedomorphosis), and recapitulation, are examples of ancient and recent adaptations in various stages of individual and population life cycles. These ontogenetic adaptations manifest themselves in behavior as well as morphology, and both are the result of physiology initiated by genetic systems. The temporal individual (including the individual life history stages and metamorphosis) and the temporal population are subject to selection as units.

ALLOMETRY AND ORTHOGENESIS

It has been noted, particularly by paleontologists, that some organisms seem to evolve beyond adaptive efficiency toward extinction. The bivalve mollusks of the genus *Gryphaea* developed extreme coiling of the shell that must have made a wide opening impossible, and opening at all difficult in old individuals (Haldane, 1932; Simpson, 1944, p. 174). The races that evolved in this direction soon became extinct, but it is not clear that this momentum in an unadaptive direction resulted in extinction.

Large deer have proportionately larger antlers than small deer, and this relationship pertains to both ontogeny and phylogeny. Such an *allometric* relationship between body size and antler growth places a limit on the size of the animal, a limit that seems to have been approximated by the extinct Irish stag.

As the limit of such a relationship between two characters is approached, selec-

tion pressure may be increased, and a slight change in the environment might eliminate the species that have an unbalanced condition (Simpson, 1944, p. 177).

The allometric formula $Y = bX^k$ has been found to apply to a large number of ontogenetic and phylogenetic series. Y and X are the measurements of the compared characters; b and k are constants. This equation can also be written $\log Y = \log b + k \log X$, meaning that any magnitude conforming to this formula will fall along a straight line if plotted on a double logarithmic grid (Huxley, 1932, p. 4). The value k gives the angle of the slope of the straight line. The value b gives the elevation of the straight line.

Robb (1935) showed that the absolute rate of increase of the preoptic region of the horse skull is different from the absolute rate of increase of the total skull length, but that the two measurements maintain a constant ratio to each other that can be expressed in the equation $Y = 0.25X^{1.23}$, in which Y is the preoptic length, X is the skull length, 0.25 is the fractional coefficient or the fraction of X that Y occupies when X equals unity, and 1.23 is the ratio of the rate of increase in Y to that in X. As pointed out by Simpson (1944), such an equation applies to the phylogenetic sequence, to existing races or species of horses of different size, to the ontogenetic development of the individual, and, in horses, probably to adults of different sizes in a single race. Ontogeny seems to repeat phylogeny in such a case, but there is no indication that this type of recapitulation is the result of any genetic or functional change.

Robb (1936, 1937) expressed the relations of the side toes (digits II and IV = Y) to the middle toe (metapodial of digit III = X) in the three-toed horses by the equation $Y = 1.4$ to $1.5X^{0.97 \text{ to } 0.98}$. However, in the ontogeny and phylogeny of the single-toed horses the equation is $Y = 0.75$ to $0.76X^{0.99 \text{ to } 1.00}$. There is thus a fairly abrupt change in b associated with a change in function of the side toes. This may be construed as a possible influence of selection upon the proportional relations of such characters. The side toes in the modern horse would probably be an encumbrance, as well as useless (p. 673).

...tionship between linear, surface, ...olume measurements of an organism ...ust be in a balanced functional proportion (p. 131). D'Arcy Thompson points out that a tenfold increase of man's linear dimensions would make it impossible for him to support his own weight, since the cross section of a thighbone would increase a hundredfold and weight would increase a thousandfold (Huxley, 1942, p. 494; see also Hiestand, 1928). This functional aspect of proportions doubtless sets up selection pressures that guide the evolution of balance and compromise (Thompson, 1917).

Seemingly intrinsic nonadaptive evolutionary tendencies sometimes leading to extinction have been termed *orthogenetic* (see Simpson, 1944, p. 150, for summary discussion). Orthogenesis involving an innate tendency for genes to mutate in a given direction may be possible in a few sequences of alleles, but it is doubtful whether such a series is to be found in paleontological sequences (Simpson, 1944, p. 156), which would be expected to result from much more complex genetic changes. Orthogenesis should be distinguished from allometric constancy in phylogenetic series (*pseudo-orthogenesis*) in which genetic change of an adaptive primary character is genetically and physiologically related to allometric secondary characters; and it must also be distinguished from evolution in a single adaptive direction, which may be explained by a constant selective pressure in a single type of environment.

Horses seem to have evolved increased adaptation to life on grassy plains through more efficient cursorial mechanisms and better adjustment to feeding on siliceous grasses. Directional trends guided by selection may be termed *orthoselection,* and do not imply any intrinsic tendency to evolve in a straight line (Plate, 1913). As might be expected, the evolution of horses exhibits divergent and convergent trends as well as different directional trends (Stirton, 1940; Weigelt, 1942; Simpson, 1944, p. 157).

Through physiological relations of differential growth rates, selection for one character, such as size in deer, may carry with it a secondary allometric character, such as size and form of antlers. There may be little selection based on the functional differences of antler size, and yet, with an increase in general size, these structures would be expected to evolve in a straight line from proportionately small to proportionately large antlers. An advantage in size might thus be ultimately overcome by a disadvantage of overdeveloped antlers, and selection might remove extremely large individuals. An optimum size during the breeding period might have a selective advantage over size greater than the optimum during the postreproductive period, when disproportioned individuals might be eliminated with little evolutionary effect upon the species. In fact, the death of some individuals may be of advantage to the population (p. 692). Such a pseudo-orthogenetic series may be adequately explained within the framework of Darwinian natural selection (Huxley, 1932; Rensch, 1939, 1943).

Most genetic variance, aside from recombination, is produced by rare and disadvantageous genes the supply of which is kept up by mutation alone, but only in so far as it includes such genes does a population usually have the genetic elasticity that permits an evolutionary response to a long-term change in environment. Haldane (1932, p. 198) showed by mathematical theory that if selection of a metrical character determined by many genes increases the optimum stature of a species by a certain quantity, then, when the mean stature reaches the new optimum, the incidence of some genes will increase even though they are past their point of adaptive balance. The stature will, so to speak, overshoot the mark, and will thus initiate a selection pressure in a reversed direction. Mutation pressure is itself hereditary and subject to selection (Simpson, 1944, p. 175), so that a degree of evolutionary momentum may produce a fluctuation of a character, first above and then below the optimal value. This mechanism may give us an explanation on Darwinian lines of some unadaptive orthogenesis, although it would apply only for a brief time with slight selection pressure. Such a momentum effect is probably of little importance in known evolutionary sequences and is unlikely to be the major factor in the extinction of any species.

Orthogenesis has been assumed to lead

to "racial senescence." The evolution of the extinct ammonites has been supposed to indicate ultimate extinction through orthogenesis. The suture lines of the shell chamber partitions with the outer shell underwent a remarkable complex development that probably strengthened the shell. Caenogenetic and recapitulative changes in the sutures have been described. In later evolution the suture line returned to a simpler type, and the shell became uncoiled, both constituting a reversion to more primitive morphological patterns (not necessarily a genetic reversion), an "archaism" that is finally associated with extinction. At the end of the Cretaceous, bizarre types with hairpin bends (*Hamites*) appeared, soon to be extinct (Haldane, 1932). Huxley (1942, p. 508) warns us that no living ammonites are known, that rate genes might produce some of the described differences in sutures and in coiling, that the adaptive significance of these characters or the other effects produced by the modifying genes are unknown, that such a phenomenon as true orthogenesis, predetermined to proceed irrespective of selective disadvantage, is exceptional and, if carried to an extreme, without a known explanatory mechanism. Directional mutation at a rate in nature that could markedly overcome counterselection is not known. It would thus be wise to await more data before assuming orthogenetic exceptions to the general adaptive evolution of organisms.

Racial senescence independent of changes in the physical and biotic environments, which would cause extinction of the specialized organism, would seem to be a highly questionable concept (Simpson, 1944, pp. 26, 31; also see p. 680, Chap. 34). However, harmful characters may evolve even greater harmfulness. The genes favoring rapid growth of such a characteristic as pollen-tube growth might be selected over competing genes producing slower growth rates, and at the same time might carry other characters harmful to the adult that would be augmented by continuous selection of the earlier function (Haldane, 1932, p. 124).

The future cannot influence present selective pressures. Selection may eliminate individuals with characters that later might save the species from extinction. So-called "racial senescence" or "species senescence"

may often be the hindsight of the biologist who detects specialization unsuited to the later changes of the environment (Simpson, 1944, p. 176; Cain, 1944, p. 241). A species may be suited to physical conditions, but unable to compete effectively with better adapted species. But this relative decrease in adaptability is not comparable to physiological aging of an individual organism. In biological evolution, organisms adjust to repeated events. Order of nature lies at the basis of heredity, development, and adaptation. Not only do individual organisms "anticipate" future functions in their development and organization, but population systems may likewise be prepared, though they are only prepared for conditions that are continuous or repeated. Sexual organisms evolved, not because asexual reproduction was immediately inferior, but because a great degree of variation within a conservative system enabled sexual species to compete successfully against those not having the capacity to recombine genetic elements.

The problems presented by these seemingly teleological phenomena are resolved by an understanding of natural selection acting upon various levels of organic integration (Hutchinson, 1948). If a group of organisms becomes adjusted to relatively stable factors in the environment, it may evolve slowly, in contrast to the rapid evolution of groups adapted to rapidly changing factors, and may be far less likely to become extinct. Tertiary genera of Pelecypoda survive at the present time far in excess of Tertiary genera of Carnivora (Simpson, 1944, p. 27).

Capacity for plastic behavior, which changes in response to experience, evolved in certain forms because similar initial learning situations were repeated. Without the repetition of events, the capacity for conditioned and learned behavior would not evolve. The evolution of the cerebral cortex in vertebrates illustrates selection of learning capacity and intelligence. With the growth of scientific prediction, man has acquired the greatest capacity for anticipating the future. He can often make the necessary adjustments in advance and control the conditions. There is little doubt that selection sorts units of social heredity and variation (nongenetic) in a manner somewhat similar to its guiding effect on germinal traits (pp. 632, 663, 686, 691, 693), and that adaptive human social evolution has occurred and will continue to be characteristic of future social progress. There is already some tendency for man to act for the benefit of unborn generations, action that has been considered invalid or meaningless by some (pp. 692, 693), but which has a sound basis in the evolutionary dynamics of population systems.

In conclusion, we question the existence of any innate evolutionary trend leading to the "senescence" or the extinction of a species. Slight genetic momentum is admissible, but is insufficient to explain orthogenesis as reported for paleontological sequences. Pseudo-orthogenesis through allometric relations of characters, and orthoselection, explain the valid examples of linear evolutionary trends. Survival under conditions that are repeated because of the order and periodicity of natural phenomena allows the cumulative development of genetic adaptations. Conditioned behavior is also dependent upon repeated events. Teleological aspects of adaptation may be explained through the action of natural selection upon temporal population systems.

SUMMARY

Living organisms universally exhibit adaptation. Ecologists are particularly concerned with exoadaptation, and physiologists with endoadaptation, but the two aspects of adaptation are fundamentally similar and have similar causations.

Adaptation is almost always complex, combining many biological mechanisms within an integrated pattern. Perfection of adaptation is not to be expected. Complex adjustments to complex factors invariably involve compromise solutions. Any single measurement of adaptation results in an oversimplification of the concept. The combination of adaptations within a single species to a variety of factors in the habitat is commonly associated with a long evolutionary history in the particular habitat.

It is necessary for the organism to be adjusted not only to the average conditions, but also to the rare extreme environmental fluctuations. Ontogenetic adjustment to the whole environment of the temporal individual is the rule.

In certain instances it can be shown that an integrated population may exhibit group adaptations similar in principle to individual adaptations.

Ancient adaptations to different environments become so fixed in the heredity that they may linger in part as functionless vestigial characters in an organism. Allometric characters explain a few phylogenetic sequences formerly included under orthogenesis. Selection may sort variations of one character physiologically associated with other characters and thus produce pseudo-orthogenesis. Racial senescence needs further verification before acceptance.

The repetition of past conditions is necessary for the cumulative effect of both germinal selection and learned behavior, and hence makes it possible for organisms unconsciously or consciously to "anticipate" and adjust to the future.

34. NATURAL SELECTION

INTRODUCTION

The principle of natural selection, together with its bearing upon progressive evolution, the origin of adaptation, and an understanding of man in his social setting, is possibly "the most important abstract biological principle ever enunciated" (Pearl, 1930a).

The essential concepts underlying the theory of natural selection (variation, heredity, overproduction, struggle for existence, differential survival) have been checked, rechecked, analyzed, and modified in special details since the day of Darwin. Controversy, both scientific and philosophical (p. 656), has raged and still rages over the theory as a whole and many of its parts.

Darwin (1859) did not always distinguish between heritable and nonheritable variation. He had no understanding of hereditary mechanisms. The concept of competition, which grew from consideration of the facts of overproduction, has been investigated since Darwin's day and has also often been misapplied in recent years. The importance of its implications and of its conscious misapplications in human affairs, both in economics and in interclass and international warfare, can hardly be overemphasized (Hofstadter, 1944). Experimental as well as observational studies of survival are numerous in recent biological literature, and the mathematical analysis of the process is at present being actively prosecuted (Chap. 18, p. 271; also pp. 646, 654, 657).

The concept of the internal integration of the individual organism and of other unitary biological systems has been and is now a field of investigation occupying the attention of thousands of biologists, including cytologists, physiologists, embryologists, psychologists, population biologists, and students of speciation. Competition between individuals seems to be essential to Darwin's original theory (see Allee, 1940). Modern investigation certainly indicates that selection often operates through competition, and that release from competition allows forms to survive that would otherwise be eliminated (Salisbury, 1936). This is particularly well illustrated in animals under domestication. Selection, however, may also operate on internal factors of viability in the absence of competition, and we might expect some adaptive evolution in an ideal world with overabundance of all the necessities of life. On the other hand, unrestricted competition may easily result in harm and even extinction to both competitors (p. 699). Competition in its relation to evolution, both biological and social, may be beneficial at an optimum and deleterious both at a minimum and at a maximum population density (p. 395). Fitness involves cooperation, and adaptations leading to coordination of parts of organisms and of individuals in populations are the result of evolution through natural selection (p. 683).

Reproductive isolation and its essential role in evolutionary diversification were not adequately understood by Darwin; but, starting with the work of Wagner (1868a), Wallace, and Gulick, this concept has expanded in the hands of geneticists, ecologists, and biogeographers. Darwin probably overemphasized natural selection as a factor in the origin of species. A better name for his great book might have been "The Origin of Adaptation."

Pearl (1930a) outlined the basic and minimal logical requisites to a proof that natural selection has altered a race. These he lists as: (A) proof of somatic difference between survivors and eliminated (p. 649); (B) proof of genetic differences between survivors and eliminated (pp. 652, 653, 687); (C) proof of effective time of elimination (p. 692); (D) proof of somatic alteration of race (pp. 653–655); (E) proof of genetic alteration of race (p. 654). Proofs on these points are summarized in the following pages.

Natural selection cannot be construed as a causative force producing genetic mutation in the strict sense, but only as a sieve that eliminates the unfit and allows the fit to pass through. In another sense, natural selection is a causative force that determines the pattern of hereditary units through selective sorting after recombination.

The basic factors initiating the evolution of adaptation must be sought in the causes of genetic variability. Mutation as seen in the laboratory nearly always reduces a structure or function. We must remember, however, that geneticists tend to choose the mutations that exhibit striking characteristics in order to treat them statistically with greater ease. Slight morphologic, behavioristic, or physiologic changes are usually not noticed, but these are just the types of mutation most liable to be involved in the evolution of natural populations. More drastic mutational effects are likely to be less viable (p. 275). Both initial mutation and recombination, however, are predominantly random so far as any adjustment to the environment is concerned, and complex adaptation must thus be conceived as evolving through selection acting as a slow sorting process that ultimately arranges the genes in a harmonious functional assemblage.

Recombination, rather than mutation, is often the most important factor producing the hereditary variation within a population that is essential to evolution, both nonadaptive and adaptive (Simpson, 1944, p. 36). Wright (1932) has succinctly stated the relation between haphazard genetic variation and adaptive evolution. "The observed properties of gene mutation —fortuitous in origin, infrequent in occurrence and deleterious when not negligible in effect—seem about as unfavorable as possible for an evolutionary process. Under biparental reproduction, however, a limited number of mutations which are not too injurious to be carried by the species furnish an almost infinite field of possible variations through which the species may work its way under natural selection."

PREADAPTATION AND HABITAT SELECTION

Before taking up the positive and negative aspects of selection, it is well to discuss the chance adaptive effects of variation (*preadaptation*), and the role of selection of a favorable habitat by the organism (called *organic selection* by Baldwin,

called its *prospective function,* in contrast with its *realized function* (Parr, 1926; Simpson, 1944, p. 184; Fig. 234). The environment also has its prospective and realized functions or fitness for organisms (p. 73). *Preadaptation* has been defined by Simpson as "the existence of a prospective function prior to its realization."

Salaman (1936) studied a wild tuber-bearing solanum (*Solanum demissum*) that lives in Mexico more than 8000 feet above sea level. Cultivation in England showed that the plant carried a recessive gene producing resistance to wart disease (*Synchitrium endobioticum*). By selection, an immune pure-breeding stock was produced.

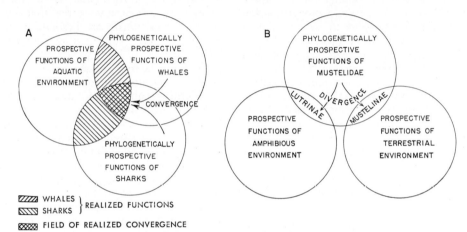

Fig. 234. Convergence and radiation in evolution of phylogenetically prospective functions of organisms through overlap with the prospective functions of their environments. A, Convergence in evolution through overlap of some of the same prospective functions of an environment by phylogenetically prospective functions of two different groups of organisms. B, Divergence in evolution through overlap of prospective functions of two different environments by the phylogenetically prospective functions of a single group of organisms. (Redrawn from Simpson.)

1896). Such adjustment precedes the subsequent action of selection through ecologic survival and elimination.

The majority of mutations studied by geneticists are not of the type that would survive under natural ecologic conditions, and many of them, such as the so-called recessive lethals, do not permit homozygous individuals to survive even under controlled laboratory conditions. There is no doubt, however, that among the myriad variations, some mutations and combinations by chance may produce characteristics that have survival value in special habitats (Gates, 1936). The potential adjustment of the organism to the environment may be

The same plant was also found to be resistant to the blight fungus (*Phytophthora infestans*) through the action of a dominant gene, although another form of *Solanum demissum* recently found in Mexico is susceptible to blight. The gene initiating resistance to blight has been transferred to the common potato by crossbreeding. In both these cases the evidence indicates that the mutations producing resistance to these diseases arose independently of the presence of the diseases, which do not occur in the native habitat of the plant in which the variations originated (see also Snyder, Baker, and Hansen, 1946).

The fact that selection must act upon

chance mutations and recombinations and that these variations arise initially with no influence by a directive ecologic factor, gives a valid basis for the principle of preadaptation. As will be discussed later (p. 647), this aspect of preadaptation applies only to changes of simple genetic factors and cannot be used to explain genetically complex and highly adapted characteristics (for a contrary opinion, see Goldschmidt, 1945).

Another aspect of preadaptation is found in the fitness of organisms adjusted to new habitats that have many factors in common with the habitats originally occupied by the ancestral forms. In some cases, new habitats are invaded without evolutionary modification. Many animals and plants introduced successfully into a region new to them exhibit such preadaptation.

Twenty-four specimens of the European rabbit were introduced into Victoria, Australia, in 1859 and in three years became a pest. They spread rapidly to Queensland and South Australia. This success was possibly because of the similarity of climate and general food in the European and Australian regions, together with the lack of competition from other placental mammals.

Bats are adjusted to nocturnal life and are able to avoid collision during flight in the dark by emitting supersonic sounds (30,000 to 70,000 cycles per second), which rebound from objects in their path. Orientation by this method is called *echolocation* (Griffin, 1944, 1946; Vesey-FitzGerald, 1947). Although such adjustments enable bats to become important members of cave communities, there is no indication that the cave environment as such created any selection pressure that influenced the nocturnal adaptation of bats.

Ewing (1933) recorded the case of the kangaroo mallophagan (*Heterodoxus longitarsus*) that belongs to a subfamily (Boopinae) all members of which are found on Australian marsupials. Through the agency of man, this biting louse was brought with its host to zoological parks and circuses, where it transferred to dogs and is now frequently more abundant on dogs than the original biting louse of the dog (*Trichodectes canis*). This introduced louse has also been recorded on coyotes (Jellison, 1942).

Other cases of adaptive dispersal into new habitats involve some genetic modification in addition to older adaptations to environmental factors in both the older and more recent habitat (Gregor, 1944). Hubbs (1938, p. 271) states: "Practically all cave-fishes, and also the blind fishes of other habitats, seem to have had ancestors which to a varying degree were preadapted to successful life in utter darkness." (Exceptions are the Characinidae of Mexican caves according to Breder, 1943; see also p. 674; Fig. 247.) Hubbs also declares (p. 272): "Although the permanent occupation of lightless caves seems to have been generally made possible by a preadaptation to such life, there is no good reason to believe that this preadaptation was complete. Blind fishes are not known to occur outside of caves, except in other more or less completely dark situations to which the blind forms seem rigidly adapted and inescapably bound."

It should also be pointed out that loss of a character, such as the eye of cave fishes, is doubtless a far simpler genetic process than the acquisition of eyes adapted to vision (p. 647), so that positive adaptation probably involves a longer period of time than regressive evolution of the same organ. Nevertheless, the slow acquisition of adaptive characteristics in one habitat may in part preadapt the organism for another habitat that shares similar ecologic factors.

As pointed out by Ferris (1943), only those changes can occur that have a pre-existing base. A change can arise and maintain itself only when and if the stage has been set for it. New adjustments presuppose previous harmonious adjustments both within the organism (White, 1945, p. 304) and between the organism and its environment. The subsequent enhancement of adaptations in a given environment invaded by a preadapted organism is termed *postadaptation* (Simpson, 1944, p. 186).

Preadaptation through genetic modification of previous adaptations may result in the invasion of a new biotic habitat. Cultivated varieties of wheat have been bred for their resistance to infection by rusts (Chester, 1942). The variety known as Kanred wheat was found to be resistant to stem rust (*Puccinia graminis*), and in 1924 over four million acres of this variety were planted in the central United States. It began to lose this resistance, however, and by 1929, 20 per cent of the acreage was lost. New races of stem rust had appeared that infected the formerly resistant wheat. Another resistant wheat variety known as Ceres was first distributed in 1926. By 1933 it was planted in five million acres in the United States and Canada, but in 1935 a physiologic race of stem rust (race 56) attacked it and, with the help of favorable weather, swept across the country in the greatest rust destruction in history, killing a fourth of the crop. Another rust-resistant wheat called Thatcher began to be raised in place of Ceres in 1934, and in 1941 it occupied the acreages formerly devoted to Ceres. A race of rust is known from South America that attacks Thatcher wheat, but by 1941 it had not yet invaded the fields of central North America.

New races of rust seem to arise soon after the new races of wheat. In many cases these new races are the result of hybridization of older races during the sexual fusions on the barberry. Other physiologic races may possibly be the result of mutation. The genetic differences are not great in either the rust or the wheat races. It is obvious that this reciprocal evolution is the result of the rise of slight genetic modifications against a background of the much more complex adaptation of the rust species to the wheat. We may thus see how the preadapted rust may originate and spread to physiologically and genetically distinctive racial populations of its host (Hart, 1944; Newton and Johnson, 1944; Yu, Wang, and Fang, 1945).

A most bizarre example of preadaptation and postadaptation that includes an intermixture of intraspecies group relations and extreme environmental conditions is found in the adjustments of the emperor penguin (*Aptenodytes forsteri*, Fig. 219; see Murphy, 1936). This bird, rarely found north of the Antarctic circle, breeds at the edge of pack ice in the vicinity of open water containing its food supply. The adult is able to shoot up out of the water, alighting feet first upon ice 1½ meters (about 5 feet) above the water surface. Unlike other penguins of different genera (including the Adélie penguin, *Pygoscelis adeliae*, the only other bird nesting on the Antarctic continent), the emperor has no available nesting material to insulate the eggs from the cold ice. Its breeding season is during the long Antarctic night. In adjusting to these extreme conditions, this bird incubates its egg by placing it on its feet between the belly and tail where a broad transverse fold of skin covers the apex of the egg. The period of incubation is between seven and eight weeks. When the bird has a full stomach, the instinct to brood is paramount; but digestion, excretion, and hunger inhibit the brooding reaction, and the egg, or young if it is hatched, is turned over to another adult. If an adult drops an egg, the egg is immediately picked up by another bird. The newly hatched chicks stay in the egg space and take regurgitated food from the adult. As they grow larger, they sit outside still on the feet of the adult, and later they squat on the ice and put the head in the "warming-chamber."

It has been observed that from one in five to one in twelve of a total colony population possessed an egg. Colonies have been estimated to contain 7500 birds, including young. Both sexes incubate the egg, and both have a bare patch of skin on the lower abdomen that is used in incubation. Only a few birds breed during a single season, but the unmated individuals show as much parental solicitude for the egg and chick as do the actual parents, thus allowing time necessary for procuring food. So strong is the instinct for egg and chick care that addled eggs, dead chicks, and even lumps of ice of the right size are tucked on the feet and covered with the feathery muff. There is so much competition for the freed young that they are often handled roughly by the adults and may even become lost or frozen during the argument. In one rookery it was estimated that the mortality among the young was 77 per cent. The average individual age is thirty-four years. The young take about one and one-half years to gain the mature coat. The downy stage lasts only four to five months, in contrast with twice this length of time in the king penguin.

Its close relative, the king penguin (*Aptenodytes patagonicus*), lives in regions with air temperatures usually above freezing and rarely if ever dropping below −18° C. The emperor penguin lives and breeds in regions with air temperatures from −18° C. to −62° C. (−80° F.). The two species do not overlap in breeding range or breeding season. The weight of the individuals of the two species conforms to Bergmann's rule (p. 119), the emperor being markedly larger, while the bills, wings, and feet remain proportionately small, thus also conforming to Allen's rule (pp. 119, 626). The emperor weighs from 57 to 94 pounds (average 70.5), while the king averages about 44 pounds. The appendages of the two species are of nearly the same absolute size. For instance, the wings average 328 mm. in the king and 326 mm. in the emperor, while the bill and foot are a little shorter in the emperor than in the king.

Most of the adaptations of the emperor penguin are also found in its more northern congener. One would thus conclude that the major adjustments for the rigorous antarctic environment had evolved in the less extreme conditions found in the circumpolar islands in the latitude of South Georgia, the Falkland Islands, and the Magellanic region. Having evolved independence of nesting materials and rocky terrain, the bird was able to invade the Antarctic continental shelf ice and survive there in the more extreme conditions. In large part, therefore, the emperor penguin was preadapted to its present rigorous habitat, though the total adaptation is both great and complex. Obviously not all the adaptations arose with the origin of this particular species, nor with the origin of the genus, but antedate the later special adjustments to special environments. On the other hand, the distinctive black head and contrasting white areas of the emperor may function for intraspecies recognition, and the white feathers with enclosed air may assist insulation. Such distinctive characters may have been selected after the isolation from the ancestors of the king penguin.

Some advocates of preadaptation are inclined to explain all functional response as resulting from habitat (organic) selection or from fortunate accidents of survival during dispersal (see Parr, 1926). Preadaptation helps to explain some instances of environmental adjustment, but there is danger of overemphasis.

Individual choice of habitat through conditioned behavior may be illustrated by the records of the return of banded birds to their nesting sites of previous years, sometimes from a distant winter range. A male bank swallow (*Riparia r. riparia*) is recorded (Stoner and Stoner, 1942) as nesting within a few feet of the spot in the colony where it had nested during three previous recorded seasons, once with the same and twice with different females. This species winters in northern South America. Such an exact nonrandom choice of nesting site must involve individual learning and memory as well as the species behavior of all bank swallows, which commonly nest in the rather restricted habitat of sand banks. Natural selection of useful changes caused by many random mutations may be distinguished from *habitat selection,* in which the organism actively moves into new conditions (Baldwin, 1896; Conklin, 1943; Thorpe, 1945).

Instinctive or hereditary orientation may also lead to a selection of the microhabitat. Termite nests built by workers of *Constrictotermes cavifrons* in the Guiana rain forest are found on the sides of smooth-barked trees (Fig. 235). The nest usually hangs from the under side of slanting trees, and it is characteristic of the species to build chevron-shaped solid ridges over and above the nest on the tree trunk. These ridges are beautifully adapted to deflect water descending the trunk and doubtless represent the consequence of selection of hereditary behavior patterns in these social insects over long periods of time. However, the colony is established by a royal pair that flies from the parental nest and, after shedding the wings, digs a shelter in the soil or in a decaying log. The workers ultimately developing from the eggs of the queen then choose the site for the nest, build at least a portion, and induce the royal pair to migrate to the new site which would have been unsuitable for the initial establishment of the colony (Emerson, 1938).

This is an example of adaptation to a complex environment with restriction to parts of the whole habitat during portions of the individual and population life cycle, succeeded by movement to chosen sites at other stages of the life cycle. Organic selection or choice of habitat may be automatic and not intelligent, reasoned, or conditioned (Thorpe, 1945), but it nevertheless involves complex behavior.

Adjustment to a more general habitat, such as a climatic zone, may be at least partially the result of directed dispersal. Migratory birds may follow the seasonal changes in isothermal lines in temperate or mountainous regions. Nonmigratory animals may slowly disperse toward favorable regions (Goldschmidt, 1933).

One should guard against an exaggeration of the role of preadaptation, valid as the concept may be. Even if a large part of the mortality of a population is based

stated that selective intensities effective in evolutionary change are of the order of 1 per cent to one-tenth of 1 per cent in each generation.

Haldane (1932, p. 94; 1936) made a mathematical analysis of the possibility of chance mutations and combinations becoming established with and without selection. If fifteen uncorrelated gene characters are each present in 1 per cent of the individuals, all fifteen would be present in only one in 10^{30} individuals. There have not been

Fig. 235. Nest of the termite, *Constrictotermes cavifrons*, in the British Guiana rain forest. On the left, side view of the entire nest constructed on the smooth bark of a slanting tree. Food is stored in the hanging portion of the nest. On the right, detail of the chevron-shaped rain-shedding ridges extending over the surface and on the side of the nest (also above the nest). Newly constructed portion is seen at the upper right.

upon pure chance and not upon the hereditary characters or the individual choice of the organism, selective factors may still guide the species in the direction of hereditary adaptation. If one supposes that 999 out of every 1000 seeds happen to fall in habitats where development of a plant species is impossible, sorting of the remainder might still be made in accordance with their genetic variability and differential survival, an influence that would be a major factor in the evolution of the plant in the direction of greater fitness, both internal and environmental (p. 603). Fisher (1936)

10^{30} individual higher plants (multicellular and sexually reproducing) during geological history of 10^9 years. Thus there is little chance of all fifteen characters occurring together unless sorted and selected. With biparental reproduction, a favorable combination of fifteen genes would immediately be dispersed. If selection favors each character so that 99 per cent of the individuals have these genes, 86 per cent of the population would have all fifteen. It would take 10,000 years for such a pattern to become established through natural selection in a favorable case, while under artificial selection such combinations are established in relatively few years. If a dominant gene increases the fitness of its carriers by one part in 1000, its frequency in a population mating at random will increase from 0.001 per cent to 99 per cent in 23,400 generations. If this difference of fitness affected viability, we should need a population of at least 16 million to detect it even with the degree of certainty afforded by a deviation equal to twice its standard error. Simpson (1944, p. 82), following Wright, says that, with a selective advantage as low as 0.0001, selection would still be a major factor in the fate of a gene in a breeding population of 5000 or more individuals (p. 654). Such survival differences would obviously be hard to detect within a population; but after frequencies have become established in different populations, it may then be possible to measure the survival values that the evolutionary process has brought about. Under artificial selection, divergencies may be detected much more rapidly.

Some investigators (Errington, 1943, p. 903; Pearl, 1930a, p. 178) seem to think that minor agents contributing to the total mortality can have no appreciable effect upon the direction of evolution, while the major agents causing the greatest mortality may select without genetic discrimination. Dewar (quoted by Pearl, 1930a) says: "From the facts that the greatest destruction is to eggs and young birds and that the forces which destroy adult birds for the most part act indiscriminately as opposed to selectively, the inference must be drawn that, speaking generally, the individuals which survive longest in the struggle for existence are the lucky ones, rather than the most fit." Great mortality, without involving genetic differential survival, must be taken into account (Salisbury, 1936) A single giant puffball produces about 7,000,000,000,000 spores, which are distributed by the wind into many lethal habitats. Large numbers of seeds of plants are distributed at random by the wind, and those that happen to alight on a favorable spot may sprout and grow to reproductive age, while all others die regardless of the favorable gene arrangements in their cells. Eggs of some invertebrates and fishes are distributed almost as completely at random. Haldane's mathematical analysis (1936)

indicates that, even though individual survival may in large part be haphazard, the influence of selection may still guide adaptive evolution as rapidly as is indicated in nature. The horns of titanotheres, the first mutations in the direction of mimetic resemblance, and slight changes in ammonite sutures, have been used as arguments against the selection theory, because of the probably small initial advantage of such characters. But as has been stated, small selective coefficients can influence adaptive evolution.

Beside the misinterpretations of the principle of preadaptation, which go to the length of assuming a small role for selection in the evolution of adaptation, the concept has sometimes been grossly misapplied. The fact that complex structures are sometimes inhibited in development by simple genetic factors has been interpreted by some to signify that these complex structures can arise in phylogeny through simple gene mutation. Villee (1942, p. 168) states: "In the course of phylogeny, one major and a few minor changes in genotype can suddenly produce dorsal appendages and then change them into wings or halteres, thus demonstrating that macroevolution is possible without the accumulation of micromutations under the pressure of selection." Villee thus agrees with the equally startling conclusions of Goldschmidt (1940), in his discussions of macroevolution (see Wright, 1941a, for a critical review).

Even though simple genetic mutations may change wings into halteres or eliminate them altogether as visible structures, this is no indication that the wings are the product of a few genes. A single mutation might influence a developmental threshold that makes possible the growth of a character that has been somatically, but not genetically, lost. If, as has been shown in many Hymenoptera, a haploid egg usually produces a male, while a diploid egg usually produces a female, it would be a rather rash conclusion (see Whiting, 1945; White, 1945) to assume that sex evolved in one jump by a mere doubling or halving of the chromosome number (see discussion by Goldschmidt, 1945). Such structures as wings, eyes, appendages, and sexual organs of *Drosophila* are modified by a large number of genes located in various chromosomes (over 100 genes modify the eye, and 140 genes modify the wing), and the genetic complexity is certainly not limited to the known mutations.

A gene is detected only when it mutates, and obviously not all the genes affecting these complex adapted structures have mutated in such a manner and at such times as to be detected by the geneticists.

That all the genes basic to the development of an insect wing could arise simultaneously and in harmony with the pre-existing genetic and embryological system is statistically highly improbable, if not fantastic, even with the long periods of time involved in organic evolution (Simpson, 1944, p. 54). It is true that wings seem to appear rather suddenly in the upper Pennsylvanian insects, and eyes appear independently in Ordovician vertebrates and Proterozoic arthropods, but the suddenness of appearance is far more easily explained by the gaps in the paleontological record than through macroevolution of such highly adapted and genetically complex organs. The concept of preadaptation has some validity, but this is pushing the theory much too far.

Sumner (1942, p. 438) quotes Darwin as saying:

"He who believes that some ancient form was transformed suddenly through an internal force or tendency into, for instance, one furnished with wings, will be almost compelled to assume, in opposition to all analogy, that many individuals varied simultaneously . . . He will further be compelled to believe that many structures beautifully adapted to all the other parts of the same creature and to the surrounding conditions have been suddenly produced; and of such complex and wonderful adaptation, he will not be able to assign a shadow of an explanation . . . To admit all this is, as it seems to me, to enter into the realms of miracle, and to leave those of Science."

Ferris (1943) expresses himself even more emphatically against macroevolution. He points out that known intergradations are at variance with the concept of macroevolution of fly mouth parts, as has been postulated by Villee (see counter critique by Goldschmidt, 1945a). Silow (1945) shows that taxonomic divergence parallels genotype differences in species of cotton with no indication of macroevolution. Hux-

ley (1942) says: "To produce adapted types by chance recombination in the absence of selection would require a total assemblage of organisms that would more than fill the universe, and overrun astronomical time." (For an opposing interpretation in the case of mimicry, see Goldschmidt, 1945; see also p. 670.)

Selection of the habitat (organic selection) may carry some preadaptive implications; such choice of conditions may also be an adaptive characteristic. Even the sprouting seed has phototropic, geotropic, and hydrotropic growth reactions that orient the growing plant to the environment. Animals commonly use their powers of locomotion to avoid unfavorable situations and to move to favorable environments and, once there, to maintain ecological position (Kendeigh, 1945; see also p. 671). The capacity to react differentially to the environment is often so complex in terms of structure, neuromechanisms, and physiology that it must be assumed that gene patterns affecting the capacity for environmental orientation are the product of long periods of selective sorting. The mutations or recombinations that initiate selection of or survival in somewhat new environments may be, at least in part, the result of simple genetic modifications with chance adaptive effects.

We may summarize our opinion of the role of preadaptation in its various aspects by stating that the concept has real validity; that it brings to our attention the random effect of recombinations and mutations so far as environmental adjustment is concerned; that it indicates in part how the organismic stage is set for further adaptive evolution; that organisms, particularly animals, may exercise conscious or unconscious choice of habitat through behavior response; but that preadaptation without natural selection cannot be used to explain the whole or even a large proportion of complex organic adaptation.

SELECTION PRESSURE

Natural selection is presumed to have been operating indirectly upon germinal patterns through organismic—especially somatic—function over long periods of time. We may well examine the indications that a survival of the fit and an elimination of the unfit actually occurs.

An accumulation of mutations may be necessary before their combination expresses itself in such a manner as to be subject to selection (Wright, 1931; Mather and Wigan, 1942). *Selection pressure** is a term used by Wright (1929) for the effect of selection on gene frequency measured by the rate of change in gene frequency per generation that it tends to produce. This rate (as is also true for mutation pressure and immigration pressure) involves a certain constant as well as the variable gene frequency of the population. This constant is the *selection coefficient (s)*, which may

* Wright (personal communication) illustrates the terms *selection pressure, selection coefficient,* and *selective value* as follows: "Taking the case of a recessive gene a, assume that whatever the frequencies of A — and aa phenotypes may be, a given number of recessives leave 100 *s* per cent fewer descendants (that reach reproductive age) than the same number of dominants. Thus, if *s* = 1.0, 100 *s* per cent is 100 per cent; and if *s* = 0.1, 100 *s* per cent is 10 per cent.

"The symbol *q* represents gene frequency (in this case, of gene a).

"The symbol Δ*q* represents the rate of change of the gene frequency *q* per generation (i.e., 100 *q* would be the percentage change in *q*).

Genotype	Selective Value (*W*)	Frequency
AA	*a*	$(1-q)^2$
Aa	*a*	$2q(1-q)$
aa	$a(1-s)$	q^2

"*Selection pressure* = Δ*q* = $-sq^2(1-q)$, or more accurately

$$\Delta q = \frac{-sq^2(1-q)}{1-sq^2}$$

"*Selection coefficient* of genotype aa is —*s*.

"*Selective value* of genotype aa is *W* = *a* (1 − *s*), where *a* is a constant such that the (weighted) average selective value of the population *W* = $a(1-sq^2)$ is the ratio of number of offspring to number in the parental population at the same phase in the life cycle.

"It should be said that constant selective values and selection coefficients cannot in general be expected for genes or even one factor genotypes. They are more likely to be applicable to the genotype as a whole considering simultaneously all pertinent loci. Selective values even of whole genotypes may, however, be functions of the gene frequencies. In this case they are variables involving one or more selection coefficients which can be defined only as constants in the variable expression for selective value. Somewhat loosely, however, one may deduce a momentary selection coefficient for a one factor genotype or even gene."

be positive or negative. Other constants are the mutation or immigration coefficients. "Selection pressure can be defined sufficiently broadly to include all processes (such as differential mortality, differential fecundity, differential emigration) which tend to change gene frequency systematically without either change of hereditary material itself (mutation) or introduction from without (immigration)" (Wright, 1948a, p. 291). Selection and inbreeding tend to reduce heritable variation. Mutation pressure or reassortment, or both, are necessary to give a continual supply of variations upon which selection may act (Wright, 1932; Dobzhansky, 1946).

Isolation is the dividing factor in phylogeny, while selection is the sorting and survival factor. Selection may act upon a linear sequence chronologically isolated in time (Simpson, 1944, p. 33; p. 626). It is a guiding factor that exhibits both intensity and direction.

Long-term effects are difficult to demonstrate experimentally in the time available to the experimenter. Occasionally short-term effects of selection can be measured (Dobzhansky, 1947, 1948). It is possible to arrange an experimental demonstration of survival in contrasting populations or species that have presumably long been reacting to selective agents. We may thus speak of certain characteristics as having *survival value.*

Sumner (1934, 1935) placed large numbers of mosquito fishes (*Gambusia patruelis*) in two cement tanks painted black and white, respectively. After seven or eight weeks, the fishes accommodated to the color of their background by means of chromatophores. Over 500 of these fishes were then placed together in a tank with a penguin introduced as a predator. In a black tank, 27 per cent black and 73 per cent white fishes were eaten in a few minutes. In a white tank, 62 per cent black and 38 per cent white fishes were eaten in a similarly short time. Fishes that harmonize in coloration with their immediate surroundings were thus shown to be less likely to be eaten by certain birds than fishes of the same species that do not so harmonize. It should be noted that selection did not act upon different germinal characteristics, but over a long period of time selection might act upon a capacity to respond differentially to environmental backgrounds. In this experiment other possible characters than the color relationship seem to have been well controlled. The capacity for plasticity of color response and adaptive coloration are both known to be genetic and different in closely related species.

Isely (1938) tested various colored species of grasshoppers on various colored in this case color may be modified by raising the young of the same species on different background colors (Faure, 1932; Hertz and Imms, 1937; James, 1944). Such plastic color differences would not be subject to evolutionary diversification, but the genetic differential in capacity to react to background color could evolve.

Dice (1947) performed a number of experiments on predator selection. He sub-

Fig. 236. A praying mantis resembling the green leaves among which it lives in Panama. (Photograph by Ralph Buchsbaum.)

backgrounds against the predatory activities of chickens, turkeys, and native birds. The nonprotected forms that did not match their backgrounds were eaten more readily than those that were protected by background resemblance. Four hundred and five, or 88 per cent, of the nonprotected forms were eaten, in contrast with fifty-four, or 12 per cent, survivors; 183, or 40 per cent, of the protected forms were eaten, in contrast with 276, or 60 per cent, survivors. The differences between grasshopper species are probably largely genetic, although jected genetic strains of the mouse, *Peromyscus maniculatus,* that varied in color, to owl predation (of *Asio wilsonianus* and *Tyto alba pratincola*) at various light intensities on different colored soils. The mice were given some protection by letting them run under a "jungle" of sticks forming a latticework $3\frac{1}{2}$ to $4\frac{1}{2}$ inches above the floor. This "jungle" forced the owls to capture the mice by sight rather than hearing.

Mice that matched their background soils had a great selective advantage, compared to those not so concealed. For example, the

number of concealed mice compared to the number of conspicuous mice taken by the barn owl (*T. alba pratincola*) in two experiments were 68:124 and 65:107. The selection indices were 0.292 and 0.244, respectively, while the chi-squares were 16.333 and 10.256, indicating high statistical significance. Dice concludes that such high selection of subspecies variation in nature would produce rapid evolution toward protective coloration (see pp. 610, 627, 668; Figs. 230, 245).

as having warning (aposematic) or concealing (procryptic) coloration, forty-five were offered, and thirty-eight, or 84 per cent, were accepted. Of the somewhat more conspicuous insects, thirty-five were offered, and two, or 6 per cent, were accepted. Of the typically conspicuous insects with warning coloration, fifty-eight were offered, and five, or 9 per cent, were accepted. The species differences in these tests are presumed to be genetic in the majority of cases on the basis of their taxonomic correlations. These

Fig. 237. A praying mantis resembling the dead brown leaves among which it lives in Panama. (Photograph by Ralph Buchsbaum.)

Carrick (1936) tested a number of species of insects against insectivorous birds that were feeding their young. He classified the specific degree of resemblance to the surroundings in five categories. Of the typically concealed insects, hidden by their extreme degree of resemblance to the colors (and often shapes) of their immediate surroundings (see Figs. 236 and 237), forty-three were offered, and seven, or 16 per cent, were accepted. Of the insects with dingy colors generally resembling the surroundings, sixty-three were offered, and fifty-three, or 84 per cent, were accepted. Of the neutral insects not readily classified

experiments are interesting in their demonstration of relative freedom from predatory attack of both the inconspicuous and the conspicuous forms, thus lending credence to the concept of background (cryptic) coloration (Figs. 236, 237 and 244), warning coloration (Fig. 238), and by inference from warning coloration, to the theories of mimicry (p. 670). It should be noted that, in Carrick's experiments, no differential survival value is demonstrated between those insects with a general resemblance to their background and those classified as neutral.

Turning from selection through predators (Errington, 1946) to the selective effect of the physical environment, Talbot (1934) shows that ants of the genus *Formica* inhabiting drier situations survived experimental drying better than other species of *Formica* that normally inhabited more humid situations (see p. 335). In this case, taxonomic correlation indicates again that these physiological characters are inherited.

Dobzhansky (1945, 1947) and Wright and Dobzhansky (1946) report differential survival of three chromosome races of *Drosophila pseudoobscura* from the same locality kept under artificial temperatures. The experimental data conform to the natural incidence of the chromosome types (Dobzhansky, 1948) during summer, fall, and winter (the spring incidence was not

Fig. 238. Panamanian frog, *Dendrobates tinctorius*, exhibiting conspicuous dark brown and blue markings (warning coloration) and provided with a poisonous mucus. (Photograph by Ralph Buchsbaum.)

Aldrich (1946) found that races of birds are usually adapted to their respective environments and that transplantations of one race to the range of another are not often successful.

Pond crayfish in eastern North America (*Cambarus diogenes, C. blandingii, C. immunis*) are more tolerant of low oxygen content of water and more resistant to heat than are stream crayfish (*C. propinquus, C. virilis*) (T. Park, 1945a). It is possible that such differences between crayfish from different habitats are the result of natural selection of physiologic characters.

experimentally repeated). Natural selection of these gene arrangements results in adaptive adjustment of the species to different conditions. Selection of heterozygotes over homozygotes results in the persistence of several types in the same locality, "buffers" the species against environmental change, and maintains a store of hereditary variability.

Dubinin and Tiniakov (1945, 1946, 1946a, 1946b, 1947) report seasonal variation in chromosome-inversion frequency in urban populations of *D. funebris* under seasonal selection pressures, but rural popula-

tions do not exhibit such seasonal cycles. The flies of bombed-out urban districts showed a decrease in chromosome-inversion frequency. Divergent urban and rural varieties seem to have resulted from a rapid environmental selection of only one of these populations. Surviving hibernating female flies were more fecund than nonhibernating controls and transmitted this fecundity to their female offspring. Natural selection evidently operates rapidly during hibernation, with resultant higher fecundity of the survivors.

Toleration of heat and radiation by animals through color adjustments (Cole, 1943; Brown and Sandeen, 1948; Parker, 1948) indicates that color adaptation is not only a response to selective pressure by predators and selection of species and sexual integration mechanisms, but is also the result of selection by factors in the physical environment.

Another approach to the action of selection pressures may be made through the study of tension zones or ecotones (pp. 476–478) between contrasting biota (Albertson and Weaver, 1945, 1946; also p. 634). The common factors on the margins of the range of a species often give an indication of the primary barriers to further distribution (Hall, 1946, p. 48). Griggs (1942, 1946) gives data indicating that a long period of climatic change has moved the tree line down on Mount Washington, New Hampshire, and that trees are now occupying a wide zone on the White Mountains that they could not colonize under present conditions. Such evidence does not indicate adaptive evolution, but does indicate the elimination of the unfit by environmental selection. Such selection by the physical environment may influence the evolution of physiological adaptations within the organism, irrespective of competition between organisms (pp. 641, 656).

White clover (*Trifolium repens*) raised from imported seed at Scalöf, Sweden, gave 100 units of green matter in the first crop, and 129 units and 137 units in the next two generations (experiments by N. Sylven reported by Gregor, 1944). The less hardy genotypes were probably eliminated in each generation by the climatic conditions in Sweden. Inbred relatively homozygous stock did not change under similar conditions.

In Australia, races of the subterranean clover (*Trifolium subterraneum*) vary in earliness of maturity. Early and midseason races were mixed and sown both in the region of Adelaide and in the higher Adelaide Hills. At Adelaide, conditions allowed the early plants to seed, but the midseason genotypes were unable to seed normally because of moisture conditions. After a few years, only the early races were found in Adelaide because of selective elimination of the midseason races, while in the Adelaide Hills only the midseason genotypes survived. Though both races in the latter area were able to seed normally, many more flowers were produced by the midseason races in the higher environment (experiments performed by C. M. Donald and discussed in Gregor, 1944).

Twelve strains of side-oats grama grass (*Bouteloua curtipendula*) on the average respond to photoperiods (p. 121) by flowering most vigorously in their normal latitude, although a few individuals in most strains grow and flower over a wider range. The species probably originated in low latitudes with short days and became secondarily adapted to the longer days of higher latitudes (Olmsted, 1944).

Wilkes (1942) found that a chalcid parasite (*Microplectron fuscipennis*) introduced for the biological control of the European spruce sawfly (*Gilpinia polytoma*) in Canada showed wide variation in its ability to establish itself in different temperature areas. Experiments demonstrated different modalities (preferenda) in a temperature gradient, and by selective breeding, strains were procured, one of which did best at 25° C. and another at 9° C. Recovery of parasites from natural regions with a low mean temperature (Parke Reserve, Quebec) indicated that natural selection modified the percentage modality in a manner similar to that produced by artificial selection in the laboratory.

Several species of insects seem to have rapidly developed populations resistant to certain insecticides since control measures were instituted (Quayle, 1943). Hydrocyanic acid tree fumigation has been used on the California red scale (*Aonidiella aurantii*) since 1886. Resistance to the insecticide was noted in 1914, and since then the scale has increased its resistance and the range of the resistant population. The resistance varies directly with population density, large populations being more resistant (Knight, 1932). Under experimental conditions, the difference in resistance of populations from different areas has been adequately demonstrated (Lindgren and Sinclair, 1944; Lindgren and Dickson, 1945). Experiments also indicate differences of resistance to methyl bromide and ethylene dioxide. Resistance depends upon a single sex-linked gene or group of closely linked genes in the X chromosome. The variation probably arose by mutation and spread by selective elimination of the non-resistant strain. Resistance has been maintained for sixty generations under experimental conditions. Crosses between resistant and nonresistant strains show intermediate resistance of the population. Resistance is a physiological character of the living insect, and not of the scaly covering.

The recent evolution of insecticide-resistant strains has also been reported for such insects as the San José scale (*Quadraspidiotus perniciosus*) to lime-sulfur spray; for the black scale (*Saissetia oleae*) to hydrocyanic acid fumigation; for larvae of the codling moth (*Carpocapsa pomonella*) to arsenical and other sprays; for the citricola scale (*Coccus pseudomagnoliarum*) to hydrocyanic acid fumigation; for the screw worm (*Cochliomyia americana*) to phenothiazine; and for the citrus thrips (*Scirtothrips citri*) to tartar emetic-sucrose spray (Quayle, 1943). The evolution of insecticide-resistant races of insects within a few years indicates the speed with which simple adaptive changes may take place under constantly applied selection, and parallels the speed of evolution under artificial selection, being in fact a negative type of artificial selection.

Adaptive evolution without selection through the agency of man is usually a much slower process, but in some cases may occur within a few thousand years. Subspecies adaptations to soils left by the Quaternary Lake Lahontan in Nevada have doubtless evolved since the late Pleistocene in five species of rodents and a species of fox (Hall, 1946, p. 61; for recent adaptive evolution, also see p. 611). Simpson (1944, p. 19) states that morphological differen-

tiation of subspecies of rodents may take place in even less than 300 generations.

Mathematical analysis indicates how selection may influence the incidence of a gene. If a new dominant gene has an advantage of 0.001 and appears by mutation with a frequency of 10^{-6}, it must appear 347 times before the odds favor its spread (Haldane, 1932, p. 200). This would require 347,000,000 individuals. In most insects and even in man, the new gene could thus start to spread in a single generation, but in the Indian elephant, with a population of 20,000 and a generation on an average of every forty years (male elephants mature at twenty years of age and females at the age of sixteen), it would be nearly a million years before such a new gene could spread to a large enough fraction of the population to be sure of spreading farther. A new recessive gene would have much less chance of spreading. In a small inbreeding population, chance would favor the continuation of such a recessive gene, thus allowing selection to begin to operate (pp. 602, 603). The time required for a novel mutation to reach high frequencies is probably less important than the mechanisms that keep it and its alleles at medium frequencies for long periods and thus make it an element in the store of variability (p. 641).

Simpson (1944, p. 66) says that a mutation of definite selective advantage (0.01) arising at the rate 0.000001 in a population of 10,000,000 is sure to become established within 25 generations, but in a population of 10,000 may require 25,000 generations—a time so long that in many cases the selective advantage or other limiting factors are likely to change. Other conditions being equal, the selection advantage would probably be different in populations of markedly different size. Wright (1940a, p. 178) says that it is probable that most mutations important in evolution have much smaller selection coefficients than can be demonstrated in the laboratory. It is even more difficult to demonstrate minute selection coefficients in the field, and yet these may be of great evolutionary importance.

Observations on the percentage incidence of a deleterious gene in a population may be indicative of selection pressure. The gene producing hemophilia in man is a sex-linked recessive to the normal allele.

Located in the X chromosome, the gene is recessive to the normal allele in the heterozygous female, but produces the disease in the male in which the action of the gene is not modified by the Y chromosome. Hemophilic males tend to die at an early age (Strandskov, 1944). Estimates indicate that 54 per cent of hemophilic males die before the fifth year, 88 per cent before the twentieth year, and 89 per cent before the twenty-first year. There is thus a strong selection against the gene carried by the male (note that not much competition is involved; see p. 641). Presumably only a homozygous female would exhibit the malady, but the incidence of the gene in the population is so low that few homozygous females have been discovered (there seems to be no well-authenticated case reported). Haldane (1938) estimated one hemophilic for every 10,000 males in London, which would give an expectation of one hemophilic female in 100,000,000. If one in 100,000 males were hemophilic, only one in 10,000,000,000 females would show hemophilia.

The selection against a deleterious gene with a similar incidence would be greater if the gene were a sex-linked dominant instead of a recessive, and less if the gene were an autosomal recessive. Selection would operate more quickly on autosomal dominants than on recessives. Deleterious autosomal recessives are strikingly abundant in certain wild populations of *Drosophila*. Dobzhansky (1942, 1946) has estimated that 98 per cent of the individuals in wild populations of *Drosophila pseudoobscura* have chromosomes carrying deleterious modifiers, semilethals, or lethals. Nearly 75 per cent carry lethals or semilethals. Of course, mutation pressure may keep an unfavorable recessive gene in equilibrium in a population in spite of selection against such a gene. Haldane (1938) estimated one mutation from normal to the hemophilic allele per 50,000 individuals in each generation in order to account for the seemingly constant incidence of this gene.

Constancy or slow change of incidence may also be accounted for through differential selection of heterozygous and homozygous individuals. A gene may be advantageous in the heterozygous and deleterious in the homozygous individuals, or *vice versa* in certain environments (Dobzhan-

sky, Holz, and Spassky, 1942; Strandskov, 1944, p. 463). Also, it should be noted that mortality may result from either organic inviability or elimination by the physical environment (pp. 624, 641, 653), from exploitation or competitive interaction (p. 656), or a combination of these factors.

Haldane (1932, p. 177) concludes that intense competition favors variable response to the environment rather than high average response. A change in the intensity of selection may reverse the relative fitness of two types, and it is not always true that intense competition means intense selection. The number of generations required for a given change in the population is inversely proportional to the intensity of selection. Selection is not very effective on populations containing only a small proportion of recessives. Selection is more rapid when dominants are favored, and slower otherwise, but the difference is not great. Mutation pressure alone must act slowly as a cause of evolution, but it certainly cannot be neglected when organisms are in a fairly constant environment over long periods.

Evolution in large populations without selection would be slow. Simpson (1944, p. 81) postulates that subspecific diversity in the horses (Equidae) might take a million to ten million years without selection, while the adaptive sequence through nine genera of horses occurred in 45 million years. This rate necessitates the existence of such a factor as selection.

Although much more experimental and quantitative data are desirable, both survival of the fit and elimination of the unfit would seem to be valid concepts that have been demonstrated both experimentally and by observation under artificial and natural conditions. Interrelated somatic and genetic characters of populations are altered by selection, thus meeting certain of Pearl's criteria for proof of the operation of natural selection (p. 641).

Granting the chance effects of recombinations and mutations, and granting a certain amount of adaptation through preadaptive factors (p. 642), we conclude that complex function based upon genetic initiation is primarily the result of selective sorting.

There is no such thing as accumulative habit, adjustment, or adaptation in physics and inorganic chemistry, except for the phenomenon of momentum, and present conditions alone determine a process (Lewis, 1946). In biology, reaction to present conditions may be determined through learned behavior from past experiences. Also, reaction to present conditions may be determined through selective sorting in past environments, and such selection effects are augmented by the repetition of the environmental factors and conditions. If orderly continuation and repetition of habitat conditions did not occur, adaptive evolution would be weak or absent. Some philosophers think that scientists base their method on a faith in the orderliness of nature. There seems to be much evidence that order and continuity are objectively real phenomena that have been discovered and partially analyzed by scientific method.

The "directiveness" of organic processes (often referred to as purposive or teleological) has its explanation in differential survival of autocatalytic systems under repeated natural conditions (see also p. 639). The organism must be viewed in its evolutionary perspective to resolve these ancient philosophical problems (see Russell, 1945, for a discussion largely avoiding evolutionary analysis; see also Hutchinson, 1948).

COMPETITION AND SELECTION

Competition (p. 395) may increase selection pressure, but it is not the only factor operating in selection (see Elton, 1930, p. 39). Some of the most obvious and widespread adaptations, such as tracheae and lungs, are adjustments to factors so pervasive as to involve no competition for a limited supply. Aside from a few habitats, oxygen occurs in sufficient abundance for all animals and plants, and the evolution of breathing adaptations is possibly through survival of the fit rather than only through survival of the fittest.

Competition or rivalry between individuals for limited necessities is a consequence of overproduction. Since Darwin's day, ample evidence as to the amount of absolute potential reproductive capacity beyond the possibility of survival has been gathered (p. 272). The partial potential reproductive capacity is the maximum possible under a given set of restricted conditions, and here we encounter selective factors operating upon what genetic variability

may be present. Competition greatly increases the action of selection upon genetic differences and creates more subtle survival distinctions. Mortality (pp. 273, 368) commonly is the result of competition and is often a selective mortality of genetic effects. Competition may be between cooperative systems, and in this way may result in the evolution of increased cooperation and decreased destructive competition (Allee, 1940).

The role of competition may be highly important, even in adaptation to a physical factor. During the drought of 1933 to 1940 in the prairies of Nebraska, Colorado, and Kansas, the cactus, *Opuntia macrorrhiza*, became abundant in former grasslands, but in the moister years of 1941 to 1943, it was largely replaced by grasses (Timmons, 1941–42; Albertson and Weaver, 1944). Dense growths of vegetation competed with the cactus for soil water and light, and by transpiration increased the humidity. Large numbers of insects were able to kill the cactus under moist conditions, though they had not been very harmful to it during the drought period. Without competition, some vegetation changes of this type might take place, but competition probably plays an important role (see T. Park (1948) for an experimental analysis of competing beetle populations).

Competition is conceived by some to be greater between individuals of the same species than between individuals of different species, and greater between taxonomically closely related species or ecologically equivalent species within the same association than between more adaptively divergent species. It is difficult to find data from which a valid generalization on these points can be made. So far as can be judged, intraspecies competition is more severe in some cases and interspecies competition in others (Hutchinson, 1948).

Genetic differentials in competition effects among litter mates within the mammalian uterus have been demonstrated (see p. 403). Wright and Eaton (1929) reported that one inbred family of guinea pigs showed the highest percentages born alive in litters of three, with litters of two and four close behind, while there is a marked drop in litters of both one and five. In another inbred family, the highest percentage born alive was in litters of one, with, on the whole, progressively more born dead with increase in size of litter. Other inbred families showed an intermediate range of mortality at birth. Control stocks not inbred showed relatively little effect of litter size, the percentage born alive averaging between 80 and 90 up to litters of five.

It might be expected that large litters would regularly be at a disadvantage compared with small ones (p. 396). But a small litter in guinea pigs may be an indication of unfavorable conditions that may more than offset the advantage derived from small numbers. The relation of size of litter to chances of death at birth is probably complex. Not only is there a differential in inbred families of guinea pigs, but a differential occurs between different groups of animals. Mortality at birth is greater in man, the larger the number of young born at one time.

During mammalian embryonic life within the uterus or marsupial pouch, and during the nesting period in birds, competition between siblings may be acute (Haldane, 1932, p. 124). At the same time, the number of young is in general inversely correlated with the amount of postembryonic parental care and protection (p. 701).

It may here be mentioned that the nestling cuckoo, parasitizing the family instincts of its foster-parents, eliminates the eggs or young that share its nest by using its hollowed back to shove its competitors out of the nest (Beebe, 1944, p. 16; Baker, 1942). No sibling nestlings have evolved such a mechanism for doing away with conspecific nest competitors—an adaptation that would be advantageous for the individual, but harmful for the species. This instance indicates that, in some cases at least, the relation of competition and cooperation within a species and between species is at least quantitatively different, and this differential sets up selection pressures that affect the evolution of intraspecific adaptations, as contrasted with interspecific adaptations (see p. 683).

In pure stands of plants, aggregated animals, and in social groups, one might imagine an increase in intraspecies competition, while in solitary and scattered forms other species might exert a stronger competitive pressure. Complete elimination is more frequent in mixed cultures of plant species than in cultures of different strains of the same species (Salisbury, 1936). In trees there seems to be a tendency toward stands of a few or single species in temperate forests under more severe conditions, while tropical forests have a much larger number of species, with fewer individuals of any given species per unit of area. A gradation in numbers of species also occurs between continental and island biotas. Darlington (1943) stated that large areas appear to be inhabited by many species of carabid beetles with sparse, unstable populations, while small areas have fewer species in denser, more stable populations. See Elton (1946), Williams (1947), and Crombie (1947), for discussions of interspecies competition in communities compared to faunas.

Recently experiments have demonstrated some of the simpler aspects of competitive relations. Gause (1934a) observed unicellular organisms under controlled conditions in order to establish types of competitive relationships. He says: "The competition between two species for a common place in the microcosm may be either (1) a competition for a certain fixed and limited amount of energy, or (2) a competition for a source of energy kept continually at a certain level." To these may be added competition for other niche factors (p. 271).

In order to investigate the first of these problems, Gause experimented with two species of yeast cells producing alcoholic fermentation (*Saccharomyces cerevisiae* and *Schizosaccharomyces kephir*). He calculated the coefficients of multiplication in these species and the factor that limited their growth (alcohol production). He then evaluated the coefficients of the struggle for existence (alcohol production per unit of yeast volume), and correlated these parameters in the form of an equation of the struggle for existence (Volterra, 1926; Gause, 1932a), and obtained an agreement in general features with the observed growth of a mixed population. Further experiments showed that under slightly different conditions (a greater content of oxygen in the nutritive medium) the complicating effect of the by-products of fermentation decreased. The forecasts of the theory coincided entirely with the values observed.

The competition between species for a source of energy kept at a certain level were investigated with Protozoa (*Parame-*

ments showed that the deficiency of food was the only limiting factor in these cases. Under such conditions there existed a competition of *P. caudatum* with *P. aurelia* for the still unutilized food resources. After

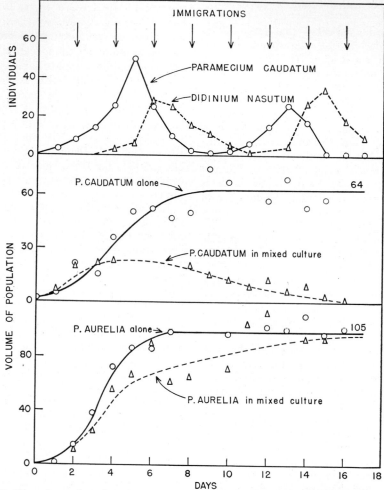

Fig. 239. The effect of exploitation and competition on populations of protozoans. Top, the reciprocal relation of populations of *Paramecium caudatum* and the predatory *Didinium nasutum* with controlled and simultaneous immigration of both species. Middle, the growth of population volume of *Paramecium caudatum* alone in a controlled environment with a fixed density of bacterial food at the beginning of the experiment compared with the population volume of *P. caudatum* in competition with *P. aurelia* under the same conditions. Bottom, the growth of population volume of *P. aurelia* alone and in competition with *P. caudatum*. (Redrawn from Gause, 1934a.)

cium caudatum and *Paramecium aurelia*). These infusoria were cultivated in a buffered, balanced Osterhout's salt solution (*pH* = 8.0), in which a suspension was made of *Bacillus pyocyaneus* (of fixed density). Bacteria do not multiply under these conditions. Specially arranged experi-

the source of energy had been utilized a redistribution of energy between two components occurred which always resulted in the complete elimination of *P. caudatum* by *P. aurelia* (Fig. 239). The corresponding equations are somewhat complicated, because the coefficients of the struggle for existence vary with time: one species may be favorable for the growth of another at the beginning of the experiment, and the depression of one species by another will only begin later.

Under natural conditions, if the food production of a given habitat remains constant, the biomass tends to remain constant, with increase of one species correlated with

foods (Lack, 1944, 1945a, 1946, 1947; Amadon, 1947; Mayr, 1948; see p. 369 for further discussion). Examples of birds that breed in a similar habitat, but occupy different regions, are the swans, *Cygnus olor* and *C. cygnus,* the curlews, *Numenius arquata* and *N. phaeopus,* and the Common and Arctic terns, *Sterna hirundo* and *S. macrura.* In each case the first-

Fig. 240. Divided range of Butler's garter snake (*Thamnophis butleri*) (eastern shaded area) produced by the invading Plains garter snake (*Thamnophis radix*) (western shaded area). (After Pope.)

a decrease in competing species. Hubbs and Eschmeyer (1938) indicate that the weight of living fishes in a lake remains constant, although fluctuations may occur in the weight of each competing species. When a species is introduced into a new region, the growth of individuals is sometimes exceptionally great because the small number of individuals results in a minimum of competition within the species (Eddy and Carlander, 1940).

The majority of closely related species with similar ecological adjustment inhabit different areas or habitats, or eat different

mentioned species breeds to the south of the second. Lack reports examples of related species that breed in the same regions, but in different habitats. These include the long-eared owl, *Asio otus,* in woods, and the short-eared owl, *A. flammeus,* in open country; the marsh harrier, *Circus aeruginosus,* in wet marshland, and the Montagu harrier, *C. pygargus,* in drier marshland and heaths; the goosander, *Mergus merganser,* mainly near rapid streams, and the red-breasted merganser, *M. serrator,* mainly near lakes or bays; the common European hare, *Lepus europaeus,* on low ground, and the mountain hare, *L. timidus,* on high ground. A form of the mountain hare, *L. anglicus,* was abundant on low ground in Britain during the Pleistocene, but became extinct when the common hare became established. In Ireland, where the common hare is absent, a form of the mountain hare still occupies low ground. The hobby, *Falco subbuteo,* and the kestrel, *F. tinnunculus,* overlap in region and habitat, but differ in their food. Among Hawaiian birds, *Phaeornis obscurus* and *P. palmeri* (Turdidae) are both found on Kauai, but one feeds mainly on fruits and berries, and the other is chiefly insectivorous. Four species of Antarctic seals occupy the same habitat, but

lated and competing forms (Mayr, 1948). Hutchinson (1948) mentions two possible exceptions to this rule: (1) where an external factor may act to rarefy the mixed population, so that the environmental possibilities are not completely exploited; (2) where continual chance oscillations of the environmental variables may continually reverse the direction of competition, so that no equilibrium can be established.

Competition of a specific nature may account for cases of geographic incompatibility of closely related organisms. Davis (1932) reported the probable invasion of the large and aggressive plains garter snake (*Thamnophis radix*) to the Illinois shores

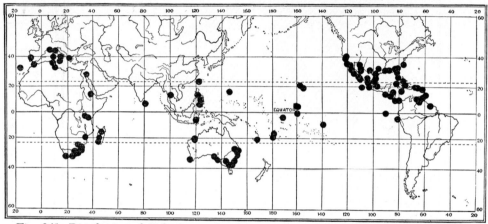

Fig. 241. Distribution of *Kalotermes,* the most primitive genus of living dry-wood termites (Kalotermitidae). Note the occurrence in peripheral geographical regions (temperate zones) and peripheral ecological regions (continental edges), as compared to the derived genera, *Neotermes* and *Glyptotermes,* in Figures 242 and 243.

have food differences. A number of cases are reported in which two related species occupy the same area and habitat, but differ in size and presumably in their types of food. These include passerine birds, woodpeckers, ducks, grebes, terns, gulls, shrews, and weasels.

There remain a few examples of closely related species of birds of similar size that seem to overlap in area and ecology. Lack, in his detailed study of the cormorant, *Phalacrocorax carbo,* and the shag, *P. aristotelis,* discloses distinct differences in both nesting habitat and food. Gause's thesis (Gause, 1934a) that two species with identical ecology cannot persist together in the same area seems to be substantiated by the data on birds and many other animals, and indicates coaction of re-

of Lake Michigan, thus separating the populations of Butler's garter snake (*T. butleri*), which ranges from western New York to Wisconsin (Fig. 240) (see also Conant, Thomas, and Rausch, 1945).

An instance of competing species of fishes is discussed by Meek (1930, p. 147). He reports that Peterson transplanted young plaice from near the mouth to the head of Limfjord, where they were naturally rare or absent, although proper food was plentiful. The viviparous blennies that live at the head of the fjord competed with the transplanted plaice for food, and the success of the plaice was found to depend upon the presence of adult cod that feed upon the blenny.

The effect of competition upon the species constitution of communities is indicated by the survival of relict types in geographically or ecologically peripheral regions where competitors are absent or reduced in number (Cole, 1946). The reptile *Sphenodon* (p. 680) survived in New Zealand in the absence of terrestrial mammals. New World marsupials have withstood the pres-

relatives that apparently could not compete after the Pleistocene arrival of the dingo dog, but survived in Tasmania in the absence of this carnivore.

The primitive termite genus, *Kalotermes*, (Fig. 241), exists in subtropical regions over the world, and in ecologically periph-

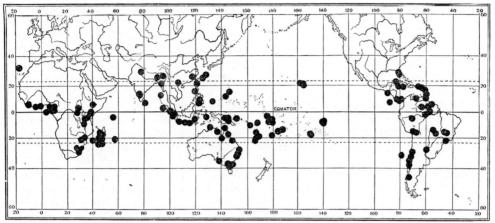

Fig. 242. Distribution of the termite genus, *Neotermes*. Note the occurrence in central continental regions of high competition in comparison with its ancestral genus, *Kalotermes*, in Figure 241.

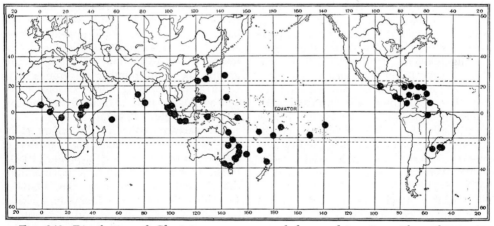

Fig. 243. Distribution of *Glyptotermes*, a genus of dry wood termites with a phragmotic soldier-head. Note the distribution in central continental regions with high competition in contrast to its ancestral genus, *Kalotermes*, in Figure 241.

sure of competition from superior placental mammals, possibly through the restriction of their activities to nocturnal periods (O. Park, 1940, p. 522), while the Australian marsupials, remaining diurnal in many instances, radiated into a great variety of habitats in the absence of such placental competitors (p. 666). The Tasmanian wolf and the Tasmanian devil had Australian

eral tropical regions, such as offshore islands, mangrove swamps, and oceanic islands, while the derived genera (*Neotermes*, Fig. 242, and *Glyptotermes*, Fig. 243) are better able to survive in areas of great competition such as are found in the continental tropical rain forests (p. 725).

Cowles and Bogert (1944) emphasize the well-known fact that relicts are more often found on islands and peninsulas, and suggest this is owing to the relatively slight temperature fluctuations characteristic of maritime climates. Specialization of course, may be correlated with survival under rather extreme physical conditions or extreme biotic conditions, or both. Likewise, primitive types might survive under both mild physical or biotic conditions. In many instances biotic factors through competition probably play an important role in the survival of relict forms.

The phenomenon of rapid or "explosive" (*tachytelic*) evolution of major groups (*megaevolution*) during a geological epoch, followed by less rapid (*horotelic*) subsequent evolution, has been questionably explained as the result of peaks of genetic mutations (p. 600). Higher rates of mutation than are commonly observed would not necessarily produce any evolutionary change (Simpson, 1944, p. 47). If mutation rate were the limiting factor, the length of generations might be expected to show a strong negative correlation with rate of evolution, but no such correlation is apparent. Explosive evolution would seem better understood as an effect associated with reduced competition or lack of competition within available niches. Under favorable conditions of partial isolation of small local inbreeding populations with occasional cross breeding between populations with unique balanced genetic patterns, an enormous potential variability exists, and selection of competing populations as contrasted with competing individuals may occur. Under exceptionally favorable ecological conditions, rapid evolution of new higher systematic categories is possible (Cain, 1944, p. 325; Wright, 1945, p. 416; Amadon, 1947). Such rapid evolution might initially exhibit a change toward general rather than special adaptation.

During the Paleocene and Eocene, placental mammals evolved into most of the modern orders from a ferungulate stock. The habitats had been largely occupied by Mesozoic reptiles with similar adaptations such as wings, streamlined shapes, carnivorous feeding adjustments, and cursorial legs. The causes of the widespread extinction of many reptile groups toward the end of the Mesozoic are not understood. Whatever the causes, the reptiles left vacant niches that in due time were occupied by ecologically equivalent placental mammals. The major orders of placental mammals had appeared by Eocene times, and no new orders evolved in the much longer period from the beginning of the Oligocene to the present. This may be explained by the fact that a niche, once occupied by an adapted form, could not be invaded by another form initially less well adapted. If unoccupied, however, the niche might be exploited by an initially poorly adapted form that in time would become adjusted through natural selection. Under reduced competition, organisms vary more widely and tend to occupy vacant niches, while an increase in competition with its more rigorous selection results in less surviving variation, more specialized adaptation, and a lessened capacity to radiate adaptively.

Before the junction of North and South America (p. 723) in the late Pliocene period, twenty-seven families of land mammals occurred in North America and twenty-nine families in South America. No families occurred in both (Didelphidae and Procyonidae are possible exceptions). After the Pliocene faunal interchange, twenty-two families were common to the two regions. South America now has twenty-nine families, and North America has twenty-three. It would appear that the advance of one group usually means the recession or extinction of a competing group, the total number of groups in a given area remaining fairly constant in recent geological time (Mayr, 1946; Simpson, 1940; Darlington, 1948).

The early radiation of the orders of insects is even more remarkable than that of the orders of mammals (Carpenter, 1930). Fossil primitive winged insects, including the Paleodictyoptera and the blattoids (roachlike insects), are found in rocks of the Pennsylvanian period and undoubtedly occurred somewhat earlier. A large number of modern orders first appear in the Permian with forerunners of still other orders known first from the Triassic and Jurassic. With the exception of the Lepidoptera, which may have evolved with the rise of the flowering plants in Cretaceous times, there was no further increase in the number of main insect orders after the Permian. In the rapid evolution of the placental mammals, the niches had probably been vacated. In the case of the insects, the niches were being created by the evolution of the plants and other terrestrial animals, and no competitors had arisen to prevent the rapid evolution into widely divergent habitats. For both mammals and insects, competition was weak during the period of greatest adaptive radiation. Contrariwise, strong competition forces the extinction of primitive forms or allows their survival only as relicts in regions or niches with weak competition (p. 679) and prevents adaptive evolution into occupied niches.

Oparin and Morgulis (1938) explain the contemporary absence of intermediate forms between inorganic systems and living organisms through the possible elimination of incipient life by highly adapted types. Before the present organisms originated, however, a slow transition from the inorganic to the organic might have taken place (see also p. 75).

Much subtle evolution in small niches probably occurs in the absence of competitors. Worthington (1940) gives an account of the speciation of a genus of cyprinid fishes of open water, *Engraulicypris*, which exhibits topographical isolation in the African lakes (Victoria, Tanganyika, Rudolf, Nyasa, and Rukwa). In Lake Edward, however, no species of *Engraulicypris* occurs, but the same niche has been filled by a cyprinodont, *Haplochilichthys pelagicus*. Most cyprinodont fishes are inhabitants of shores and swamps, and this is the only species of the family that has become highly modified toward plankton feeding in open water. Worthington thinks that the evidence points to a rapid evolution of these adaptations since the Pleistocene arid period, which separated the two major pluvial periods in central Africa, and draws the conclusion that "where a good niche exists, vacant for reasons of isolation, some species will fill it rapidly, even though considerable structural alterations are involved in the process." The time involved in this case is considered to be of the order of 15,000 to 40,000 years. The last pluvial period in Africa seems to have coincided with the last glacial period in Europe. The retreat of the continental glaciers began 30,000 to 40,000 years ago (p. 81).

Some authors (Bertalanffy, 1937; Frieling, 1940) express the opinion that major evolution of the larger categories has come to an end, and only minor speciation or ra-ciation is now possible, particularly because of the presence of man. Just (1944) thinks that such generalizations are unwarranted. Occupied niches probably prevent adaptive evolution of forms that would otherwise radiate, but the evolution of new organisms creates new biotic niches. The advent of man may result in evolutionary spurts of certain organisms at the same time that extinction or reduction of populations occurs for many other species. To some extent future evolution will be directed or profoundly influenced by man, but it seems safe to say that much will take place in spite of or because of his influence.

Kropotkin (1902) concluded that intraspecies competition is always harmful. His view is in contrast with the Spencerian concept that progressive evolution depends almost wholly upon competition, whether intraspecies or interspecies. Both these early interpreters of biological theory based their assumptions upon a meager accumulation of data, and their generalizations were oversimplified and somewhat subjective. In organic evolution, intraspecies and interspecies competition doubtless have a strong effect through selective elimination; on the other hand, selection likewise may tend to mollify both types of competition. Competition usually seems to have an optimum, too little and too much both acting to the detriment of the species (p. 395) and thus creating selective pressures that guide the evolution of the competitive system itself. The effect of competition may grade all the way from a slight population pressure, which would tend to space competing individuals in relation to territory, food, or mates (see p. 413), to a drastic lethal elimination of the loser of a dual combat. It is pointed out elsewhere (pp. 692, 706) that death of individuals is not necessarily harmful to the species. The elimination of the genetically unfit individuals results in adaptive evolution.

Competition between individuals within a group, or between groups, may select genetic capacities for learning and for cooperative social organization. Guhl and Allee (1944) compared organized and unorganized flocks of hens that were presumably without important genetic differences. The organized flock had less individual combat, consumed more food, and laid more eggs. It is quite conceivable that a genetic capacity to organize through experience could be selected and result in the evolution of social organization based upon nongenetic individual or group differences (pp. 631, 632, 639, 686, 691, 693).

Simpson (1944, p. 31) says:

"From every point of view there is an essential difference between variation of individuals within a group and variation between groups, but the two are often inadequately distinguished. Natural selection, for instance, acts on both, but its action on intergroup variation can produce nothing new; it is purely an eliminating, not an originating, force. Despite its critics, the action of natural selection on intragroup (or interindividual) variation is essentially an originating force: it produces definitely new sorts of groups (populations), and the interbreeding group is the essential unit in evolution. Action on intra-individual variation also occurs, but, again, can only eliminate, not originate, types of individuals or of individual reactions."

One may take partial exception to Simpson's conclusion. Elimination of individuals may affect the genetic composition and adaptational response of the group. Elimination of groups may affect selection pressures on competing or dependent groups with consequent changes in gene incidence and patterns. It is admitted that reproductive isolation interferes with further exchange of genes between two populations with consequent inability to produce new characters through reassortment. Selection, however, guides the development of hereditary patterns, whether operating on intraspecies subgroups or on the whole species in its relation to other species, and consequently is largely responsible for progressive evolution. Otherwise, it would be difficult to explain both intraspecies and interspecies adaptations by any known principles, and both have doubtless evolved (see pp. 684, 695, 728).

Selection may be interpreted as exerting a pressure toward the determination of new genetic patterns by a succession of choices. Selection may thus produce a balance between species and between individuals within a species (p. 684), as well as between parts of an organism. Wright (1945, p. 416) concludes that selection between partially isolated groups is perhaps the greatest creative factor, making possible selection of genetic systems as wholes

rather than the mere selection of allele effects. He also states that drastic elimination of families and orders, and the compensatory adaptive radiation of successful groups, are highly creative.

We conclude that selection is the only mechanism that adequately explains the evolution of complex endoadaptation and exoadaptation and that competition exerts a strong but not exclusive influence in enhancing selection pressures. Competition usually has an optimal value in exerting selection pressures resulting in progressive evolution. Competition may be either above or below the optimum in any given case and is thus itself subject to modifying selective pressures (see Hutchinson, 1948, for a discussion of circular causal systems).

ADAPTIVE RADIATION AND CONVERGENT EVOLUTION

The student of phylogeny of any division of the animal or plant kingdom has long been aware that the main branches, at least, represent adaptive adjustments either to internal efficiencies or particular environments. For example, the subclasses of mammals are distinguished by their embryonic development—within an egg, a marsupium, or a uterus. An adaptation increasing the internal efficiency of the organism may be termed a *general adaptation*. Secondarily, the orders of mammals seem to be associated with special adjustments to the respective environments, such as food specializations, locomotor specializations, or special means of defense. Intraspecies aggregation relations are important (Chap. 23), stemming in part from the sex and family adjustments of all mammals and moving toward special herd, flock, or pack organizations in some of the orders and lower taxonomic categories. Thus, an *adaptive radiation* of internal characters, intraspecies characters, and interspecies characters is exhibited by the mammals (Fig. 234). Every large group of organisms shows similar radiate evolution. (Rapid or "explosive" radiation is discussed on pp. 600, 662).

Adaptive radiation is illustrated by many examples among the vertebrates. Mesozoic reptiles and Tertiary mammals are oft-cited cases. The bills of birds show remarkable adjustments to food types and food position (Amadon, 1947; Lack, 1947).

With their vast number of species, adaptive radiation is seen on the grandest scale among insects, and among the insects the beetles (Coleoptera) are the best example. The two most obvious general characters distinguishing the beetles—the largest order of organisms in number of families, genera, and species—are complete metamorphosis and the thickened tough elytra. The mode of metamorphosis is associated with a high degree and variety of caenogenetic adaptations, while the adaptive significance of the elytra includes relative protection from predatory attack and from environmental physical extremes. Some of the specialized adjustments resulting from radiate evolution in the beetles are listed here.

Specialized Adaptations of Beetles

Hypermetamorphosis with several larval types (*Epicauta marginata*)
Neoteny (*Phengodes plumosa*)
Sexual dimorphism (*Lucanus elephas*)
Male clasping organs (*Dytiscus fasciventris*)
Luminescent organs (*Photinus scintillans*)
Family integration (*Popilius disjunctus = Passalus cornutus*)
Stridulation (*Popilius disjunctus*)
Rapid flight (*Cicindela repanda*)
Swimming (*Dytiscus marginalis*)
Surface swimming (*Dineutes americanus*)
Water skating by secretion lowering surface tension at rear (*Stenus croceatus*)
Rapid running (*Cicindela dorsalis*)
Jumping (*Haltica chalybea*)
Fossorial legs (*Clivina dentipes*)
Flattened shape under submerged stones (*Psephenus herricki* larva)
Flattened shape under bark (*Hololepta fossularis; Denroides bicolor* larva)
Divided eye with upward and downward vision (*Gyrinus ventralis*)
Eyeless cave beetle (*Pseudanophthalmus eremita*)
Aquatic air storage under elytra (*Dytiscus fasciventris*)
Diurnal activity (*Cicindela lepida*)
Nocturnal activity (*Tetracha virginica*)
Defensive ejection (*Brachinus fumans*)
Defense by thoracic snapping (*Alaus oculatus*)
Hole-plugging phragmotic head (*Cicindela* larva)
Death feigning (*Boletotherus cornutus*)
Case bearing (*Chlamys plicata* larva)
Concealing coloration (*Goes tigrina;* Fig. 244)
Warning coloration (*Thonalmus suavis*)
Mimicry (*Calocosmus venustus*)
Caterpillar eating (*Calosoma scrutator*)
Snail eating (*Cychrus andrewsii*)
Aphid eating (*Coccinella 9-notata*)
Scale-insect eating (*Smilia misella*)

External parasitism (*Platypsylla castoris; Amblyopinus schmidti*)
Termitophilous symphile with glandular appendages (*Spirachtha mirabilis;* Fig. 259).
Myrmecophilous synechthran escaping by agility (*Tachyura incurva*)
Myrmecophilous synechthran with defensive ejection (*Megastilicus formicarius*)

Fig. 244. Cerambycid beetle (*Goes tigrina*), illustrating concealing (cryptic) coloration on the bark of a white oak, Falls Church, Virginia. (Courtesy of Bureau of Entomology and Plant Quarantine, U. S. Department of Agriculture.)

Myrmecophilous synoekete (*Batrisodes globosus*)
Myrmecophilous symphile with trichomes (*Adranes lecontei*)
Carrion eating (*Nicrophorus americanus*)
Dung rolling (*Ateuchus sacer*)
Eating dried insects (*Anthrenus museorum*)
Hair and feather eating (*Anthrenus scrophulariae*)
Leaf eating (*Leptinotarsa decemlineata*)
Leaf mining (*Chalepus dorsalis* larva)
Pith boring (*Languria mozardi*)
Boring in decayed wood (*Alaus oculatus* larva)
Boring in solid wood (*Physocnemum brevilineum*)
Seed boring (*Bruchus pisorum*)
Seed and flour eating (*Tribolium confusum*)
Acorn boring (*Balaninus nasicus*)
Pollen and nectar eating (*Chauliognathus pennsylvanicus*)
Sap eating (*Ips quadriguttatus*)
Fungus eating (*Megalodacne heros*)
Living and eating in pores of fungi (*Cylindrosella dampfi*)
Fungus cultivation (*Ips calligraphus*)

Several of these adaptations may be present in the same insect, and some of the adaptations may be characteristic of higher categories, such as families, while others may distinguish species. Certain adaptations have convergently and independently evolved in numerous phylogenetic branches. Some adaptations are highly successful and common, while others are comparatively rare.

Radiate evolution, of course, is found in physiological sequences as well as in morphological characters. The physiological adaptations of both plants and animals to desert conditions are an illustration. The differential toleration of closely related species of ants to different degrees of humidity (p. 652) probably represents radiate evolution.

Behavior radiation is sometimes apparent. Wheeler (1930) discusses the possible phylogenetic stages in the caenogenetic evolution of the pit-making behavior of ant lions (Myrmeleonidae). The ancestral Hemerobiid-like forms had predatory larvae that walked about and fed on the juices of their prey. The maxilla enclosed in a groove on the ventral side of the mandible formed a sucking tube. The next stage in evolution is represented by lethargic larvae (*Palpares*) that bury themselves in sand and detritus. The third stage is seen in larvae that make pitfalls, but move both forwards and backwards (*Myrmocaelurus*). Finally, in *Myrmeleon,* we find a sedentary, pit-making ant lion with exclusive retrograde locomotion.

When different stocks radiating into similar habitats become adapted to the same ecological factor or combination of factors, the environmental influence upon evolution through selection becomes clearer. If the compared structures are homologous, the evolution is termed *parallel;* if the compared structures are analogous, the evolution is called *convergent* (Simpson, 1937; Richardson, 1942; see p. 631, Fig. 234). It may be assumed that parallel evolution is the result of one or a few genetic changes, sometimes even of homologous genes or parallel mutations, while convergent evolution is genetically more complex, and commonly involves selection of different genetic characters in two or more species within the same environment. Parallel evolution may be somewhat adaptive, or may be neutral or nonadaptive (Gates, 1936). Convergent ecological types may sometimes be found in similar but geo-graphically separated environments, thus giving rise to the concept of *ecological equivalence* (pp. 470, 471, 492, 493). Convergence may occur in unrelated organisms that compete in the same general habitat. The factor or factors to which the convergent types have become adapted determine the degree of their competition.

A notable example of convergence of ecologically equivalent organisms in geographically separated similar habitats is found in the adaptive similarities of the marsupials of Australia to various types of placental mammals in the rest of the world. It is generally conceded that Australia became separated from the Indomalayan continental mass during the Mesozoic before the rise of placental mammals, so that only monotremes and marsupials were present in the original Australian mammalian fauna. There are only a few species of placental land mammals, in addition to bats, indigenous to Australia. These are the dingo dog, probably brought in by Pleistocene man, and a few rodents which could have been transported by natural rafts in relatively recent times (Raven, 1935). Marsupials (phalangers) reached the Celebes, but did not become established in Borneo, possibly because of more severe placental competition (Mayr, 1944). Thus, the main marsupial fauna of Australia and Tasmania evolved during the Tertiary without competition from the more efficient placental mammals, and remarkable ecological equivalents were independently evolved. The Tasmanian wolf (*Thylacinus cynocephalus*) is a marsupial convergent with the canine carnivores; the banded anteater (*Myrmecobius fasciatus*) is a marsupial convergent with the South American anteaters; the marsupial mole (*Notoryctes typhlops*) is astonishingly convergent with the golden moles of South Africa; the locomotion of the kangaroo is duplicated by various jumping rodents; and the flying phalangers are convergent with the flying squirrels and colugo (the so-called flying lemur).

Convergent evolution may be seen in the adaptations to specialized food (Fig. 164). Those mammals that have become adjusted to a diet of ants and termites have cylindrical tongues and a reduction of the teeth. Convergent evolution of this feeding apparatus in five orders of mammals is found in the spiny anteater (Monotremata),

cised; discrimination is shown by the ejection or destruction of the egg or by desertion of the nest; the evolution of resemblance between the eggs of cuckoos and those of their normal foster parents is brought about by the constant destruction, by the latter, of the cuckoos' eggs most unlike their own, and the survival of those most like them (also see p. 615).

Adaptive radiation of a single phylogenetic line into various habitats and the convergent evolution of many lines within the same habitat amply illustrate the slow effect of environmental selection pressures. Both the genetic complexity of adaptation and the subtlety of the ecological factors are evident. Mimetic resemblance has been a controversial problem in biology for a long time. This concept is still in need of more thorough analysis. Nevertheless, mimicry exemplifies the convergent evolution of species through natural selection with a convincing or at least a supporting quantity of factual material.

ECOLOGICAL POSITION AND HOMEOSTASIS

Once an organism has evolved to fit a particular combination of ecological factors, the maintenance of *ecological position* becomes an important aspect of survival and adaptation. As a result of environmental changes and periodicities such as seasonal fluctuations, certain ecological factors may move to another region, thus tending to leave the organism in an unfavorable habitat. Orientation behavior (p. 648) and locomotion are commonly adaptations that keep the animal within a moving favorable environment. Both the ability to stay within a favorable stable habitat and the ability to move with the shift of favorable conditions are adaptations for maintaining ecological position.

Many organisms hold ecological position by means of various adaptations for attachment. Examples are the suckers, thread, and streamlined shape of the larva of the black fly (Simuliidae) living in rapid water where the danger of being swept into the unfavorable pond environment is ever present. The danger of dislodgement is overcome by a great variety of animals adjusted to life on rocky sea shores by means of attachment organs or boring devices. In this connection, it is noteworthy that the holdfast cell is the first specialized somatic cell of the simple filamentous algae. The attachment organ of the large brown algae (kelps) is particularly well developed.

If the adaptations for maintaining ecological position fail, great mortality in the unfavorable environment is to be expected. This expectation is borne out by studies of elimination under extreme conditions at the borders of habitats and among accidentally dispersed individuals (Storey, 1937; Miller, 1940; Dendy, 1944; see also p. 634).

Stable environments without great fluctuation in conditions are naturally favorable habitats for organisms, provided the essentials for life are available. The deep sea and the cave environment are particularly stable in their physical conditions. Organisms have moved into these habitats in their phylogenetic history in spite of the absence of a primary plant food supply.

Habitats affording proper food and effective protection from predatory and parasitic enemies may be favorable for a given species, whereas other areas with similarity of physical conditions may be untenable. The pika (*Ochotona princeps*) of western North America lives only in talus slopes which combine protection from predatory enemies with dry shelter for the storage of their plant food. These rodents do not move more than thirty feet away from the talus environment (Hall, 1946, p. 49).

Certain desert reptiles are limited in their toleration to a range of temperature that is exceeded in their general habitat. These reptiles often show physiological adjustment to extreme temperatures, but they move to shade or burrow when the ground surface temperature approaches the tolerable limit (Cowles and Bogert, 1944).

Migrating birds find a favorable climatic environment by moving north and south with the change of seasons, or up and down in mountainous districts. It is interesting to note that the stimulus initiating migration of some birds is the length of daylight, probably acting through the pituitary gland secretory effect on the gonads and thence to behavior responses. Survival, however, is not determined by the direct response to light, but rather by climatic and food factors.

In the relatively stable temperature conditions of the tropics migration may be correlated with fluctuations of food. The pennant-winged nightjar (*Cosmetornis vexillarius*) of tropical Africa crosses the equator twice each year. It breeds in southern Africa from September to November. In February it migrates northward, often crossing the central African rain forest, to the grass country of Uganda, Uele, the Sudan, and Nigeria. This migration follows the beginning of the wet season, when winged termites, the usual food of this bird, are flying (Chapin, 1916).

Many organisms have evolved an ability to modify their environment in the direction of relative stability. The important physiological principle of *homeostasis* (maintenance of constant conditions; p. 631) is also an ecological principle. Examples are afforded by the beavers, which build dams, and by those social insects that build nests. The termite nest functions primarily to maintain a constant high humidity (Emerson, 1938; p. 428). A careful study of the humidity within a mound nest of an Australian termite (*Nasutitermes exitiosus*) was made by Fyfe and Gay (1938). They conclude:

"In brief, the structures and composition of the mound strongly tend to retain the moisture produced by the metabolism of the termites in the mound, but the temperature maintained by the living termites and the special properties of the mound material prevent the deposition of free water in the central regions. The system balances the amount of water produced by metabolism by the amount lost by diffusion and evaporation, and provides a buffer mechanism to compensate variations in the rate of production and loss."

Man, by intelligent behavior and scientific knowledge, is rapidly increasing the modification and control of his environment. He not only changes the physiographic features of the earth, but profoundly modifies the fauna and flora, and in addition develops domestic plants and animals adapted to his needs. He also tends more and more to control his social interactions and to evolve social division of labor and integration. Environmental modifications that are made without ecological knowledge or long-term social perspective may necessitate conservation measures if permanent harm or decreased homeostasis is to be avoided.

Spencer postulated an increasing independence of the environment accompanying increasing complexity of organization. One of the major aspects of adaptation is the control of the external environment through the incorporation of the environment of one organismic level within the system of a higher level (p. 694). Thus the immediate surroundings of each living unit are brought under control and allow an organic evolution of the environment (pp. 695, 698). Homeostasis is not only characteristic of the cell environment in the multicellular organism and the individual environment in the aggregated species population (p. 694), but to a certain extent it is also characteristic of the evolving ecological community (p. 728).

REGRESSIVE EVOLUTION

It has been observed that an evolutionary regression of structural adaptations may occur, leaving vestigial organs that often persist long after the function has disappeared (see Palingenesis, p. 635). Animals are known with vestigial eyes, legs, wings, lungs, teeth, mouths, and even heads, as well as innumerable other organs and organ systems.

Regressive evolution is by no means confined to a few forms living in special habitats, but is a universal phenomenon. Every living organism seems to have lost functional adaptations characteristic of its ancestors. The environment is involved in this regressive evolution, first, because special ecological selection pressures have decreased or vanished in certain instances, and, second, because there is a convergent degeneration of analogous as well as of homologous functional structures in different organisms in similar habitats.

Sometimes one function of an organ regresses and may be replaced by another function. The ears of mammals are complex organs with the elements of the middle ear traceable back through the jaw apparatus of reptiles, amphibians, and fishes to primitive gill-bar structures of the jawless fishes (Westoll, 1943a). In this instance we see a modification of breathing structures into structures for eating and finally into accessory organs of hearing, with a reduction of some parts and a development of others (Romer, 1933, pp. 308–314; see also Fig. 246).

In some cases a character may become harmful to an organism, and selection pressure will act to reduce it (pp. 637, 677). Simpson (1944, p. 88) cites instances among closely related mollusks in which some lose their shells because the shell impedes locomotion and requires much food

and in others vestigial structures may be identified and homologized with the functional organs of more primitive animals, both living and fossil.

Probably the best studied examples of convergent regression are found in the cave habitat, in which pigment (Pavan, 1946; Rasquin, 1947) and photoreceptive organs have degenerated among various animals.

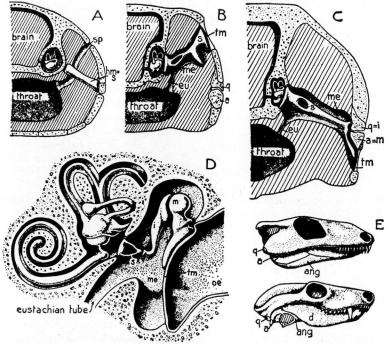

Fig. 246. The evolution of the vertebrate ear. *A*, Cross section of a fish skull through the internal ear, consisting of sacs and semicircular canals only. *B*, Cross section of an amphibian skull, showing the modification of the fish hyomandibular bone to form the stapes. *C*, Cross section of a mammal-like reptile skull. *D*, Cross section of the skull of man, showing the malleus and incus modified from skull bones that formed the jaw joint in the lower forms. *E*, A primitive land animal and a mammal-like reptile, showing the relation of the eardrum to the jaw joint. *a*, articular bone; *d*, dentary bone; *eu*, eustachian tube; *hm*, hyomandibular bone; *i*, incus; *m*, malleus; *me*, cavity of middle ear; *oe*, cavity of outer ear; *q*, quadrate bone; *s*, staples; *sp*, spiracle; *tm*, tympanic membrane. (From Romer.)

for its development, while others develop stronger shells because of their value as a protection from predators and from environmental dangers. *Chiton* with a strong well-developed shell and *Noomonia* without a shell seem to have evolved fairly recently from a common ancestor with a moderately developed shell.

In other cases, as in the eyes of cave animals, the organ does not take on another function, nor is its presence harmful, but it seems merely to lose its value to the organism. No vestige is left in some species,

Eyes are reduced in cave species of salamanders, fishes, beetles, millipedes, crayfish, isopods, amphipods, harvestmen, and spiders. Even the eye spots of cave flatworms are absent or reduced. Convergent regression is also apparent within many of these groups (Hubbs, 1938; Van Name, 1936, p. 465).

The absence of a character may be owing to its lack of development in evolutionary history (genetic absence), or to regressive evolution (probably partial genetic presence). The regression of a character in two different organisms may be analogous in some cases and homologous in others. In the instance of analogous absence of a character, the common ancestor may be presumed to have had the character in question. In the case of homologous absence of a character, the common ancestor also lacked the character. The loss of eyes in various species of cave isopods (Asellidae) exemplifies the point. These cave crustaceans were formerly classified under the generic name of *Caecidotea* on the assumption that the regressive characters were homologous. Evidence now indicates the separate convergent evolution of eyeless cave forms within the genus *Asellus,* and the polyphyletic group *Caecidotea* consequently is placed in synonymy with *Asellus* (Miller, 1933; Van Name, 1936, p. 465).

In laboratory animals, eye reduction often results from simple genetic mutations (Chase, 1944, 1945). It seems probable that reduction of eyes in cave or subterranean forms is genetically complex. Wide variation in the degree of regression of different parts of the eye and associated structures is found among the various blind species.

An ecocline within an interbreeding population of characinid fishes from eyed river forms (*Astyanax mexicanus,* Fig. 247), which have a widespread variation in eye size, to blind cave forms (*Anoptichthys jordani;* Fig. 247), has been described from La Cueva Chica in the state of San Luis Potosi in Mexico (Breder, 1942, 1943, 1943a). The gradation, from "normal" eyes of various sizes through uncovered sunken eyes and covered sunken eyes to blind forms with little eye structure, is correlated with a gradation in loss of pigmentation. These regressive characters are more pronounced the farther the fishes are from the light and the mouth of the cave. Five generations of blind forms raised in the light retained the blind condition. Mating of eyed, pigmented fishes with blind, light-colored fishes produced all eyed and pigmented forms. Specimens with degenerate eyes on only one side, however, indicate some possibility of physiological degeneration even with the same heredity.

These data suggest that a number of alleles or multiple genes control the expression of the characters under differential selection, migration, and physiological conditions of the river population compared with the cave population. The interbreeding population would indicate either a hybridization between the river and cave forms, or that the cave form is an ecotype (ecological subspecies) of the river form, rather than a separate genus, as originally described (Pavan, 1946; see p. 612). The two populations may have been isolated at one time, and this isolation may have broken down from subterranean connections or possible flooding. Then again, the two populations may be under different selection pressures at the two ends of the cline, a partial isolation at the mouth of the cave giving rise to the observed stepped cline.

Another cave fish showing greater eye reduction and absence of a connecting optic nerve has been found in the neighboring cave, Cueva de los Sabinos (Breder, 1944). It shows further regressive evolution and modification of the skull. The direction of this modification is indicated by Breder through the comparison of polar coordinates (Fig. 247) of the normal and two blind forms, as well as the reactions of the fishes to light. The sensory apparatus shows reduction in the evolutionary series except in the organs of taste, and possibly in the olfactory mechanisms (Breder and Rasquin, 1943). The eyed fishes use dark retreats only when escaping or when the dark water has a higher temperature.

The blind Cueva Chica fishes avoid light, while the blind Cueva de los Sabinos forms are indifferent to it. The river fishes school while the blind ones do not, and those from the river school with their own type on the basis of sight, thus tending to avoid cave forms. Such behavior differences may well produce the partial isolation between the river and cave types (Breder and Gresser, 1941). The tendency of eyed fishes to enter caves is the result of negative phototaxis, positive rheotaxis, and positive thermotaxis. The blind Cueva Chica forms tend to stay in the cave because they do not school, are negatively phototactic, positively rheotactic, and move toward warmer water.

It is assumed that blind individuals would not survive long in the river with normal predators. In an experimental pool, half simulating cave conditions and half open pond, out of an initial population of ten blind types and nine river types, one blind and four eyed fishes survived a season under predation pressure from frogs and insects.

Darlington (1936) described the convergent regression of the hind wings in various genera of carabid beetles, in all of which nonfunctional vestiges of the hind wings are present. The reduced hind wing is an example of a vestige of an ancestral character functional only in the adult stage. Controversy still exists over recapitulation of ancestral adult structures (de Beer, 1938, p. 58, 1940; see also p. 636).

Various external parasites such as fleas, sucking lice, and Mallophaga are wingless, and the mesothoracic wings of certain flies, including the sheep tick (*Melophagus ovinus*), have undergone extreme regressive evolution. In other examples, one sex has lost the wings, while the other retains functional wings. The female gypsy moth (*Porthetria dispar*) has well-developed wings, but is incapable of sustained flight, while the male has functional wings. The female of the white-marked tussock moth (*Hemerocampa leucostigma*) has small wing rudiments useless for flight, while the male has functional wings. The male of a termitophilous braconid (*Termitobracon emersoni*) has reduced wings, while the female has normal functional wings (Brues, 1923). Some of the summer generations of the woolly apple aphid (*Eriosoma lanigerum*) lack wings without even a vestige, while other summer generations of females may be winged, and the fall sexual generation of males and females is wingless (see pp. 123, 347, 703).

One of the most extreme cases of regressive evolution is found in the adult stage of the crustacean *Sacculina*, parasitic upon crabs. The parasite is attached to the host by rootlike projections that penetrate throughout the crab and absorb nutriment. The appendages, muscles, nerves, sensory organs, and digestive tract are all degenerate, and only the reproductive organs of the parasite are unimpaired. If it were not for the free-swimming larva with jointed appendages, it is doubtful whether the crustacean affinities of the parasite could have been recognized.

Regression of metabolic functions is probably characteristic of the evolution of parasites. One may assume that free-living forms commonly synthesize some essential

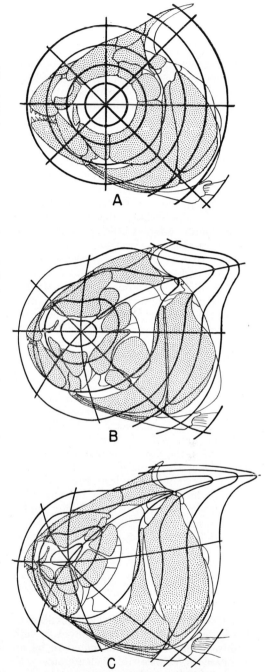

Fig. 247. Transformations of polar coordinates centered in the eye of fishes exhibiting regressive evolution. A, Normal-eyed river fish (*Astyanax mexicanus*); B, fully blind derived form (*Anoptichthys jordani*) from a cave (La Cueva Chica); C, fully blind derived form from a cave (Cueva de los Sabinos). (Redrawn from Breder.)

substances, while closely related parasites are dependent upon their hosts for certain vital essentials (p. 695).

Although the phylogeny of the viruses is almost wholly unknown, it is possible that these protein molecules, which resemble genes in their protein constitution and their autocatalytic reproduction, may be the extreme in regressive evolution of the cell, still dependent through parasitism upon the cellular constitution of other organisms (Burnet, 1945; Darlington, 1944).

In some instances, convergent degeneration of homologous structures in parasites, coupled with convergent evolution of adaptive structures, makes the study of the phylogenetic relationships difficult (Van Cleave, 1941).

Regressive evolution may take place at any level of biological integration (p. 693). The simplicity of Amoeba is probably the result of regressive evolution from the more complex Flagellata. Most of the cases of phylogenetic regression cited in the preceding pages are multicellular organisms.

The absence of a free-living tadpole stage in the Surinam toad (*Pipa pipa*), and of the free-living larva of the tsetse fly (*Glossina*) and the sheep tick (*Melophagus ovinus*) must be interpreted as regressive evolution of a certain stage in the life cycle of the metamorphic organism. In these viviparous flies, the larvae are nourished within the body of the female and pupate immediately after emergence from the mother.

Stages in the life cycle of cyclomorphic populations may also be lost during evolution. Many rusts (Uredinales) exhibit a rather definite tendency toward a simplification of their life history as compared with that of the ancestral types with greater polymorphism, more highly developed sexuality, and heterecious adjustments (p. 614). The life cycle of the Anthozoa and of hydra, with polyps only, and possibly of the Scyphozoa with reduced polyps or with medusae only, may be presumed to be an evolution from ancestral coelenterates with metagenetic life cycles.

Integrated polymorphic populations such as those found in the social Hymenoptera have on numerous occasions lost their worker caste in association with the evolution of social parasitism. Examples include the wasp, *Vespula austriaca*, which lives in the nest of *Vespula rufa* in Europe; *Vespula adulterina*, which lives in the nest of *Vespula arenaria* in the United States (Taylor, 1939); various species of the bee genus *Psithyrus*, which parasitize species of the bumblebee genus, *Bombus*, and doubtless have evolved from *Bombus;* and ants of fourteen genera and seventeen species, including *Wheeleriella santschii*, a parasite of *Monomorium salomonis* in North Africa, and *Anergates atratulus*, a parasite of *Tetramorium cœspitum* in Europe. Many gradations are known that indicate the phylogenetic stages leading toward extreme social parasitism.

Degeneration of the nesting and parental instincts has occurred convergently several times among birds (Friedmann, 1929; Miller, 1946). Examples are known among cowbirds (Icteridae), cuckoos (Cuculidae), weavers (Ploceidae), honeyguides (Indicatoridae), and ducks (Anatidae). These are all extreme examples in which the parasites lay their eggs in the nests of other unrelated species, and the young are raised by the foster parents. Closely related species show various degrees of loss of the nesting and parental instincts that may be considered to represent phylogenetic series. First came the loss of nest construction (*Molothrus badius*). Second, the brooding and feeding of the young was lost (*M. rufo-axillaris*). Finally, territoriality and pair formation disappeared (*M. ater*).

The gradual evolution of infertility, hybrid inviability, or noncrossability, often exhibited between species, is to be considered a regression of the reproductive function between populations, with a consequent permanent reproductive isolation between the species (pp. 622, 623). This phenomenon is so common that many authors define the species as physiologically incapable of interbreeding with other species, either because of psychological, physiological, or genetic incapacities (Dobzhansky, 1941, p. 373; Mayr, 1942, p. 120; see also p. 626).

The genetic basis for the evolution of infertility and inviability has been discussed particularly by Muller (1942). Interesting cases are known among plants in which fertility has regressed through a lack of chromosomal balance, but may be regained through allopolyploidy (Darlington, 1940; see also p. 625). Polyploid species may arise among plants because of self-fertilization or vegetative reproduction, but would appear rarely if at all among exclusively sexually reproducing animals. Parthenogenetic generations with an occasional sexual generation might allow speciation through polyploidy in certain animals (Hughes-Schrader, 1948; p. 623).

Examples illustrating the gradations toward intersterility or psychological impairment of interbreeding between contiguous populations are to be seen in circular chains of subspecies such as the deer mouse, *Peromyscus maniculatus,* and the Old World warbler, *Phylloscopus trochiloides,* in which crossing occurs between each contiguous subspecies, except that where the two ends of the chain happen to occupy the same territory they are reproductively isolated (Mayr, 1942, pp. 183, 184; see also p. 610).

Porter (1941) experimented with frog hybrids produced by fertilization of enucleated eggs. The embryos showed abnormal development when the eggs of northern forms of *Rana pipiens* were fertilized by spermatozoa of southern forms, or the eggs of southern forms were fertilized by spermatozoa from northern forms. The amount and direction of the abnormality were correlated with the amount and direction of the difference in climatic adaptation of the respective parental species. Muller (1942), in discussing this case, states "that the genotypic difference responsible for the hybrid incapacitation did not arise as a consequence of selection for that effect itself, but for something quite different, namely, in the given case, adaptation to development at higher or lower temperatures, respectively."

In some instances, selection against a character that has become harmful may occur (pp. 637, 673). At the same time, direct positive selection pressure does not account adequately for the evolution of a great many cases of loss of function, although a slight selection in favor of economy of growth is possible.

Pertaining to this economy theory of regression, Walls (1942) states:

"An old idea was that where the eye had become useless, there was a positive incentive for eliminating the organ, since this would save energy both in adulthood and—especially—during growth. This notion seems ridiculous nowadays, for the proportion of a growing animal's food-intake which goes to enlarge the eye is negligible. Most of the energy released from food goes for motor and secretory activity, and only a very small part of the food is converted into new protoplasm. Nor does the disappearance of an eye leave a hole in the head—its volume is occupied by tissues (mainly muscle) which consume just as much energy as the eye had done."

A number of other theories have been advanced to explain regressive evolution (see Breder, 1944, for a review). In some cases the character undergoing reduction might be harmful in a new habitat (p. 673). The eye of a mole might be a source of infection in a subterranean burrow, but the eye is likewise reduced in burrowing snakes in which the ocular scale prevents any danger of infection.

Needham (1930) claimed that all vestigial organs have an embryological function through induction of growth of other parts. In some organs, such as the notochord in vertebrate embryos, embryological functions have been demonstrated, but this theory places a tremendous burden upon investigators to establish embryological utility for all the relict adaptations known, such as the embryonic teeth and pelvic bones of whales, or the showy flowers of some species of dandelions (*Taraxacum*) that produce their seeds through obligatory apomixis* (Huxley, 1942).

Simpson (1944, p. 39) says "that degenerating structures are highly variable" and "this may be advanced as an empirical evolutionary generalization." The comparative variation of functional molars and nonfunctional wisdom teeth in man is an example. If selection pressures were operating upon a functional degeneration, variability would probably be less.

Several generalizations, each the result of considerable experimental evidence, seem, in combination, to give an adequate understanding of the mechanisms of regressive evolution. (1) Each gene or genetic factor affects many characters. Genes with manifold effects are said to be *pleiotropic* (Dobzhansky and Holz, 1943). (2) Each character is affected by many genes. These characters are said to be *multiple factor* or *polygenic characters* (Mather, 1943). (3) Mutation of any single gene may occur at a

---

* *Apomixis* is development without fertilization, but with retention of the sexual structures.

statistically predictable rate. This tendency is referred to as *mutation pressure*. (4) The effect of the majority of mutations on a functional character is commonly deleterious or degenerative (Timoféeff-Ressovsky, 1940; Mather, 1943; Silow, 1945). (5) Selection acts upon the whole organismic unit or population as a system as well as upon the parts somewhat independently (Sturtevant, 1938; Emerson, 1939).

It follows that elimination or weakening of a selective pressure may in time result in degeneration of the functional character through the action of mutation pressure (p. 696). Also, if selection favors an increased development of one character while another character has a diminished survival value in a given habitat, there will be a shift in the alleles in many gene systems with a consequent degeneration of the character that is losing importance. This secondary effect of positive selection pressure is probably responsible for all rapid regressive evolution of a harmless character, because the effect of mutation pressure in the absence of selection would be a slow process (Wright, 1929, 1932; Fisher, 1930, p. 20). Through the combined action of these principles, we have a reasonable explanation of nonfunctional vestigial structures and some recapitulative development (see Robb, 1937; Wilson, 1941; Holmes, 1944a; see also p. 636).

At the same time, we can understand why relict adaptations or vestigial structures are commonly still visible after their function has ceased. The complex genetic system basic to the development of a complex adaptive character cannot be eliminated suddenly without affecting many other vital characters and processes. Large numbers of the genes have become so much involved in the development of other adaptive characters through the action of selection over long periods of time that much of the gene complex activating the growth of a character that has lost survival value may be retained, even though portions of the gene pattern may have become modified as the selection pressure fluctuated.

Proof that the genes may be largely intact even when a given character has undergone evolutionary degeneration may be demonstrated in the segmented, sexual, and social forms. If one segment has legs reduced, while other segments retain legs, obviously the genes for legs are not lost, and the reduction must depend upon a threshold of development. This threshold, in turn, may be determined by other genes and thus be inherited (Wright, 1934, 1934a). If one sex has lost its wings, while the other sex retains them, the loss is not through the loss of the gene complex, but rather in developmental thresholds under the influence of genetic, physiologic, or ecologic factors. An apterous worker ant must have the gene pattern for the functional wings of its parents. Similarly, blind and wingless soldier termites must have the basic genetic system that produces functional eyes and wings in their parents, even though this soldier type is characteristic of its genus, family, and order (Emerson, 1947). We are led to the conclusion that organisms retain ancient genes that have been selected and incorporated into complex interrelated systems and that gave rise to adaptive characters in ancient environments, even though the visible vestiges of these relict adaptations may have disappeared entirely.

Inasmuch as genes not only initiate the development of morphological attributes within a proper physiological and ecological environment, but are also foundational to the development of physiological patterns (Needham, 1930) and behavior (Emerson, 1938), we should expect to find vestigial activities and recapitulative tendencies in the physiology and psychology of organisms (p. 636).

The interrelationship of the genetic, physiologic, psychologic, and ecologic influences in regressive evolution has often been misunderstood. The Ozark cave salamander (*Typhlotriton spelaeus*) demonstrates some of these interrelationships. The eggs of this salamander are laid in pools outside the caves and develop into eyed and pigmented larvae (Noble and Marshall, 1929; Bishop, 1944). Normally these larvae move into the caves. In the dark, the eyelids become fused and much pigmentation is lost, but, if experimentally kept in the light, these cave modifications do not develop. A closely related and possibly ancestral species (*T. nereus*) lives in the same vicinity, but usually not near caves. If it enters a cave it also loses much of its pigment, but its eyelids do not fuse. In both cases the genes for eyes and pigment are obviously present. Physiologic thresholds are under the influence of modifying genes during evolution. Hence, we may expect to find eyed and pigmented salamanders that do not become blind or pale in the absence of light, blind and pale cave salamanders with all the requisite genes for normal eye and pigment development, and eyeless white salamanders that breed true in perpetual light.

Leach (1944) suggests that the loss of the forebrain during regressive evolution of amphioxus has resulted in the loss of the pituitary gland with its thyrotropic hormones. The thyroid (endostyle) is thus supposed to have degenerated and carried with it other systems dependent upon it. In criticism of this theory, it should be emphasized that endocrine effects in the invertebrate chordates are poorly understood, and it may well be that they have not evolved so far as in the vertebrates. Secondly, if the endocrines had as important general functions as they show in the higher vertebrates, it is unlikely that they would degenerate, even though the brain and head were otherwise useless. Amphioxus probably evolved from an ancestor with a much better developed head, but, in becoming adapted to a sedentary sand-burrowing life, the selection pressure for maintaining head structures was possibly lessened. The head could have undergone regressive evolution as new adaptations arose, but only if the survival value of its other functions were not so great as that of the new balanced system as a whole. Selection is surely sorting organisms in terms of developmental processes, physiological integration, and ecological adaptations.

Dollo's so-called "law of the irreversibility of evolution" (see W. K. Gregory, 1936; Huxley, 1942, p. 503; Cave and Haines, 1944) may apply to the loss of complex adaptations. Reversible mutations certainly occur, but it would usually require too many within a balanced system to have a genetically similar structure evolve, once it has regressed. Fish gills do not reappear in whales, even though the embryo recapitulates gill clefts. The gill of the primitive aquatic arthropod does not reappear in the aquatic insect after a long ancestry on land. We find, instead, a convergent adaptation undoubtedly with a different genetic background (Muller, 1939).

If slight genetic inhibitions prevent the growth of a structure that has been lost, it is possible that modification of these inhibiting genes might allow the character to reappear. For example, Wright (1934a) raised heterozygous guinea pigs that developed the primitive pentadactyl foot. Castle produced true-breeding pentadactyl guinea pigs in 1906 that were apparently atavistic. Robb (1937) discusses cases of apparent atavistic appearance of the side toes in modern horses.

There is no more reason to look upon the degeneration of locomotor and sensory organs in a parasite as something to be decried than to regret the evolution of animals from a chlorophyl-bearing ancestor, with the consequent loss of the beautiful capacity to carry on photosynthesis (Freeman, 1937; see p. 254). Parasites are dependent upon their hosts, animals are dependent upon plants, green plants are dependent upon direct radiant energy. Regressive evolution does not lead to extinction any more than does progressive evolution. It may lead to dependence and necessary integration with more complete biological systems (p. 695). So does progressive evolution. The scientist has no valid reasons for an emotional attitude toward these evolutionary tendencies that move the organism in the direction of harmonious adjustment to a changing environment.

In summary, regressive evolution is a universal phenomenon affecting many former adaptive characters of organisms and organismic systems. It is the result of principles that apply also to progressive evolution, and the explanation of the process gives us a better perspective on many aspects of natural selection.

RETARDATION OF EVOLUTION

Considerable differences in evolutionary rate occur among different organisms, and an understanding of the factors involved in retardation should explain the existence of primitive relicts ("living fossils") and should also place the causes of evolutionary change in sharper relief.

Simpson (1944, p. 144) follows Handlirsch in classifying relicts as (1) numerical (groups once abundant and now rare), (2) geographic (groups once widespread and now geographically restricted), (3) phylogenetic (ancient groups exhibiting little evolution), and (4) taxonomic (groups once highly varied and now reduced to a few species). A single relict species may fit several of these categories, and all these types are probably indications of evolutionary retardation as the result of competition with more successful and more recent groups (p. 661) or of rapid changes in the habitat occupied.

The most extreme examples of relicts are those monotypic families and orders that the systematists recognize as single representatives of large branches springing from near the base of the phylogenetic tree. Examples include the ginkgo tree (*Ginkgo biloba*), the only remaining species of the order Ginkgoales, which, through the possession of motile sperm cells, represents the primitive transition leading to the higher seed plants in which a passive sperm nucleus is transported in the pollen tube; the recently discovered lobe-finned fish (*Latimeria chalumnae*) found off South Africa, which belongs to a group that had been thought to be extinct since Cretaceous times; the famous *Sphenodon* of New Zealand, a generalized reptile of the order Rhynchocephalia, long known from fossils found in other parts of the world; and the primitive Australian termite, *Mastotermes darwiniensis,* the sole living species of the family Mastotermitidae, which displays many transitional characters connecting modern termites to their roachlike ancestors.

Besides these monotypic branches, numerous groups of primitive types may have a number of living species, but show little indication of evolutionary change over long periods of time. Illustrative examples are provided by the horseshoe crabs, branching from the base of the chelicerate arthropods, and including the Atlantic and Indo-Pacific genus *Limulus,* which has existed from Triassic times to the present; the brachiopod genus *Lingula,* which exhibits little evolution since the Ordovician; the lungfishes, with the genera *Neoceratodus, Lepidosiren,* and *Protopterus,* little changed from the Triassic to the present; and the opossums, only slightly modified from their Cretaceous forebears.

Simpson (1944) shows that land carnivores have, on the average, evolved about ten times faster than pelecypods. He also concludes (on p. 143) that slowly evolving

(*bradytelic*) groups have the longest geological history; lines evolving at a standard rate (*horotelic*) are less likely to survive over long periods; and the rapidly evolving (*tachytelic*) groups become extinct more quickly. Relicts may be found in groups exhibiting all these evolutionary rates.

Stebbins (1945), after discussing a number of bradytelic higher plants, concludes that slow evolution is brought about by population structure, environment, and type of adaptation, rather than through inherent genetic properties of the species (see Orthogenesis p. 638).

The known factors that might tend to produce stability or retardation of evolution over long intervals may be listed as follows: (1) long life cycle; (2) prevention of hereditary reassortment; (3) lack of mutation; (4) small, relatively homozygous populations; (5) equilibrium as a consequence of Mendelian mechanisms; (6) lack of partial or complete reproductive isolation; (7) absence of certain types of selection pressure, particularly competition; (8) the limitations of successful mechanisms; (9) an excellent, balanced adaptation to a relatively stable and long-existing habitat, with severe selective elimination of new variations (see Cain, 1944, pp. 376–382).

Long time intervals between generations might be presumed to retard evolution (pp. 600, 654, 662; see also Worthington, 1937), but Simpson (1944, p. 137) indicates no paleontological proof that number of generations influences rate of evolution in a given period. The rapid emergence of strains among the asexual bacteria may be in part the result of a rapid sequence of generations.

Reassortment being impossible in asexual or completely parthenogenetic forms (p. 628), variability is possible only through mutation. With the absence of sexual reproduction, therefore, we may expect to find the pace of evolution slowed or stopped, unless there is a compensatory increase in mutation pressure (see p. 641), population size, or reduction of time between generations. A possible example of such stability is found in the flagellate protozoan (*Macrotrichomonas pulchra*) occurring in the intestines of widely separated species of the termite genus *Glyptotermes* (Kirby, 1942), that probably originated in

Mesozoic times (Fig. 243). The habitat of these intestinal flagellates is also extremely stable, and adaptation may be so high as to prevent the survival of genetic modifications.

Mutation is a basic cause of variability upon which evolution depends (see pp. 600, 601, 638, 662). Genes can be detected only through their mutation. If a gene has not mutated, the geneticist is unable to gather evidence of its existence. General effects of groups of genes may be postulated from a study of chromosome deletions (McClintock, 1944).

Differences in mutation rate suggest a differential in gene stability. The relative stability of plasmagenes, plastogenes, nuclear genes, and chromosome systems may also differ (Darlington, 1944; see also p. 602). We may thus expect some hereditary units to maintain chemical structure over long periods of time, ages that would make genetic homology conceivable through long geological intervals. In some cases it may be assumed that the whole gene maintains stability with constant physiological effects (Cushing, 1945), while other genes mutate to produce divergent physiological effects in the development of the same character. In other instances the gene may mutate toward a series of alleles while the basic homologous gene structure is maintained together with certain of its physiological effects.

From the idea that the observed genes constitute the whole of the genetics of a structure, some authors have assumed that homology does not necessarily rest upon the genetic constitution (Harland, 1933; de Beer, 1938), a conclusion not in accord with the probable stability of many genes or the general effects of the genes in an allelic series. In conformity with the theory of the high mutation pressure of every locus during geological time, the explanation of the continuance of a homologous organ would be based upon the selective incorporation of each mutation. In an organ like the vertebrate eye, seemingly homologous in all vertebrates since Ordovician times, it would not be assumed, according to this theory, that the basic genes initiating the development of the eye are the same or similar in fish and mammal. Rather, it would be assumed that all had mutated many times, but that each muta-

tion was selected in terms of its function in the eye and gradually replaced the older genes that may have served a similar function somewhat less efficiently in the ancient eye (or organism). This concept places the burden of the explanation of homologous structures maintained through long geological ages upon selection rather than upon genetic stability.

Trivial unadaptive structures may be characteristic of higher taxonomic groups through millions of years of speciation. Emerson (1942a) cites the case of a useless subsidiary tooth in the mandible of certain primitive termites (*Stolotermes:* Hodotermitidae) that is also characteristic of an entire somewhat advanced family (Rhinotermitidae). If secondarily produced by a favored gene complex, such characters may be explained by gene stability, while it would be difficult to think that direct selection could be sufficiently strong to maintain them. If homology is based upon constant selection, there is no reason to assume that the secondary, nonadaptive effects of genes would remain stable while the selection of numerous mutations is causing a shift in the gene pattern. With this evidence of the stability of genes, we may still rest the concept of homology upon some degree of constancy of the genetic system through geological time.

Inbreeding in small populations may reduce the field of variability through the homozygous fixation of genes and the prevention of reassortment (Wright, 1940a, p. 167; see also pp. 407, 602).

As a consequence of the Mendelian mechanism, Hardy (1908) pointed out that the relative frequencies of various genes in the population are maintained from generation to generation, regardless of the absolute values of their initial frequencies. This equilibrium is to be expected only in a sexually reproducing, random breeding population in which the genotypes are equivalent with respect to natural selection, in which immigration does not occur, and in which mutation pressure is zero. This concept has been reconsidered and somewhat modified by Wright (1931), Haldane (1932), Fisher (1930), and Kollross (1944). Hardy's theory pertains to the average condition only without disturbing factors. Under natural conditions it would be expected

encies would fluctuate
one, and in time would
from the incidence that
ristic of the population.
eeding population, the
more likely is it that the gene frequencies
would conform to Hardy's theory; and the
smaller the population, the sooner would
fixation of chance variations occur. The
effective size of the population depends in
part upon the sexual behavior and the numbers of breeding males and females, and
may be closer to the smaller of these two
numbers, particularly to the number of
females.

The various forms of reproductive isolation between populations result in the
divergence of species (Chap. 32, p. 606). A
lack of reproductive isolation would prevent the branching of the phylogenetic
tree, and all evolution would be linear. In
the infraspecies populations, a lack of partial isolation in large randomly breeding
groups would result in the swamping of
each favorable combination as soon as it
arose (pp. 602, 646), and no selection between competing races could occur (pp.
603, 616, 649). Partial and complete reproductive isolation tends to speed evolution. Lack of isolation would have a retarding effect.

If an organism has been able to adjust
to an environment in which competition
does not develop to any great extent, it
may survive with a primitive organization
through ages without becoming extinct or
evolving adaptations to fit a more rigorous
habitat (see pp. 655, 662). It is characteristic of primitive relicts to be either
geographically or ecologically protected.
Sphenodon was able to survive in New
Zealand, where mammalian predators were
absent before the advent of white man.
Several primitive termites, notably the
Termopsinae, survive in temperate regions
out of competition with the more highly
specialized tropical termites. The ginkgo
tree would probably have become extinct
in recent centuries were it not for its protection by man in the temple gardens of
the Orient. The monotremes of Australia
and New Guinea would probably not have
survived competition of placental mammals.
It is likely that they have survived marsupial competition through specialized aquatic

life in the case of the duckbill, and spiny
protection in *Echidna* (Gregory, 1947).

It is not by chance that Australia has the
most abundant fauna of primitive types—
notably primitive mammals, primitive ants,
and primitive termites. All these Australian
animals evolved during Mesozoic times and
were cut off during the Cretaceous from
the rest of the world. The primitive groups
of Australia survived to the present time
with little change in the absence of competition from the more highly evolved Tertiary relatives arising on other continents.
Many primitive mammals of South America became extinct with the Pliocene invasion by superior northern groups. The
survivors either had good protection (porcupines, armadillos), were nocturnal (opossums), or had evolved specialized adaptations to little occupied niches (sloths, anteaters). Of course, such survival of primitive forms results from many subtle and
complicated factors that can no longer be
fully analyzed, but the facts indicate the
importance of lack of competition in the
survival of otherwise primitive organisms
that have evolved slowly, compared with
their contemporaries in more competitive
environments. Absence of competition allows slowly evolving forms to survive.

Specialization results in limitations toward further evolution. A species with its
current organization may reach an evolutionary *cul de sac* because its possible field
of adaptive values has already been exploited, and change giving advantage over
other organisms becomes improbable (see
pp. 632, 643). The more complete the
adaptation to a given set of stable ecologic
factors, the less chance there is for further
evolution (Fig. 229).

Simpson (1944, p. 149) says: "Organic
change is so nearly universal that a state
of 'evolutionary motion' is inherent in phyletic survival. It is probable that the continuous application of some sort of force,
such as selection pressure, is necessary to
maintain a state of rest and that the mere
removal of restraint may be followed by
acceleration" (see pp. 662, 666).

Selection tends to stabilize the species
by the elimination of deleterious genes over
long periods of time (Haldane, 1936).
The stronger the selection pressure, particularly on small populations, the more the
field of variability is limited. Selection acts

upon the various levels of gene integration and gene pattern, sometimes eliminating the new and less effective variations, sometimes eliminating the older and less effective systems. Effectivity will vary with changes in the organismic system and in the habitat. If a form is highly adapted to a durable stable environment, genetic modification is more likely to be selectively eliminated than if the organism is less well adapted (Simpson, 1944, p. 141, 149), and a rapid adaptive evolution may be followed by a retardation of the further evolution of both endoadaptations and exoadaptations.

Lack of ecological opportunity results in a retardation of evolution (pp. 600, 662). The more developed the special adaptation, the more likely will be the extinction of the form when the environment changes. The more rapidly the environment changes, the greater are the number of forms that become extinct.

For purposes of analysis, experimental control of different factors, or observation of natural instances in which only one or a few factors vary and all others remain constant, is desirable. Evolution usually occurs as the result of a large number of variable pressures influencing the populations at the same time and at different times, and the isolation of all such factors may be practically impossible in any given case. Not only is there a multiplicity of factors with varying quantitative effects, but these factors strike a certain balance in successfully evolving organisms, so that variation in one may influence a reciprocal variation in another (Fig. 229; see also Mather, 1943). Wright (1932) summarized this viewpoint as follows:

"The most general conclusion is that evolution depends on a certain balance among its factors. There must be gene mutation, but an excessive rate gives an array of freaks, not evolution; there must be selection, but too severe a process destroys the field of variability, and thus the basis for further advance; prevalence of local inbreeding within a species has extremely important evolutionary consequences, but too close inbreeding leads merely to extinction. A certain amount of cross-breeding is favorable but not too much. In this dependence on balance the species is like a living organism."

Balance between opposing systematic pressures may produce stability. The tendency toward the selective elimination of a gene may be opposed by its reintroduction by mutation or immigration. The frequency of two alleles of the same gene may be maintained by selection favoring the heterozygote over either homozygote. There may be little chance of particularly favorable mutations occurring if they can arise only through a succession of unfavorable mutations. Wright (1948) says that equilibrium frequencies of genes are restored through such balanced pressures resulting in the stability of subspecies and species in spite of continuing mutations, continual interbreeding at a low rate with neighboring populations, and continuing selection.

An examination of the factors negating evolutionary change gives perspective on the mechanisms of evolutionary advance. Many existing organisms have evolved slowly or have stopped evolving. Some are on the verge of extinction. As is true in evolutionary progress and regression, retardation results from numerous factors, often acting in complicated interrelationship (Wright, 1948a).

ORGANISMIC LEVELS AND SELECTION

Biologists have become increasingly aware that there are different levels of organismic integration and that these levels may be arranged in phylogenetic order. Higher levels incorporate lower levels (Schmid, 1941; Gerard, 1942; Needham, 1943). Such levels are discussed under a number of terms: the gene and virus with molecular organization; the cell with protoplasmic parts; the cell colony and multicellular organism with cellular parts; the metamorphic organism with larval and adult stages; the colonial organism with zooids, and the metameric organism with segments.

Where direct protoplasmic connections are broken, intraspecies population units at various levels of integration are recognized and referred to under various terms: the species composed of individual organisms; the cyclomorphic population with periodic polymorphism; the aggregation, school, flock, and herd with gradations of population integration (p. 393); the sex pair with sexual dimorphism; the family with reciprocal adjustments between parents and offspring; and the society in the strict sense (Chap. 24) with marked division of labor between adults of the same sex (p. 687).

These intraspecies populations may be integrated through physiologic or behavioristic mechanisms that are nongenetic as such. The capacity to differentiate may be genetic, but the different resulting forms may not differ genetically. On the other hand, some of these populations may be dimorphic or polymorphic with a genetic difference for each form.

Where germinal continuity is broken, interspecies populations are coordinated largely through coaction (pp. 437, 698). Terms such as predator, prey, parasite, host, guest, symbiote, biocoenose, society (in the wide sense), sere, biome, community, ecosystem, and so forth, are used for the parts and for the whole units. The terms, both for the various integrated units and their parts, are often inexact and grade into one another. Further classification by addition and division may be carried on indefinitely.

At this point we shall consider the fact that these levels of individual and group coordination are subject to selection as units and are often under the influence of different selection pressures for different arrangements within the same organismic system. The existence of complex internal adaptation between parts of an organism or population, with division of labor and integration within the whole system, is explicable only through the action of selection upon whole units from the lowest to the highest. Conversely, these integrated levels would not exist as entities unless selection acted upon each whole system.*

At the species level, genes that tended to mutate excessively would be deleterious to the population system, even though some of the characters produced by such genes might be advantageous to the individual. One might, therefore, expect selection to exert a control over the rate of mutation. An optimal rate of mutation and recombination is probably adaptive, and the rate is maintained through selection of the sur-

viving species even though many individual variants are eliminated (Sturtevant, 1939; Just, 1944; Simpson, 1944, p. 37).

Wright (1937a) points out: "It is the harmonious development of all characteristics that determines the success of an organism, not the absolute grades of the separate characters and still less the composition with respect to a single series of alleles." This conclusion doubtless applies to all organismic systems and is basic to our understanding of organismic integration and survival at all levels—the individual, the intraspecies population, the interspecies population, and the community.

Density is a phenomenon that has a series of optimal ranges for a given species under environmental conditions that regularly recur, so that there may be undercrowding as well as overcrowding with greater survival at the optimum (p. 395). One would therefore expect that selection would operate on those aspects of natality, mortality, and dispersal that have a genetic basis. Doubtless many environmental factors also directly affect the abundance of any given species and its balance and unbalance in the community (Kendeigh and Baldwin, 1937; Errington, 1934).

If selection does sort some genetic traits influencing population size, population numbers would often be as characteristic of species and even some higher categories as are other adaptive characters. Populations of individuals should theoretically show growth and maturity as do populations of cells in a multicellular organism (pp. 264, 282; Chap. 21). Although this field of investigation is in its infancy, and many complexities confuse the analysis of any given case (Thompson, 1939; Errington, 1946), there are some definite indications that such intrinsic control of population numbers has evolved. The more integrated the population, the more it takes on supraorganismic aspects, and the greater is the tendency for inherited and adaptive density control (Strandskov and Ondina, 1947).

Numerous authors have questioned the possibility of certain evolutionary tendencies because they have concentrated upon a part of the system instead of recognizing the unity of the whole species system. Elton (1930, p. 47) points out that in large scale emigration most of the migrants

---

* This action of selection upon whole population systems was sensed by Darwin, Spencer, and Weismann, and has been elaborated and analyzed in the light of modern biology by more recent authors (Marshall, 1936; Wright, 1930, 1937, 1945; Sturtevant, 1938; Allee, 1938, 1940, 1943; Emerson, 1939, 1939a, 1942, 1943, 1947; Mather, 1943; T. Park, 1945; Gerard and Emerson, 1945; Howells, 1947).

perish, but he also says, contrary to our opinion, that the instinct to emigrate cannot have been produced by natural selection (see pp. 642, 645, 671).

Another aspect of the evolution of populations deserves attention. Pearl (1930a) stated that somatic differences that do not rest upon a genetic basis would have no evolutionary significance. Suppose that an emigrating lemming did not differ genetically from a nonemigrating one (this has not been proved or disproved so far as we know). If the sacrifice of the emigrating individuals had survival value to the population as a whole, emigrating behavior might well evolve under natural selection of the whole system. The genetic pattern might produce emigrating behavior only at certain environmental thresholds that would behavioristically differentiate the individuals that emigrate from those that remain on the breeding grounds. Populations without this genetic characteristic would perish because the emigration would not diminish the population in conformity to the food supply (pp. 286, 706). The population in which some individuals show emigrating behavior under adverse conditions would survive and perpetuate the genetic pattern because of the sacrifice of the emigrants. The tendency in some species of locusts or grasshoppers to develop solitary and emigrating phases (p. 543), one of which regularly invades new territory where it ultimately perishes, may be the result of evolution involving the sacrifice of large numbers of the population.

The number of pollen spores produced by pines, which depend on the random distribution of pollen by wind, is much greater than the number of spores per given unit produced by an insect-pollinated plant, such as the yucca or the tulip tree. Fishes that spread their eggs at random and take no care of the young lay many more eggs per fish than do fishes that make nests and protect their young. Birds that are subjected to a greater mortality rate tend to have larger clutch-sizes (Moreau, 1944; see also p. 701). These balanced interrelationships of a whole population to its environment are best understood as the result of evolutionary adaptation through natural selection of population units (p. 684).

Wright (1932, 1948a) postulated that the breeding population size together with a given breeding structure may have an optimum for evolutionary advance—large enough to promote variability and to allow an effective selection pressure, and small enough to allow a certain random fluctuation of gene frequencies. With a genetic control of population numbers, size of population might become characteristic of surviving species if other factors remain fairly constant. Baker (1947) states that "those factors which reduce the reproductive capacity of a strain are *per se* selected against," a conclusion with which we are not in agreement.

There may be an evolutionary trend in the direction of a smaller reproductive potential associated with increased shelter and protection (p. 274), as in tree-nesting birds. Or the trend may be in the opposite direction. A larger reproductive potential is often associated with greater vicissitudes in the life cycle, as in the parasitic roundworms (Fig. 251) as compared with free-living roundworms (Baylis, 1938), and in tapeworms (Fig. 250) as contrasted with free-living flatworms. Mutualism within the population may be more beneficial in large colony populations, as may be seen in the more specialized termite and ant societies in contrast with their primitive ancestral societies or with their solitary ancestors (p. 272).

There seems to be a general tendency for the population numbers (or biomass) of social insect colonies to increase in the evolution of vegetarian and scavenger types, and to decrease in those that have evolved social exploitation (i.e., thief ants, slave-making ants, or socially parasitic ants, bees, and wasps), while the population sizes of the colonies of predatory species are roughly between those of these other feeding types.

The evolution of increase or decrease in size (number of cells) of an organism, and size of a population (number of individuals) may result from somewhat similar evolutionary forces. Both trends in either individual organisms or populations may result in adaptation to and even control over environmental fluctuations in particular instances.

Those groups that exhibit *cyclomorphosis* indicate clearly the result of selection on species populations. Cyclomorphosis (p. 118) is a term usually used for cyclic changes in form exhibited by entomostracans (Crustacea) (Fig. 21). The term may be appropriately applied to all populations exhibiting periodic polymorphism. Examples include malarial protozoans (p. 701), flukes (Fig. 249), tapeworms (Fig. 250), and aphids (pp. 123, 612, 703). Cyclomorphic species exhibit a life cycle of a population and not just of an individual metamorphic organism (Huff and Coulston, 1946).

Many generations may occur in a year among Cladocera adapted to flotation, turbulence, and locomotion near the surface of fresh water (Coker, 1939). Density and viscosity of the water change with temperature. Pure liquid water is most dense at 4° C. and is less dense above and below this temperature (p. 93). Winter forms need less adjustment to flotation and motion than summer forms, and certain species of Cladocera (*Bosmina*) undergo seasonal changes in shape, offering more surface to the less dense and less viscous warmer water and less surface to the more viscous colder water. Certain plankton protozoa (*Ceratium*), rotifers (*Asplanchna*), and diatoms likewise exhibit seasonal cyclomorphic changes in form.

It is obvious that the genetic constitution may be identical in these distinct phases of the population life cycle. Reproduction is asexual or parthenogenetic for most of the generations, so that thousands of individuals belonging to a single clone carry identical heredity, while the generations within the clone differ strikingly in their morphologic and physiologic adaptations.

The evolution of such cyclic polymorphism must be explained through the selection of a genetic system in the species as a whole that responds to different stimuli by differential development in different environments, just as different structural adaptations develop in the soma of an organism from genetically identical cells in different physiological settings. In other words, the winter-adapted cladoceran must not only respond to the environment of the individual in January, but must have a genetic pattern capable of responding differently to the summer environment several generations hence. It follows that the unit of selection cannot be only the genetic pattern of the individual in its habitat, but must be also the genetic pattern of the whole species population in its seasonal environment (see also p. 664).

Likewise the population of a species of malarial protozoan is selected as a unit both in relation to its mosquito host and to its vertebrate host environment and to different tissues in each (p. 701). In malarial and other parasites, the physiologic adaptation of different generations of the same species is both subtle and intricate.

A great many aggregations of the higher vertebrates exhibit individual behavior differences that unify the population system. As with physiologic and instinctive reactions in some types of emigrating populations (lemmings, grasshoppers) and in cyclomorphic species, conditioned, learned, and intelligent behavior is not necessarily based upon genetic differences between the individuals responding differently, but is explained as resulting from the action of selection on the whole unitary population in favor of a capacity for plastic response. Even a flock of inbred hens arranges itself in a peck order, and such a genetic capacity for conditioning might have been selected during the evolution of the species (pp. 413, 663). The capacity for somatic adaptation certainly evolves and is an important basis for the evolution of the brain capacity and intelligence found among higher vertebrates (pp. 639, 693).

Wheeler (1928b, p. 12) lists the stages of the evolution of the insect (especially hymenopteran) family and society as follows:

1. The insect mother merely scatters her eggs in the general environment in which the individuals of her species normally live. In some cases the eggs are placed near the larval food.

2. She places her eggs on some portion of the environment (leaves, and the like) which will serve as food for the hatching larvae.

3. She supplies her eggs with a protective covering. This stage may be combined with (1) or (2).

4. She remains with her eggs and young larvae and protects them.

5. She deposits her eggs in a comparatively safe or specially prepared situation (nest) with a supply of food easily accessible to the hatching young (mass provisioning).

6. She remains with the eggs and young and protects and continuously feeds the latter with prepared food (progressive provisioning).

7. The progeny are not only protected and fed by the mother, but eventually cooperate with her in rearing additional broods of young, so that parent and offspring live together in an annual or perennial society.

Wheeler designates the first five categories as *infrasocial;* those of the sixth as *subsocial;* and only the seventh as *social* (*sensu stricto*). Division of labor among the adults is characteristic of the seventh category. These stages are not necessarily phylogenetic in their linear sequence, although they may often indicate evolutionary order.

As has already been seen in the gradations of integration in various types of aggregations (Chap. 23), principles of family organization are not the only principles of group coordination. Although insect societies are doubtless primarily developments of family systems, adaptive group life may emerge from aggregations of adults not necessarily associated with family and sex relations.

The term "social" may be used in a general sense to include "all groupings of individuals which are sufficiently integrated so that natural selection can act on them as units" (Allee, 1940). In this general sense every individual organism belongs to a society. Each species population is integrated through the continuity of the germ plasm. In addition, various degrees of elaboration of other mechanisms of social coordination give rise to a multiplicity of population types (Chaps. 18–24; pp. 605, 625, 684).

It is significant that the highest systems of intraspecies organismic and population cooperation, with the exception of some sexual adjustments, are coordinated individual units produced by asexual reproduction, parthenogenesis, or intense inbreeding. By this means, any genes promoting cooperation are spread into a large organization. The cells of a multicellular organism or the segments of a metameric organism have the same genes. The generations of cyclomorphic species, such as aphids and cestodes, usually have the same genetic constitution. Mating among social insects is commonly between brother and sister, thus tending to establish single rare mutations in large populations, which may then be selected as integrated units. Castes of social insects are not produced by genetic differentiation of the individuals (p. 428).

Snell (1932) accepts the point of view that the mating flight in the social Hymenoptera selects fit males, which are haploid and therefore without distinction between the phenotypic and genotypic individuals. The female progeny from a single mating are identical in at least one-half of their germ plasm, because only one kind of spermatozoan is produced. Spermatozoa from a single mating in ants fertilize the eggs of the queen for a period as long as fifteen years, with a total progeny that may reach 1,800,000. Large numbers of these offspring may be haploid males and reproductive diploid females which, if mated brother to sister, would again be likely to spread a gene originally appearing in a grandparent to an enormous population.

Swarming, the result of an increase in numbers and of the presence of a new, young, fertile queen, divides colonies of honeybees (see p. 423). This behavior seems to have evolved long ago; the honeybee queen has lost the ability to found a new colony without large numbers of workers. Probably colony subdivision is the result of the joint action of several instincts that benefit the species as a whole. Instincts may become overt under certain stimuli and do not necessarily indicate genetic differences between swarming and nonswarming bees.

Let us now consider genetically differentiated classes within an integrated population. Selection may result in a permanent genetically determined polymorphism within a species. Timoféeff-Ressovsky (1940) records the seasonal fluctuation of the relative numbers of black and red forms of the ladybird beetle, *Adalia bipunctata*, in the vicinity of Berlin (Fig. 248). Over a period of three years, the black genotypes were less numerous than the red genotypes in April, and more numerous in October. There are about three generations of the beetle per year in this locality, and Timoféeff-Ressovsky explains the polymorphism on the basis of selection favoring one genotype in the spring and the other genotype in the fall. The color differences, of course, may be secondary effects of the genes selected through physiological fitness.

Another type of genetically determined permanent polymorphism of a seemingly functional value is described by Ford (1940). Two forms of the nymphalid butterfly, *Hypolimnas dubius,* occur in East Africa. One form is supposed to be a mimic of the two species, *Amauris albimaculata*

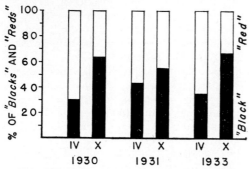

Fig. 248. The relative frequencies of black and red beetles (*Adalia bipunctata*) in April and October during three different years in the vicinity of Berlin, Germany. (Redrawn from Timoféeff-Ressovsky.)

and *A. echeria.* The other form supposedly mimics *Amauris niavius dominicanus.* The two forms differ in color, pattern, and behavior, but the different form patterns are expressed through the action of a single gene and its allele. Ford explains the evolution of a dimorphic species that mimics two different species on the assumption that, in Batesian mimicry, selection against the mimic increases as the numbers approach those of the model. If a mimicking species can become polymorphic, a much larger population can survive.

If further study of the survival of these populations in relation to each other and to their predators tends to substantiate Ford's speculations, we may have an example of the evolution of a population adjustment based upon genetic classes in contrast with the much more common nongenetic polymorphism. In spite of the single gene difference between the dimorphic forms of the mimic, such an evolution could occur gradually and be polygenic, only the threshold of expression being controlled by the single gene. Otherwise we must assume mutations that chance to resemble the model species in a variety of characters with elimination of the nonmi-

metic variations (Ford, 1936) and, in a few instances, selection of genes with different adaptive effects in terms of their incidence in the whole population. Such striking adaptation as that of mimicry would be more likely to be polygenic (p. 670).

Genetically determined forms may maintain their relative proportions in a population with differential survival. For instance, if the male sex has a higher mortality than the female, the resulting selection would not change the sex ratio in future generations if one sex were homozygous for the sex chromosomes (XX) and the other were heterozygous (XY).

The group functions must be highly adaptive, as in sexual adaptation in higher organisms, before genetic determination can produce classes on the basis of homozygous and heterozygous individuals, or through some other genetic mechanism. Sex determination in the lower forms is commonly on the basis of physiologic differentiation without genetic differences of the sexes, and it is usually in the higher organisms that we find genetic determination of sex (the mating types of *Paramecium* may be an exception; Sonneborn, 1939, 1941).

In the Hymenoptera and in a few other arthropods, *haplodiploidy* occurs—that is, the males develop from unfertilized haploid eggs and the females from fertilized diploid ones. White (1945, p. 267) says: "From the point of view of reproductive economy haplodiploidy is an infinitely plastic system in which (given sufficient time) selection can bring about any sex ratio which is in the interest of the species." Considering the fact that the sterile castes of the social Hymenoptera are always genetic females, this ability to produce large populations of females is important in the convergent evolution of strictly social Hymenoptera (pp. 690, 691). The termites, however, evolved a social system with sterile castes with no haplodiploidy, both soldiers and workers being sterile males and females.

Controversy has raged over Darwin's theory of sexual selection through individual (sometimes unilateral) choice. This theory, as a special aspect of natural selection, was thought to explain the evolution of courtship displays and the evolution of structural, physiological, and behavioristic adaptations for combat between males. Recently, various authors have been inclined to treat sexual adaptation and other types of group adjustment as similar in basic origin to endoadaptation within the organism.

Many groups of invertebrates, including flatworms, oligochaetes, leeches, and most mollusks, are hermaphroditic. Other groups such as echinoderms, arthropods, and vertebrates are with few exceptions bisexual. Bisexuality has convergently evolved from hermaphroditism many times, and hermaphroditism has also arisen through bisexual forms a number of times (White, 1945, p. 228). It is obvious that sexual tissues (male or female) were originally without genetic differentiation, that in some bisexual forms there is no genetic determination, and that it was in the later stages of the evolution of sex that genetic determination arose, and is particularly well developed in the insects and vetebrates.

The intricate interplay of sexual, familial, and species mechanisms of attraction indicates various levels of group coordination resulting from identical physiological or behavior adaptations (Noble and Curtis, 1939). Selection sorts more efficient mechanisms through survival of the whole system. In sexual mechanisms the survival unit is the sex pair, and not the individual as such. Marshall (1942) points out that display and courtship often occur after and not before the period when the birds are paired, so that courtship is subsequent to choosing a mate.

Display is not always confined to one sex, but is often used for mutual stimulation. Communal display by large numbers of individuals may be useful in stimulating each individual female, even though many of the males at the bottom of the peck order may not copulate (J. W. Scott, 1942).

Predators may produce a selective pressure favoring concealing coloration instead of conspicuous sexual coloration, particularly in the brooding female. Bright-colored females are often found in hole-nesting birds and in female-courting species such as the phalaropes (Huxley, 1938). The male phalarope is dull-colored, builds the nest, incubates the eggs, and tends the young.

Newts (*Triturus* spp.) exhibit courtship attitudes after the males have dropped their spermatophores. If the males do not perform, the females do not pick up the spermatophores. Huxley (1941) points out that the female cannot know that a particular spermatophore has been dropped by a particular· male, so that Darwinian sexual selection is hardly possible in this instance.

It should be emphasized that other physiological attributes of sex do not function in sex attraction and can hardly be selected in the Darwinian sense of sexual selection. For example, female sex hormones stimulate the development of mammary glands in mammals. These glands are clearly an adaptation of the mother for the benefit of the young, and thus help to coordinate the family. They can hardly be assumed to evolve through the selection of females by males that would choose more effective mammary glands, nor can the offspring select its mother, but selection may well operate on the family unit as a whole toward the evolution of efficient parental care.

Many angiosperm flowers are adapted for display (p. 249), not to attract an individual of the opposite sex, but to attract the animals that transfer the pollen to another flower, thus setting the stage for ultimate union of the gametes. There is thus a sexual function and a sexual display, but obviously no such mechanism could evolve through individual sexual selection. The species population as well as its component individuals constitutes the unit of selection in the evolution of flowers. (Interspecies populations are also units of selection; see p. 698.) Lewis (1942) assembles evidence pointing to the evolution of diecious organisms from hermaphrodites or monoclinous types, usually with a monecious intermediary. Animals are usually diecious—an adjustment better suited to their motility. Plants are usually hermaphroditic with adaptations for cross fertilization—an adjustment better suited to their sessile life. Both gain greater evolutionary potentialities through reassortment of chromosomes in sexual union. Greater variability is an important basis for adaptive evolution, provided it is not too drastic (Mather, 1943). Whereas reassortment of existing genes is probably a more important mechanism in the origin of species than is gene mutation (pp. 600, 641), gene mutation rather than gene frequency is probably more important in the origin of higher taxonomic categories.

Darwin, in developing his theory of individual sexual selection, did not always recognize that the male-female pair could be a unit upon which selection could act as a whole. At certain levels of integration there may be an evolution of sterility. This is exemplified at the level of the organism by the somatic cells and at the population level by the sterile castes of social insects. It would be wholly illogical (see p. 599) to interpret the evolution of sterility by means of the survival of unit somatic cells in the organism, or the survival of sexless individuals in the society.

In colonies of honeybees, drones are usually produced at the time of queen production when they may function in fertilizing new queens. Queens lay unfertilized eggs in drone cells made with somewhat thicker walls than cells in which workers are raised (p. 434). The various behavior mechanisms that enable the workers and the queens to regulate the numbers of queens, drones, and workers in the colony at various seasons and under various conditions are almost entirely unknown, but there is no doubt that a remarkable population balance is maintained. Only a few drones copulate with the few young queens. The others have no function in the colony and are disposed of in the most direct way by the workers. This population control is most dramatically illustrated at the time of drone elimination, which usually occurs in the fall when the nectar flow diminishes. Workers appear to herd the drones into corners of the colony and cut them off from a food supply. The weakened drones are ultimately dragged out and left to die outside the hive entrance. In one instances on observation hive had the exit closed at the time of the drone slaughter. The workers cut up the bodies of the drones and dropped the remains through a crack in the bottom of the hive so that a conspicuous mound of drone parts accumulated directly below the hive. Queenless colonies may tolerate drones indefinitely.* This functional behavior for population control in the honeybee is characteristic of the species, and thus is probably the product of adaptive evolution. The regulation of numbers

* Personal communication from O. W. Park.

in a colony of social insects is analogous to the regulation of numbers of cells and cell types in a multicellular organism.

The action of natural selection on the population or organismic unit as a whole does not preclude independent selection of parts of higher systems. Through independent assortment, chromosomes may be selected independently of other chromosomes in the cells, and through crossover mechanisms, genes within a chromosome may be independently selected in relation to other genes in the system. At other levels of integration we may also expect to find a degree of differential selection of parts. This would seem to be illustrated by the evolution of secondary sexual characters that function during competition for mates between members of the same sex (intrasexual selection).

Intrasexual selection, together with selection of sex pairs, may be involved in the evolution of certain types of sexual behavior. Wheeler (1928, pp. 145–165) reviewed numerous cases of insect and spider courtship that indicate a relationship between the food and sex drives. The food drive originates as an individual adaptation, while the sex drive is a population adaptation. A behavior pattern functioning for the acquisition of food may be in part transformed by evolutionary processes into acquisition of mates.

Instances are known in which (1) the males regurgitate food droplets that are imbibed by the female before or during copulation (Cardiacephala myrmex of the dipterous family Micropezidae); (2) the males secrete a glandular substance upon which the females feed before, during, or after copulation (the tree cricket Oecanthus niveus); (3) the male is devoured by the female after copulation (the mantid, Mantis religiosa, and many spiders, including Pisaura mirabilis); (4) the male captures and paralyzes its prey and presents it to the female, who devours it during copulation (several species of the dipterous family Empididae, including Empis borealis); (5) the male presents the female with prey or a substitute object such as a flower part which she "plays with" during copulation (various species of the empidid genus Hilara); and (6) the male catches and kills a minute insect and encloses it in an envelope made of an oral secretion that

the female manipulates during copulation (several species of the empidid genus *Hilara*).The males of the micropezid fly, *Nerius fuscus,* combat each other for the possession of the female without the loser being killed by the winner.

Beebe (1944a) describes a combat between male elephant beetles (*Megasoma elephas*) in the presence of the female. The function of the conspicuous horns of the male during combat is evidently to tip over the opposing male, thus allowing the victor to copulate with the female, who seems to exert no individual choice. Somewhat similar combats occur between males of the Hercules beetle, *Dynastes hercules* (Beebe, 1947).

Secondary sexual characters might also be used for combating or threatening predaceous enemies, but the female might then be expected to have evolved similar defensive adaptations, unless, by division of labor, she was defended by the male. Defense of the females by males is sometimes seen, particularly among birds and mammals, but could hardly account for the evolution of the horns of dynastid beetles. Whether a genetic difference inducing horns in the males is selected differentially on the basis of individual combat is also a question. Such structures are known to be developed through allometric growth and might evolve indirectly by selection of size differences. This is also true of the antlers of the majority of male deer (Huxley, 1932; see also p. 638). Secondary sexual characters confined to one sex might have general survival value for the species if they functioned for species recognition, sex recognition, sexual stimulation, coition, fertilization, territoriality, defense of the individual male, defense of the female, or defense of the family (Huxley, 1938, 1938a).

These possible functions of the horns of the dynastid beetles seem unlikely. It is possible to explain the evolutionary adaptation of some sex characters through intrasexual selection in a sense close to the original Darwinian concept. At the same time we must remember that we have no proof that the winning male is genetically superior to the loser, or that the loser may not find another female. There seems to be a supply of unmated males and females in many populations. It may still be possible to explain this peculiar evolution of intrasexual competitive adaptation on the basis of species selection rather than individual selection.

Birds have probably evolved territorial behavior (p. 412) through more efficient spacing of breeding, nesting, and feeding functions. An individual bird or mammal may win a combat in its own territory and lose to the same opponent in the opponent's territory (p. 414). Species exhibiting territorial behavior, however, probably have a selective advantage.

Both genetically similar and genetically different classes of individuals may occur in certain populations, one set of mechanisms integrated with the other set in a functional whole. Sexual division of labor in the social Hymenoptera may be based upon genetic differences—the males being haploid and the females diploid (p. 688). At the same time, the female castes, consisting of reproductives, workers, and soldiers, are not genetically different, but are the result of physiological differentiation (Gregg, 1942). There is little doubt that such a society evolved through basic sexual and family systems.

Likewise, human society evolved social coordination through sexual and family patterns. Sex behavior based upon initial genetic differentials is still of fundamental importance in human social life; the human family, like the family in other mammals, is a physiological integration between parents and offspring with familial adaptations, such as the mammary glands, genetically and physiologically an evolution of more basic sex patterns. On top of these systems, a social organization has evolved that is based upon conditioned response, intelligence, and symbolic learning; each individual has the capacity to fit numerous different social niches by means of education. The foundation for the nongenetic psychological division of labor may be traced back through various vertebrate aggregations (pp. 411, 664, 686).

Whether the population is integrated through nongenetic or genetic mechanisms, or both, there are many examples of what would appear to be an evolution of individual or class sacrificial action or behavior. Somatic cells sacrifice the capacity to reproduce new organisms and often die functioning for the benefit of the whole organism. A part of an animal, for example the tail of a lizard, may be shed when the animal is attacked, an action that has been thought to contribute to the survival of the individual, which then regenerates a new tail. Brilliant coloration of the tail may even be associated with the specific mechanisms for shedding the tail without loss of blood.

Maternal instinct subjects the individual mother to a higher mortality rate when she attempts to protect her young or eggs (Haldane, 1932, p. 207; see also 339, 416). A honeybee worker is often killed while protecting the colony. The sting of the worker is barbed and is often left in the stung animal together with a portion of the abdomen. In contrast, the queen has a smooth unbarbed sting. A soldier termite has highly evolved defensive adaptations, frequently is killed defending the society, and exhibits regressive evolution of the reproductive organs. During periods of disturbance, the soldiers of some species (*Nasutitermes, Coptotermes,* and the like) concentrate at the point of danger (Fig. 149). In none of these does the individual in question typically differ genetically from other individuals making up the unit population. Physiological and environmental thresholds determine the manifestation of the function of the individual, but the function itself may well determine the survival of the reproductive individual, thus perpetuating any genetic enhancement of functional efficiency.

Wright (1945) develops a mathematical genetic theory to explain the possibility of the fixation of a character valuable to the population, but disadvantageous at a given time to the individual organisms. He believes that some form of intergroup selection is necessary for the establishment of socially advantageous but individually disadvantageous mutations. Conditions for such creative evolution of social units seem to be met among the social insects. Considerable inbreeding within small, partially isolated populations occurs, together with occasional crossing between reproductives from different colonies. Intraspecies but intercolony competition may occur.

If whole populations are adaptive, it seems possible that adaptations producing *beneficial death* of the individual—death for the benefit of the population—might evolve.* Numerous cases of beneficial death are known at the level of the multicellular organism. For instance, the sapwood cells of a tree function after their death when they then transport water and minerals from the roots to the leaves. The functional insect wing is largely a dead structure (only some living cells, glands, and blood may be present), and in the termite wing, a basal suture has evolved that enables the outer portion of the wing to be efficiently discarded after the colonizing flight. At the sexual level, the male is often eaten by the female after copulation (p. 690). At the population level, the tumble weed or Russian thistle (*Salsola pestifer*), introduced into the dry semideserts and prairies of North America from the steppes of Russia, breaks off near the ground, and its dried dead branches form a stiff round mass that, when rolled over the plains by the wind, disperses its seeds. This obviously does not benefit the individual plant, but insures the spread and ultimate survival of the new generation. From these considerations, it follows that the physiological effects of aging and senescence may be adaptations for the benefit of the species (see Physiological Longevity, p. 273).

Cannibalism, as exhibited by numerous groups of insects (p. 370), may benefit the population system. This behavior pattern causing the beneficial death of individuals in overcrowded populations may be the result of adaptation within a population system.

Pearl (1930a) states: "No death of an individual occurring in . . . the post-reproductive period can possibly be selective, in the sense of having any effect upon the race." Pearl here seems to view the reproductive individual as the only unit upon which selection may act. We do not at all agree to this limitation. If the postreproductive (or for that matter, sterile) individual is integrated within a supraorganismic unit, its selection may influence survival of the reproductive individuals and thus indirectly have a profound influence upon the further evolution of the race.

* *Beneficial death* is defined here in a specific way as it is related to that mortality resulting from particular adaptations. In other places (pp. 418, 603, 685, 706) we stress the fact that death may be beneficial without such adaptational implication.

Proof that such a selection of postreproductive or sterile individuals influences evolution is amply demonstrated in the phylogeny of the social insects. The most conclusive case is in the adaptive evolution of the nasute soldier of the termites (Figs. 148 and 149). This soldier caste is completely sterile (the rare abnormal alate-soldier intercaste described by Adamson, 1940, does not affect this conclusion). The nasute soldier has evolved from mandibulate soldier types (Fig. 263), and the evidence points to the conclusion that this evolution is toward increased defensive adaptation with associated regressive evolution of the mandibles. The effective function of the soldier in the defense of the colony helps select the queen capable of producing such soldiers. The genetic characteristics of the reproductives may thus be sorted through selective survival as effectively as the genetic characters of the gametes are selected through the function of the sterile somatic cells and organs incorporated with the gametes within the multicellular individual. Consequently, it is necessary to recognize the selection of whole integrated population units in order to understand adequately well-known facts of evolution.

We have already discussed (p. 676) the regression of supraorganismic adaptations, a parallel to regressive evolution in individual organisms that emphasizes the analogy of organism and supraorganism. Some authors think that it is philosophically unsound to derive any valid scientific meaning from the analogies between two different integrative levels. According to this viewpoint, integrative mechanisms within a unicellular organism yield no knowledge applicable to integrative mechanisms between cells of a multicellular organism; and comparisons of multicellular coordination with social coordination (either insect or human) is deemed fallacious. Similarities between two levels are regarded as "purely formal and therefore meaningless" (Novikoff, 1945, 1945a). Simpson (1941, p. 18) says: "The biologist who elevates the organism-epiorganism metaphor into a standard for social interpretation and recommendation is guilty of the most reckless, unjustified, and nonscientific extrapolation."

It is true that in comparing distinct integrative levels, homologies (resemblances with a common genetic basis) cannot be assumed, although we have seen (pp. 689, 690) that the identical mechanisms of one level may sometimes integrate a higher level. Similarities may, however, be convergent and therefore analogous, and a comparison of similar pressures guiding unlike organisms toward analogous functions is significant. The principles that order similarities and differences may be formulated by study, comparison, and evaluation of the data. Much scientific research is based upon this observational and analytic method. Care must be taken to study truly functional similarities and differences, and not to be led astray by verbalisms, euphonious metaphors, or purely chance resemblances (Gerard and Emerson, 1945; Schneirla, 1946).

The theory of emergent evolution has been applied to the concept of organismic levels. This theory recognizes that new or novel properties and characteristics emerge from new combinations. Complex associations have properties that are not merely the sum of the properties of the constituent parts (Jennings, 1927; Wheeler, 1928a; Nabours, 1930, 1930a; Morgan, 1933; Wright, 1935; Needham, 1943). Wheeler emphasizes the fact that emergent characteristics may be losses as well as gains, so that the whole is not necessarily more than the sum of its parts, but may be less.

Some proponents of the theory of emergent evolution state that the novel properties arising from interaction are fundamentally unpredictable from a knowledge of the unassociated parts. This philosophical aspect of the theory is beyond our field of enquiry. In essence, emergent evolution emphasizes the basic necessity for the study of wholes, as contrasted to the study of parts, and adds a certain dignity to synthetic sciences. Biology is the study of the properties of whole systems as well as of parts, and ecology, among the various subsciences of biology, tends to be holistic in its approach.

Human social evolution is beyond the scope of this book. Biological evolution involves germinal changes. Social evolution of man involves cultural changes. We hold, however, that the social scientist may find many significant parallels in biological and social evolutionary mechanisms (Brody, 1944; Emerson, 1947; see pp. 630, 632, 639, 686, 691). We also think that human

society has many supraorganismic characteristics. Cannon (1941) said, "The body
politic exhibits many processes which resemble those found in the body physiologic;
the analogies are so close and so numerous,
not only for nations but also for industry,
as to intimate strongly that there are indeed general principles of organization,
widely applicable to complex aggregations
of collaborating parts." As in the nonhuman
species, the integrated cooperative group
may be an important unit of selection, so
that survival may well be in relation to
humanity as a whole, rather than for the
benefit of the few at the expense of the
many. Sacrifice by some individuals for the
good of the group, and sacrifice by some
infraspecies groups for the good of the
species, are exhibited in both biological
and social systems; thus many ethical
principles have a biological foundation
(Gerard, 1942a; Allee, 1943).

As in the evolution of nonhuman population units, the benefits to the whole system is not independent of the benefit to
the individuals composing the group. The
surviving system in all probability will be
neither one in which the group exploits the
individuals composing it, nor in which the
individuals exploit the group. Rather, it
may be expected that surviving populations
will be coordinated under the formula "one
for all and all for one."

Lest the concept of the evolution of the
biological supraorganism be used to advo-
cate totalitarianism, either of the fascist or
communist type, we sound a note of warning. The social unit, whether a class, a
tribe, a nation, or the species as a whole,
has probably evolved somewhat as the
biological population has: through a certain
degree of variation, selection of favorable
variations in relation to both the environment and to the organismic system, and
transmission of the surviving variations to
succeeding generations. Whether human
social evolution moves toward autocracy,
fascism, communism, or democracy probably depends upon how these political
systems influence the primary factors of
social functioning, including, of course,
social evolution. Variation may be analogized with the creative arts and sciences,
natural selection with social selection
through optimal competition, and germinal
heredity with transmission through sym-

bolic communication of cultural patterns
(social heredity). Animal and plant breeders have improved varieties through the
application of evolutionary principles.
Through the application of intelligent "artificial" selection of social units, human
social evolution could also advance more
rapidly toward greater function, greater
integration, and more effective control over
the environment (Cannon, 1941). Elimination of nonconformists may destroy the degree of social variability upon which progressive social evolution depends (see Muller, 1948).

In résumé, the generalizations of this division lead to the broad conclusion that
selection operates on parts and wholes of
genetically connected intraspecies populations (i.e., on species, cyclomorphic populations, aggregated populations, sex pairs,
family units, and on societies) in a manner similar to the action of selection
on protoplasmically connected organisms
(Weismann, 1893, p. 327). Efficient functional coordination within each unit is
comparable to the adjustment of the unit
as a whole to its surroundings. Adaptation
toward a balanced relationship and internal
relative constancy (homeostasis) has obviously developed within each system during phylogeny, and the more inclusive
systems incorporate, at least in partial or
modified form, the external environment of
those less inclusive.

Populations, however, are usually far
more loosely integrated than are protoplasmically continuous organisms. Even the
social insect supraorganism is more soundly
analogized with a primitive multicellular organism such as a sponge, than with a
highly complex coordinated vertebrate organism.

SUMMARY

A number of broad conclusions may be
drawn from this discussion of the role of
natural selection. Natural selection of
genetic variations is the primary guiding
factor directing evolution toward increased
endoadaptation and exoadaptation. Chance
genetic variation, chance dispersal, and
orientation behavior may enable preadapted
forms with genetically simple new adaptive
modifications to become established in new
habitats where natural selection in time will
develop more complex adjustments. The

ability of selection pressure, largely but not exclusively the result of competition, to sort genetic variations through their somatic effects is demonstrated by both observation and experiment. Adaptive mechanisms enable organisms to maintain their ecological position and partially to control their environment. Ancient complex and currently less valuable adaptations secondarily regress through positive selection of other functions, but because of their genetic relationship to evolving adaptations and beneficial functions, the genetic pattern is maintained in part and is exhibited by vestigial characters. Interbreeding between populations may regress, leading to permanent reproductive isolation. Extreme reduction or extreme increase of variation, isolation, or selection leads to the retardation or cessation of evolution. Selection operates upon organismic and population (supraorganismic) systems. Circular evolutionary effects are the rule (see Hutchinson, 1948). Thus, variation and isolation set the stage for the guiding action of selection, and selection in turn guides the mechanisms of variation and isolation. Evolutionary trends are in the direction of increased homeostasis within the organism, the species population, and the ecosystem.

35. EVOLUTION OF INTERSPECIES INTEGRATION AND THE ECOSYSTEM

INTRODUCTION

The evolution of the ecosystem, more particularly the evolution of interspecies integration, culminates in the balance of nature within the community. The *ecosystem* may be defined as the interacting environmental and biotic system.

The activities of the community may be summed up in the *action* of the physicochemical habitat upon the organisms, the *reaction* of organisms upon the physical factors, and the *coaction* of the organisms upon each other (Clements and Shelford, 1939; see also p. 348).

The evolution of interspecies integration involves the genetic modification of the ecologically associated organisms in relation to each other, in the aggregate resulting in the evolution of the community as a whole.

Progression of the community through succession and development of contemporary species associations is discussed elsewhere (Chap. 29). Succession and development may be conceived as the ontogeny of the community and its parts. The evolution of interspecies integration may be thought of as the phylogeny of the definitive grouping of species within the community.

As an example, the prairie community of the Miocene had much taxonomic and ecologic similarity to the prairie community of the present day, although the species composing these associations were different in the Miocene. In some cases, the species have gradually evolved within a similar habitat, and there is a genetic continuity between the organisms of the Miocene and present prairies (see Stirton, 1947). Sometimes a species evolves with changes in its habitat. In other instances, species have entered the prairies from other contiguous habitats and have gradually become adjusted. On occasion, a distant species may have entered the region and later evolved toward a balanced adjustment with the older established species. Selection pressures within the whole community gradually produce a balanced relation of the species to each other and to their physical environment.

Species in a given association have often come from several different regions, and their origin may be traced by their taxonomic relations. Mayr (1946) finds elements in the North American bird fauna that may be classified according to their ancestral origin in any one of the following categories: Pantropical, Panboreal, Old World, North American, Pan-American, and South American.

Weir (1946) discusses the environmental influence in releasing genes from their adaptive function so that establishment of mutations with new adaptive functions may not be prevented by selection. He points out that favorable mutations of genes already possessing vital catalytic functions are improbable. Also, there is a size limit of the nucleus for an increase in gene number. If other organisms in the biocoenose, however, supply certain physiological needs, genes in a given organism may become adaptively neutral, and are thus free to mutate toward other functions. The evolution of greater interdependence between organisms is correlated with progressive evolution (see pp. 676 and 679).

Species may be adapted to more than one community. The larvae and pupae of mosquitoes are adjusted to aquatic communities, while the winged adults fit terrestrial and aerial conditions. The herbivorous larvae are eaten by pond fishes, while the predaceous adults suck the blood of terrestrial vertebrates and may transmit malaria or yellow fever to their vertebrate prey. Thus, the same species of mosquito is incorporated into different communities that must be spatially close to each other, but it takes a different place in the food web in these different associations.

The borderline between contiguous communities is important in the life of a mosquito adapted to each. Hess and Hall (1943) report a high positive correlation between the population density of *Anopheles quadrimaculatus* larvae and the "intersection value," defined as the number of meters of "intersection line" per square meter of water surface. The "intersection line" is the junction between water-air, water-plant, and plant-air, such as the perimeter of a floating leaf where it intersects the water surface.

Swynnerton (1940) has reported that each of the twenty-one species of tsetse flies has different behavior and ecological adjustments. Each requires more than one vegetational type at a time, and these types must be in contact with each other. He calls this "concurrence of requirements." "*Glossina morsitans,* for instance, needs savanna wooding to rest and breed in, and vleis (temporary marshes) to search food in. Continuous uniform savanna wooding will not support it, while ant-heaps (termite mounds) with heavy vegetation, near or at the contact of this and the vleis, add much to the suitability of the general vegetational concurrence." Beecher (1942) also found that certain bird species nest in greatest density at the junction line (ecotone) between two communities. He refers to such distributions as producing an "edge effect" (pp. 476–478).

The adjustments of an organism to two or more associations obviously influence the evolution of the species assemblage. As an example, the crayfishes of the Allegheny Mountains are different species in the streams of the Atlantic and Mississippi drainages because, although the head waters may be close and ecologically nearly equivalent, there is no way for most of the species to cross the divide. In contrast, the insect species of these same streams, which have an adult flying stage, are usually found in both drainage systems because the divide is no barrier to their distribution.

Possibly even more striking are the community relations of migratory birds during their annual flight from wintering to breeding areas, the pelagic feeding and littoral breeding activities of penguins and seals, the marine feeding and fresh-water spawning of various Pacific salmon, and the fresh-water feeding and marine breeding of the migratory eels of Europe and North America. Obviously, these animals must be adapted to different sets of factors at the same time or in different periods of their life cycles, and the evolution of the different associations of which they form an element is influenced by their adaptations and their periodicities.

Occasionally, species at the base of food chains may also be found in communities of different types. Waksman (1945) points out that many soil micro-organisms are also characteristic of littoral sea waters and must influence the pattern of these distinctive communities.

These complexities make biocoenoses and communities less definable than are most individual organisms, and there is no doubt that considerable interdependence between associations occurs—so much so, that a degree of evolutionary integration and balance exists that brings all life together with its environment into an ecosystem with some unity (Egler, 1942). Even while many dynamic changes are affecting portions of the total pattern, long-term relative stability and independence of each community system exist and justify the separation of communities and their parts. Many ecological principles must be coordinated in order to understand both the stable unity and the evolution of the ecosystem.

In the following pages, we attempt to analyze the evolutionary processes integrating different species, and we shall then review aspects of the more complex assemblages found in the biocoenoses and communities.

ACTION

Community evolution involves the action or effect of the physicochemical habitat upon organisms. Adaptations to the physical environment result from a long process of sorting through natural selection (p. 640). The community often contains species in different taxonomic categories with similar adjustments to similar ecological factors (Convergent Evolution, p. 666; see also Gleason, 1939).

For example, the existence of sand cherry (*Prunus pumila*) and marram grass (*Ammophila arenaria*) side by side in an Indiana foredune association is probably not the result of any important interaction between these species, but is rather the consequence of similar adaptations of both species to climatic, light, soil, and moisture conditions. Likewise, the presence of an ant lion larva (*Myrmeleon immaculatus*), a tiger beetle larva (*Cicindela lepida*), a seaside locust (*Trimerotropis maritima*), and a sand spider (*Geolycosa pikei*) in a poplar dune association does not indicate adaptation to each other, but rather structural, physiological, and behavioristic adjustment to rather extreme conditions of substrate, temperature, and moisture, characteristic of this stage in the sand dune succession (Wheeler, 1930).

Cole (1946) has analyzed the cryptozoa (terrestrial fauna in the dark habitat under stones, logs, and bark of trees) and finds that this fauna (as studied under boards), although similar in various geographic regions, lacks interspecies integration and is largely the result of common habitat requirements and tolerances. Such an assemblage does not exhibit the interspecies adaptations of a biocoenose, but may have many organisms that avoid the stiffer competition of the more integrated associations.

Temporal changes in physical conditions may give rise to a succession of species adapted to each stage in the development of the community. Obviously, adaptive evolution is a slower process than the change in the factors during ecological succession in the development of the dunes associations. Only succession taking hundreds of thousands of years might enable a certain number of organisms to become adapted to the changing conditions. Possibly the organisms could keep up with the environmental modifications if competition with better adjusted species were reduced or absent.

The physicochemical environment may affect the composition of an assemblage of organisms that shows no evolved integration and represents only a statistical entity. Such a grouping is at the bottom of an ascending series of interspecies systems.

REACTION

The reaction of the organisms upon the environment often changes the physical, and indirectly the biotic factors, to which many species are adjusted (Jennings, 1944). The gradual accumulation of humus, through the incorporation of decaying vegetation and animal matter into the soil, alters the moisture-holding capacity and the rate of evaporation from the surface. This factor is responsible for much of the successional sequence found in the Indiana sand dunes from the drier foredunes to the mesic woodlands (pp. 566–569). Many organisms living in the climax forest on the dunes are thus dependent upon the community sequence, but nevertheless have not necessarily become adapted to each other, but rather to the physical conditions resulting from the reaction of organisms on their environment.

A good example is the succession of ant species in these dunes (Talbot, 1934). The ants in this series are generalized scavengers or predators. The foredune has a mean average daily evaporation about three times that of the beech-maple climax, and a decrease in evaporation rate may be demonstrated through the community sequence on sand from the foredunes to the climax forest. *Pheidole bicarinata* is found nesting in soil from the foredunes through the oak stage. *Paratrechina parvula obscuriventris* nests in the soil of the pine and oak stages. *Monomorium minimum* is found from the pine dunes through the oak stages. *Formica truncicola obscuriventris* nests in the soil of the oak associes. *Myrmica scabrinodis* nests in the soil from the pine dunes through the beech-maple climax. *Formica fusca* var. *subaenescens* nests in both the soil and logs of the oak-maple and beech-maple climax.

This sequence illustrates an indirect effect of the reaction of organisms on their environment without correlation with adaptive coaction. The interspecies relations of these ants are rather general and not limited to one or a few species of other organisms.

In contrast, a succession of gall insects in the same series is doubtless produced by the coaction between the species of insects and the host plants to which they are limited (p. 699).

The most dramatic effects of animals on the community are found in the activities of forms that control their own environment by building nests or other structures, such as those of the social insects (p. 425), beavers, and man. Before the dawn of history, the beavers had a greater physiographic influence than man. One-tenth of the flat meadow land of parts of the Rocky Mountain region is the result of their work (Hill, 1943; p. 672).

It is a truism that organisms are adapted to many factors in the environment (p. 634). Different combinations of factors may result in entirely different community composition, as was pointed out in the preceding pages (Chap. 26). Likewise, it is apparent that many organisms are adjusted to more than one distinct community as well as to different parts of the same community. As we have just seen (p. 696), the remarkable caenogenetic evolution of the larval stages of numerous animals allows for double or multiple community relations, particularly among the insects with complete metamorphosis. Selection pressures unquestionably are produced by these environmental modifications, and in time the germinal patterns of the evolving organisms in turn cause a degree of organic evolution of the physical as well as of the biotic environment (p. 672).

COACTION

Many intraspecies populations evolve as units, and the broad concept of individuality must include various levels of population integration (p. 683). Such intraspecies populations have been referred to as supraorganisms, superorganisms, or epiorganisms (Emerson, 1939; Gerard, 1942). The problem that now confronts us is the possibility that interspecies associations evolve as supraorganismic units. This question is properly an important aspect of the evolution of biocoenoses and communities, and the reality of ecosystems is substantiated if the answer is in the affirmative. The evolution of the mechanisms of community integration is largely concerned with the origin of coaction between organisms.

Clements and Shelford (1939) say that coactions constitute the chief bonds in the community (p. 348). The elementary unit with which we are dealing in this division is the coactive species pair. Relations between two species (*coaction*) may be roughly classified under *disoperation* (both harmed through a deleterious effect or mutual elimination), *exploitation* (one organism benefits, while the other is harmed), *toleration* (neither harmed), and cooperative *mutualism* (both benefit).

There may be every gradation between these categories, and contrasting aspects of the relation of two organisms may occur at different stages in their development, or even at the same time. For example, the larva of a histerid beetle (Fig. 258) living with termites in British Guiana was observed eating young termites at the same moment that worker termites were licking exudate organs on its abdomen. Thus this insect, while deriving many advantages from the termite hosts, was both harming and benefiting the society to which it had become conspicuously adapted.

A basic "proto-cooperation" (p. 395) between organisms may set a stage for later evolution, but may not have evolved through selection. Preadaptation (p. 642) may involve cooperative relations on occasion. Proto-cooperative relationships may also be conceived of as the fitness of the biotic environment—to paraphrase Henderson's concept (p. 73).

Interspecies integration, when viewed in evolutionary terms, is the result of the operation of natural selection on pairs of species or upon larger associations in relation to the reciprocal interactions.

DISOPERATION

Instances of direct mutual harm between species are not known to us, but a few cases of mutual elimination through over-exploitation exist (see p. 395; Gause, 1934a). Because of negative selection, disoperation would be most likely when two organisms come in contact for the first time and have no common evolutionary history within the same community. Unless one of the species is preadapted (p. 642) to the other, disoperation may occur.

Many introduced organisms that become pests or cause epidemic disease are examples of such disoperation. The simplest cases are those in which man does not insert himself in a dominant role within the community.

The chestnut bark disease or chestnut blight, caused by an ascomycete fungus (*Endothia parasitica*), originally a parasite of oriental chestnuts (*Castanea mollissima, C. Henryi*, and *C. sequinii*), was introduced into the United States from China about 1904. This foreign fungus has since nearly wiped out the native chestnut (*Castanea dentata*), once the most abundant tree in eastern deciduous forests. With the death of the host, the fungus also lost its major food supply. The parasite survives on other species of American chestnuts and also on species of oaks, but is less common on these hosts and has not eliminated these species (Craighead, 1916).

Cases of drastic disoperation are not easily found in nature, because of the obvious long-continued selection against such a relationship. Indications of previous elimination of populations are fairly abundant, although the factors involved may only be surmised. With the exception of bank and cliff swallows, which nest in or on relatively inaccessible steep banks or cliffs, all colonial ground-nesting birds, including penguins, auks, murres, skimmers, petrels, tropic birds, gannets, cormorants, pelicans, and flamingos, now breed only on islands or otherwise inaccessible situations. It seems possible that such a distribution is the result of survival in regions where disoperative relations do not occur, and elimination in continental regions might have taken place through disoperation between such ground-nesting birds and their predators. However, we have no knowledge concerning the secondary elimination of the predators or what other factors may have been influential in such instances.

EXPLOITATION

Exploitation with unilateral benefit to one of the species is characteristic of the majority of known cases of coaction between two species, and the effect on the struggle for existence is marked.

Characteristic community organization exemplified by the food web (pp. 508–522) and pyramid of numbers (pp. 522–525) is largely the result of exploitation. The food relations within the food web are usually the result of long evolutionary action. For example, insects whose food is limited to a species or higher taxonomic category of plants are usually adjusted to special biochemical traits of their hosts, and therefore have evolved a coactive relationship. The evolution of gall structures formed by plant tissues under the stimulation of the gall-producing animal is an example of unilateral exploitation of the morphogenetic capacities of the plant host without benefit to the plant (Agar, 1943, p. 186).

Mordvilko (1928) states that the evolution of plant lice (aphids) often runs parallel to the evolution of their plant hosts (see Patch, 1938). The primary host of each species of Adelginae is always a spruce (*Picea*), and the secondary host is always another conifer (Abietineae). The phylogenetic origin of genera of aphids is sometimes associated with a change of host genera (Mordvilko, 1934). For example, the genus *Euceraphis* on the birch (*Betula*) gave rise to the genera *Drepanosiphum* and *Drepanaphis* on maples (*Acer*).

Along with their hosts, specialized herbivorous or phytophagous insects exhibit a rather clear successional sequence in the Indiana dunes series, although the ecological factors are different from those affecting the succession of predatory and scavenging ant species. For example, the pine spittle insect (*Aphrophora parallela*) is found on several species of pine and on the Norway spruce; the clustered midrib gall (*Cynips nigricens*) is found on the white and burr oaks, and the woolly leaf gall (*Callirhytis lanata*) is found on the under side of the leaves of several species of the red oak group. The gall wasp genus *Neuroterus* has seventeen species in New

York state, all confined to the species of the white oak group, and most of them to a single species of oak.

Predation has strongly influenced the evolution of both the exploiter and the exploited. Worthington (1940) postulates an astonishingly rapid adaptive radiation of fishes in Lakes Victoria, Kioga, Edward, and George in Africa (p. 611), and points out that Lakes Albert and Rudolf have no such evolution of endemic forms, though similar ecologic conditions have been established for at least as long a period. Lakes Victoria and Kioga have fifty-eight endemic cichlids, Lakes Edward and George have eighteen, Lake Albert has two, and Lake Rudolf three.

Lakes Albert and Rudolf have large active predators, the Nile perch (*Lates*) and the tiger fish (*Hydrocyon*), while in Lakes Victoria and Edward, the only large predators that survived the arid period, or that regained access subsequently, are the rather inactive lungfishes and certain catfishes. In other lakes with the same potentialities the predators prevented a parallel rapid evolution. Lake Nyasa survived the Pleistocene arid period because of its great depth. Species of the genus *Barilius* are less active predators than *Lates* and *Hydrocyon*, which are absent from Lake Nyasa. Nearly twice as many species of endemic cichlid fishes (171) have evolved in Lake Nyasa, as compared with Lake Tanganyika, where there are eighty-nine endemic cichlid species together with *Hydrocyon* and two species of *Lates*. The great evolution of cichlids in Lake Tanganyika as compared with that of Lake Victoria may be explained by the much greater age and depth of Lake Tanganyika (Hesse, Allee, and Schmidt, 1937).

Gause (1934a) experimented upon laboratory controlled predator-prey relations (p. 371).

"The destruction of one species by another has been studied with *Paramecium caudatum* being devoured by another infusoria, *Didinium nasutum*. Experiments showed that this biological system presents no oscillations in the numbers of individuals peculiar to itself, and that in spite of abundant food for *Paramecium* the latter are completely destroyed by predators which perish in their turn later on. However, oscillations appear if we admit a controlled and simultaneous immigration of predators and prey into the microcosm (Fig. 239). There-

fore, it is not the interaction itself, as would be expected from the mathematical theory developed by Lotka (1920) and by Volterra (1926), but the constant interference from without that leads to the oscillation in numbers. . . . In our experiments an anlaysis was made of the role of cover or refuge for the prey in the processes of the struggle for existence. This showed that when the number of individuals becomes reduced, and the conditions in the microcosm complicated, instead of the 'deterministic' processes subject to differential equations we are confronted with 'probabilities of change' in one direction or another."

DeBach and Smith (1941) discuss "inherent" oscillations in host-parasite systems. Experiments on populations of housefly puparia and one of their parasitic species, *Mormoniella vitripennis*, reacting through seven generations, followed the theoretical predictions of Nicholson and Bailey (1935) closely. DeBach and Smith think that the periodicity is inherent in the predator-prey relation, but they introduce conditions that Gause considers external, so that probably no basic difference in principle is involved in the two treatments (pp. 384, 705, Fig. 239).

Ullyett (1936) studied host selection by the chalcid, *Microplectron fuscipennis*. He showed that the insect was able to distinguish to some extent between parasitized and unparasitized hosts and also to choose proper hosts in contrast with hosts that could not serve for the completion of the parasite life cycle. Local concentrations of parasites indicated intensive searching for hosts in a local region. Lloyd (1938) concludes from his studies of host selection by the egg-parasitic chalcid, *Ooencyrtus kuvanae*, that eggs suitable for the offspring are generally chosen, and that the fraction of the eggs found rises as the host density diminishes. Salt (1936) studied the effect of host density on parasite density under experimental conditions (see p. 383). He used the chalcid egg parasite, *Trichogramma evanescens*, with its host, the eggs of the moth, *Sitotroga cerealella*. Five females, capable of depositing 108 eggs, produced 84.4 progeny per 100 available hosts, while fifty females, capable of depositing 1080 eggs, produced only 29.8 progeny per 100 available hosts because of the competition for food when several parasite eggs are laid in the same host egg. Of these 29.8 progeny, 12.8

were females, many of which were abnormal.

These relationships produce local fluctuation of numbers in both parasite and host populations and move toward eventual equilibrium. Concentrations of egg laying often give rise to local concentrations of numbers. Galls of a given species of aphid, cynipid, or other gall insect, are often common in a small area or even on an individual plant, and are rare under similar ecological conditions a short distance away.

Some authors believe that evolution tends toward reduction of reproductive potential in some forms such as those birds and fishes that evolve protected nests for the care of the young, or that nest in areas with natural protection. Beebe (1906) said many years ago: "The number of eggs which a bird lays has been found to bear a definite relation to the amount of danger to which the species is exposed." Moreau (1944) thinks that clutch size and mortality rate react upon each other and are in mutual adjustment.

Clutch size is characteristic of species of birds (Averill, 1933; Stresemann, 1934, p. 373; Moreau, 1944). When the eggs in the nest reach the number characteristic of the species, the bird usually ceases laying. If, however, the eggs are removed by an experimenter, many birds will continue to lay until the number common to the species is reached. In chickens, selective breeding has increased the genetic capacity for egg production. In species under natural conditions, there would seem to be an intrinsic psycho-physiological mechanism that maintains a number of eggs characteristic for each species, this number being presumably optimal for the species under the given conditions.

There are evolutionary tendencies toward increased reproductive capacity and greater density of populations in some forms such as the termite, in which the more primitive and less socialized species have queens with low egg-laying capacity that produce only a few (less than ten) eggs daily, while in the more highly social species, with much larger and better coordinated colony populations, the queens may lay several thousand eggs daily. The phylogenetic relationships of these forms leave no doubt that there was an evolutionary increase in egg-laying capacity.

The selection pressure toward augmented reproductive potential in this case is probably mainly associated with the greater social homeostasis (p. 672) possible with large colony populations (see p. 274). The conspicuous continued evolution of the soldier caste toward increased defensive adaptation against predators, together with an increase in the proportional number of soldiers in certain highly successful genera (for example in *Nasutitermes*, Fig. 149), is indicative of a fairly strong evolutionary response to predation pressures.

Egg-laying capacity has also certainly increased during the evolution of parasitic cestode worms from the free-living ancestral flatworms. In these parasites this evolutionary tendency is probably connected with the necessity for overcoming high egg mortality because of the slight chance of infesting the secondary host (Fig. 250; p. 709). It is also interesting to note that parasitic cuckoos lay many more eggs (thirteen to eighteen) than their nonparasitic relatives (two to six).

Invasion of the host body has probably occurred through evolutionary stages that gradually became more and more adjusted to parasitism (Freeman, 1937; von Brand, 1946, pp. 279–284; see also p. 255). Taliaferro (1948) suggests bacterial stages leading to parasitism as follows: (1) the free-living putrefactive bacteria living on decaying matter, (2) the putrefactive organism living in the lower intestine of animals, (3) the tetanus organism living on necrotic tissue, (4) true parasites such as the typhoid bacillus, which is established in the body. Other evolutionary invasions of hosts may occur through predation, seen in the phylogeny of mites, lice, and fleas. Some parasites evolve from external to internal parasitism, for example, the lung mites (*Halarachne*) of seals, the lung mites (*Pneumonyssus*) of Old World monkeys, and the chigoe fleas (*Tunga penetrans*), the female of which burrows under the skin of various animals, including man.

The fact that some parasites are in reality adjusted to an interspecies predator-prey relationship, rather than to a single host species, indicates a long establishment of such interspecies systems. The complex life cycle (Cyclomorphosis, p. 685) of malaria in man and anopheline mosquitoes affords a good illustrative example. Bird malaria is adjusted to birds and culicine mosquitoes in a similar type of life cycle.

Many instances of cyclomorphic populations adjusted to a number of aspects of the community are found among the parasitic worms—flukes (Fig. 249), tapeworms (Fig. 250), nematodes (Fig. 251), and acanthocephalans (Thomas, 1944). In many cases two hosts are involved, and in

host and enter either another snail of the same or a different species, or some other invertebrate such as an insect larva, and encyst. In some cases, the cercarias encyst within the redia or sporocyst without leaving the first host. Some species are transmitted passively to a second or third intermediate host. The cercarias of some families (Opisthorchidae, Heterophyidae, Strigeidae) invade the skin of fishes or amphib-

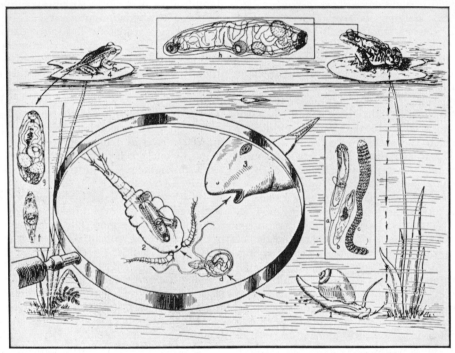

Fig. 249. Life cycle of a fluke (*Halipegus eccentricus*). Eggs passed in the feces of the frog (5) are eaten by a snail, *Physa* or *Helisoma* (1). The eggs hatch (a) and become sporocysts (b), each of which develops three or more rediae (c). Within a month each of the rediae has 50 or more cercaria (d) that may be eaten by *Cyclops* (2), in which they develop into mesocercaria in the body cavity. The tadpole (3) sucks up the infected *Cyclops*. The young flukes (f) migrate from the stomach to the mouth (g), and the adult fluke (h) finally migrates to the auditory tube of the adult frog (5). (From Thomas.)

some instances three or even four. The first intermediate host of all digenetic flukes is a mollusk, except in *Cercaria loosii*, which infects the marine annelid, *Hydroides hexagonus*, of the Atlantic coast of the United States (Martin, 1944).

Digenetic trematodes show a variety of types of life cycles. The cercarias of some (Fasciolidae, Notocotylidae, Paramphistomidae), on leaving the first host, encyst in the open and survive only if ingested by a suitable final host. Others (Echinostomatidae, Lepodermatidae) leave the snail

ians and encyst in the host tissues, there to be later ingested by a final host. The cercarias of the blood flukes (Schistosomatidae) leave the molluscan host and penetrate the skin of a fish, bird, or mammal directly, and migrate to the host circulatory system (Bartsch, 1946).

Such types of life cycles may have evolved one from the other. A possible free-living adult resembling a cercaria may have been characteristic of the ancestral types (Baylis, 1938). Baer (1933) observed that the number of genera of trematodes increase from the elasmobranchs to the mammals, indicating specialization parallel to that of the hosts.

Cyclomorphic populations with two hosts are also found among herbivorous insects. For example, the aphid (*Hormaphis hamamelidis*) causing the cone gall of the witch hazel (*Hamamelis virginiana*) has various species of birches for alternate hosts (*Betula nigra, B. papyracea, B. spinosa*). The winter eggs of this aphid are laid

causing the spiny gall of the witch hazel also has various species of birches for alternate hosts (*Betula alba, B. fontinalis, B. nigra, B. papyracea, B. pendula, B. pumila*). Both the witch hazels (Hamamelidaceae) and the birches (Betulaceae) are ancient types of plants.

The two species of aphids, although classified in different genera, have a close morphological relationship and similar life cycle. These species exemplify cyclic iso-

Fig. 250. Life cycle of a tapeworm (*Diphyllobothrium oblongatum*). The eggs (1–3) develop a coracidium (4), which hatches in the water. *Diaptomus oregonesis* (5) eats the coracidium and develops a procercoid (5A). Herring or minnows (6) eat the *Diaptomus*, and plerocercoids (6A, 6B, 6C) develop and encyst on the stomach wall or mesenteries. Infected fish are fed to young birds by their parents, and the mature tapeworms (7A, 7B, 7C) develop and are shed (7) into the water with the feces. (From Thomas.)

on the twigs of the witch hazel. The stem mother hatches from one of these eggs in the spring and attacks the lower surface of the leaves. Her continuous secretory stimulation causes the cone-shaped gall to develop on the upper surface. The generation produced in these galls migrates to birches upon which a number of generations are produced that differ markedly from each other. The forms and the number of generations seem to be fixed genetically and are not modified by the environment (see pp. 123, 347). In the fall, a generation that migrates to the witch hazel produces a wingless sexual generation, the females of which lay winter eggs. The aphid (*Hamamelistes spinosus*)

lation (p. 616), the sexual generation of *Hormaphis* occurring in August through October, and that of *Hamamelistes* in June. Mordvilko (1928, 1935) thinks that the ancestors of these aphids first evolved in subtropical regions where birches were lacking, and that the witch hazel spread north and the birches south. When the two plants came to live in the same region, the life cycle of the aphids as we see it today could have arisen.

Parasitic fungi like the rusts (Uredinales) often have complicated life cycles that include alternate hosts (pp. 614, 643). The white pine blister rust has a uredo stage on currants and gooseberries.

The adaptations of cyclomorphic species

to alternate hosts show how evolution brings about adjustment to the community as a system, and also indicate the long duration of the associations and relations within the community. Of course, these organisms are not only adjusted to different

In summary, we may say that reciprocal evolution of exploited and exploiting forms has occurred, that the selection pressures through exploitation gradually sort organisms in relation to each other, and that these evolutionary relationships create

Fig. 251. Life cycle of a nematode (*Cammallanus trispinosis*). The larval worms (1) pass out of the intestine of a turtle with the feces and are eaten by *Cyclops*. The worms (2) develop in the body cavity. If the *Cyclops* is eaten by a damsel fly, dragon fly, fish or newt, the worms (3) attach to the intestinal walls, and if these hosts are eaten by a turtle, the adult worms (4) infect the small intestines. (From Thomas.)

biotic aspects of the community, but show many adaptations to the physical factors as well. In other words, a combination of factors in the ecosystem has exerted selection pressures guiding the evolution of organisms toward adaptation to the system as a unit.

highly important interacting, interdependent, integrated systems of species.

TOLERATION

It has already been mentioned (p. 699) that extreme disoperation tends to be eliminated through natural selection. A predator or a parasite that causes a great decrease in the numbers of its prey or hosts is also eliminating its own food supply, so that exploitation has elements of disoperation. Disoperation is more severe when a parasite or predator attacks a single species of host or prey, and is probably less acute when many species are exploited. More efficient adaptation, however, is attained through specialization, and these two tendencies lead toward a balanced compromise, depending upon the quantitative pressures involved in each case. Natural selection must favor adaptations that tend to bring opposing systems into equilibrium, with a resulting evolution, at least in numerous instances, approaching toleration between species, one of which exploits the other (Baylis, 1938).

Animals depend upon plants directly or indirectly for carbohydrates, certain essential amino acids, and certain vitamins. Plants in turn have become dependent to a degree upon the activities of animals through the nitrogen, carbon, and phosphorus cycles (pp. 497–499), the geological influence of animals as soil modifiers (Chap. 16), and through their role in controlling plant enemies, dispersing seeds, and as pollinating agents. A balanced equilibrium between plants and plant-eating animals may be favorable to both.

It is an interesting hypothesis that plants have slowly become adjusted to the evolution of herbivores through various regenerative and protective devices. Grasses, through growth from the base of the leaf, are adjusted to the grazing herbivores and thus dominate the prairies where other types of plants that grow at the end of the stem are largely eliminated (Gunderson and Hastings, 1944). Cacti, through the development of spines, survive in desert areas where the plant population is reduced by the lack of water; without the spines these same plants would probably be eliminated by the larger herbivores. Cattle readily eat the prickly pear (Opuntia) when the spines are burned off by man. Camels have become adjusted to feeding on desert plants and will even eat the spiny prickly pear that has been introduced into North Africa. Other desert plants may be equally spiny or, like the creosote bush (Larrea), may evolve a repellent taste that gives as effective protection as spines. The

herbivores, near the bottom of the food chain, are in turn exploited by the predators and parasites that tend to keep their numbers down and thus prevent the overexploitation of the plants.

Animals that are likely to be attacked by predators have evolved defensive adaptations such as the spines of porcupines and hedgehogs; the poisonous spines of various caterpillars (e.g., Io); the stinging apparatus of scorpion fishes and of bees; the secretion of repellent fluids by millipedes, termite soldiers, ants, and toads; the protective coloration of walking sticks, sargassum fishes, and mice; the swiftness of escape of antelopes, squirrels, and crayfish; all matching the evolution of the predaceous adaptations of their enemies. The whole community tends, through the process of natural selection operating on complex coactions, to attain a relative equilibrium sufficient to carry the quantitative pattern of interspecies relations over long periods of time.

Equilibrium is here regarded as the condition in which the rate of change of population density on the average is approximately zero, and is, of course, independent of absolute density (Smith, 1939). An overall equilibrium may be established for average densities even for populations that may fluctuate periodically in relation to both regular and irregular environmental variations. Elton (1930) says: "The numbers of wild animals are constantly varying to a greater or less extent, and the variations are usually irregular in period and always irregular in amplitude." This statement is essentially true, but does not contra-indicate the attainment of a comparative balance in nature based upon long-term population relations (pp. 305, 391, 507–522).

The gross equilibrium of communities can sometimes be detected through the introduction of a species that has not evolved with the system (p. 723). A good example is the effect of the gypsy moth (Porthetria dispar), introduced into Massachusetts in 1869. By 1890 so much destruction of forest and shade trees had occurred that the State Board of Agriculture instituted control measures and the pest was reduced considerably. In 1900 the state appropriations were discontinued with consequent rapid increase and spread that still continue, in spite of vigorous attempts to control the pest. The caterpillars defoliate large areas of forest trees, and one complete defoliation will kill a pine or a hemlock (Sheals and Brown, 1944). Several native predators and parasites have helped reduce the moth populations, but the depredations are still much more severe in New England forests than they are in the original European habitat.

into the Hawaiian Islands and soon afterward came close to wiping out the sugar cane industry. The insect was later found to be native to Australia, where it was neither common nor considered a pest. Parasites and predators were introduced into Hawaii from Australia and were so effective in controlling the leaf-hopper that it is no longer seriously injurious (Zimmerman, 1943; see also J. H. Smith, 1944).

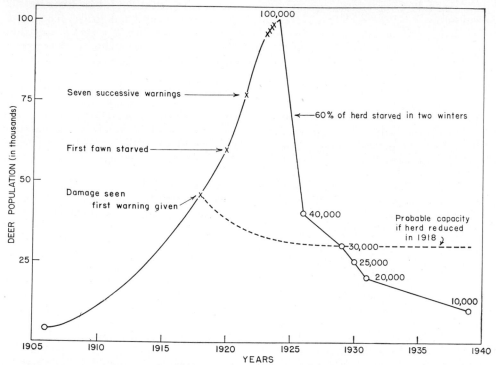

Fig. 252. The effect of removal of predators on populations of deer on the Kaibab plateau in Arizona (727,000 acres). Six hundred pumas were removed in 1907–1917, 74 in 1918–1923, and 142 in 1924–1939. Eleven wolves were removed in 1907–1923 and were exterminated by 1926. Three thousand coyotes were removed in 1907–1923 and 4388 in 1923–1939. (Redrawn from Leopold.)

For control purposes, many species of predators and parasites of the gypsy moth have been brought into New England, and the search continues for others. Some of these enemies, including ten species of parasites, have become established and give promise of checking the populations of the moth. However, the equilibrium reached through long evolution of the community in Europe has not been attained during the relatively short history of this species in New England (see also Dowden, 1946).

About 1900, the sugar cane leaf-hopper (*Perkinsiella saccharicida*) was introduced

Predation is not always wholly deleterious for the species preyed upon. A balance or relative equilibrium may develop that is somewhat beneficial to both predator and prey. The deer population in the Kaibab plateau of Arizona was probably originally adjusted to its food supply and to its predators. Pumas and wolves seem to have kept the number of deer well below the carrying capacity of the range. The original population is estimated to have been about 4000 deer. After the shooting of the pumas, the deer population increased beyond the carrying capacity of its winter food supply. The herd declined from 100,000 to 40,000 in 1924–1925, and from 30,000 to 20,000 in 1929 to 1931. The normal carrying capacity of the Kaibab plateau is estimated to be about 30,000 deer, and this number does not damage the plant forage as do excessive population eruptions. In 1939 the population stood at about 10,000, with few pumas and a depleted range (Leopold, 1943; Fig. 252).

It would seem that an optimal number of predators keeps the deer population in better adjustment to its food supply, and the plants are also indirectly benefited by these predators in the community. The original population of predators on the Kaibab plateau kept the deer below the carrying capacity of the range, but too many were eliminated by man for benefit to either the deer or the forage plants. Leopold (1943a) suggests that wolves be allowed to increase in overbrowsed areas of Wisconsin in order to benefit the deer (see also Sears, 1937, p. 261; Cartwright, 1944).

The best illustrations of the evolution of toleration are the host-parasite relations of certain pathogenic organisms (p. 260). Huff (1938) gives a summary discussion and interpretation of the facts indicating reciprocal evolution of hosts and parasites.

The hemoflagellates of the family Trypanosomidae were originally parasites of invertebrates, particularly of insects. Many species are found only in insect digestive tracts and are transmitted through the feces of the hosts. Tsetse flies (*Glossina*) transmit African sleeping sickness of man and nagana of animals; the sand fly (*Phlebotomus*) transmits the oriental sore; reduviid bugs transmit Chagas' disease; and *Trypanosoma lewisi* of rats is transmitted by rat fleas.* The pathogenicity of some of these species—for example, the African sleeping sickness of man—is great, while *T. lewisi* of rats and *T. duttoni* of house mice are nonpathogenic. *T. lewisi* increases in numbers for about 4–7 days after the infection of the rat. An antibody (ablastin) then inhibits further reproduction of the parasites, but does not kill them (Taliaferro, 1941). Also, specific trypanolysins that kill many parasites are acquired on about the tenth day of infection. The

* *Trypanosoma equiperdum*, which causes a venereal disease of equines (dourine), lacks an insect vector and is an exception.

course of infection for *T. lewisi* and *T. duttoni* in their respective hosts is similar, but the *T. duttoni* population does not rise parallel with that of *T. lewisi*, and the mouse has a natural immunity through macrophage function that is similar in effect to the acquired immunity through macrophage function in the rat (Taliaferro and Pavlinova, 1936; Taliaferro, 1938).

The trypanosomes of the native game animals of Africa are comparatively harmless to their natural hosts, but two (*T. gambiense* and its close relative, *T. rhodesiense*) are highly pathogenic to man, while all attempts to infect man with *T. brucei* have failed, although morphologically it is indistinguishable from the other two species and is probably the ancestral species of the human parasites. *Trypanosoma gambiense* in man produces chronic sleeping sickness with well marked nervous symptoms, while *T. rhodesiense* in man causes a toxic disease without nervous symptoms. *Trypanosoma brucei* produces a disease in laboratory animals like that produced in man by *T. rhodesiense*. Hoare (1943) thinks that *T. brucei* originally occurred in antelopes and gave rise to the two species in man, *T. gambiense* being somewhat older in man than *T. rhodesiense*. *Trypanosoma brucei* is nonpathogenic in antelopes, but produces the disease nagana in cattle (p. 476).

Huff concludes that there is a strong likelihood that the trypanosomes have been adapted to insect hosts much longer than to vertebrates, to wild game animals of Africa much longer than to man or cattle, and that evolution toward toleration has probably occurred in the older associations. Natural immunity may have evolved in some instances, while in others there has been an evolution of mechanisms producing acquired immunity. Acquired immunity, however, is not always the result of an evolutionary reaction to the specific parasite.

Malarial protozoans indicate that their major phyletic evolution (megaevolution) has been more closely tied to that of their insect vectors than to their vertebrate hosts (Huff, 1945). *Plasmodium* is found in the blood of man, apes, monkeys, bats, birds, and lizards, and is transmitted to these hosts by mosquitoes. *Haemoproteus* occurs in birds, turtles, and snakes. The hippoboscid flies transmit the *Haemoproteus* of birds, while the vector for the reptile types is unknown. The vertebrate host of *Leucocytozoon* is always a bird, and the two species for which the life cycle is known are transmitted by blackflies (Simuliidae). In all three genera, the asexual cycle is in the vertebrate, most of the sexual cycle is in the fly, and no free-living stage occurs (see p. 686). Sporozoans (*Lankesteria culicis*) related to malarial parasites infect mosquitoes without an intermediate host.

The evolutionary parallelism between the original hosts and the parasites would be expected to be greater than between the more recent hosts. Also, one would expect greater adjustment to the original hosts. This adaptation would result from natural selection, since the strains of parasites having the greatest pathogenicity would probably be eliminated through the death of the host (Disoperation, p. 699). Likewise, the more susceptible of the hosts would succumb to the effects of the parasite. Through the closer phylogenetic relationship of the fly vectors compared with that of the vertebrate hosts, one would assume that malarial protozoans evolved primarily with the Diptera.

Huff (1938) found that infected and noninfected mosquitoes showed no significant differences in (*a*) ability to lay viable eggs, (*b*) length of life after a blood meal, (*c*) length of time between a blood meal and oviposition, and (*d*) number of eggs laid after a blood meal. He concludes that there are no pathological effects in the mosquitoes, although the vertebrate hosts may suffer from the disease. Again, toleration in the older parasite-host adjustment is indicated, while pathogenicity is characteristic of the more recent parasite-host relationship.

Hoare (1943) states:

"In a non-susceptible animal (or plant) various factors may prevent a parasite from setting up an infection. Thus, the character of the digestive juices may not be suitable for hatching the cysts of intestinal protozoa, or the serum may possess natural parasiticidal properties which affords protection against infection with blood protozoa. It is known, for instance, that the oocysts of coccidia, when ingested by animals other than natural hosts, pass unchanged through the alimentary tract. The resistance of man to infection with *Trypanosoma brucei* is probably due to the fact that normal human serum kills this trypanosome, whereas it has no effect upon *T. gambiense*. The other race, *T. rhodesiense,* appears to occupy an intermediate position—in the human body it resists the action of serum, but may lose this property after passages through other animals."

Huff and Coulston (1946) postulate several barriers that may prevent an infection by malarial parasites. First, phagocytic cells or humoral substances may destroy the sporozoites before they reach the appropriate host cells. Secondly, there may be cellular or humoral interference with the change of parasites from tissue cells to erythrocytes. Thirdly, the host may develop immunity to the parasite in the erythrocyte stages. These hazards to the parasites differ in different species of hosts. The saurian malarial parasite, *Plasmodium mexicanum,* produces gametocytes in its normal host lizard, *Scleroporus ferrariperezi,* but not in the lizard, *Crotaphytus collaris.* The ability to form gametocytes was regained when the parasite was experimentally transferred to close relatives of the normal host (*Scleroporus olivaceus* and *S. undulatus*).

Physiological characteristics of parasites in combination with ecological adjustment of hosts may influence the evolution of the parasite-host relationship. The ciliate protozoan, *Balantidium coli,* chiefly occurring in domestic pigs, is nonpathogenic in the pig and is often pathogenic in man. It feeds mainly on starch, which is abundant in the intestine of a pig, but is scarce in the intestine of man. Insufficiency of starch in the human intestine may induce the ciliate to attack the walls with consequent symptoms of balantidiosis (Hoare, 1943, p. 142).

Ball (1943) takes exception to the absolute rule that "a high degree of pathogenicity of a parasite is *prima facie* evidence of a recent and still imperfect development of the host-parasite relation." He states that "evolution may, in many cases, have brought about a mutual adaptation between host and parasite resulting in relative harmlessness of the relation, but in other instances no such decrease in pathogenicity seems to have occurred; and in still others as the parasite becomes better adapted for life in its host, it has become rather more than less capable of producing

Carteria or *Chlamydomonas*). The organs of nutrition degenerate, so that the flagellate functions as an organ in the animal. The flatworms live on the products of the symbiotes, but in a later stage digest the flagellates, lay eggs, and die. Thus, in this instance, the animal is dependent upon the symbiotes for its existence, but the flagellates are also free-living, and do not seem to have evolved toward dependence upon *Convoluta*.

Gilbert (1944) demonstrates that alga-inhabited eggs of *Ambystoma maculatum* have lower mortality, develop more rapidly, and hatch earlier than do alga-free eggs. The larvae from alga-inhabited eggs are both larger and more advanced. The algae, in this case, multiply within the egg envelopes, and apparently benefit from the association. Gohar (Yonge, 1944) has given experimental evidence that the corals belonging to the family Xeniidae (Alcyonacea) are incapable of predatory activity and starve in the presence of animal food in the dark. In the light, animals harboring zooxanthellae are healthy and vigorous, even without animal food.

Mutualism between these symbiotes and their animal hosts is a possibility, but it is questionable whether the symbiotes have undergone evolutionary adaptation to their hosts. The possibility of preadaptive mutualism has been demonstrated between algae (*Chlorella pyrenoidosa*) and chick connective tissue cells in tissue culture (Buchsbaum and Buchsbaum, 1934; Buchsbaum, 1937a; see also p. 246).

Fungi are actively cultivated by several groups of insects, including the ambrosia beetles (some Scolytidae and all Platypodidae), the fungus-growing ants (Attini), and the fungus-growing termites (Macrotermitinae) (Wheeler, 1907, 1923, 1928b; Hegh, 1922; Heim, 1940; Weber, 1941, 1945; Brues, 1946). The ambrosia beetles are cosmopolitan, the fungus-growing ants are found only in the tropical and warm temperate regions of the New World, and the fungus-growing termites are confined to the warm regions of the Orient and Africa. The fact that the genera within each of these insect groups are phylogenetically related indicates that the insects have evolved in relation to the fungus-growing behavior (p. 246).

The ambrosia beetles burrow in wood, but do not eat it. These fungus-eating beetles have weak maxillae, in contrast with the strong maxillae of their bark-eating and wood-eating relatives. They are somewhat social in their behavior, adults and young living together in connected burrows. The adult beetles feed the larvae and remove larval excrement. Large larvae sometimes protect small larvae. In certain genera, the larvae are located in small pockets in the sides of the burrows. The beetles "plant" the spores of the fungi in the new burrows after carrying the spores from the parental burrow. Brushes of hairs on the front of the head are a common adaptation for transporting the spores. Some beetles carry fungal material in their stomachs. After "planting," the fungi grow upon the sides of the chambers in the sapwood.

The fungi are reported to be specific for particular beetles, irrespective of the kind of wood in which the burrows are made. The fungi are partly nourished by the excrement of the larvae. These facts indicate that the fungi have also evolved in relation to the beetles, and an evolution of mutualism may be presumed (Chamberlin, 1939).

The attine ants indicate a phylogenetic sequence in the development of their fungus-growing behavior. The more primitive genera use the gathered excrement of caterpillars and beetles for a substrate in which the fungus mycelium grows, and from which they harvest mycelial tufts or spherical bodies (bromatia). The more specialized genera (i.e., *Atta*, Fig. 253) cut pieces of leaves from growing trees and transport these leaf fragments to their underground nest, where minute workers, which never leave the nest, make a spongy substrate from the leaves upon which the fungus grows.

A pellet of fungus mycelium is transported by the new queen in an infrabuccal pocket. After digging a burrow in the ground after her nuptial flight, the female expels the fungal pellet. Hyphae soon develop, and the growing fungus is manured by anal droplets. The worker ants develop in about forty days or more and soon take over the care of the fungus bed. The first mature workers, a few days after their appearance, break out of the nest and immediately bring in pieces of leaves which are chewed up and inserted in the fungus garden. Manuring ceases, and the fungus is now entirely cultivated by the workers. The spherical bromatia are harvested and used for food by the entire colony. The larvae are fed with the bromatia, and the ants eat little food other than the fungus.

The knowledge of the taxonomy and phylogeny of the fungi cultivated by the transported and "planted" by the reproductive pair is not known. The fungus species are usually not specific for the termite species or genera, and are also free-living, so that it is doubtful whether the fungus has evolved any mutualistic adaptations. Heim (1940) says that some species of fungi (*Collybia albuminosa*) are found only in termite nests and are dependent upon

Fig. 253. Leaf-cutting ants (*Atta*) carrying portions of leaves to their subterranean nest, where fungus is cultivated on a substrate of chewed leaves. Note the individual at the left, riding back to the nest on the leaf carried by another worker. (Photograph by Ralph Buchsbaum.)

attine ants is not sufficient to establish their reciprocal evolution with the ants.

The fungus-growing termites (Macrotermitinae) cultivate fungi on the excrement of the workers. The claylike excrement is built into rather elaborate structures or gardens with involutions that provide a large surface with abundant aeration. Ventilation tunnels often connect the fungus gardens with the surface wall of the mound, but do not penetrate into the open air (Grassé, 1937). Small spherical bodies develop from the mycelium and are harvested and fed to the reproductive pair and to the nymphs by the workers. Adult workers and soldiers feed almost exclusively on cellulose contained in grass, leaves, and wood. The means by which the fungus is termites for their existence. If this be true, some degree of mutualism has evolved in both fungus and termite species.

Many plants, for example, the burdock (*Arctium minus*), have evolved adaptations whereby the seeds cling to the fur of mammals and are thus dispersed (p. 251). Both hooks and adhesive surfaces have evolved (Ridley, 1930). These adaptations are as distinct as the numerous adjustments for seed dispersal by wind and by water. There is no indication, however, that the mammal in any way benefits by the clinging seed in its fur.

On the other hand, fruits, by their edibility, fragrance, changing color, and position, induce birds and other animals to transport mature seeds (Ridley, 1930;

Gunderson and Hastings, 1944; see p. 251). Experiments show, in some instances, that seeds germinate more rapidly after subjection to the digestive juices of birds and numerous seeds pass unharmed through the alimentary canal. Some birds swallow the fruit and expectorate the seeds. They commonly feed young birds only with the fruit, depositing the seeds in the vicinity of the nest. Birds seem to be the most effective of all animals in distributing seeds over wide areas, and many, such as the orioles, have sharp, pointed bills adapted to fruit-eating. The reciprocal evolution of fruits and animals (particularly birds) probably originated and expanded during the Tertiary period.

Phillips (1926) discussed the influence of the feeding habits of the South African wild pig (*Potamochoerus choeropotamus*) upon the germination and dispersal of forest tree seeds. Of twenty-six species of tree seeds studied, about a third of the species are mostly destroyed by passage through the pig; about a third are assisted; and about a third are partially destroyed, but the survivors germinate more readily. Phillips concludes that the pigs benefit the forests by assisting in the dispersal and germination of the seeds of a number of tree species, and by providing numerous improved seed beds through their "rooting" activities. Harm to the forest is slight, although it might increase if the pig population increased.

The relation between pollinating insects and flowering plants, found in all terrestrial communities and at the surface of some fresh-water communities, affords the most important example of mutualism (McDougall, 1941). The adaptive interactions of plants and animals with reference to pollination are described in Chapter 17, page 248. Other instances of mutualism discussed in this division are either less convincing examples of reciprocal evolution, or, if truly mutual, are less important in large community systems.

Lutz (1924, 1933) showed that flowers have ultraviolet patterns, invisible to the eye of man, to which pollinating insects react. He discounts the theory that variations of flower colors are adaptations to insects through the action of selection pressure exerted by the insects. However, other types of pollinating mechanisms in flowers

are obviously specifically adjusted to the structural and behavior characteristics of particular insects, and there is every reason to assume that flower color is also adaptive to insects and that insects exert some selective pressure influencing the evolution of the flowers. Some colors of plants are surely nonadaptive, however—for example, the turning of leaves to yellow and red in the autumn—and some colors invisible to man may be adaptive (Lutz, 1933a).

Gunderson and Hastings (1944) give the postulated stages of adaptation of insects to flowers as follows: (1) insects generally with biting mouth parts, not adapted to but occasionally visiting flowers; (2) insects partly adapted to flower visits—short-tongued bees and some flies (partially effective in cross pollination); (3) fully adapted flower visitors with both structure and behavior fitted for obtaining nectar and pollen, while at the same time they effect cross pollination—long-tongued bees, butterflies, and hawk-moths. Correspondingly, we find a large variety of flower adaptations to insect pollination (Ames, 1944; Craigie, 1927; Rau, 1945; see also p. 249).

Haldane (1932) discusses some of the disadvantages as well as the advantages accruing to the insect-pollinated plant. Wind pollination is fairly efficient and does not necessitate the energy expended in the growth of petals, nectar, and odor. Insect pollination must limit the distribution of the plant, particularly when mutual adaptation is confined to a single species of pollinator for a single species of plant. Differential maturity of anther and stigma, dimorphic flowers, and diecious plants insure cross pollination, but make the transfer of pollen more precarious.

Selection has reversed the direction of evolution in some types of flowers (Huxley, 1942, p. 109) from animal pollination toward self pollination and wind pollination. It thus may be assumed that, in such cases, a delicate selective pressure exists, first favoring and then suppressing mutualism.

In some instances mutualism may revert to exploitation, as in the orchid, *Cryptostylis leptochila*, that stimulates ichneumonid flies (*Lissopimpla semipunctata*) to simulate copulation with its flowers, which resemble the female flies in form and color (Coleman, 1927, 1938).

Let us now consider some of the reported examples of mutualism found between species of animals.

McAnally and Phillipson (1944) state that the diet of ruminants consists of large quantities of cellulose and other carbohydrates that are indigestible except by the aid of bacteria (p. 712), and that protozoans probably do not play a vital part in the digestion of these materials. Species of protozoans of the genus *Diplodinium* inhabit the rumen of cattle, are capable of digesting cellulose (Hungate, 1943), and may be considered mutualistic. Other protozoan genera in the rumen of cattle do not digest cellulose.

In many ways the most remarkable example of evolutionary mutualism known is that between the intestinal flagellates of wood-eating termites and roaches and their hosts. Largely through the work of Cleveland (1924, 1925, 1925a, 1926, 1928), Cleveland, Hall, Sanders, and Collier (1934), Hungate (1938, 1939, 1941, 1944a), and Kirby (1937, 1944), we now have a fairly clear understanding of the mutualism that has evolved between these insects and their intestinal flagellates. Experimental evidence is conclusive that an interdependence between these associated animals exists. Some of the protozoans seem to be commensals or parasites in the hindgut of the insects, but a large number of species ingest wood particles, and the cellulose is broken down by the specific enzymes cellulase and cellobiase in the body of the protozoan. The resulting products, including sugar (dextrose), are then squeezed back into the midgut, where they are absorbed by the termite or roach. Neither the roaches nor the termites that normally harbor these intestinal flagellates can survive long without the protozoans unless they are fed a diet other than cellulose. It is now certain that the protozoans are the agents that enable these insects to feed upon hard wood.

Cleveland, Hall, Sanders, and Collier (1934) give many details of the morphological adjustments of the wood-roach (*Cryptocercus punctulatus*) to the protozoan faunule (Fig. 254). Because of the remarkable functional adaptations of the hindgut of *Cryptocercus* to the symbiotic protozoans, there would seem to be no question that the evolution of many of these structures was the result of selection of the efficient interspecies system as a functional unit. The hindgut of the termites does not show such striking morphological adaptations for harboring and controlling the protozoa, but the physiological adjustments are doubtless the result

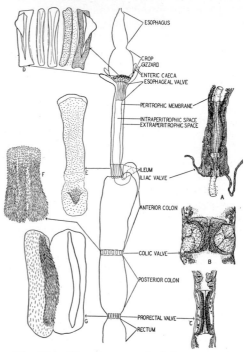

Fig. 254. Alimentary canal of the protozoan-harboring roach, *Cryptocercus punctulatus,* showing position and structure of valves. Central figure: flattened inner surface; *A, B, C,* longitudinal sections; *D, E, F, G,* surface views of portions of valves showing one or more of the chitinous bars of which the valves are composed. (From Cleveland, Hall, Sanders, and Collier.)

of a long evolution of the mutualistic relationship.

Hungate (1939) postulates the mutualistic relations of termites and protozoans as follows:

"(1) The termite comminutes the wood and transports it to the hind-gut where (2) the protozoa digest it and (3) metabolize it anaerobically, thereby deriving their necessary energy and forming metabolic products which (4) are absorbed by the termite and oxidized to satisfy its energy requirements, an action which not only serves the termite but also aids the protozoa by (5) removing harmful metabolic products. In addition, the oxygen needs of the termite maintain a low oxygen tension which (6) permits the protozoa to survive and at the same time insures that their metabolism shall be anaerobic and result in products useful to the termite. The unique conditions which the protozoa require and which the termite supplies may explain in part the restricted distribution of the protozoa."

Perhaps the best evidence for the dependence of the protozoa on their roach and termite hosts is the fact that all the species of flagellates of the orders Polymastigina and Hypermastigina so far recorded from these insects are wholly confined to the termites or the single species of wood-eating roach. Of the eight families of hypermastigotes, six are found in both *Cryptocercus punctulatus* and in termites, although, with one exception (*Trichonympha*), the genera are exclusively found either in the roach or the termites. Of the polymastigotes, one family (Pyrsonymphidae) has one genus in the roach and two genera exclusively in termites. Another family (Trichomonadidae) has one genus in the roach, in termites and in other insects, while eight genera of the subfamily Devescovininae are confined to termites.

Many of the protozoa are species-specific or are confined to closely related groups of host species. In some instances closely related species of the same protozoan genus occur in a single host species and appear to have originated in this narrow ecological niche (p. 628). These protozoans seem to be incapable of an independent existence, and contrary to the potentialities of most free-living flagellates, nearly all are incapable of forming cysts that might enable them to survive periodically unfavorable conditions. The protozoan phylogeny seems to be largely correlated with the phylogeny of their hosts—so much so that both Cleveland and Kirby think that the mutualism goes back to the ancestors of the roaches and the termites.

Martynov (1937) presents evidence that the modern order of roaches (Blattodea or Blattaria), with their parchment-like forewings, could not be the ancestors of termites (Isoptera) with their membranous wings, even though primitive roaches are well represented in Pennsylvanian rocks (Carpenter, 1930). Martynov thinks that the common ancestor belonged to an ex-

tinct hypothetical order of Devonian or Carboniferous age.

All the species of the four primitive families of termites (Mastotermitidae, Kalotermitidae, Hodotermitidae, and Rhinotermitidae) have intestinal flagellates, and there is fair circumstantial evidence that these families were well established in the Mesozoic age. It may therefore be assumed that this mutualistic relationship between the insects and their intestinal flagellates has been in existence and evolving for 150 to 250 million years. In 1948, 528 species of termites were known to harbor these flagellates, and from them about 250 species of flagellates have been described. Numerous additional species of termites and protozoans await description.

It is also fairly obvious that the family and social life of the roaches and termites evolved in part as a necessary adjustment for the transmission of the protozoa, and that the difference in colonizing behavior between the roaches and the termites is also associated with differences in the mode of protozoan infection. Cleveland, Hall, Sanders, and Collier (1934, p. 209) say:

"Once the protozoan infection is acquired in *Cryptocercus*, it is never lost until death; and any individual after acquiring it is capable of living by itself during the rest of its life. This, however, is in direct contrast to termites (even lower ones where the reproductive individuals do not lose the ability to feed on wood) since the protozoa are lost at each moult, and colony life is essential in order that reinfection from non-moulting individuals may take place. On the other hand, two sexually mature first form reproductive adult termites may leave the colony and start a new one; but this is impossible in *Cryptocercus*, for sexually mature adults very probably do not moult and, unless they do, they could not infect their young with protozoa. Hence, in order to start a new colony, it is necessary for nymphs to accompany adults, so that when the nymphs moult they can transmit protozoa to the young which the adults in the meantime have produced."

It should be noted in this connection that all termite species have winged colonizing reproductives, while *Cryptocercus* is wingless in both sexes.

It seems that in this case at least we are forced to the conclusion that the mutualistic relationship has resulted in the evolution of something closely approaching an interspecies supraorganism about as well integrated as parts of an individual organism, with selection operating on the system as a functional whole, and favoring greater living efficiency for the mutualistic partners (Emerson, 1947; see also p. 721).

It is noteworthy that this mutualism, attained and evolved over great periods of time, has nevertheless been lost in the evolution of the most advanced termites (Termitidae). Circumstantial evidence, particularly from zoogeography, points to the origin of the family Termitidae by Cretaceous times. These higher termites have not only diverged into the largest number of species (1333 described by 1947), but they are without question the most successful termites in tropical regions the world over and have advanced far beyond their primitive relatives in the integration of their social systems and in their remarkable nest-building instincts. Although many feed on leaves, grass, fungi, and animal excrement, they also feed on cellulose in the same hard wood that may also be occupied by the flagellate-harboring termites.

The physiology of digestion has not been studied in these advanced termites, but they must have some ability to digest cellulose without the assistance of intestinal flagellates, which are lacking in their intestines. Hungate (1938) reports that the termite, *Zootermopsis angusticollis* (Hodotermitidae), digests one-third of the total amount of wood digested without the aid of its protozoa. Possibly this ability has been expanded in the Termitidae.

Thus, the flagellate-termite mutualism may have been an inhibiting factor in the evolution of higher social functions, and once rid of it, a great advance and further adaptive radiation of the social system could take place. Further progressive evolution is more in the direction of controlling the intrasocial environment (p. 672) than an adaptation toward diverse external habitats. Much more information is needed before valid conclusions may be drawn, but it appears that in this instance interspecies mutualism is less efficient than intraspecies internal organic adaptation and social adjustment.

It may be possible that evolutionary mechanisms leading to adaptive modification may be speeded up when operating through a single germ plasm, rather than through the two or more germ plasms involved in a mutualistic association. If this be true, it may help to explain the generalization that the integration of the individual organism and of the intraspecies population is far more advanced than the integration of interspecies systems in the community.

The evolution of the ants, remarkably convergent to that of the termites, had no

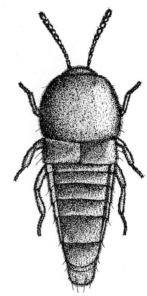

Fig. 255. *Perinthus vestitus*, a staphylinid synoekete in the nest of the termite, *Nasutitermes octopilis*, in British Guiana.

interspecies mutualism to start with, but evolved extreme intraspecies population integration. Both the more advanced ant and termite populations, with a degree of social control of their habitats, have set the stage for the evolution of a mutualistic relation between the social insects and many other organisms (p. 253). The cultivation of fungi has already been discussed (pp. 713, 714). The relations of the *myrmecophiles* and *termitophiles** to their hosts afford another illuminating example of mutualism.

* We here refer to organisms living in the galleries with ants and termites by the established terms, *myrmecophiles* and *termitophiles*, though regretting the anthropomorphism (p. 8). Organisms occupying the nests of these social insects are called *myrmecocoles* or *termitocoles*, including those forms not living in the galleries of the hosts (O. Park, 1929).

The various types of organisms commonly found living in close association with social insects, particularly with the ants and termites, are classified by Wasmann (1920) in five ecological categories on the basis of their relationship to their

Fig. 256. *Trachopeplus setosus*, a staphylinid symphile from the nest of the termite, *Nasutitermes nigriceps*, in British Guiana.

hosts: (1) *synechthrans*, or persecuted predators; (2) *synoeketes*, or tolerated scavengers (Fig. 255); (3) *trophobionts*, living in the trophoporic field, usually outside the nest, but attended for their secre-

bionts and symphiles return some compensation to the social insects and receive considerable attention from their hosts, much of which is doubtless beneficial to the symbiote, thus establishing a true mutualistic relation. As might be expected, there are various gradations and peculiar combinations of relationships between these various insects and their hosts, but Wasmann's classification seems to have stood the test of time, and the majority of new species discovered fall readily into one or the other of these categories. In some instances there is reason to believe that the categories represent evolutionary sequences.

Wheeler (1928b), in an expanded and modified version of Wasmann's classification, gives several examples of relationships that are less readily classified into these categories. For instance, the first instar larva of a Queensland moth, *Cyclotorna monocentra*, is an ectoparasite on a species of leaf hopper (Cicadellidae) that is attended on a tree and "milked" by the ant, *Iridomyrmex sanguineus*. The caterpillar is carried to the ant's nest, where it trans-

Fig. 257. *Termitonicus mahout*, a staphylinid synoekete that rides on the heads of the workers of the termite, *Velocitermes beebei*, and takes portions of the food passed from one worker to another.

tions; (4) *symphiles*, or true guests within the nest, that return exudates to their hosts who feed and guard them (Fig. 256); (5) *parasites*, both external and internal.

The synechthrans, synoeketes, and parasites may be included under various aspects of exploitation and toleration. The tropho-

forms into a second stage larva that exudes a liquid upon which the ants feed. This larva sucks the juices from ant grubs. The mature caterpillar follows the ants back to a tree, where it pupates. Here is certainly a peculiar combination of relationships that could be partially classified under the categories of trophobiont, synechthran, symphile, and parasite.

The staphylinid beetle, *Termitonicus mahout* (Fig. 257), rides on the heads of worker termites, *Velocitermes beebei*, and imbibes nutritive liquids passed by mouth between the termites. This unusual type of termitophile may be classified as a synoekete, although most synoeketes are scavengers, with little direct contact with their hosts.

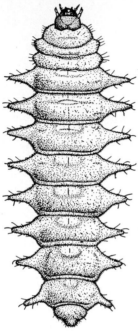

Fig. 258. Larva of a histerid beetle from the nest of *Velocitermes beebei* in British Guiana. While termite workers were licking the abdominal exudatoria, the larva was feeding on young termites.

The adaptive evolution of myrmecophilous symphiles is illustrated by the convergent appearance of trichome glands in separately evolved groups of beetles, including the Staphylinidae, Clavigerinae (Pselaphidae), Paussidae, Histeridae, and other insects (Wheeler, 1926). Through some sort of stimulation, perhaps odor, these red or golden setae at the openings of clustered unicellular glands are licked and sucked by the ants (O. Park, 1932).

The symphiles in termite nests exhibit convergent evolution of glandular structures that secrete a fatty exudate (McIndoo, 1923). In some cases, particularly in larval insects (Fig. 258), but rarely in adults (Fig. 259), the "exudatoria" may be numerous outgrowths from the body wall (Silvestri, 1920). Especially in adult symphiles, the exudate glands are usually distributed over swollen body surfaces (Emerson, 1935; Seevers, 1937; see Figs. 256, 260). Insects showing swollen soft whitish bodies are termed *physogastric*. Physogastry has appeared convergently many times within the staphylinid beetles, and also in several other groups of insects, particularly among the termitophilous flies (Fig. 260).

The true symphiles are commonly monoxenous, each species living only in the nests of one host species. Speciation of the termitophiles often parallels speciation of the hosts (Emerson, 1935).

Some ants procure a large part of their food from trophobiotic aphids and scale insects. In a number of instances an aphid species is dependent upon the ants for its existence, but in no instance is the ant dependent upon a given species of aphid or other trophobiont.

Ants and termites benefit even less from their symphiles. The symphiles are always dependent upon their hosts, often during different stages in their life cycles, but there is no reason to believe that these social insects could not survive in the absence of their mutualistic symphiles. A degree of mutualism has evolved between the hosts and their myrmecophiles and termitophiles, but the adaptations and the benefits pertain much more to the guests than to the hosts. The social life of the ants and termites evolved in large part independently of the guests, which exploit the social mechanisms and the socially controlled environment with only a moderate return to their hosts. Again we find that the organism and the social supraorganism exhibit a greater degree of cooperative integration than is to be found in the interspecies system.

In drawing conclusions from our brief survey of mutualistic relations, it is apparent that evolution has guided numerous organisms into a mutually beneficial cooperation, occasionally approaching the degree of cooperation characteristic of the parts of an individual organism. In addition to the more obvious and more extreme cases discussed, innumerable organisms doubtless benefit from subtle physiological, behavioristic, and population relationships that are largely uninvestigated.

an interspecies supraorganism. An interspecies system with organismic attributes surely exists (p. 440) and is a highly en-

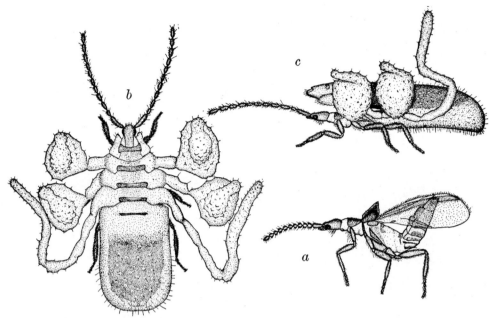

Fig. 259. Termitophilous staphylinid beetles from the nests of *Constrictotermes cavifrons* in British Guiana: *a, Spirachtha schioedtei* recently emerged from pupa case, in profile; *b, Spirachtha mirabilis* from above, physogastric form with three pairs of abdominal exudatoria; *c,* same, in profile, showing recurved abdomen with lateral exudate glands.

Considering the high degree of cooperation at the individual and population level of integration, it is somewhat surprising to find that the evolution of interspecies co-

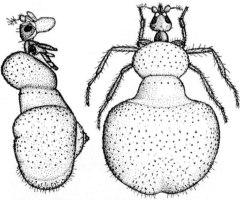

Fig. 260. *Ptochomyia* sp., a physogastric termitophilous fly (Termitoxeniidae) with reduced wings from the nest of *Macrotermes natalensis,* Belgian Congo.

operation is less obvious and more difficult to demonstrate. This conclusion should not be used to argue against the existence of

lightening ecological concept (for an opposed interpretation, see Bodenheimer, 1938).

The action of natural selection in guiding the evolution of genetically continuous intraspecies systems produces a degree of cooperative interrelationship not attained to such a marked degree when selective pressures guide genetically isolated organisms with ecological continuity.

THE INTERSPECIES SUPRAORGANISM

In the foregoing discussion of the evolution of interspecies systems, species pairs have been chosen in the main because they illustrate the simple, fundamental ecological relations between genetically discontinuous organisms. However, even a brief survey of any biocoenose reveals a great multiplicity and intertwining of innumerable interrelationships. There is danger that the whole may not be perceived from a focus on its basic parts.

The complexity of a small biocoenose may be partially illustrated by a diagram (Fig. 261) of the factoral relations (Emerson, 1939a). The arrows indicate the direction of the effect and are double-pointed if there is a reciprocal interaction between the factors. Organisms are boxed to distinguish them from other factors. Theoretically, each arrow could be evaluated quantitatively in terms of direct factors. Population growth and regular or irregular periodic fluctuations would produce quantitative variations in the influence of so many factors that such a static diagram is hardly more than a single frame in a long motion picture of ontogenetic and phylogenetic processes. Even with all the

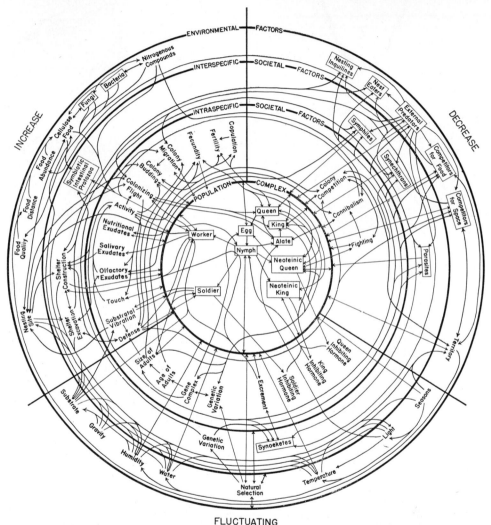

FLUCTUATING

Fig. 261. Diagram of the factoral complex influencing the population of a typical termite of the family Rhinotermitidae. Arrows indicate the direction of the effect.

or indirect effect upon the biocoenose. Diagrams illustrating even closely related associations would show striking qualitative and quantitative differences among population factors, differences that could often be arranged in an evolutionary order. The majority of these would probably be variations in the degree of influence of certain knowledge so far gained concerning any given biocoenose, this single frame is doubtless a gross oversimplification. Complete knowledge will never be obtained, but the slow process of establishing tiny relationships between the parts of this immense whole is both fascinating and highly valuable to mankind.

Any one of the large community systems is made up of many biocoenotic parts with varying degrees of independence and interdependence. Each part of the whole ecosystem exhibits a degree of independence, and relatively high degrees of independence characterize the major communities of the globe (p. 436).

In addition to the physical boundaries of biocoenoses and communities that are often fairly obvious, subtle *biotic barriers* occur at boundary lines or regions (Cain, 1944, p. 16). The evidence for the existence of biotic barriers—biotic limitations to dispersal and survival—may serve to give us a glimpse of some of the properties of biocoenoses and communities conceived as large and highly complex interspecies units. Boundaries assist in defining entities and may later be used in the further analysis and synthesis of the systems they limit.

If natural selection gradually results in balanced competition, exploitation, toleration, and mutualism leading to the adaptive integration of the biocoenose or community, one might expect to find that organisms from other associations would not always fit into such a balanced and coordinated system, even though the physical environment were favorable. Favorable niches in long-established systems would be saturated with forms adapted to the biotic as well as to the physical conditions (Robertson and Pearse, 1945).

The concept of biotic barriers may be tested by introducing animals and plants from foreign associations and observing the results. In most instances such tests have not been performed consciously. With the advent of modern transportation, many organisms are inadvertently introduced into ancient balanced communities. These unwitting experiments may be studied with profit.

The introduced organism sometimes seems to be preadapted to the new environment, both physical and biotic. Such a species may overrun the new habitat to the detriment of the whole community. An example is the introduction of the European rabbit into Australia (p. 643), where this placental mammal found little competition from the native marsupials, and an abundance of food in a climate not dissimilar to its original habitat.

An instance without such drastic effects upon the natural community is found in the introduction of the pheasant (*Phasianus colchicus torquatus*) into North America, where it is kept within bounds by the impact of the habitat and the sportsman. Errington (1946) states that introduced pheasants and Hungarian partridges (*Perdix perdix*), co-occupying the same tract of land with bobwhite quail (*Colinus virginianus*) in Wisconsin, lived at the expense of the quail, while native grouse did not affect quail populations, possibly because of less ecological overlap.

The introduction of the common honeybee (*Apis mellifica*) to the New World by the early European colonists is another example of an animal that adjusts to the community without previous evolutionary adaptation to the particular species assemblage. Once brought in, honeybees would doubtless be abundant in the New World even without domestication by man.

Ancient invasions of preadapted animals are indicated by correlated taxonomic, zoogeographic, and paleontologic patterns. At the time of the late Pliocene or early Pleistocene land connection between South and Central America about two million years ago, physical and climatic highways for dispersal were established (p. 662). Many mammals, including pumas, jaguars, small cats, deer, peccaries, tapirs, and squirrels, invaded South America from the north and sometimes evolved endemic genera, while others originating in South America, including the armadillos and porcupines, invaded Central and North America. Ground sloths apparently reached North America earlier, possibly via island connections, while procyonid carnivores and monkeys invaded South America by the same means (Mayr, 1946).

Biotic barriers did not prevent the dispersal of these animals, but other species with equal physical opportunities did not move into the new available regions. Parasites of these dispersing mammals often moved with their hosts (Jellison, 1942).

Although some preadapted organisms succeed in entering new regions, it is noteworthy that the majority of introduced species that maintain themselves succeed only in the highly modified environment of man or in the impoverished biota of islands and are largely excluded by the more complex natural environment of continental communities (Allan, 1936). Species in the United States, such as the house mouse, house rat, German roach, Mediterranean fruit fly, European cornborer, and English sparrow, succeed mainly under the protection of human agriculture or architecture.

Just what prevents these organisms from invading those communities not modified by man is not known in detail, but it is fairly obvious that there is a biotic barrier. It is true that most successfully introduced animals succeed under climatic conditions similar to those of their native habitat, and the number of pests introduced into the United States from temperate Europe and Asia far outweigh the number originating in the American tropics with an easy access by land.

However, climate is hardly the explanation for their limitation to the crops and dwellings of man. A few species adapted to warm climates may extend their normal climatic range by living in heated dwellings—for example, the Argentine ant, *Iridomyrmex humilis,* in University of Chicago buildings, and the common eastern termite, *Reticulitermes flavipes,* in buildings in Superior, Wisconsin. In many other organisms, the factor preventing the extension of range seems to involve the biotic environment.

First let us examine a few examples of introduced animals that succeed only in a man-modified habitat. The English sparrow (*Passer domesticus*) is a fairly critical case. This species was first introduced into New York City in 1850, and more individuals were subsequently again released in the same area. The sparrows rapidly spread over most of the United States. The numbers of individuals, however, are in direct proportion to the degree of environmental modification wrought by man. The greatest abundance is reached in the cities where few native birds are to be found, the numbers decrease on the edge of town and in the country districts where native birds are more abundant, and the sparrow is about as rare in virgin woods or prairies as native birds are rare in the centers of large metropolitan areas (see Bumpus, 1898).

Other examples in which introduced animals are limited to human habitats are found among insect pests causing serious economic damage. The Mediterranean fruit fly (*Ceratitis capitata*) was discovered in Florida in 1929 attacking citrus fruits and avacado pears. Although it spread over about a third of the state, it was completely exterminated by state and federal agencies in 1930 through the control of the citrus and avacado crops at a cost of seven million dollars. In the laboratory it was found that this fly could be raised on a great many different kinds of wild fruits, but it was never found in wild host plants away from cultivated orchards in Florida. In Hawaii the Mediterranean fruit fly completes its life cycle in the introduced wild guava.

The yellow fever vector, *Aedes aegypti,* introduced into Brazil, spread only through human habitats in cities and rural regions, but did not invade natural habitats similar to those originally harboring these mosquitoes in Africa.

The mosquito, *Anopheles gambiae,* native to the tropical belt of Africa, was introduced into eastern Brazil in 1930 and rapidly spread over 12,000 square miles north and west, but always in the vicinity of human habitations. Malaria of a virulent form accompanied the introduction of this species. In the first half of 1938, 100,000 cases and 14,000 deaths occurred. Non-human communities were not invaded, thus making complete eradication possible by 1940 through the joint efforts of the Rockefeller Foundation and the Brazilian government (Soper and Wilson, 1942).

In 1942, *Anopheles gambiae* invaded upper Egypt, reaching within 200 miles of Cairo. Again, the mosquito successfully bred only in the vicinity of human habitations. Again, it carried virulent malaria that caused the death of 130,000 persons. By early 1945 the species was completely eradicated from the area of its introduction by appropriate control measures.

The termite, *Cryptotermes dudleyi,* was introduced from the Orient into Panama as early as 1890 and is still a common termite in Panamanian houses, but it has not invaded the natural communities inhabited by closely related native species (Emerson, 1947). In one instance, this termite occupied furniture in a house within 40 feet of dense native rain forest; a thorough search for the species in the natural habitat failed to disclose its presence, although ecologically equivalent termites were abundant. The inability of introduced termites to invade native habitats, particularly on continents, is illustrated by other species numerous enough to indicate a general rule (Emerson, 1936).

Secondly, let us consider a number of examples of successful introduction or invasion of ecologically simple habitats in which man has not necessarily played a modifying role. In these cases the introduced form may become established in the simple natural community, but be unable to invade a more complex community. Islands and island-like habitats do not have such strong biotic barriers as may be present on the edges of continental communities (see p. 661).

the endemic land birds in the south Atlantic island of Tristan da Cunha (Murphy, 1938). The introduced ant, *Pheidole megacephala*, probably originally from central Africa (Weber, 1943), has destroyed many endemic species of ants in the Hawaiian Islands, West Indies, and Madeira. Wheeler, (1928b, p. 320) says that *P. megacephala* does not invade virgin forest in Australia, but is successful in neighboring habitats modified by man. On Madeira, *P. megacephala* was in turn replaced by another introduced ant, *Iridomyrmex humilis*. Still another ant, *Plagiolepis longipes*, introduced into Reunion from Cochin China, replaced endemic species of ants (Wheeler, 1926).

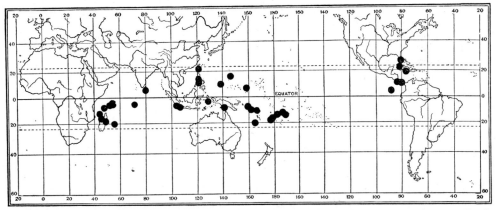

Fig. 262. Distribution of various species of *Prorhinotermes*, a genus of termites confined to islands or shores of mainlands that may recently have been islands. The species are probably dispersed in floating logs. They survive in areas of low competition in the tropics, but have been unable to survive in continental areas of high competition.

For example, the mongoose was introduced on Caribbean islands and South American shores where it has reached pest proportions, but it has been unable to invade the continental rain forest a few miles inland from the region of its marked success along the shore. Likewise, the house mouse may enter and survive natural conditions if introduced on islands or into regions of low competition such as occur in coastal Chile.[*]

Endemic species on islands have often succumbed to introduced forms. House rats on Lord Howe Island off the coast of Australia caused the extinction of endemic birds (Hesse, Allee, and Schmidt, 1937). Introduced hogs and rats eliminated all

[*] Personal communication from W. H. Osgood.

The same species introduced on an island may be successful, but fail to become established on a continent. The biotic barriers of continental communities may be effective for millions of years. For example, the termite genus *Prorhinotermes* (Fig. 262) is found on Ceylon, but is absent from India; it is found on Madagascar, Mauritius, and the Seychelles, but not in Africa; in the Netherlands East Indies, but not on the Malay peninsula; on Formosa, but not on the China coast; on various oceanic islands of the Pacific, but not in Australia; and in the West Indies and the coastal mangrove swamps of Florida and Central America (which may have been islands in recent geological times), but is rare or absent in the interior. Speciation in this genus has occurred in the various isolated island habitats, thus indicating ancient distribution. Thus, for long periods of time, what appears to be the biotic barrier of the continental communities has prevented the establishment of this otherwise tropicopolitan group of insects that probably has been continually dispersed in floating logs.

Phalangers are the only marsupials that have successfully invaded the Celebes. Mayr (1944) thinks it likely that phalangers have repeatedly landed on Borneo, but have been unable to withstand the predation by the abundant placental mammals. Borneo was recently part of the Indomalayan continent, while the Celebes have probably been insular through Tertiary times.

We do not know the exact nature of the biotic barriers that exclude these various animals from habitats foreign to them. The introduced or invading organism first must have the biotic essentials, such as food, to enable it to exist (p. 634). There is some indication that phytophagy or predation may exclude some organisms. Various degrees of competition may exclude others.

Phytophagy is probably the reason why many vegetable and ornamental plants fail to survive when introduced by man into natural communities. In the vicinity of a biological station in the British Guiana rain forest, leaf-cutting ants (*Atta*) destroyed such plants almost as soon as leaves were produced.

Predation seems to exclude certain introduced animals from native habitats. The Norway rat (*Rattus norvegicus*) lives far away from buildings in Wisconsin during the spring, summer, and fall, but the winter population under corn shocks is nearly annihilated, particularly by the great horned owl, *Bubo virginianus* (Errington, 1946).

Biotic restriction to certain natural habitats is surmised by Barney and Anson (1920), who suggested that the pigmy sunfish, *Elassoma zonatum*, which is populous in thick submerged vegetation, would succumb to predator fishes outside this habitat.

An example that possibly illustrates an ancient barrier of predators may be drawn from termite distribution. In the subfamily Nasutitermitinae (Fig. 263), the most primitive genera (*Syntermes, Cornitermes, Armitermes*, and so forth) are confined to the neotropical region, while specialized derived genera (*Nasutitermes* and *Subulitermes*) are tropicopolitan. The primitive genera all have mandibulate soldiers exhibiting gradations of defensive adaptation progressing in the direction of the nasute soldier, which has regressively lost its functional mandibles and protects the colony from such general predators as ants by the forceful ejection of a chemically irritating viscid fluid from a frontal projection of the head (p. 426; Fig. 149). From the present distribution of *Nasutitermes* and *Subulitermes* and their relatives, including many indigenous derived genera in such regions as Australia, Indomalaya, Africa, and South America, it may be presumed that dispersal of these nasute groups occurred during Cretaceous times or earlier. The primitive genera of the subfamily were doubtless in existence at the time when *Nasutitermes* and *Subulitermes* invaded the Old World from South America. There is no indication that a geographic, climatic, or food barrier existed. The flying powers of the primitive genera and the nasute genera are about equally weak. The obvious adaptive difference between the genera in the phylogenetic sequence is in the defensive ability of the soldiers. The most probable hypothesis is that a predatory barrier prevented the dispersal of the less defended genera, while the more specialized and defended genera were able to overcome this barrier.

Competition with ecologically equivalent species is possibly the major biotic barrier in the majority of cases. Ecological investigations are insufficient at present, however, to allow more than a guess concerning the exact nature and quantitative effects of the excluding factors. Competition with remotely related species seems to operate in some instances, while in others the competition is between closely related species. It has already been pointed out (p. 656) that ecological equivalence is likely to be greater the more closely related the species are phylogenetically.

We may imagine that native birds, better adapted through long selection to their natural habitat, succeed in excluding the English sparrow through direct competition. A flicker (*Colaptes auratus*) has been seen destroying nests of sparrows with eggs and young occupying former flicker holes in telephone poles on the outskirts of a town (Ithaca, New York). Wrens (*Troglodytes aëdon*) have ultimately won nesting sites from sparrows in such "tension zones" or ecotones as the vicinity of houses in the Indiana sand dunes (Breed, 1945). More such observations would lead us to a better understanding of the exact nature

Pliocene times.

Experiments show that a species may exclude another closely related and ecologically similar one (p. 657). Two species of flour beetles, *Tribolium confusum* and *T. castaneum,* are competitive under experimental conditions (Birch, Park, and Frank, 1946). When parasitized by a sporo-

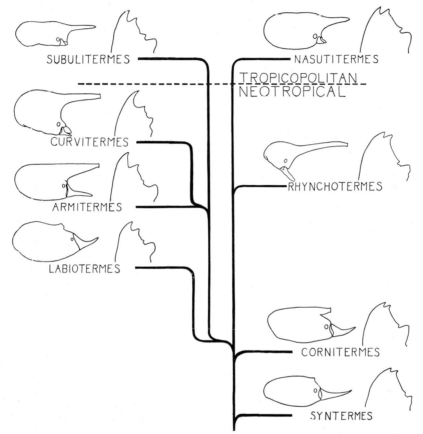

Fig. 263. Phylogenetic tree of certain genera of termites (Nasutitermitinae), showing profiles of the heads of the soldier caste and the imago-worker mandibles. Convergent development of the "squirt gun" and reciprocal convergent reduction of the soldier mandible are shown in *Subulitermes* and *Nasutitermes,* both of which are tropicopolitan, while the more primitive genera with mandibulate soldiers are all neotropical.

of the biotic barrier limiting the successful invasion of this "foreigner."

Eight genera of termites originating in South America have reached no farther than Costa Rica since the Pliocene connection, while one genus (*Tenuirostritermes*), originating in Central America, has been unable to push south of northern South America. One may postulate competition between termite genera as a possible explanation for this mutual exclusion since

zoan (*Adelina tribolii*), *T. confusum* usually replaces *T. castaneum* in mixed cultures, because *T. castaneum* is more susceptible to the pathogenic effects of the parasite. In nonparasitized cultures, *T. castaneum* usually eliminates *T. confusum,* probably in part because of the higher reproductive potential of *T. castaneum* (T. Park, 1948). These experiments show how competition between closely related species differs in effect through the influence of another species in the interspecies system.

A convincing case of biotic antagonism between related species is seen among the house rats. The black rat (*Rattus rattus*), originating in tropical Asia, was the common house rat of Europe during medieval times until it came into competition in the eighteenth century with the Norway rat (*R. norvegicus*), originating in temperate Asia. After the spread of these species around the world, each became established in the climatic zone of its origin and each in general prevented and still prevents the successful invasion of its area by its competitor. Local conditions produce some exceptions to the general correlation of climate and relative abundance of the two competing species.

Elton (1946) studied eighty-two animal and plant communities from different parts of the world and found that 86 per cent of the animal genera and 84 per cent of the plant genera included only a single species. The corresponding average number of species per genus was 1.38 and 1.22. In the faunal lists of large regions, such as Britain, 50 per cent of the genera have single species, and the average number of species per genus is 4.23. The explanation of this difference seems to be competition between closely allied species within the same association (Crombie, 1947).

A multiplicity of such biotic antagonisms together with biotic limitations is probably the explanation of biotic barriers in general. The barriers often consist of closely related and ecologically equivalent species, genera, or families, but in some cases convergent ecological equivalents may form a competitive barrier. The absence of proper food also may prevent the spread of specialized herbivores, carnivores, or parasites, and predators may prevent the establishment of an unadjusted prey species.

It may be concluded from these data that the community maintains a certain balance, establishes a biotic border, and has a certain unity paralleling the dynamic equilibrium and organization of other living systems. Natural selection operates upon the whole interspecies system, resulting in a slow evolution of adaptive integration and balance. Division of labor, integration, and homeostasis characterize the organism and the supraorganismic intraspecies population (p. 435). The interspecies system has also evolved these characteristics of the organ-

ism and may thus be called an ecological supraorganism (Emerson, 1946).

Objections to the concept of the community supraorganism (p. 698) are largely the result of (1) the handicaps in gathering phylogenetic data on population numbers, (2) the failure to recognize that coaction often creates selective pressures on genetic patterns, and (3) the failure to comprehend that the unit upon which selection acts may be either an integrated intraspecies or interspecies population.

The evolution of populations parallels some aspects of the evolution of organisms. When parallels are recognized, they are sometimes dismissed as "mere analogies" without realizing that these analogies may not always be chance similarities, but may be convergent as the result of similar evolutionary pressures. Because primitive organismic or supraorganismic integration does not exhibit the specialization and cooperative interdependence of the most highly integrated systems, basic coordination may not be recognized.

Because genetic continuity is often broken and is replaced by environmental continuity, the community is fundamentally different from intraspecies populations or individual organisms, but it also partakes of certain aspects of organismic integration, division of labor, and structure, and maintains ecological homeostasis. The concept of the interspecies supraorganism has some real scientific basis and is useful both in relating many facts in ecology and in directing our investigations toward the relations of the parts of the coordinated whole (Lotka, 1944).

SUMMARY AND CONCLUSIONS

Interactions between different species of organisms and interactions between organisms and their environment produce selection pressures. Reciprocal genetic patterns evolve by means of such selection and produce interspecies adaptations, interdependence, and integration. Harmful disoperation between species eliminates itself. Exploitation tends to evolve toward toleration and mutualism. The evolution of mutualism between species has not progressed so far as cooperation between parts of an individual or between individuals in an intraspecies population. The evolution of division of labor and integration between species results in a biotic system that may appropriately be called an interspecies supraorganism. The incorporation and control of the physical habitat by the interspecies supraorganism produces a unitary ecosystem. Homeostatic equilibrium within the ecosystem (balance of nature) is in large part the result of evolution.

CONCLUSION OF SECTION V ON ECOLOGY AND EVOLUTION

Ecology contributes important facts and principles to the general theory of evolution. In particular, the environmental influences on hereditary variation, the role of reproductive isolation, and the origin and maintenance of adaptation through natural selection are prime subjects of ecological investigation, shared in part with other fields of biology.

Evolution gives an essential perspective to our view of the organism, the species, and the community. It adds a different time dimension to the ontogenetic dimension (also time) and to the spatial dimensions. Many facts may be arranged in an order along this evolutionary dimension that could not be detected through the study of the ecological relations of existing species and their developmental stages. We should be aware, however, that the consideration of evolutionary phases of ecology introduces difficulties of scientific method and interpretation not met in dealing with the descriptions and analysis of existing community structure and function. Sometimes our conclusions rest upon circumstantial evidence of events that happened many millions of years ago and left only vague traces of their occurrence.

The analytic study of the parts of a system, and the synthetic study of the whole system, are both necessary, and each is inadequate without the other. Lotka (1945) has emphasized the necessity of envisaging the evolving system as a whole —the aggregate of past and present coexisting species in their inorganic and organic environment—for any adequate treatment of evolution.

Through the action of the habitat upon living systems, the reaction of these upon the environment often resulting in an organic evolution of the physical environment, and the coaction between organismic units of various levels of integration upon each other, we find that life and habitat are integrated into an evolving ecosystem (Egler, 1942), ultimately incorporating the entire biosphere of the earth (Vernadski, 1929, 1945). The unity of the biosphere is the resultant of the complex interaction of many factors—a complexity so great that many competent biologists have failed to recognize the existence of the unitary whole. Our attempts to analyze and synthesize the ecological aspects of the biosphere are necessarily superficial; the principles that emerge at this stage of our knowledge are often out of perspective, overemphasized, and oversimplified.

"I have often thought," wrote Liebig to his friend Duclaux, "in my long and practical career and at my age [69 years] how much pains and how many researches are necessary to probe to the depths a rather complicated phenomenon. The greatest difficulty comes from the fact that we are too much accustomed to attribute to a single cause that which is the product of several, and the majority of our controversies come from that."

Oversimplification is an error often committed by scientists in their drive to discover basic principles that relate diverse facts. If the terms are general enough to incorporate complex phenomena, they are likely to be hazy and ambiguous. Nevertheless, on occasion fundamental principles may be stated in language that has meaning to most readers and in a manner that brings order to vast accumulations of knowledge.

We may thus summarize the section on Ecology and Evolution—and indeed the book as a whole—by repeating a principle discussed by Leake (1945): The probability of survival of individual living things, or of populations, increases with the degree with which they harmoniously adjust themselves to each other and their environment. This principle is basic to the concept of the balance of nature, orders the subject matter of ecology and evolution, underlies organismic and developmental biology, and is the foundation for all sociology.

Principles that assort facts in meaningful order have not fulfilled their purpose unless they stimulate further fact finding, further discovery of relationships, further synthesis, and ultimately contribute to the evolution of human wisdom.

BIBLIOGRAPHY AND AUTHOR INDEX

The page citations following the items in the bibliography give the location of reference to the given title in the text and replace the customary author index. Occasional titles without text reference have been retained. Generalized citations to authors not restricted to the precise titles listed here may be found in the general index.

Abbe, Cleveland, 1905. 1st Report on the Relation between Climates and Crops. U. S. Dept. of Agr., Weather Bureau. [Compiled 1891.] pp. 18, 19, 27.

Abel, Othenio, 1929, Paläobiologie und Stammesgeschichte. Jena, Fischer. p. 57.

Absolon, Karl, 1900. Vorläufige Mittheilung über einige neue Collembolen aus den Höhlen des mährischen Karstes. Zool. Anz., 23: 265–269. p. 36.

Adams, C. C., 1901. Base Leveling and Its Faunal Significance. Am. Nat., 35: 839–852. p. 155.

——— 1909. The Ecological Succession of Birds. Ann. Rept. Mich. Geol. Surv., 1908: 121–154. p. 47.

——— 1913. Guide to the Study of Animal Ecology. New York, Macmillan. pp. 24, 25, 35, 36, 46, 49, 54.

——— 1915. An Ecological Study of Prairie and Forest Invertebrates. Bull. Illinois Lab. Nat. Hist., 11: 33–280. p. 514.

——— 1915a. The Variations and Ecological Distribution of the Snails of the Genus Io. Mem. Nat. Acad. Sc., 12: 1–92. p. 54.

Adams, Francis, 1849. The Genuine Work of Hippocrates. Translated from the Greek with a Preliminary Discourse and Annotations. London, Sydenham Society, 2 vols. p. 14.

Adams, R. H., 1941. Stratification, Diurnal and Seasonal Migration in a Deciduous Forest. Ecol. Monogr. 11: 190–227. pp. 488, 489.

Adams, W. S., and Nicholson, S. B., 1933. The Nature of the Solar Cycle. Proc. Nat. Acad. Sc., 19: 371–375. p. 86.

Adamson, A. M., 1940. New Termite Intercastes. Proc. Roy. Soc. London, s. B., 129: 35–53. p. 693.

Adolph, E. F., 1932. The Vapor Tension Relation of Frogs. Biol. Bull., 62: 112–125. pp. 184, 187.

——— 1933. Exchanges of Water in the Frog. Biol. Rev., 8: 224–240. p. 184.

——— 1943. Physiological fitness for the Desert. Federation Proc., 2: 158–164. p. 183.

——— and Associates, 1947. Physiology of Man in the Desert. New York, Interscience. p. 183.

Agar, W. E., 1943. A Contribution to the Theory of the Living Organism. Melbourne, Melbourne Univ. Press. p. 699.

Agassiz, Alexander, 1888. Three Cruises of the "Blake." Boston, Houghton Mifflin, 2 vols. p. 40.

——— 1906. Reports on the Scientific Results of the Expedition to the Eastern Tropical Pacific. V. General Report of the Expedition. Mem. Mus. Comp. Zool., 33: 88 pp. p. 19.

Agassiz, E. C., 1885. Louis Agassiz, His Life and Correspondence. Boston, Houghton Mifflin, 2 vols. p. 33.

Agassiz, Louis, 1848–1854. Bibliographia Zoologiae. London, Roy. Society. 4 vols. p. 5.

——— 1869. Report upon Deep-Sea Dredgings in the Gulf Stream, during the Third Cruise of the U. S. Steamer Bibb. Bull. Mus. Comp. Zool., 1: 363–386. p. 39.

Albertson, F. W., and Weaver, J. E., 1944. Nature and Degree of Recovery of Grassland from the Great Drought of 1933 to 1940. Ecol. Monogr., 14: 393–479. pp. 578, 656.

———, ——— 1945. Injury and Death or Recovery of Trees in Prairie Climate. Ecol. Monogr., 15: 393–433. p. 653.

———, ——— 1946. Reduction of Ungrazed Mixed Prairie to Short Grass as a Result of Drought and Dust. Ecol. Monogr., 16: 449–463. pp. 578, 653.

Aldrich, John W., 1946. Significance of Racial Variation in Birds to Wildlife Management. J. Wildlife Management, 10: 86–93. p. 652.

Alexander, Gordon, 1945. Natural Hybrids between Dendroica coronata and D. auduboni. Auk, 62: 623–626. p. 624.

Alexander, P., and Barton, D. H. R., 1943. The Excretion of Ethylquinone by the Flour Beetle. Biochem. J., 37: 463–465. p. 355.

Allan, H. H., 1936. Indigene Versus Alien in the New Zealand Plant World. Ecology, 17: 187–193. p. 724.

Allanson, M., and Deansley, R., 1934. The Reaction of Anoestrus Hedgehogs to Experimental Conditions. Proc. Roy. Soc. London, s. B., *116:* 170–185. p. 123.

Allard, H. A., 1935. The Natural History of the Box Turtle. Scient. Monthly, *45:* 325–339. p. 552.

Allee, W. C., 1911. Seasonal Succession in Old Forest Ponds. Tr. Ill. Acad. Sc., *4:* 126–131. pp. 53, 530.

—— 1912. An Experimental Analysis of the Relation between Physiological States and Rheotaxis in Isopoda. J. Exper. Zool., *13:* 270–344. p. 539.

—— 1914. The Ecological Importance of the Rheotactic Reaction of Stream Isopods. Biol. Bull., *27:* 52–66. p. 2.

—— 1919. Note on Animal Distribution Following a Hard Winter. Biol. Bull., *34:* 96–104. p. 179.

—— 1923. Studies in Marine Ecology. I. The Distribution of Common Littoral Invertebrates of the Woods Hole Region. Biol. Bull., *44:* 167–191. pp. 115, 160, 173, 174, 455.

—— 1923a. Studies in Marine Ecology. III. Some Physical Factors Related to the Distribution of Littoral Invertebrates. Biol. Bull., *44:* 205–253. p. 458.

—— 1923b. Studies in Marine Ecology. IV. The Effect of Temperature in Limiting the Geographical Range of Invertebrates of the Woods Hole Littoral. Ecology, *4:* 341–354. p. 458.

—— 1926. Measurement of Environmental Factors in the Tropical Rain-Forest of Panama. Ecology, *7:* 273–302. pp. 231, 480, 549.

—— 1926a. Distribution of Animals in a Tropical Rain-Forest with Relation to Environmental Factors. Ecology, *7:* 445–468. pp. 480, 482, 486, 488, 489, 514, 549.

—— 1926b. Studies in Animal Aggregations: Causes and Effects of Bunching in Land Isopods. J. Exper. Zool., *45:* 255–277. pp. 480, 539.

—— 1927. Symposium: Needed Lines of Investigation in American Entomology. Insect Ecology. Ann. Entom. Soc. Amer., *20:* 439–444. p. 547.

—— 1927a. Animal Aggregations. Quart. Rev. Biol., *2:* 367–398. pp. 59, 537.

—— 1930. Concerning Community Studies. Ecology, *11:* 621–630. p. 518.

—— 1931. Animal Aggregations. A Study in General Sociology. Chicago, Univ. of Chicago Press. pp. 69, 235, 347, 355, 357, 360, 393, 395, 404, 408, 415, 487, 537, 538.

—— 1932. Animal Life and Social Growth. Baltimore, Williams & Wilkins. pp. 69, 564.

—— 1934. Concerning the Organization of Marine Coastal Communities. Ecol. Monogr., *4:* 541–554. p. 160.

—— 1934a. Recent Studies in Mass Physiology. Biol. Rev., *9:* 1–48. pp. 71, 347, 358, 386.

—— 1938. The Social Life of Animals. New York, Norton. pp. 69, 235, 328, 347, 356, 357, 396, 398, 399, 403, 407, 413, 604, 684.

—— 1940. Concerning the Origin of Sociality in Animals. Scientia, *1940:* 154–160. pp. 72, 396, 641, 656, 684, 687.

—— 1941. Integration of Problems Concerning Protozoan Populations with Those of General Biology. Am. Nat., *75:* 473–487. pp. 72, 331.

—— 1942. Social Dominance and Subordination among Vertebrates. Biol. Symposia, *8:* 139–162. p. 413.

—— 1943. Where Angels Fear to Tread: A Contribution from General Sociology to Human Ethics. Science, *97:* 514–525. pp. 684, 694.

—— 1945. Human Conflict and Cooperation: The Biological Background. In Bryson, Finkelstein, and MacIver, Approaches to National Unity. Conference on Sci., Phil., and Religion. New York, Harpers, pp. 321–364. pp. 397, 403, 413, 418.

—— 1947. Animal Sociology. Encyclopaedia Britannica, *1947:* 971d–971r. pp. 397, 418.

—— 1949. Extrapolation in Comparative Sociology. Scientia, *84.* p. 395.

—— and Bowen, Edith, 1932. Studies in Animal Aggregations: Mass Protection against Colloidal Silver among Goldfishes. J. Exper. Zool., *61:* 185–207. p. 360.

—— Collias, N. E., and Lutherman, C. Z., 1939. Modification of the Social Order in Flocks of Hens by the Injection of Testosterone Propionate. Physiol. Zoöl., *12:* 412–440. p. 413.

—— and Douglis, Marjorie B., 1945. A Dominance Order in the Hermit Crab, *Pagurus longicarpus* Say. Ecology, *26:* 411–412. p. 411.

—— and Evans, Gertrude, 1937. Some Effects of Numbers Present on the Rate of Cleavage and Early Development in *Arbacia.* Biol. Bull., *72:* 217–232. pp. 356, 396, 402.

—— Finkel, A. J., and Hoskins, W. H., 1940. The Growth of Goldfish in Homotypically Conditioned Water; A Population Study in Mass Physiology. J. Exper. Zool., *84:* 417–443. p. 357.

—— and Frank, P., 1948. Ingestion of Colloidal Material and Water by Goldfish. Physiol. Zool., *21:* 381–390. p. 169.

—— and Lutherman, C. Z., 1940. An Experimental Study of Certain Effects of Temperature on Differential Growth of Pullets. Ecology, *21:* 29–33. p. 120.

—— and Park, T., 1939. Concerning Ecological Principles. Science, *89:* 166–169. p. 72.

—— and Wilder, Janet, 1939. Group Protection for *Euplanaria dorotocephala* from Ultra-violet Radiation. Physiol. Zool., *12:* 110–135. p. 398.

Allen, E. J., 1909, Mackerel and Sunshine. J. Marine Biol. Assn. U.K., *8:* 394–406. p. 346.

Allen, G. M., 1939. Bats. Cambridge, Harvard Univ. Press. p. 140.

—— 1942. Extinct and Vanishing Mammals of the Western Hemisphere. Spec. Publ. Am. Comm. for Interm. Wild Life Prot., *11:* 620. p. 399.

Allen, J. A., 1892. The Geographic Distribution of North American Mammals. Bull. Am. Mus. Nat. Hist., *4:* 199–243. p. 114.

Allen, W. E., 1934. The Primary Food Supply of the Sea. Quart. Rev. Biol., *9:* 161–180. pp. 71, 448.

Allgeier, R. J., Hafford, C., and Juday, C. 1941. Oxidation-Reduction Potentials and pH of Lake Waters and of Lake Sediments. Tr. Wis. Acad. Sc., *33:* 115–133. pp. 195, 196.

Alsterberg, Gustav, 1927. Die Sauerstoffschichtung der Seen. Bot. Notiser., *1927:* 255–274. p. 193.

Altenburg, E., 1946. The "Viroid" Theory in Relation to Plasmagenes, Viruses, Cancer and Plastids. Am. Nat., *80:* 559–567. pp. 602, 712.

Alverdes, Friedrich, 1927. Social Life in the Animal World. New York, Harcourt, Brace. p. 415.

Amadon, Dean, 1947. Ecology and the Evolution of Some Hawaiian Birds. Evolution, *1:* 63–68. pp. 659, 662, 664.

Ames, Oakes, 1944. The Pollinia of Orchids. Bull. Am. Orchid Soc., *13:* 190–194. p. 715.

Andrewartha, H. G., 1940. The Environment of the Australian Plague Locust (*Chortoicetes terminifera* Walk.) in South Australia. Roy. Soc. S. Australia, *64:* 76–94. p. 338.

—— 1945. Some Differences in the Physiology and Ecology of Locusts and Grasshoppers. Bull. Ent. Res., *35:* 379–389.

Andrews, E. A., 1904. Breeding Habits of Crayfish. Am. Nat., *38:* 165–206. p. 46.

—— 1940. The snail, *Neritina virginea* L., in a Changing Salt Pond. Ecology, *21:* 335–346. p. 340.

Angström, Anders, 1925. The Albedo of Various Surfaces of Ground. Geog. Ann., *7:* 323–342. p. 231.

Annuaire d'Observatoire municipal de Montsouris (Paris), 1888. (*Piche evaporometre*, p. 254.) p. 19.

Anonymous, 1874. Notes and News. Academy and Literature, *6:* 262. p. 21.

—— 1938. Soils and Men. Yearbook U. S. Dept. of Agr., 1938: 1–1232. p. 216.

—— 1939. Food and Life. Yearbook U. S. Dept. of Agr. 1939: 1–1165. p. 526.

—— 1939a. Fire Control Handbook, Region Two. Forest Service, U. S. Dept. of Agr. p. 210.

—— 1943. Winter Get-together: Fish Aggregations. Animal Kingdom, *46:* 129–132. p. 104.

Antevs, Ernst, 1925. The Retreat of the Last Ice Sheet in Eastern Canada. Mem. Canad. Geol. Surv., *146:* 1–141. p. 528.

—— 1938. Rainfall and Tree Growth in the Great Basin. Publ. Carnegie Inst. Wash., *469:* 1–97. p. 82.

Ariëns Kappers, J., 1942. Orthogenesis and Progressive Appearance of Early-Ontogenetic Form Relations in the Adult Stages during Human Evolution with a Possible Explanation for Them. Acta Biotheoretica, *6:* 165–184. p. 636.

Arnold, F. A., 1943. Role of Fluorides in Preventative Chemistry. J. Am. Dent. A., *30:* 499–508. p. 221.

Arrhenius, O., 1922. Hydrogen Ion Concentration, Soil Properties and Growth of Higher Plants. Ark. Bot., *18:* 1–54. p. 223.

Arrhenius, S., 1915. Quantitative Laws in Biological Chemistry. London, Bell. pp. 75, 107.

Arthur, J. C., 1929. The Plant Rusts. New York, Wiley. p. 614.

Atkins, W. R. G., 1926. A Quantitative Consideration of Some Factors Concerned in Plant Growth in Water. J. Conseil Intern. Explor. Mer., *1:* 1–28, 29–58. p. 203.

—— and Lebour, M. V., 1923. The Hydrogen-Ion Concentration in the Soil and of Natural Waters in Relation to the Distribution of Snails. Proc. Roy. Dub. Soc., *17:* 233–240. p. 223.

Audubon, J. J., 1827–1838. The Birds of America. London, published by the author, 4 vols. p. 33.

Auerbach, C., and Robson, J. M., 1944. Production of Mutations by Allyl Isothiocyanate. Nature, *154:* 81. p. 600.

——, —— and Carr, J. G., 1947. The Chemical Production of Mutations. Science, *105:* 243–247. p. 599.

Austin, Mary L., 1948. The Killing Action and Rate of Production of Single Particles of Paramecin 51. Physiol. Zoöl., *21:* 69–86. p. 390.

Autuori, M., 1941. Contribuição para o conhecimento da saúva. Arq. Inst. biol., *12:* 197–228. p. 310.

Averill, C. K., 1933. Geographical Distribution in Relation to Number of Eggs. Condor, *35:* 93–97. p. 701.

Avery, O. T., MacLeod, C. M., and McCarty, Maclyn, 1944. Studies on the Chemical Nature of the Substance Inducing Transformation of Pneumococcal Types. J. Exper. Med., *79:* 137–157. p. 601.

Axelrod, D. I., 1941. The Concept of Eco-species in Tertiary Paleobotany. Proc. Nat. Acad. Sc., *27:* 545–551. p. 626.

Babcock, S. M., 1912. Metabolic Water: Its Production and Role in Vital Phenomena. Res. Bull. Wisc. Agr. Exp. Sta., *22:* 87–181. pp. 184, 187.

Bachmetjew, P., 1901. Experimentelle ento-mologische Studien. I. Temperaturver-hältnisse bei Insekten. Leipzig: Engel-mann. p. 45.

—— 1901a. Die Lage des anabiotischen Zustandes auf der Temperaturkurve der wechselwärmen Thiere. Biol. Zentralb., *21:* 672–675. p. 45.

—— 1907. Experimentelle entomologische Stu-dien vom physikalisch-chemischen Stand-punkt aus; vol. II. Einfluss der äussern Factoren auf Insekten. Leipzig: Engel-mann. pp. 20, 45, 102, 121.

Bacot, A., and Martin, C. J., 1924. The Re-spective Influences of Temperature and Moisture upon the Survival of the Rat Flea (*Xenopsylla cheopis*) Away from Its Host. J. Hyg., *23:* 98–105. p. 634.

Baer, J. G., 1933. L'adaptation des helminthes à leur hôtes. Bull. Soc. neuchâtel. Sc. nat., *58:* 57–76. pp. 615, 702.

Baier, C. R., 1935. Studien zur Hydrobakterio-logie stehender Binnengewässer. Arch. Hydrobiol., *29:* 183–264. p. 497.

Bailey, Vernon, 1905. Biological Survey of Texas. North Am. Fauna, *25:* 1–222. p. 438.

—— 1925. A Biological Survey of North Da-kota. North Am. Fauna, *49:* 1–226. p. 468.

—— 1933. Cave Life of Kentucky, Mainly in the Mammoth Cave Region. Am. Midl. Nat., *14:* 385–635. p. 439.

Baily, J. L., Jr., 1939. Physiological Group Dif-ferentiation in *Lymnaea columella*. Am. J. Hygiene, Monogr. Ser., *14:* 1–133. p. 607.

Baker, E. C. S., 1942. Cuckoo Problems. Lon-don, Witherby. pp. 615, 657, 670.

Baker, J. R., 1936. Nomograms for Saturation Deficiency. J. Animal Ecol. *5:* 94–96. p. 480.

—— and Ranson, R. M., 1933. Factors Af-fecting the Breeding of the Field Mouse (*Microtus agrestis*). III. Locality. Proc. Roy. Soc. Lond., s. B., *113:* 486–495. p. 123.

Baker, W. K., 1947. A Study of the Isolating Mechanisms Found in Drosophila arizon-ensis and Drosophila mojavensis, in Studies in the Genetics of Drosophila V. Isolating Mechanisms. Univ. Texas Publ., *4720:* 126–136. p. 685.

Balduf, W. V., 1935. The Bionomics of En-tomophagous Coleoptera. St. Louis: Swift. p. 494.

Baldwin, J. M., 1896. A New Factor in Evolu-tion. Am. Nat., *30:* 441–475, 536–553. pp. 642, 645.

Ball, G. H., 1943. Parasitism and Evolution Am. Nat., *77:* 345–364. pp. 260, 708.

Baltzer, F., 1925. Untersuchungen über die Entwicklung und Geschlechtsbestimmung der Bonellia. Pub. Staz. Zool. Napoli, *6:* 223–285. p. 409.

Baly, E. C. C., 1929. Photosynthesis. Smith-sonian Inst. Ann. Rept., 237–244. p. 75.

Banta, A. M., 1907. The Fauna of Mayfield's Cave. Publ. Carnegie Inst. Wash., *67:* 1–114. p. 439.

—— 1939. Environmental Conditions and Daphnia Characteristics. Publ. Carnegie Inst. Wash., *513:* 229–252. p. 524.

—— 1939a. Adaptation and Evolution. Publ. Carnegie Inst. Wash., *513:* 253–264. p. 603.

—— and Brown, L. A., 1939. Control of the Male and Sexual Egg Production. [Chap-ter VII, pp. 106–129]. Papers Dept. Genetics, Carnegie Inst. Wash., *39:* 1–285. p. 410.

—— and Wood, T. R., 1928. A Thermal Race of Cladocera Originating by Mutation. Z. indukt. Abstamm. u. Vererb. lehre., 1928, Suppl. *1:* 397–398. [Proc. 5th Int. Congr. Genetics, *1:* 397–398.] p. 616.

—— with the collaboration of Wood, T. R., Brown, L. A., and Ingle, L., 1939. Studies on the Physiology, Genetics, and Evolu-tion of Some Cladocera. Carnegie Inst. Wash., Department of Genetics, Paper *39:* 1–285. p. 70.

Baranov, F., 1916. On the Question of the Bi-ological Basis of Fisheries. Rept. Dept. Fisheries and Scientific and Industrial Invest., *1* [in Russian]. p. 377.

—— 1925. On the Question of the Dynamics of the Fishing Industry. Bull. Fishery Economics, 8 [in Russian]. p. 377.

Barber, G. W., 1926. The Factors Responsible for the Decrease of the European Corn Borer in New England during 1923 and 1924. Ecology, *7:* 148–162. pp. 386–389.

Barbour, Thomas, 1934. Reptiles and Amphib-ians: Their Habits and Adaptations. 2nd ed. Boston, Houghton Mifflin. p. 553.

Barden, Albert, 1942. Activity of the Lizard, *Cnemidophorus sexlineatus*. Ecology, *23:* 336–344. pp. 545, 558.

Barnes, H. F., 1930. On Some Factors Govern-ing the Emergence of Gall Midges (Ceci-domyiidae: Diptera). Proc. Zool. Soc. London, 1930: 381–393. p. 552.

Barnes, T. C., 1937. Textbook of General Phys-iology. Philadelphia, Blakiston. pp. 106, 107.

Barney, R. L. and Anson, B. J., 1920. Life History and Ecology of the Pigmy Sunfish, *Elassoma zonatum*. Ecology, *1:* 241–256. p. 726.

Barott, H. G., 1937. Effect of Temperature.

Humidity, and Other Factors on Hatch of Hen's Eggs and on Energy Metabolism of Chick Embryos. Tech. Bull., U. S. Dept. of Agr., 553: 1–45. p. 190.

Bartholomew, G. A., Jr., 1942. The Fishing Activities of the Double Crested Cormorants on San Francisco Bay. Condor, 44: 13–21. p. 411.

—— 1943. Daily Movements of Cormorants on San Francisco Bay. Condor, 45: 3–18. p. 411.

Bartsch, Paul, 1946. The Human Blood Flukes. Scient. Monthly. 63: 381–390. p. 702.

Baskett, T. S., 1947. Nesting and Production of the Ring-Necked Pheasant in North-Central Iowa. Ecol. Monogr., 17: 1–30. p. 340.

Batchelder, C. H., 1915. Migration of Ilyanassa obsoleta, Litorina litorea and Litorina rudis. Nautilus, 29: 43–46. p. 542.

—— 1926. An Ecological Study of a Brackish-Water Stream. Ecology, 7: 55–71. p. 542.

Bates, H. W., 1863. The Naturalist on the River Amazons . . . . London, Murray, 2 vols. pp. 23, 33.

Bates, Marston, 1944. Observations on the Distribution of Diurnal Mosquitoes in a Tropical Forest. Ecology, 25: 159–170. pp. 490, 592.

—— 1945. Observations on Climate and Seasonal Distribution of Mosquitoes in Eastern Colombia. J. Animal Ecol., 14: 17–26. pp. 534, 539.

—— 1946. The Natural History of Yellow Fever in Colombia. Scient. Monthly, 63: 42–52.

Baylis, H. A., 1938. Helminths and Evolution. In de Beer, G. R., Evolution. Oxford, Clarendon Press, pp. 249–270. pp. 615, 685, 702, 705.

Bayliss, W. M., 1918. Principles of General Physiology. 2nd Ed. London, Longmans. [4th ed., 1924 and 1931.] pp. 49, 51, 138, 437, 500, 509.

Beadle, L. C., 1943. Osmotic Regulation and the Faunas of Inland Waters. Biol. Rev., 18: 172–183. p. 171.

Beall, Geoffrey, 1941. The Monarch Butterfly, Danaus archippus Fab. I. General Observations in Southern Ontario. II. The Movement in Southern Ontario. Canad. Field Nat., 55: 123–129, 133–136. pp. 100, 366.

—— 1941a. Method of Estimating the Population of an Agricultural Pest over Areas of Many Square Miles. Canad. J. Res., 19: 267–277. p. 366.

Beamer, R. H., 1928. Studies on the Biology of Kansas Cicadidae. Kansas Univ. Sc. Bull., 18: 155–263. p. 543.

Beard, J. S., 1944. Climax Vegetation in Tropical America. Ecology, 25: 127–158. p. 482.

Béclard, M. J., 1858. Influence de la lumière sur les animaux. Compt. rend. Acad. Sci. Paris, 46: 441–443. p. 20.

Bedford, • Duke of, and Marshall, F. H. A., 1942. On the Incidence of the Breeding Season in Mammals after Transference to a New Latitude. Proc. Roy. Soc., London, s. B., 130: 396–399. p. 631.

Beebe, William, 1906. The Bird. New York, Holt. p. 701.

—— 1908. Preliminary Report on an Investigation of the Seasonal Changes of Color in Birds. Am. Nat., 42: 34–38. p. 123.

—— 1928. Beneath Tropic Seas, A Record of Diving among Coral Reefs of Haiti. New York, Putnams. pp. 456, 462.

—— 1929. Deep Sea Fishes of Hudson Gorge. Zoologica, 12: 1–19. p. 450.

—— 1932. Exploration of the Deep Sea. Science, 76: 344. pp. 124, 450.

—— 1932a. A Half Mile in the Bathysphere. Bull. New York Zool. Soc., 35: 143–180. p. 450.

—— 1934. Half Mile Down. New York, Harcourt, Brace. pp. 124, 448.

—— 1934a. Oceanographical Work at Bermuda of the New York Zoology Society. Science, 80: 495–496. p. 451.

—— 1944. The Book of Naturalists. New York, Knopf. p. 657.

—— 1944a. The Function of Secondary Sexual Characters in Two Species of Dynastidae (Coleoptera). Zoologica, 29: 53–58. p. 691.

—— 1947. Notes on the Hercules Beetle, Dynastes hercules (Linn.), at Rancho Grande, Venezuela, with Special Reference to Combat Behavior. Zoologica, 32: 109–116. p. 691.

Beecher, W. J., 1942. Nesting Birds and the Vegetation Substrate. Chicago, Chicago Ornithol. Soc. pp. 478, 494, 572, 574, 696.

Beeman, Elizabeth A., 1947. Aggressive Behavior of Normal, Castrate and Androgen Treated Castrate C 57 Black and Bagg Albino Male Mice. Physiol. Zoöl., 20: 373–405. p. 414.

Behre, E. H., 1928. Some Distribution Relations of Fresh Water Fishes in Panama West of the Canal Zone. Ecology, 9: 421–428. p. 174.

Beklemischev, V. N., 1931. Osnovnye poniātiā biotsenologii v prilozhenii k zhivotnym komponentam nazemnykh soobshchestb. [Ueber die Anwendung einiger Grundbegriffe der Biocönologie auf tierische Komponente der Festlandbiocoenosen.] Bull. Plant Prot. (Entomol.), 1: 277–358. (Russian text, summary in German.) p. 531.

Belding, D. L., 1942. Textbook of Clinical Parasitology, Including Laboratory Identification and Technic. New York, Appleton-Century. p. 514.

—— and Lane, F. C., 1911. The Life History

and Growth of the Quahaug (*Venus mercenaria*). Rep. Mass. Comm. Fisheries and Game, 1910: 18–128. p. 50.

Bělehrádek, J., 1935. Temperature and Living Matter. Berlin, Borntraeger. pp. 74, 107, 108, 111.

Bellevoye et Laurent, 1897. Bull. Soc. Étude Sc. Nat. Reims. (vide Thompson, W. R., 1939.) p. 28.

Belt, Thomas, 1874. The Naturalist in Nicaragua. London, Bumpus. pp. 23, 33.

Belyea, H. C., 1925. Wind and Exposure as Limiting Factors in the Establishment of Forest Plantations. Ecology, 6: 238–240. p. 481.

Benedict, F. G., and Lee, R. C., 1938. Hibernation and Marmot Physiology. Publ. Carnegie Inst. Wash., 497: 239 pp. p. 105.

Bennett, M. K. 1949. Population and Food Supply: the Current Scare. Sci. Mon., 68: 17–26. p. 578.

Bennitt, Rudolf, 1932. Diurnal Rhythm in the Proximal Pigment Cells of the Crayfish Retina. Physiol. Zoöl. 5: 65–69. p. 546.

Benoist, R., 1924. La végétation de la Guiane française. Bull. Soc. Bot. France, 71: 1169–1177. p. 482.

Benson, S. B., 1933. Concealing Coloration among Some Desert Rodents of the Southwestern United States. Univ. Calif. Publ. Zool., 40: 1–70. pp. 590, 667, 668.

Bentley, E. W., Gunn, D. L., and Ewer, D. E., 1941. The Biology and Behavior of *Ptinus tectus* Boie (Ptinidae), a Pest of Stored Products. I. The Daily Rhythm of Locomotor Activity, Especially in Relation to Light and Temperature. J. Exper. Biol., 18: 182–195. p. 559.

Bequaert, Joseph, 1922. The Predaceous Enemies of Ants. Bull. Am. Mus. Nat. Hist., 45: 271–331. p. 257.

Bernard, Merrill, 1942. Precipitation. In Physics of the Earth, IX., O. E. Meinzer, ed., pp. 32–55. p. 178.

Bert, Paul, 1870. Leçons sur la physiologie comparée de la respiration. Paris, Bailliere. p. 23.

—— 1876. Sur l'influence de la chaleur sur les animaux inférieurs. Compt. rend. Soc. Biol. Paris., 28: 168–169. p. 21.

—— 1878. La pression barométrique. Recherches de physiologie expérimentale. Paris, G. Masson. pp. 23, 135.

—— 1943. Barometric Pressure. Researches in Experimental Physiology (transl. by Mary A. and Fred A. Hitchcock). Columbus, College Book Co., [1878]. p. 135.

Bertalanffy, L. v., 1937. Das Gefüge des Lebens. Leipzig, Tübner. p. 663.

Best, C. H., and Taylor, N. B., 1943. The Physiological Basis of Medical Practice. Baltimore, Williams & Wilkins. p. 140.

Beudant, F. S., 1816. Mémoire sur la possibilité de faire vivre des mollusques fluviatiles dans les eaux salines, etc. J. Phys., 83: 268–284. p. 20.

Bews, J. W., 1935. Human Ecology. London, Oxford University Press. p. 69.

Bezold, Albert von, 1857. Untersuchungen über die Vertheilung von Wasser, organischer Materie und anorganischen Verbindungen im Thierreiche. Ztschr, wiss. Zool., 8: 487–524. p. 19.

Bidder, H. F., and Schmidt, C., 1852. Die Verdauungssaefte und der Stoffwechsel. Mitau and Leipzig, Reyher. p. 21.

Bigelow, H. B., 1925. Plankton of the Offshore Waters of the Gulf of Maine. Bull. U. S. Bur. Fisheries, 40 (pt. 2): 1–509. pp. 448, 450.

—— and Welsh, W. W., 1924. Fishes of the Gulf of Maine. Bull. U. S. Bur. Fish., 40 (pt. 1): 1–567. p. 126.

Bills, C. E., 1936. Radiation and the Vitamins. In Duggar, B. M., 1936. Biological Effects of Radiation. New York: McGraw-Hill. p. 128.

Binz, C., and Schulz, H., 1879. Die Arsengiftwirkungen vom chemischen Standpunkt betrachtet. Arch. f. exper. Path. u. Pharmacol., 11: 200–230. p. 19.

Birch, L. C., 1945. The Biotic Potential of the Small Strain of *Calandra oryzae* and *Rhizopertha dominica*. J. Anim. Ecol., 14: 125–127. p. 391.

—— 1948. The Intrinsic Rate of Increase of an Insect Population. J. Anim. Ecol., 17: 15–26. p. 294.

—— and Andrewartha, H. G., 1942. The Influence of Moisture on the Eggs of *Austroicetes cruciata* Sauss. (Orthoptera), with Reference to Their Ability to Survive Desiccation. Australian J. Exper. Biol. & Med. Sc., 20: 1–8. p. 277.

——, —— 1944. The Influence of Drought on the Survival of Eggs of *Austroicetes crusiata*, Sauss. (Orthoptera) in South Australia. Bull. Ent. Res., 35: 243–250. p. 278.

——, Park, T., and Frank, M. B., 1946. The Effect of Interspecies Competition on the Fecundity of Tribolium confusum Duval and Tribolium castaneum Herbst. Anat. Rec., 96: 82 (abstract). p. 727.

Bird, R., 1930. Biotic Communities of the Aspen Parkland of Central Canada. Ecology, 11: 355–442. pp. 468, 477, 513, 531.

Birge, E. A., 1893. Notes on Cladocera. III. Tr. Wis. Acad. Sc., 9: 275–317. p. 42.

—— 1898. Plankton Studies on Lake Mendota. II. Crustacea of Plankton from July, 1894, to December, 1896. Tr. Wis. Acad. Sc., 11: 274–448. p. 42.

—— 1898a. The Relation between the Areas of Inland Lakes and the Temperature of the Water. Proc. Am. Fish. Soc., 27: 99–105. p. 335.

—— 1904. The Thermocline and Its Biological Significance. Tr. Amer. Micro. Soc., 25: 5–33. p. 47.

—— 1915. The Heat Budgets of American and European Lakes. Tr. Wis. Acad. Sc., 18: 1–47. p. 92.

—— 1916. The Work of the Wind in Warming a Lake. Tr. Wis. Acad. Sc., 18: 341–391. pp. 92, 96.

—— and Juday, C., 1911. The Inland Lakes of Wisconsin. The Dissolved Gases of the Water and Their Biological Significance. Bull. Wis. Geol. & Nat. Hist. Surv., 22. pp. 51, 92, 446, 538.

——, —— 1912. A Limnological Study of the Finger Lakes of New York. Bull. Bur. Fish., 32: 529–609. p. 92.

——, —— 1914. The Inland Lakes of Wisconsin. The Hydrography and Morphometry of the Lakes. Bull. Wis. Geol. & Nat. Hist. Surv., 27, Sc. Ser., 9.

——, —— 1922. The Inland Lakes of Wisconsin. The Plankton. I. Its Quantity and Chemical Composition. Bull. Wis. Geol. & Nat. Hist. Surv., 64: 1–222. pp. 497, 504.

——, —— 1934. Particulate and Dissolved Organic Matter in Inland Lakes. Ecol. Monogr. 4: 440–474. p. 444.

Bishop, S. C., 1941. The salamanders of New York. Bull. New York Mus., 324: 1–365. p. 487.

—— 1944. A New Neotenic Plethodont Salamander, with Notes on Related Species. Copeia, 1944: 1–5. p. 678.

Bissonnette, T. H., 1935. Sexual Photoperiodicity in Animals. J. Heredity, 26: 284–286. p. 124.

—— 1936. Sexual Photoperiodicity. J. Heredity, 27: 171–180. p. 121.

—— 1936a. Sexual Photoperiodicity. Quart. Rev. Biol., 11: 371–386. p. 121.

—— and Bailey, E. E., 1944. Experimental Modification and Control of Molts and Changes of Coat-Color in Weasels by Controlled Lighting. Ann. N. Y. Acad. Sc., 45: 221–260. p. 123.

—— and Wadlund, A. P. R., 1931. Spermatogenesis in Sturnus vulgaris: Refactory Period and Acceleration in Relation to Wave Length and Rate of Increase of Light Ration. J. Morph., 52: 403–420. p. 124.

——, —— 1932. Duration of Testis Activity of Sturnus vulgaris in Relation to the Type of Illumination. J. Exper. Biol., 9: 339–350. p. 124.

——, and Wilson, E., 1939. Shortening Daylight Periods between May 15 and September 12 and the Pelt Cycle of the Mink. Science, 89: 418–419. p. 123.

Bitancourt, A. A., 1941. Expressao matematica do crescimento de formigueiros de "Atta sexdens rubropilosa" representado pelo au-

mento do numero de olheiros. Arch. Inst. Biol. 12: 229-236. p. 310.

Blackman, F. F., 1905. Optima and Limiting Factors. Ann. of Bot., 19: 281–295. p. 198.

Blackman, M. W., and Stage, H. H., 1924. Succession of Insects in Dying, Dead and Decaying Hickory. Bull. New York State Coll. Forestry, 24: 1–269. p. 570.

Blair, W. Frank, 1947. Estimated Frequencies of the Buff and Gray Genes (G, g) in Adjacent Populations of Deer-Mice (Peromyscus maniculatus blandus) Living on Soils of Different Colors. Contrib. Lab. Vertebrate Biol. 36: 1–16. pp. 610, 668.

—— 1947a. Variation in Shade of Pelage of Local Populations of the Cactus-Mouse (Peromyscus eremicus) in the Tularosa Basin and Adjacent Areas of Southern New Mexico. Contrib. Lab. Vertebrate Biol., 37: 1–7. pp. 610, 668.

Blaisdell, F. S., 1912. Hibernation in Cicindela senilis. Entom. News, 23: 156–159. p. 538.

Blake, I. H., 1926. A Comparison of the Animal Communities of Coniferous and Deciduous Forests. Illinois Biol. Monogr., 10, (No. 4): 1–148. pp. 514, 537.

Blakeslee, A. L., 1948. Stars of Death . . . Nat. Hist., 57: 75–77. p. 125.

Blatchley, W. S., 1920. Orthoptera of Northeastern America. Indianapolis, Nature Pub. Co. p. 617.

Blatz, W. C., Millichamp, D., and Charles, M., 1937. The Early Social Development of the Dionne Quintuplets. Univ. Toronto Studies, Child Dev. Ser., 13. [Also in Collected Studies on the Dionne Quintuplets. Univ. Toronto Press.] p. 413.

Blegvad, H., 1916. On the Food of Fishes in the Danish Waters within the Skaw. København Ber. Biol. Sta. 24: 17–72. p. 459.

—— 1925. Continued Studies on the Quantity of Fish-Food in the Sea Bottom. København Ber. Biol. Sta. 31: 27–56. p. 459.

—— 1930. Quantitative Investigations of the Bottom Invertebrates in the Kattegat with Special Reference to the Plaice Food. København Ber. Biol. Sta. 36: 3–55. p. 459.

Blewett, M., and Fraenkel, G., 1944. Intracellular Symbiosis and Vitamin Requirements of Two Insects, Lasioderma serricorne and Sitodrepa panicea. Proc. Roy. Soc. London, s. B., 132: 212–221. p. 248.

Bliss, C. I., 1941. Statistical Problems in Estimating Populations of Japanese Beetle Larvae. J. Econ. Entom., 34: 221–232. pp. 364, 366.

——, Cressman, A. W., and Broadbent, B. M., 1935. Productivity of the Camphor Scale and the Biology of Its Egg and Crawler Stages. J. Agr. Res., 50: 243–266. p. 278.

Blumenthal, H., 1935. Das Tarsalorgan der

Spinnen. Z. Morph. Ökol. Tiere., *29:* 667–719. p. 189.

Bodenheimer, F. S., 1925. On Predicting the Developmental Cycles of Insects. I. *Ceratitis capitata.* Wied., Bull. Soc. Entom. Egypte, 1924: 149–157. p. 60.

—— 1930. Studien zur Epidemiologie, Ökologie, und Physiologie der afrikanischen Wanderheuschrecke (*Schistocerca gregaria,* Forsk). Z. Angew. Ent., *15:* 1–125, *16:* 433–450. p. 209.

—— 1937. Population Problems of Social Insects. Biol. Rev., *12:* 393–430. pp. 310, 419.

—— 1937a. Studies in Animal Populations. II. Seasonal Population Trends of the Honey-Bee. Quart. Rev. Biol., *12:* 406–425. p. 71.

—— 1938. Problems of Animal Ecology. London, Oxford Univ. Press. pp. 69, 209, 272, 273, 276, 279, 282, 286, 349, 508, 526, 600, 721.

Böhm, Anton, 1931. Distribution and Variability of Ceratium in the Northern and Western Pacific. B. P. Bishop Mus. Bull., *87:* 1–46. p. 502.

Böker, Hans, 1935. Einführung in die vergleichende biologische Anatomie der Wirbeltiere. Jena, Gustav Fischer. p. 132.

Bonar, James, 1885. Malthus and His Work. New York, Harper. p. 25.

Bond, R. M., 1933. A Contribution to the Study of the Natural Food-Cycle in Aquatic Environments. Bull. Bingham Oceanogr. Coll., *4:* 1–89. pp. 444, 500, 514.

Bornebusch, C. II., 1930. The Fauna of Forest Soil. Verhandl. Internat. Kongr. Forst. Versuchsanst. Stockholm, 1919: 541–545. p. 486.

—— 1930a. The Fauna of Forest Soil. Det Forstlige Forsøgsvaesen I, Danmark, *11,* (No. 1): 1–224. p. 486.

Borradaile, L. A., 1923. The Animal and Its Environment. London, Frowde, Hodder, and Stoughton. p. 55.

—— and Potts, F. A., 1935. The Invertebrata. New York, Macmillan. p. 259.

Botero, Giovanni, 1590. Della ragion di stato, libri dieci. Con tre libre delle cause della grandezza, e magnificenza delle città. Ferrara, Baldini. p. 25.

Boussingault, J. B. J. D., 1845. Rural Economy in Its Relations with Chemistry, Physics, and Meteorology. Transl. G. Law. New York, Appleton. [Orig. 1837.] p. 18.

Bouvier, E. L., 1922. The Psychic Life of Insects. New York, Century. p. 553.

Bouyoucos, G. J., 1921. A New Classification of the Soil Moisture. Soil Science, *11:* 33–47. p. 220.

Boyce, J. M., 1946. The Influence of Fecundity and Egg Mortality on the Population

Growth of *Tribolium confusum* Duval. Ecology, *27:* 290–302. p. 371.

Boyle, Robert, 1670. New Pneumatical Experiments about Respiration. Philos. Tr. Roy. Soc., London, 5 (62): 2011–2032; (63): 2035–2056. pp. 16–17, 135.

Bracket, F. S., 1936. Measurement and Application of Visible and Near Visible Radiation. In Duggar, B. M., Biological Effects of Radiation. New York, McGraw-Hill, pp. 123–209. p. 90.

Bragg, A. N., 1945. The Spadefoot Toads in Oklahoma with a Summary of Our Knowledge of the Group. II. Am. Nat., *79:* 52–72. p. 620.

—— 1945a. Notes on the Psychology of Frogs and Toads. J. Gen. Psychol., *32:* 27–37. p. 620.

Brand, Theodor von, 1946. Anaerobiosis in Invertebrates. Normandy, Mo., Biodynamica. pp. 190, 701.

Braun, E. Lucy, 1916. The Physiographic Ecology of the Cincinnati Region. Bull. Ohio Biol. Surv., *7:* 116–211. p. 586.

—— 1935. Undifferentiated Deciduous Forest Climax and the Association Segregate. Ecology, *16:* 375–402. p. 575.

—— 1947. Development of the Deciduous Forests of Eastern North America. Ecol. Monogr. *17:* 211–219. p. 575.

Braun, W., 1945. Factors Controlling Bacterial Dissociation. Science, *101:* 182–183. p. 601.

Braun-Blanquet, J., 1932. Plant Sociology: The Study of Communities. New York, McGraw-IIill. pp. 34, 36, 577.

Breder, C. M., Jr., 1934. Ecology of an Oceanic Fresh-Water Lake, Andros Island, Bahamas, with Reference to Its Fishes. Zoologia, *18:* 57–88. p. 169.

—— 1942. Descriptive Ecology of La Cueva Chica, with Especial Reference to the Blind Fish, *Anoptichthys.* Zoologica, *27:* 7–16. p. 674.

—— 1942a. A Consideration of Evolutionary Hypotheses in Reference to the Origin of Life. Zoologica, *27:* 131–143. p. 598.

—— 1943. Problems in the Behavior and Evolution of a Species of Blind Cave Fish. Tr. New York Acad. Sc., *5:* 168–176. pp. 643, 674.

—— 1943a. Apparent Changes in Phenotypic Ratios of the Characins at the Type Locality of *Anoptichthys jordani* Hubbs and Innes. Copeia, 1943: 26–30. p. 674.

—— 1944. Ocular Anatomy and Light Sensitivity Studies on the Blind Fish from Cueva de los Sabinos, Mexico. Zoologica, *29:* 131–143. pp. 674, 675, 677.

—— and Gresser, E. B., 1941. Correlations between Structural Eye Defects and Behavior in the Mexican Blind Characin. Zoologica, *26:* 123–132. p. 674.

—— and Rasquin, P., 1943. Chemical Sensory Reactions in the Mexican Blind Characins. Zoologica, *28:* 169–199. p. 674.

Breed, F. S., 1945. Sand-Hill Sketches. Chicago, Univ. Chicago Mag., *37:* 10–11. p. 727.

Brehm, A. E., 1896. From North Pole to Equator. London, Blackie. p. 33.

―― 1911–1918. Thierleben, 4th ed. [Various authors.] Leipzig, Bibliographisches Institut., 13 vols. pp. 23, 33, 467, 514.

Brehm, V., 1930. Einführung in die Limnologie. Berlin, Springer. p. 56.

Bremer, H., 1926. Über die tageszeitliche Konstanz im Schlüpftermine der Imagines einiger Insekten, und ihre experimentella Beeinflussbarkeit. Ztschr. wiss. Insektenbiol., *21:* 209–216. p. 553.

Brenchley, W. E., 1943. Minor Elements and Plant Growth. Biol. Rev., *18:* 159–171. p. 221.

Britton, W. E., 1923. Guide to the Insects of Connecticut. Part IV. The Hemiptera. Coccidae. Bull. Connecticut Geol. & Nat. Hist. Surv., *34:* 346–382. p. 494.

Brody, Samuel, 1944. Science and Social Wisdom. Scient. Monthly, *59:* 203–214. p. 693.

―― 1945. Bioenergetics and Growth. New York, Reinhold. p. 183.

Brooks, Allan, 1926. Past and Present Big Game Conditions in British Columbia and the Predatory Mammal Question. J. Mammalogy, *7:* 37–40. p. 60.

Brooks, C. E. P., 1925. The Distribution of Thunderstorms over the Globe. London, Meteorol. Office, Geophysics Mem., *3:* 145–164. p. 157.

―― 1926. Climate through the Ages. London, Benn. pp. 80, 81, 83, 86, 88.

Brooks, J. L., 1946. Cyclomorphosis in Daphnia. I. An Analysis of *D. retrocurva* and *D. galeata.* Ecol. Monogr., *16:* 409–447. pp. 118, 534.

Brooks, W. K., 1899. Foundations of Zoology. New York, Macmillan. [2nd ed., 1915, New York, Columbia Univ. Press.] p. 13.

Brown, E. M., 1943. Some Effects of Soil and Air Temperature on the Growth of Certain Grass Species. Scient. Monthly, *53:* 283–285. p. 475.

Brown, F. A., Jr., 1939. Responses of the Swimbladder of the Guppy. *Lebistes reticulatus,* to Sudden Pressure Decreases. Biol. Bull., *76:* 48–58. p. 139.

―― and Rollo, M., 1940. Light and Molt in Weaver Finches. Auk, *57:* 486–498. p. 123.

―― and Sandeen, Muriel I., 1948. Responses of the Fiddler Crab, Uca, to Light and Temperature. Physiol. Zoöl., *21:* 361–371. pp. 620, 653.

―― and Webb, H. Marguerite, 1948. Temperature Relations of an Endogenous Daily Rhythmicity in the Fiddler Crab, Uca. Physiol. Zoöl., *21:* 371–381. p. 558.

Brown, L. A., 1929. The Natural History of Cladocerans in Relation to Temperature. I. Distribution and the Temperature Limits for Vital Activities. Am. Nat., *63:* 248–264. p. 99.

Brown, W. H., 1919. Vegetation of Philippine Mountains: The Relation between the Environment and Physical Types at Different Altitudes. Manila, Philippine Bur. Sc.

Brown, W. J., 1945. Food-plants and Distribution of the Species of *Calligrapha* in Canada, with Descriptions of New Species (Coleoptera, Chrysomelidae). Canad. Ent., *77:* 117–133. p. 613.

Brownlee, J., 1915. Studies in the Meaning and Relationship of Birth and Death Rates. J. Hyg., *15:* 11–35. p. 26.

Brückner, E., 1890. Klimaschwankungen seit 1700 Vienna. Geogr. Abh. *4* (2). p. 86.

Brückner, John, 1767. Théorie du système animal. Leyden, Jean Luzac. [Transl., 1768, A Philosophical Survey of the Animal Creation. London.] p. 25.

Brues, C. T., 1923. Termitobracon, a Termitophilous Braconid from British Guiana. Zoologica, *3:* 427–432. p. 675.

―― 1927. Animal Life in Hot Springs. Quart. Rev. Biol., *2:* 181–203. p. 514.

―― 1939. Studies on the Fauna of Some Thermal Springs in the Dutch East Indies. Proc. Am. Acad. Arts & Sc., *73:* 71–95. pp. 21, 103.

―― 1946. Insect Dietary; An Account of the Food Habits of Insects. Cambridge, Harvard. pp. 241, 514, 713.

―― and Dunn, R. C., 1945. The Effect of Penicillin and Certain Sulpha Drugs on the Intracellular Bacteroids of the Cockroach. Science, *101:* 336–337. p. 712.

Brunner, J., 1912. Tracks and Tracking. New York, Outing Publishing Co. p. 50.

Bryson, H. R., 1931. The Interchange of Soil and Subsoil by Burrowing Insects. J. Kansas Entom. Soc. *4:* 17–24. p. 485.

―― 1933. The Amount of Soil Brought by Insects to the Surface of a Watered and an Unwatered Plot. J. Kansas Entom. Soc., *6:* 81–90. p. 485.

Buchanan, R. E., and Fulmer, E. I., 1930. Effects of Environment upon Microorganisms. Baltimore, Williams & Wilkins. p. 173.

Buchbinder, Leon, 1942. The Bactericidal Effects of Daylight and Sunlight on Chained Gram Positive Cocci in Simulated Room Environment: Theoretical and Practical Considerations. Aerobiology. Publ. Am. A. Adv. Sci., *17:* 267–270. p. 127.

Bucher, W. H., 1938. Key to Papers Published by an Institute for the Study of Modern Sediments in Shallow Seas. J. Geol., *46:* 726–755. p. 57.

Buchholtz, J. T., 1945. Embryological Aspects

of Hybrid Vigor in Pines. Science, *102:* 135–142. p. 625.

Buchner, Paul, 1921. Tier und Pflanze in intrazellularer Symbiose. Berlin, Borntraeger.

——— 1930. Tier und Pflanze in Symbiose. Berlin, Borntraeger. pp. 56, 248, 712.

Buchsbaum, Ralph, 1937. Readings in Ecology. Chicago, Univ. Chicago Bookstore. pp. 569, 573.

——— 1937a. Chick Tissue Cells and *Chlorella* in Mixed Cultures. Physiol. Zoöl., *10:* 373–379. p. 713.

——— and Buchsbaum, M., 1934. An Artificial Symbiosis. Science, *80:* 408–409. pp. 246, 713.

Buck, J. B., 1935. Synchronous Flashing of Fireflies Experimentally Induced. Science, *81:* 339–340. p. 554.

——— 1937. Studies on the Firefly. I. The Effect of Light and Other Agents on Flashing in *Photinus pyralis,* with Special Reference to Periodicity and Diurnal Rhythm. Physiol. Zoöl., *10:* 45–58. pp. 546, 554.

——— 1937a. Studies on the Firefly. II. The Signal System and Color Vision in *Photinus pyralis.* Physiol. Zoöl., *10:* 412–419. pp. 546, 554.

Buffon, L. L. de, 1749-1769. Histoire Naturelle générale et particuliére. Paris, Plonteaux, 13 vols. [with numerous editions]. pp. 23, 25, 29, 42.

Bullen, G. E., 1909. Plankton Studies in Relation to Western Mackerel Fishery. J. Marine Biol. Assn.U.K., *8:* 269–302. p. 346.

Bumpus, H. G., 1898. The Elimination of the Unfit as Illustrated by the Introduced Sparrow, *Passer domesticus.* Biol. Lectures, Marine Biol. Lab., Woods Hole, *6:* 209–226. p. 724.

Bundesen, H., Lemon, H., *et al.,* 1927. Ultraviolet Radiation from Sunlight and Incandescent Lamps. J. A. M. A., *89:* 187–189. p. 90.

Burke, V., 1934. Interchange of Bacteria between the Freshwater and the Sea. J. Bacteriol., *27:* 201–205. p. 501.

Burnet, F. M., 1940. Biological Aspects of Infectious Disease. Cambridge, Cambridge University Press. p. 380.

——— 1945. Virus as Organism. Evolutionary and Ecological Aspects of Some Human Virus Diseases. Cambridge, Harvard Univ. Press. pp. 255, 676.

Burrows, William, 1942. Synergistic Aspects of Bacterial Populations. Biol. Symposia, *8:* 89–104. p. 410.

——— and Cordon, T. C., 1936. The Influence of the Decomposition of Organic Matter on the Oxidation-Reduction Potential of Soils. Soil Sc., *42:* 1–10. p. 195.

Buswell, A. M., and Boruff, C. S., 1931. Pollution Studies of Illinois River. Circ. Illinois Water Surv. Div., *12:* 52–59. p. 515.

Butler, L., 1945. Distribution and Genetics of the Color Phases of the Red Fox in Canada. Genetics, *30:* 39–50. p. 603.

Buxton, P. A., 1923. Animal Life in Deserts, A Study of the Fauna in Relation to the Environment. London, Arnold. pp. 514, 539, 668.

Byers, H. G., Kellogg, C. E., Anderson, M. S., and Thorp, J., 1938. Formation of Soil, In Soils and Men. Yearbook of Agriculture for 1938 [U. S. Dept. of Agr.]: 948–978. p. 218.

Byers, H. R., 1944. General Meteorology. New York, McGraw-Hill. pp. 140, 145.

Cain, S. A., 1939. The Climax and Its Components. Am. Midl. Nat., *21:* 146–181. p. 577.

——— 1943. The Tertiary Character of the Cove Hardwoods of the Great Smoky Mountains National Park. Bull. Torrey Bot. Club. *70:* 213–235. p. 575.

——— 1944. Foundations of Plant Geography. New York, Harper. pp. 575, 597, 606, 623, 639, 662, 680, 723.

——— 1945. A Biological Spectrum of the Flora of the Great Smoky Mountains National Park. Butler Univ. Bot. Stud., *8:* 1–14. p. 575.

Caldwell, G. T., 1931. Studies in Water Metabolism of the Cat. Physiol. Zoöl., *4:* 324–359. p. 186.

Calhoun, J. B., 1944–46. Twenty-four Hour Periodicities in the Animal Kingdom. J. Tenn. Acad. Sc., *19:* 179–200; 252–262; *20:* 228–232; 291–308; 373–378; *21:* 208–216; 281–282. p. 558.

——— 1945. Diel Activity Rhythms of the Rodents *Microtus ochrogaster* and *Sigmodon hispidus hispidus.* Ecology, *26:* 251–273. p. 558.

Calkins, G. N., 1926. The Biology of the Protozoa. Philadelphia, Lea and Febiger. p. 502.

———, and Summers, F. M., 1941. Protozoa in Biological Research. New York, Columbia. pp. 69, 360.

Calman, W. T., 1939. Instincts of the Herd. Nature, *144:* 5–6. p. 31.

Calvert, P. P., 1899. Massing of Coccinellidae. Entom. News, *10:* 68. p. 538.

Cameron, A. E., 1917. The Insect Association of a Local Environmental Complex in the District of Holmes Chapel, Cheshire. Tr. Roy. Soc., Edinburgh, *52:* 37–78. pp. 466, 467, 477.

Campbell, Robert Samuel, 1940. Range Management Research Methods in the Western United States. Herbage Reviews, *2:* 121–138. p. 475.

——— 1946. Determination of Grazing Values of Native Vegetation on Southern Pine Forest Ranges. Ecology, *27:* 195–204. p. 578.

——— and Rhodes, R. R., 1944. Forest Grazing

in Relation to Beef Cattle Production in Louisiana. Bull. Louisiana Univ., *380:* 3–43. p. 475.

Campbell, Robert Seymour, 1941. Vertical Distribution of the Plankton Rotifera in Douglas Lake, Michigan, with Special Reference to Depression Individuality. Ecol. Monogr., *11:* 1–19. p. 447.

Candolle, A. de, 1865. De la germination sous les degrés divers de témperature constante. Biblioth. Univ. Revue Suisse., *14:* 243–282. p. 18.

Candolle, A. P. de, 1806. Expériences relatives à l'influence de la lumière sur quelques végétaux. Acad. Sc. Paris. Mem., *1:* 329–350. p. 18.

Cannon, Walter B., 1941. The Body Physiologic and the Body Politic. Science, *93:* 1–10. pp. 631, 694.

Carlson, T., 1913. Über Geschwindigkeit und Grösse der Hefevermehrung in Würze. Biochem. Ztschr. *57:* 313–334. p. 307.

Carnap, Rudolf, 1938. Logical Foundation of the Unity of Science. In Int. Encyclopedia of Unified Science, *1:* 42–62. p. 13.

Carnes, E. K., 1912. Colecting Ladybirds by the Ton. Monthly Bull. Comm. Horticulture, Sacramento, California, *1:* 71–81. p. 538.

Carpenter, C. R., 1934. A Field Study of the Behavior and Social Relations of Howling Monkeys. Comp. Psych. Monogr., *10:* 1–168. pp. 413, 416, 554.

—— 1940. A Field Study of the Behavior and Social Relations of the Gibbon. Comp. Psych. Monogr., *16:* 1–212. p. 413.

—— 1942. Sexual Behavior of Free-Ranging Rhesus Monkeys. I. Specimens, Procedures and Behavioral Characteristics of Estrus. II. Periodicity of Estrus, Homosexual, Autocratic and Non-conformist Behavior. J. Comp. Psychl., *33:* 113–162. pp. 413, 414, 416, 417.

Carpenter, F. M., 1930. Review of Our Present Knowledge of the Geological History of the Insects. Psyche, *37:* 15–34. pp. 662, 717.

Carpenter, G. D. H., 1920. A Naturalist on Lake Victoria. London, Unwin. p. 669.

—— 1936. *Pseudacraea eurytus* (L.) and Its Models in the Budongo Forest, Bunyoro, Western Uganda (Lepidoptera). Proc. Roy. Ent. Soc., London, A., *11:* 22–28. p. 670.

—— 1936a. The Facts of Mimicry Still Require Natural Selection for Their Explanation. Proc. Roy. Soc., London, s. B., *121:* 65–67. p. 670.

Carpenter, J. R., 1934. Diurnal Fluctuations in Communities Adjoining the Forest Edge near Urbana, Illinois. Proc. Oklahoma Acad. Sc., *14:* 29–31. p. 544.

—— 1935. Fluctuations in Biotic Communities. I. Prairie-Forest Ecotone of Central Illinois. Ecology, *16:* 203–212. pp. 478, 546.

—— 1936. Daily Fluctuations in Insect Populations in the Prairie-Forest Ecotone of North America. Proc. 12th. Internat. Cong. Zool. Lisbon, pp. 969, 979. pp. 549, 557.

—— 1938. An Ecological Glossary. Norman, Univ. of Oklahoma Press. pp. 9, 69, 478, 531, 546, 574.

—— 1939. Special Review. Recent Russian Work on Community Ecology. J. Anim. Ecol., *8:* 354–386. p. 71.

—— 1940. Insect Outbreaks in Europe. J. Anim. Ecol., *9:* 108 147. p. 330.

—— 1940a. The Grassland Biome. Ecol. Monogr. *10:* 617–684. pp. 441, 468, 472, 475, 476, 514.

Carrick, Robert, 1936. Experiments to Test the Efficiency of Protective Adaptations in Insects. Tr. Roy. Ent. Soc., London, *85:* 131–140. p. 651.

Carr-Saunders, A. M., 1922. The Population Problem; A Study in Human Evolution. Oxford, Clarenden Press. p. 57.

Cartwright, C. W., 1944. The "Crash" Decline in Sharp-Tailed Grouse and Hungarian Partridge in Western Canada and the Role of the Predator. Tr. Ninth North American Wildlife Conference, *9:* 324–330. pp. 376, 707.

Caspari, Ernst, 1948. Cytoplasmic Inheritance. In Demerec, M. (ed.): Advances in Genetics. *2:* 1–66. pp. 602, 622.

Castle, W. E., 1946. Genes which Divide Species or Produce Hybrid Vigor. Proc. Nat. Acad. Sc., *32:* 145–149. p. 623.

Cattell, J. M., 1936. The Physiological Effect of Pressure. Biol. Rev., *11:* 441–476. pp. 137, 138.

Caullery, M. and Comas, M., 1928. Le déterminisme du sex chez un nématode parasite des larves de chironomes. Compt. rend. Acad. Sc. Paris, *186:* 646–647. p. 409.

Cave, A. J. E., and Haines, R. W., 1944. Meristic Variation and Reversibility of Evolution. Nature, *154:* 579–580. p. 679.

Chace, F. A., 1940. Plankton of the Bermuda Oceanographic Expeditions. IX. The Bathypelagic Caridean Crustacea. Zoologica, *25:* 117–209. pp. 450, 451, 514.

Chalkley, H. W., 1930. On the Relation between the Resistance to Heat and the Mechanism of Death in Paramecium. Physiol. Zoöl., *3:* 425–440. p. 175.

Challenger Expedition. 1880–1895. Report on the Scientific Results of the Voyage of H. M. S. Challenger, during the Years 1873–76. London, Challenger Office, 40 vols. pp. 38, 39.

Chamberlin, W. J., 1939. The Bark and Timber Beetles of North America. Corvallis, Oregon, O.S.C. Cooperative Assoc. p. 713.

Chandler, A. C., 1944. Introduction to Parasitology. 7th ed. New York, Wiley. pp. 258, 260, 261.

Chandler, D. C., 1942. Limnological Studies of Western Lake Erie. II. Light Penetration and Its Relation to Turbidity. Ecology, 23: 41–52. p. 445.

—— 1942a. Limnological Studies of Western Lake Erie. III. Phytoplankton and Physical-Chemical Data from November, 1939, to November, 1940. Ohio J. Sc., 42: 24–44. pp. 446, 504.

Chapin, J. P., 1916. The Pennant-Winged Nightjar of Africa and Its Migration. Bull. Am. Mus. Nat. Hist., 35: 73–81. p. 672.

Chapman, F. M., 1900. Bird Studies with a Camera with Introductory Chapters on the Outfit and Methods of the Bird Photographer. New York, Appleton. p. 45.

—— 1917. The Distribution of Bird-Life in Colombia; A Contribution to a Biological Survey of South America. Bull. Am. Mus. Nat. Hist., 36: 1–729. p. 595.

—— 1918. Our Winter Birds. New York, Appleton. p. 535.

—— 1933. Autobiography of a Bird-Lover. New York, Appleton-Century. pp. 461, 539.

—— 1934. Handbook of Birds of Eastern North America. 2nd rev. ed. New York, Appleton-Century. pp. 118, 539.

Chapman, R. N., 1920. The Life-Cycle of the Coleoptera (Including the Strepsiptera). Ann. Entom. Soc. Am., 13: 174–180. p. 534.

—— 1928. The Quantitative Analysis of Environmental Factors. Ecology, 9: 111–122. pp. 61, 370, 391, 392, 404, 508, 518.

—— 1931. Animal Ecology with Especial Reference to Insects. New York, McGraw-Hill. pp. 45, 69, 107, 135, 215, 227, 235, 272, 345, 526.

—— 1933. The Cause of Fluctuations of Populations of Insects. Proc. Hawaii Entom. Soc., 8: 279–297. p. 71.

—— and Baird, Lillian, 1934. The Biotic Constants of Tribolium confusum Duval. J. Exper. Zool., 68: 293–304. pp. 371, 405.

—— Mickel, C. E., Parker, J. R., Miller, G. E., and Kelley, E. G., 1926. Studies in the Ecology of Sand Dune Insects. Ecology, 7: 416–427. pp. 549, 557.

Chapman, V. J., 1941. An Introduction to the Study of Algae. London, Macmillan. pp. 454, 458.

Chase, H. B., 1944. Studies on an Anophthalmic Strain of Mice. IV. A Second Major Gene for Anophthalmia. Genetics, 29: 264–269. p. 674.

—— 1945. Studies on an Anophthalmic Strain of Mice. V. Associated Cranial Nerves and Brain Centers. J. Comp. Neurol., 83: 121–139. p. 674.

Cheatum, E. P., 1934. Limnological Investigation on Respiration, Annual Migratory Cycle and Other Related Phenomena in Fresh Water Pulmonate Snails. Tr. Am. Micr. Soc., 53: 348–407. p. 542.

Chejfec, M., 1928. Die Lebensdauer von Paramecium caudatum in Abhängigkeit von der Nahrungsmenge. Acta Biol. Exper., 4: 73–118. p. 406.

Chen, S. C., 1937. Social Modification of the Activity of Ants in Nest Building. Physiol. Zoöl., 10: 420–436. p. 411.

—— 1937a. The Leaders and Followers among the Ants in Nest Building. Physiol. Zoöl., 10: 437–455. pp. 411, 415.

Chen, T. T., 1945. Induction of Conjugation in Paramecium bursaria. Proc. Nat. Acad. Sc., 31: 404–410. p. 409.

—— 1946. Varieties and Mating Types in Paramecium bursaria. I. New Variety and Types, from England, Ireland, and Czechoslovakia. Proc. Nat. Acad. Sc., 32: 173–181. p. 622.

—— 1946a. Conjugation in Paramecium bursaria. II. Nuclear Phenomena in Lethal Conjugation between Varieties. J. Morphol., 79: 125–262. p. 622.

Chenoweth, H. E., 1917. The Reactions of Certain Moist Forest Mammals to Air Conditions and Its Bearing on Problems of Mammalian Distribution. Biol. Bull., 32: 183–201. p. 480.

Chester, K. S., 1942. The Nature and Prevention of Plant Diseases. Philadelphia, Blakiston. p. 643.

Chevillard, L., 1935. Contribution à l'étude des échanges respiratoires de la Souris blanche adulte. IV. Généralités des faits observés sur la Souris. Variation de leur importance avec la taille de l'homeotherme. Ann. Physiol. physicochemie Biol., 11: 1055–1088. p. 98.

Child, C. M., 1940. Social Integration as a Biological Process. Am. Nat., 74: 389–397. p. 72.

Chittenden, F. H., 1896. Insects Affecting Cereals and Other Dry Vegetable Foods. U. S. Dept. of Agr., Bur. Ent. Bull., 4: 112–131. p. 354.

Christie, J. R., 1929. Some Observations on Sex in the Mermithidae. J. Exper. Zool., 53: 59–76. p. 409.

Chu, T., and Pai, S., 1944. The Relation between Annelid Natural Fission and Regeneration in Stylaria fossularis. Physiol. Zoöl., 17: 159–166. p. 356.

Chumley, J., 1910. Bibliography of Limnological Literature. In Murray and Pullar's Bathymetrical Survey of the Scottish Fresh-Water Lochs, 1: 659–753. p. 52.

Church, J. E., 1942. Snow and Snow Surveying; Ice. Physics of the Earth, 9: 83–149. pp. 94, 96, 179.

Church, P. E., 1942. The Annual Temperature Cycle of Lake Michigan. I. Cooling from

Late Autumn to the Terminal Point, 1941–42. Univ. of Chicago Inst. Meteorol., Misc. Rept., *4:* 1–48.

Clark, A. H., 1914. Nocturnal Animals. J. Wash. Acad. Sc. *4:* 139–142. p. 553.

—— 1925. Animals of Land and Sea. New York, Van Nostrand. p. 459.

—— 1927. Geography and Zoology. Ann. A. Am. Geogr., *17:* 101–145. p. 237.

Clark, Frances N., 1925. The Life History of *Leuresthes tenuis,* an Atherine Fish with Tide Controlled Spawning Habits. Calif. Fish & Game Comm. Bull., *10:* 1–58. p. 84.

Clark, L. B., 1941. Factors in the Lunar Cycle which May Control Reproduction in the Atlantic Palolo. Coll. Net., *16:* 66–67. p. 84.

—— 1941a. Factors in the Lunar Cycle which May Control Reproduction in the Atlantic Palolo. Biol. Bull., *81:* 278. p. 84.

Clark, W. M., 1928. Determination of Hydrogen Ions. Baltimore, Williams & Wilkins. p. 56.

Clarke, F. W., 1924. The Data of Geochemistry. 5th ed. U.S.G.S. Bull., *770.* pp. 157, 199, 498.

—— and Wheeler, W. C., 1922. The Inorganic Constituents of Marine Invertebrates. U.S.G.S. Prof. Papers, *124:* 1–62. p. 206.

Clarke, G. L., 1933. Diurnal Migration of Plankton in the Gulf of Maine and Its Correlation with Changes in Submarine Irradiation. Biol. Bull., *65:* 402–436. pp. 554, 555.

—— 1934. Factors Affecting Vertical Distribution of Copepods. Ecol. Monogr., *4:* 530–540. p. 554.

—— 1936. On the Depth at which Fish Can See. Ecology, *17:* 452–456. p. 126.

—— 1938. Light Penetration in the Caribbean Sea and in the Gulf of Mexico. J. Mar. Res., *1:* 85–94.

—— 1939. The Utilization of Solar Energy by Aquatic Organisms. Publ. Am. A. Adv. Sc., *10:* 27–38. p. 124.

—— 1939a. Variation in the Transparency of Three Areas of the Atlantic throughout the Year. Ecology, *20:* 529–543. p. 124.

—— 1939b. The Relation between Diatoms and Copepods as a Factor in the Productivity of the Sea. Quart. Rev. Biol., *14:* 60–64. p. 71.

—— 1946. Dynamics of Production in a Marine Area. Ecol. Monogr., *16:* 321–335. pp. 519, 520, 521.

——, Edmondson, W. T., and Ricker, W. E., 1946. Mathematical Formulation of Biological Productivity. Ecol. Monogr., *16:* 336–337. pp. 519, 522.

—— and Gellis, S. S., 1935. The Nutrition of Copepods in Relation to the Food-Culture Cycle of the Sea. Biol. Bull., *68:* 231–246. p. 444.

—— and Zinn, D. J., 1937. Seasonal Production of Zoöplankton off Woods Hole with Special Reference to Calanus finmarchicus. Biol. Bull., *73:* 464–487. p. 534.

Clarke, J. E., Margerie, I., and Marshall, R., 1924. Report on Phenological Observation in the British Isles, 1922–23. Q. J. Roy. Meteorol. Soc., *50:* 277–323. pp. 118, 519.

Clausen, C. P., 1940. Entomophagous Insects. New York, McGraw-Hill. pp. 70, 494.

Clausen, J., Keck, D. D., and Hiesey, W. M., 1940. Experimental Studies on the Nature of Species. I. Effect of Varied Environments on Western North American Plants. Publ. Carnegie Inst. Wash., *520:* 1–452. p. 628.

——, ——, —— 1945. Experimental Studies on the Nature of Species. II. Plant Evolution through Amphiploidy and Autoploidy with Examples from the Madiinae. Pub. Carnegie Inst. Wash., *564:* 1–174. p. 626.

Clausen, R. G., 1934. Body Temperature of Fresh Water Fishes. Ecology, *15:* 139–144. pp. 97, 494.

Clemens, W. A., 1917. An Ecological Study of the Mayfly Nymph *Chirotones.* Univ. Toronto Studies, (Biol.) *17.* pp. 156, 157.

Clements, F. E., 1905. Research Methods in Ecology. Lincoln, Univ. Pub. Co. pp. 34, 530.

—— 1916. Plant Succession: An Analysis of the Development of Vegetation. Publ. Carnegie Inst. Wash. *242:* 1–512. p. 530.

—— 1924. Methods and Principles of Palaeoecology. Year Book, Carnegie Inst. Wash., *32:* 319. p. 57.

—— 1928. Plant Succession and Indicators; A Definitive Edition of Plant Succession and Plant Indicators. New York, Wilson. p. 577.

—— and Chaney, R. W., 1936. Environment and Life in the Great Plains. Publ. Carnegie Inst. Wash. *24,* Suppl., pp. 1–54. pp. 83, 475.

—— and Shelford, V. E., 1939. Bio-ecology. New York, Wiley. pp. 11, 34, 47, 62, 69, 85, 87, 227, 348, 395, 406, 441, 449, 450, 459, 462, 466, 475, 514, 528, 531, 571, 574, 576, 577, 578, 580, 586, 590, 596, 695, 698.

Cleveland, L. R., 1924. The Physiological and Symbiotic Relationships between the Intestinal Protozoa of Termites and Their Host, with Special Reference to *Reticulitermes flvipes* Kollar. Biol. Bull., *46:* 177–225. pp. 62, 716.

—— 1925. Toxicity of Oxygen for Protozoa in Vivo and in Vitro; Animals Defaunated without Injury. Biol. Bull., *48:* 455–468. p. 716.

Cleveland, L. R., 1925a. The Ability of Termites to Live Perhaps Indefinitely on a Diet of Pure Cellulose. Biol. Bull., *48*: 289–293. p. 716.

—— 1926. Symbiosis among Animals with Special Reference to Termites and Their Intestinal Flagellates. Quart. Rev. Biol., *1*: 51–60. pp. 712, 716.

—— 1928. Further Observations and Experiments on the Symbiosis between Termites and Their Intestinal Protozoa. Biol. Bull., *54*: 231–237. p. 716.

—— 1947. The Origin and Evolution of Meiosis. Science, *105*: 287–289. p. 629.

——, Hall, S. R., Sanders, E. P., and Collier, Jane, 1934. The Wood-Feeding Roach *Cryptocercus*, Its Protozoa, and the Symbiosis between Protozoa and Roach. Mem. Am. Acad. Arts & Sc., *17*: 185–342. pp. 62, 629, 712, 716, 717.

Clowes, G. H. A., and Smith, H. W., 1923. The Influence of Hydrogen Ion Concentration on the Fertilization and Growth of Certain Marine Eggs. Am. J. Physiol., *64*: 144–159. p. 175.

Cobb, N. A., 1915. Nematodes and Their Relationships. Yearbook U. S. Dept. of Agr., 1914: 456–490. p. 484.

Cockerell, T. D. A., 1931. Rocky Mountain Bees. II. The Genus Andrena. Am. Mus. Novitates, *458*: 1–20. p. 617.

Coe, W. R., 1936. Sexual Phases in *Crepidula*, J. Exper. Zool., *72*: 455–477. p. 409.

Coker, R. E., 1934. Influence of Temperature on Form of the Freshwater Copepod. *Cyclops vernalis* Fischer. Intern. Rev. Ges. Hydrobiol. Hydrograph., *30*: 411–447. p. 119.

—— 1938. Life in the Sea. Scient. Monthly, *46*: 299–322; 416–432. pp. 447, 460, 499, 501, 514.

—— 1939. The Problem of Cyclomorphosis in Daphnia. Quart. Rev. Biol., *14*: 137–148. pp. 118, 119, 686.

—— 1947. This Great and Wide Sea. Chapel Hill, Univ. of North Carolina Press. pp. 37, 85, 165, 448, 499, 501, 502, 514, 596.

Cole, LaMont C., 1943. Experiments on Toleration of High Temperature in Lizards with Reference to Adaptive Coloration. Ecology, *24*: 94–108. pp. 590, 653.

—— 1946. A Study of the Cryptozoa of an Illinois Woodland. Ecol. Monogr., *16*: 49–86. pp. 361, 364, 394, 537, 661, 697.

—— 1946a. A Theory for Analyzing Contagiously Distributed Populations. Ecology, *27*: 329–341. p. 365.

Coleman, Edith, 1927. Pollination of the Orchid *Cryptostylis leptochila*. Victorian Nat., *44*: 20–22. p. 715.

—— 1938. Further Observations on the Pseudocopulation of the Male *Lissopimpla semipunctata* Kirby (Hymenoptera Parasitica) with the Australian Orchid, *Crypt-*

ostylis leptochila F. v. M. Proc. Roy. Ent. Soc. London, s. A., *13*: 82–83. p. 715.

Collias, N. E., 1943. Statistical Analysis of Factors which Make for Success in Initial Encounters between Hens. Am. Nat., *77*: 519–538. p. 414.

—— 1944. Aggressive Behavior among Vertebrate Animals. Physiol. Zoöl., *17*: 83–123. pp. 413, 418.

Colquhoun, M. K., and Morley, A., 1943. Vertical Zonation in Woodland Bird Communities. J. Animal Ecology, *12*: 75–81. pp. 488, 489.

Comstock, J. H., 1933. An Introduction to Entomology. Rev. ed. Ithaca, Comstock. pp. 514, 518.

Comte, A., 1830. Cours de philosophie positive. Paris, Schleicher, 6 vols. p. 31.

Conant, Roger, Thomas, E. S., and Rausch, R. L., 1945. The Plains Garter Snake. Thamnophis radix, in Ohio. Copeia, 1945: 61–68. pp. 590, 660.

Conard, H. S., 1939. Plant Associations on Land. Am. Mid. Nat., *21*: 1–26. p. 43.

Conklin, E. G., 1943. Man, Real and Ideal. New York: Scribner. p. 645.

—— 1944. Jean Baptiste-Pierre Antoine de Monet Chevalier de Lamarck, Genetics, *29*: i–iv. p. 30.

Conklin, E. S., 1927. Principles of Abnormal Psychology. New York, Holt. p. 553.

Cook, A. J., 1898. Massing in Coccinellidae. Entom. News, *9*: 117. p. 538.

Cook, D. B., 1943. History of a Beaver Colony. J. Mammal., *24*: 12–18. p. 401.

Cook, S. F., and Scott, K. G., 1933. The Nutritional Requirements of *Zootermopsis (Termopsis) angusticollis*. J. Cell & Comp. Physiol., *4*: 95–110. p. 430.

Cook, W. C., 1921. Studies on the Flight of Nocturnal Lepidoptera. Rep. State Ent. Minn., *18*: 43–56. p. 188.

—— 1924. The Distribution of the Pale Western Cutworm, *Porosogrotis orthogonia* Morr: A Study in Physical Ecology. Ecology, *5*: 60–69. pp. 60, 187.

Cooke, A. H., 1895. Molluscs. In Cambridge Natural History, *3*: 1–459. p. 20.

Cooke, W. W., 1917. Bird Migration. In Pearson, T. G., Birds of America. New York, Garden City Pub. Co., pp. xxxi–xliv. p. 118.

Cooper, J. B., 1942. An Exploratory Study on African Lions. Comp. Pysch. Monogr., *17*: 1–48. p. 417.

Cooper, L. H. N., 1937. On the Ratio of Nitrogen to Phosphorus in the Sea. J. Mar. Biol. A., *22*: 177–182. p. 201.

—— 1938. Redefinition of the Anomaly of the Nitrate-Phosphate Ratio. J. Mar. Biol. A., *23*: 179. p. 201.

Cooper, W. S., 1926. The Fundamentals of Vegetational Change. Ecology, *7*: 391–413. p. 577.

Copeland, J. J., 1936. Yellowstone Thermal Myxophyceae. Ann. New York Acad. Sc., 36: 1–232. p. 103.

Cott, H. B., 1940. Adaptive Coloration in Animals. New York, Oxford Univ. Press. p. 70.

Coulter, J. M., Barnes, C. R., and Cowles, H. C., 1911. A Textbook of Botany. New York: American Book Co., 2 vols. pp. 480, 501, 548.

Coward, T. A., 1912. The Migration of Birds. Cambridge, Cambridge Univ. Press. p. 539.

Cowles, H. C., 1899. The Ecological Relations of the Vegetation of the Sand Dunes of Lake Michigan. Bot. Gaz., 27: 95–117; 167–202; 281–308; 361–391. pp. 47, 563, 567.

—— 1901. The Plant Societies of Chicago and Vicinity. Bull. Geog. Soc. Chicago, 2: 1–76. pp. 42, 43, 155, 436, 463, 563, 567.

—— 1901a. The Physiographic Ecology of Chicago and Vicinity; A Study of the Origin, Development, and Classification of Plant Societies. Bot. Gaz., 31: 73–182. [Repr., Ann Arbor, Edwards Bros.] p. 563.

—— 1911. The Causes of Vegetative Cycles. Bot. Gaz., 51: 161–183. p. 567.

Cowles, R. B., 1945. Heat-Induced Sterility and Its Possible Bearing on Evolution. Am. Nat., 79: 160–175. p. 632.

—— and Bogert, C. M., 1944. A Preliminary Study of the Thermal Requirements of Desert Reptiles. Bull. Am. Mus. Nat. Hist., 83: 261–296. pp. 590, 634, 661, 671.

Cowles, R. P., 1930. A Biological Study of the Offshore Waters of Chesapeake Bay. Bull. Bur. Fish., 46: 277–381. p. 341.

Craig, C. F., and Faust, E. C., 1943. Clinical Parasitology. 3rd ed. Philadelphia, Lea and Febiger. p. 258.

Craig, Wallace, 1908. The Voices of Pigeons Regarded as a Means of Social Control. Am. J. Sociol., 14: 86–100. p. 45.

—— 1917. On the Ability of Animals to Keep Time with an External Rhythm. J. Animal Behavior, 7: 444–448. p. 554.

Craighead, F. C., 1916. Insects in Their Relation to the Chestnut Bark Disease. Science, 43: 133–135. p. 699.

Craigie, J. H., 1927. Discovery of the Function of the Pycnia of the Rust Fungi. Nature, 120: 765–767. p. 715.

Crampton, H. E., 1916. Studies on the Variation, Distribution, and Evolution of the Genus Partula. The Species Inhabiting Tahiti. Publ. Carnegie Inst. Wash. 228: 1–313. p. 609.

—— 1925. Studies on the Variation, Distribution and Evolution of the Genus Partula. The Species of the Mariana Islands, Guam and Saipan. Publ. Carnegie Inst. Wash., 228A: 1–116. p. 609.

—— 1932. Studies on the Variation, Distribution and Evolution of the Genus Partula. The Species Inhabiting Moorea. Publ. Carnegie Inst. Wash., 410: 1–335. p. 609.

Crane, Jocelyn, 1941. Crabs of the Genus Uca from the West Coast of Central America. Zoologica, 26: 145–208. pp. 412, 620, 710.

—— 1941a. On the Growth and Ecology of Brachyuran Crabs of the Genus Ocypode. Zoologica, 26: 297–310. p. 611.

—— 1944. On the Color Changes of Fiddler Crabs (Genus Uca) in the Field. Zoologica, 29: 161–168. p. 620.

Crawford, S. C., 1933. A Survey of Nocturnal Vertebrates in the Kartabo Region of British Guiana. J. Animal Ecol., 2: 282–288. p. 547.

—— 1934. The Habits and Characteristics of Nocturnal Animals. Quart. Rev. Biol., 9: 201–214. p. 71.

Creaser, E. P., 1931. Some Coinhabitants of Burrowing Crayfish. Ecology, 12: 243–244. pp. 438, 439, 538, 539.

Cressman, A. W., Bliss, C. I., Kessels, L. T., and Dumestre, J. O., 1935. Biology of the Camphor Scale and a Method for Predicting the Time of Appearance in the Field. J. Agr. Res., 50: 267–283. p. 278.

Crombie, A. C., 1942. The Effect of Crowding upon the Oviposition of Grain-Infesting Insects. J. Exper. Biol., 19: 311–340. pp. 350, 355.

—— 1943. The Effect of Crowding upon the Natality of Grain-Infesting Insects. Proc. Zool. Soc., London, s. A., 113: 77–98. pp. 355, 371, 405.

—— 1944. On Intraspecific and Interspecific Competition in Larvae of Graminivorous Insects. J. Exper. Biol., 20: 135–151. p. 350.

—— 1945. On Competition between Different Species of Graminivorous Insects. Proc. Roy. Soc., London, s. B., 132: 362–395. pp. 271, 369, 370.

—— 1946. Further Experiments on Insect Competition. Proc. Roy. Soc. London, s. B., 133: 76–109. p. 271.

—— 1947. Interspecific Competition. J. Anim. Ecology, 16: 44–73. pp. 369, 610, 616, 617, 623, 657, 728.

Cross, E. C., 1940. Periodic Fluctuations in Numbers of the Red Fox in Ontario. J. Mammalogy, 21: 294–306. p. 367.

Cruz, S. R. and Romanoff, A. L., 1944. Effect of Oxygen Concentration on the Development of the Chick Embryo. Physiol. Zoöl., 17: 184–187. p. 190.

Cushing, J. E. Jr., 1945. A Comparative Study of Complement. II. The Interaction of Components of Different Species. J. Immunol., 50: 75–89. p. 681.

Custer, C. P., 1928. The Bee that Works in Stone; Perdita opuntiae. Psyche, 35: 69–84. p. 225.

Cutright, P. R., 1940. The Great Naturalists Explore South America. New York, Macmillan. p. 461.

Dach, Herman von, 1943. The Effect of pH on Pure Cultures of *Euglena mutabilis*. Ohio J. Sc., *43:* 47–48. p. 174.

Daggy, Tom, 1946. The Ecology and Taxonomy of the Immature Stages of Certain Wood-Inhabiting Coleoptera of the Chicago Region. Northwestern Univ., Summ. Doct. Diss., *14:* 227–231. p. 570.

Dahl, F., 1898. Experimentell-statistische Ethologie. Verh. Deutsch. Zool. Gesellsch., *8:* 121–131. p. 36.

—— 1901. Was ist ein Experiment, was Statistik in der Ethologie? Biol. Centralbl., *21:* 675–681. p. 42.

Daily, W. A., 1938. A Quantitative Study of the Phytoplankton of Lake Michigan Collected in the Vicinity of Evanston, Illinois. Butler Univ. Stud. Bot., *4:* 65–83. p. 504.

Dallinger, W. H., 1887. The President's Address. J. Roy. Micr. Soc., pp. 185–199. p. 22.

Dalquest, W. W., and Scheffer, V. B., 1944. Distribution and Variation in Pocket Gophers, *Thomomys talpoides*, in the State of Washington. II. Am. Nat., *78:* 423–450. p. 609.

Damann, K. E., 1940. Phytoplankton Study of Lake Michigan at Evanston, Illinois. Tr. Illinois Acad. Sc., *33:* 68–70. p. 504.

Dana, J. D., 1852–1855. Crustacea. [Report] U. S. Exploring Expedition . . . 1838–42. Under the command of C. Wilkes, *13:* 1–1618. p. 35.

—— 1853. On an Isothermal Oceanic Chart Illustrating the Geographic Distribution of Marine Animals. Am. J. Sc., (2) *16:* 314–327. p. 35.

D'Ancona, Umberto, 1942, La Lotta per L'Esistenza. Torino, Giulio Einaudi. p. 271.

Dannevig, A., 1933. The Number of Vertebrae in *Gadus virens* L. from the Norwegian Skagerak Coast. Cons. Perm. Intern. Explor. Mer. J. Conseil., *8:* 355–356. p. 119.

Darling, F. F., 1937. A Herd of Red Deer. A Study in Animal Behaviour. New York, Oxford Univ. Press. pp. 69, 103, 415, 416.

—— 1938. Bird Flocks and the Breeding Cycle. A Contribution to the Study of Avian Sociality. Cambridge, Cambridge University Press. pp. 69, 103, 402.

Darlington, C. D., 1940. Taxonomic Species and Genetic Systems. In Huxley, J., The New Systematics. Oxford: Clarendon Press, pp. 137–160. p. 676.

—— 1944. Heredity, Development and Infection. Nature, *154:* 164–169. pp. 602, 676, 681.

Darlington, P. J. Jr., 1936. Variation and Atrophy of Flying Wings of Some Carabid Beetles. Ann. Ent. Soc. Am., *29:* 136–179. p. 675.

—— 1938. Experiments on Mimicry in Cuba, with Suggestions for Future Study. Tr. Roy. Ent. Soc., London, *87:* 681–696. p. 669.

—— 1938a. The Origin of the Fauna of the Greater Antilles, with Discussion of Dispersal of Animals over Water and through the Air. Quart. Rev. Biol., *13:* 274–300. pp. 146, 149.

—— 1943. Carabidae of Mountains and Islands: Data on the Evolution of Isolated Faunas, and an Atrophy of Wings. Ecol. Monogr., *13:* 37–61. pp. 147, 600, 657.

—— 1948. The Geographical Distribution of Cold-Blooded Vertebrates, Quart. Rev. Biol., *23:* 1–26, 105–123. p. 662.

Darwin, Charles, R., 1842. On the Structure and Distribution of Coral Reefs. London [Amer. ed., 1901, New York, Appleton]. pp. 456, 570, 596.

—— 1859. The Origin of Species by Means of Natural Selection or the Preservation of Favored Races in the Struggle for Life. London, Murray [numerous editions]. pp. 25, 26, 31, 330, 513, 514, 516, 640.

—— 1871. Descent of Man and Selection in Relation to Sex. London, Murray. 2 vols. [Amer. ed., 1871, New York, Appleton. 2 vols.] p. 32.

—— 1875. Insectivorous Plants. London, Murray. [Amer. ed., 1883, New York, Appleton]. p. 437.

—— 1881. The Formation of Vegetable Mould, through the Action of Worms. London, Murray. pp. 24, 484.

——, and Wallace, A., 1858. On the Tendency of Species to Form Varieties; and on the Perpetuation of Varieties and Species by Natural Means of Selection. J. Linn. Soc., London, Zoology, *3:* 45–62. p. 25.

Darwin, Erasmus, 1794. Zoonomia, or the Laws of Organic Life. London. [Amer. ed. 1809, Boston, Thomas and Andrews. Vol. 1, part 1.] p. 29.

—— 1800. Phytologia. London, Johnson. p. 29.

Daubenmire, R. F., 1936. The "Big Woods" of Minnesota: Its Structure, and Relation to Climate, Fire, and Soils. Ecol. Monogr., *6:* 235–268. p. 482.

—— 1938. Merriam's Life Zones of North America. Quart. Rev. Biol., *13:* 327–332. pp. 72, 114, 593.

Davenport, Charles B., 1897–1899. Experimental Morphology. London and New York, Macmillan, 2 vols. pp. 19, 20, 21, 22, 24.

—— 1903. The Animal Ecology of the Cold Spring Harbor Sand Split, with Remarks on the Theory of Adaptation. Decennial Pub. Univ. Chicago, *10:* 157–176. p. 48.

—— 1908. Experimental Morphology. 2d. ed. New York, Macmillan. p. 44.

Davidson, F. A., 1927. Relation of Taurine Cattle to Climate. Econ. Geog., 3: 466–485. p. 104.

—— 1933. Temporary High Carbon Dioxide Content in an Alaskan Stream at Sunset. Ecology, 14: 238–240. p. 343.

—— and Vaughn, Elizabeth, 1941. Relation of Population Size to Marine Growth and Time of Spawning Migration in the Pink Salmon of Southeastern Alaska. J. Mar. Research, 4: 231–246. p. 396.

Davidson, James, 1938. On the Ecology of the Growth of the Sheep Population in South Australia. Tr. Roy. Soc. S. Australia, 62: 141–148. p. 310.

—— 1938a. On the Growth of the Sheep Population in Tasmania. Tr. Roy. Soc. S. Australia, 62: 342–346. pp. 310, 317.

—— 1944. On the Growth of Insect Populations with Successive Generations. Australian J. Exper. Biol. & Med. Sc., 22: 95–103. pp. 310, 320.

Davidson, V. S., 1930. The Tree Layer Society of the Maple-Red Oak Climax Forest. Ecology, 11: 601–606.

—— 1932. The Effect of Seasonal Variability upon Animal Species in Total Populations in a Deciduous Forest Succession. Ecol. Monogr. 2: 305–333. p. 531.

—— and Shackleford, M. W., 1929. Diurnal Variations in the Vernal Invertebrate Population of a Central Oklahoma Prairie. Proc. Oklahoma Acad. Sc., 9: 54–59. p. 557.

Davis, D. D., 1932. Occurrence of *Thamnophis butleri* Cope in Wisconsin. Copeia, 1932: 113–118. p. 660.

Davis, David E., 1942. The Phylogeny of Social Nesting Habits in the Crotophaginae. Quart. Rev. Biol., 17: 115–134. p. 71.

—— 1945. The Annual Cycle of Plants, Mosquitoes, Birds and Mammals in Two Brazilian Forests. Ecol. Monogr., 15: 243–295. pp. 85, 531.

Davis, J. H., Jr., 1940. The Ecology and Geologic Rôle of Mangroves in Florida. Publ. Carnegie Inst. Wash., 517: 303–412. p. 460.

Davis, T. A. W., and Richards, P. W., 1934. The Vegetation of Moraballi Creek, British Guiana: An Ecological Study of a Limited Area of Tropical Rain Forest. Part II. J. Ecology, 22: 106–155. p. 482.

Davis, W. M., 1928. The Formation of Coral Reefs. Scient. Monthly, 36: 289–301. p. 456.

—— 1928a. The Coral Reef Problem. Am. Geogr. Soc. Spec. Publ., 9: 1–596. p. 596.

Davis, W. T., 1925. *Cicada tibicen*, a South American Species, with Records and Descriptions of North American Cicadas. J. New York Entom. Soc., 33: 35–51. p. 543.

Davison, Charles, 1944. Earthquake. Encyclopaedia Britannica, pp. 844–854. p. 130.

Dawson, J., 1911. The Biology of Physa. Behavior Mon., 1: 1–120. p. 50.

DeBach, Paul, and Smith, H. S., 1941. Are Population Oscillations Inherent in the Host-Parasite Relation? Ecology, 22: 363–369. pp. 326, 384, 700.

DeBary, A., 1879. Die Erscheinung der Symbiose. Strassburg, Tübner. pp. 243, 710.

deBeer, G. R. (editor), 1938, Evolution; Essays on Aspects of Evolutionary Biology. Oxford, Clarenden Press. pp. 70, 598, 675, 681.

—— 1940. Embryos and Ancestors. Oxford, Clarenden Press. pp. 636, 675.

Deegener, P., 1918. Die Formen der Vergesellschaftung im Tierreiche. Ein Systematisch-soziologischer Versuch. Leipzig, Veit. p. 32.

Deevey, E. S., Jr., 1941. Limnological Studies in Connecticut. VI. The Quantity and Composition of the Bottom Fauna of Thirty-six Connecticut and New York Lakes. Ecol. Monogr., 11: 413–455. p. 453.

—— 1944. Pollen Analysis and History. Am. Scientist, 32: 39–53. pp. 82, 83.

—— 1947. Life Tables for Natural Populations of Animals. Quart. Rev. Biol., 22: 283–314. p. 294.

Delage, Yves, and Goldsmith, Marie, 1912. The Theories of Evolution. Trans. by André-Tridon. London, Palmer. p. 32.

Demoor, J. 1894. Contribution à l'étude de la physiologie de la cellule (independance functionnelle du protoplasma et du noyan). Arch. de biol., 3: 163–244. p. 19.

Dendy, A., 1895. The Cryptozoic Fauna of Australasia. Rept. Sixth Meeting Australian A. Adv. Sc., 6: 99–119. p. 364.

—— 1914. Outlines of Evolutionary Biology. 2nd ed. London, Constable. pp. 29, 30.

Dendy, J. S., 1944. The Fate of Animals in Stream Drift when Carried into Lakes. Ecol. Monogr., 14: 333–357. pp. 155, 671.

Dermen, Haig, 1940. Colchicine Polyploidy and Technique. Bot. Rev., 6: 599–635. p. 625.

Desneux, J., 1948. Les Nidifications souterraines des *Apicotermes*, Termites de l'Afrique tropicale. Rev. Zool. Bot. Afric., 41: 1–54. p. 633.

Detlefsen, J. A., 1925. The Inheritance of Acquired Characters. Physiol. Rev., 5: 244–278. p. 599.

DeTurk, E. E. (ed.), 1948. Freedom from Want, a Survey of the Possibilities of Meeting the World's Food Needs. Chron. Bot., 11: 210–283. p. 515.

De Vries, Hugo, 1884. Eine Methode zur

Analyse der Turgorkraft. Jahrb. wiss. Bot., 14: 427–601. p. 20.

Dice, L. R., 1931. The Occurrence of Two Subspecies of the Same Species in the Same Area. J. Mammalogy, 12: 210–213. p. 610.

—— 1940. Relationships between the Wood-Mouse and the Cotton-Mouse in Eastern Virginia. J. Mammalogy, 21: 14–23. p. 621.

—— 1940a. The Relation of Genetics to Geographical Distribution and Speciation; Speciation. II. Am. Nat., 74: 289–298. p. 625.

—— 1945. Minimum Intensities of Illumination under which Owls Can Find Dead Prey by Sight. Am. Nat., 79: 385–416. p. 627.

—— 1947. Effectiveness of Selection by Owls of Deer-Mice (Peromyscus maniculatus) which Contrast in Color with Their Background. Contrib. Lab. Vert. Biol., Univ. Michigan, 34: 1–20. pp. 627, 650.

Dill, D. B., 1938. Life, Heat and Altitude. Cambridge, Harvard. pp. 183, 191.

Ditman, L. P., Voght, G. B., and Smith, D. R., 1943. Undercooling and Freezing of Insects. J. Econ. Ent., 36: 304–311. p. 101.

Diver, C., 1936. The Problem of Closely-Related Species and the Distribution of Their Populations. Proc. Roy. Soc., London, s. B., 121: 62–65. p. 618.

—— 1940. The Problem of Closely Related Species Living in the Same Area. In Huxley, J., The New Systematics, pp. 303–328. p. 618.

Dixey, F. A., 1920. The Geographical Factor in Mimicry. Tr. Ent. Soc., London, 1920: 208–211. p. 669.

Dobell, C. (transl.), 1932. Leeuwenhoek and His "Little Animals." Amsterdam, Swets and Zeitlinger. p. 37.

Dobzhansky, Theodosius, 1941. (1st ed., 1937.) Genetics and the Origin of Species. New York, Columbia. pp. 70, 187, 598, 606, 617, 618, 619, 623, 626, 629, 676.

—— 1942. Studies on the Genetic Structure of Natural Populations. Yr. Book Carnegie Inst. Wash., 41: 228–234. p. 655.

—— 1945. Genetic Structure of Natural Populations. Yr. Book Carnegie Inst. Wash., 44: 127–134. p. 652.

—— 1946. Genetics of Natural Populations. XIII. Recombination and Variability in Populations of Drosophila pseudoobscura. Genetics., 31: 269–290. pp. 649, 655.

—— 1946a. Lysenko's "Genetics." J. Heredity, 37: 5–9. p. 599.

—— 1947. Adaptive Changes Induced by Natural Selection in Wild Populations of Drosophila. Evolution, 1: 1–16. pp. 649, 652.

—— 1948. Genetics of Natural Populations. XVI. Altitudinal and Seasonal Changes

Produced by Natural Selection in Certain Populations of Drosophila pseudoobscura and Drosophila persimilis. Genetics, 33: 158–176. pp. 649, 652.

—— and Epling, C., 1944. Contributions to the Genetics, Taxonomy, and Ecology of Drosophila pseudoobscura and Its Relatives. Publ. Carnegie Inst. Wash., 554: 1–183 p. 607.

—— and Holz, A. M., 1943. A re-examination of the Problem of Manifold Effects of Genes in Drosophila melanogaster Genetics, 28: 295–303. p. 677.

—— Holz, A. M., and Spassky, B., 1942. Genetics of Natural Populations. VIII. Concealed Variability in the Second and the Fourth Chromosomes of Drosophila pseudoobscura and Its Bearing on the Problem of Heterosis. Genetics, 27: 464–490. p. 655.

—— and Koller, P. C., 1938. An Experimental Study of Sexual Isolation in Drosophila. Biol. Zentralbl., 58: 589–607. p. 619.

—— and Wright, S., 1943. Genetics of Natural Populations. X. Dispersion Rates in Drosophila pseudoobscura. Genetics, 28: 304–340. p. 366.

Doflein, Franz, 1914. Das Tier als Glied des Naturganzen. Leipzig, Teubner. [Vol. 2 of Hesse and Doflein, Tierbau und Tierleben.] pp. 239, 242, 250.

Donaldson, H. H., 1924. The Rat. Philadelphia, Mem. Wistar Inst., 6.

Doty, M. S., 1946. Critical Tide Factors that Are Correlated with the Vertical Distribution of Marine Algae and Other Organisms along the Pacific Coast. Ecology, 27: 315–328. p. 455.

Doubleday, T., 1841 (3rd ed., 1853). The True Law of Population Shewn to Be Connected with the Food of the People. London, Smith, Elder. p. 26.

Douglass, A. E., 1928. Climatic Cycles and Tree Growth: A Study of the Annual Rings of Trees in Relation to Climate and Solar Activity. Publ. Carnegie Inst. Wash., No. 289, vol. 2. p. 528.

—— 1936. Climatic Cycles and Tree Growth: A Study of the Annual Rings of Trees in Relation to Climate and Solar Activity. Publ. Carnegie Inst. Wash., 289: 3 vols. pp. 86, 87.

Douglis, Marjorie B., 1948. Social Factors Influencing the Hierarchies of Small Flocks of the Domestic Hen: The Interaction between Resident and Part-time Members of Organized Flocks. Physiol. Zoöl., 21: 147–182. p. 414.

Doutt, J. K., 1942. A Review of the Genus Phoca. Ann. Carnegie Mus., 29: 61–125. p. 609.

Dowden, P. B., 1946. Parasitization of the Oriental Moth (Cnidocampa flavescens

(Walk)) by *Chaetexorista javana* B. and B. Ann. Ent. Soc. Amer., *39:* 225–241. p. 706.

Dowdeswell, W. H., Fisher, R. A., and Ford, E. B., 1940. The Quantitative Study of Populations in the Lepidoptera. I. *Polyommatus icarus* Rott. Ann. Eugenics, *10:* 123–136. p. 366.

Dowdy, W. W., 1944. The Influence of Temperature on Vertical Migration of Invertebrates Inhabiting Different Soil Types. Ecology, *25:* 449–460. p. 537.

Downes, A., and Blunt, T. P., 1877. Researches on the Effect of Light upon Bacteria and Other Organisms. Proc. Roy. Soc., London, *26:* 488–500. p. 20.

—— 1878. On the Influence of Light upon Protoplasm. Proc. Roy. Soc., London, *28:* 199–212. p. 20.

Doyere, M. P. L. N., 1840–1842. Mémoire sur les tartigrades. Ann. Sc. Nat., (2), Zool., *14:* 269–361; *17:* 193–205; *18:* 5–35. p. 21.

Draper, J. W., 1844. On the Decomposition of Carbonic-Acid Gas and the Alkaline Carbonates, by the Light of the Sun. Am. J. Sc., *46:* 398–400. p. 20.

Draper, J. W., and Edwards, D. J., 1932. Some Effects of High Pressure on Developing Marine Forms. Biol. Bull., *63:* 99–107. p. 138.

Drew, G. H., 1912. Report of Investigations on Marine Bacteria Carried on at Andros Island, Bahamas, British West Indies, in May, 1912. Yearbook Carnegie Inst. Wash., *11:* 136–144. p. 446.

Dreyer, W. A., 1932. The Effect of Hibernation and Seasonal Variation of Temperature on the Respiratory Exchange of *Formica ulkei* Emery. Physiol. Zoöl., *5:* 301–331. p. 538.

—— 1938. Seasonal Weight and Total Water Content of the Mound-Building Ant, *Formica exsectoides* Forel. Ecology, *19:* 38–49. pp. 102, 538.

—— 1942. Further Observations on the Occurrence and Size of Ant Mounds with Reference to Their Age. Ecology, *23:* 486–490. p. 428.

Dropkin, V. H., 1941. Host Specificity Relations of Termite Protozoa. Ecology, *22:* 200–202. p. 429.

Dubinin, N. P., and Tiniakov, G. G., 1945. Seasonal Cycles and the Concentration of Inversions in Populations of *Drosophila funebris.* Am. Nat., *79:* 570–572. p. 652.

——, —— 1946. Seasonal Cycle and Inversion Frequency in Populations. Nature, *157:* 23–24. p. 652.

——, —— 1946a. Structural Chromosome Variability in Urban and Rural Populations of *Drosophila funebris.* Am. Nat., *80:* 393–396. p. 652.

——, —— 1946b. Natural Selection and Chromosomal Variability in Populations of *Drosophila funebris.* J. Heredity, *37:* 39–44. p. 652.

——, —— 1947. Inversion Gradients and Selection in Ecological Races of *Drosophila funebris.* Am. Nat., *81:* 148–153. p. 652.

Dublin, L. I., and Lotka, A. J., 1925. On the True Rate of Natural Increase as Exemplified by the Population of the United States, 1920. J. Am. Stat. A., *20:* 305–339. p. 283.

——, —— 1936. Length of Life. A Study of the Life Table. New York, Ronald. pp. 69, 281, 286, 293, 294.

Dubos, R. J., 1928. Influence of Environmental Conditions on the Activities of Cellulose Decomposing Organisms in the Soil Ecology, *9:* 12–28. p. 484.

Duggar, B. M., 1936. Effects of Radiation on Bacteria. In Duggar, B. M., 1936, Biological Effects of Radiation, New York, McGraw-Hill. 2 vols., pp. 1119–1149. p. 127.

Duncan, H. G., 1929. Race and Population Problems. New York, Longmans. p. 271.

Dunham, G. C., 1940. Military Preventive Medicine. Harrisburg, Military Service Pub. Co. p. 70.

Dunn, E. R., 1931. The Amphibians of Barro Colorado Island. Occ. Papers Boston Soc. Nat. Hist., *5:* 403–421. p. 486.

—— 1935. The Survival Value of Specific Characters. Copeia, 1935: 85–98. p. 517.

Dunn, L. C., and Dobzhansky, T. H., 1946. Heredity, Race, and Society. New York, Penguin Books. p. 3.

DuRietz, G. E., 1930. Fundamental Units of Biological Taxonomy. Sv. Bot. Tidskr., *24:* 333–428. p. 577.

—— 1930a. Classification and Nomenclature of Vegetation. Sv. Bot. Tidskr., *24:* 489–503. p. 577.

DuShane, G. P., 1938. Neural Fold Derivatives in the Amphibia. Pigment Cells, Spinal Ganglia and Rohon-Beard Cells. J. Exper. Zool., *78:* 485–502. p. 636.

—— and Hutchinson, C., 1944. Differences in Size and Developmental Rate between Eastern and Midwestern Embryos of *Ambystoma maculatum.* Ecology, *25:* 414–423. p. 607.

Dutrochet, R. J. H., 1837. Observations sur les modifications qu'impriment à la circulation du Chara flexilis les changement de température, l'action d'agents mecanique, etc. Compt. rend. Acad. d. sc., *5:* 775–784. p. 21.

Dutton, H. J., and Juday, C., 1944. Chromatic Adaptation in Relation to Color and Depth of Freshwater Phytoplankton and Large Aquatic Plants. Ecology, *25:* 273–282.

Ecological Society of America, 1933–1935. Tentative Glossary of Ecological Terms.

[Committee on Nomenclature, Reports. Distributed in mimeographed form.] p. 531.

Eddy, S., and Carlander, K. D., 1940. The Effect of Environmental Factors upon the Growth Rates of Minnesota Fishes. Proc. Minn. Acad. Sc., 8: 14–19. p. 659.

Edmondson, W. T., 1944. Ecological Studies of Sessile Rotatoria. Part I. Factors Affecting Distribution. Ecol. Monogr., 14: 31–66. pp. 340, 366.

—— 1945. Ecological Studies of Sessile Rotatoria. Part II. Dynamics of Populations and Social Structures. Ecol. Monogr., 15: 141–172. p. 366.

—— 1946. Factors in the Dynamics of Rotifer Populations. Ecol. Monogr., 16: 357–372. p. 534.

Edwards and Colin, M. M., 1834. Influence de la température sur la germination. Ann. Sc. Nat. Bot. (2) 1: 257–270. p. 18.

Edwards, G. A., and Irving, L., 1943. The Influence of Temperature and Season upon the Oxygen Consumption of the Sand Crab, Emerita talpoida Say. J. Cell. & Comp. Physiol., 21: 169–182. p. 631.

Edwards, W. F., 1824. De l'influence des agens physique sur la vie. Paris, Crochard. [Trans. Hodgkin and Fisher, 1838. Philadelphia, Haswell, Barrington and Haswell.] pp. 20, 21.

Ege, Richard, 1918. On the Respiratory Function of the Air Stores Carried by Some Aquatic Insects (Corixidae, Dytiscidae and Notonecta). Ztschr. allg. Physiol., 17: 81–124. p. 195.

Eggleton, F. E., 1931. A Limnological Study of the Profundal Bottom Fauna of Certain Fresh-Water Lakes. Ecol. Monogr., 1: 231–332. pp. 451, 453.

—— 1937. Productivity of the Profundal Benthic Zone in Lake Michigan. Papers Michigan Acad. Sc., 22: 593–611. p. 453.

—— 1939. Role of the Bottom Fauna in the Productivity of Lakes. Pub. Am. A. Adv. Sc., 10: 123–131. pp. 451, 452, 453, 508.

Egler, Frank E., 1942. Vegetation as an Object of Study. Philosophy of Sc., 9: 245–260. pp. 577, 696, 729.

Ehrlich, P., 1891. Experimentelle untersuchungen über immunität. I. Ueber Ricin. II. Ueber Abrin. Deutsche med. Wochenschr., 17: 976–979; 1218–1219. p. 19.

Eifert, Virginia, S., 1941. Birds in Your Back Yard. Illinois State Mus., Pop. Sc. Ser., 2: 1–240. p. 535.

Eigenbrodt, H. J., 1925. The Somatic Effects of Certain Environmental Conditions on a Homozygous Race of Drosophila. Ph. D. thesis, Univ. Ill. p. 408.

Eigenmann, C. H., 1909. Cave Vertebrates of America; A Study in Degenerative Evolution. Pub. Carnegie Inst. Wash., 104: 1–241. pp. 36, 48, 439.

Ekman, Sven, 1935. Tiergeographie des Meeres. Leipzig, Akademische Verlagsgesellschaft. pp. 69, 78, 214, 596, 597.

Eldridge, Seba, 1925. The Organization of Life. New York, Crowell. p. 599.

Ellis, Carleton, and Wells, A. A., 1941. The Chemical Action of Ultra-violet Rays. Rev. by F. F. Heyroth. New York, Reinhold. pp. 88, 90, 128, 131.

Ellison, Lincoln, 1946. The Pocket Gopher in Relation to Soil Erosion on Mountain Range. Ecology, 27: 101–114. p. 578.

Elton, Charles, 1924. Periodic Fluctuations in the Numbers of Animals: Their Causes and Effects. J. Exper. Biol., 2: 119–163. pp. 60, 86, 367.

—— 1925. Plague and the Regulation of Numbers in Wild Mammals. J. Hyg., 24: 138–163. pp. 60, 148.

—— 1925a. The Dispersal of Insects to Spitzbergen. Tr. Ent. Soc. London, 1925: 289–299. p. 148.

—— 1927. Animal Ecology. New York, Macmillan; London, Sidgwick and Jackson, (2nd edition, 1935; 3rd edition, 1947). pp. 55, 69, 256, 257, 511, 514, 515, 516, 517, 522, 570.

—— 1930. Animal Ecology and Evolution. New York, Oxford Univ. Press. pp. 8, 55, 58, 603, 656, 684, 705, 710.

—— 1932. Territory among Wood Ants (Formica rufa L.) at Picket Hill. J. Anim. Ecol., 1: 69–76. p. 266.

—— 1933. The Ecology of Animals. London, Methuen. pp. 8, 69.

—— 1936. Ecology's Survey of the Living Universe. Ency. of Mod. Knowl., 2: 1029–1036. London, The Amalgamated Press, Ltd. p. 386.

—— 1942. Voles, Mice and Lemmings. Problems in Population Dynamics. Oxford, Clarendon Press. pp. 27, 69, 85, 87, 269, 323, 324, 330, 367, 374, 543, 586.

—— 1946. Competition and the Structure of Ecological Communities. J. Anim. Ecol., 15: 54–68. pp. 368, 657, 728.

Emerson, A. E., 1926. Development of a Soldier of Nasutitermes (Constrictotermes) cavifrons (Holmgren) and Its Phylogenetic Significance. Zoologica, 7: 69–100. p. 635.

—— 1933. The Mechanism of Tandem Behavior Following the Colonizing Flight in Termites (abstract). Anat. Rec., 57 (supp.): 61–62. p. 433.

—— 1935. Termitophile Distribution and Quantitative Characters as Indicators of Physiological Speciation in British Guiana Termites. Ann. Entom. Soc. Amer., 28: 369–395. pp. 615, 720.

—— 1936. Distribution of Termites. Science, 83: 410–411. p. 725.

—— 1938. Termite Nests—A Study of the Phylogeny of Behavior. Ecol. Monogr., 8:

247–284. pp. 420, 434, 440, 599, 633, 634, 636, 645, 669, 672, 678.

—— 1939. Social Coordination and the Superorganism. Am. Midl. Nat., *21:* 182–209. pp. 72, 420, 440, 599, 678, 684, 698.

—— 1939a. Populations of Social Insects. Ecol. Monogr., *9:* 287–300. pp. 272, 393, 419, 420, 423, 684, 722.

—— 1942. Basic Comparisons of Human and Insect Societies. Biol. Symposia, *8:* 163–176. pp. 420, 632, 684.

—— 1942a. The Relations of a Relict South African Termite (Isoptera, Hodotermitidae, *Stolotermes*). Am. Mus. Novitates, 1187: 1–12. p. 681.

—— 1943. Ecology, Evolution and Society. Am. Nat., *77:* 97–118. pp. 420, 605, 606, 618, 684.

—— 1945. Taxonomic Categories and Population Genetics. Ent. News, *56:* 14–19. p. 625.

—— 1946. The Biological Basis of Social Cooperation. Tr. Ill. Acad. Sc., *39:* 9–18. p. 728.

—— 1947. Why Termites? Scient. Monthly, *64:* 337–345. pp. 420, 599, 633, 678, 684, 693, 718, 724.

Emerson, P. S., 1930. Principles of Soil Technology. New York, Macmillan. pp. 216, 222.

Emerson, Sterling, 1944. The Induction of Mutations by Antibodies. Proc. Nat. Acad. Sc., *30:* 179–183. p. 601.

Emlen, J. T., 1940. Sex and Age Ratios in Survival of the California Quail. J. Wildlife Manag., *4:* 92–99. p. 283.

—— and Lorenz, F. W., 1942. Pairing Responses of Free-Living Valley Quail to Sex Hormone Implants. Auk, *59:* 369–378. p. 413.

Emsweller, S. L., and Stewart, M. B., 1944. The Origin of *Lilium testaceum.* J. Heredity, *35:* 301–308. p. 625.

Enders, R. K., 1935. Mammalian Life Histories from Barro Colorado Island, Panama. Bull. Mus. Comp. Zool., *78:* 385–502. p. 558.

Engler, H. G. A., and Drude, O. [editors], 1896–1928. Die Vegetation der Erde. Sammlung pflanzengeographischer Monographien. Leipzig, Engelmann, 15 vols. p. 582.

Epling, Carl, 1947. Actual and Potential Gene Flow in Natural Populations. Am. Nat., *81:* 104–113. p. 624.

—— and Dobzhansky, Theodosius, 1942. Genetics of Natural Populations. VI. Microgeographic Races in Linanthus parryae. Genetics, *27:* 317–332. p. 608.

Erickson, Ralph O., 1945. The *Clematis Fremontii* var. *Riehlii* Population in the Ozarks. Ann. Missouri Bot. Garden, *32:* 413–460. p. 603.

Ernst, F. A., 1928. Fixation of Atmospheric

Nitrogen. New York, Van Nostrand. p. 157.

Errington, Paul L., 1934. Vulnerability of Bob-White Populations to Predation. Ecology, *15:* 110–127. p. 684.

—— 1937. Food Habits of Iowa Red Foxes during a Drought Summer. Ecology, *18:* 53–61. p. 269.

—— 1937a. What Is the Meaning of Predation? Smithsonian Inst., Annual Rep., 1936: 243–252. pp. 71, 375.

—— 1939. Reactions of Muskrat Populations to Drought. Ecology, *20:* 168–186. p. 338.

—— 1940. Natural Restocking of Muskrat-Vacant Habitats. J. Wildlife Manag., *4:* 173–185. p. 402.

—— 1941. An Eight-Winter Study of Central Iowa Bob-whites. Wilson Bull., *53:* 85–101. p. 326.

—— 1943. An Analysis of Mink Predation upon Muskrats in North-Central United States. Res. Bull. Iowa Agr. Exper. Sta., *320:* 797–924. pp. 402, 647.

—— 1945. Some Contributions of a Fifteen-Year Local Study of the Northern Bobwhite to a Knowledge of Population Phenomena. Ecol. Monogr., *15:* 1–34. p. 403.

—— 1946. Predation and Vertebrate Populations. Quart. Rev. Biol., *21:* 144–177; 221–245. pp. 377, 651, 684, 723, 726.

—— Hamerstrom, Frances, and Hamerstrom, F. N., 1940. The Great Horned Owl and Its Prey in North-Central United States. Res. Bull. Iowa Agr. Exper. Sta., *277:* 759–850. p. 370.

Espinas, A. V., 1877 (2nd ed., 1878). Des sociétés animales. Paris, Baillière. pp. 23, 30, 32, 418.

Essig, E. O., 1931. A History of Entomology. New York, Macmillan. p. 27.

—— 1942. College Entomology. New York, Macmillan. pp. 514, 517.

Esterly, C. O., 1917. The Occurrence of a Rhythm in the Geotropism of Two Species of Plankton Copepods when Certain Recurring External Conditions Are Absent. Pub. Univ. California Zool., *16:* 393–400. pp. 554, 555.

Evans, L. T., 1936. The Development of the Cochlea in the Gecko (*Gymnodactylus kotschyi*), with Special Reference to the Cochlea-lagena Ratio and Its Bearing on Vocality and Social Behavior. Anat. Rec., *64:* 187–201. p. 552.

Ewing, H. E., 1933. Some Peculiar Relationships between Ectoparasites and Their Hosts. Am. Nat., *67:* 365–373. pp. 614, 643.

—— 1938. The Sucking Lice of American Monkeys. J. Parasitol., *24:* 13–33. p. 614.

Fabre, J. H., 1879–1907. Souvenirs entomologiques. Paris, Delegrave, 10 vols. pp. 24, 33.

Farr, W., 1843. Causes of Mortality in Town Districts. Fifth Ann. Rept. Reg. Gen. of Births, Deaths and Marriages in England (2nd ed.), pp. 406–435. pp. 26, 27, 347.

—— 1875. A Letter to Reg. Gen. on Mortality in the Registration Districts of England during the Years 1861–1870. Suppl. to 35th Ann. Rept. of Reg. Gen. of Births, Deaths and Marriages in England (for year 1872). pp. 26, 27.

Faure, J. C., 1932. "The Phases of Locusts in South Africa." Bull. Ent. Res., 23: 293–427. pp. 408, 650.

Faussek, Vigor, 1907. Biologische Untersuchungen in Transkaspien. Verh. Russ. Geogr. Gesells., Abt. Allgemeine Geographie, 27: 1–191. [Review by E. Schultz, Biol. Zentralbl., 14: 97–100.] p. 163.

Fautin, R. W., 1941. Development of Nestling Yellow-Headed Blackbirds. Auk, 58: 215–232. p. 402.

Fawcett, E. W., and Gibson, R. O., 1934. The Effect of Pressure on a Number of Organic Reactions in the Liquid Phase. J. Chem. Soc., 1934: 386–395. p. 137.

Fayrer, J., 1872. The Thanatophidia of India. London, Churchill. p. 19.

Fearon, W. R., 1933. A Classification of the Biological Elements, with a Note on the Biochemistry of Beryllium. Sc. Proc. Roy. Dublin Soc., 20: 531–535. pp. 73, 76.

Felt, E. P., 1905–1906. Insects Affecting Park and Woodland Trees. Mem. New York State Mus., 8: v. 1: 1–333; v. 2: 333-801. pp. 494, 518.

—— 1917. Key to American Insect Galls. Bull. New York State Mus., 200: 1–310. p. 491.

—— 1940. Plant Galls and Gall Makers. Ithaca, Comstock. p. 491.

Fenton, C. L., 1935. Viewpoints and Objects of Paleoecology. J. Paleont., 9: 63–78. p. 57.

Fenton, G. R., 1947. The Soil Fauna: With Special Reference to the Ecosystem of Forest Soil. J. Animal Ecol., 16: 76–93. p. 465.

Ferris, G. F., 1943. Some Fundamental Concepts in Insect Morphology. Microentomology, 8: 2–7. pp. 643, 648.

Feuerbach, L., 1846–1890. Sämmtliche Werke. Leipzig, O. Wigand, 10 vols. p. 30.

Feyerabend, Cessa, 1943. The Budgerigar or Shell Parrakeet as a Talker. Chicago, Amer. Budgerigar Soc., p. 410.

Fichter, Edson, 1939. An Ecological Study of Wyoming Spruce-Fir Arthropods with Reference to Stratification. Ecol. Monogr., 9: 184–215. pp. 488, 490.

Fiebrig, K., 1912. Schlafende Insekten. Ztschr. Naturwiss., 48: 315–364. p. 553.

Filinger, G. A., 1931. The Effect of Temperature on Feeding and Development of the Leaf-Tyer Phlyctaenia ferrugalis. J. Econ. Ent., 24: 52–54. p. 113.

Finkel, A. J., Allee, W. C., and Garner, H. R., 1942. Copper and the Acceleration of Early Cleavage of Arbacia Eggs. J. Cell. & Comp. Physiol., 20: 179–187. p. 205.

Finlay, C. J., 1912. Trabajos selectos. Havana, Republica de Cuba. p. 28.

Fischel, W., 1927. Beiträge zur Soziologie des Haushuhns. Biol. Zentralbl., 47: 678–696. p. 415.

Fisher, J., and Vevers, H. G., 1944. The Changes in the World Numbers of the Gannet in a Century. J. Animal Ecol., 13: 49–62. p. 402.

—— and Waterson, G., 1941. The Breeding Distribution, History and Population of the Fulmar in the British Isles. J. Animal Ecol., 10: 204–272. p. 402.

Fisher, R. A., 1930. The Genetical Theory of Natural Selection. Oxford, Clarendon Press. pp. 427, 598, 678, 681.

—— 1936. The Measurement of Selective Intensity. Proc. Roy. Soc., London, s. B., 121: 58–62. p. 646.

—— 1937. The Relation between Variability and Abundance Shown by the Measurements of the Eggs of British Nesting Birds. Proc. Roy. Soc., London, s. B., 122: 1–26. p. 602.

—— 1941. Statistical Methods for Research Workers. 8th ed. London, Oliver and Boyd.

Flanders, S. E., 1937. Habitat Selection by Trichogramma. Ann. Ent. Soc. Amer., 30: 208–210. p. 612.

—— 1939. The Role of Arrhenotoky in the Adaptation of Insects. Science, 90: 82. pp. 427, 434.

—— 1945. Is Caste Differentiation in Ants a Function of the Rate of Egg Deposition? Science, 101: 245–246. p. 428.

—— 1946. Haploidy as a Factor in the Polymorphic Differentiation of the Hymenoptera. Science, 103: 555–556. pp. 424, 428.

Fleming, J. A., 1939. Terrestrial Magnetism and Electricity. Physics of the Earth. 8: 1–778. Chap. 1. The Earth's Magnetism and Magnetic Surveys, pp. 1–58. p. 157.

Fleming, R. H., 1939. The Control of Diatom Populations by Grazing. J. Conseil Explor. Mer., 14: 3–20. p. 312.

Flint, W. P., 1914. On the Capture of Living Insects by the Corn-Field Ant (Lasius niger americanus). J. Econ. Ent., 7: 476–478. p. 559.

Foerster, R. E., 1944. The Relation of Lake Population Density to Size of Young Sockeye Salmon, Oncorhynchus nerka. J. Fish. Res. Bd. Canada, 6: 267–280. p. 396.

—— and Ricker, W. E., 1941. The Effect of Reduction of Predaceous Fish on Survival of Young Sockeye Salmon at Cultus Lake. J. Fish. Res. Bd. Canada, 5: 315–336. p. 373.

Foggie, A., 1947. Some Ecological Observations on a Tropical Forest Type in the Gold Coast. J. Ecology, *34:* 88–106. p. 483.

Folsom, J. W., 1922. Entomology with Special Reference to Its Ecological Aspects. Philadelphia, Blakiston. p. 55.

——, and Wardle, R. A., 1934. Entomology with Special Reference to Its Ecological Aspects. 4th ed. Philadelphia, Blakiston. p. 514.

Forbes, Edward, 1843. Report on the Molluscs and Radiata of the Aegean Sea, and on Their Distribution Considered as Bearing on Geology. Rept. Br. A. Adv. Sc., *13:* 130–193. pp. 34, 36.

—— 1844. On the Light Thrown on Geology by Submarine Researches; [etc.] Edinburgh New Philos. J. *36:* 318–327. pp. 34, 36, 37, 38.

Forbes, S. A., 1880. The Food of Birds. Bull. Illinois Lab. Nat. Hist., *1:* 86–161. p. 517.

—— 1882. The Regulative Action of Birds upon Insect Oscillations. Bull. Illinois Lab. Nat. Hist., *1,* No. 6: 1–32. p. 517.

—— 1887. The Lake as a Microcosm. Bull. Sc. A. Peoria, 1887: 77–87. [Reprinted with emendations in Illinois Nat. Hist. Surv. Bull., *15:* 537–550, 1925]. pp. 32, 36, 42, 453, 508, 514, 522.

—— 1895. Noxious and Beneficial Insects. Rept. Ill. State Entomologist, *19:* 1–206. pp. 28, 29, 42.

—— 1895a. On Contagious Disease in the Chinch-bug *Blissus leucopterus* Say. Rept. Ill. State Entomologist, *19:* 16–176. p. 28.

—— 1907. An Ornithological Cross-Section of Illinois in Autumn. Bull. Ill. State Lab. Nat. Hist., *7:* 305–335. p. 46.

—— 1907a. On the Local Distribution of Certain Illinois Fishes: An Essay in Statistical Ecology. Bull. Ill. Lab. Nat. Hist., *7:* 1–19. p. 46.

—— 1909. The General Entomological Ecology of the Indian Corn Plant. Am. Nat., *43:* 286–301. p. 48.

—— and Richardson, R. E., 1919. Some Recent Changes in Illinois River Biology. Ill. Nat. Hist. Survey Bull., *13:* 140–156. pp. 51, 515.

Ford, E. B., 1936. The Genetics of *Papilio dardanus* Brown (Lep.). Tr. Roy. Ent. Soc. London, *85:* 435–466. pp. 670, 688.

—— 1937. Problems of Heredity in the Lepidoptera. Biol. Rev., *12:* 461–503. p. 670.

—— 1940. Polymorphism and Taxonomy. In Huxley, J., The New Systematics, pp. 493–513. p. 688.

Ford, John, 1937. Research on Populations of *Tribolium confusum* and Its Bearing on Ecological Theory: A Summary. J. Anim. Ecol., *6:* 1–14. p. 71.

—— 1937a. Fluctuations in Natural Population of Collembola and Acarina. J. Anim. Ecol., *6:* 98–111. p. 319.

Forel, F. A., 1867. Einige Beobachtungen über die Entwicklung des zelligen Muskelgewebes. Beiträge zur Entwicklungs geschichte der Najaden. Würzburg, Doctor's thesis.

—— 1869. Introduction à l'étude de la faune profonde du lac Léman. Bull. Soc. Vaud. Sc. Nat., *10:* 217. pp. 23, 41.

—— 1892–1904. Le Léman, monographie limnologique. Lausanne, Rouge, 3 vols. pp. 37, 40, 41.

——, 1901. Handbuch der Seenkunde. Allgemeine Limnologie. Stuttgart, Englehorn. pp. 47, 95.

Formosov, A. N., 1946. Snezhnyĭ pokrov v zhĭznĭ mlekopĭtanaunshchĭkh ĭ ptits USSR. [Snow Cover as an Environmental Factor; Its Importance in the Life of Mammals and Birds.] (Russian text, summary in French.) Mat. k Pozn. Fauny ĭ Florĭ USSR, n. s., Otdel Zool., *5:* (XX), 1–150. p. 180.

Forskål, Pehr, 1775. Descriptiones animalium, avium, amphibiorum, piscium, insectorum, vermium; quae in itinere orientali observavit P. Forskål, ... Hauniae, Moelleri. p. 28.

Forsythe, W. E., and Christison, F., 1930. A Study of the Ultra-Violet Radiation from the Sun and Heated Tungsten. J. Opt. Soc. Amer., *20:* 396–410. p. 90.

Foster, T. D., 1937. Productivity of a Land Snail, *Polygyra thyroides* (Say). Ecology, *18:* 545–546. p. 526.

Fraenkel, G. S., and Blewett, M., 1944. The Utilization of Body Water in Insects. Bull. Ent. Res., *36:* 127–139. p. 187.

—— and Gunn, D. L., 1940. The Orientation of Animals. Kineses, Taxes and Compass Reactions. New York, Oxford Univ. Press. pp. 24, 70.

France, R. H., 1913. Das Edaphon. Untersuchungen zur Oekologie der bodenbewohnenden Mikroorganismen. München: Deutsch. mikrolog. Gesellschaft. p. 510.

—— 1914. Das Edaphon als Lebensgemeinschaft bodenbewohnender Mikroorganismen. Naturwissenschaften, *5:* 111–112. pp. 235, 510.

—— 1922. Das Leben im Ackerboden. 12th ed. Stuttgart, Cosmos.

Franklin, Benjamin, 1751. Concerning the Increase of Mankind, Peopling of Countries, etc. In the Writings of Benjamin Franklin, A. H. Smith, ed. New York, Macmillan, *3:* 63–73. p. 25.

Freeman, E. M., 1937. In Praise of Parasitism. Scient. Monthly, *44:* 67–76. pp. 679, 701, 712.

Freeman, G. L., 1935. Diurnal Variations in Performance and Energy Expenditure.

754 BIBLIOGRAPHY AND AUTHOR INDEX

Evanston: Northwestern Univ. Press. p. 560.

Friedmann, Herbert, 1929. The Cowbirds; A Study in the Biology of Social Parasitism. Springfield, Ill., Thomas. pp. 633, 676.

—— 1937. Birds Collected by the Childs Frick Expedition to Ethiopia and Kenya Colony. Part II. Passeres. Bull. U. S. Nat. Mus., *153:* 1–506. p. 123.

—— 1946. Ecological Counterparts in Birds. Scient. Monthly, *63:* 395–398. p. 668.

Friedrichs, K., 1930. Zur Epidemiologie des Kiefernspanners, Ztschr. Angew. Ent., *16:* 197–205. p. 228.

Frieling, H., 1940. Der Ganzheitsbegriff in der Systematik. Grundsätzliches über Rasse und Art, sowie Bemerkungen über Berechtigung und Bedeutung der höheren systematischen Kategorien. Acta Biotheoretica, *5:* 117–138. p. 663.

Frisch, Karl von, 1923. Ueber die "Sprache" der Bienen. Jena, Fischer. p. 250.

—— 1942. Die Werbetänse der Bienen und ihre Auslösung. Naturwiss., *30:* 269–277. p. 433.

—— 1943. Versuche über die Lenkung des Bienenfluges durch Duftstoffe. Naturwiss., *31:* 445–460. p. 433.

—— 1946. Die Tänze der Bienen. Österreich Zool. Zeitschr., *1:* 1–48. p. 433.

Frison, T. H., 1929. Fall and Winter Stoneflies or Plecoptera of Illinois. I. Nat. Hist. Surv. Bull., *18:* 345–409. p. 102.

—— 1935. The Stoneflies, or Plecoptera of Illinois. Nat. Hist. Surv. Bull., *30:* 218–471. p. 102.

Fritsch, F. E., 1935. The Structure and Reproduction of the Algae. Vol. I. New York, Macmillan. p. 503.

Fritsch, K., 1851. Ueber die jährliche Vertheilung der Käfer, Sb. Akad. Wiss. Wien, (math.-natur.), *6:* 3–42. p. 534.

—— 1851a. Resultate zweijähriger Beobachtunger über die jährliche Vertheilung der Käfer. Sb. Akad. Wiss. Wien., (math-natur.) *7:* 689–710. p. 534.

Frobisher, Martin, 1944. Fundamentals of Bacteriology. 3rd ed. Philadelphia, Saunders. pp. 497, 498.

Frost, S. W., 1923. A Study of the Leaf-Mining Diptera of North America. Mem. Cornell Agr. Exper. Sta. 78: 1–228. p. 491.

—— 1942. General Entomology. New York, McGraw-Hill. pp. 490, 491, 554.

Frost, W. H., 1927. Epidemiology. Nelson Loose-Leaf System, Public Health-Preventive Medicine, Vol. 2, Chap. 7, pp. 163–190. New York, Nelson. pp. 60, 380.

Frothingham, E. H., 1915. The Northern Hardwoods Forest: Its Composition, Growth and Management. Bull. U. S. Dept. of Agri., *285:* 1–80. p. 575.

Fryxell, F. M., 1927. The Physiography of the Region of Chicago. Chicago, Univ. of Chicago Press. p. 567.

Fuller, G. D., 1911. Evaporation and Plant Succession. Bot. Gaz., *52:* 193–208. pp. 480, 567.

—— 1914. Evaporation and Soil Moisture in Relation to the Succession of Plant Associations. Bot. Gaz., *58:* 193–234. pp. 436, 480, 567.

—— 1925. The Vegetation of the Chicago Region. Chicago, Univ. of Chicago Press. pp. 436, 567.

Fuller, M. L., 1906. Total Amount of Free Water in the Earth's Crust. U.S.G.S., Water Survey Papers, *160:* 59–72. p. 178.

Fulton, B. B., 1933. Inheritance of Song in Hybrids of Two Subspecies of *Nemobius fasciatus* (Orthoptera). Ann. Ent. Soc. Amer., *26:* 368–376. p. 621.

—— 1941. A Luminous Fly Larva with Spider Traits. Ann. Ent. Soc. Amer., *34:* 289–303. p. 558.

Fyfe, R. V., and Gay, F. J., 1938. The Humidity of the Atmosphere and the Moisture Conditions within Mounds of *Eutermes exitiosus* Hill. Pamphlets Australia Council Sc. & Indust. Res., *82:* 1–22. pp. 429, 672.

Gabrielson, I. N., 1941. Wildlife Conservation. New York, Macmillan. p. 70.

Galambos, Robert, and Griffin, D. R., 1942. Obstacle Avoidance by Flying Bats: The Cries of Bats. J. Exper. Zool., *89:* 475–490. p. 140.

Galt, William, 1940. The Principle of Cooperation in Behavior. Quart. Rev. Biol., *15:* 401–410. pp. 71, 72.

Galtsoff, P. S., 1924. Limnological Observations on the Upper Mississippi. Bull. U. S. Bur. Fish., *39:* 347–438. p. 155.

—— 1925. Regeneration after Dissociation. (An Experimental Study on Sponges). J. Exper. Zool., *42:* 183–251. pp. 356, 397.

—— 1930. The Fecundity of the Oyster. Science, *72:* 97–98. p. 272.

—— 1943. Copper Content of Sea Water. Ecology, *24:* 263–65. p. 205.

—— Chipman, W. A., Hasler, A. D., and Engle, J. B., 1938. Preliminary Report on the Decline of the Oyster Industry of the York River, Va., and the Effects of Pulp-Mill Pollution on Oysters. Bur. Fisheries Rept., 37. p. 342.

Gamow, George, (1940) 1945. The Birth and Death of the Sun. New York, Penguin. p. 42.

Garner, M. R., 1934. The Relation of Numbers of *Paramecium caudatum* to Their Ability to Withstand High Temperatures. Physiol. Zoöl., 7: 408–434. p. 175.

Garner, W. W., 1936. Photoperiodism. In Duggar, B. M., 1936, *Op. cit.*, pp. 677–714. p. 21.

—— and Allard, H. A., 1920. Effect of the Relative Length of the Day and Night and Other Factors of the Environment on Growth and Reproduction in Plants. J. Agr. Res., *18:* 553–606. pp. 121, 534, 545.

Gasparin, Comte de A. E., 1843–1848. Cours d'agriculture. Paris, La Maison Rustique, 4 vols. [esp. vol. 2, 1844]. p. 18.

Gates, F. C., 1911. Summer-Bird Life in the Vicinity of Havana, Illinois, in Its Relation to the Prominent Plant Associations. Wilson Bull., *23:* 1–27. p. 52.

Gates, Mary, and Allee, W. C., 1933. Conditioned Behavior of Isolated and Grouped Cockroaches on a Simple Maze. J. Comp. Psychol., *15:* 331–358. p. 410.

Gates, R. R., 1936. Mutations and Natural Selection. Am. Nat., *70:* 505–516. pp. 642, 666.

Gause, G. F., 1931. The Influence of Ecological Factors on the Size of Population. Am. Nat., *65:* 70–76. pp. 307, 334.

—— 1932. Ecology of Populations. Quart. Rev. Biol., *7:* 27–46. pp. 71, 402.

—— 1932a. Experimental Studies on the Struggle for Existence. I. Mixed Population of Two Species of Yeast. J. Exper. Biol., *9:* 389–402. p. 657.

—— 1934. The Struggle for Existence. Baltimore, Williams & Wilkins. pp. 69, 302, 307, 368, 371, 373, 386, 391, 406.

—— 1934a. Experimental Analysis of Vito Volterra's Mathematical Theory of the Struggle for Existence. Science, *79:* 16–17. pp. 326, 657, 658, 660, 699, 700.

—— 1935. Vérifications expérimentales de la théorie mathématique de la lutte pour la vie. Actualités Scientifiques et Industrielles, *277:* 1–61. pp. 11, 69, 326, 369.

—— 1935a. Experimental Demonstration of Volterra's Periodic Oscillations in the Numbers of Animals. J. Exper. Biol., *12:* 44–48.

—— 1936. The Principles of Biocoenology. Quart. Rev. Biol., *11:* 320–336. p. 71.

——, Nastukova, O. K., and Alpatov, W. W., 1934. The Influence of Biologically Conditioned Media on the Growth of a Mixed Population of *Paramecium caudatum* and *P. aurelia.* J. Anim. Ecol., *3:* 222–230. p. 328.

Gebien, Hans, 1920. Käfer aus der Familie Tenebrionidae. Hamburg. Univ. Abhandl. Gebiet Auslandsk., *5:* (C) p. 163.

Geddes, P., and Thompson, J. A., 1911. Evolution. New York, Holt. p. 31.

Geiger, Rudolf, 1942. Das Klima der bodennahen Luftschicht. Braunschweig, Vieweg. Ed. 2, pp. 98, 147, 211, 212, 228, 231, 232.

Gellis, S. S., and Clarke, G. L., 1935. Organic Matter in Dissolved and in Colloidal Form as Food for *Daphnia magna.* Physiol. Zoöl., *8:* 127–137. pp. 444, 500.

Gerard, R. W., 1940. Organism, Society and Science. Scient. Monthly, *50:* 340–350; 403–412; 530–535. p. 72.

—— 1942. Higher Levels of Integration. Biol. Symposia, *8:* 67–87. pp. 683, 698.

—— 1942a. A Biological Basis for Ethics. Philos. Sc., *9:* 92–120. p. 694.

—— and Emerson, A. E., 1945. Extrapolation from the Biological to the Social. Science, *101:* 582–585. pp. 684, 693.

Gersbacher, W. M., 1937. Development of Stream Bottom Communities in Illinois. Ecology, *18:* 359–390. pp. 570, 571.

Gerstell, R., 1939. Certain Mechanics of Winter Quail Losses Revealed by Laboratory Experimentation. Tr. Fourth N. A. Wildlife Inst., *1939:* 462–467. pp. 98, 363, 398.

Gesner, Conrad, 1551–1587. Historiae Animalium. Tiguri, 5 vols. p. 16.

Getman, F. H., and Daniels, F., 1931. Outlines of Theoretical Chemistry. 5th ed. New York, Wiley. p. 111.

Gibson, W. W., 1947. An Ecological Study of the Spiders of a River-Terrace Forest in Western Tennessee. Ohio J. Sc., *47:* 38–44. p. 490.

Giese, A. C., 1945. Ultraviolet Radiation and Life. Physiol. Zoöl., *18:* 223–250. p. 75.

Gilbert, G. K., 1914. The Transportation of Debris by Running Water. U. S. Geol. Survey, Prof. Papers, *86:* 1–263. p. 154.

Gilbert, P. W., 1944. The Alga-Egg Relationship in *Ambystoma maculatum,* A Case of Symbiosis. Ecology, *25:* 366–369. p. 713.

Gilmour, Darcy, Waterhouse, D. F., and McIntyre, G. A., 1946. An Account of Experiments Undertaken to Determine the Natural Population Density of the Sheep Blowfly, *Lucilia cuprina* Wied. Council for Scientific and Industrial Research (Australia), Bull. No. *195:* 1–39. pp. 269, 366.

Ginsburg, Benson, and Allee, W. C., 1942. Some Effects of Conditioning on Social Dominance and Subordination in Inbred Strains of Mice. Physiol. Zoöl., *15:* 485–506. p. 414.

Gish, O. H., 1939. Atmospheric Electricity. Physics of the Earth, *8:* 149–230. p. 157.

Glass, Bentley, 1944. The Effect of X-rays upon the Action of a Specific Gene in Drosophila melanogaster. Genetics, *29:* 436–446. p. 600.

Gleason, H. A., 1926. The Individualistic Concept of the Plant Association. Bull. Torrey Bot. Club, *53:* 7–26. pp. 71, 577.

—— 1936. Is the Synusia an Association? Ecology, *17:* 444–451. p. 478.

—— 1939. The Individualistic Concept of the Plant Association. Am. Mid. Nat., *21:* 92–110. p. 697.

Glick, P. A., 1939. The Distribution of Insects, Spiders and Mites in the Air. U. S. Dept. of Agr., Tech. Bull., *673:* 1–150. p. 148.

Glick, P. A., 1942. Insect Population and Migration in the Air. Publ. Am. A. Adv. Sc., *17:* 88–98.

Glover, J. W., 1921. United States Life Tables, 1890, 1901, 1910, and 1901–1910. U. S. Bureau of Census. p. 301.

Gloyd, H. K., 1940. The Rattlesnakes Genera *Sistrurus* and *Crotalus*. A Study in Zoogeography and Evolution. Spec. Pub. Chicago Acad. Sc., *4:* 1–270. pp. 466, 471.

Godden, W., 1939. "Trace" Elements in Human and Animal Nutrition. Chemistry and Industry, *58:* 791–796. p. 80.

Goldie, A. H. R., 1936. Some Characteristics of the Mean Annual Circulation over the British Isles. Q. J. Roy. Met. Soc., *62:* 81–102. p. 86.

Goldschmidt, R. B., 1933. Lymantria. Bibliogr. Genet., *11:* 1–186. p. 646.

—— 1938. Physiological Genetics. New York, McGraw-Hill. pp. 3, 118.

—— 1940. The Material Basis of Evolution. New Haven, Yale. pp. 598, 647.

—— 1945. Mimetic Polymorphism. A Controversial Chapter of Darwinism. Quart. Rev. Biol., *20:* 147–164; 205–230. pp. 643, 647, 648, 670.

—— 1945a. Evolution of Mouth Parts in Diptera. A Counter Critique. Pan-Pacific Entom., *21:* 41–47. p. 648.

Goodale, H. D., 1942. Further Progress with Artificial Selection. Am. Nat., *76:* 515–519. p. 668.

Goode, J. Paul, 1943. Goode's School Atlas, Physical, Political, and Economic, for American Schools and Colleges. Rev. Ed. Chicago, Rand McNally. pp. 143, 152, 580.

Gordon, R. B., 1940. The Primeval Forest Types of Southwestern New York. New York State Mus. Bull., *231:* 1–102. p. 575.

Gottschall, R. Y., and Jennings, O. E., 1933. Limnological Studies at Erie, Pennsylvania. Tr. Am. Micr. Soc., *52:* 181–191. p. 504.

Graham, H. W., 1941. An Oceanographic Consideration of the Dinoflagellate Genus *Ceratium*. Ecol. Monogr., *11:* 99–116. pp. 449, 450, 501, 502.

Graham, M., 1935. Modern Theory of Exploiting a Fishery, and Application to North Sea Trawling. J. Conseil Explor. Mer., *10:* 264. pp. 312, 377.

—— 1938. The Trawl Fisheries: A Scientific and National Problem. Nature, *142:* 1143–1146. p. 378.

—— 1948. Rational Fishing of the Cod of the North Sea. London, Edward Arnold & Co. p. 377.

Graham, S. A., 1920. Factors Influencing the Subcortical Temperatures of Logs. Rept. Minnesota State Entom., *18:* 26–42. p. 560.

—— 1922. Effect of Physical Factors in the Ecology of Certain Insects in Logs. Rept. Minnesota State Entom., *19:* 22–40. p. 560.

—— 1924. Temperature as a Limiting Factor in the Life of Subcortical Insects. J. Econ. Ent., *17:* 377–383. p. 560.

—— 1925. The Felled Tree Trunk as an Ecological Unit. Ecology, *6:* 397–411. pp. 514, 560.

—— 1939. Principles of Forest Entomology. 2nd ed. New York, McGraw-Hill. pp. 514, 560.

Gran, H. H., 1912. Pelagic Plant Life. In Murray and Hjort, Depths of the Ocean, pp. 307–386. pp. 450, 502.

—— 1931. On the Conditions for Production of Plankton in the Sea. Conseil. Perm. Intern. Explor. Mer., Rapp. et Proc. Verb., *75:* 37–46. p. 204.

Grassé, P. P., 1937. Recherches sur la systématique et la Biologie des Termites de l'Afrique Occidentale Française. Ann. Soc. Entomol. France, *56:* 1–100. p. 714.

Grave, B. H., 1922. An Analysis of the Spawning Habits and Spawning Stimuli of *Chaetopleura apiculata* Say. Biol. Bull., *42:* 234–256. p. 544.

Grave, Caswell, and Nicoll, P. A., 1939. Studies of Larval Life and Metamorphosis in *Ascidia nigra* and Species of *Polyandrocarpa*. Papers Tortugas Lab., Carnegie Inst. Wash., *32:* 1–46.

Gray, James, 1920. The Relation of the Animal Cell to Electrolytes. I. A Physiological Study of the Egg of the Trout. J. Physiol., *53:* 308–319. p. 171.

Green, D. E., 1941. Enzymes and Trace Substances. In Advances in Enzymology, Nord, F. F. and Werkman, C. H., New York, Interscience.

Green, R. G., and Evans, C. A., 1940. Studies on a Population Cycle of Snowshoe Hares on the Lake Alexander Area. I. Gross Annual Censuses, 1932–1939. J. Wildlife Manag., *4:* 220–240. p. 268.

Greenberg, Bernard, 1947. Some Relations between Territory, Social Hierarchy and Leadership in the Green Sunfish (*Lepomis cyanellus*). Physiol. Zoöl., *20:* 267–299. pp. 411, 413.

Greene, E. L., 1909. Landmarks of Botanical History. Smithsonian Misc. Coll., *54:* 1–329. pp. 15, 16.

Greenwood, Major, 1932. Epidemiology, Historical and Experimental. Baltimore, Johns Hopkins. pp. 60, 396.

—— 1935. Epidemics and Crowd-Diseases. An Introduction to the Study of Epidemiology. New York, Macmillan. p. 69.

——, Hill, A. B., Topley, W. W. C., and Wilson, J., 1936. Experimental Epidemiology. Medical Res. Coun. (Gt. Brit.), Special Report Series, 209. p. 380.

Gregg, Robert E., 1942. The Origin of Castes in Ants with Special Reference to *Phei-*

dole morrisi Forel. Ecology, *23:* 295–308. pp. 421, 428, 601.

Gregor, J. W., 1932. Experimental Methods in Taxonomy. 6th Intern. Congr. Genetics, *2:* 71–73. p. 626.

—— 1944. The Ecotype. Biol. Rev., *19:* 20–30. pp. 626, 643, 653.

Gregory, Tappan, 1936. Mammals of the Chicago Region. Program Activities, Chicago Acad. Sc., *7:* 13–75. pp. 438, 558.

Gregory, W. K., 1936. On the Meaning and Limits of Irreversibility of Evolution. Am. Nat., *70:* 517–528. p. 679.

—— 1946. The Roles of Motile Larvae and Fixed Adults in the Origin of the Vertebrates. Quart. Rev. Biol., *21:* 348–364. p. 636.

—— 1947. The Monotremes and the Palimpsest Theory. Bull. Am. Mus. Nat. Hist., *88:* 1–52. p. 682.

Griffin, D. R., 1944. Echolocation by Blind Men, Bats and Radar. Science, *100:* 589–590. p. 643.

—— 1946. Supersonic Cries of Bats. Nature, *158:* 46. p. 643.

—— and Galambos, R., 1941. The Sensory Basis of Obstacle Avoidance by Flying Bats. J. Exper. Zool., *86:* 481–506. p. 140.

Griggs, R. F., 1934. The Edge of the Forest in Alaska and the Reasons for Its Position. Ecology, *15:* 80–96. p. 477.

—— 1942. Indications as to Climatic Changes from the Timberline of Mount Washington. Science, *95:* 515–519. p. 653.

—— 1946. The Timberlines of Northern America and Their Interpretation. Ecology, *27:* 275–289. p. 653.

Grinnell, Joseph, 1923. The Burrowing Rodents of California as Agents in Soil Formation. J. Mammalogy, *4:* 137–149. p. 465.

——, Dixon, J., and Linsdale, J. M., 1930. Vertebrate Natural History of Northern California through the Lassen Peak Region. Berkeley, Univ. of Calif. Press. (Univ. of Calif. Publ. Zool. Vol. 35.) pp. 56, 117.

—— and Storer, T. I., 1924. Animal Life in the Yosemite. Berkeley, Univ. of Calif. Press. pp. 56, 116, 117.

Griscom, Ludlow, 1932. The Distribution of Bird-Life in Guatemala: A Contribution to a Study of the Origin of Central American Bird-Life. Bull. Am. Mus. Nat. Hist., *64:* 1–439.

Grisebach, A. H. R., 1838. Ueber den Einfluss des Klimas auf die Begrenzung der natürlichen Floren. Linnaea, *12:* 159–200. p. 34.

—— 1872. Die Vegetation der Erde nach ihrer klimatischen Anordnung. Ein Abriss der vergleichenden Geographie der Pflanzen. Leipzig, Engelman, 2 vols. p. 582.

Grison, P., 1944. Rythme d'activité chez Lep-

tinotarsa decemlineata Say et leur importance pour l'étude du phototropisme. Bull. Soc. Zool. France, *68:* 100–105. p. 558.

Griswold, Grace H., and Crowell, Mary F., 1936. The Effect of Humidity on the Development of the Webbing Clothes Moth (*Tineola bisselliella* Hum.) Ecology, *17:* 241–250. p. 188.

Gross, A. O., 1928. The Heath Hen. Mem. Bost. Soc. Nat. Hist., *6:* 491–588. p. 328.

Grüber, A., 1889. Biologische Studien an Protozoen. Biol. Zentralbl., *9:* 14–23. p. 20.

Gudger, E. W., 1921. Rains of Fishes. Nat. Hist., *21:* 607–619. p. 149.

Gudoshchikova, W. J., 1927. Sutochnaiā mīgratsiiā zhībotnykh b komplekse assofsii. [Diurnal Migrations of Insects in a Complex of Plant Associations]. Trav. Inst. Rech. Biol. Perm, *1:* 299–328 (Russian text, summary in English.) p. 557.

Guhl, A. M., and Allee, W. C., 1944. Some Measurable Effects of Social Organization in Flocks of Hens. Physiol. Zoöl., *17:* 320–347. pp. 414, 417, 663.

——, Collias, N. E., and Allee, W. C., 1945. Mating Behavior and the Social Hierarchy in Small Flocks of White Leghorns. Physiol. Zoöl., *18:* 365–390. pp. 414, 417.

—— and Warren, D. C., 1946. Number of Offspring Sired by Cockerels Related to Social Dominance in Chickens. Poultry Science, *25:* 460–472. p. 417.

Gulick, Addison, 1932. Biological Peculiarities of Oceanic Islands. Quart. Rev. Biol., *7:* 405–427. pp. 71, 148.

Gulick, J. T., 1888. Divergent Evolution through Cumulative Segregation. J. Linn. Soc., (Zool.) *20:* 189–274. p. 30.

—— 1905. Evolution, Racial and Habitudinal. Publ. Carnegie Inst. Wash., *25:* 1–269. pp. 30, 609.

Gunderson, Alfred, and Hastings, G. T., 1944. Interdependence in Plant and Animal Evolution. Scient. Monthly, *59:* 63–72. pp. 705, 715.

Gunn, D. L., 1940. The Daily Rhythm of Activity of the Cockroach, *Blatta orientalis* Linnaeus. I. Actograph Experiments, Especially in Relation to Light. J. Exper. Biol., *17:* 267–278. p. 558.

—— and Pielou, D. P., 1940. The Humidity Behavior of the Mealworm Beetle, *Tenebrio molitor* L. III. The Mechanism of the Reaction. J. Exper. Biol., *17:* 307–317. p. 558.

Gunter, Gordon, 1941. Death of Fishes due to Cold on the Texas Coast, January, 1940. Ecology, *22:* 203–208. p. 334.

Gustafson, A. F., Guise, C. H., Hamilton, W. J., Jr., and Ries, H., 1947. 2nd. ed. Conservation in the United States. Ithaca, Comstock Pub. Co. pp. 515, 578.

Haeckel, Ernst, (1869) 1870. Ueber Ent-wickelungsgang u. Aufgabe der Zoologie. Jenaische Z., 5: 353–370. pp. 34, 42.

―― 1890. Plankton-Studien. Jena, Fischer. [Transl. in Rept. U. S. Fish Comm. for 1889–1891, 17: 565–641]. p. 36.

Haldane, J. B. S., 1932. The Causes of Evolution. London, Longmans. pp. 625, 633, 635, 636, 637, 638, 639, 646, 654, 655, 657, 681, 692, 715.

―― 1936. Primary and Secondary Effects of Natural Selection. Proc. Roy. Soc., London, s. B., 121: 67–69. pp. 647, 682.

―― 1938. The Location of the Gene for Haemophilia. Genetica, 20: 423–430. p. 655.

Hale, M., 1677. The Primitive Origination of Mankind. London, Shrowsbery. p. 25.

Hall, E. R., 1946. Mammals of Nevada. Berkeley, U. California Press. pp. 608, 624, 653, 654, 671.

Hall, F. G., 1922. The Vital Limits of Exsiccation of Certain Animals. Biol. Bull., 42: 31–51. pp. 19, 183.

Hall, R. P., and Shottenfeld, H. 1941. Maximum Density and Phases of Death in Populations of Glaucoma piriformis. Physiol. Zoöl., 14: 384–393. p. 319.

Hamilton, J., 1885. Hibernation of Coleoptera. Canad. Entomologist, 17: 35–38. p. 538.

Hamilton, W. J., Jr., 1932. The Food and Feeding Habits of Some Eastern Salamanders. Copeia, 1932: 83–86. p. 487.

―― 1936. The Food and Breeding Habits of the Raccoon. Ohio J. Sc., 36: 131–140.

―― 1937. The Biology of Microtine Cycles. J. Agr. Res., 54: 779–790. pp. 367, 530.

―― 1937a. Activity and Home Range of the Field Mouse, Microtus p. pennsylvanicus (Ord.). Ecology, 18: 255–263. p. 547.

―― 1939. American Mammals. Their Lives, Habits, and Economic Relations. New York, McGraw-Hill. pp. 105, 119, 466, 484, 514, 535, 539, 543.

―― 1940. Life and Habits of Field Mice. Scient. Monthly, 50: 425–434. p. 469.

―― 1940a. The Feeding Habits of Larval Newts with Reference to Availability and Predilection of Food Items. Ecology, 21: 351–356. p. 517.

―― 1940b. Summer Food of the Robin Determined by Fecal Analysis. Wilson Bull., 52: 179–182. p. 517.

―― 1943. The Mammals of Eastern United States. An Account of Recent Land Mammals Occurring East of the Mississippi. Ithaca, Comstock. pp. 494, 535, 547.

―― and Cook, D. B., 1940. Small Mammals and the Forest. J. Forestry, 38: 468–473. p. 484.

Hammond, E. C., 1938. Biological Effects of Population Density in Lower Organisms. Part I. Quart. Rev. Biol., 13: 421–438. pp. 71, 72.

―― 1939. Biological Effects of Population Density in Lower Organisms. Part II. Quart. Rev. Biol., 14: 35–59. pp. 71, 72.

Hammond, P. F., and Goslin, R., 1933. The Effect of Humidity on the Rate of Evaporation. Ecology, 14: 411–413. p. 480.

Hansen, A. A., 1921. The Terminology of the Ultimate Vegetation. Ecology, 2: 125–126. p. 577.

Hanson, F. B., and Heys, F., 1930. A Possible Relation between Natural (Earth) Radiation and Gene Mutation. Science, 71: 43–44.

Hanson, H. C., 1938. Ecology of the Grassland. Bot. Rev., 4: 51–82. p. 477.

―― and Whitman, W., 1938. Characteristics of Major Grassland Types in Western North Dakota. Ecol. Monogr., 8: 57–114. pp. 468, 472.

Hardy, A. C., 1924. The Herring in Relation to Its Animate Environment. Part I. Min. Agr. & Fish., Fishery Investigations, (2) 7: 1–53. pp. 59, 514, 516.

―― 1939. Ecological Investigations with the Continuous Plankton Recorder: Object, Plan and Methods. Hull Bull. Marine Ecol., 1: 1–57. p. 317.

Hardy, G. H., 1908. Mendelian Proportions in a Mixed Population. Science, 28: 49–50. p. 681.

Hardy, Ross, 1945. The Influence of Types of Soil upon the Local Distribution of Some Mammals in Southwestern Utah. Ecol. Monogr., 15: 71–108. p. 668.

Hargitt, G. T., 1944. What Is Germ Plasm? Science, 100: 343–348. p. 599.

Harland, S. C., 1933. The Genetical Conception of the Species. C. R. Acad. Sc. U.S.S.R., 4: 181–186. [Reprinted in Tropical Agriculture, 11: 51–53, 1934.] p. 681.

Harms, J. W., 1934. Wandlungen des Artgefüges unter natürlichen und künstlichen Umweltsbedingungen. Beobachtungen an tropischen Verlandungszonen und am verlandenden Federsee, Tübingen, Heine. p. 70.

Harper, Francis, 1945. Extinct and Vanishing Mammals of the Old World. Spec. Publ. Am. Comm. Intern. Wildlife. Prot., 12. pp. 399, 400.

Harshberger, J. W., 1911. Phytogeographic Survey of North America. New York, Stechert. p. 575.

Hart, Helen, 1944. Stem Rust on New Varieties and Hybrids. Phytopathol., 34: 884–899. p. 644.

Hartley, P. H. T., 1947. Predation by Sparrow-Hawk Populations. Review of "De Sperwer als Roofvijand van Zangvogels" by L. Tinbergen. Ecology, 28: 326–328. p. 374.

Harvey, E. N., 1940. Living Light. Princeton, Princeton Univ. Press. p. 125.

Harvey, H. W., 1928. Biological Chemistry and

Physics of Sea Water. London, Cambridge Univ. Press. pp. 56, 84, 85, 191, 202, 204.

—— 1939. Substances Controlling the growth of a Diatom. J. Mar. Biol. Assoc., 23: 409–520. pp. 204, 206.

—— 1940. Nitrogen and Phosphorus Required for the Growth of Phytoplankton. J. Mar. Biol. Assoc., 24: 115–123. p. 125.

—— 1945. Recent Advances in the Chemistry and Biology of Sea Water. Cambridge, University Press. p. 56.

Hase, A., 1926. Über Warmeentwicklung in Kolonien von Wachsmottenraupen. Naturwiss., 41: 995–997. p. 362.

Hasler, A. D., 1935. The Physiology of Digestion of Plankton Crustacea. 1. Some digestive Enzymes of Daphnia. Biol. Bull., 68: 207–214. p. 444.

—— 1938. Fish Biology and Limnology of Crater Lake, Oregon. J. Wildlife Man., 2: 94–103. p. 125.

Haviland, Maud D., 1926. Forest, Steppe and Tundra. Cambridge, University Press. pp. 466, 514, 515, 585.

Hawkes, O. A. M., 1920. Observations on the Life History, Biology, and Genetics of the Ladybird Beetle Adalia bipunctata (Mulsant). Proc. Zool. Soc., London, 1920: 475–490. p. 538.

Hawes, R. S., 1939. The Flood Factor in the Ecology of Caves. J. Animal Ecol., 8: 1–5. p. 439.

Hayes, W. P., 1927. Prairie Insects. Ecology, 8: 238–250. pp. 473, 514.

—— 1929. Morphology, Taxonomy and Biology of Larval Scarabaeoides. Illinois Biol. Monogr., 12: 1–119. p. 472.

Headlee, T. J., 1914. Effects of Temperature and Moisture on the Rate of Insect Metabolism. J. Econ. Ent., 7: 413–417. p. 110.

—— 1917. Some Facts Relative to the Influence of Atmospheric Humidity on Insect Metabolism. J. Econ. Entom., 10: 31–38. pp. 51, 187.

—— 1921. Climate and Insect Investigations. Rep. New Jersey Agr. Exper. Sta., 367–369. p. 187.

—— 1921a. The Mosquitoes of New Jersey and Their Control. Bull. New Jersey Agr. Exper. Sta., 348: 1–229. p. 485.

—— 1945. The Mosquitoes of New Jersey and Their Control. New Brunswick, Rutgers Univ. Press.

Heape, Walter, 1932. Emigration Migration and Nomadism. Cambridge, Heffer. p. 69.

Hebard, M., 1934. The Dermaptera and Orthoptera of Illinois. Bull. Ill. Nat. Hist. Surv., 20: 125–279. p. 617.

Heer, Oswald, 1835. Die vegations Verhältnisse des Südöstlichen Teiles des Kantons glarus. Mitt. Geb. Theoret. Erdkunde., Zurich. pp. 34, 36.

Hegh, E., 1922. Les Termites. Bruxelles, Imprimerie Industrielle & Financière. pp. 420, 633, 713.

Hegner, R., Root, F. M., Augustine, D. L., and Huff, C. G., 1938. Parasitology. New York, Appleton-Century. pp. 256, 396.

Heilbrunn, L. V., 1943. An Outline of General Physiology. 2nd ed. Philadelphia, W. B. Saunders Company. pp. 104, 107, 128, 172, 239.

——, Harris, D. L., LeFevre, P. G., Wilson, W. L., and Woodward, A. A., 1946. Heat Death, Heat Injury and Toxic Factor. Physiol. Zoöl., 19: 404–430. p. 104.

Heim, R., 1940. Les champignonières des termites et les grands champignons d'Afrique tropicale. Rev. Bot. Appl., 20: 121–127. pp. 713, 714.

Heinicke, A. J., and Childers, N. F., 1937. The Daily Rate of Photosynthesis of a Young Apple Tree of Bearing Age. Mem. Cornell Univ. Agr. Exper. Sta., 201: 3–52. p. 507.

Henderson, L. J., 1913. The fitness of the Environment. New York, Macmillan. pp. 49, 73, 76.

—— 1914. The Functions of an Environment. Science, 39: 524–527. p. 77.

—— 1917. The Order of Nature. Cambridge, Harvard. p. 77.

—— 1922. Water. Scient. Monthly, 15: 404–416. pp. 76, 181.

Henrici, A. T., 1939. The Distribution of Bacteria in Lakes. Pub. Am. A. Adv. Sc., 10: 39–64. pp. 445, 451, 500.

Henry, W. A., and Morrison, F. E., 1923. Feeds and Feeding; A Handbook for the Student and Stockman. 18th ed. Madison, Henry-Morrison. p. 472.

Hensen, V., 1887. Ueber die Bestimmung des Planktons oder des im Meere treibenden Materials an Pflanzen und Thieren. Ber. Komm. wiss. Unters. deutschen Meere, Kiel, 5: 1–107. pp. 36, 37.

—— 1891. Die Plankton-Expedition und Haeckel's Darwinismus. In Über einige Aufgaben und Ziele der beschreibenden Naturwissenschaften. Kiel und Leipzig, Lipsius und Tischer. p. 36.

Hentschel, E., 1923. Grundzüge der Hydrobiologie. Jena, Fischer. p. 56.

Herdman, W. A., 1923. Founders of Oceanography. An Introduction to the Science of the Sea. London, Arnold. pp. 37, 38, 39, 40.

Herms, W. B., 1907. An Ecological and Experimental Study of the Sarcophagidae with Relation to Lake Beach Debris. J. Exper. Zool., 4: 45–83. pp. 394, 534.

—— 1939. Medical Entomology. New York, Macmillan. pp. 28, 70, 261, 514.

Herre, W., 1943. Zur Frage der Kausalität von Domestikationserscheinungen. Zool. Anz., 141: 196–214. p. 600.

Herrick, F. H., 1911. Natural History of the

American Lobster. Bull. U. S. Bur. Fisheries, *29:* 149–408. p. 50.

Hertwig, Oskar, 1883. Die Symbiose oder das Genossenschaftsleben im Tierreich. Jena, Fischer. p. 32.

Hertz, A., and Imms, A. D., 1937. On the Responses of the African Migratory Locust to Different Types of Background. Proc. Roy. Soc., London, s. B., *122:* 281–297. p. 650.

Hess, A. D., and Hall, T. F., 1943. The Intersection Line as a Factor in Anopheline Ecology. J. Nat. Malaria Soc., *2:* 93–98. p. 696.

Hess, W. N., 1920. Notes on the Biology of Lampyridae. Biol. Bull., *38:* 39–76. p. 554.

Hesse, Richard, 1921. Das Herzgewicht der Wirbeltiere. Zool. Jahrb; Allg. Zool. Physiol. *38:* 243–364. p. 120.

—— 1924. Tiergeographie auf oekologischer Grundlage. Jena, Fischer. pp. 55, 221.

——, Allee, W. C., and Schmidt, K. P., 1937. Ecological Animal Geography. New York, Wiley. pp. 56, 69, 92, 119, 120, 131, 134, 162, 169, 181, 187, 189, 456, 459, 463, 464, 466, 476, 513, 514, 539, 578, 580, 582, 596, 700, 725.

——, ——, —— 1948. Animal Geography. Encyclopaedia Britannica.

—— and Doflein, F., 1935–1943. Tierbau und Tierleben in ihrem Zusammenhang betrachet. 2nd ed. Jena, Fischer, 2 vols. p. 69.

Hetherington, Alford, 1932. The Constant Culture of *Stentor coeruleus*. Arch. Protistenkunde, *76:* 118–129. p. 174.

Hettner, A. H., 1923. Der Gang der Kultur über die Erde. Leipzig, Teubner. p. 57.

Hewatt, W. G., 1935. Ecological Succession in the *Mytilus californianus* Habitat as Observed in Monterey Bay, California. Ecology, *16:* 244–251. p. 570.

—— 1937. Ecological Studies on Selected Marine Intertidal Communities of Monterey Bay, California. Am. Mid. Nat., *18:* 161–206. p. 570.

Hewitt, C. G., 1921. The Conservation of Wild Life in Canada. New York, Scribner. p. 60.

Hewitt, L. F., 1937. Oxidation-Reduction Potentials in Bacteriology and Bio-chemistry. London County Council Gazette, No. 3200. p. 196.

Heyward, Frank, 1939. The Relation of Fire to Stand Composition of Longleaf Pine Forests. Ecology, *20:* 287–304. p. 157.

Hickson, S. J., 1906. Coelenterata and Ctenophora. Cambridge Nat. Hist., *1:* 245–426. p. 214.

Hiestand, W. A., 1928. A Correlation of Strength and Weight in Insects. Ann. Ent. Soc. Amer., *21:* 601–607. p. 638.

Higginbotham, A. C., 1939. Studies on Amphibian Activity. I. Preliminary Report on the Rhythmic Activity of *Bufo a. americanus* Holbrook and *Bufo fowleri* Hinckley. Ecology, *20:* 58–70. p. 558.

—— 1947. Notes on the Oxygen Consumption and Activity of Catfish. Ecology, *28:* 462–464. p. 558.

Higgins, Elmer, 1934. Fishery Biology. Its Scope, Development, and Applications. Quart. Rev. Biol., *9:* 275–291. p. 71.

Hill, J. A., 1936. United States Life Tables. 1929 to 1931, 1920 to 1929, 1919 to 1921, 1909 to 1911, 1901 to 1910, 1900 to 1902. U. S. Bureau of Census. p. 295.

Hill, J. E., 1943. Beaver Engineers. Nat. Hist., *52:* 41. p. 698.

Hill, L., 1912. Caisson Sickness and the Physiology of Work in Compressed Air. London, Arnold. p. 137.

Hill, N. P., 1945. The 1944 Hurricane in New England. Auk. *62:* 410–413. p. 146.

Hincks, W. D., and Dibb, J. R., 1935. Passalidae. Coleopterorum Catalogus: *142:* 1–118. p. 560.

Hingston, R. W. G., 1925. Animal Life at High Altitudes. Geogr. Jour., *65:* 186–198. pp. 136, 147.

—— 1932. A Naturalist in the Guiana Forest. New York, Longmans. pp. 236, 435, 592.

Hinshelwood, C. N., 1944. Bacterial Growth. Biol. Rev., *19:* 150–163. p. 601.

Hinton, M. A. C., 1931. Rats and Mice as Enemies of Mankind. 3rd ed. Brit. Mus., Econ. Ser., *8:* 1–70. p. 401.

Hisaw, F. L., and Gloyd, H. K., 1926. The Bull Snake as a Natural Enemy of Injurious Rodents. J. Mammalogy, *7:* 200–205. p. 467.

Hitchcock, D. I., 1945. Selected Principles of Physical Chemistry. Section 1, pp. 1–91 of Physical Chemistry of Cells and Tissues by Rudolf Höber. Philadelphia, Blakiston.

Hjort, Johan (editor), 1933. Essays on Population. (A Compendium.) Hvalrådets Skrifter, 7. p. 69.

—— 1938. The Human Value of Biology. Cambridge, Harvard Univ. Press. pp. 70, 72.

——, Jahn, G., and Ottestad, P. 1933. The Optimum Catch. Hvalrådets Skrifter, 7: 92–127. pp. 71, 377.

Hoare, C. A., 1940. Studies on the Behaviour of *Trypanosoma evansi* in Tsetse-flies with Special Reference to Its Phylogeny. Parasitology, *32:* 105–121. p. 628.

—— 1943. Biological Races in Parasitic Protozoa. Biol. Rev., *18:* 137–144. pp. 602, 625, 628, 707, 708.

Hobbs, Horton H., Jr., 1942. The Crayfishes of Florida. Univ. of Florida Publication. Biol. Sc., 3 (2): 1–179. p. 226.

Hobbs, W. H., 1943. Wind and Soil. Scient. Monthly *62:* 289–300. p. 218.

Hofstadter, Richard, 1944. Social Darwinism

in American Thought. Philadelphia, Univ. of Pennsylvania Press. p. 641.

Hogben, L. T., 1931. Some Biological Aspects of the Population Problem. Biol. Rev., 6: 163–180. pp. 71, 304, 347.

—— 1933. Nature and Nurture. New York, Norton. p. 3.

—— 1940. Problems of the Origin of Species. In Huxley, J., The New Systematics, pp. 269–286. p. 617.

Hogg, J., 1854. Observations on the Development and Growth of Lymnaeus stagnalis. Q. J. Micros. Soc., 2: 91–103. pp. 22, 355.

Holdaway, F. G., 1932. An Experimental Study of the Growth of Populations of the "Flour Beetle" Tribolium confusum Duval, as Affected by Atmospheric Moisture. Ecol. Monogr., 2: 261–304.

—— 1933. The Composition of Different Regions of Mounds of Eutermes exitiosus Hill. J. Council Sc. Ind. Res., 6: 160–165. p. 431.

——, Gay, F. J., Greaves, T., 1935. The Termite Population of a Mound Colony of Eutermes exitiosus Hill. J. Counc. Sc. Ind. Res., 8: 42–46. p. 422.

Hollaender, Alexander, 1942. Abiotic and Sublethal Effects of Ultraviolet Radiation on Microrganisms. Publ. Am. A. Adv. Sc., 17: 156–165. p. 127.

Holmes, Arthur, 1947. A Revised Estimate of the Age of the Earth. Nature, 159: 127–128. p. 74.

Holmes, S. J., 1916. Studies in Animal Behavior. Boston, Badger. p. 23.

—— 1944. The Problem of Organic Form. IV. Chemical Equilibrium and Organic Interaction. Scient. Monthly, 59: 253–260, 379–383.

—— 1944a. Recapitulation and Its Supposed Causes. Quart. Rev. Biol., 19: 319–331. pp. 637, 678.

Holmquist, A. M., 1926. Studies in Arthropod Hibernation. Ann. Ent. Soc. Amer., 19: 395–429. pp. 102, 487, 537, 538.

—— 1928. Notes on the Life History and Habits of the Mound-Building Ant, Formica ulkei Emery. Ecology, 9: 70–87. p. 538.

—— 1928a. Studies in Arthropod Hibernation. II. The Hibernation of the Ant, Formica ulkei Emery. Physiol. Zoöl., 1: 325–357. p. 538.

—— 1931. Studies in Arthropod Hibernation. III. Temperatures in Forest Hibernacula. Ecology, 12: 387–400. p. 102.

Holzapfel, Ruth A., 1937. The Cyclic Character of Hibernation in Frogs. Quart. Rev. Biol., 12: 65–84. p. 105.

Hooker, Davenport, 1944. The Origin of Overt Behavior. Univ. of Michigan Lecture, No. 1 Ann Arbor. p. 636.

Hoover, E. E., 1937. Experimental Modification of the Sexual Cycle in Trout by Control of Light. Science, 86: 425–426.

Hopkins, A. D., 1918. Periodic Events and Natural Law as Guides to Agricultural Research and Practice. U. S. Mon. Weather Rev., Suppl., 9: 1–42. p. 118.

—— 1920. The Bioclimatic Law. J. Wash. Acad. Sc., 10: 34–40. p. 118.

Horstmann, Ernst, 1935. Die tagesperiodischen Pigmentwanderungen im Facettenauge von Nachtschmetterlingen. Biol. Centralbl., 55: 93–97. p. 546.

Höst, Per, 1942. Effects of Light on the Moults and Sequence of Plumage in the Willow Ptarmigan. Auk, 59: 388–403. p. 123.

Hough, A. F., and Forbes, R. D., 1943. The Ecology and Silvics of Forests in the High Plateaus of Pennsylvania. Ecol. Monogr., 13: 299–320. p. 575.

Hovanitz, William, 1942. Genetic and Ecologic Analyses of Wild Populations in Lepidoptera. I. Pupal Size and Weight Variation in Some California Populations of Melitaea chalcedona. Ecology, 23: 175–188. p. 606.

—— 1943. Hybridization and Seasonal Segregation in Two Races of a Butterfly Occurring Together in Two Localities. Biol. Bull., 85: 44–51. p. 606.

Howard, H. E., 1920. Territory in Bird Life. London, Murray. p. 412.

Howard, L. O., 1897. A Study in Insect Parasitism: A Consideration of the Parasites of the White-Marked Tussock Moth, with an Account of Their Habits and Interrelations and with Descriptions of New Species. Tech. Ser. U. S. Dept. of Agr., 5: 5–57. p. 28.

—— 1925. The Needs of the World as to Entomology. Ann. Entom. Soc. Amer., 18: 1–21. pp. 515, 516.

—— 1930. A History of Applied Entomology. Smithsonian Misc. Coll., 84: 1–564. p. 27.

—— and Fiske, W. F., 1911. The Importation into the United States of the Parasites of the Gipsy Moth and the Brown-Tail Moth. Bull. U. S. Bur. Entom., 91: 1–344. p. 331.

Howe, R. W., and Oxley, T. A., 1944. The Use of Carbon Dioxide Production as a Measure of Infestation of Grain by Insects. Bull. Entom. Res., 35: 11–22. p. 269.

Howell, A. B., 1944. Speed in Animals. Chicago, Univ. of Chicago Press. pp. 631, 632.

Howell, A. H., 1938. Revision of the North American Ground Squirrels, with a Classification of the North American Sciuridae. N. Amer. Fauna, 56: 1–256. p. 438.

Howells, Thomas H., 1947. Lamarckian-Darwinian Reorientation. Psychological Rev., 54: 24–40. pp. 599, 684.

Hubbard, H. G., 1893. The Insect Guests of the Florida Land Tortoise. Insect Life, 6: 302–315. pp. 438, 514.

Hubbs, C. L., 1922. Variations in the Number

of Vertebrae and Other Meristic Characters of Fishes Correlated with the Temperature of Water during Development. Am. Nat., 56: 360–372. p. 119.

Hubbs, C. L., 1930. The High Toxicity of Nascent Oxygen. Physiol. Zoöl., 3: 441–460. p. 193.

—— 1938. Fishes from the Caves of Yucatan. Carnegie Inst. Wash. Publ., 491: 261–295. pp. 643, 673.

—— 1944. Concepts of Homology and Analogy. Am. Nat., 78: 289–307. p. 635.

—— and Eschmeyer, R. W., 1938. The Improvement of Lakes for Fishing. A Method of Fish Management. Fish. Res. Bull., Mich. Dept. Conservat. Inst., 2: 1–233. p. 659.

—— and Hubbs, Laura C., 1946. Breeding Experiments with the Invariably Female, Strictly Matroclinous Fish, *Mollienisia formosa*. Genetics, 31: 218. p. 623.

—— and Miller, R. R., 1942. Mass Hybridization between Two Genera of Cyprinid Fishes in the Mohave Desert, California. Papers Mich. Acad. Sc. Arts & Letters, 28: 343–378. p. 625.

Hudson, W. H., 1912. The Naturalist in La Plata. London, Dent. [1st ed. 1892] p. 23.

Huff, C. G, 1938. Studies on the Evolution of some Disease-Producing Organisms. Quart. Rev. Biol., 13: 196–206. pp. 256, 707, 708.

—— 1945. A Consideration of the Problem of Evolution of Malarial Parasites. Rev. Inst. Salubridad Enfermedades Tropicales, 6: 253–258. p. 707.

—— and Coulston. F., 1946. The Relation of Natural and Acquired Immunity of Various Avian Hosts to the Cryptozoites and Metacryptozoites of *Plasmodium gallinaceum* and *Plasmodium relictum*. J. Infect. Diseases, 78: 99–117. pp. 686, 708.

Huffaker, C. B., 1944. The Temperature Relations of the Immature Stages of the Malarial Mosquito, *Anopheles quadrimaculatus* Say, with a Comparison of the Developmental Power of Constant and Variable Temperatures in Insect Metabolism. Ann. Ent. Soc. Amer., 37: 1–27.

Huggins, C. B., and Blocksom, B. H., Jr., 1936. Changes in Outlying Bone Marrow Accompanying a Local Increase of Temperature within Physiological Limits. J. Exper. Med., 64: 253–274. p. 120.

Hughes-Schrader, Sally, 1948. Cytology of Coccids (Coccoidea-Homoptera). In Demerec, M. (ed.): Advances in Genetics, 3: 127–203. pp. 623, 677, 712.

Hull, T. G., 1930. Diseases Transmitted from Animals to Man. Springfield, Ill., Thomas. p. 261.

Humbolt, Alexander von, 1850. Views of Nature: or Contemplations on the Sublime Phenomena of Creation; with Scientific Illustrations. London, Bell. p. 461.

Humphrey, Tryphena, 1944. Primitive Neurons in the Embryonic Human Central Nervous System. J. Comp. Neur., 81: 1–45. p. 636.

Humphreys, W. J., 1931. The Atmosphere; Origin and Composition. Physics of the Earth, 3: 1–14. pp. 189, 190.

—— 1942. Ways of the Weather. Lancaster, Jacques Cattell Press. pp. 82, 91, 140.

Hungate, R. E., 1938. Studies on the Nutrition of Zootermopsis. II. The Relative Importance of the Termite and the Protozoa in Wood Digestion. Ecology, 19: 1–25. pp. 716, 718.

—— 1939. Experiments on the Nutrition of Zootermopsis. III. The Anaerobic Carbohydrate Dissimilation by the Intestinal Protozoa. Ecology, 20: 230–245. p. 716.

—— 1941. Experiments on the Nitrogen Economy of Termites. Ann. Ent. Soc. Amer., 34: 467–489. p. 716.

—— 1943. Further Experiments on Cellulose Digestion by the Protozoa in the Rumen of Cattle. Biol. Bull., 84: 157–163. p. 716.

—— 1944. Studies on Cellulose Fermentation. I. The Culture and Physiology of an Anaerobic Cellulose-Digesting Bacterium. J. Bacteriol., 48: 499–513. p. 712.

—— 1944a. Quantitative Analyses on the Cellulose Fermentation by Termite Protozoa. Ann. Ent. Soc. Amer., 36: 730–739. p. 716.

Hungerford, H. B., and Williams, F. X., 1912. Biological Notes on Some Kansas Hymenoptera. Entom. News, 23: 241–260. p. 467.

Huntington, Ellsworth, 1914. The Climatic Factor as Illustrated in Arid America. Pub. Carnegie Inst. Wash., 192: 95–157. p. 528.

—— 1919. World Power and Evolution. New Haven, Yale Univ. Press. pp. 208, 209.

—— 1924. Civilization and Climate. New Haven, Yale Univ. Press. p. 57.

—— 1932. Matamek Conference on Biological Cycles. Matamek Factory, Canadian Labrador. p. 87.

—— 1945. Mainsprings of Civilization. New York, Wiley. pp. 73, 85.

—— and Cushing, S. W., 1921. Principles of Human Geography. New York, Wiley. p. 57.

Huntsman, A. G., 1921. The Effect of Light on Growth in the Mussel. Tr. Roy. Soc. Canada, 15: 23–28. p. 121.

—— 1924. Limiting Factors for Marine Animals. I. The Lethal Effect of Sunlight. Contr. Canad. Biol., (N.S.) 2: 83–88. p. 121.

—— 1937. The Cause of Periodic Scarcity in Atlantic Salmon. Tr. Roy. Soc. Canada, 31: 17–27. p. 321.

—— 1938. North American Atlantic Salmon J. Conseil Explor. Mer (Extrait du Rapports et Procès-Verbaux, CI), 4: 11–15. p. 321.

Hurd, A. M., 1920. Effect of Unilateral Mono-chromatic Light and Group Orientation on the Polarity of Germinating *Fucus* Spores. Bot. Gaz., *70:* 25–50. pp. 121, 408.

Huskins, C. L., 1931. The Origin of Spartina townsendii. Genetica, *12:* 531–538. p. 625.

Hutchinson, G. E., 1938. On the Relation between the Oxygen Deficit and the Productivity and Typology of Lakes. Int. Rev. Hydrobiol., *36:* 336–355. pp. 194, 196.

—— 1941. Limnological Studies in Connecticut. IV. Mechanism of Intermediary Metabolism in Stratified Lakes. Ecol. Monogr., *11:* 21–60. pp. 96, 206, 519.

—— 1941a. Ecological Aspects of Succession in Natural Populations. Am. Nat., *75:* 406–418. pp. 174, 202.

—— 1942. *Nati Sunt Mures, et Facta Est Confusio.* Review of Voles, Mice and Lemmings by Charles Elton. Quart. Rev. Biol., *17:* 354–357. p. 367.

—— 1943. The Biogeochemistry of Aluminum and of Certain Related Elements. Quart. Rev. Biol., *18:* 1–29; 128–153; 242–262; 331–363. pp. 73, 206, 216, 222.

—— 1943a. Thiamin in Lake Waters and Aquatic Organisms. Arch. Biochem., *2:* 143–150.

—— 1943b. Food, Time and Culture. Tr. New York Acad. Sc., (2) *5:* 152–154. p. 526.

—— 1944. Nitrogen in the Biogeochemistry of the Atmosphere. Am. Scientist, *32:* 178–195. pp. 75, 508.

—— 1947. A Note on the Theory of Competition between Two Social Species. Ecology, *28:* 319–321. p. 370.

—— 1948. Teleological Mechanisms: Circular Causal Systems in Ecology. Ann. New York Acad. Sci., *50:* 221–246. pp. 386, 639, 656, 660, 664, 695.

Hutchison, Lynn, 1947. Analysis of the Activity of the Fresh-Water Snail, *Viviparus malleatus* (Reeve). Ecology, *28:* 335–345. p. 558.

Huxley, J. S., 1930. The Maladaptation of Trout Spermatozoa to Fresh Water. Nature, *125:* 494.

—— 1932. Problems of Relative Growth. London, Methuen. pp. 637, 638, 691.

—— 1938. Darwin's Theory of Sexual Selection and the Data Subsumed by It, in the Light of Recent Research. Am. Nat., *72:* 416–433. pp. 619, 689, 691, 710.

—— 1938a. The Present Standing of the Theory of Sexual Selection. In de Beer, G. R., Evolution. Oxford, Clarendon Press. pp. 11–42. pp. 691, 710.

—— 1939. Clines: An Auxiliary Method in Taxonomy. Bijdr. Dierk., *27:* 491–520. pp. 624, 626, 627.

—— 1939a. Ecology and Taxonomic Differentiation. J. Ecol., *27:* 408–420. p. 602.

—— (Ed.) 1940. The New Systematics. Oxford, Clarendon Press. pp. 70, 117, 598.

—— 1941. The Courtship of Animals. In Huxley, The Uniqueness of Man. London, Chatto & Windus, pp. 190–206. p. 689.

—— 1942. Evolution, The Modern Synthesis. New York, Harper. pp. 70, 598, 606, 625, 638, 639, 648, 677, 679, 715.

Hyman, L. H., 1925. On the Action of Certain Substances on Oxygen Consumption. Biol. Bull., *49:* 288–322. p. 175.

—— 1929. The Effect of Oxygen Tension on Oxygen Consumption in Planaria and some Echinoderms. Physiol. Zoöl., *2:* 505–534. p. 194.

—— 1932. Relation of Oxygen Tension to Oxygen Consumption in Nereis virens. J. Exper. Zoöl., *61:* 209–221. p. 194.

—— 1937. Studies on the Morphology, Taxonomy, and Distribution of North American Triclad Turbellaria. VIII. Some Cave Planarians of the United States. Tr. Am. Micr. Soc., *56:* 457–477. p. 439.

—— 1940. The Invertebrates: Protozoa through Ctenophora. New York, McGraw-Hill. p. 183.

Imms, A. D., 1924. A General Textbook of Entomology, Including the Anatomy, Physiology, Development and Classification of Insects. New York, Dutton. p. 514.

Irwin, M. R. and Cole, L. J., 1936. Immunogenetic Studies of Species and of Species Hybrids in Doves, and the Separation of Species-specific Substances in the Backcross. J. Exper. Zool., *73:* 85–108. p. 625.

—— 1936a. Immunogenetic Studies of Species and Species Hybrids from the Cross of Columba livia and Streptopelia risoria. J. Exper. Zool., *73:* 309–318. p. 625.

Isely, F. B., 1938. Survival Value of Acridian Protective Coloration. Ecology, *19:* 370–389. pp. 466, 650.

—— 1938a. The Relations of Texas Acrididae to Plants and Soils. Ecol. Monogr., *8:* 551–604. pp. 466, 514.

—— 1941. Researches Concerning Texas Tettigoniidae. Ecol. Monogr., *11:* 457–475. p. 466.

Ives, R. L., 1947. Behavior of Dust Devils. Bull. Am. Meteorol. Soc., *28:* 168–174. p. 149.

Jackson, C. H. N., 1933. On the True Density of Tsetse Flies. J. Anim. Ecol., *2:* 204–209. pp. 269, 366.

—— 1936. Some New Methods in the Study of Glossina morsitans. Proc. Zool. Soc., London, 1936: 811–896. pp. 269, 366.

—— 1939. The Analysis of an Animal Population. J. Anim. Ecol., *8:* 238–246. pp. 269, 366.

Jackson, H. S., 1931. Present Evolutionary Tendencies and the Origin of Life Cycles in the Uredinales. Mem. Torrey Bot. Club, *18:* 1–108. pp. 614, 623.

Jacobs, M. K., 1935. Diffusion Processes. Ergebn. Biol., *12:* 1–160. p. 166.

Jacot, A. P., 1935. Wild Life of the Forest Carpet. Scient. Monthly, *40:* 425–430. p. 486.

—— 1935a. Molluscan Populations of Old Growth Forests and Rewooded Fields in the Asheville Basin of North Carolina. Ecology, *16:* 603–605. p. 486.

—— 1936. Soil Structure and Soil Biology. Ecology, *17:* 359–379. p. 484.

—— 1936a. Spruce Litter Reduction. Canad. Entomologist, *68:* 31–32. p. 486.

—— 1939. Reduction of Spruce and Fir Litter by Minute Animals. J. Forestry, *37:* 858–860. pp. 465, 486.

—— 1940. The Fauna of the Soil. Quart. Rev. Biol., *15:* 28–58. pp. 486, 510.

James, H. G., 1944. Colour Changes in Mantis religiosa L. Canad. Ent., *76:* 113–116. p. 650.

Janisch, E., 1932. The Influence of Temperature on the Life History of Insects. Tr. Ent. Soc., London, *80:* 137–168. p. 107.

—— and Maercks, H., 1933. Ueber die Berechnung der Kettenlinie als Ausdruck für die Temperaturabhängigkeit von Lebenserscheinungen. Arb. Biol. Reichsanst. Land-Forstw., *20:* 259–268.

Jeannel, Renee, 1926–1930. Monographie des Trechinae, Morphologie comparée et distribution geographique d'un groupe de Coléoptères. L'Abeille, *32:* 221–550; *33:* 1–592; *35:* 1–808; Suppl., Les Trechini cavernicoles *34:* 59–122. p. 439.

Jeffreys, Harold, 1939. Theory of Probability. Oxford, Clarendon Press. p. 222.

Jellison, W. L., 1942. Host Distribution of Lice on Native American Rodents North of Mexico. J. Mammal., *23:* 245–250. pp. 643, 723.

Jenkins, D. W., 1944. Territory as a Result of Despotism, and Social Organization in Geese. Auk, *61:* 30–47. p. 413.

Jennings, H. S., 1906. Behavior of the Lower Organisms. New York, Columbia Univ. Press. pp. 24, 44.

—— 1927. Some Implications of Emergent Evolution; Diverse Doctrines of Evolution—Their Relation to the Practice of Science and of Life. Hanover, N. H: The Sociological Press. p. 693.

—— 1938. Sex Reaction Types and Their Interrelations in *Paramecium bursaria.* Proc. Nat. Acad. Sc., *24:* 112–120. p. 408.

—— 1940. The Beginnings of Social Behavior in Multicellular Organisms. Science, *92:* 539–546.

—— 1944. Changes in the Surrounding Medium Produced by Free-Living Cells. In Alexander, J., Colloid Chemistry, *5:* 1162–1174. p. 697.

—— 1945. Social Life and Interrelationships in Certain Protozoa. Sociometry, *8:* 9–20. p. 408.

—— and Opitz, Pauline, 1944. Genetics of Paramecium bursaria. IV. A Fourth Variety from Russia. Lethal Crosses with an American Variety. Genetics, *29:* 576–583. p. 622.

Jewell, M. E., 1935. An Ecological Study of the Fresh-water Sponges of Northern Wisconsin. Ecol. Monogr., *5:* 461–504. p. 204.

—— 1939. An Ecological Study of the Freshwater Sponges of Wisconsin, II. The Influence of Calcium. Ecology, *20:* 11–28. p. 341.

—— and Brown, H. W., 1929. Studies on Northern Michigan Bog Lakes. Ecology, *10:* 427–475. pp. 174, 204.

Jewett, Stanley G., 1944. Hybridization of Hermit and Townsend Warblers. Condor, *46:* 23–24. p. 624.

Johnson, C. G., 1942. Insect Survival in Relation to the Rate of Water Loss. Biol. Rev., *17:* 151–177.

Johnson, G. E., 1931. Hibernation in Mammals. Quart. Rev. Biol., *6:* 439–461. pp. 71, 105.

Johnson, N. K., and Davies, E. L., 1927. Some Measurements of Temperatures Near the Surface in Various Kinds of Soils. Q. J. Roy. Meteorol. Soc., *53:* 45–59. p. 98.

Johnson, W. H., 1933. Effects of Population Density on the Rate of Reproduction in *Oxytricha.* Physiol. Zoöl., *6:* 22–54. pp. 358, 406, 407.

—— 1937. Experimental Populations of Microscopic Organisms. Am. Nat., *71:* 5–20. p. 407.

—— 1938. The Effect of Light on the Vertical Movements of *Acartia clausi* (Giesbrecht). Biol. Bull., *75:* 106–118. p. 554.

—— 1941. Population of Ciliates. Am. Nat., *75:* 438–457. p. 402.

Johnson, W. L., 1945. Age and Growth of the Black and White Crappies of Greenwood Lake, Indiana. Invest. Indiana Lakes & Streams, *2:* 297–324. p. 618.

Johnson, W. M., 1945. Natural Revegetation of Abandoned Crop Land in the Ponderosa Pine Zone of the Pike's Peak Region in Colorado. Ecology, *26:* 363–374. p. 578.

Johnstone, James, 1908. Conditions of Life in the Sea. A Short Account of Marine Biological Research. Cambridge, University Press. pp. 36, 46, 198.

—— 1923. An Introduction to Oceanography. London, Arnold. pp. 136, 137, 162.

——, Scott, A., and Chadwick, H. C., 1924. The Marine Plankton, with Special Reference to Investigations Made at Port Erin, Isle of Man, during 1907–1914. A Handbook for Students and Amateurs. Liverpool, Univ. Press. p. 448.

Jollos, V., 1932. Variabilität und Vererbung bei

Mikroorganismen in ihrer Bedeutung für die Medizin. Klin. Wochenschr., *11:* 1–16. p. 602.

Jones, J. W., 1939. Salmon of the Cheshire Dee, 1937 and 1938. Proc. & Tr., Liverpool Biol. Soc., *52:* 19–80. p. 283.

Jones, Sarah E., 1946. Variations in Abundance of Certain Invertebrates in William Trelease Woods. Amer. Mid. Nat., *35:* 172–192. pp. 531, 533.

Jordan, D. S., 1905. A Guide to the Study of Fishes. New York, Holt, 2 vols. p. 245.

—— and Kellogg, V. L., 1915. Evolution and Animal Life. New York, Appleton. p. 49.

Jordan, E. O., and Burrows, W., 1945. Textbook of Bacteriology. 14th Ed. Philadelphia, W. B. Saunders Company, p. 381.

Jordan, Karl, 1905. Der Gegensatz zwischen geographischer und nichtgeographischer Variation. Ztschr. wiss. Zool., *83:* 151–210. p. 618.

Jörgensen, E., 1920. Mediterranean Ceratia. Rep. Danish Oceanogr. Exped. 1908–1910 to the Mediterranean and adjacent seas, *2:* 1–110. p. 502.

Juday, Chancey, 1896. The Plankton of Turkey Lake. Proc. Indiana. Acad. Sc., *1896:* 287–296. p. 42.

—— 1904. The Diurnal Movement of Plankton Crustacea. Tr. Wis. Acad. Sc., *14:* 534–568. p. 550.

—— 1921. Observations on the Larvae of Corethra punctipennis Say. Biol. Bull., *40:* 271–286. pp. 453, 556.

—— 1922. Quantitative Studies of the Bottom Fauna in the Deeper Waters of Lake Mendota. Tr. Wis. Acad. Sc., *20:* 461–493. p. 453.

—— 1938. Fish Records for Lake Wingra. Tr. Wis. Acad. Sc., *31:* 533–534. p. 526.

—— 1940. The Annual Energy Budget of an Inland Lake. Ecology, *21:* 438–450. pp. 92, 519, 520, 521, 522.

—— 1942. The Summer Standing Crop of Plants and Animals in Four Wisconsin Lakes. Tr. Wis. Acad. Sc., *34:* 103–135. pp. 203, 527.

——, Birge, E. A., and Meloche, V. W., 1935. The Carbon Dioxide and Hydrogen Ion Content of the Lake Waters of Northeastern Wisconsin. Tr. Wis. Acad. Sc., *29:* 1–82. p. 175.

——, ——, —— 1938. Mineral Content of the Lake Waters of Northeastern Wisconsin. Tr. Wis. Acad. Sc., *31:* 223–276. p. 203.

Jurine, Louis, 1798. Experiments on Bats Deprived of Sight. Transl. from J. Physique for 1798. Philos. Mag., *1:* 136–140. p. 140.

Juritz, C. F., 1920. Analysis of Droppings of Caterpillar (*Antheraea cytherea*). Chemical News, *121:* 181. p. 487.

Just, Theodor (editor), 1939. Plant and Animal Communities. Am. Mid. Nat., *21:* 1–255. p. 69.

—— 1944. The Rates of Evolutionary Processes. Proc. Indiana Acad. Sc., *53:* 14–27. pp. 663, 684.

Kahn, M. C., Celestin, W., and Offenhauser, W., 1945. Recording of Sounds Produced by Certain Disease-Carrying Mosquitoes. Science, *101:* 335–336. p. 619.

Kalmus, Hans, 1935. Periodizität und Autochronie (Ideochronie) als zeitregelnde Eigenschaften der Organismen. Biol. Gen., *11:* 93–114. p. 553.

—— 1940. Diurnal Rhythms in the Axolotl Larva and in Drosophila. Nature, *145:* 72–73. pp. 553, 558.

—— 1941. The Resistance to Desiccation of *Drosophila* Mutants Affecting Body Colour. Proc. Roy. Soc., London, s. B., *130.* 185–201. p. 668.

Kammerer, Paul, 1909. Allgemeine Symbiose und Kampf ums Dasein als gleichberechtigte Triebkrafte der Evolution. Arch. Rass. Gesell. Biol., *6:* 585–608. p. 32.

Kanitz, Aristides, 1915. Temperatur und Lebensvorgänge. Berlin, Borntraeger. p. 107.

Karsten, G., 1907. Das Indische Phytoplankton. Wiss. Ergeb. deutsch. Tiefsee Exped., *2:* 221–548. p. 448.

Kashkarov, D., and Kurbatov, V., 1930. Preliminary Ecological Survey of the Vertebrate Fauna of the Central Kara-kum Desert in West Turkestan. Ecology, *11:* 35–60. p. 514.

Kato, K., 1933. Is Nomeus a Harmless Inquiline of Physalia? Tokyo Imp. Proc., *9:* 537–538. p. 245.

Keeble, F. W., 1910. Plant-Animals: A Study in Symbiosis. Cambridge: Univ. Press. pp. 457, 544.

—— and Gamble, F. W., 1904. The Colour-Physiology of Higher Crustacea. Phil. Tr. Roy. Soc., London, B., *196:* 295–388. p. 22.

Keegan, H. L., and Andrews, T. F., 1942. Effects of Crotalid Venom on North American Snakes. Copeia, *1942:* 251–254. p. 19.

Keith, A., 1942. A Postscript to Darwin's "Formation of Vegetable Mould through the Action of Worms." Nature, *149:* 716–720. p. 24.

Kellerman, K. F., 1926. A Review of the Discovery of Photoperiodism; The Influence of the Length of Daily Light Periods upon the Growth of Plants. Quart. Rev. Biol., *1:* 87–94. pp. 534, 545.

Kellogg, V. L., 1913. Distribution and Species Forming of Ecto-parasites. Am. Nat., *47:* 129–158. pp. 258, 259.

Kendall, James, 1923. Smith's College Chemistry. New York, Century. p. 195.

Kendeigh, S. C., 1932. A Study of Merriam's Temperature Laws. Wilson Bull., *44:* 129–143. p. 115.

—— 1934. The Role of Environment in the

Life of Birds. Ecol. Monogr., *4:* 301–417. pp. 98, 494.

Kendeigh, S. C., 1942. Analysis of the Losses in the Nesting of Birds. J. Wildlife Manag., *6:* 19–26. p. 334.

—— 1944. Measurement of Bird Populations. Ecol. Monogr., *14:* 67–106. pp. 326, 478.

—— 1945. Community Selection by Birds on the Helderberg Plateau of New York. Auk, *62:* 418–436. pp. 494, 495, 648.

—— 1946. Breeding Birds of the Beech-Maple-Hemlock Community. Ecology, *27:* 226–245. p. 575.

—— 1947. Bird Population Studies in the Coniferous Forest Biome during a Spruce Budworm Outbreak. Dept. Lands, Forests Canada, Div. Research, Biol. Bull., *1:* 1–100. p. 483.

—— and Baldwin, S. P., 1928. Development of Temperature Control in Nestling House Wrens. Am. Nat., *62:* 249–278. p. 98.

——, —— 1937. Factors Affecting Yearly Abundance of Passerine Birds. Ecol. Monogr., *7:* 91–123. p. 684.

Kendrew, W. G., 1938. Climate: A Treatise on the Principles of Weather and Climate. Oxford Univ. Press. pp. 140, 143.

Kennedy, C. H., 1927. Some Non-Nervous Factors that Condition the Sensitivity of Insects to Moisture, Light and Odors. Ann. Ent. Soc. Amer., *20:* 87–106. p. 187.

—— 1928. Evolutionary Level in Relation to Geographic, Seasonal and Diurnal Distribution of Insects. Ecology, *9:* 367–379. p. 553.

Kerner von Marilaun, A., 1863. Das Pflanzenleben der Donauländer. Innsbruck. p. 34.

Kesteven, G. L., 1947. Population Studies in Fisheries Biology. Nature, *159:* 10–12. p. 377.

Ketchum, B. H., 1939. The Absorption of Phosphate and Nitrate by Illuminated Cultures of *Nitzschia closterium*. Am. J. Bot., *26:* 399–407. p. 203.

—— 1947. The Biochemical Relations between Marine Organisms and Their Environment. Ecol. Monogr., *17:* 309–315.

Key, K. H. L., 1942. An Analysis of the Outbreaks of the Australian Plague Locust (*Chortoicetes terminifera* Walk) during the Seasons 1937–38 and 1938–39. Bull. Australian C. S. I. R., 146. p. 338.

Kidder, G. W., 1941. Growth Studies on Ciliates. V. The Acceleration and Inhibition of Ciliate Growth in Biologically Conditioned Medium. Physiol. Zoöl., *14:* 209–226. pp. 359, 408.

Kimball, H. H., 1924. Records of Solar Radiation Intensity and Their Relation to Daylight Intensity. U. S. Mon. Weather. Rev., *52:* 473–479. p. 90.

—— 1931. Physics of the Earth. III. Meteor-ology. Bull. Nat. Res. Council. 79, Washington, Nat. Acad. Sc. p. 140.

—— and Hand, I. F., 1936. The Intensity of Solar Radiation as Received at the Surface of the Earth and Its Variation with Latitude, Altitude, the Season of the Year, and the Time of Day. In Duggar, B. M., 1926. Biological Effects of Radiation. Chap. 5, pp. 211–226. p. 89.

Kimball, R. F., 1939. Mating Types in *Euplotes*. Am. Nat., *73:* 451–456. p. 408.

—— 1943. Mating Types in the Ciliate Protozoa. Quart. Rev. Biol., *18:* 30–45. p. 408.

King, A. F. A., 1883. Mosquitoes and Malaria. Pop. Sc. Monthly, *23:* 644–658. p. 29.

King, H. D., 1916. The Relation of Age to Fertility in the Rat. Anat. Rec., *11:* 269–288. p. 285.

—— 1929. Life Processes and Size of the Body and Organs of the Gray Norway Rat during Ten Generations in Captivity. Am. Anat. Mem., *14:* 1–106. p. 279.

Kinsey, A. C., 1929. The Gall Wasp Genus Cynips. A Study in the Origin of Species. Indiana Univ. Stud., *16:* 1–577. p. 491.

—— 1936. The Origin of Higher Categories in Cynips. Indiana Univ. Pub. (Sci. Ser.) *4:* 1–334. pp. 70, 610, 613.

Kirby, H., Jr., 1937. Host-Parasite Relations in the Distribution of Protozoa in Termites. Univ. of Calif. Publ. Zool., *41:* 189–212. pp. 629, 716.

—— 1942. Devescovinid Flagellates of Termites. II. The Genera Caduceia and Macrotrichomonas. Univ. of Calif. Publ. Zool., *45:* 93–166. p. 680.

—— 1942a. Deverscovinid Flagellates of Termites. III. The Genera Foaina and Parajoenia. Univ. of Calif. Publ. Zool., *45:* 167–246. p. 629.

—— 1944. The Structural Characteristics and Nuclear Parasites of Some Species of *Trichonympha* in Termites. Univ. of Calif. Publ. Zool., *49:* 185–282. p. 716.

Kirk, R., 1944. The Evolution of Leishmania Infections in Man. Tr. Roy. Soc. Trop. Med. & Hyg., *38:* 61–70. p. 628.

Klaauw, C. J. van der, 1936. Zur Aufteilung der Ökologie in Autökologie und Synökologie, im Lichte der Ideen als Grundlage der Systematik der zoologischen Disziplinen. Acta Biotheoretica, *2:* 195–241. p. 72.

Klages, K. M. W., 1942. Ecological Crop Geography. New York, Macmillan. pp. 183, 207.

Klauber, L. M., 1939. Studies of Reptile Life in the Arid Southwest. Bull. Zool. Soc., San Diego, *14:* 1–100. p. 590.

Klebs, Georg, 1896. Die Bedingungen der Fortpflanzung bei einigen Algen und Pilzen. Jena. Fischer. p. 19.

Kleitman, Nathaniel, 1929. Sleep. Physiol. Rev., *9:* 624–665. p. 553.

—— 1933. Studies on the Physiology of

Sleep. VIII. Diurnal Variation in Performance. Am. J. Physiol., *104:* 449–456. p. 553.

—— 1939. Sleep and Wakefulness. Chicago, Univ. of Chicago Press. pp. 553, 560.

·· ——, Titelbaum, S., and Hoffman, H., 1937. The Establishment of the Diurnal Temperature Cycle. Am. J. Physiol., *119:* 48–54. p. 559.

Klugh, A. B., 1923. A Common System of Classification in Plant and Animal Ecology. Ecology, *4:* 366–377. p. 577.

—— 1927. The Ecology, Food Relations and Culture of Fresh-Water Entomostraca. Tr. Roy. Canad. Inst., *16:* 15–98. pp. 444, 514.

—— and Martin, J. R., 1927. The Growth-Rate of Certain Marine Algae as Related to Depth of Submergence. Ecology, *8:* 221–232. pp. 449, 450.

Knauthe, K., 1907. Das Süsswasser, chemische, biologische, und bakteriologische Untersuchungsmethoden unter besonderer Berücksichtigung der Biologie und der fischereiwirtschaftlichen Praxis. Neudamm. p. 47.

Knibbs, G. H., 1917. The Mathematical Theory of Population, of Its Character and Fluctuations, and of the Factors which Influence Them. Census of the Commonwealth of Australia, *1:* Appendix A. p. 289.

Knight, B. C. J. G., 1945. Growth Factors in Microbiology. In Vitamins and Hormones, R. S. Harris and K. V. Thimann, editors. New York, Academic Press, vol. 3, pp. 108–228b. p. 225.

Knight, H. H., 1941. The Plant Bugs, or Miridae, of Illinois. Bull. Illinois Nat. Hist. Surv., *22:* 1–234. p. 494.

Knight, Hugh, 1932. Some Notes on Scale Resistance and Population Density. J. Ent. Zool., *24:* 1–11. p. 654.

Knowlton, F. H., 1909. Birds of the World: A Popular Account. . . . New York, Holt. p. 257.

Knuth, Paul, 1898–1905. Handbuch der Blütenbiologie. Leipzig, Englemann, 3 vols. pp. 33, 248.

—— 1906–1909. Handbook of Flower Pollination. Oxford: Univ. Press, 3 vols.

Kofoid, C. A., 1897. On Some Important Sources of Error in the Plankton Method. Science, *0:* 829–832. p. 36.

—— 1903. The Plankton of the Illinois River, 1894–1899, with Introductory Notes upon the Hydrography of the Illinois River and Its Basin. Bull. Ill. State Lab. Nat. Hist., *6:* 95–629. pp. 36, 41, 47.

—— and Swezy, Olive, 1921. The Free-Living Unarmored Dinoflagellata. Mem. California Univ., *5:* 1–538. p. 502.

Köhler, W., 1925. The Mentality of Apes. New York, Harcourt, Brace. p. 411.

Kollros, Catharine L., 1944. A Study of the Gene, Pearl, in Populations of *Tribolium castaneum* Herbst. Ph.D. Thesis, Univ. of Chicago Library. p. 681.

Komarek, E. V., and Spencer, D. A., 1931. A New Pocket Gopher from Illinois and Indiana. J. Mammal. *12:* 404–408. p. 608.

Korringa, P. 1947. Relations Between the Moon and Periodicity in the Breeding of Marine Animals. Ecol. Monogr., *17:* 347–381. p. 544.

Korstian, C. F., 1937. Perpetuation of Spruce on Cut-over and Burned Lands in the Higher Southern Appalachian Mountains. Ecol. Monogr., *7:* 126–167. pp. 479, 578.

Kostitzin, V. A., 1934. Symbiose, parasitisme et évolution. (Etude mathématique). Actualités Sc. et Industr., *96:* 1–47. Paris, Hermann. p. 69.

—— 1937. Biologie mathématique. Paris, Armand Colin. pp. 70, 369.

Krafka, Joseph, 1920. The Effect of Temperature upon Facet Number in the Bar-Eyed Mutant of *Drosophila,* Pts. I, II, and III. J. Gen. Physiol., *2:* 409–462. p. 51.

Krecker, F. H., and Lancaster, L. Y., 1933. Bottom Shore Fauna of Western Lake Erie; A Population Study to a Depth of Six Feet. Ecology, *14:* 79–93. p. 160.

Krogh, August, 1914. On the Influence of Temperature on the Rate of Embryonic Development. Ztschr. Allg. Physiol., *29:* 29–36. pp. 107, 112.

—— 1914a. On the Rate of Development and CO_2 Production of Chrysalides of *Tenebrio molitor* at Different Temperatures. Ztschr. Allg. Physiol., *16:* 178–190. pp. 108, 109, 113.

—— 1930. Über die Bedeutung von gelösten organischen Substanzen bei Ernährung von Wassertieren. Ztschr. vergl. Physiol., *12:* 668–681. p. 444.

—— 1931. Dissolved Substances as Food of Aquatic Organisms. Biol. Rev., *6:* 412–442. pp. 444, 500.

—— 1934. Conditions of Life in the Ocean. Ecol. Monogr., *4:* 422–429. pp. 40, 137, 138, 499, 500, 522.

—— 1934a. Conditions of Life at Great Depths in the Ocean. Ecol. Monogr., *4:* 430–439. p. 500.

—— 1939. Osmotic Regulation in Aquatic Animals. Cambridge, Univ. Press. pp. 107, 168, 169, 170.

Kropotkin, P., 1902. Mutual Aid, A Factor in Evolution. New York, McClure Phillips. [1914, Knopf.] pp. 32, 663.

Kudo, R. R., 1931. Handbook of Protozoology. Springfield, Thomas. p. 502.

Kühne, W., 1859. Untersuchungen über Bewegungen und Veränderungen der contraktilen Substanzen. Arch. Anat. & Phys. 748–835. p. 21.

—— 1864. Untersuchungen über das Protoplasma und die Contractilität. Leipzig, Engelmann. pp. 19, 20.

Kurtz, A. K., and Edgerton, H. A., 1939. Statistical Dictionary of Terms and Symbols. New York, Wiley. p. 265.

Kusnetzow, S. I., and Karzinkin, G. S., 1931. Direct Count Method for the Quantitative Study of Bacteria in Water and Some Considerations on the Causes which Produce a Zone of Oxygen Minimum in Lake Glubokoje. Centralbl. Bakter., Abt. II, 83: 169–174.

Lack, David, 1944. Ecological Aspects of Species-Formation in Passerine Birds. Ibis, 86: 260–286. pp. 610, 616, 659.

—— 1945. The Galapagos Finches (Geospizinae). A Study in Variation. Occ. Papers Calif. Acad. Sc., 21: 1–151. p. 621.

—— 1945a. The Ecology of Closely Related Species with Special Reference to Cormorant (Phalacrocorax carbo) and Shag (P. aristotelis). J. Anim. Ecol., 14: 12–16. p. 659.

—— 1946. Competition for Food by Birds of Prey. J. Anim. Ecol., 15: 123–129. pp. 11, 616, 659.

—— 1947. Darwin's Finches. Cambridge Univ. Press; New York, Macmillan. pp. 368, 621, 659, 664.

—— and Venables, L. S. V., 1939. The Habitat Distribution of British Woodland Birds. J. Anim. Ecol., 8: 39–71. p. 494.

Lafleur, L. J., 1941. Theoretical Biochemistry. Acta Biotheoretica, 5: 177–183. p. 73.

Lamarck, J. B. P. A., de., 1809. Philosophie Zoologique. Paris, Baillière, 2 vols. [Trans. by Elliot, Hugh, 1914. London, Macmillan.] pp. 29, 30.

—— 1815–1822. Historie Naturelle des Animaux sans vertèbres. Paris, Verdiere. 7 vols. pp. 29, 30.

Lampert, Kurt, 1925. Das Leben der Binnengewässer. 3rd ed. Leipzig, Tauchnitz. [1st ed. 1899; 2nd. 1910.] pp. 37, 40, 41.

Lange, F. A., 1925. The History of Materialism. New York, Harcourt, Brace, 3 vols. [orig. German ed. 1865.] p. 31.

Langford, R. R., 1938. Diurnal and Seasonal Changes in the Distribution of the Limnetic Crustacea of Lake Nipissing, Ontario. Pub. Ontario Fish. Res. Lab. Ser., Toronto Univ. Biol. Ser., 45: 1–142. p. 446.

Lankester, E. R., 1889. Zoology. Encyclopaedia Britannica, 9th ed. 24: 799–820. pp. 17, 42.

Larsen, Ellinor B., 1943. Problems of Heat Death and Heat Injury. K. Danske Vidensk. Selsk., Biol. Meddels., 19: 1–52. p. 104.

Larson, Floyd, and Whitman, W., 1942. A Comparison of Used and Unused Grass-

land Mesas in the Badlands of South Dakota. Ecology, 23: 438–445. p. 578.

Laurens, Henry, 1933. The Physiological Effects of Radiant Energy. New York, Chemical Catalog Co. p. 88.

Leach, W. J., 1944. The Archetypal Position of Amphioxus and Ammocoetes and the Role of Endocrines in Chordate Evolution. Am. Nat., 78: 341–357. p. 679.

Leake, C. D., 1945. Ethicogenesis. Scient. Monthly, 60: 245–253. p. 729.

LeBarron, R. K., and Neetzel, J. R., 1942. Drainage of Forested Swamps. Ecology, 23: 457–465. p. 578.

Lecoq, Henri, 1854. Etude sur la Géographie botanique de l'Europe et en particulier sur la végétation du plateau central de France. I. Paris, Baillière. p. 34.

Ledebur, J. von, 1937. Ueber Sekretion und Resorption in der Schwimmblase des Flussbarsches. Ztschr. Vergl. Physiol., 21: 646–657 p. 139.

Leeson, H. S., 1941. The Effect of Temperature upon the Hatching of Eggs of Pediculus humanus corporis DeGeer (Anoplura). Parasitology, 38: 243–249. p. 99.

Leeuwenhoek, A. van, 1676. Letter No. 18 discovers protozoa. (Written from Delft in Holland on Oct. 9.) p. 37.

—— 1702. Letter No. 144 discovers rotifers. p. 19.

—— 1932. Leeuwenhoek and His "Little Animals." C. Dobell, transl. Amsterdam, Swets and Zeitlinger. p. 37.

Lefevre, G., and Curtis, W. C., 1912. Studies on the Reproduction and Artificial Propagation of Fresh-Water Mussels. Bull. U. S. Bur. Fisheries, 30: 105–201. p. 50.

Leighly, John, 1937. A Note on Evaporation. Ecology, 18: 180–198. pp. 181, 182, 189.

Lenz, F., 1928. Einführung in die Biologie der Süsswasserseen. Berlin, Springer. p. 56.

—— 1931. Untersuchungen über die Vertikalverteilung der Bodenfauna im Tiefensediment von Seen. Verh. Int. Ver. theor. u. angew. Limnol., Budapest, 5: 232–260. p. 453.

Leopold, Aldo, 1933. Game Management. New York, Scribner. pp. 68, 70, 370, 399.

—— 1943. Deer Irruptions. Wis. Conserv. Bull. August, 1943. [Reprinted in Wis. Conserv. Dept. Publ., 321: 1–11.] pp. 706, 707.

—— 1943a. The Flambeau. Wis. Conserv. Bull., 8: 13–17. p. 707.

—— and Jones, Sara E., 1947. A Phenological Record for Sauk and Dane Counties, Wisconsin, 1935–1945. Ecol. Monogr., 17: 81–122. p. 531.

Leslie, A. S., and Shipley, A. E. (editors), 1912. The Grouse in Health and in Disease. Being the Popular Edition of the Report of the Committee of Inquiry on

Grouse Disease. London, Smith, Elder & Co. p. 68.

Leslie, P. H., and Park, T., 1949. Intrinsic Rate of Natural Increase of *Tribolium castaneum* Herbst. Ecology, *30:* 469–477. p. 294.

Leslie, P. H., and Ranson, R. M., 1940. The Mortality, Fertility and Rate of Natural Increase of the Vole (*Microtus agrestis*) as Observed in the Laboratory. J. Anim. Ecol., *9:* 27–52. pp. 280, 283.

Lesne, Pierre, 1896. Moers du Limosina sacra, Meig. (famille Muscidae, tribu Bordorinae). Phénomènes de transport mutuel ches les Animaux articules. Origines du parasitisme chez les Insectes dipteres. Bull. Soc. Ent. France, 1896: 162–165.

Lewis, C. B., and Bletchly, J. D., 1943. The Emergence Rhythm of the Dung-Fly, *Scopeuma* (= *Scatophaga*) *stercoraria* (L.). J. Anim. Ecol., *12:* 11–19. pp. 552, 553, 558.

Lewis, D., 1942. The Evolution of Sex in Flowering Plants. Biol. Rev., *17:* 46–67. p. 689.

Lewis, G. N., 1946. Thermodynamics of an Ice Age: The Cause and Sequence of Glaciation. Science, *104:* 43–47. p. 656.

Lewis, I. M., 1934. Bacterial Variation with Special References to Behavior of Some Mutabile Strains of Colon Bacteria in Synthetic Media. J. Bacter., *28:* 619–637. pp. 601, 628.

Liebig, Justus, 1840 (4th ed. 1847). Chemistry in Its Application to Agriculture and Physiology. London, Taylor and Walton. pp. 20, 198, 205, 224.

Light, S. F., 1942–1943. The Determination of the Castes of Social Insects. Quart. Rev. Biol., *17:* 312–326; *18:* 46–63. p. 428.

——— 1944. Experimental Studies on Ectohormonal Control of the Development of Supplementary Reproductives in the Termite Genus Zootermopsis (formerly Termopsis). Univ. of Calif. Publ. Zool., *43:* 413–454. p. 428.

Lillie, F. R., and Just, E. E., 1913. Breeding Habits of the Heteronereis Form of *Nereis limbata* at Woods Hole, Mass. Biol. Bull., *24:* 147–169. pp. 84, 544.

——— and Knowlton, F., 1897. On the Effect of Temperature on the Development of Animals. Zool. Bull., *1:* 179–193. p. 21.

Lincoln, F. C., 1935. The Migration of North American Birds. U. S. Dept. of Agr., Cir. No. 363: 1–72. pp. 539, 541.

Lindeman, R. L., 1941. The Developmental History of Cedar Creek Bog, Minnesota. Am. Mid. Nat., *25:* 101–112. pp. 509, 520.

——— 1941a. Seasonal Food-Cycle Dynamics in a Senescent Lake. Am. Mid. Nat., *26:* 636–673. p. 509.

——— 1942. The Trophic-Dynamic Aspect of Ecology. Ecology, *23:* 399–418. pp. 453, 508, 509, 510, 519, 520, 525, 577.

Linder, F. E., and Grove, R. D., 1943. Vital Statistics Rates in the United States 1900–

1940. Washington, U. S. Govt. Printing Office. pp. 293, 318.

Lindgren, D. L., and Dickson, R. C., 1945. Repeated Fumigation with HCN and the Development of Resistance in the California Red Scale. J. Econ. Ent., *38:* 296–299. p. 654.

——— and Sinclair, W. B., 1944. Relation of Mortality to Amounts of Hydrocyanic Acid Recovered from Fumigated Resistant and Nonresistant Citrus Scale Insects. Hilgardia, *16:* 303–315. p. 654.

Lindsey, A. A., 1940. Recent Advances in Antarctic Bio-geography. Quart. Rev. Biol., *15:* 456–465. p. 71.

Lippmaa, Theodor, 1939. The Unistratal Concept of Plant Communities (the Unions). Am. Mid. Nat., *21:* 111–145. p. 442.

Lister, J., 1858. On the Cutaneous Pigmentary System of the Frog. Philos. Tr. Roy. Soc., London, *148:* 627–643. p. 22.

Livingston, B. E., 1916. A Single Index to Represent both Moisture and Temperature Conditions as Related to Plants. Physiol. Res., *1:* 421–440. p. 207.

Lloyd, D. C., 1938. A Study of Some Factors Governing the Choice of Hosts and Distribution of Progeny by the Chalcid *Ooencyrtus kuvanae* Howard. Philos. Tr. Roy. Soc. London, s. B., *229:* 275–322. p. 700.

Lloyd, F. E., 1942. The Carnivorous Plants. Waltham, Mass. Chron. Botanica. p. 232.

Loeb, Jacques, 1888. Die Orientierung der Thiere gegen das Licht und die Schwerkraft der Erde (thierischer Heliotropismus und thierischer Geotropismus). Sitzber. Phys.-Med. Ges. Würzburg, 1888: 1–10. p. 24.

——— 1918. Forced Movements, Tropisms and Animal Conduct. New York, Lippincott. pp. 24, 50.

——— and Northrup, J. R., 1917. On the Influence of Food and Temperature upon the Duration of Life. J. Biol. Chem., *32:* 103–121.

Loew, O., 1891. Die chemischen Verhältnisse des Bakterienlebens. Zentralbl. Bakteriol. u. Parasitenk., *9:* 757–760. p. 19.

Lohmann, H., 1901. Ueber das Fischen mit Netzen aus Müllergaze Nr. 20 zu dem Zwecke quantitativer Untersuchungen des Auftriebs. Wiss. Meeresunt., *5:* 45–66. p. 36.

——— 1912. Die Probleme der Modernen Planktonforschung. Verh. der Deutschen Zool. Ges., 1912: 16–109. p. 37.

Longley, W. H., 1922. The Instincts and Adaptations of Several Species of Tortugas Fishes. Anat. Rec., *23:* 131. p. 160.

Loosanoff, V. L., and Engle, J. B., 1947. Feeding of Oysters in Relation to Density of Microorganisms. Science, *105:* 260–261. p. 525.

Lorenz, Konrad, 1935. Der Kumpan in der

Umwelt des Vogels. J. Ornith., *83:* 137–213. p. 7.

Lorimer, Frank, and Osborn, F., 1934. Dynamics of Population. Social and Biological Significance of Changing Birth Rates in the United States. New York, Macmillan. p. 69.

Lotka, A. J., 1920. Analytical Notes on Certain Rhythmic Relations in Organic Systems. Proc. Nat. Acad. Sc., Washington, *7:* 410–415. p. 700.

—— 1925. Elements of Physical Biology. Baltimore, Williams & Wilkins. pp. 57, 60.

—— 1932. The Growth of Mixed Populations: Two Species Competing for a Common Food Supply. J. Wash. Acad. Sc., *22:* 461–469. p. 369.

—— 1934. Théorie analytique des associations biologiques. Actualités Scientifiques et Industrielles, *187:* 1–45. pp. 70, 326.

—— 1936. Modern Trends in the Birth Rate. Ann. Am. Acad. Polit. & Soc. Sc., 1936 (Nov.), 1–13. p. 288.

—— 1944. Evolution and Thermodynamics. Science & Society, *8:* 161–171. pp. 598, 728.

—— 1945. The Law of Evolution as a Maximal Principle. Human Biol., *17:* 167–194. pp. 598, 729.

Lowrie, D. C., 1942. The Ecology of the Spiders of the Xeric Dunelands in the Chicago Area. Bull. Chicago Acad. Sc., *6:* 161–189. p. 567.

Lubbock, John, 1883. Ants, Bees and Wasps. 6th ed. London, Paul and Trench. p. 24.

Lucas, C. E., 1938. Some Aspects of Integration in Plankton Communities. J. Conseil. Explor. Mer., *13:* 309–322. p. 71.

—— 1940. Ecological Investigations with the Continuous Plankton Recorder: the Phytoplankton in the Southern North Sea, 1932–37. Hull Bull. Marine Ecol., *1:* 73–170. pp. 317, 323.

Ludwig, Daniel, 1928. The Effects of Temperature on the Development of an Insect (*Popillia japonica* Newman). Physiol. Zoöl., *1:* 358–389. pp. 110, 111, 112.

—— 1937. The Effect of Different Relative Humidities on Respiratory Metabolism and Survival of the Grasshopper, *Chrotophaga viridifasciata* De Geer. Physiol. Zoöl., *10:* 342–351. p. 184.

Ludwig, Wilhelm, and Boost, Charlotte, 1939. Über das Wachstum von Protistenpopulationen und den allelokatalytischen Effekt. Archiv Protistenkunde, *92:* 453–484. p. 359.

Lull, R. S., 1920. Organic Evolution. New York, Macmillan. p. 466.

Lund, H. O., 1938. Studies on Longevity and Productivity in *Trichogramma evanescens.* J. Agr. Res., *56:* 421–440. p. 335.

Lundbeck, J., 1926. Die Bodentierwelt norddeutscher Seen. Arch. Hydrobiol., Suppl., *7:* 1–473. p. 452.

Lunn, Elizabeth T., 1939. The Ecology of the Forest Floor, with Special Reference to Microarthropods. Northwestern Univ., Summ. Doct. Diss., *7:* 233–237. pp. 480, 526.

Lutz, F. E., 1924. Apparently Non-selective Characters and Combinations of Characters, Including a Study of Ultraviolet in Relation to the Flower-Visiting Habits of Insects. Ann. New York Acad. Sc., *29:* 181–283. p. 715.

—— 1933. "Invisible" Colors of Flowers and Butterflies. Nat. Hist., *33:* 565–576. p. 715

—— 1933a. Experiments with "Stingless Bees" (*Trigona cressoni parastigma*) Concerning Their Ability to Distinguish Ultraviolet Patterns. Am. Mus. Novit., *641:* 1–26. p. 715.

Lutz, H. J., 1930. The Vegetation of Hearts Content, a Virgin Forest in Northwestern Pennsylvania. Ecology, *11:* 1–29. p. 575.

Luyet, B. J., and Gehenio, P. M., 1938. The Lower Limit of Vital Temperatures. A Review. Biodynamica, *1:* 1–92. pp. 98, 99, 103.

Lydekker, Richard, 1901. The New Natural History. New York, Merrill and Baker, 6 vols. p. 514.

Lyford, W. H., Jr., 1943. The Palatability of Freshly Fallen Forest Tree Leaves to Millipeds. Ecology, *24:* 252–261. p. 486.

Lyman, C. P., 1943. Control of Coat Color in the Varying Hare, *Lepus americanus* Erxl. Bull. Mus. Comp. Zool., *93:* 393–461. p. 122.

Lyman, F. E., 1943. Swimming and Burrowing Activities of May Fly Nymphs of the Genus Hexagenia. Ann. Ent. Soc. Amer., *36:* 250–256.

Lyon, M. W., 1936. Mammals of Indiana. Am. Mid. Nat., *17:* 1–384. p. 608.

Lyon, T. L., and Buckman, H. O., 1927. The Nature and Properties of Soil. New York, Macmillan. pp. 216, 220, 222.

Lysenko, T. D., 1946. Heredity and Its Variability. New York, King's Crown Press. [Translated from the Russian by Th. Dobzhansky.] p. 599.

MacArthur, J. W., and Baillie, W. H. T., 1926. Sex Differences in Mortality and Metabolic Activity in *Daphnia magna.* Science, *64:* 229–230. p. 114.

—— 1929. Metabolic Activity and Duration of Life. J. Exper. Zool., *53:* 243–268. pp. 113, 114.

MacBride, E. W., 1936. A Discussion on the Present State of the Theory of Natural Selection. Proc. Roy. Soc., London, s. B., *121:* 69–72. p. 599.

—— 1936a. Insect Colouration and Natural Selection. Nature, *138:* 365–366. p. 599.

Macdonald, G. A., Shephard, F. P., and Cox, D. C., 1947. The Tsunami of April 1, 1946, in the Hawaiian Islands. Pac. Sc., 1: 21–37. pp. 131, 578.

MacFarlane, R., 1905. Notes on Mammals Collected in the Northern Mackenzie River District, Northwest Territories of Canada, with Remarks on Explorers and Explorations of the Far North. Proc. U. S. Nat. Mus., 28: 673–764. p. 374.

MacGill, Elsie I., 1945. On the Biology of *Dysdercus howardi*, Ballou. III. The Effect of Temperature and Humidity on the Life-Cycle. Bull. Ent. Res., 35: 301–308. p. 188.

MacGillivray, A. D., 1916. Guide to the Insects of Connecticut. Part III. The Hymenoptera. Tenthredinoidea. Bull. Connecticut Geol. & Nat. Hist. Surv., 22: 25–175. p. 494.

MacGinitie, G. E., 1939. Littoral Marine Communities. Am. Mid. Nat., 21: 28–55. p. 160.

MacLagen, D. S., 1932. The Effect of Population Density upon Rate of Reproduction with Special Reference to Insects. Proc. Roy. Soc., London, s. B., 111: 437–454. pp. 404, 405.

—— 1940. Sunspots and Insect Outbreaks; An Epidemiological Study. Proc. Univ. of Durham Philosophical Soc., 10: 173–199. p. 367.

—— and Dunn, E., 1936. The Experimental Analysis of the Growth of an Insect-Population. Proc. Roy. Soc., Edinburgh, 55: 126–139. pp. 350, 405.

MacLulich, D. A., 1937. Fluctuations in the Numbers of the Varying Hare (*Lepus americanus*). Univ. of Toronto Studies, Biol. Ser., No. 43. pp. 71, 87, 269, 323, 367, 374.

Macnab, J. A., 1944. Faunal Aspection in the Coast Range Mountains of Northwestern Oregon. Ph.D. thesis, Univ. of Nebraska.

McAnally, R. A., and Phillipson, A. T., 1944. Digestion in the Ruminant. Biol. Rev., 19: 41–54. p. 716.

McAtee, W. L., 1907. Census of Four Square Feet. Science, 26: 447–449. p. 48.

—— 1917. Showers of Organic Matter. Monthly Weath. Rev., 45: 217–224. p. 149.

—— 1932. Effectiveness in Nature of the So-called Protective Adaptations in the Animal Kingdom, Chiefly as Illustrated by the Food Habits of Nearctic Birds. Smithsonian Misc. Coll., 85(7): 1–201. pp. 514, 517.

—— 1936. The Malthusian Principle in Nature. Scient. Monthly, 42: 444–456. p. 375.

—— 1937. Survival of the Ordinary. Quart. Rev. Biol., 12: 47–64. p. 71.

—— 1947. The Cats-to-Clover Chain. Scient. Monthly, 65: 241–242. p. 514.

McClintock, Barbara, 1944. The Relation of Homozygous Deficiencies to Mutations and Allelic Series in Maize. Genetics, 29: 478–502. p. 681.

McClure, H. E., 1937. Barren Land Bogs. The Beaver, 1937 (Mar.), 2–8.

—— 1943. Ecology and Management of the Mourning Dove, *Zenaidura macroura* (Linn.), in Cass County, Iowa. Iowa State Coll. Res. Bull., 310: 357–415. p. 339.

—— 1945. Effects of a Tornado on Bird Life. Auk, 62: 414–418. p. 147.

McColloch, J. W., and Hayes, W. P., 1922. The Reciprocal Relation of Soil and Insects. Ecology, 3: 288–301. pp. 485, 487.

McCook, H. C., 1877. Mound-Making Ants of the Alleghenies, Their Architecture and Habits. Tr. Entom. Soc. Amer., 6: 253–296. p. 559.

McCoy, O. R., 1932. Size of Infection as an Influence on the Persistence of Adult Trichina in Rats. Science, 75: 364–365. p. 401.

McDougall, K. D., 1943. Sessile Marine Invertebrates of Beaufort, North Carolina. Ecol. Monogr., 13: 321–374. p. 457.

McDougall, W. B., 1941. Plant Ecology. 3rd ed. Philadelphia, Lea and Febiger. p. 715.

McGibbon, W. H., 1944. Cellular Antigens in Species and Species Hybrids in Ducks. Genetics, 29: 407–419. p. 625.

McIndoo, N. E., 1923. Glandular Structure of the Abdominal Appendages of a Termite Guest (Spirachtha). Zoologica, 3: 367–381. p. 720.

McKendrick, A. G., 1940. The Dynamics of Crowd Infection. Edinburgh Med. J., 47: 117–136. p. 382.

McMurtrey, J. E., Jr., and Robinson, W. O., 1938. Neglected Soil Constituents that Affect Plant and Animal Development. Yearbook, U. S. Dept. of Agr., 1938: 807–830. p. 221.

McVaugh, Rogers, 1943. The Vegetation of the Granitic Flat-Rocks of the Southeastern United States. Ecol. Monogr., 13: 119–165. p. 463.

Machiavelli, N., 1882. History of Florence. Transl. by C. E. Detmold. Boston, Osgood. (Orig. ed. 1521–25). p. 25.

Maheu, Jacques, 1926. La flora cavernicole americaine. Bull. Soc. Bot. France, 73: 39–57. p. 439.

Malaquin, A., 1901. Le parasitisme évolutiv des Monstrillidae. Arch. Zool. Exper. Gen., 9: 81–232. p. 409.

Malthus, T. R., 1798. An Essay on the Principle of Population. London, Johnson. [Various ed., e.g., 1914, repr. of 7th ed., Everymans Library, 2 vols. 1909, New York, Macmillan, in Economic Classics.] pp. 25, 29, 271.

Mann, W. M., 1923. New Genera and Species of Termitophilous Coleoptera. Zoologica, 3: 323–366. p. 615.

Manning, W. M., and Juday, R. E., 1941. The Chlorophyll Content and Productivity of Some Lakes in Northeastern Wisconsin. Trans. Wis. Acad. Sc., *33*: 363–393. pp. 505, 507.

Manson-Bahr, P. H., 1940. Manson's Tropical Diseases. 11th ed. Baltimore, Williams & Wilkins. p. 628.

Marchal, P., 1897. L'équilibre numérique des espèces et ses rélations avec les parasites chez les insectes. C. R. Soc. Biol., Paris, *49*: 129. p. 28.

Marcovitch, S., 1923. Plant Lice and Light Exposure. Science, *58*: 537–538. p. 123.

Marlatt, C. L., 1907. The Periodical Cicada. Bull. Bur. Entom., U. S. Dept. Agr., *71*: 1–181. p. 543.

Marshall, F. H. A., 1936. Sexual Periodicity and the Causes which Determine It. Phil. Tr. Roy. Soc., London, s. B., *226*: 423–456. p. 684.

——— 1942. Exteroceptive Factors in Sexual Periodicity. Biol. Rev., *17*: 68–90. p. 689.

——— and Bowden, F. P., 1934. The Effect of Irradiation with Different Wave Lengths on the Oestrus Cycle of the Ferret, with Remarks on the Factors Controlling Sexual Periodicity. J. Exper. Biol., *11*: 409–422.

Martin, M., 1698. A Late Voyage to St. Kilda, the Remotest of All the Hebrides, or Western Isles of Scotland. London, Brown and Goodwin. p. 33.

Martin, W. E., 1944. Studies on Trematodes of Woods Hole. IV. Additional Observations upon *Cercaria loosii* Stunkard Developing in an Annelid. Tr. Am. Microsc. Soc., *63*: 237–243. p. 702.

Martynov, A. V., 1937. Wings of Termites and Phylogeny of Isoptera and of Allied Groups of Insects. "A l'Academicien N. V. Massonov." Moscow, Acad. Sc. USSR., pp. 83–150. p. 717.

Mashtaler, G. A., 1937. Pristosovni osoblivosti u gidri (*Hydra fusca* L.). [Adaptability in Hydra.] Works Odessa State Univ. (Biol.), *2*: 65–74. (Russian text, summary in English.) p. 255.

Mast, S. O., 1911. Light and the Behavior of Organisms. New York, Wiley. p. 50.

——— 1912. The Value of the Ciliate, *Didinium*, in the Study of Biology. Science, *36*: 871–873. p. 538.

——— 1917. The Relation between Spectral Color and Stimulation in the Lower Organisms. J. Exper. Zool., *22*: 471–528. p. 538.

——— and Pace, D. M., 1933. Synthesis from Inorganic Compounds of Starch, Fats, Proteins and Protoplasm in the Colorless Animal, *Chilomonas paramecium*. Protoplasma, *20*: 326–358. p. 345.

———, ——— 1938. The Effect of Substances Produced by *Chilomonas paramecium* on Rate of Reproduction. Physiol. Zoöl., *11*: 359–382. pp. 358, 406.

———, ——— 1946. The Nature of the Growth-Substance Produced by *Chilomonas paramecium*. Physiol. Zoöl., *19*: 223–235. pp. 358, 396, 408.

Masure, R. H., and Allee, W. C., 1934. The Social Order in Flocks of the Common Chicken and the Pigeon. Auk, *51*: 307–327. p. 413.

Mather, K., 1943. Polygenic Inheritance and Natural Selection. Biol. Rev., *18*: 32–64. pp. 602, 603, 677, 678, 683, 684, 689.

——— and Wigan, L. G., 1942. The Selection of Invisible Mutations. Proc. Roy. Soc. London, s. B., *131*: 50–64. p. 649.

Mather, K. F., 1939. Earth Structure and Earth Origin. Science, *89*: 65–70. p. 130.

Mathes, F. E., 1942. Glaciers. Meinzer, 1942, Hydrology, pp. 149–219. p. 178.

Matheson, Robert, 1930. The Utilization of Aquatic Plants as Aids in Mosquito Control. Am. Nat., *44*: 56–86. p. 193.

Matthew, W. D., 1915. Climate and Evolution. Ann. New York Acad. Sc., *24*: 171–328. [Republished 1939. Sp. Publ. New York Acad. Sc., *1*: 1–223.] pp. 464, 597.

Matthews, L. H., 1932. Lobster-Krill. Anomuran Crustacea that Are the Food of Whales. Discovery Repts., *5*: 467–484. p. 394.

——— 1944. Parturition in the Kangaroo. Proc. Zool. Soc., London, s. A., *113*: 117–120. p. 630.

Maury, M. F., 1858. Explanations and Sailing Directions to Accompany the Wind and Current Charts. 8th ed. Washington, Harris, 2 vols. p. 39.

Maxwell, Clerk, 1854. On a Particular Case of the Descent of a Heavy Body in a Resting Medium. Cambridge and Dublin Math. J., *9*: 145–148. [Also in Scientific Papers, *1*: 115–118.] p. 156.

Mayer, A. G., 1908. The Annual Breeding Swarm of the Atlantic Palolo. Papers Tortugas Lab., Carnegie Inst. Wash., *1*: 105–112. p. 544.

Mayr, Ernst, 1942. Systematics and the Origin of Species. New York, Columbia Univ. Press. pp. 70, 598, 606, 607, 608, 610, 611, 612, 613, 616, 619, 621, 626, 628, 676, 677.

——— 1944. Notes on the Zoogeography of Timor and Sumba. Bull. Am. Mus. Nat. Hist., *83*: 123–194. pp. 666, 726.

——— 1945. Birds of the Southwest Pacific. New York, Macmillan.

——— 1946. History of the North American Bird Fauna. Wilson Bull., *58*: 1–41. pp. 238, 662, 695, 723.

——— 1946a. Experiments on Sexual Isolation in Drosophila. VII. The Nature of the Isolating Mechanisms between Drosophila pseudoobscura and Drosophila persimilis. Proc. Nat. Acad. Sc., *32:* 128–137. p. 619.

—— 1947. Ecological Factors in Speciation. Evolution, *1* (4): 263–288. pp. 610, 611, 616.

—— 1948. The Bearing of the New Systematics on Genetical Problems. The Nature of Species in Demerec, M. (ed.): Advances in Genetics, *2:* 127–203. pp. 606, 659, 660.

—— and Serventy, D. L., 1944. The Number of Australian Bird Species. Emu, *44:* 33–40. p. 600.

Meek, A., 1930. The Progress of Life: A Study in Psycho-genetic Evolution. New York, Longmans. p. 660.

Meinertzhagen, R., 1927. Ladakh with Special Reference to Its Natural History. Geogr. J., *70:* 129–163. p. 147.

Meinzer, O. E., (Ed.), 1942. Hydrology. Physics of the Earth. 9, pp. 1–712. pp. 154, 178.

—— and Wenzel, L. K., 1942. Movement of Ground Water and Its Relation to Head, Permeability and Storage. In Meinzer, 1942, Hydrology, pp. 445–477. pp. 177, 178.

Mell, R., 1935. Grundzüge einer Oekologie der chinesischen Lepidopteren. 1. Die "bioklimatische Regel" und die Erscheinungszeiten von Lepidopteren. Biol. Zentralbl., *55:* 2–16. p. 118.

Mellanby, Kenneth, 1932. The Effect of Atmospheric Humidity on the Metabolism of the Fasting Mealworm (*Tenebrio molitor*). Proc. Roy. Soc., London, s. B., *111:* 376–390.

—— 1934. Effects of Temperature and Humidity on the Clothes Moth Larva, *Tineola biselliella* Hum. (Lepidoptera). Ann. Applied Biol., *21:* 476–482.

—— 1940. The Activity of Certain Arctic Insects at Low Temperature. J. Anim. Ecol., 9: 296–301. pp. 102, 558.

—— 1940a. The Daily Rhythm of Activity of the Cockroach, *Blatta orientalis* L. II. Observations and Experiments on a Natural Infestation. J. Exper. Biol., *17:* 278–286. p. 558.

Merriam, C. H., 1890. Results of a Biological Survey of the San Francisco Mountain Region and Desert of the Little Colorado, Arizona. North American Fauna, *3:* 1–136. p. 114.

—— 1892. The Geographic Distribution of Life in North America. Proc. Biol. Soc. Wash., 7: 1–64. [Repr. 1893, in Smithsonian Inst., Annual Rept., 1891: 365–415.] pp. 33, 114.

—— 1894. Laws of Temperature Control of the Geographic Distribution of Terrestrial Animals and Plants. Nat. Geog. Mag., *6:* 229–238. p. 114.

—— 1899. Life Zones and Crop Zones. Bull. Biol. Sur., *10:* 9–79. pp. 33, 114, 595.

—— 1899a. Zone Temperatures. Science, *9:* 116. p. 114.

Merwin, Ruth, M., 1945. Some Group Effects on the Rate of Cleavage and Early Development of Frog Eggs (*Rana pipiens*). Physiol Zoöl., *18:* 16–34. pp. 356, 402.

—— and Allee, W. C., 1943. The Effect of Low Concentrations of Carbon Dioxide on the Cleavage Rate in Frog's Eggs. Ecology, *24:* 61–69. p. 197.

Metcalf, C. L., and Flint, W. P., 1939. Destructive and Useful Insects: Their Habits and Control, 2nd ed. New York, McGraw-Hill. pp. 70, 514.

Meyer, K. F., 1925. The "Bacterial Symbiosis" in the Concretion Deposits of Certain Operculate Land Mollusks of the Families Cyclomastidae and Annulariidae. J. Infect. Dis., *36:* 1–107. p. 710.

Michaelis, L., 1930. Oxidation-Reduction Potentials. Philadelphia, Lippincott. p. 196.

Michal, K., 1931. Die Beziehung der Populationsdichte zum Lebensoptimum und Einfluss des Lebensoptimum auf das Zahlenverhältnis der Geschlechter bei Mehlwurm und Stubenfliege. Biol. Generalis, *7:* 631–646. p. 361.

Mikulski, J. S., 1936. The Effect of Constant and Alternating Temperatures on the Survival of Some Developmental Stages of *Tribolium confusum* Duval. Bull. Internat. Acad. Polonaise Sc. & Lettr., (math. natur) B, Sc. Nat., Pt. 2, 1936: 361–372. p. 110.

—— 1936a. On the Changes of Developmental Velocity of Some Developmental Stages of *Tribolium confusum* when Influenced by Constant and Alternating Temperatures. Bull. Internat. Acad. Polonaise Sc. & Lettr. (math. natur) B, Sc. Nat., Pt. 2, 1936: 373–385. p. 110.

Mill, J. S., 1848. (8th ed., 1879.) A System of Logic. New York, Harper. p. 42.

Miller, A. H., 1937. Structural Modifications in the Hawaiian Goose (*Nesochen sandvicensis*). A Study in Adaptive Evolution. Univ. of Calif. Publ. Zool., *42:* 1–80. p. 631.

—— 1938. Problems of Speciation in the Genus *Junco*. Proc. 8th Intern. Ornith. Congr. Oxford (1934): 277–284. p. 625.

—— 1939. Analysis of Some Hybrid Populations of Juncos. Condor, *41:* 211–214. p. 625.

—— 1942. Habitat Selection among Higher Vertebrates and Its Relation to Intraspecific Variation. Am. Nat., *76:* 25–35. p. 608.

—— 1946. Social Parasites among Birds. Scient. Monthly, *62:* 238–246. p. 676.

Miller, E. C., 1938. Plant Physiology. New

York, McGraw-Hill. pp. 103, 166, 190, 199, 206, 220.

Miller, E. M., 1940. Mortality of Fishes Due to Cold on the Southeast Florida Coast, 1940. Ecology, *21:* 420–421. p. 671.

—— 1942. The Problem of Castes and Caste Differentiation in Prorhinotermes simplex (Hagen). Bull. Univ. of Miami, *15:* 3–27. p. 428.

—— and Miller, D. B., 1943. A Preliminary Study on the Distribution and Habits of South Florida Termites. Proc. Fla. Acad. Sc., *6:* 101–107. p. 617.

Miller, M. A., 1933. A New Blind Isopod, *Asellus californicus,* and a Revision of the Subterranean Asellids. Univ. of Calif. Publ. Zool., *39:* 97–110. p. 674.

Miller, W. C., 1932. The Pupa-Case Building Activities of *Passalus cornutus* Fab. Ann. Entom. Soc. Amer., *25:* 709–713. p. 560.

Mills, A. S., 1929. Periodical Cicada Observations. J. Econ. Entom., *22:* 594. p. 543.

Milne-Edwards, H., 1857, 1881. Leçons sur la physiologie et l'anatomie comparée de l'homme et des animaux. Paris, Masson, 14 vols. p. 23.

Miner, J. R., 1933. Pierre-Francois Verhulst, the Discoverer of the Logistic Curve. Human Biology, *5:* 673–689. p. 25.

Möbius, Karl, 1877. Die Auster und die Austernwirtschaft. Berlin [Transl., 1880, The Oyster and Oyster Culture. Rept. U. S. Fish Comm., 1880: 683–751.] pp. 22, 35, 436, 508.

Moewus, F., 1933. Untersuchungen über die Sexualität und Entwicklung von Chlorophyceen. Arch. Protistenk., *80:* 469–526. p. 408.

—— 1940. Carotinoid-Derivate als geschlechtsbestimmende Stoffe von Algen. Biol. Zentrabl., *60:* 143–166. p. 408.

Mohr, C. O., 1943. Cattle Droppings as Ecological Units. Ecol. Monogr., *13:* 275–298. pp. 469, 533, 567, 568, 569.

Mohr, E., 1933. The Status of the Wisent on December 31, 1932. J. Mammalogy, · *14:* 260–262. p. 400.

Moleschott, M. J., 1855. Recherches sur l'influence de la lumière sur la production de l'acide carbonique par les animaux. Ann. Sc. Nat., (Zool.) *4:* 209–224. p. 21.

Moore, C. R., and Quick, W. J., 1924. The Scrotum as a Temperature Regulator for the Testes. Am. J. Physiol., *68:* 70–79. p. 120.

——, Simmons, G. F., Wells, L. J., Zalesky, M., and Nelson, W. O., 1934. On the Control of Reproductive Activity in an Annual-Breeding Animal. Anat. Rec., *60:* 279–289. p. 103.

Moore, J. A., 1939. Temperature Tolerance and Rates of Development in the Eggs of Amphibia. Ecology, *20:* 459–478. p. 108.

—— 1941. Isolating Mechanisms in the Genus

Rana. Anat. Rec., 81 (Suppl.): 71. p. 620.

—— 1946. Incipient Intraspecific Isolating Mechanisms in Rana pipiens. Genetics, *31:* 304–326. p. 620.

—— 1946a. Hybridization between Rana palustris and Different Geographical Forms of Rana pipiens. Proc. Nat. Acad. Sc., *32:* 209–212. p. 620.

Moore, W. G., 1942. Field Studies on the Oxygen Requirements of Certain Fresh-Water Fishes. Ecology, *23:* 319–329. p. 343.

Mordvilko, A., 1928. The Evolution of Cycles and the Origin of Heterœcy (migrations) in Plant Lice. Ann. Mag. Nat. Hist., (10) *2:* 570–582. pp. 612, 699, 703.

—— 1934. On the Evolution of Aphids. Archiv Naturg. Abt. B, *3:* 1–60. pp. 699, 703.

—— 1935. Die Blattläuse mit unvollständigem Generationszyklus und ihre Entstehung. Ergeb. Fortschr. Zool., *8:* 36–328. p. 613.

Moreau, R. E., 1934. A Contribution to Tropical African Bird-Ecology. J. Anim. Ecol. *3:* 41–69. pp. 495, 701.

—— 1944. Clutch-Size: A Comparative Study, with Special Reference to African Birds. Ibis, 1944: 286–347. p. 685.

Morgan, Ann H., 1939. Field Book of Animals in Winter. New York, Putnams. pp. 69, 536.

Morgan, C. Lloyd, 1891. Animal Life and Intelligence. Boston, Ginn. p. 23.

—— 1894. An Introduction to Comparative Psychology. (2nd ed., 1906). New York, Scribners. p. 23.

—— 1933. The Emergence of Novelty. London, Williams and Norgate. p. 693.

Morgan, T. H., 1924. Are Acquired Characters Inherited? Yale Rev., July, 1924. p. 599.

—— 1930. The Apparent Inheritance of an Acquired Character and Its Explanation. Am. Nat., *64:* 97–114. p. 599.

—— 1932. The Scientific Basis of Evolution. New York, Norton. p. 598.

Morgan, W. T. J., 1944. Transformation of Pneumococcal Types. Nature, *153:* 763–764. p. 601.

Morland, D. M. T., 1930. On the Causes of Swarming in the Honey Bee (*Apis mellifera* L.): An Examination of the Brood Food Theory. Ann. Applied Biol., *17:* 137–149. pp. 423, 427.

Morris, H. W., 1920. Observations on the Insect Fauna of a Permanent Pasture in Cheshire. Ann. Applied Biol., *7:* 141–155. p. 473.

Morrison, J. P. E., 1932. A Report on the Mollusca of the Northeastern Wisconsin Lake District. Tr. Wis. Acad. Sc., *27:* 359–396. pp. 203, 204.

Mosauer, Walter, 1930. A Note on the Sidewinding Locomotion of Snakes. Am. Nat., *64:* 179–183. p. 669.

—— 1935. The Reptiles of a Sand Dune Area

and Its Surroundings in the Colorado Desert, California. Ecology, *16:* 13–27. p. 669.

Moulton, F. R. (editor), 1939. The Migration and Conservation of Salmon. Pub. Am. A. Adv. Sc., *8:* 1–106. p. 69.

—— 1939a. Problems of Lake Biology. Pub. Am. A. Adv. Sc., *10:* 1–142. p. 69.

—— 1942. Aerobiology. Pub. Am. A. Adv. Sc., *17:* 1–289. p. 148.

—— 1942a. Fluorine and Dental Health. Pub. Am. A. Adv. Sc., *19:* 1–101. p. 221.

Müller, Hermann, 1873. Die Befruchtung der Blumen durch Insekten and die gegenseitigen Anpassungen beider. Leipzig, Engelmann. p. 33.

—— 1883. The Fertilization of Flowers. Tr. by D'Arcy Thompson. London, Macmillan. p. 33.

Muller, H. J., 1939. Reversibility in Evolution Considered from the Standpoint of Genetics. Biol. Rev., *14:* 261–280. p. 679.

—— 1942. Isolating Mechanisms, Evolution and Temperature. Biol. Symposia, *6:* 71–125. pp. 606, 616, 625, 676, 677.

—— 1948. The Crushing of Genetics in the USSR. Bull. Atomic Scientists, *12:* 369–371. p. 694.

Müller, P. E., 1870. Note sur les Cladocères des grands lacs de la Suisse. Arch. Sci. Phys. & Nat., *37:* 317–340. pp. 40, 41.

Müntzing, Arne, 1937. Multiple Alleles and Polymeric Factors in Galeopsis. Hereditas, *23:* 371–400. p. 625.

Murphy, R. C., 1928. Antarctic Zoogeography and Some of Its Problems. In Problems of Polar Research. Am. Geog. Soc., Special Pub., *7:* 355–379. p. 179.

—— 1936. Oceanic Birds of South America. New York, Am. Mus. Nat. Hist. 2 vols. pp. 609, 644.

—— 1938. The Need of Insular Exploration as Illustrated by Birds. Science, *88:* 533–539. p. 725.

Murray, John, 1895. Report on the Scientific Results of the Voyage of H.M.S. Challenger. A Summary of the Scientific Results. Part I. London, H. M. Stationary office. pp. 37, 39.

—— and Hjort, J., 1912. Depths of the Ocean. London, Macmillan. pp. 37, 49, 137, 448, 450, 460, 596.

Muttkowski, R. A., 1918. The Fauna of Lake Mendota—A Qualitative and Quantitative Survey with Special Reference to the Insects. Tr. Wis. Acad. Sc., *19:* 374–482. p. 51.

Myers, George S., 1936. Report on the Fishes Collected by H. C. Raven in Lake Tanganyika in 1920. Proc. U. S. Nat. Mus., *84:* 1–15. p. 611.

Nabours, R. K., 1930. A Third Alternative: Emergent Evolution. Scient. Monthly, *31:* 453–456. p. 693.

—— 1930a. Emergent Evolution and Hybridism. Science, *71:* 371–375. p. 693.

Najjar, V. A., and Barrett, Rachel, 1945. The Synthesis of B Vitamins by Intestinal Bacteria. In Vitamins and Hormones, R. S. Harris and K. V. Thimann, ed. *3:* 23–48. p. 247.

Nash, C. B., 1944. Natural Selection and the Birth-Rate. Am. Nat., *78:* 534–543. p. 709.

Naumann, E., 1929. The Scope and Chief Problems of Regional Limnology. Int. Rev. ges. Hydrobiol. Hydrogr., *22:* 423–444.

—— 1932. Grundzuge der regionalen Limnologie. Die Binnengewässer, *11:* 1–176.

Neave, Ferris, 1944. Racial Characteristics and Migratory Habits in *Salmo gairdneri.* J. Fish. Res. Bd. Canada, *6:* 245–251. p. 619.

Needham, J. G., 1900. Insect Drift on the Shore of Lake Michigan. Occ. Mem. Chicago Entom. Soc., *1:* 1–8. p. 534.

—— 1904. Beetle Drift on Lake Michigan. Canad. Entom., *36:* 294–295. p. 534.

—— 1917. The Insect Drift of Lake Shores. Canad. Entom., *49:* 129–137. p. 534.

—— 1920. Burrowing Mayflies of Our Larger Lakes and Streams. Bull. U. S. Bur. Fisheries, *36:* 269–292. p. 50.

—— 1937. (ed.) Culture Methods for Invertebrate Animals. Ithaca, Comstock. p. 69.

—— and collaborators, 1941. A Symposium on Hydrobiology. Madison, Univ. of Wis. Press. p. 69.

——, Frost, S. W., and Tothill, Beatrice H., 1928. Leaf-Mining Insects. Baltimore, Williams & Wilkins. p. 491.

——, Juday, C., Moore, E., Sibley, C. K., and Titcomb, J. W., 1922. A Biological Survey of Lake George, N.Y. State of N.Y. Conservation Comm., 3–78. pp. 59, 92.

—— and Lloyd, J. T., 1916. The Life of Inland Waters. Ithaca, Comstock. pp. 37, 49.

Needham, Joseph, 1930. The Biochemical Aspect of the Recapitulation Theory. Biol. Rev., *5:* 142–158. pp. 677, 678.

—— 1931. Chemical Embryology. Cambridge, Cambridge Univ. Press, 3 vols.

—— 1943. Time: The Refreshing River. London, George Allen & Unwin, Ltd. pp. 598, 683, 693.

Nehring, Alfred, 1890. Ueber Tundren und Steppen der Jetzt-und Vorzeit, mit besonderer Berücksichtigung ihrer Fauna. Berlin, Rummler. p. 590.

Neumayer, G. von, 1906. Anleitung zu wissenschaftlichen Beobachtungen auf Reisen. 3rd ed. Hanover, 2 vols. p. 46.

Newbigin, M. I., 1913. Animal Geography. The Faunas of Natural Regions of the Globe. Oxford, Clarendon Press.

—— 1936. Plant and Animal Geography. London, Methuen. p. 216.

Newman, H. H., Freeman, F. N., and Holzinger, K. J., 1937. Twins: A Study of

Heredity and Environment. Chicago, Univ. of Chicago Press. p. 3.

Newton, Alfred, 1874. The Migration of Birds. Nature, *10:* 415–416. p. 21.

Newton, Margaret, and Johnson, T., 1944. Physiologic Specialization of Oat Stem Rust in Canada. Canad. J. Res., Sect. C. Bot. Sc., *22:* 201–216. p. 644.

Neyman, J., 1939. On a New Class of "Contagious" Distributions, Applicable in Entomology and Bacteriology. Ann. Math. Stat., *10:* 35–57. p. 365.

Nice, Margaret M., 1933. The Theory of Territorialism and Its Development. In Fifty Years' Progress of American Ornithology. Lancaster, A.O.U., pp. 89–100. p. 412.

——— 1934. Song Sparrows and Territory. Condor, *36:* 49–57. p. 605.

——— 1937. Studies in the Life History of the Song Sparrow I. Tr. Linn. Soc. New York, *4:* 1–247. pp. 326, 412, 605.

——— 1939. The Watcher at the Nest. New York; Macmillan. p. 412.

——— 1941. The Role of Territory in Bird Life. Am. Mid. Nat., *26:* 441–487. pp. 412, 605.

——— 1943. Studies in the Life History of the Song Sparrow. II. The Behavior of the Song Sparrow and Other Passerines. Tr. Linn. Soc. New York, *6:* 1–328. p. 411.

Nichol, Hugh, and Thornton, H. G., 1941. Competition between Related Strains of Nodule Bacteria and Its Influence on Infection of the Legume Host. Proc. Roy. Soc., London, s. B., *130:* 32–59. p. 711.

Nichols, G. E., 1917. The Interpretation and Application of Certain Terms and Concepts in the Ecological Classification of Plant Communities. Plant World, *20:* 305–319; 341–353. p. 577.

——— 1923. A Working Basis for the Ecological Classification of Plant Communities. Ecology, *4:* 11–23; 154–177. p. 531.

——— 1935. The Hemlock-White Pine-Northern Hardwood Region of Eastern North America. Ecology, *16:* 403–422. p. 575.

Nichols, J. T., 1931. Notes on the Flocking of Shore Birds. Auk, *48:* 181–185. pp. 415, 575.

Nicholson, A. J., 1933. The Balance of Animal Populations. J. Anim. Ecol., *2:* 132–178. pp. 71, 332, 371, 380, 710.

——— and Bailey, V. A., 1935. The Balance of Animal Populations. Part I. Proc. Zool. Soc., London, 1935: 551–598. pp. 380, 381, 384, 385, 700.

Nickles, J., 1865. Influence of Light on the Production of Proto-Organisms. Am. J. Sc., *89:* 79–97. p. 20.

Nielsen, E. S., 1934. Untersuchungen über die Verbreitung, Biologie und Variation der Ceratien im südlichen stillen Ozean. Dana Reports, *4:* 1–67. pp. 448, 502, 506.

Nikiforoff, C. C., 1938. Soil Organic Matter and Soil Humus. Yearbook, U. S. Dept. of Agr., 1938: 929–939. p. 225.

——— 1942. Soil Dynamics. Sigma Xi Quart., *30:* 36–50. pp. 216, 484.

Noble, G. K., 1931. The Biology of the Amphibia. New York, McGraw-Hill. p. 105.

——— 1939. The Role of Dominance in the Social Life of Birds. Auk, *56:* 264–273. p. 414.

——— and Bradley, H. T., 1933. The Mating Behavior of Lizards; Its Bearing on the Theory of Sexual Selection. Ann. New York Acad. Sc., *35:* 25–100. p. 552.

——— and Curtis, B., 1939. The Social Behavior of the Jewel Fish, *Hemichromis bimaculatus.* Bull. Am. Mus. Nat. Hist., *76:* 1–76. p. 689.

——— and Marshall, B. C., 1929. The Breeding Habits of Two Salamanders. Am. Mus. Nov., *347:* 1–12. p. 678.

Nordenskiold, Erik, 1932. The History of Biology: A Survey. New York, Knopf. pp. 16, 17.

Norman, J. R., 1931. A History of Fishes. London, Ernest Benn. p. 104.

Northrup, J. H., 1926. Carbon Dioxide Production and Duration of Life of *Drosophila* Cultures. J. Gen. Physiol., *9:* 319–324. p. 114.

Nott, J. C., 1848. On the Origin of Yellow Fever. New Orleans. Med. & Surg. J., *4:* 563–601. p. 28.

Novikoff, A. B., 1945. The Concept of Integrative Levels and Biology. Science, *101:* 209–215. p. 693.

——— 1945a. Continuity and Discontinuity in Evolution. Science, *102:* 405–406. p. 693.

Noyes, B., 1922. Experimental Studies on the Life-History of a Rotifer Reproducing Parthenogenetically *(Proales decipiens).* J. Exper. Zool., *35:* 225–255. p. 275.

Nuttall, G. H. F., 1899. On the Role of Insects, Arachnids, and Myriapods as Carriers in the Spread of Bacterial and Parasitic Diseases of Man and Animals—A Critical Historical Study. Johns Hopkins Hosp. Rep., *8:* 1–154. p. 29.

Odum, E. P., 1941, 1942. Annual Cycle of the Blackcapped Chickadee. Auk, *58:* 314–333; 518–535; *59:* 499–531. p. 413.

——— 1943. The Vegetation of the Edmund Niles Huyck Preserve, New York. Am. Mid. Nat., *29:* 72–88. p. 575.

Oesting, Ralph, and Allee, W. C., 1935. Further Analysis of the Protective Value of Biologically Conditioned Fresh Water for the Marine Turbellarian, *Procerodes wheatlandi.* IV. The Effect of Calcium. Biol. Bull., *68:* 314–326. pp. 169, 360.

Ogle, C., 1934. Climatic Influence on the Male Albino Mouse. Am. J. Physiol., *107:* 635–640.

Ohle, Waldemar, 1934. Chemische und physikalische Untersuchungen norddeutscher Seen. Arch. Hydrobiol., *26:* 386–464; 584–658. pp. 203, 205.

Olmsted, C. E., 1944. Growth and Development in Range Grasses. IV. Bot. Gaz., *106:* 46–74. p. 653.

Olson, H. W., 1928. The Earthworms of Ohio. Bull. Ohio Biol. Surv., *17:* 47–90. p. 484.

Oosting, H. J., 1948. The Study of Plant Communities: An Introduction to Plant Ecology. San Francisco, Freeman. pp. 345, 574, 577, 578.

—— and Anderson, L. E., 1939. Plant Succession on Granite Rock in Eastern North Carolina. Bot. Gaz., *100:* 750–768. p. 464.

Oparin, A. I., 1938. The Origin of Life. Tr. by Sergius Morgulis. New York, Macmillan. pp. 75, 663.

Ortman, A. E., 1905. The Mutual Affinities of the Species of the Genus *Cambarus,* and Their Dispersal over the United States. Proc. Am. Philos. Soc., *44:* 91–136.

Osborn, Fairfield, 1944. The Pacific World. New York, Norton. p. 142.

——1948. Our Plundered Planet. Boston, Little, Brown and Co., pp. 515, 578.

Osborn, Herbert, 1902. A Statistical Study of Variations in the Periodical Cicada. Science, *16:* 345–346. p. 543.

Ostenfeld, C. H., 1908. On the Ecology and Distribution of the Grass-Wrack (*Zostera marina*) in Danish Waters. Rep. Danish Biol. Sta., *16:* 1–62. p. 46.

Ottestad, Per, 1933. A Mathematical Method for the Study of Growth. Hvalrådets Skrifter, *7:* 30–54. p. 71.

Pace, D. M., 1944. The Relation between Concentration of Growth-Promoting Substance and Its Effect on Growth in *Chilomonas paramecium*. Physiol. Zoöl., *17:* 278–288. p. 358.

Packard, A. S., 1863. A List of Animals Dredged near Carabou Island, Southern Labrador during July and August, 1860. Canad. Nat., *8:* 401–429. p. 35.

—— 1888. The Cave Fauna of North America, with Remarks on the Anatomy of the Brain and Origin of the Blind Species. Mem. Nat. Acad. Sc., *4:* (Mem. 1): 1–156. pp. 36, 439.

—— 1894. On the Origin of the Subterranean Fauna of North America. Am. Nat., *28:* 727–751. p. 36.

Packard, W. H., 1905. On Resistance to Lack of Oxygen and on a Method of Increasing This Resistance. Am. J. Physiol., *15:* 30–41. p. 45.

Pantin, C. F. A., 1931. The Adaptation of *Gunda ulvae* to Salinity. I. The Environment. J. Exper. Biol., *8:* 63–72.

Pardi, L., 1948. Dominance Order in *Polistes* Wasps. Physiol. Zoöl., *21:* 1–13. pp. 411, 430.

Park, Orlando, 1929. Ecological Observations upon the Myrmecocoles of *Formica ulkei* Emery, Especially *Leptinus testaceus* Mueller. Psyche, *36:* 195–215. pp. 244, 514, 718.

—— 1930. Studies in the Ecology of Forest Coleoptera. Seral and Seasonal Succession of Coleoptera in the Chicago Area, with Observations on Certain Phases of Hibernation and Aggregation. Ann. Entom. Soc. Am., *23:* 57–80. pp. 436, 487, 534, 535, 537, 538, 542, 567.

—— 1931. The Measurement of Daylight in the Chicago Area and Its Ecological Significance. Ecol. Monogr., *1:* 189–230. pp. 91, 231, 436, 480, 535, 536, 567.

—— 1931a. Studies in the Ecology of Forest Coleoptera. II. The Relation of Certain Coleoptera to Plants for Food and Shelter, Especially Those Species Associated with Fungi in the Chicago Area. Ecology, *12:* 188–207. pp. 436, 437, 514, 533, 567, 570.

—— 1932. The Myrmecocoles of *Lasius umbratus mixtus aphidicola* Walsh. Ann. Ent. Soc. Amer., *25:* 77–88. pp. 514, 720.

—— 1935. Studies in Nocturnal Ecology. III. Recording Apparatus and Further Analysis of Activity Rhythm. Ecology, *16:* 152–163. p. 560.

—— 1935a. Beetles Associated with the Mound-Building Ant, *Formica ulkei* Emery. Pschye, *42:* 216–231. p. 514.

—— 1937. Studies in Nocturnal ecology. VI. Further Analysis of Activity in the Beetle, *Passalus cornutus,* and Description of Audio-Frequency Recording Apparatus. J. Anim. Ecol., *6:* 239–253. pp. 188, 480, 558, 560.

—— 1938. Studies in Nocturnal Ecology. VII. Preliminary Observations on Panama Rain Forest Animals. Ecology, *19:* 208–223. pp. 547, 549, 550.

—— 1940. Nocturnalism—The Development of a Problem. Ecol. Monogr., *10:* 485–536. pp. 71, 546, 553, 557, 558, 661.

—— 1941. Quantitative Determination of Rhythmicity in Organisms. Ohio. J. Sc., *41:* 39–45. pp. 546, 558.

—— 1941a. Concerning Community Symmetry. Ecology, *22:* 164–167. pp. 72, 439, 558, 560, 561, 578.

—— 1942. A Study in Neotropical Pselaphidae. Northwestern Univ. Stud. Biol. & Med., *1:* 1–403. p. 557.

—— 1947. The Pselaphid at Home and Abroad. Sci. Mon., *65:* 27–42. p. 487.

——, Allee, W. C., and Shelford, V. E., 1939. A Laboratory Introduction to Animal Ecology and Taxonomy. Chicago, Univ. of Chicago Press. pp. 69, 203, 502, 514, 522, 531.

——, Barden, A. A., Jr., and Williams, E. C., Jr., 1940. Studies in Nocturnal Ecology.

IX. Further Analysis of Activity of Panama Rain Forest Animals. Ecology, *21:* 122–134. pp. 480, 488, 547, 548, 549.

Park, Orlando, Lockett, J. A., and Myers, D. J., 1931. Studies in Nocturnal Ecology with Special Reference to Climax Forest. Ecology, *12:* 709–727. pp. 480, 546, 549, 550, 551, 559.

—— and Noskin, Vivian, 1947. Studies in Nocturnal Ecology, XIV. Activity of the Flour Beetle, *Tribolium confusum,* as a Test of a Theory of Activity. Anat. Rec., *99:* 89. pp. 558, 559.

——, Roberts, T. W., and Harris S. J., 1941. Preliminary Analysis of Activity of the Cave Crayfish, *Cambarus pellucidus.* Am. Nat., *75:* 154–171. pp. 439, 558, 559.

—— and Sejba, O., 1935. Studies in Nocturnal Ecology. IV. *Megalodacne heros.* Ecology, *16:* 164–172. p. 547.

—— and Strohecker, H. F., 1936. Studies in Nocturnal Ecology. V. An Experiment in Conducting Field Classes at Night. Ohio J. Sc., *36:* 46–54. pp. 67, 206, 480, 514, 547, 549, 557, 559.

Park, Thomas, 1932. Studies in Population Physiology: The Relation of Numbers to Initial Population Growth in the Flour Beetle, *Tribolium confusum* Duval. Ecology, *13:* 172–181. p. 404.

—— 1933. Studies in Population Physiology. II. Factors Regulating Initial Growth of *Tribolium confusum* Populations. J. Exper. Zool., *65:* 17–42. pp. 364, 371, 404, 405.

—— 1939. Analytical Population Studies in Relation to General Ecology. Am. Mid. Nat., *21:* 235–255. pp. 72, 264, 302.

—— 1941. The Laboratory Population as a Test of a Comprehensive Ecological System. Quart. Rev. Biol., *16:* pt. 1, 274–293; pt. II, 440–461. pp. 71, 72, 353, 406.

—— 1942. Integration in Infra-Social Insect Populations. Biol. Symposia, *8:* 121–138. p. 272.

—— 1945. Ecological Aspects of Population Biology. Scient. Monthly, *60:* 311–313. p. 684.

—— 1945a. A Further Report on Toleration Experiments by Ecology Classes. Ecology, *26:* 305–308. pp. 539, 652.

—— 1946. Some Observations on the History and Scope of Population Ecology. Ecol. Monogr., *16:* 313–320. pp. 68, 346.

—— 1948. Experimental Studies of Interspecies Competition. I. Competition between Populations of the Flour Beetles, *Tribolium confusum* Duval and *Tribolium castaneum* Herbst. Ecol. Monogr., *18:* 265–308. pp. 369, 370, 656, 727.

—— and Burrows, W., 1942. The Reproduction of *Tribolium confusum* Duval in a Semisynthetic Wood-Dust Medium. Physiol. Zoöl., *15:* 476–484. p. 355.

—— Gregg, R. E., and Lutherman, C. Z., 1940. Toleration Experiments by Ecology Classes. Ecology, *21:* 109–111. p. 539.

——, Gregg, E. V., and Lutherman, C. Z., 1941. Studies in Population Physiology. X. Inter-Specific Competition in Populations of Granary Beetles. Physiol. Zoöl., *14:* 395–430. pp. 319, 329, 368, 369.

——, Miller, E. V., and Lutherman, C. Z., 1939. Studies in Population Physiology. IX. The Effect of Imago Population Density on the Duration of the Larval and Pupal Stages of *Tribolium confusum* Duval. Ecology, *20:* 365–373. p. 353.

—— and Woollcott, Nancy, 1937. Studies in Population Physiology. VII. The Relation of Environmental Conditioning to the Decline of *Tribolium confusum* Populations. Physiol. Zoöl., *10:* 197–211. p. 353.

Parker, G. H., 1948. Animal Colour Changes and Their Neurohumours. Cambridge University Press. pp. 634, 653.

Parker, H. W., 1935. A New Melanic Lizard from Transjordania and Some Speculations Concerning Melanism. Proc. Zool. Soc., London, 1935: 137–142. p. 590.

Parker, J. R., 1930. Some Effects of Temperature and Moisture upon *Melanoplus mexicanus* Saussaure and *Camnula pellucida* Scudder (Orthoptera). Bull., Univ. of Montana. Agr. Exper. Sta., *223:* 1–132. pp. 102, 110, 111, 113.

Parr, A. E., 1926. Adaptiogenese und Phylogenese; zur Analyse der Anpassungserscheinungen und ihre Entstehung. Abh. Theor. organ. Ent., *1:* 1–60. pp. 642, 645.

Parr, L. W., 1938. "Citrate" Mutation in Bacteria. Heredity, *29:* 381–384. p. 628.

Patch, Edith M., 1910. Gall aphids of the elm. Bull. Maine Agr. Exper. Sta., *181:* 193–240. p. 613.

—— 1938. Food-Plant Catalogue of the Aphids of the World. Bull. Maine Agr. Exper. Sta., *393:* 1–431. pp. 494, 699.

Patten, William, 1916. Cooperation as a Factor in Evolution. Proc. Am. Philos. Soc., *55:* 503–532. p. 32.

—— 1920. The Grand Strategy of Evolution. Boston, Badger.

Patterson, J. T., 1942. Isolating Mechanisms in the Genus *Drosophila.* Biol. Symposia, *6:* 271–287. p. 606.

—— 1943. Studies in the Genetics of Drosophila. III. The Drosophilidae of the Southwest. Univ. of Texas Pub., 4313. p. 366.

—— 1946. A New Type of Isolating Mechanism in Drosophila. Proc. Nat. Acad. Sc., *32:* 202–208. p. 622.

—— 1947. The Insemination Reaction and Its Bearing on the Problem of Speciation in the Mulleri Subgroup. Univ. of Texas Pub. *4720:* 41–77. p. 622.

——, McDanald, Linda W., and Stone, W. S., 1947. Sexual Isolation between Members of the Virilis Group of Species. Univ. of Texas Pub., *4720:* 7–31. p. 619.

—— and Wheeler, M. R., 1947. Two Strains of Drosophila peninsularis with Incipient Reproductive Isolation. Univ. of Texas Pub., *4720:* 116–125. p. 623.

Pauchon, A., 1880. Recherches sur le rôle de la lumière dans la germination. Paris. p. 18.

Pavan, C., 1946. Observations and Experiments on the Cave Fish *Pimelodella kronei* and Its Relatives. Am. Nat., *80:* 343–361. pp. 673, 674.

Pavillard, J., 1935. Remarques sur le phytoplankton du Pacific intertropical. Ecology, *16:* 308–316. pp. 447, 448.

Pavlychenko, T. K., 1937. Quantitative Study of the Entire Root System of Weed and Crop Plants under Field Conditions. Ecology, *18:* 62–79. pp. 466, 467.

Payne, Nellie M., 1926. Freezing and Survival of Insects at Low Temperatures. Quart. Rev. Biol., *1:* 270–282. pp. 102, 538.

—— 1927. Measures of Insect Cold Hardiness. Biol. Bull., *52:* 449–457. p. 538.

—— 1927a. Two Factors of Heat Energy Involved in Insect Cold Hardiness. Ecology, *8:* 194–196. p. 538.

—— 1928. Cold Hardiness in the Japanese Beetle, *Popilia japonica* Newman. Biol. Bull., *55:* 163–179. p. 538.

—— 1929. Absolute Humidity as a Factor in Insect Cold Hardiness with a Note on the Effect of Nutrition on Cold Hardiness. Ann. Entom. Soc. Amer., *22:* 601–620. p. 538.

Pearls, L. M., 1927. Some Phases of the Relation of Temperature to the Development of Insects. Bull., West Va. Agr. Exper. Sta., *208:* 1–62. p. 110.

Pearl, Raymond, 1903. The Movements and Reactions of Fresh-Water Planarians: A Study in Animal Behaviour. Quart. J. Microsc. Sc., *46:* 509–714. p. 45.

—— 1914. The Service and Importance of Statistics to Biology. Quart. Pub. Am. Statis. A., *1914:* 40–48. p. 55.

—— 1921. The Vitality of the Peoples of America. Am. J. Hyg., *1:* 592–674.

—— 1922. The Biology of Death. Philadelphia, Lippincott. p. 56.

—— 1924. Studies in Human Biology. Baltimore, Williams & Wilkins. pp. 56, 302.

—— 1928. The Rate of Living. New York, Knopf. pp. 56, 275.

—— 1930. The Biology of Population Growth. New York, Knopf. (First edition, 1925.) pp. 56, 61, 307, 313, 318, 347.

—— 1930a. Requirements of a Proof that Natural Selection Has Altered a Race. Scientia, *47:* 175–186. pp. 640, 641, 647, 685, 692.

—— 1932. The Influence of Density of Population upon Egg Production in *Droso-*

phila melanogaster. J. Exper. Zool., *63:* 57–84. p. 349.

—— 1937. On Biological Principles Affecting Populations: Human and Other. Am. Nat., *71:* 50–68. pp. 71, 264.

—— 1939. The Natural History of Population. London, Oxford Univ. Press. p. 69.

—— 1940. Introduction to Medical Biometry and Statistics. 3rd ed. Philadelphia, W. B. Saunders Company. pp. 288, 289, 292, 294, 295, 301.

—— and Doering, C. R., 1923. A Comparison of the Mortality of Certain Lower Organisms with That of Man. Science, *57:* 209–212. p. 275.

—— and Gould, Sophia A., 1936. World Population Growth. Human Biology, *8:* 399–419. p. 313.

—— and Miner, J. R., 1935. Experimental Studies on the Duration of Life. XIV. The Comparative Mortality of Certain Lower Organisms. Quart. Rev. Biol., *10:* 60–79. p. 71.

——, ——, and Parker, S. L., 1927. Experimental Studies on the Duration of Life. XI. Density of Population and Life Duration in *Drosophila.* Am. Nat., *61:* 289–318. p. 403.

—— Park, T., and Miner, J. R., 1941. Experimental Studies on the Duration of Life. XVI. Life Tables for the Flour Beetle *Tribolium confusum* Duval. Am. Nat., *75:* 5–19. p. 298.

—— and Parker, S. L., 1922. Experimental Studies on the Duration of Life. IV. Data on the Influence of Density of Population on the Duration of Life in *Drosophila.* Am. Nat., *56:* 312–321. pp. 349, 396.

——, —— 1924. Experimental Studies on the Duration of Life. X. The Duration of Life of *Drosophila melanogaster* in the Complete Absence of Food. Am. Nat., *58:* 193–218. p. 275.

—— and Reed, L. J., 1920. On the Rate of Growth of the Population of the United States since 1790 and Its Mathematical Representation. Proc. Nat. Acad. Sc., *6:* 275–288. pp. 25, 27, 302.

——, —— 1923. On the Mathematical Theory of Population Growth. Metron., *3:* 6–19.

——, —— and Kish, J. F., 1940. The Logistic Curve and the Census Count of 1940. Science, *92:* 486–488. p. 313.

Pearse, A. S., 1920. Distribution and Food of the Fishes of Green Lake, Wisconsin, in Summer. Bull. U. S. Bur. Fish., *37:* 255–272. p. 194.

—— 1926. Animal Ecology. (2nd ed., 1939.) New York. McGraw-Hill. pp. 42, 55, 69, 161, 167, 171, 254, 272, 411.

—— 1936. The Migration of Animals from Sea to Land. Durham, N. C., Duke Univ. Press. pp. 69, 583.

—— 1939. Animal Ecology. 2nd ed. New

York, McGraw-Hill. pp. 441, 466, 528, 539, 542, 544, 570, 572, 578.

Pearse, A. S., 1942. Introduction to Parasitology. Springfield, Thomas. p. 258.

—— 1943. Effects of Burning-over and Raking-off Litter on Certain Soil Animals in the Duke Forest. Am. Mid. Nat., 29: 406–424. pp. 479, 480, 484.

—— 1946. Observations on the Microfauna of the Duke Forest. Ecol. Monogr., 16: 127–150. p. 484.

—— and Achtenberg, H., 1920. Habits of Yellow Perch in Wisconsin Lakes. Bull. U. S. Bur. Fish., 36: 293–366. p. 50.

——, Humm, H. J., and Wharton, G. W., 1942. Ecology of Sand Beaches at Beaufort, North Carolina. Ecol. Monogr., 12: 135–190. pp. 457, 500.

——, Patterson, M. T., Rankin, J. S., and Wharton, G. W., 1936. Ecology of Passalus cornutus Fabricius, a Beetle which Lives in Rotting Logs. Ecol. Monogr., 6: 455–490. p. 560.

Pearson, Karl, 1937. The Grammar of Science. London, Dent (Everyman's Library Edition; first ed. 1892) p. 5.

Peckham, G. W., and Peckham, Elizabeth G., 1898. On Instincts and Habits of the Solitary Wasps. Bull. Wis. Geol. Nat. Hist. Surv., 2: 1–245. pp. 24, 33, 518, 550.

——, —— 1905. Wasps, Social and Solitary. Boston, Houghton, Mifflin. pp. 24, 33.

Pennak, R. W., 1939. The Microscopic Fauna of the Sandy Beaches. Pub. Am. A. Adv. Sc., 10: 94–106. p. 452.

—— 1946. The Dynamics of Fresh-Water Plankton Populations. Ecol. Monogr., 16: 339–355. pp. 504, 534.

Peters, N., 1934. Die Bevölkerung des Südatlantischen Ozeans mit Ceratien. Wiss. Ergeb. deut. atlant. Exped. Meteor. 1925–1927, 11: 1–69. p. 502.

Petersen, C. G. J., 1889–1893. Det Videnskabelige Udbytte af Kanonbaaden "Hauchs" Tvogter i de Danske Have Inderfor Skagen i Aarene 1883–1886 . . . Copenhagen. p. 36.

—— 1913. Valuation of the Sea. II. The Animal Communities of the Sea Bottom and Their Importance for Marine Zoogeography. København Ber. Biol. Stat., 21: 1–44; Appendix, 1–68. pp. 160, 458.

—— 1914. [The Animal Associations of the Sea-Bottom in the North Atlantic.] København Ber. Biol. Stat., 22: 89–96. p. 458.

—— 1915. On the Animal Communities of the Sea Bottom in the Skagerak, the Christiana Fjord and the Danish Waters. København Ber. Biol. Stat., 23: 1–28. pp. 160, 458.

—— 1915a. A Preliminary Report of the Investigations on the Valuation of the Sea. København Ber. Biol. Stat., 23: 29–32. p. 458.

—— 1918. Havbunden og Fiskenes Ernaering.

København Ber. Biol. Stat., 25: 1–57. p. 458.

—— 1918a. The Sea Bottom and Its Production of Fish Food. København Ber. Biol. Stat., 26: 1–62. p. 458.

—— and Jensen, P. B., 1911. Valuation of the Sea. 1. Animal Life of the Sea-Bottom, Its tion of Fish Food. København Ber. Biol. Stat., 20: 1–76. p. 51.

Petersen, Walburga, 1926. Seasonal Succession of Animals in a Chara-Cattail Pond. Ecology, 7: 371–377. p. 530.

—— 1929. The Relation of Density of Population to Rate of Reproduction in Paramecium caudatum. Physiol. Zoöl., 2: 221–254. pp. 358, 402.

Petersen, Wilhelm, 1932. Die Arten der Gattung Swammerdamia Hb. (Lep.). Mit Bemerkungen zur Mutationslehre. Arch. Naturg., (n.f.) 1: 197–224. p. 614.

Petry, E. J., and Visher, S. S., 1926. South Dakota. In Shelford, 1926, Naturalist's Guide to the Americas. pp. 548–556. p. 466.

Pfeffer, W. F. P., 1871. Die Wirkung farbigen Lichtes auf die Zersetzung der Kohlensäure in Pflanzen. Leipzig, Engelmann. p. 20.

—— 1877. Osmotische Untersuchungen. Leipzig, Engelmann. p. 20.

Pfeffer, W., 1900–1906. Physiology of Plants (Eng. ed.) Oxford, Clarendon Press, 3 vols. p. 19.

Phelps, Austin, 1946. Growth of Protozoa in Pure Culture. J. Exper. Zool., 102: 277–292.

Phifer, L. D., and Thompson, T. G., 1937. Seasonal Variation in the Surface Water Of San Juan Channel. J. Mar. Res., 1: 34–53. p. 200.

Philip, C. B., 1927. Diurnal Fluctuations in the Hydrogen Ion Activity of a Minnesota Lake. Ecology, 8: 73–89. pp. 547, 549.

Philip, George, 1934. Philip's Centenary General Atlas of the World, 4th ed. Chicago, Rand McNally. p. 458.

Philip, U. and Haldane, J. B. S., 1939. Relative Sexuality in Unicellular Algae. Nature, 143: 334. p. 408.

Phillips, E. F., and Demuth, G. S., 1914. The Temperature of the Honeybee Cluster in Winter. Bull. U. S. Dept. of Agr., 93: 1–16. p. 97.

Phillips, J. F. V., 1926. "Wild Pig" (Potamochoerus choeropotamus) at the Knysna: Notes by a Naturalist. So. Afr. J. Sc., 23: 655–660. p. 715.

—— 1934–1935. Succession, Development, the Climax, and the Complex Organism: An Analysis of Concepts. J. Ecol., 22: 554–571; 23: 210–246, 488–508. pp. 72, 564, 577, 582.

Pia, J., 1933. Kohlensäure und Kalk. Die Binnengewässer, 13: 1–183.

Picado, C., 1911. Bromeliacés épiphytes comme milieu biologique. Compt. rend. Acad. Sc., Paris, *153:* 960–963. p. 438.

—— 1913. Les Bromeliacés épiphytes considérées comme milieu biologique. Bull. Sc. Ent. France et Belgique, *7:* 215–360. p. 438.

Pickles, Walter, 1935. Populations, Territory and Interrelations of the Ants *Formica fusca, Acanthomyops niger* and *Myrmica scabrinodis* at Garforth (Yorkshire). J. Anim. Ecol., *4:* 22–31. p. 419.

—— 1936. Populations and Territories of the Ants, *Formica fusca, Acanthomyops flavus* and *Myrmica ruginodis,* at Thornhill (Yorks.) J. Anim. Ecol., *5:* 262–270. p. 419.

—— 1937. Populations, Territories and Biomasses of Ants at Thornhill, Yorkshire, in 1936. J. Anim. Ecol., *6:* 54–61. pp. 419, 525.

—— 1938. Populations, Territories and Biomasses of Ants at Thornhill, Yorkshire, in 1937. J. Anim. Ecol., *7:* 370–380. pp. 266, 419.

—— 1940. Fluctuations in the Populations, Weights, and Biomasses of Ants at Thornhill, Yorkshire, from 1935–1939. Tr. Roy. Entom. Soc., London, *90:* 467–485. p. 419.

Pielou, D. P., and Gunn, D. L., 1940. The Humidity Receptors of the Mealworm Beetle, *Tenebrio molitor.* I. The Reaction to Differences of Humidity. II. The Humidity Receptors. III. The Mechanism of the Reaction. J. Exper. Biol., *17:* 286–294; 295–306; 307–316. pp. 189, 558.

Pierce, W. D., Cushman, R. A., and Hood, C. E., 1912. The Insect Enemies of the Cotton Boll Weevil. U. S. Dept. of Agr., Bur. Entom. Bull., *100:* 1–99. p. 52.

Pieron, Henri, 1913. Le problème physiologique du sommeil. Paris. p. 553.

Pilsbry, H. A., 1894–1935. Manual of Conchology, Second Series, Vols. 5–52. Philadelphia, Acad. Nat. Sc. p. 609.

Pirsch, G. B., 1923. Studies on the Temperature of Individual Insects with Special Reference to the Honey Bee. J. Agr. Res., *24:* 275–288. p. 97.

Pirschle, K., 1938. Die Bedeutung der Spurenelemente für Ernährung, Wachstum und Stoffwechsel der Pflanzen. I. Li, Na, Rb, Cs, Be, Sr, Ba, B, As, Sb, Bi, Se, Te, Mo, W. Ergeb. Biol., *15:* 67–168. p. 205.

Pitelka, F. A., 1941. Distribution of Birds in Relation to Major Biotic Communities. Am. Mid. Nat., *25:* 113–137. p. 494.

Plate, Ludwig H., 1913. Selektionsprinzip und Probleme der Artbildung. Leipzig & Berlin, Engelmann. p. 638.

Plateau, F., 1871. Recherches physico-chimiques sur les articules aquatiques. Mém. Acad. Belgique, *36:* p. 20.

Plough, H. H., 1941. Spontaneous Mutability in *Drosophila.* Cold Spring Harbor Symposia on Quant. Biol., *9:* 127–136. p. 600.

—— 1942. Temperature and Spontaneous Mutation. Biol. Symposia, *6:* 9–20. p. 600.

Plunkett, C. R., 1926. The Interaction of Genetic and Environmental Factors in Development. J. Exper. Zool., *46:* 181–244. p. 408.

—— 1944. The Primary Physicochemical Basis of Organic Evolution, In Alexander, J., Colloid Chemistry, *5:* 1173–1197. p. 630.

Polimanti, O., 1911. Activité et repos chez les animaux marine. Bull. Inst. Gen. Psych., *11:* 125–163. p. 553.

Pólya, G., 1931. Sur quelques points de la théorie des probabilités. Ann. Inst. Henri Poincaré, *1:* 117–162. p. 365.

Pool, R. J., Weaver, J. E., and Jean, F. C., 1918. Further Studies in the Ecotone between Prairie and Woodland, Univ. of Nebraska Bot. Surv., *18:* 1–47. p. 477.

Pope, C. H., 1937. Snakes Alive and How They Live. New York, Viking. p. 537.

—— 1939. Turtles of the United States and Canada. New York, Knopf. p. 487.

—— 1941. Copulatory Adjustment in Snakes. Field Mus. Nat. Hist. (Zool.), *24:* 249–252. p. 618.

—— 1944. Amphibians and Reptiles of the Chicago Area. Chicago, Chicago Nat. Hist. Mus. p. 659.

Porter, K. R., 1941. Developmental Variations Resulting from the Androgenetic Hybridization of Four Forms of Rana pipiens. Science, *93:* 439. p. 677.

Portier, P., 1918. Les Symbiotes. Paris, Masson. p. 712.

Post, Hamp von, 1868. Försök till iakttagelser i djur-och växt-statistik. Öfversigt Svenska Vetenskaps akad., *24:* 53–79. p. 34.

Potter, Jane H., 1947. Some Observations on the Relation of Breed in Hens to Their Social Rank and to Their Success in Initial Pair Contacts. Master's thesis. Univ. of Chicago Libraries. p. 414.

—— 1949. Dominance Relations Between Different Breeds of Domestic Hens. Physiol. Zoöl., *22:* 261–279. p. 414.

Potzger, J. E., 1946. Phytosociology of the Primeval Forest in Central-Northern Wisconsin and Upper Michigan, and a Brief Post-Glacial History of the Lake Forest Formation. Ecol. Monogr., *16:* 211–250. p. 575.

—— and Wilson, I. T., 1941. Post-Pleistocene Forest Migration as Indicated by Sediments from Three Deep Inland Lakes. Am. Mid. Nat., *25:* 270–289. p. 545.

Pouchet, Georges, 1872. Note sur le rôle des nerfs dans les changements de coloration des poissons. J. Anat. Physiol., *8:* 71–74.

—— 1876. Changements de coloration sans l'influence des nerfs. J. Anat. Physiol., *12:* 1–90, 113–165. p. 22.

Pough, R. H., 1946. Audubon Bird Guide. Eastern Land Birds. New York, Doubleday. p. 539.

Pound, Roscoe, and Clements, F. E., 1898. A Method of Determining the Abundance of Secondary Species. Minn. Bot. Studies, 2: 19–24. p. 36.

Powell, W. M., and Clarke, G. L., 1936. The Reflection and Absorption of Daylight at the Surface of the Ocean. J. Optical Soc. Amer., 26: 111–120. p. 124.

Powers, E. B., 1934. Certain Conditions of Existence of Fishes, Especially as Concerns Their Internal Environment. Ecology, 15: 69–79.

—— 1939. Chemical Factors Affecting the Migratory Movements of the Pacific Salmon. Publ. Am. A. Adv. Sc., 8: 72–85. p. 175.

——, Rostorfer, H. H., Shipe, Lula M., and Rostorfer, Theresa H., 1938. The Relation of Respiration of Fishes to Environment. XII. Carbon Dioxide Tension as a Factor in Various Physiological Respiratory Responses in Certain Fresh-Water Fishes. J. Tennessee Acad. Sc., 13: 220–245.

Powsner, L., 1935. The Effects of Temperature on the Duration of Developmental Stages of Drosophila melanogaster. Physiol. Zoöl., 8: 474–512. pp. 107, 111.

Pratt, D. M., 1943. Analysis of Population Development in Daphnia at Different Temperatures. Biol. Bull., 85: 116–140. p. 334.

Pratt, Robertson, and Fong, Jane, 1940. Studies on Chlorella vulgaris. III. Growth of Chlorella and Changes in the Hydrogen-Ion and Ammonium-Ion Concentrations in Solutions Containing Nitrate and Ammonium Nitrogen. Am. J. Bot., 27: 735–743. p. 199.

Prenant, Marcel, 1934. Adaptation, écologie et biocoenotique. Actualités Sc. et Industr. Paris, Hermann. p. 70.

Prescott, G. W., 1939. Some Relationships of Phytoplankton to Limnology and Aquatic Biology. Pub. Am. A. Adv. Sc., 10: 65–78. pp. 203, 446, 505.

Preyer, W., 1886–1887. Ueber die Bewegungen der Seesterne. Mitth. Zool. Stat. Neapel, 7: 27–127, 191–233. p. 23.

—— 1891. Ueber die Anabiose. Biol. Zentrabl., 11: 1–5. p. 19.

Price, Dorothy, 1941. Rat Prostate and Seminal Vesicle Grafts in Relation to the Age and Sex of the Hosts. Physiol. Zoöl., 14: 145–162. p. 356.

Prytherch, H. F., 1934. The Role of Copper in the Setting, Metamorphosis and Distribution of the American Oyster, Ostrea virginica. Ecol. Monogr., 4: 47–107. pp. 205, 436.

Pütter, A., 1909. Die Ernährung der Wasser-tiere und der Stoffhaushalt der Gewässer. Jena, Fischer. p. 444.

—— 1911. Vergleichende Physiologie. Jena, Fischer. p. 49.

Quastel, J. H., 1947. The Metabolism of Nitrogen in Soil. Endeavour, 6: 129–134. p. 711.

Quayle, H. J., 1943. The Increase in Resistance in Insects to Insecticides. J. Econ. Ent., 36: 493–500. pp. 653, 654.

Quetelet, A., 1835. Sur l'homme et le développement de ses facultés ou essai de physique sociale. Paris, Bachelier, 2 vols. pp. 25, 26.

—— 1846. Sur le Climat de la Belgique. Des Phénomènes périodiques des plantes. Annales de l'Observatoire Royal de Bruxelles, 5: 1–183. p. 18.

Rahm, P. G., 1922. Biologische und physiologische Beiträge zur Kenntnis der Moosfauna. Ztschr. Allg. Physiol., 20: 1–34. p. 99.

Rahn, Otto, 1945. Microbes of Merit. Lancaster, Jacques Cattell Press. p. 497.

Raillet, A., 1895. Traité de zoologie médicale et agricole. 2nd ed. Paris, Assilin and Houzeau. p. 272.

Raitt, D. S., 1939. The Rate of Mortality of the Haddock of the North Sea Stock, 1919–38. Rapp. Conseil Explor. Mer., 110 p. 379.

Rakestraw, M. W., 1936. The Occurrence and Significance of Nitrite in the Sea. Biol. Bull., 71. 133–167. p. 200.

Ramaley, Francis, 1940. The Growth of a Science. Univ. of Colo. Studies, 26: 3–14. pp. 14, 15, 16.

Ramann, E., 1911. Regenwürmer und Kleintiere im deutschen Waldboden. Intern. Mitt. Bodenkunde, 1: 138–164. p. 484.

——, Schellhorn, C. R., and Krause, M., 1899. Anzahl und Bedeutung der niederen Organismen in Wald- und Moorböden. Ztschr. Forst. u. Jagdwes., 31: 575–606. p. 484.

Ranson, R. M., 1941. Pre-Natal and Infant Mortality in a Laboratory Population of Voles (Microtus agrestis). Proc. Zool. Soc., London, s. A., 111: 45–57. p. 279.

Rasmussen, A. T., 1916. Theories of Hibernation. Am. Nat., 50: 609–625. pp. 98, 105.

Rasquin, Priscilla, 1947. Progressive Pigmentary Regression in Fishes Associated with Cave Environments. Zoologica, 32: 35–42. p. 673.

Rau, Phil, 1935. Jungle Bees and Wasps of Barro Colorado Island (with Notes on Other Insects). Kirkwood, Missouri, The Author. p. 546.

—— 1945. The Yucca plant, Yucca filamentosa, and the Yucca Moth, Tegeticula (Pronuba) yuccasella Riley: An Ecologico-Behavior Study. Ann. Missouri Bot. Garden, 32: 373–394. p. 715.

—— and Rau, Nellie, 1916. The Sleep of Insects: An Ecological Study. Ann. Entom. Soc. Amer., 9: 227–274. p. 553.

Raunkiaer, C., 1934. The Life Forms of Plants and Statistical Plant Geography. Oxford, Clarendon Press. p. 518.

Raup, H. M., 1941. Botanical Problems in Boreal America. II. The Development and Distribution of Plant Communities. Bot. Rev., 7: 209–248. p. 83.

Raven, H. C., 1935. Wallace's Line and the Distribution of Indo-Australian Mammals. Bull. Am. Mus. Nat. Hist., 68: 179–293. p. 666.

Rawles, Mary, 1936. A Study in the Localization of Organ-Forming Areas in the Chick Blastoderm of the Head-Process Stage. J. Exper. Zool., 72: 271–315. p. 356.

Rawson, D. S., 1934. Productivity Studies in Lakes of the Kamloops Region, British Columbia. Bull. Biol. Bd. Can., 42: 1–31. p. 194.

—— 1939. Some Physical and Chemical Factors in the Metabolism of Lakes. Pub. Am. A. Adv. Sc., 10: 9–26. pp. 96, 194, 196, 444, 496.

Rayner, M. C., and Neilson-Jones, W., 1944. Problems in Tree Nutrition; An Account of Researches Concerned Primarily with the Mycorrhizal Habit in Relation to Forestry and with Some Biological Aspects of Soil Fertility. London, Faber and Faber. p. 712.

Réaumur, René, A. F. de, 1734–42. Mémoires pour servir à l'histoire des insectes. Paris, Impr. Royale, 6 vols. pp. 17, 18, 363.

—— 1735. Observations du thermômetre. Mem. Acad. Roy. Sc., Paris, pp. 545–576. pp. 18, 107.

—— 1926. The Natural History of Ants. Translated and annotated by W. M. Wheeler. New York, Knopf. p. 17.

Redfield, A. C., 1939. The History of a Population of Limacina retroversa during Its Drift across the Gulf of Maine. Biol. Bull., 76: 26–47. p. 366.

Reed, Guilford, and Klugh, A. B., 1924. Correlation between Hydrogen Ion Concentration and Biota of Granite and Limestone Pools. Ecology, 5: 272–275. p. 174.

Regan, C. T., 1937. Natural History. New York, Hillman-Curl.

Regnard, Paul, 1891. Recherches experimentales sur les conditions physiques de la vie dans les eaux. Paris, Acad. Med. p. 137.

Reich, Karl, 1938. Studies on the Physiology of Amoeba. II. The Allelocatalytic Effect in Amoeba Cultures Free of Bacteria. Physiol. Zoöl., 11: 347–358. pp. 358, 408.

Reid, W. M., 1945. The Relationship between Glycogen Depletion in the Nematode Ascaridia galli (Schrank) and Elimination of the Parasite by the Host. Am. J. Hyg., 41: 150–155.

Reighard, J., 1903. The Natural History of Amia calva Linnaeus. Mark Anniversary Volume, 57–109. p. 46.

Reinhard, H. J., 1927. The Influence of Parentage, Nutrition, Temperature and Crowding on Wing Production in Aphis gossypii Glover. Bull. Texas Agr. Exper. Sta., 353: 5–19.

Reinheimer, H., 1913. Evolution by Cooperation: A Study in Bio-economics. London, Paul, Trench, Trubner. p. 32.

Reinke, J., 1883, 1884. Untersuchungen über die Einwirkung des Lichtes auf die Sauerstoffausscheidung der Pflanzen. Part I. Mitt. Bot. Ztg., 41: 697–707, 713–723, 732–738; Part II, 42: 1–10, 17–29, 33–46, 49–59. p. 20.

Rensch, Bernhard, 1939. Typen der Artbildung. Biol. Rev., 14: 180–222. p. 638.

—— 1943. Die paläontologischen Evolutionsregeln in zoologischer Betrachtung. Biol. gen., 17: 1–55. p. 638.

Reynolds, W. E., 1920. The Cycles and Super-Cycles of Nature. Science Progress, 15: 250–264. p. 553.

Rhoad, A. O., 1941. Investigations in the Ecophysiology of Farm Animals under Gulf-Coast Climatic Conditions; A Scale of Heat Tolerance for Animals. MS. prepared for Ecol. Soc. Amer., Dallas Meeting, Dec. 1941. p. 104.

Rhodes, E. C., 1940. Population Mathematics. I. J. Roy. Statis. Soc., 103: 61–89. p. 72.

—— 1940a. Population Mathematics. II. J. Roy. Statis. Soc., 103: 218–245. p. 72.

—— 1940b. Population Mathematics. III. J. Roy. Statis. Soc., 103: 362–387. p. 72.

Ribbands, C. R., 1944. Differences between Anopheles melas and Anopheles gambiae. II. Salinity Relations of Larvae and Maxillary Palp Banding of Adult Females. Ann. Trop. Med. & Parasitol., 38: 87–99. p. 611.

Rice, Lucile, A., 1946. Studies on Deciduous Forest Animal Populations during a Two-Year Period with Differences in Rainfall. Am. Mid. Nat., 35: 153–171. p. 531.

Rice, T. D., and Alexander, L. T., 1938. The Physical Nature of Soil. In Soils and Men. Yearbook, U. S. Dept. of Agr., 1938: 887–928. p. 216.

Richards, O. W., 1932. The Second Cycle of Growth of a Population of Yeast. Archiv. Protist., 78: 263–301. p. 316.

Richardson, Frank, 1942. Adaptive Modifications for Tree-Trunk Foraging in Birds. Univ. of Calif. Publ. Zool., 46: 317–368. pp. 666, 668.

Ricker, W. E., 1934. A Critical Discussion of Various Measures of Oxygen Saturation in Lakes. Ecology, 15: 348–363.

—— 1937. Physical and Chemical Characteristics of Cultus Lake, British Columbia.

J. Fish. Res. Bd. Canada, 3: 450–468. p. 204.

Ricker, W. E., 1938. "Residual" and Kokanee Salmon in Cultus Lake. J. Fish. Res. Bd. Canada, 4: 192–218. pp. 617, 620.

—— 1940. On the Origin of Kokanee, a Fresh-Water Type of Sockeye Salmon. Tr. Roy. Soc., Canada, 34, Sect. 5: 121–135. p. 617.

—— 1940a. Relation of "Catch per Unit Effort" to Abundance and Rate of Exploitation. J. Fish. Res. Bd. Canada, 5: 43–70. p. 377.

Rickett, H. W., 1920. A Quantitative Survey of the Flora of Lake Mendota. Science, 52: 641–642. p. 462.

—— 1922. A Quantitative Study of the Larger Aquatic Plants of Lake Mendota. Tr. Wis. Acad. Sc., 20: 501–527. pp. 462, 504.

—— 1924. A Quantitative Study of the Larger Aquatic Plants of Green Lake, Wisconsin. Tr. Wis. Acad. Sc., 21: 381–414. pp. 462, 504.

Ridley, H. N., 1930. The Dispersal of Plants throughout the World. Ashford, Kent, Reeve. p. 714.

Riley, C. V., 1892. Parasitism in Insects. Proc. Ent. Soc., Wash., 2: 397–431. p. 518.

Riley, G. A., 1937. The Significance of the Mississippi River Drainage for Biological Conditions in the Northern Gulf of Mexico. J. Mar. Res., 7: 60–74. p. 201.

—— 1941. Plankton Studies. III. Long Island Sound. Bull. Bingham Oceanographic Collection, 7(3): 1–93. pp. 519, 521, 522.

—— 1941a. Plankton Studies. IV. Georges Bank. Bull. Bingham Oceanographic Collection, 7(4): 1–73. p. 522.

—— 1943. Physiological Aspects of Spring Diatom Flowerings. Bull. Bingham Oceanographic Collection, 8: 1–53. p. 313.

—— 1944. The Carbon Metabolism and Photosynthetic Efficiency of the Earth as a Whole. Am. Scientist, 32: 132–134. pp. 199, 522.

Riley, N. D., 1944. Minutes of Symposium on the Interrelations of Plants and Insects. Proc. Roy. Entom. Soc., London, s. C., 8: 54–55. p. 441.

Riley, W. A., and Johannsen, O. A., 1938. Medical Entomology; A Survey of Insects and Allied Forms which Affect the Health of Man and Animals. 2nd ed. New York, McGraw-Hill. pp. 70, 261, 514.

Risso, A., 1826. Histoire naturelle des principales productions de l'Europe mériodionale. Paris, Levrault, 5 vols.

Rivers, T. M., 1947. Epidemic Diseases. Proc. Am. Philos. Soc., 91: 88–94. p. 380.

Robb, R. C., 1935. A Study of Mutations in Evolution. Part I. Evolution of the Equine Skull. Part. II. Ontogeny in the Equine Skull. J. Genetics, 31: 39–46, 47–52. p. 637.

—— 1936. A Study of Mutations in Evolution.

Part 3. The Evolution of the Equine Foot. J. Genetics, 33: 267–273. p. 637.

—— 1937. A Study of Mutations in Evolution. Part 4. The Ontogeny of the Equine Foot. J. Genetics, 34: 477–486. pp. 637, 678, 679.

Robbins, W. J., 1944. The Importance of Plants. Science, 100: 440–443.

Roberts, B., 1940. The Breeding Behaviour of Penguins with Special Reference to Pygoscelis papua. Brit. Graham Land Exp. 1934–1937. Scientific Rept., 1: 195–254. p. 402.

Robertson, Charles, 1889–1898. Flowers and Insects. Bot. Gaz., 14: 297–304: 1889; 17: 65–71: 1892; 21: 72–81: 1896; 25: 229–245: 1898. p. 534.

—— 1928. Flowers and Insects. Ecology, 9: 505–527. p. 534.

—— 1929. Flowers and Insects; Lists of Visitors of 453 Flowers. Lancaster, Privately Printed. p. 534.

Robertson, F. W., and Sang, J. H., 1944. The Ecological Determinants of Population Growth in a Drosophila Culture. I. Fecundity of Adult Flies. Proc. Roy. Soc. London, s. B., 132: 258–277. pp. 347, 349, 396.

Robertson, J. H., and Pearse, C. K., 1945. Artificial Reseeding and the Closed Community. Northwest Sc., 19: 58–66. p. 723.

Robertson, T. B., 1921. Experimental Studies on Cellular Reproduction. II. The Influence of Mutual Contiguity upon Reproductive Rate in Infusoria. Biochem. J., 15: 612–619. p. 357.

—— 1923. The Chemical Basis of Growth and Senescence. Philadelphia, Lippincott. p. 56.

—— 1927. On Some Conditions Effecting the Viability of Infusoria and the Occurrence of Allelocatalysis therein. Australian J. Exper. Biol. & Med. Sc., 2: 83–90. pp. 402, 407, 408.

Robinson, G. W., 1936. Soils, Their Origin, Constitution, and Classification. London, Thomas Murby. pp. 216, 222.

Robinson, W., 1928. Water Conservation in Insects. J. Econ. Ent., 21: 897–902. p. 186.

Robson, G. C., and Richards, O. W., 1936. The Variation of Animals in Nature. New York, Longmans. pp. 70, 598.

Rogers, C. G., 1938. Textbook of Comparative Physiology. New York, McGraw-Hill. pp. 171, 239.

—— and Lewis, E. M., 1914. The Relation of the Body Temperature of the Earthworm to That of Its Environment. Biol. Bull., 27: 262–268. p. 97.

——, —— 1916. The Relation of the Body Temperature of Certain Cold-Blooded Animals to That of Their Environment. Biol. Bull., 31: 1–15. p. 97.

Romanes, G. J., 1883. Animal Intelligence. New York, Appleton. p. 23.

―― 1885. Jellyfish, Starfish, and Sea Urchins. London, Paul, Trench. p. 23.

Romell, L. G., 1930. Forest Soil Research in Relation to Forestry with Particular Reference to the Northeast. J. Forestry, 28: 841–848. p. 484.

―― 1935. An Example of Myriapods as Mull Formers. Ecology, 16: 67–71. pp. 484, 486.

Romer, A. S., 1933. Man and the Vertebrates. Chicago, Univ. of Chicago Press. pp. 132, 673.

―― 1945. Vertebrate Paleontology. 2nd ed. Chicago, University of Chicago Press.

Rooney, W. J., 1939. Earth Currents. Physics of the Earth, 8: 270–307. p. 157.

Roosevelt, Theodore, 1910. African Game Trails. New York, Scribner. pp. 550, 552, 553.

Root, A. I., Root, E. R., Root, H. H., and Dreyell, M. J., 1945. The ABC and XYZ of Bee Culture. Medina, Ohio, A. I. Root. p. 257.

Rösch, G. A., 1927. Über die Bautätigkeit im Bienenvolk und das alter der Baubienen. Ztschr. vergl. Physiol., 6: 264–298. p. 427.

―― 1930. Untersuchungen über die Arbeitsteilung im Bienenstaat. 2. Teil: Die Tätigkeiten der Arbeitsbienen unter experimentell veränderten Bedingungen. Ztschr. vergl. Physiol., 12: 1–71. pp. 426, 427.

Roscoe, H. E., 1867. On the Chemical Intensity of Total Daylight at Kew and Pará. 1865, 1866 and 1867. Phil. Tr. Roy. Soc., London, 157: 555–570. p. 18.

Rosenvinge, M. L. K., 1889. Influence des agents extérieurs sur l'organization polaire et dorsiventrale des plantes. Rev. Gen. Bot., 1: 125–135. p. 408.

Ross, J. C., 1847. Antarctic Voyage. A Voyage of Discovery and Research in the Southern and Antarctic Regions. London, Murray, 2 vols. p. 38.

Ross, John, 1819. A Voyage of Discovery for the Purpose of Exploring Baffins Bay and Inquiring into the Probability of a North West Passage. London, Murray. p. 38.

Rossolimo, L., and Kusnezowa, S., 1934. Donnoe gasootdelenîe, kak faktor kîslorodnogo rezhîma ozer. [Die Boden-gasausscheidung als Faktor des Sauerstoffhaushaltes der Seen.] Arb. Limnol. Sta. Kossino, 17: 87–117. (Russian text, summary in German.) p. 193.

Roth, L. M., 1943. Studies on the Gaseous Secretion of Tribolium confusum Duval. II. The Odoriferous Glands of Tribolium confusum. Ann. Entom. Soc. Amer., 36: 397–424. p. 355.

―― 1944. Studies on Tribolium confusum Duval. III. Abnormalities Produced in Tribolium confusum Duval by Exposure to

Acetic and Hydrochloric Acids. Ann. Entom. Soc. Amer., 37: 235–254. p. 355.

―― and Howland, R. B., 1941. Studies on the Gaseous Secretion of Tribolium confusum Duval. I. Abnormalities Produced in Tribolium confusum Duval by Exposure to a Secretion Given off by the Adults. Ann. Entom. Soc. Amer., 34: 151–172. p. 355.

Rowan, W., 1925. Relation of Light to Bird Migration and Developmental Changes. Nature, 115: 494–495. p. 541.

―― 1926. On Photoperiodism, Reproductive Periodicity, and Annual Migration of Birds and Certain Fishes. Proc. Boston Soc. Nat. Hist., 38: 147–189. pp. 534, 541.

―― 1927. Migration and Reproductive Rhythm in Birds. Nature, 119: 351–352. p. 541.

―― 1929. Experiments in Bird Migration. I. Manipulation of the Reproductive Cycle: Seasonal Histological Changes in the Gonads. Proc. Boston Soc. Nat. Hist., 39: 151–208. p. 541.

―― 1931. The Riddle of Migration. Baltimore, Williams & Wilkins. pp. 69, 121, 122, 124.

―― 1932. Experiments in Bird Migration. III. The Effects of Artificial Light, Castration and Certain Extracts on the Autumn Movements of the American Crow (Corvus brachyrhynchos). Proc. Nat. Acad. Sc., 18: 639–654. p. 541.

Rübel, Eduard, 1935. The Replaceability of Ecological Factors and the Law of the Minimum. Ecology, 16: 336–341. p. 224.

Rubner, M., 1908. Das problem der Lebensdauer und Seine Beziehungen zu Wachstum und Ernährung. Munich und Berlin, Oldenbourg. p. 113.

Rummell, R. S., 1946. Some Effects of Competition from Cheatgrass Brome on Crested Wheatgrass and Bluestem Wheatgrass. Ecology, 27: 159–167. p. 578.

Russell, C. P., 1932. Seasonal Migration of Mule Deer. Ecol. Monogr., 2: 1–46. p. 541.

Russell, E. S., 1927. The Vertical Distribution of Marine Macroplankton. V. The Distribution of Animals Caught in the Ring-Trawl in the Daytime in the Plymouth Area. J. Marine Biol. A. United Kingdom, 14: 557–608. p. 447.

―― 1927a. The Vertical Distribution of Plankton in the Sea. Biol. Rev., 2: 213–263. p. 555.

―― 1928. The Vertical Distribution of Macroplankton. VII. Observations on the Behaviour of Calanus finmarchicus. J. Marine Biol. A. United Kingdom, 15: 429–454. p. 555.

―― 1931. Some Theoretical Considerations on the Overfishing Problem. J. Conseil. Explor. Mer., 6. p. 377.

―― 1934. The Behaviour of Animals. An Introduction to Its Study. New York, Longmans. p. 70.

Russell, E. S., 1942. The Overfishing Problem. Cambridge, Cambridge University Press. pp. 51, 69, 322, 377.

—— 1945. The Directiveness of Organic Activities. Cambridge, Cambridge University Press. p. 656.

—— and Yonge, C. M., 1928. The Seas. London, Warne. pp. 203, 454, 458, 502, 514, 531, 555.

Russell, John, 1937. Soil Conditions and Plant Growth. London, Longmans. pp. 216, 223.

Russell, R. J., 1941. Climatic Change through the Ages. Yearbook, U. S. Dept. of Agric., 1941: 67–97. pp. 80, 83, 86.

Ruthven, A. G., 1906. An Ecological Survey in the Porcupine Mountains and Isle Royale, Michigan. Ann. Rept. Mich. Geol. Surv., 1905: 17–55. p. 48.

Rylov, W. M., 1935. Das Zooplankton der Binnengewässer. Die Binnengewässer, 15: 1–272. p. 446.

Sachs, Julius, 1863. Die vorübergehenden Starre-Zustande periodisch beweglicher und reizbarer Pflanzenorgane. Flora, 46: 449–459; 465–472; 481–489; 497–506.

—— 1864. Wirkung farbigen Lichts auf Pflanzen. Bot. Ztg., 22: 353–358; 361–367; 369–372. p. 20.

—— 1872. Ueber den Einfluss der Luft-temperatur und des Tageslichts auf die stundlichen und täglichen Aenderungen des Langenwachsthums (Streckung) der Internodien. Arb. Bot. Inst. Wurzburg, 1: 99–192. p. 20.

—— 1882. Vorlesungen über pflanzenphysiologie, Leipzig, Engelmann. p. 19.

Saham, M. N., and Srivastava, B. N., 1936. A Text Book of Heat. Allahabad, Indian Press. p. 91.

St. Hilaire, I. Geoffroy, 1859. Histoire générale des règnes organiques. Vol. 2, p. 285. pp. 34, 42.

Salaman, R. N., 1936. [A Discussion on the Present State of the Theory of Natural Selection.] Proc. Roy. Soc., London, s. B., 121: 72–73. p. 642.

Salisbury, E. J., 1923. The Influence of Earthworms on Soil Reaction and the Stratification of Undisturbed Soils. J. Linn. Soc. (Botany), 46: 415–425. p. 223.

—— 1936. Natural Selection and Competition. Proc. Roy. Soc., London, s. B., 121: 47–49. pp. 641, 647, 657.

Salisbury, R. D., and Alden, W. C., 1899. The Geography of Chicago and Its Environs. Bull. Geog. Soc. Chicago, 1: 1–63. pp. 565, 566.

Salt, George, 1934. Experimental Studies in Insect Parasitism. II. Superparasitism. Proc. Roy. Soc. London, s. B., 114: 455–476. p. 383.

—— 1936. Experimental Studies in Insect Parasitism. IV. The Effect of Superparasitism on Populations of Trichogramma evanescens. J. Exper. Biol., 13: 363–375. pp. 383, 386, 700.

—— 1941. The Effects of Hosts upon Their Insect Parasites. Biol. Rev., 16: 239–264. p. 383.

Salt, R. W., and Mail, G. A., 1943. The Freezing of Insects. A Criticism and an Explanation. J. Econ. Ent., 36: 126–127. pp. 100, 101.

Sanborn, C. C., 1922. Chicago Winter Birds. Zoöl. Leaflet, Field Mus. Nat. Hist., 2: 1–12. p. 535.

—— 1925. Mammals of the Chicago Area. Zoöl. Leaflet, Field Mus. Nat. Hist., 8: 1–23.

Sanctuary, W. C., 1932. A Study in Avian Behavior to Determine the Nature and Persistency of the Order of Dominance in the Domestic Fowl and to Relate These to Certain Physiological Reactions. Master's thesis. Library of Mass. State Coll., Amherst, Mass. p. 417.

Sanders, N. J., and Shelford, V. E., 1922. A Quantitative and Seasonal Study of a Pine-Dune Animal Community. Ecology, 3: 306–321. pp. 59, 557.

Sanderson, E. D., 1908. The Influence of Temperature in the Northern Distribution of Insects. J. Econ. Ent., 1: 245–262. p. 115.

—— and Peairs, L. M., 1914. The Relation of Temperature to Insect Life. Tech. Bull., N. H. Coll. Agr. Exper. Sta. 7. pp. 107, 112.

Sandon, H., 1927. The Composition and Distribution of the Protozoan Fauna of the Soil. Edinburgh, Oliver and Boyd. p. 484.

Saussure, H. B. de, 1779–1796. Voyages dans les Alpes . . . Neuchâtel, Fauche, 3 vols. p. 21.

Savely, H. E., 1939. Ecological Relations of Certain Animals in Dead Pine and Oak Logs. Ecol. Monogr., 9: 321–385. pp. 242, 361, 512, 514, 560, 561, 570.

Schäfer, E. A., 1907. On the Incidence of Daylight as a Determining Factor in Bird Migration. Nature, 77: 159–163. p. 21.

Scharrer, Berta, 1948. Hormones in Insects. In Pincus, G., and Thimann, K. V., ed. The Hormones: Chemistry, Physiology and Applications. New York, Academic Press, chap. 4. p. 136.

Schechter, Victor, 1943. Tolerance of the Snail Thais floridana to Waters of Low Salinity and the Effect of Size. Ecology, 24: 493–499.

Schick, R., 1932. Photoperiodismus. Der Zuchter, 4: 122–135. p. 534.

Schjelderup-Ebbe, Thorleif, 1922. Beiträge zur sozial-psychologie des Haushuhns. Zeit. Psych., 88: 225–252. p. 413.

—— 1935. Social Behavior of Birds. In Carl

Murchison: A Handbook of Social Psychology, pp. 947–972. Worcester, Mass., Clark Univ. Press. p. 414.

Schmankewitsch, W. J., 1875. Über des Verhältniss der Artemia salina Miln. Edw. zur Artemia Mühlhousenii Miln. Edw. und dem Genus Branchipus Schaeff. Ztschr. wiss. Zool., 25, Suppl., pp. 103–116. [Abstract, 1879, Nature, 29: 274. p. 20.

Schmid, E., 1941. Der Stufenbau der Materie und die biologischen Wissenschaften. Vierteljahrschr. naturforsch. Ges. Zürich, 86: viii–ix. p. 683.

Schmidt, Johannes, 1925. On the Content of Oxygen in the Ocean on Both Sides of Panama. Science, 61: 592–593. p. 193.

Schmidt, K. P., 1936. Guatemalan Salamanders of the Genus Oedipus. Zool. Ser. Field Mus. Nat. Hist., 20: 135–166. pp. 594, 595.

—— 1938. Herpetological Evidence for the Postglacial Eastward Extension of the Steppe in North America, Ecology, 19: 396–407. p. 590.

—— 1945. A Naturalist's Glimpse of the Andes. Scient. Monthly, 60: 335–346. p. 239.

Schmieder, R. G., 1947. More about Dancing Bees. Entomol. News, 58: 152–154. p. 433.

Schneirla, T. C., 1933. Studies on Army Ants in Panama. J. Comp. Psychol., 15: 267–301. pp. 410, 415.

—— 1938. A Theory of Army-Ant Behavior Based upon the Analysis of Activities in a Representative Species. J. Comp. Psychol., 25: 51–90. pp. 431, 487.

—— 1940. Further Studies on the Army-Ant Behavior Pattern. Mass Organization in the Swarm-Raiders. J. Comp. Psychol., 29: 401–460. p. 487.

—— 1944. The Reproductive Functions of the Army-Ant Queen as Pace Makers of the Group Behavior Pattern. J. New York Ent. Soc., 52: 153–192. p. 431.

—— 1945. The Army-Ant Behavior Pattern: Nomad-Statary Relation in the Swarmers and the Problem of Migration. Biol. Bull., 88: 166–193. p. 431.

—— 1946. Problems in the Biopsychology of Social Organization. J. Abnormal & Soc. Psych., 41: 385–402. pp. 395, 410, 430, 432, 435, 693.

—— 1947. A Study of Army-Ant Life and Behavior under Dry Season Conditions with Reference to Reproductive Functions. Am. Mus. Nov., 1336: 1–20. p. 431.

Scholander, P. F., 1940. Experimental Investigation on the Respiratory Function in Diving Mammals and Birds. Norske Vidensk. Akad. Oslo Evalradets Skrift. Sci. Results Mar. Biol. Res., 22: 1–131. p. 138.

Schonland, B. F. J., 1939. Thunder-Clouds, Shower Clouds, and Their Electrical Effects. Physics of the Earth, 8: 657–678. p. 157.

Schopfer, W. H., 1943. Plants and Vitamins. Waltham, Chronica Botanica Press. p. 128.

Schreiner, Oswald, and Brown, B. E., 1938. Soil Nitrogen. Yearbook U. S. Dept. of Agr., 1938: 361–376. p. 199.

Schrödinger, Erwin, 1945. What Is Life? The Physical Aspect of the Living Cell. Cambridge, Univ. Press. p. 598.

Schröter, C., and Kirchner, O., 1896, 1902. Die Vegetation des Bodensees. Schriften Ver. gesch. Bodensees Umgeb., 25: 1–119; 31: 1–86. pp. 42, 48.

Schwarz, E. A., 1891. Massing of Coccinellidae. Entom. News, 2: 169. p. 538.

Sclater, W. L., 1900. Mammals of South Africa. London, R. H. Porter, 2 vols. p. 415.

Scofield, C. S., 1938. Soil, Water Supply, and Soil Solution in Irrigation Agriculture. In Yearbook, U. S. Dept. of Agr., 1938: 704–716. p. 222.

Scott, J. P., 1942. Genetic Differences in the Social Behavior of Inbred Strains of Mice. J. Heredity, 33: 11–15. p. 414.

Scott, J. W., 1909. Some Egg-Laying Habits of Amphitrite ornata Verrill. Biol. Bull., 17: 327–340. p. 544.

—— 1942. Mating Behavior of the Sage Grouse. Auk, 59: 477–498. pp. 417, 689.

Scott, T. G., 1941. A Method of Estimating the Red Fox Population. Iowa State Coll. J. Sc., 15: 155–159. p. 269.

Scott, Will, and Opdyke, D. F., 1941. The Emergence of Insects from Winona Lake. Inves. Indiana Lakes & Streams, 2: 5–15. p. 453.

Scott, W. N., 1936. An Experimental Analysis of the Factors Governing the Hour of Emergence of Adult Insects from Their Pupae. Tr. Roy. Ent. Soc., London, 85: 303–329. p. 553.

Scrivenor, J. B., Burkill, I. H., Smith, M. A., Corbet, A. S., Shaw, H. K. A., Richards, P. W., and Zeumer, F. E., 1943. A Discussion of the Biogeographic Division of the Indo-Australian Archipelago. Proc. Linn. Soc. Lond., 154: 120–165. p. 9.

Sdobnikov, V. M., 1935. Vzaĭmootnosheniĭa severnogo olenia s zhĭvotnym mĭrom tundry i lesa [Relations between the Reindeer and Animal Life of the Tundra and Forest]. Trans. Arctic Inst. 24: 5–66. (Russian text, English summary.) pp. 181, 401, 416.

Sears, J. W., 1947. Relationships within the Quinaria Species Group of Drosophila. Univ. of Texas Pub., 4720: 137–156. p. 613.

Sears, Paul B., 1935. Glacial and Postglacial Vegetation. Bot. Rev., 1: 37–51. pp. 82, 83.

—— 1935a. Deserts on the March. Norman, Univ. of Oklahoma Press. pp. 468, 580.

Sears, Paul B., 1937. This Is Our World. Norman, Univ. of Oklahoma Press. p. 707.

—— 1948. Forest Sequence and Climatic Change in Northeastern North America Since Early Wisconsin Time. Ecology, 29: 326–333.

Sebenzow, B. M., and Adova, A. N., 1929. La réaction actuelle du milieu dans l'écologie d' Anopheles maculipennis. Bull. Soc. Pathol Exotique, 22: 584–606. p. 174.

Seebohm, H., 1888. The Geographical Distribution of the Family Charadriidae. London, Sotheran. p. 21.

Seevers, C. H., 1937. New Species of Termitophilous Staphylinidae from Tropical America and the Solomon Islands. Ann. Ent. Soc. Amer., 30: 1–23. pp. 615, 720.

Semon, Richard, 1894. Beobachtungen über die Lebensweise und Fortpflanzung der Monotremen nebst Notizen über ihre Körpertemperatur. Denkschr. Med. nat. Ges. Jena, 5: 1–15. p. 98.

Semper, K. G., 1881. Animal Life as Affected by the Natural Conditions of Existence. New York, Appleton. pp. 19, 21, 22, 23, 42, 58.

Sendtner, Otto, 1854. Vegetations verhältnisse Südbayerns nach den Grundsätzen der Pflanzen-Geographie und mit Bezugnahme auf Landskultur geschildert. München, Literarisch-artistische Anstalt. p. 23.

Sengün, A., 1944. Experimente zur sexuellmechanishen Isolation. Istanbul Univ. Fen Fakultesi Mecmuasi (B) 9: 239–253. p. 618.

Seton, E. T., 1909. Life Histories of Northern Animals. New York, Scribner, 2 vols. pp. 46, 180, 181, 467, 472, 514, 543.

—— 1925. On the Study of Scatology. J. Mammalogy, 6: 47–49. p. 269.

—— 1925–1928. Lives of Game Animals. New York, Doubleday, Doran, 4 vols. p. 374.

Sette, Oscar E., 1943. Studies on the Pacific Pilchard or Sardine (Sardinops caerulea). I. Structure of a Research Program to Determine How Fishing Affects the Resource. Fish & Wildlife Service, Special Scientific Reports, 19: 1–27. p. 377.

Severens, J. M., and Tanner, F. W., 1945. The Inheritance of Environmentally Induced Characters in Bacteria. J. Bact., 49: 383–393. p. 601.

Severin, H. H. P., and Severin, H. C., 1911. An Experimental Study on the Death-Feigning of Belostoma flumineum Say and Nepa apiculata Uhler. Behavior Monographs, 1: 1–44. p. 50.

Severtzoff, S. A., 1934. On the Dynamics of Populations of Vertebrates. Quart. Rev. Biol., 9: 409–437. p. 71.

Seward, A. C., 1909. Darwin and Modern Science. Cambridge, University Press. p. 48.

Shackleford, M. W., 1929. Animal Commu-nities of an Illinois Prairie. Ecology, 10: 126–154. pp. 59, 514, 531.

Shaftesbury, Anthony [Earl of], 1900. Characteristics of Men, Manners, Opinions, Times, etc. New York, Dutton, 2 vols. [1st ed. 1711.] p. 30.

Sharpe, F. R., and Lotka, A. J., 1911. A Problem in Age-Distribution. Philosophical Magazine, 1911, 21: 435. p. 293.

Shcherbakov, A. P., 1935. Intensīvnots' obmena ī prodolzhītel'nost' zhīznī drosophila. I. Vvodnye zamechaniiā ī obzor literatury. II. Prodolzhītel'nost' zhīznī ī intensīvnost' obmena u Drosophila melanogaster prī raznoĭ plotnostī nacelenii ā. [Metabolic Rate and Duration of Life in Drosophila. 1. Introductory Remarks and Review of the Literature. 2. Longevity and Metabolic Rate at Different Population Densities.] Arch. Biol. Sc., 38: 639–655. (Russian text, summary in English.) p. 403.

Sheals, R. A., and Brown, R. C., 1944. The Present Outlook on the Gypsy Moth Problem. J. Forestry, 42: 393–407. p. 706.

Shelford, V. E., 1907. Preliminary Notes on the Distribution of the Tiger Beetles (Cicindela) and Its Relation to Plant Succession Biol. Bull., 14: 9–14. p. 47.

—— 1911. Ecological Succession. I. Stream Fishes and the Method of Physiographic Analysis. Biol. Bull., 21: 9–34. pp. 54, 155, 156, 572.

—— 1911a. Ecological Succession. II. Pond Fishes. Biol. Bull., 21: 9–34. p. 54.

—— 1911b. Ecological Succession. III. A Reconnaissance of Its Causes in Ponds with Particular Reference to Fish. Biol. Bull., 22: 1–38. pp. 54, 573.

—— 1911c. Physiological Animal Geography. J. Morph., 22: 551–618. pp. 54, 198, 573.

—— 1912. Ecological Succession. IV. Vegetation and the Control of Land Animal Communities. Biol. Bull., 23: 59–99. p. 54.

—— 1912a. Ecological Succession. V. Aspects of Physiological Classification. Biol. Bull., 23: 331–370. p. 54.

—— 1913. Animal Communities in Temperate America. Bull. Geog. Soc. Chicago, 5: 1–368. [Reprinted 1937, Univ. of Chicago Press.] pp. 49, 155, 394, 436, 441, 514, 534, 537, 567, 570, 572, 573, 576, 577.

—— 1913a. The Reactions of Certain Animals to Gradients of Evaporating Power of Air. A Study in Experimental Ecology. Biol. Bull., 25: 79–120. p. 480.

—— 1914. Modification of the Behavior of Land Animals by Contact with Air of High Evaporating Power. J. Animal Behavior, 4: 31–49. pp. 480, 539.

—— 1914a. A Comparison of the Responses of Sessile and Motile Plants and Animals. Am. Nat., 48: 641–674. p. 539.

—— 1915. Principles and Problems of Ecology as Illustrated by Animals. J. Ecol., 3: 1–23. pp. 277, 280, 467.

—— 1918. Conditions of Existence. In Ward and Whipple, Fresh-Water Biology, chap. 2. p. 544.

—— 1925. The Hydrogen Ion Concentration of Certain Western American Inland Waters. Ecology, 6: 279–287. p. 174.

—— 1926. Naturalist's Guide to the Americas. (Ed.) Baltimore, Williams & Wilkins. p. 586.

—— 1927. An Experimental Investigation of the Relations of the Codling Moth to Weather and Climate. Bull. Ill. Nat. Hist. Surv., 16: 307–440. pp. 60, 207, 208.

—— 1929. Laboratory and Field Ecology. Baltimore, Williams & Wilkins. pp. 2, 55, 107, 112, 167, 517, 531.

—— 1931. Some Concepts of Bioecology. Ecology, 12: 455–467. pp. 564, 577.

—— 1932. Basic Principles of the Classification of Communities and Habitats and the Use of Terms. Ecology, 13: 105–120. pp. 208, 577.

—— 1932a. An Experimental and Observational Study of the Chinch Bug in Relation to Climate and Weather. Bull. Ill. Nat. Hist. Surv., 19: 487–547. p. 211.

—— 1932b. Life Zones, Modern Ecology, and the Failure of Temperature Summing. Wilson Bull., 44: 144–157. p. 115.

—— 1943. The Abundance of the Collared Lemming in the Churchill Area, 1929–1940. Ecology, 24: 472–484. p. 339.

—— 1945. The Relative Merits of the Life-Zone and Biome Concepts. Wilson Bull., 57: 248–252. p. 593.

—— and Allee, W. C., 1913. The Reactions of Fishes to Gradients of Dissolved Atmospheric Gases. J. Exper. Zool., 14: 207–266. p. 51.

—— and Flint, W. P., 1943. Populations of the Chinch Bug in the Upper Mississippi Valley from 1823–1940. Ecology, 24: 435–456. p. 475.

—— and Gail, F. W., 1922. A Study of Light Penetration into Sea Water Made with the Kunz Photoelectric Cell with Particular Reference to the Distribution of Plants. Pub. Puget Sound Biol. Sta., 3: 141–176. pp. 110, 150.

—— and Olson, Sigurd, 1935. Sere, Climax and Influent Animals with Special Reference to the Transcontinental Coniferous Forest of North America. Ecology, 16: 375–402. pp. 9, 511, 577, 585.

——, Weese, A. O., Rice, L. A., Rasmussen, D. I., Wismer, N. M., and Swanson, J. H., 1935. Some Marine Biotic Communities of the Pacific Coast of North America. Ecol. Monogr., 5: 249–354. pp. 35, 160, 459.

Sherff, E. E., 1913. Evaporation Conditions at Skokie Marsh. Plant World, 16: 154–160. p. 228.

Shimer, H. W., 1903. Fossorial Adaptations. Am. Nat., 37: 819–825. p. 466.

Shlaifer, Arthur, 1938. Studies in Mass Physiology: Effect of Numbers upon the Oxygen Consumption and Locomotor Activity of Carassius auratus. Physiol. Zoöl., 11: 408–424. p. 352.

—— 1939. An Analysis of the Effect of Numbers upon the Oxygen Consumption of Carassius auratus. Physiol. Zoöl., 12: 381–392. pp. 352, 410.

Shortess, G. S., 1942. The Relation between Temperature, Light, and Rate of Locomotion in Peranema trichophorum and Response to Changes in Temperature. Physiol. Zoöl., 15: 184–195.

Shreve, F., 1914. The Role of Winter Temperatures in Determining the Distribution of Plants. Am. J. Bot., 1: 194–202. p. 115.

Shull, A. F., 1936. Evolution. New York, McGraw-Hill. p. 70.

—— 1942. The Mechanism through which Light and Heat Influence Genetic Factors for Wing Development in Aphids. J. Exper. Zool., 89: 183–195. p. 123.

—— 1946. Inheritance in Lady Beetles. IV. The Form of the Chitinous Male Genitalia in Crosses of the Species Hippodamia quinquesignata and H. convergens. Genetics, 31: 291–303. p. 618.

Silow, R. A., 1945. The Genetics of Species Development in the Old World Cottons. J. Genetics, 46: 62–77. pp. 648, 678.

Silvestri, Filippo, 1920. Contribuzione alla Conoscenza dei Termitidi e Termitofili. II. Termitofili. Boll. Lab. Zool. Portici, 14: 265–319. p. 720.

Simony, F., 1850. Die Seen des Salzkammergutes. Sitzb. Akad. Wiss., Wien (m. n.), 4: 542–566. p. 41.

Simpson, G. G., 1937. Super-Specific Variation in Nature and in Classification. Am. Nat., 71: 236–267. p. 666.

—— 1940. Mammals and Land Bridges. J. Wash. Acad. Sc., 30: 137–163. p. 662.

—— 1941. The Role of the Individual in Evolution. J. Wash. Acad. Sc., 31: 1–20. p. 693.

—— 1944. Tempo and Mode in Evolution. New York, Columbia Univ. Press. pp. 598, 600, 602, 609, 634, 637, 638, 639, 641, 642, 643, 647, 648, 649, 654, 655, 662, 664, 673, 677, 679, 680, 682, 683, 684.

—— 1945. The Principles of Classification and a Classification of Mammals. Bull. Am. Mus. Nat. Hist., 85: 1–350. p. 407.

—— and Roe, Anne, 1939. Quantitative Zoology. Numerical Concepts and Methods in the Study of Recent and Fossil Animals. New York, McGraw-Hill. pp. 69, 265, 268.

Sinclair, J. G., 1922. Temperatures of the Soil and Air in a Desert. U. S. Mon. Weather Rev., 50: 142–144. p. 219.

Sinnott, E. W., 1946. Substance or System: The

Riddle of Morphogenesis. Am. Nat., *80:* 497–505. p. 631.

Skinner, C. E., and Mellem, Ethel M., 1944. Further Experiments to Determine the Organisms Responsible for Decomposition of Cellulose in Soils. Ecology, *25:* 360–365. p. 484.

Smaragdova, N. P., 1936. The Interaction between Phytophagous and Predatory Mites in Relation to Their Environment and Concentration. Bull. Biol. Med. Exper., *2:* 2–3. p. 370.

Smith, Adam, 1759. Theory of Moral Sentiments. London, Millar. p. 30.

—— 1776. An Inquiry into the Nature and Causes of the Wealth of Nations. London, Strahan and Cadell, 2 vols. p. 30.

Smith, Carroll N., and Cole, M. M., 1941. Effect of Length of Day on the Activity and Hibernation of the American Dog Tick, *Dermacentor variabilis* (Say). Ann. Entom. Soc. Amer., *34:* 426–432. p. 558.

Smith, E. V., 1916. Effect of Light on the Development of Young Salmon. Pub. Puget Sound Marine Sta., *1:* 89–107. p. 121.

Smith, Folmer, 1933. Researches on the Influence of Natural and Artificial Light on Plants. I. On the Influence of Length of Day. Meld. Norges Landbukshoiskole, *13:* 1–228. p. 20.

Smith, Geoffrey, 1909. Crustacea. Cambridge Natural History, *4:* 1–17, 55–217. p. 245.

Smith, G. M., 1938. Cryptogamic Botany. Vol. I. Algae and Fungi. New York, McGraw-Hill. p. 503.

—— 1946. The Nature of Sexuality in *Chlamydomonas.* Am. J. Bot., *33:* 625–630. p. 408.

Smith, Harry M., 1943. Reproductive Success in the Eastern Red-Wing (*Agelaius a. phoeniceus*) in Relation to Darling's Hypothesis. Ecology, *24:* 183–208. p. 402.

Smith, H. S., 1935. The Role of Biotic Factors in the Determination of Population Densities. J. Econ. Entom., *28:* 873–898. pp. 71, 331, 332, 344, 391.

—— 1939. Insect Populations in Relation to Biological Control. Ecol. Monogr., *9:* 311–320. p. 705.

—— et al., 1933. The Efficiency and Economic Effects of Plant Quarantines in California. Bull. Univ. of Calif. Coll. Agr., *555:* 1–276. p. 401.

Smith, Homer, W., 1930. The Absorption and Excretion of Water and Salts by Marine Teleosts. Am. J. Physiol., *93:* 480–505. p. 169.

—— 1931. Observations on the African Lungfish, *Protopterus aethiopicus,* and on Evolution from Water to Land Environments. Ecology, *12:* 164–181. p. 583.

—— 1932. Water Regulation and Its Evolution in Fishes. Quart. Rev. Biol., *7:* 1-26. p. 171.

—— 1936. The Retention and Physiological Role of Urea in the Elasmobranchii. Biol. Rev., *11:* 49–82. p. 169.

Smith, J. H., 1944. Ladybird Beetles. Queensl. Agr. J., *58:* 181–185. p. 706.

Smith, S. I., 1874. Sketch of the Invertebrate Fauna of Lake Superior. Rept. U. S. Fish Comm., 1872–1873; 690–707. p. 41.

Smith, Theobald, 1934. Parasitism and Disease. Princeton, Princeton Univ. Press. pp. 254, 257, 258, 401.

—— and Kilbourne, F. L., 1893. Investigations into the Nature, Causation and Prevention of Texas or Southern Cattle Fever. Bull. Bur. Animal Industry, U. S. Dept. of Agr., *1:* 1–301. pp. 28, 29.

Smith, V. G., 1928. Animal Communities of a Deciduous Forest Succession. Ecology, *9:* 479–500. pp. 59, 531, 532, 533, 577.

Smith, W. C., 1939. Some Notes on Irish Sea Plaice. Proc. & Tr. Liverpool Biol. Soc., *52:* 6–18. p. 282.

Snell, G. D., 1932. The Rôle of Male Parthenogenesis in the Evolution of the Social Hymenoptera. Am. Nat., *66:* 381–384. p. 687.

Snow, L. M., 1902. The Microcosm of the Drift-Line. Am. Nat., *36:* 855–864. p. 534.

Snyder, T. E., 1935. Our Enemy the Termite. Ithaca, Comstock. (2nd ed., 1948.) p. 617.

Snyder, W. C., Baker, K. F., and Hansen, H. N., 1946. Interpretation ,of Resistance to Fusarium Wilt in Tomato. Science, *103:* 707–708. p. 642.

Sonneborn, T. M., 1937. Sex, Sex Inheritance and Sex Determination in *Paramecium aurelia.* Proc. Nat. Acad. Sc., *23:* 378–385.

—— 1939. *Paramecium aurelia*: Mating Types and Groups; Lethal Interactions, Determination and Inheritance. Am. Nat., *73:* 390–413. p. 688.

—— 1941. Sexuality in Unicellular Organisms. In Calkins and Summers, Protozoa in Biological Research. New York, Columbia Univ. Press., pp. 666–709. pp. 622, 688.

—— 1942. Development and Inheritance of Serological Characters in Variety I of Paramecium aurelia. Rec. Gen. Soc. Amer., *11:* 90. pp. 408, 601, 602.

—— 1942a. Sex Hormones in Unicellular Organisms. Cold Spring Harbor Symposia in Quant. Biol., *10:* 111–124.

—— 1943. Gene and Cytoplasm. I. The Determination and Inheritance of the Killer Character in Variety 4 of Paramecium aurelia. Proc. Nat. Acad. Sc., *29:* 329–338. p. 601.

—— 1945. Gene Action in Paramecium. Ann. Missouri Bot. Garden, *32:* 213–221. p. 602.

—— 1945a. The Dependence of the Physiological Action of a Gene on a Primer and the Relation of Primer to Gene. Am. Nat., *79:* 318–339. p. 602.

—— 1947. Recent Advances in the Genetics

of Paramecium and Euplotes. Advances in Genetics, *1*: 263–358. pp. 398, 408.

—— 1948. Introduction: Symposium on Plasmogenes, Genes and Characters in *Paramecium aurelia*. Am. Nat., *82*: 6–34. p. 602.

—— and Dippell, Ruth V., 1946. Mating Reactions and Conjugation between Varieties of Paramecium aurelia in Relation to Conceptions of Mating Type and Variety. Physiol. Zoöl., *19*: 1–18. pp. 409, 622.

Soot-Ryen, T., 1924. Faunistische Untersuchungen im Ramfjorde. Trömso Mus. Årshefter, 45, No. *6*: 1–106. p. 458.

Soper, F. L., and Wilson, D. B., 1942. Species Eradication. A Practical Goal of Species Reduction in the Control of Mosquito-Borne Disease. J. Nat. Malaria Soc., *1*: 5–24. pp. 401, 724.

Soper, H. E., 1929. The Interpretation of Periodicity in Disease Prevalence. J. Roy. Stat. Soc., London, *92*: 34–61. p. 382.

Soper, J. D., 1921. Notes on the Snowshoe Rabbit. J. Mammalogy, *2*: 102–104. p. 60.

Southern, H. N., Watson, J. S., and Chitty, D., 1946. Watching Nocturnal Animals by Infra-Red Radiation. J. Animal Ecol., *15*: 198–202. p. 547.

Spallanzani, L., 1787 (1st ed. 1776). Opuscules d. physique, animale et végétale, etc. Trans. Jean Senebier. Pavia and Paris, 3 vols. pp. 19, 21.

Spärck, R., 1929. Preliminary Survey of the Results of Quantitative Bottom Investigations in Iceland and Faroe Waters, 1926–1927. Rapp. Cons. Internat. Expl. Mer, 57 (No. 2): 1–28. p. 458.

—— 1933. Contribution to the Animal Ecology of the Franz Joseph Fjord and Adjacent Waters. Medd. om. Grönl., *100*: 5–37. p. 458.

—— 1937. Benthonic Animal Communities of the Coastal Waters. The Zoology of Iceland, *1* (pt. 6): 1–45. [Copenhagen, Levin and Munksgaard.] p. 458.

Spencer, Baldwin, 1896. Amphibia. Rep. Horn Sc. Exped. Centr. Australia, *2*: 152–175. p. 105.

Spencer, Herbert, 1852. A Theory of Population, Deduced from the General Law of Animal Fertility. Westminster. Rev., *57*: 468–501. p. 26.

—— 1855. Principles of Psychology. [3rd ed., 1890. London, Williams and Norgate, 2 vols.; 1914, New York, Appleton, 2 vols.]

—— 1863. First Principles. London, Williams and Norgate. p. 27.

—— 1864–1867. The Principles of Biology. London, Williams and Norgate, 2 vols. [various ed.] p. 26.

—— 1892–1893. The Principles of Ethics. New York, Appleton, 2 vols. p. 31.

Spett, G., 1925. Beobachtungen über Geselligkeit (Koloniebildung) bei über-wintern-

den Käfern der Gattung Saprinus. Ztschr. wissen. Insektenbiologie, *20*: 5–8. p. 538.

Spiegelman, S., and Kamen, M. D., 1946. Genes and Nucleoproteins in the Synthesis of Enzymes. Science, *104*: 581–584. p. 602.

—— and Lindegren, C. C., 1944. A Comparison of the Kinetics of Enzymatic Adaptation in Genetically Homogeneous and Heterogeneous Populations of Yeast. Ann. Missouri Bot. Garden, *31*: 219–233. p. 602.

——, —— and Lindegren, Gertrude, 1945. Maintenance and Increase of a Genetic Character by a Substrate-Cytoplasmic Interaction in the Absence of the Specific Gene. Proc. Nat. Acad. Sc., *31*: 95–102. p. 602.

Stangeland, C. E., 1904. Pre-Malthusian Doctrines of Population. Studies in History, Economics and Public Law, *21*: 1–356. p. 25.

Stanier, R. Y., 1941. Studies on Marine Agar-Digesting Bacteria. J. Bact., *42*: 527–560. p. 500.

Stanley, John, 1942. A Mathematical Theory of the Growth of Populations of the Flour Beetle *Tribolium confusum* Duval. V. The Relation between the Limiting Value of Egg-Populations in the Absence of Hatching and the Sex-Ratio of the Group of Adult Beetles Used in a Culture. Ecology, *23*: 24–31. p. 371.

Starling, J. H., 1944. Ecological Studies of the Pauropoda of the Duke Forest. Ecol. Monogr., *14*: 291–310. p. 484.

Stebbins, G. L., Jr., 1945. Evidence for Abnormally Slow Rates of Evolution, with Particular Reference to the Higher Plants and the Genus Drosophila. Lloydia, *8*: 84–102. p. 680.

Stebbins, R. C., 1944. Some Aspects of the Ecology of the Iguanid Genus *Uma*. Ecol. Monogr., *14*: 311–332. p. 634.

Steinberg, R. A., 1938. Correlation between Biological Essentiality and Atomic Structure of the Chemical Elements. J. Agr. Res., *57*: 851–858. p. 73.

Steiner, A., 1929. Temperaturuntersuchungen in Ameisennestern mit Erdkuppeln, im Nest von *Formica exsecta*, Nyl., und in Nestern unter Steinen. Z. vergl. Physiol., *9*: 1–66. p. 362.

Steinhaus, E. A., 1946. Insect Microbiology. Ithaca, Comstock. pp. 243, 248, 710, 712.

Steuer, Adolf, 1911. Leitfaden der Planktonkunde. Leipzig, Teubner. p. 460.

Stiles, Walter, 1946. Trace Elements in Plants and Animals. New York, Macmillan. pp. 205, 221.

Stirrett, G. M., 1938. A Field Study of the Flight, Oviposition and Establishment Periods in the Life Cycle of the European Corn Borer, *Pyrausta nubilalis* Hbn., and the Physical Factors Affecting Them. Scient. Agr., *18:* 355–656. p. 389.

Stirton, R. A., 1940. Phylogeny of North American Equidae. Bull. Dept. Geol. Sc., Univ. of Calif., *25:* 165–198. p. 638.

—— 1947. Observations on Evolutionary Rates in Hypsodonty. Evolution, *1:* 32–41. p. 695.

Stoddard, H. L., 1932. The Bobwhite Quail, Its Habits, Preservation, and Increase. New York, Scribner. pp. 68, 70, 326, 367, 374.

Stoner, Dayton, and Stoner, Lillian C., 1942. A Seven-Year-Old Bank Swallow. Science, *96:* 273–274. p. 645.

Storey, Margaret, 1937. The Relation between Normal Range and Mortality of Fishes due to Cold at Sanibel Island, Florida. Ecology, *18:* 10–26. pp. 635, 671.

—— and Gudger, E. W., 1936. Mortality of Fishes Due to Cold at Sanibel Island, Florida, 1886–1936. Ecology, *17:* 640–643. p. 635.

Stork, J. W., and Renouf, L. P. W., 1933. Plant and Animal Ecology. London, Murray. p. 69.

Stout, A. B., 1945. Classes and Types of Intraspecific Incompatibilities. Am. Nat., *79:* 481–508. p. 622.

Strandine, E. J., 1940. A Quantitative Study of the Periodical Cicada with Respect to Soil of Three Forests. Am. Mid. Nat., *24:* 177–183. pp. 543, 544.

—— 1941. Quantitative Study of a Snail Population. Ecology, *22:* 86–91. pp. 480, 526.

—— 1941a. Effect of Soil Moisture and Algae on the Survival of a Pond Snail during Periods of Relative Dryness. Nautilus, *54:* 128–130. p. 539.

Strandskov, H. H., 1941. The Distribution of Human Genes. Scient. Monthly, *52:* 203–215. pp. 264, 603.

—— 1944. Physiological Aspects of Human Genetics, Five Human Blood Characteristics. Physiol. Rev., *24:* 445–466. pp. 605, 655.

—— and Ondina, Doris, 1947. A Comparison of the Percentages of Stillbirths among Single and Plural Births in the Total, the "White" and the "Colored" U. S. Populations. Am. J. Phys. Anthrop., *5:* 40–54. p. 684.

Strel'nikov, I. D., 1936. Deistvie solnechnoi radiatsii i mikroklimata na temperaturu tela i povedenie lichinok saranchi *Locusta migratoria* L. (Effect of Solar Radiation and Microclimate on the Body Temperature and the Behavior of the Larvae of L. migratoria.) Trudy Zoologicheskogo Instituta Akademii Nauk USSR (Trav. Inst. Zool. Acad. Sc., USSR), *2:* 637–733. p. 97.

Stresemann, Erwin, 1934. Aves. Kükenthal's Handbuch der Zoologie, *7:* 1–899. p. 701.

Strickland, A. H., 1947. The Soil Fauna of Two Contrasted Plots of Land in Trinidad, British West Indies. J. Animal Ecol., *16:* 1–10. p. 537.

Strohecker, H. F., 1937. An Ecological Study of Some Orthoptera of the Chicago Area. Ecology, *18:* 231–250. p. 567.

—— 1938. Measurement of Solar Ultra-Violet in the Chicago Area. Ecology, *19:* 57–80. pp. 91, 127, 436, 480, 566, 567, 568.

Strøm, K. M., 1931. Feforvatn. A Physiographical and Biological Study of a Mountain Lake. Arch. Hydrobiol., *22:* 491–536. p. 194.

Stuart, C. A., and Cooper, H. J., 1932. Food as a Sex Determining Factor in *Moina macrocopa*. Physiol. Zoöl., *5:* 70–91. p. 410.

——, McPherson, M., and Cooper, H. J., 1931. Studies on Bacteriologically Sterile *Moina macrocopa* and Their Food Requirements. Physiol. Zoöl., *4:* 87–100. p. 444.

Sturtevant, A. H., 1938. Essays on Evolution. II. On the Effects of Selection on Social Insects. Quart. Rev. Biol., *13:* 74–76. pp. 678, 684.

—— 1939. High Mutation Frequency Induced by Hybridization. Proc. Nat. Acad. Sc., *25:* 308–310. p. 684.

—— 1944. Can Specific Mutations be Induced by Serological Methods? Proc. Nat. Acad. Sc., *30:* 176–178. p. 601.

—— 1944a. *Drosophila pseudoobscura.* Ecology, *25:* 476–477. p. 625.

Summerhayes, V. S., and Elton, C. S., 1923. Contributions to the Ecology of Spitsbergen and Bear Island. J. Ecol., *11:* 214–286. pp. 59, 514.

Sumner, F. B., 1910. An Intensive Study of the Fauna and Flora of a Restricted Area of the Sea Bottom. Bull. U. S. Bur. Fish., *28:* 1225–1263. p. 46.

—— 1932. Genetic, Distributional, and Evolutionary Studies of the Subspecies of Deer Mice (Peromyscus). Bibliographia Genetica, *9:* 1–106. pp. 69, 607, 627.

—— 1934. Does "Protective Coloration" Protect? Results of Some Experiments with Fishes and Birds. Proc. Nat. Acad. Sc., *20:* 559–564. p. 649.

—— 1935. Studies of Protective Color Change. III. Experiments with Fishes both as Predators and Prey. Proc. Nat. Acad. Sc., *21:* 345–353. p. 649.

—— 1942. Where Does Adaptation Come In? Am. Nat., *76:* 433–444. pp. 632, 648.

Sutton, G. M., 1931. The Blue Goose and Lesser Snow Goose on Southampton Island, Hudson Bay. Auk, *48:* 335–364. p. 619.

Sverdrup, H. U., Johnson, M. W., and Fleming, R. H., 1942. The Oceans. Their Physics, Chemistry, and General Biology. New York, Prentice-Hall. pp. 4, 69, 80, 109, 137, 138, 140, 149, 150, 151, 153,

165, 172, 178, 189, 192, 195, 199, 200, 201, 202, 204, 240, 243, 284, 333, 366, 448, 450, 454, 460, 500, 511, 514, 554, 555, 596.

Sweadner, W. R., 1937. Hybridization and the Phylogeny of the Genus Platysamia. Ann. Carnegie Mus., 25: 163–242. p. 625.

Sweetman, H. L., 1936. The Biological Control of Insects. Ithaca, Comstock. pp. 23, 70.

Swinnerton, H. H., 1938. Development and Evolution. Nature, 142: 459–462. p. 636.

Swynnerton, C. F. M., 1921. An Examination of the Tsetse Problem in North Mossurise, Portuguese East Africa. Bull. Ent. Res., 11: 315–385. p. 60.

—— 1936. The Tsetse Flies of East Africa. Tr. Roy. Entom. Soc., London, 84: 1–597. p. 70.

—— 1940. How Forestry May Assist towards the Control of the Tsetse Flies. Appendix II. In Troup, R. S., 1940. Colonial Forest Administration, Oxford Univ. Press, pp. 439–440. p. 696.

Szymanski, J. S., 1918. Versuche über Aktivität und Ruhe bei Säuglingen. Pflüger's Arch., 172: 424–429. p. 559.

Talbot, Mary, 1934. Distribution of Ant Species in the Chicago Region, with Reference to Ecological Factors and Physiological Toleration. Ecology, 15: 416–439. pp. 436, 567, 652, 697.

—— 1943. Population Studies of the Ant, Prenolepis imparis Say. Ecology, 24: 31–44. pp. 418, 424.

—— 1945. Population Studies of the Ant Myrmica schencki ssp. emeryana Forel. Ann. Ent. Soc. Amer., 38: 365–372. p. 419.

—— 1946. Daily Fluctuations in Aboveground Activity of Three Species of Ants. Ecology, 27: 65–70. p. 559.

—— and Kennedy, C. H., 1940. The Slave-Making Ant, Formica sanguinea subintegra Emery, Its Raids, Nuptial Flights and Nest Structure. Ann. Ent. Soc. Amer., 33: 560–577. p. 424.

Taliaferro, W. H., 1938. Ablastic and Trypanocidal Antibodies against Trypanosoma duttoni. J. Immunol., 35: 303–328. p. 707.

—— 1941. Populations of Blood-Dwelling Species. Am. Nat., 75: 458–472. p. 707.

—— 1948. Parasitism. Encyclopaedia Brittanica. p. 701.

—— and Huff, C. G., 1940. The Genetics of the Parasitic Protozoa. Pub. A. A. Adv. Sc., 12: 57–61. p. 602.

—— and Pavlinova, Y., 1936. The Course of Infection of Trypanosoma duttoni in Normal and in Splenectomized and Blockaded Mice. J. Parasitol., 22: 29–41. p. 707.

Tansley, A. G., and Chipp, T. F., 1926. Aims and Methods in the Study of Vegetation. London, Crown Agents. pp. 530, 577, 578.

Tarde, Gabriel, 1903. Inter-Psychology. Internat. Quart., 7: 59–84. p. 410.

Taylor, Griffith, 1916. The Control of Settlement by Humidity and Temperature. Commonwealth Bur. Met., 14: 1–32. p. 208.

—— 1918. Geographical Factors Controlling the Settlement of Tropical Australia. Queensland Geog. J., 32–33: 1–67. p. 207.

—— 1927. Environment and Race. London, Oxford Univ. Press. p. 577.

Taylor, L. H., 1939. Observations on Social Parasitism in the Genus Vespula Thomson. Ann. Ent. Soc. Amer., 32: 304–315. p. 676.

Taylor, W. P., 1927. Ecology or Bio-Ecology. Ecology 8: 280–281. p. 527.

—— 1934. Significance of Extreme or Intermittent Conditions in Distribution of Species and Management of Natural Resources, with a Restatement of Liebig's Law of Minimum. Ecology, 15: 374–379. p. 635.

—— 1935. Some Animal Relations to Soils. Ecology, 16: 127–136. p. 484.

—— 1935a. Significance of the Biotic Community in Ecological Studies. Quart. Rev. Biol., 10: 291–307. p. 71.

—— and Lay, D. W., 1944. Ecologic Niches Occupied by Rabbits in Eastern Texas. Ecology, 25: 120–121. p. 476.

Tehon, L. R., 1928. Methods and Principles of Interpreting the Phenology of Crop Pests. Bull. Ill. Nat. Hist. Surv., 17: 321–346. p. 211.

Terao, Arata, and Tanaka, T., 1928. Population Growth of the Water-Flea, Moina macrocopa Strauss. Proc. Imper. Acad. (Japan), 4: 550–552. pp. 307, 333.

——, —— 1928a. Influence of Temperature upon the Rate of Reproduction in the Water-Flea, Moina macrocopa Strauss. Proc. Imper. Acad. (Japan), 4: 553–555. p. 334.

——, —— 1928b. Influence of Density of Population upon the Rate of Reproduction in the Water-Flea Moina macrocopa Strauss. Proc. Imper. Acad. (Japan), 4: 556–558. p. 334.

Terzaghi, Karl, 1942. Soil Moisture. Physics of the Earth, 9: 331–365. p. 158.

Thamdrup, H. M., 1932. Faunistische und ökologische Studien über dänische Oribatiden. Zool. Jahrb., Syst., 62: 289–330. p. 486.

Thienemann, August, 1925–1935. Die Binnengewässer. . . . Stuttgart, Schweizerbarth, 15 vols. p. 501.

—— 1926. Limnologie. Breslau, Jedermanns Bücherei. pp. 56, 501, 508.

—— 1926a. Der Nahrungskreislauf im Wasser. Verh. deutsch. Zool. Ges., 31: 29–79. pp. 508, 510.

—— 1932. Die Tierwelt der Nepenthes Kannen. Tropische Binnengewässer, *3:* 1–54. p. 232.

Thienemann, August, 1939. Grundzüge einer allgemeinen Oekologie. Arch. Hydrobiol., *35:* 267–285.

Thimann, K. V., 1941. Action of Light on Organisms. Sigma Xi Quart., *29:* 23–35. p. 506.

Thomas, A. S., 1943. The Vegetation of the Karamoja District, Uganda. J. Ecology, *31:* 149–178. p. 476.

Thomas, F., 1941. Über Schutzanpassung, Katalepsie und Tagesrhythmik der Spannerraupen. Biol. Gen., *15:* 75–108. p. 631.

Thomas, L. J., 1944. Researches in Life Histories of Parasites of Wildlife. Tr. Ill. Acad. Sc., *37:* 7–24. pp. 702, 703, 704.

Thompson, D. H., 1931. The Fishing Industry of Illinois River. Circ. Illinois Water Surv. Div., *12:* 69–72. p. 515.

—— 1931a. Variation in Fishes as a Function of Distance. Tr. Ill. Acad. Sc., *23:* 276–281. p. 607.

—— and Hunt, F. D., 1930. The Fishes of Champaign County: A Study of the Distribution and Abundance of Fishes in Small Streams. Illinois Nat. Hist. Surv. *19:* 5–101. p. 342.

Thompson, D'Arcy W., 1917. On Growth and Form. Cambridge: Univ. Press. (1942 ed.) pp. 132, 157, 638.

Thompson, W. F., 1937. Theory of the Effect of Fishing on the Stock of Halibut. Rep. Internat. Fish. Comm., *12:* 1–22. p. 377.

—— and Bell, F. H., 1934. Biological Statistics of the Pacific Halibut Fishery. (2) Effect of Changes in Intensity upon Total Yield and Yield per Unit of Gear. Rep. Internat. Fish Comm., *8:* 1–49. p. 377.

—— and Thompson, Julia B., 1919. The Spawning of the Grunion (*Leuresthes tenuis*). Calif. Fish & Game Comm. Fish Bull., *3:* 1–29. pp. 84, 544.

Thompson, W. L., 1928. Effect of Hurricane on the Abundance of Some Insects. Florida Ent., *12:* 40–41. p. 146.

Thompson, W. R., 1928. A Contribution to the Study of Biological Control and Parasite Introduction in Continental Areas. Parasitology, *20:* 90–112. p. 331.

—— 1939. Biological Control and the Theories of the Interactions of Populations. Parasitology, *31:* 299–388. pp. 25, 72, 331, 380, 386, 684.

Thomson, J. A., 1911. The Biology of the Seasons. New York, Holt. p. 544.

Thornthwaite, C. W., 1931. The Climates of North America According to a New Classification. Geogr. Rev., *21:* 633–655. p. 468.

—— 1940. Atmospheric Moisture in Relation to Ecological Problems. Ecology, *21:* 17–28. pp. 181, 182, 189, 480.

—— 1940a. The Relation of Geography to Human Ecology. Ecol. Monogr., *10:* 343–348. p. 516.

Thorpe, W. H., 1940. Ecology and the Future of Systematics. In Huxley, J., The New Systematics, pp. 341–364. pp. 613, 615.

—— 1945. The Evolutionary Significance of Habitat Selection. J. Animal Ecol., *14:* 67–70. pp. 605, 610, 616, 645.

Thorson, Thomas, and Svihla, A., 1943. Correlation of Habitats of Amphibians with Their Ability to Survive the Loss of Body Water. Ecology, *24:* 374–381.

Tiffany, L. H., 1934 The Plankton Algae of the West End of Lake Erie. Contr. Stone Lab., *6:* 1–113.

—— 1938. Algae, the Grass of Many Waters. Springfield, Thomas. pp. 503, 505.

Tilden, J. W., and Mansfield, G. S., 1944. Notes on Three Species of the Genus *Coenonycha* Horn. Pan-Pacific Ent., *20:* 115–117. p. 614.

Timmons, F. L., 1941–1942. The Rise and Decline of Cactus in Kansas. Kansas State Agr. Bienn. Rept., *33:* 37–46. p. 656.

Timoféeff-Ressovsky, N. W., 1936. Some Genetic Experiments on Relative Viability. Proc. Roy. Soc., London, s. B., *121:* 45–47.

—— 1940. Mutations and Geographical Variation. In Huxley, J., The New Systematics, pp. 73–136. pp. 117, 607, 678, 687, 688.

—— 1940a. Sulla questione dell' isolamento biologico entro popolazioni specifiche. Sci. Genetica, *1:* 317–325. p. 606.

Tinbergen, L., 1946. De Sperwer als Roofvijand van Zangvogels. Ardea, *34:* 1–213. pp. 374, 710.

Tinbergen, N., 1933. Die ernährungsökologischen Beziehungen zwischen *Asio otus otus* L. und ihren Beutetieren, inbesondere den *Microtus*-Arten. Ecol. Monogr., *3:* 445–492. p. 374.

—— 1942. An Objectivistic Study of the Innate Behavior of Animals. Bibliotheca Biotheretica., Ser. D., *1:* 39–98. Leiden, Brill. p. 7.

Tisserand, E., 1875. Mémoire sur la végétation dans les hautes latitudes. Mémoires de la société Centrale d'Agriculture. (vide Abbe, 1905.) p. 18.

Tonney, F. O., and DeYoung, C. R., 1931. Smoke Eradication to Save the Health Value of Urban Sunshine. Am. J. Pub. Health, *21:* 344–354. p. 127.

Topley, W. W. C., 1933. An Outline of Immunity. Baltimore, Wood. p. 261.

Townsend, Grace, 1939. The Spawning Reaction and Spawning Integration of *Nereis limbata* with Emphasis upon Chemical Stimulation. Univ. of Chicago Libraries [Ph. D. Thesis]. p. 84.

Transeau, E. N., 1926. The Accumulation of Energy by Plants. Ohio J. Sc., *26:* 1–10. pp. 506, 507.

—— 1935. The Prairie Peninsula. Ecology, *16:* 423–437. p. 590.

——, Sampson, H. C., and Tiffany, L. H.,

1940. Textbook of Botany. New York, Harper. pp. 484, 498, 507, 548, 574.

Treadwell, A. L., 1915. Internal Factors Producing the Swarming of the Atlantic Palolo. Science, 41: 438. p. 544.

Trembley, A., 1744. Mémoires pour servir à l'histoire d'un genre de polypes d'eau douce à bras en forme de cornes. Leyden, Verbeek. p. 24.

Tressler, W. L., 1939. The Zooplankton in Relation to the Metabolism of Lakes. Pub. Am. A. Adv. Sc., 10: 79–93. p. 447.

Trew, C. J., 1727. Beschreibung der grossen Amerikanischen Aloa, wobei das tägliche Wachsthum des Stengels der im Jahr 1726, zu Nürnberg verglükten Aloe erläutert wird. Nürnberg, Adelburner. p. 20.

Trewartha, G. T., 1940. The Cover of the Driftless Cuestaform Hill Land: Presettlement Record and Post Glacial Geology. Tr. Wis. Acad. Sc., 32: 361–388. p. 82.

—— 1943. An Introduction to Weather and Climate. New York, McGraw-Hill.

Trewavas, Ethelwynn, 1935. A Synopsis of the Cichlid Fishes of Lake Nyasa. Ann. Mag. Nat. His. (10) 16: 65–118. p. 611.

—— 1938. Lake Albert Fishes of the Genus Haplochromis. Ann. Mag. Nat. Hist., (11) 1: 435–449. p. 611.

Tschermak, Elisabeth, 1941. Untersuchungen über die Beziehungen von Pilz und Alge im Flechtenthallus. Oesterreich Bot. Ztschr., 90: 233–307. p. 711.

Turesson, Göte, 1922. The Genotypical Response of the Plant Species to the Habitat. Hereditas, 3: 211–350. p. 626.

—— 1931. The Geographical Distribution of the Alpine Ecotype of Some Eurasiatic Plants. Hereditas, 15: 329–346. p. 626.

Turrill, W. B., 1936. Natural Selection and the Distribution of Plants. Proc. Roy. Soc., London, s. B., 121: 49–52. p. 624.

—— 1946. The Ecotype Concept. A Consideration with Appreciation and Criticism Especially of Recent Trends. New Phytol., 45: 34–43. p. 626.

Twenhofel, W. H., 1942. Physical Changes Produced by the Water of the Earth. Physics of the Earth, 9: 592–655. p. 154.

Uichanco, L. B., 1924. Studies on the Embryogeny and Postnatal Development of the Aphidae with Special Reference to the History of the "Symbiotic Organ" or "Mycetom." Philippine. J. Sc., 24: 143–247. p. 712.

Ullrich, F. T., 1915. The Relation of Evaporation and Soil Moisture to Plant Succession in a Ravine. Bull. Illinois Lab. Nat. Hist., 12: 1–16. p. 480.

Ullyett, G. C., 1936. Host Selection by Microplectron fuscipennis Zett. (Chalcidae. Hymenoptera). Roy. Soc., London, s. B., 120: 253–291. p. 700.

Ulrich, A. T., 1933. Die Makrofauna der Waldstreu. Mitt. Forstwirtsch. Forstwiss., 4: 283–323. p. 486.

Utida, Syunro, 1941. Studies on Experimental Population of the Azuki Bean Weevil, Callosobruchus chinensis (L.). II. The Effect of Population Density on Progeny Populations under Different Conditions of Atmospheric Moisture. Mem. Coll. Agr. Kyoto Imp. Univ., 49: 1–20. p. 335.

Uvarov, B. P., 1921. A Revision of the Genus Locusta with a New Theory as to the Periodicity and Migration of Locusts. Bull. Entomol. Res., 12: 135–163.

—— 1923. Notes on Locusts of Economic Importance, with Some New Data on the Periodicity of Locust Invasion. Bull. Entomol. Res., 14: 31–39.

—— 1928. Grasshoppers and Locusts. London. Imp. Bur. Entom. pp. 408, 466, 543,

—— 1931. Insects and Climate. Trans. Entom. Soc. London, 79: 1–247. pp. 69, 100, 102, 136, 186, 188, 211, 228, 333, 337, 339, 363.

Valentine, J. M., 1931. The Olfactory Sense of the Adult Mealworm Beetle Tenebrio molitor (Linn.). J. Exper. Zool., 58: 165–220.

—— 1932. Classification of the Genus Pseudanophthalmus Jeannel with Descriptions of New Species and Notes on Distribution. J. Elisha Mitchell Sc. Soc., 47: 261–280. p. 439.

—— 1943. Insect Taxonomy and Principles of Speciation. J. Wash. Acad. Sc., 33: 353–358. p. 609.

—— 1945. Speciation and raciation in Pseudanophthalmus. Tr. Conn. Acad. Arts & Sc., 36: 631–672. p. 609.

Van Beneden, J. P., 1876. Animal Parasites and Messmates. New York, Appleton. pp. 32, 243.

Van Cleave, H. J., 1931. Some Biological Effects of Drought. Scient. Monthly, 33: 301–306. p. 539.

—— 1941. Relationships of the Acanthocephala. Am. Nat., 75: 31–47. p. 676.

Vandel, A., 1942. Recherches sur la génétique et la sexualité des Isopodes terrestres. VIII. Les modalités de l' incubation chez les Isopodes volvationnels. Bull. Biol. France et Belgique, 76: 336–346. p. 631.

Van Deventer, W. C., 1936. A Winter Bird Community in Western New York. Ecology, 17: 491–499. p. 478.

Van Dyke, E. C., 1919. Tendency of Insects to Collect on Ridges and Mountain Snow fields. Entom. News, 30: 241–244. p. 538.

Van Dyke, J. C., 1902. The Desert. New York, Scribner. p. 539.

Van Name, W. G., 1936. The American Land and Fresh-Water Isopod Crustacea. Bull. Am. Mus. Nat. Hist., 71: 1–535. pp. 631, 673, 674.

Van Niel, C. B., 1931. On the Morphology and Physiology of the Purple and Green Sulphur Bacteria. Arch. Mikrobiol., *3*: 1–112. p. 497.

—— 1935. Photosynthesis of Bacteria. Cold Spring Harbor Symposia on Quantitative Biology, *3*: 138–150. p. 497.

—— 1936. On the Metabolism of the Thiorhodaceae. Arch. Mikrobiol., *7*: 323–358. p. 497.

Van't Hoff, T. H., 1884. Études de dynamic chimique. Amsterdam, Müller. p. 107.

Varga, L., 1934. Wandelweg und heutiger Stand der Pütter'schen Theorie. Arch. Hydrobiol., *26*: 255–278. p. 444.

Varley, G. C., 1941. On the Search for Hosts and the Egg Distribution of Some Chalcid Parasites of the Knapweed Gall-Fly. Parasitology, *33*: 47–66. p. 381.

—— 1947. The Natural Control of Population Balance in the Knapweed Gall-Fly (*Urophora jaceana*). J. Anim. Ecol., *16*: 139–187. pp. 271, 385, 389.

Vaughan, T. W., 1912. Summary of the Results Obtained from a Study of the Recent Madreporaria of the Hawaiian Islands and Laysan. Proc. 7th Intern. Zool. Cong., Boston, pp. 932–943. p. 214.

—— 1919. Corals and the Formation of Coral Reefs. Smithsonian Inst. Annual Rept., 1917: 189–276. p. 570.

Verhulst, P. F., 1838. Notice sur la loi que la population suit dans son accroissement. Corresp. Math. et Phys., *10*: 113–121. pp. 25, 26.

Vernadsky, W. I., 1929. La Biosphere. Paris, Alcan. pp. 77, 729.

—— 1945. The Biosphere and the Noosphere. Am. Scientist, *33*: 1–12. p. 729.

Vernon, H. M., 1928. Industrial Fatigue in Relation to Atmospheric Conditions. Physiol. Rev., *8*: 130–150.

Verrill, A. E., 1866. On the Polyps and Echinoderms of New England with Descriptions of New Species. Proc. Bost. Soc. Nat. Hist., *10*: 333–357. p. 35.

—— 1873. Report on the Invertebrates of Vineyard Sound and Adjacent Waters. Rept. U. S. Fish Comm., 1871–1872: 295–544. p. 455.

—— 1897. Nocturnal Protective Coloration of Mammals, Birds, Fishes, Insects, etc. Am. Nat., *31*: 99–103. p. 546.

—— 1901. A Remarkable Instance of the Death of Fishes, at Bermuda in 1901. Am. J. Sc., (4) *12*: 88. p. 99.

—— 1902. Comparisons of the Bermudian, West Indian, and Brazilian Coral Faunae. Tr. Conn. Acad. of Arts & Sc., *11*: 169–206. p. 214.

—— and Smith, S. I., 1874. Report on the Invertebrate Animals of Vineyard Sound and Adjacent Waters. Rept. U. S. Comm. Fish and Fisheries, 1871–1872: 295–852. pp. 35, 458.

Verworn, Max, 1889. Psycho-physiologische Protisten-studien. Experimentelle untersuchungen. Jena, Fischer.

—— 1899a. General Physiology. London, Macmillan. p. 98.

Vesey-Fitzgerald, B., 1947. The Senses of Bats. Endeavour, *6*: 36–41. p. 643.

Vestal, A. G., 1913. An Associational Study of Illinois Sand Prairie. Bull. Illinois Lab. Nat. Hist., *10*: 1–96. p. 466.

Villee, Claude A., Jr., 1942. A Study of Hereditary Homoeosis: The Mutant Tetraltera in Drosophila melanogaster. Univ. of Calif. Pub. Zool., *49*: 125–183. p. 647.

Vladimerova, M. S., and Smirnov, E. S., 1938. The Struggle for Food in Homogeneous and in Mixed Populations of *Musca domestica* and *Phormia groenlandica*. Meditsinskaia Parazitologiia i Parazitarnye Bolezni, 7: 755–777. p. 370.

Vogt, William, 1948. Road to Survival. New York, Sloane. pp. 515, 578.

Volterra, Vito, 1926. Variazioni e fluttuazioni del numero d'individui in specie animali conviventi. Mem. accad. Lincei, (6) *2*: 31–113. pp. 60, 326, 657, 700.

—— 1931. Variation and Fluctuations of the Number of Individuals in Animal Species Living Together. In Chapman, R. N. 1931. Animal Ecology. New York, McGraw-Hill, pp. 409–448. pp. 11, 326.

Voûte, A. D., 1943. Classification of Factors Influencing the Natural Growth of a Population of Insects. Acta Biotheoretica, *7*: 99–116. p. 332.

—— 1946. Regulation of the Density of the Insect-Populations in Virgin-Forests and Cultivated Woods. Arch. Néerlandaises Zool., *7*: 435–470. p. 332.

Wagner, Moritz, 1868. Über die Darwinsche Theorie in Bezug auf die geographische Verbreitung der Organismen. Sitzber. bayer. Akad. Wiss. (Math.-natur.) 1868 (1): 359–395. p. 30.

—— 1868a. Die Darwinsche Theorie und das Migrationsgesetz der Organismen. Leipzig, Duncker und Humblot. p. 641.

Waksman, S. A., 1916. Studies on Soil Protozoa. Soil Science, *1*: 135–152. p. 52.

—— 1932. Principles of Soil Microbiology. 2nd ed. Baltimore, Williams & Wilkins. pp. 216, 484, 486, 497, 498.

—— 1934. The Rôle of Bacteria in the Cycle of Life in the Sea. Scient. Monthly, *38*: 35–49. p. 500.

—— 1941. Aquatic Bacteria in Relation to the Cycle of Organic Matter in Lakes. In Symposium on Hydrobiology. Madison, Univ. of Wis. Press, pp. 86–105. p. 510.

—— 1945. Soil Microbiology as a Field of Science. Science, *102*: 339–344. p. 696.

—— and Carey, Cornelia L., 1935. Decomposition of Organic Matter in Sea Water by Bacteria. I. Bacterial Multiplication in

Stored Sea Water. J. Bacteriol. *29:* 531–543. p. 500.

——, —— 1935a. Decomposition of Organic Matter in Sea Water by Bacteria. II. Influence of Addition of Organic Substances upon Bacterial Activities. J. Bacteriol., *29:* 545–561. p. 500.

—— and Renn, C. E., 1936. Decomposition of Organic Matter in Sea Water by Bacteria. III. Factors Influencing the Rate of Decomposition. Biol. Bull., *70:* 472–483. p. 500.

Wald, George, 1942. Visual Systems and the Vitamins A. Biol. Symposia, *7:* 43–71. p. 668.

Wallace, A. R., 1876. The Geographical Distribution of Animals . . . . New York, Macmillan, 2 vols. p. 597.

—— 1881. Island Life. New York, Harper. pp. 33, 597.

—— 1894. The Malay Archipelago. London, Macmillan. [7th ed. 1st. ed., 1869] pp. 23, 33.

Wallace, Robert, 1761. Various Prospects of Mankind, Nature and Providence. London, Millar. p. 25.

Wallich, G. C., 1862. North Atlantic Sea-Bed. London, Van Voorst. p. 39.

Walls, G. L., 1931. The Occurrence of Colored Lenses in the Eyes of Snakes and Squirrels, and Their Probable Significance. Copeia, 1931: 125–127. p. 546.

—— 1942. The Vertebrate Eye and Its Adaptive Radiation. Bloomfield Hills, Michigan, Cranbrook Press. pp. 70, 546, 677.

Waloff, Nadejda, 1941. The Mechanisms of Humidity Reactions of Terrestrial Isopods. J. Exper. Biol., *18:* 115–135. p. 558.

Wanless, H. R., 1938. Geological Records of a Rhythmic Nature. Tr. Illinois Acad. Sc., *31:* 7–14. p. 528.

Ward, E. B., 1940. A Seasonal Population Study of Pond Entomostraca in the Cincinnati Region. Am. Mid. Nat., *23:* 635–691. p. 335.

Ward, H. B., 1899. The Freshwater Biological Stations of the World. Science, *9:* 497–507. p. 41.

—— 1899a. Freshwater Investigations during the Last Five Years. Tr. Am. Micr. Soc., *20:* 261–336. pp. 41, 42.

—— and Whipple, G. C., 1918. Fresh-Water Biology. New York, Wiley. p. 49.

Warden, C. J., Jenkins, T. N., and Warner, L. H., 1935–1940. Comparative Psychology. 1935, Principles and Methods. 1936, Vertebrates. 1940, Plants and Invertebrates. New York, Ronald, 3 vols. pp. 23, 70, 128, 135, 157, 558.

Wardle, R. A., 1929. The Problems of Applied Entomology. New York, McGraw-Hill. pp. 56, 258.

—— and Buckle, P. 1923. The Principles of Insect Control. New York, Longman. p. 56.

Warming, J. E. B., 1895. Plantesamfund-

grundträk af den ökologiska plantegeografi. Copenhagen . . . (German trans., 1896, Lehrbuch der ökologischen Pflanzengeographie. Berlin.) p. 36.

—— 1909. Oecology of Plants. Oxford, Clarendon Press. pp. 34, 441, 472, 484, 501, 577, 578.

Washburn, M. F., 1908. The Animal Mind. New York, Macmillan. p. 45.

Wasmann, Eric, 1901. Biologie oder Ethologie? Biol. Centralbl., *21:* 391–400. p. 42.

—— 1920. Die Gastpflege der Ameisen ihre biologischen und philosophischen Probleme. Berlin, Borntraeger. p. 719.

Waterman, T. H., Nunnemacher, R. F., Chase, F. A., Jr., and Clarke, G. L., 1939. Diurnal Vertical Migrations of Deep-Water Plankton. Biol. Bull., *76:* 256–279. p. 139.

Weaver, J. E., 1920. Root Development in the Grassland Formation. Pub. Carnegie Inst. Wash., *292:* 1–155. p. 466.

—— 1943. Replacement of True Prairie by Mixed Prairie in Eastern Nebraska and Kansas. Ecology, *24:* 421–435. pp. 475, 477.

—— and Bruner, W. E., 1945. A Seven-Year Quantitative Study of Succession in Grassland. Ecol. Monogr., *15:* 297–319. p. 577.

—— and Clements, F. E., 1929. Plant Ecology. New York, McGraw-Hill. [2nd ed. 1938.] pp. 184, 216, 220, 222, 246, 577, 590.

—— and Himmel, W. J., 1931. The Environment of the Prairie. Bull. Conserv. & Surv. Div., Univ. of Nebraska, *5:* 1–50. p. 477.

Webb, Glenn R., 1947. The Mating-Anatomy Technique as Applied to Polygyrid Landsnails. Am. Nat., *81:* 134–147. p. 619.

Weber, Neal A., 1941. The Biology of the Fungus-Growing Ants. Part VII. The Barro Colorado Island, Canal Zone, Species. Revista d. Entom., *12:* 93–130. pp. 484, 713.

—— 1943. The Ants of the Imatong Mountains, Anglo-Egyptian Sudan. Bull. Mus. Comp. Zool., *93:* 263–389. p. 725.

—— 1945. The Biology of the Fungus-Growing Ants. Part VIII. The Trinidad, B. W. I., Species. Revista d. Entom., *16:* 1–88. p. 713.

Weese, A. O., 1924. Animal Ecology of an Illinois Elm-Maple Forest. Ill. Biol. Monogr., *9:* 249–437. pp. 59, 485, 487, 514, 537.

Weigelt, J., 1942. Paläontologie als Heuristik. Jen. Ztschr. Naturw., *75:* 243–278. p. 638.

Weir, J. A., 1946. A Source of Genes for Evolutionary Progress. Records Genetics Soc. Amer., *15:* 74–75. p. 695.

Weismann, August, 1877. Das Thierleben im Bodensee. Lindau, Stettner. p. 41.

—— 1893. The All-Sufficiency of Natural Selection. A Reply to Herbert Spencer. The Contemporary Review, *64:* 309–338. pp. 31, 599, 694.

Weiss, H. B., 1920. Coleoptera Associated with

Pleurotus ostreatus. Entom. News, *31:* 296–297. p. 437.

Weiss, H. B., 1920a. Coleoptera Associated with *Polyporus versicolor.* Psyche, *27:* 137–139. p. 437.

—— 1920b. Insect Enemies of Polyporoid Fungi. Am. Nat., *54:* 443–447. p. 437.

Welch, d'A. A., 1938. The Distribution and Variation of *Achatinella mustelina* Mighels in the Waianae Mountains, Oahu. Bull., Bishop Mus., *152:* 1–164. p. 610.

—— 1942. Distribution and Variation of the Hawaiian Tree Snail *Achatinella apexfulva* Dixon in the Koolau Range, Oahu. Smithsonian Misc. Coll., *103:* 1–236. pp. 610.

Welch, P. S., 1935. Limnology. New York, McGraw-Hill. pp. 40, 41, 47, 69, 92, 95, 124, 194, 203, 333, 366, 446, 451, 452, 504, 514, 519, 555, 556.

—— 1935a. Additional Data on Submerged Depression Individuality in Douglas Lake, Michigan. Papers Michigan Acad. Sc., *20:* 737–750.

Weldon, W. F. R., 1898. Opening Address in Section D of the British Association. Nature, *58:* 499–506. p. 27.

—— 1898a. Organic Variations and Their Interpretation. Nature, *58:* 595–596.

Wellenstein, G., 1928. Beiträge zur Biologie der roten Waldameise (*Formica rufa,* L.,) mit besonderer Berücksichtigung klimatischer und förstlicher Verhältnisse. Z. angew. Entom., *14:* 1–68. p. 362.

Wells, W. W., 1940. Ecological Studies on the Pinnotherid Crabs of Puget Sound. Univ. of Wash. Pub. Oceanogr., *2:* 19–50. p. 257.

Welsh, J. H., 1930. Reversal of Phototropism in a Parasitic Water Mite. Biol. Bull., *61:* 165–169. p. 245.

—— 1935. Further Evidence of a Diurnal Rhythm in the Movement of Pigment Cells in Eyes of Crustaceans. Biol. Bull., *68:* 247–253. p. 546.

—— 1938. Diurnal Rhythms. Quart. Rev. Biol., *13:* 123–139. pp. 546, 553.

——, Chace, F. A., and Nunnemacher, R. F., 1937. The Diurnal Migration of Deep-Water Animals. Biol. Bull., *73:* 185–196. p. 555.

Welty, J. C., 1934. Experiments in Group Behavior of Fishes. Physiol. Zoöl., *7:* 85–128. p. 411.

Wenrich, D. H., 1935. Host-Parasite Relations between Parasitic Protozoa and Their Hosts. Proc. Am. Philos. Soc., *75:* 605–650. p. 258.

—— 1944. Comparative Morphology of the Trichomonad Flagellates of Man. Am. J. Trop. Med., *24:* 39–50. p. 628.

—— 1944a. Morphology of the Intestinal Trichomonad Flagellates in Man and of Similar Forms in Monkeys, Cats, Dogs, and Rats. J. Morphol., *74:* 189–211. p. 628.

Wenstrom, W. H., 1942. Weather and the Ocean of Air. Boston, Houghton, Mifflin. pp. 140, 141, 144, 157.

Westoll, T. S., 1943. The Origin of the Primitive Tetrapod Limb. Proc. Roy. Soc., London, s. B., *131:* 373–393. p. 632.

—— 1943a. The Hyomandibular of *Eusthenopteron* and the Tetrapod Middle Ear. Proc. Roy. Soc., London, s. B., *131:* 393–414. p. 672.

Wheeler, M. R., 1947. The Insemination Reaction in Intraspecific Matings of Drosophila. Univ. of Texas Pub., *4720:* 78–115. p. 622.

Wheeler, W. M., 1887. On the Distribution of Coleoptera along the Lake Michigan Beach of Milwaukee County. Proc. Nat. Hist. Soc. Wis., 1887: 132–140. p. 534.

—— 1902. 'Natural History,' 'Œctology' or 'Ethology'? Science, N. S., *15:* 971–976.

—— 1907. The Fungus-Growing Ants of North America. Bull. Am. Mus. Nat. Hist., *23:* 669–807. pp. 420, 713.

—— 1911. The Ant-Colony as an Organism. J. Morphol., *22:* 307–325. pp. 52, 437.

—— 1918. A Study of Some Ant Larvae with a Consideration of the Origin and Meaning of the Social Habit Among Insects. Proc. Am. Philos. Soc., *57:* 293–343. p. 430.

—— 1919. The Phoresy of *Antherophagus.* Psyche, *26:* 145–152.

—— 1921. A Study of Some Social Beetles in British Guiana and of Their Relations to the Ant-Plant Tachigalia. Zoologica, *3:* 35–126. p. 420.

—— 1923. Social Life Among the Insects. New York, Harcourt, Brace. pp. 32, 52, 410, 418, 438, 560, 713.

—— 1926. Ants, Their Structure, Development and Behavior. (1st ed., 1910) New York, Columbia Univ. Press. pp. 45, 420, 484, 487, 720, 725.

—— 1927. The Physiognomy of Insects. Quart. Rev. Biol., *2:* 1–36. p. 233.

—— 1928. Foibles of Insects and Men. New York, Knopf. p. 690.

—— 1928a. Emergent Evolution and the Development of Societies. New York, Norton. pp. 420, 693.

—— 1928b. The Social Insects, Their Origin and Evolution. New York, Harcourt, Brace. pp. 420, 429, 430, 686, 713, 719, 725.

—— 1930. Demons of the Dust. New York, Norton. pp. 666, 697.

—— 1939. Essays in Philosophical Biology. Cambridge, Harvard Univ. Press. p. 70.

Whelpton, P. K., 1936. An Empirical Method of Calculating Future Population. J. Am. Statis. A., *31:* 457–473. p. 314.

Whipple, G. C., 1927. The Microscopy of Drinking Water. 4th ed. New York, Wiley. p. 95.

Whitaker, D. M., 1931. Some Observations on the Eggs of *Fucus* and upon Their Mutual Influence in the Determination of the

Development Axis. Biol. Bull., *61:* 294–309. pp. 121, 408.

White, Benjamin, 1938. The Biology of Pneumococcus. New York, Commonwealth Fund. p. 601.

White, Gilbert, 1789. The Natural History and Antiquities of Selborne in the County of Southhampton. . . . London, White, [various ed.] p. 33.

White, M. J. D., 1945. Animal Cytology and Evolution. Cambridge, University Press. pp. 598, 623, 625, 628, 629, 643, 647, 688, 689.

Whitehouse, Eula, 1933. Plant Succession on Central Texas Granite. Ecology, *14:* 391–405. p. 463.

Whiting, P. W., 1945. The Evolution of Male Haploidy. Quart. Rev. Biol., *20:* 231–260. p. 647.

Whitman, C. O., 1898. Animal Behavior. Biol. Lectures, Woods Hole, *6:* 285–338. p. 24.

—— 1919. Behavior in Pigeons. Pub. Carnegie Inst. Wash., *257:* 1–161. p. 24.

Wiebe, A. H., 1931. Dissolved Phosphorus and Inorganic Nitrogen in Water of the Mississippi River. Science, *73:* 652.

Wiegand, Karl M., 1935. A Taxonomist's Experience with Hybrids in the Wild. Science, *81:* 161–166. p. 625.

Wiesner, B. P., and Sheard, N. M., 1934. The Duration of Life in an Albino Rat Population. Proc. Roy. Soc., Edinburgh, *55:* 1–22. pp. 276, 279.

Wigan, L. G. 1944. Balance and Potence in Natural Populations. J. Genetics, *46:* 150–160. p. 603.

Wigglesworth, V. B., 1938. The Regulation of Osmotic Pressure and Chloride Concentration in the Haemolymph of Mosquito Larvae. J. Exper. Biol., *15:* 235–247. pp. 170, 171.

—— 1939. The Principles of Insect Physiology. London, Methuen. pp. 101, 136.

Wildt, Rupert, 1942. The Geochemistry of the Atmosphere and the Constitution of the Terrestrial Planets. Rev. Modern Physics, *14:* 151–159. pp. 177, 178.

Wilkes, A., 1942. The Influence of Selection on the Preferendum of a Chalcid (Microplectron fuscipennis Zett.) and Its Significance in the Biological Control of an Insect Pest. Proc. Roy. Soc., London, s. B., *130:* 400–415. p. 653.

Willet, H. C., 1931. Dynamic Meteorology. Physics of the Earth, *3:* 133–233. pp. 89, 140, 145.

—— 1944. Descriptive Meteorology. New York, Academic Press. pp. 140, 144, 145.

Williams, A. B., 1936. The Composition and Dynamics of a Beech-Maple Climax Community. Ecol. Monogr., *6:* 317–408. pp. 85, 122, 480, 481.

Williams, C. B., 1930. The Migration of Butterflies. London, Oliver and Boyd. pp. 100, 539.

—— 1938. Recent Progress in the Study of Some North American Migrant Butterflies. Ann. Ent. Soc. Amer., *31:* 211–239. pp. 100, 539.

—— 1947. The Generic Relations of Species in Small Ecological Communities. J. Animal Ecol., *16:* 11–18. p. 657.

——, Cockbill, G. F., Gibbs, M. E., and Downes, J. A., 1942. Studies in the Migration of Lepidoptera. Tr. Roy. Ent. Soc. London, *92:* 101–280. p. 366.

Williams, E. C., Jr., 1941. An Ecological Study of the Floor Fauna of the Panama Rain Forest. Bull. Chicago Acad. Sc., *6:* 63–124. pp. 486, 487, 488, 523, 526, 557.

Williams, F. X., 1928. The Natural History of a Philippine Nipa House with Descriptions of New Wasps. Philippine J. Sc., *35:* 53–118. p. 514.

Willis, J. C., 1922. Age and Area; A Study in Geographical Distribution and Origin of Species. Cambridge, Univ. Press. pp. 56, 215.

—— 1940. The Course of Evolution by Differentiation or Divergent Mutation rather than by Selection. Cambridge, Univ. Press. p. 215.

—— 1942. Evolution in Plants by Kaleidoscopic Mutations. Proc. Roy. Soc., London s. B., *131:* 161–169.

Wilson, E. B., 1945. Some Points in Epidemiological Theory. Am. Scientist, *33:* 246–252. p. 380.

——, and Puffer, R. R., 1933. Least Squares and Laws of Population Growth. Proc. Am. Acad. Arts & Sc., *68:* 285–382. p. 304.

Wilson, H. V., 1907. On Some Phenomena of Coalescence and Regeneration in Sponges. J. Exper. Zool., *5:* 245–258. p. 397.

—— 1910. Development of Sponges from Dissociated Tissue Cells. Bull. U. S. Bur. Fish., *30:* 1–30. p. 356.

—— 1941. The Recapitulation Theory or Biogenetic Law in Embryology. Am. Nat., *75:* 20–30. p. 678.

Wilson, I. T., and Opdyke, D. F., 1941. The Distribution of the Chemical Constituents in the Accumulated Sediment of Tippecanoe Lake. Investigations Indiana Lakes and Streams, *2:* 16–43. p. 444.

Wilson, J. W., 1932. Coleoptera and Diptera Collected from a New Jersey Sheep Pasture. J. New York Entom. Soc., *40:* 77–92. p. 469.

Wilson, L. R., 1935. Lake Development and Plant Succession in Vilas County, Wisconsin. Part I. The Medium Hard Water Lakes. Ecol. Monogr., *5:* 207–247. p. 504.

—— 1937. A Quantitative and Ecological Study of the Larger Aquatic Plants of Sweeney Lake, Oneida County, Wisconsin. Bull. Torrey Bot. Club, *64:* 199–208. p. 504.

—— 1939. Rooted Aquatic Plants and Their Relation to the Limnology of Fresh-Water

Lakes. Pub. Am. A. Adv. Sc., *10:* 107–122. pp. 451, 504.

Wilson, P. W., 1940. The Biochemistry of Symbiotic Nitrogen Fixation. Madison, Univ. of Wisconsin Press. pp. 497, 711.

Winsor, C. P., 1932. The Gompertz Curve as a Growth Curve. Proc. Nat. Acad. Sc., *18:* (No. 1) 1–8. p. 304.

—— 1934. Mathematical Analysis of Growth of Mixed Populations. Cold Spring Harbor Symposia on Quant. Biol., *2:* 181–187. pp. 369, 373.

—— 1937. Controlling Factors in Drosophila Population Growth. Quart. Rev. Biol., *12:* 348–351. p. 275.

—— and Winsor, Agnes A., 1935. Longevity and Fertility in the Pond Snail *Lymnaea columella.* J. Wash. Acad. Sc., *25:* 302–307. p. 396.

Wolcott, G. N., 1924. Hormigas. Circ. Est. Expt. Insular, Rio Piedras, Porto Rico, *75:* 3–11. p. 473.

—— 1937. An Animal Census of Two Pastures and a Meadow in Northern New York. Ecol. Monogr., *7:* 1–90. pp. 466, 468, 473, 517, 526.

—— 1942. The Requirements of Parasites for More than Hosts. Science, *96:* 317–318. p. 634.

Wolcott, R. H., 1933. Animal Biology. New York, McGraw-Hill. 2d. ed., 1940. pp. 594, 595.

Wolfenbarger, D. O., 1946. Dispersion of Small Organisms. Am. Mid. Nat., *35:* 1–152.

Wolfson, Albert, 1945. The Role of the Pituitary Fat Deposition, and Body Weight in Bird Migration. Condor, *47:* 95–127. pp. 121, 539, 541.

Wollaston, T. V., 1854. Insecta Maderensia; Being an Account of the Insects of the Islands of the Madeiran Group. London, Van Voorst. p. 147.

Wollny, E., 1891. [Review.] Forsch. Agr.-Physik, *14:* 176–180. [Review of Serafini and Arata: Ueber den Einfluss des Waldes auf die vom Winde fortgetragenen Microorganismen der Luft. Boll. R. Acc. Med. Roma, *16:* Fasc. 8.] p. 19.

Woltereck, R., 1932. Races, Associations and Stratification of Pelagic Daphnids in Some Lakes of Wisconsin and Other Regions of the United States and Canada. Tr. Wis. Acad. Sc., *27:* 487–522. p. 447.

Wood, T. W., 1867. Remarks on the Coloration of Chrysalids. J. Proc. Ent. Soc., London, 1867: xcix. p. 20.

Woodbury, A. M., 1933. Biotic Relationships of Zion Canyon, Utah, with Special Reference to Succession. Ecol. Monogr., *3:* 147–245. pp. 577, 578.

Woodruff, L. L., 1911. The Effect of Excretion Products of *Paramecium* on Its Rate of Reproduction. J. Exper. Zool., *10:* 551–581. pp. 396, 564.

—— 1912. Observations on the Origin and Sequence of the Protozoan Fauna of Hay Infusions. J. Exper. Zool., *12:* 205–264. p. 564.

—— 1913. The Effect of Excretion Products of Infusoria on the Same and on Different Species, with Special Reference to the Protozoan Sequence in Infusions. J. Exper. Zool., *14:* 575–582. p. 564.

—— 1938. Philosophers in Little Things. Univ. of Oklahoma Bull., (n.s.), *739:* 21–33. p. 484.

Woodworth, J. B., 1894. The Relation between Base-Leveling and Organic Evolution. Am. Geologist, *16:* 209–235. p. 155.

Worthington, E. B., 1931. Vertical Movements of the Fresh-Water Macroplankton. Int. Rev. ges. Hydrobiol. u. Hydrogr., *25:* 394–436. pp. 554, 556.

—— 1937. On the Evolution of Fish in the Great Lakes of Africa. Int. Rev. ges. Hydrobiol. u. Hydrogr., *35:* 304–317. pp. 609, 611, 680.

—— 1940. Geographical Differentiation in Fresh Waters with Special Reference to Fish. In Huxley, J., 1940. The New Systematics, pp. 287–302. pp. 609, 611, 663, 700.

Wray, D. L., and Brimley, C. S., 1943. The Insect Inquilines and Victims of Pitcher Plants in North Carolina. Ann. Entom. Soc. Amer., *36:* 128–137. p. 437.

Wright, Sewall, 1921. Correlation and Causation. J. Agr. Res., *20:* 557–585. p. 392.

—— 1922. The Effect of Inbreeding and Crossbreeding on Guinea Pigs. Bull. U. S. Dept. of Agr., *1090:* 1–61. p. 403.

—— 1926. The Biology of Population Growth. A Review. J. Am. Statis. A., 1926: 493–497. p. 304.

—— 1928. The Rate of Living—By Raymond Pearl. A Review. J. Am. Statis. A., 1928: 336–338. p. 275.

—— 1929. Fisher's Theory of Dominance. Am. Nat., *63:* 274–279. pp. 403, 649, 678.

—— 1930. The Genetical Theory of Natural Selection. J. Heredity, *21:* 349–356. p. 684.

—— 1931. Evolution in Mendelian Populations. Genetics, *16:* 97–159. pp. 407, 649, 681.

—— 1932. Roles of Mutation, Inbreeding, Crossbreeding and Selection in Evolution. Proc. 6th Int. Congress of Genetics, *1:* 356–366. pp. 407, 600, 604, 641, 649, 678, 683, 685.

—— 1934. Genetics of Abnormal Growth in the Guinea Pig. Cold Spring Harbor Symposia on Quant. Biology, *2:* 137–147. pp. 427, 678.

—— 1934a. A Mutation of the Guinea Pig, Tending to Restore the Pentadactyl Foot when Heterozygous, Producing a Monstrosity when Homozygous. Genetics, *20:* 84–107. pp. 678, 679.

—— 1935. The Emergence of Novelty. J. Heredity, *26:* 369–373. p. 693.

—— 1937. The Distribution of Gene Frequencies in Populations. Proc. Nat. Acad. Sc., *23:* 307–320. pp. 603, 684.

—— 1937a. The Distribution of Gene Frequencies in Populations. Science, *85:* 504. p. 684.

—— 1940. Breeding Structure of Populations in Relation to Speciation. Am. Nat., *74:* 232–248. p. 72.

——1940a. The Statistical Consequences of Mendelian Heredity in Relation to Speciation. In Huxley, J., 1940. The New Systematics, pp. 161–183. pp. 654, 681.

—— 1941. On the Probability of Fixation of Reciprocal Translocations. Am. Nat., *75:* 513–522. p. 603.

——1941a. The Material Basis of Evolution. Scient. Monthly, *53:* 165–170. p. 647.

—— 1942. Statistical Genetics and Evolution. Bull. Am. Math. Soc., *48:* 223–246. p. 603.

—— 1945. Tempo and Mode in Evolution. A Critical Review. Ecology, *26:* 415–419. pp. 407, 602, 603, 616, 662, 664, 684, 692.

—— 1946. Isolation by Distance under Diverse Systems of Mating. Genetics, *31:* 39–59. p. 605.

—— 1948. Evolution. Encyclopaedia Britannica. p. 683.

—— 1948a. On the Roles of Directed and Random Changes in Gene Frequency in the Genetics of Populations. Evolution, *2:* 279–294. pp. 603, 649, 683, 685.

—— and Dobzhansky, Theodosius, 1946. Genetics of Natural Populations. XII. Experimental Reproduction of Some of the Changes Caused by Natural Selection in Certain Populations of Drosophila pseudoobscura. Genetics, *31:* 125–156. p. 652.

—— and Eaton, O. N., 1929. The Persistence of Differentiation among Inbred Families of Guinea Pigs. Tech. Bull. U. S. Dept. of Agr., *103:* 1–45. p. 656.

Wright, W. H., 1944. Present and Post-War Health Problems in Connection with Parasitic Diseases. Science, *99:* 207–213.

Yocom, H. B., 1928. The Effect of the Quantity of Culture Medium on the Division Rate of Oxytricha. Biol. Bull., *54:* 410–417. p. 358.

Yonge, C. M., 1930. A Year on the Great Barrier Reef: The Story of Corals and of the Greatest of Their Creations. New York, Putmans. p. 456.

—— 1938. The Prosobranchs of Lake Tanganyika. Nature, *142:* 464–466. p. 612.

—— 1944. Experimental Analysis of the Association between Invertebrates and Unicel-

lular Algae. Biol. Rev., *19:* 68–80. pp. 710, 712, 713.

—— and Nichols, A. G., 1931. Studies, etc. V. The Effect of Starvation in Light and in Darkness on the Relation Between Corals and Zooxanthellae. Gr. Barrier Reef Expd. Sci. Rept., *1:* 13–57. p. 246.

Yu, T. F., Wang, H. R., and Fang, C. T., 1945. Varietal Resistance and Susceptibility of Wheat to Flag Smut (Urocystis tritici Koern). IV. Further Studies on Physiologic specialization in Urocystis tritici Koern. Phytopath., *35:* 332–338. p. 644.

Yule, G. U., 1924. An Introduction to the Theory of Statistics. 7th ed. London, Griffin.

Yung, Emile, 1878. Contributions à l'histoire de l'influence des milieux physiques sur les êtres vivants. Arch. Zool. Exper., *7:* 251–282. p. 20.

Zeller, E., 1931. Outlines of the History of Greek Philosophy. London, Paul, Trench, Trubner. p. 15.

Zeuthen, E., 1939. Hibernation of Spongilla. Ztschr. Vergl. Physiol., *26:* 527–547. p. 102.

Zimmerman, E. C., 1938. Cryptorhynchinae of Rapa. Bull. Bishop Mus., *151:* 1–75. p. 613.

—— 1943. On Wheeler's Paper Concerning Evolution and the Nemertean *Gorgonorhynchus.* Am. Nat., 77: 373–376. p. 706.

Zinsser, H., and Wilson, E. B., 1932. Bacterial Dissociation and a Theory of the Rise and Decline of Epidemic Waves. J. Prev. Med., *6:* 497–514. p. 382.

Zirkle, Conway, 1941. Natural Selection before the "Origin of Species." Proc. Am. Phil. Soc., *84:* 71–123. p. 29.

—— 1946. The Early History of the Idea of the Inheritance of Acquired Characters and of Pangenesis. Tr. Am. Phil. Soc., *35:* 91–151. p. 599.

ZoBell, C. E., 1934. Microbiological Activities at Low Temperatures with Particular Reference to Marine Bacteria. Quart. Rev. Biol., *9:* 460–466. p. 499.

—— 1943. The Effect of Solid Surfaces upon Bacterial Activity. J. Bacteriol., *46:* 39–54. p. 177.

—— 1946. Marine Microbiology; A Monograph on Hydrobacteriology. Waltham, Chronica Botanica. pp. 158, 173, 192, 200, 243, 445, 446, 499, 500.

—— and McEwen, G. F., 1935. The Lethal Action of Sunlight upon Bacteria in Sea Water. Biol. Bull., *68:* 93–106. p. 445.

Zon, Raphael, 1941. Climate and the Nation's Forests. Yearbook, U. S. Dept. of Agr., 1938: 477–498.

Zuckerman, S., 1932. The Social Life of Monkeys and Apes. New York, Harcourt, Brace. p. 416.

SUBJECT INDEX

Names of authors are to be found in the Bibliography and Author Index, and names of persons included here are only for references not specifically associated with bibliographic titles. Italic folios indicate illustrations.

Biome(s), 8, 63, 684
  concept, as applied to islands, 583
    relation to climatic zones, 583
  seral aspects of, 571–577
  terrestrial, minor, 595
  world distribution, 580–597
    pattern, 581, 582
Biome-type(s), 580, 583
  marine, 595
  tropical forest, 592
  world distribution, 580–597
Biometricians, 27
Biometry, historical aspects, 46, 54, 55
Bio-social facilitation, 395, 410. See also Social.
Biosphere, 77, 148, 158, 729
Biota of soil, 225
Biotic balance, principle of, 507, 508
  equilibrium, 710
  factors, 57, 234, 697
    in relation to individuals, 227–262
  potential, 61, 392
  pressure, 235
  region, distinguished from biome, 580
  succession, 564, 565, 695
  zonation, in mountains, 592, 646, 653, 660, 671
Biotope, 568
Birch, 699, 703
Bird(s), adaptation to environment, 652
  body temperature, 98
  clutch size, 701
  colonies, 699
  community adjustment, 723
    integration, 696
  convergent evolution, 668, 676
  day-length and feeding, 126
  diel periodicity, 548, 549
  disoperation among, 699
  ecotone, 478
  feet, 164
  flight, 132, 136, 634
  food habits, 517
  of forest edge, 478
    stratification, 488, 489, 494, 495
  grassland, 470, 668
  ground-nesting, 699
  habitat selection, 494, 495, 659, 660
  homing, magnetism and, 157
  hurricane transport, 146
  interspecies competition, 726
  leadership in, 415

Bird(s), migration, 21, 99, 117, 118, 121, 157, 186, 238, 531, 539, 540, 541, 542, 552, 607, 608, 671, 672, 696
  minimum breeding population, 402
  mortality, 647
  mutualism, 251
  nesting losses of, 334
  nests, 494, 644, 657, 689, 691, 699, 701, 726, 727
  North American-European waifs, 148
  parasites, 703, 709
  prairie, predation, 474
  regressive evolution, 676
  seasonal changes, 122
    distribution, 122
  seed dispersal and, 715
  sexual selection, 689
  skeletal weight, 132
  stratal abundance of, 489
    equivalents in grassland communities, 470
  succession, 47
  territorial behavior, 691
  territories, 412
  vitamin source, 128
Birge, E. A., 41, 51
Birge's thermocline rule, 94
Birth and death rates, 290, 293
  rate, 287, 289
    crude, 288
    species potential and, 273
    specific, 289
Birth-death ratio, 293
Bison bonasus, 399, 400
Bjerknes theorem, 149, 150
Black Sea, oxygen lack, 193
Blattidae, 301, 487. See also Roaches.
Blissus, 208, 210, 211, 247, 474, 475
Blood, cells, red, destruction of, 344
  evolutionary ecology, 171
  groups, 264, 603
  suckers, 241, 256, 696, 708. See also Mosquitoes, Tsetse flies.
Blood-worms, 453
Blytt-Sernander hypothesis, 82, 83
Bobwhite huddle, 398
Bodenheimer, F. S., 274
Bog(s) forest, 574, 577, 578
  pH, 173
  soils, 218
  succession, 573, 574
Bohr's invasion coefficient, 191
Boll weevil complex, 53

Bone marrow, red, and temperature, 120
Bonellia, sex determination, 409, 410
Bones, 132, 677. See also Allometry, Morphology.
Bonitation, 209, 210
Botflies, 236
Bottom characteristics, 159–163
  communities, 159–163, 571, 632
  deposits, 160, 161
Brachiopoda, 680
Brain, 679, 686
Braun-Blanquet, J., 48
Breathing adaptations. See Respiration.
Breeding activity, 644
  Amphibia, latitudinal, 108
  cross, 613
  mammalian, photoperiodicity, 124, 631
  population, minimum, 402, 403. See also Population size.
  structure, effect of, 602–605, 606, 607, 608, 682, 685
Brentidae, 491
Bridges, land, 78, 148
Brooks, W. K., 54
Bruce, David, 28
Brückner cycle, 85, 86
Bryocoles, water relations, 185
Bryophytes, 603
Bryozoa, 712
Bubonic plague, 337
Budding. See Colonization.
Buffers, 222, 601, 672. See also Homeostasis, Insulation.
  chemical, 173
Buffon, L. L. de, 17
Bug(s), 187, 188, 208, 210, 473, 512, 707. See also Hemiptera.
  chinch. See Blissus.
  death feigning, 50
  squash, 474
Buoyancy, water, 136, 137
Buprestidae, 490, 491
Bureau of Animal Population, 63, 269
Burrowers, 161, 163, 225–227, 425, 439, 465, 666, 671, 677, 679, 713. See also Wood eaters.
Burrowing, water saving, 185
Butterflies, 99, 134, 539, 669, 670, 688, 715

Tide, levels, San Francisco, 455

Tilth, 222

Time, 631, 646, 648, 663, 680, 681, 697, 704, 709, 717, 729. See also *Age; Evolution, rate of; Geological periods; Isolation, chronological; Longevity; Ontogeny; Phylogeny; Succession.*

variations in, 80

Time-temperature hyperbola, 108

Toads, 534, 620, 705. See also *Amphibia.*

Tolerance, acid, 173

Toleration, 45, 51, 173, 174, 348, 628, 652, 653, 666, 671, 719. See also *Mortality, Survival.*

differential, light, 121

evolution of, 698, 704, 712, 719, 723, 728

of parasitism, 260, 704–710

physiology, history, 17–23

spectrum, 539

temperature, 21, 22, 74, 98, 99, 104, 616, 634, 671

Tornadoes, 146

Totalitarianism, 694

Trace concentrations, 167, 172, 190, 205, 221

Tracheal system, 185

Tractional load, streams, 154

Trade winds, 144

Tradition, 604, 605

Transient visitants, 122, 540

Transparency index of water, 124

Transplants, embryonic, 397

Transport, aerial, 134, 146, 148, 149, 613, 647, 692, 714, 715. See also *Dispersion, Migration, Pollination, Seed dispersal, Transportation.*

Transportation, 134, 146, 148, 149, 625, 723, 728. See also *Dispersion, Distribution.*

by water, 714, 725, 726

by winds, 613, 647, 692, 714, 715. See also *Dispersion, Migration, Pollination, Seed dispersal, Transport.*

Tree(s), holes, 485, 486, 570

rings, 82, 87

stratum. See *Canopy.*

as substrates, 158

Tree-climbing adaptations. See *Adaptations, Feet, Tails.*

Tree-line, 83, 653

Trematodes. See *Flukes.*

Triassic, 662, 680

Tribolium, 61, 110, 187, 267, 298, 309, 319, 352–355, 364, 369, 370, 559, 727

populations, 299, 308, 403, 404, 405, 406

Trichogramma evanescens, 335, 383, 384

Trigger action in populations, 339. See also *Threshold.*

Trilobites, 631

Trogidae, 534

Trogoderma, 286, 319, 369

Trophallaxis, 410, 430, 431, 432, 433, 435

Trophic levels, 509, 510, 511, 519

Trophoporic field, 421, 719, 722

Tropics, 78, 228, 600, 631, 657, 671, 682, 718, 725, 726, 727, 728

width of, coastal variation, 78

Tropisms, 648

Troposphere, 142

True rate of natural increase, 293, 294

Trypanosomes, 707

Tsetse flies, 476, 628, 629, 676, 696, 707

Tsunami, 578

Tundra, 80, 401, 583, 584

animals, 583

seasonal color-change, 584

Tunnelers in dead rootlets, 465

Turbellaria. See *Flat worms, Planaria.*

Turbidity, 125, 155

effects on fishes, 455

Turesson, G. W., 48

Turtles, 552, 704, 707

Twilight and eye size, 126, 129

zone, ocean, 124

Twins, identical, 3

Typhoons, 146

Tyroglyphidae, 465

Uca, territories, 412. See also *Crabs.*

Ultraviolet, group protection from, 398

coloration of flowers, 128, 715

radiation, 74, 75, 87, 88, 127, 128, 129, 566

Unbalance, community, 507, 508, 514, 515, 516, 543, 544, 578–581

Undercooling, insects, 100, 101, 102

Undercrowding, 396, 401–407, 684

Unfitness of environment, 77

Units, biological, 30, 319, 420, 426, 435, 440, 602, 605, 631, 637, 639, 640, 641, 649, 664, 672, 676, 678, 683–695, 695–729. See also *Levels of integration.*

Urbanization, consequences of, 578–581. See also *Barriers.*

VAGILITY, 213, 214, 215, 605, 607, 608, 609, 610. See also *Dispersion, Distribution, Locomotion.*

Values, survival. See *Survival values.*

Van't Hoff rule, 107, 600

Vapor pressure, 181, 182, 184, 187, 189

Variation(s), genetic, 427, 623, 624, 629, 638, 639, 640, 641, 642, 649, 652, 654, 655, 656, 662, 680, 681, 682, 683, 684, 685, 687, 688, 689, 694, 695, 709, 722, 729. See also *Gene recombination, Mutations.*

ecology and, 599–605

in relation to population numbers, population rhythms and dispersion, 602

nonadaptive, 604, 630, 641, 655, 670, 677, 683, 715. See also *Ecophene.*

nongenetic, 639, 640, 649, 664, 684, 686, 687, 691, 692, 694, 709. See also *Adaptability, Ecophene.*

in space, 78, 627

Varves, 82, 131, 528

Vectors, insect, 28, 707, 708, 709, 724. See also *Diseases, Host-parasite relations.*

Vegetarian. See *Herbivores, Phytophages.*

Vegetation, blanketing effect of, 230, 479

littoral, 452

mats and oxygen, 193

rooted, in Wisconsin lakes, 504

world, 581. See also *Biomes.*

Velocity, hurricane, 146

law of, 166

stream, 154, 155

20195